Dear Student,

This textbook was carefully selected by your instructor and you will notice that there are various page deletions and this was intentional.

This textbook matches the course needs and provides a substantial cost saving.

Best wishes for a successful semester!

# Intermediate Algebra

## Marvin L. Bittinger

Custom Edition for Delaware County Community College
MAT 100

Taken from:

*Intermediate Algebra,* Eleventh Edition
by Marvin L. Bittinger

**Learning Solutions**

New York   Boston   San Francisco
London   Toronto   Sydney   Tokyo   Singapore   Madrid
Mexico City   Munich   Paris   Cape Town   Hong Kong   Montreal

Cover Art: Courtesy of Photodisc/Getty Images.

Taken from:

*Intermediate Algebra,* Eleventh Edition
by Marvin L. Bittinger
Copyright © 2011 by Pearson Education, Inc.
Published by Addison-Wesley
Boston, Massachusetts 02116

This special edition published in cooperation with Pearson Learning Solutions.

Pearson Learning Solutions, 501 Boylston Street, Suite 900, Boston, MA 02116
A Pearson Education Company
www.pearsoned.com

Printed in the United States of America

8  9  10  V092  15  14  13  12


000200010270583210

LB

ISBN 10: 0-558-80893-X
ISBN 13: 978-0-558-80893-8

# Contents

# For Extra Help

## Student Supplements

### New! Worksheets for Classroom or Lab Practice
(ISBN: 978-0-321-61374-5)

These classroom- and lab-friendly workbooks offer the following resources for every section of the text: a list of learning objectives, vocabulary practice problems, and extra practice exercises with ample work space.

### Student's Solutions Manual (ISBN: 978-0-321-61375-2)
By Judith Penna

Contains completely worked-out annotated solutions for all the odd-numbered exercises in the text. Also includes fully worked-out annotated solutions for all the exercises (odd- and even-numbered) in the Mid-Chapter Reviews, the Summary and Reviews, the Chapter Tests, and the Cumulative Reviews.

### Chapter Test Prep Videos

Chapter Tests can serve as practice tests to help you study. Watch instructors work through step-by-step solutions to all the Chapter Test exercises from the textbook. Chapter Test Prep videos are available on YouTube (search using BittingerInterAlgPB) and in MyMathLab. They are also included on the Video Resources on DVD described below and available for purchase at www.MyPearsonStore.com.

### Video Resources on DVD Featuring Chapter Test Prep Videos
(ISBN: 978-0-321-64063-5)

- Complete set of lectures covering every objective of every section in the textbook
- Complete set of Chapter Test Prep videos (see above)
- All videos include optional English and Spanish subtitles.
- Ideal for distance learning or supplemental instruction
- DVD-ROM format for student use at home or on campus

### InterAct Math Tutorial Website (www.interactmath.com)

Get practice and tutorial help online! This interactive tutorial website provides algorithmically generated practice exercises that correlate directly to the exercises in the textbook. Students can retry an exercise as many times as they like with new values each time for unlimited practice and mastery. Every exercise is accompanied by an interactive guided solution that provides helpful feedback for incorrect answers, and students can also view a worked-out sample problem that steps them through an exercise similar to the one they're working on.

### MathXL® Tutorials on CD (ISBN: 978-0-321-61373-8)

This interactive tutorial CD-ROM provides algorithmically generated practice exercises that are correlated at the objective level to the exercises in the textbook. Every practice exercise is accompanied by an example and a guided solution designed to involve students in the solution process. Selected exercises may also include a video clip to help students visualize concepts. The software provides helpful feedback for incorrect answers and can generate printed summaries of students' progress.

## Instructor Supplements

### Annotated Instructor's Edition (ISBN: 978-0-321-61369-1)

Includes answers to all exercises printed in blue on the same page as the exercises. Also includes the student answer section, for easy reference.

### Instructor's Solutions Manual (ISBN: 978-0-321-61371-4)
By Judith Penna

Contains brief solutions to the even-numbered exercises in the exercise sets. Also includes fully worked-out annotated solutions for all the exercises (odd- and even-numbered) in the Mid-Chapter Reviews, the Summary and Reviews, the Chapter Tests, and the Cumulative Reviews.

### Printed Test Forms (ISBN: 978-0-321-61370-7)
By Laurie Hurley

- Contains one diagnostic test and one pretest for each chapter, plus two cumulative tests per chapter, beginning with Chapter 2.
- New! Includes two versions of a short mid-chapter quiz.
- Provides eight test forms for every chapter and eight test forms for the final exam.
- For the chapter tests, four free-response tests are modeled after the chapter tests in the main text, two tests are designed for 50-minute class periods and organized so that each objective in the chapter is covered on one of the tests, and two tests consist of multiple-choice questions. Chapter tests also include more challenging Synthesis questions.
- For the final exam, three test forms are organized by chapter, three forms are organized by question type, and two forms are multiple-choice tests.

### Instructor's Resource Manual
(ISBN: 978-0-321-61376-9)

- Features resources and teaching tips designed to help both new and adjunct faculty with course preparation and classroom management.
- New! Includes a mini-lecture for each section of the text with objectives, key examples, and teaching tips.
- Additional resources include general first-time advice, sample syllabi, teaching tips, collaborative learning activities, correlation guide, video index, and transparency masters.

# Additional Media Supplements

### MyMathLab® Online Course (access code required)

MyMathLab is a series of text-specific, easily customizable online courses for Pearson Education's textbooks in mathematics and statistics. Powered by CourseCompass™ (our online teaching and learning environment) and MathXL® (our online homework, tutorial, and assessment system), MyMathLab gives instructors the tools they need to deliver all or a portion of their course online, whether their students are in a lab setting or working from home. MyMathLab provides a rich and flexible set of course materials, featuring free-response exercises that are algorithmically generated for unlimited practice and mastery. Students can also use online tools, such as video lectures, animations, interactive math games, and a multimedia textbook, to independently improve their understanding and performance. Instructors can use MyMathLab's homework and test managers to select and assign online exercises correlated directly to the textbook, and they can also create and assign their own online exercises and import TestGen tests for added flexibility. MyMathLab's online gradebook—designed specifically for mathematics and statistics—automatically tracks students' homework and test results and gives the instructor control over how to calculate final grades. Instructors can also add offline (paper-and-pencil) grades to the gradebook. MyMathLab also includes access to the **Pearson Tutor Center** (www.pearsontutorservices.com). The Tutor Center is staffed by qualified mathematics instructors who provide textbook-specific tutoring for students via toll-free phone, fax, email, and interactive Web sessions. MyMathLab is available to qualified adopters. For more information, visit our website at www.mymathlab.com or contact your sales representative.

### MathXL® Online Course (access code required)

MathXL® is a powerful online homework, tutorial, and assessment system that accompanies Pearson Education's textbooks in mathematics or statistics.

With MathXL, instructors can

* create, edit, and assign online homework and tests using algorithmically generated exercises correlated at the objective level to the textbook.
* create and assign their own online exercises and import TestGen tests for added flexibility.
* maintain records of all student work tracked in MathXL's online gradebook.

With MathXL, students can

* take chapter tests in MathXL and receive personalized study plans based on their test results.
* use the study plan to link directly to tutorial exercises for the objectives they need to study and retest.
* access supplemental animations and video clips directly from selected exercises.

MathXL is available to qualified adopters. For information, visit our website at www.mathxl.com, or contact your Pearson sales representative.

**TestGen®** (www.pearsoned.com/testgen) enables instructors to build, edit, and print tests using a computerized bank of questions developed to cover all the objectives of the text. TestGen is algorithmically based, allowing instructors to create multiple but equivalent versions of the same question or test with the click of a button. Instructors can also modify test bank questions or add new questions. The software and test bank are available for download from Pearson Education's online catalog.

**PowerPoint® Lecture Slides** present key concepts and definitions from the text. Slides are available to download from within MyMathLab and from Pearson Education's online catalog.

**Pearson Math Adjunct Support Center** (http://www.pearsontutorservices.com/math-adjunct.html) is staffed by qualified instructors with more than 100 years of combined experience at both the community college and university levels. Assistance is provided for faculty in the following areas: suggested syllabus consultation, tips on using materials packed with your book, book-specific content assistance, and teaching suggestions, including advice on classroom strategies.

# Review of Basic Algebra

## Real-World Application

The rate of triplet and higher-order multiple births in the United States is $\frac{161.8}{100,000}$.
Write scientific notation for this birth rate.

*Source:* U.S. National Center for Health Statistics

*This problem appears as Exercise 86 in Section R.7.*

# R.1

## PART 1 OPERATIONS
## The Set of Real Numbers

## OBJECTIVES

**a** Use roster notation and set-builder notation to name sets, and distinguish among various kinds of real numbers.

**b** Determine which of two real numbers is greater and indicate which, using < and >; given an inequality like $a < b$, write another inequality with the same meaning; and determine whether an inequality like $-2 \leq 3$ or $4 > 5$ is true.

**c** Graph inequalities on the number line.

**d** Find the absolute value of a real number.

To the student:

At the front of the text, you will find a Student Organizer card. This pullout card will help you keep track of important dates and useful contact information. You can also use it to plan time for class, study, work, and relaxation. By managing your time wisely, you will provide yourself the best possible opportunity to be successful in this course.

Find the opposite of each number.

**1.** 9

**2.** $-6$

**3.** 0

*Answers*

1. $-9$   2. 6   3. 0

### a  Set Notation and the Set of Real Numbers

A **set** is a collection of objects. In mathematics, we usually consider sets of numbers. The set we consider most in algebra is **the set of real numbers**. There is a real number for every point on the real-number line. Some commonly used sets of numbers are **subsets** of, or sets contained within, the set of real numbers. We begin by examining some subsets of the set of real numbers.

The set containing the numbers $-5, 0$, and 3 can be named $\{-5, 0, 3\}$. This method of describing sets is known as the **roster method**. We use the roster method to describe three frequently used subsets of real numbers. Note that three dots are used to indicate that the pattern continues without end.

---

**NATURAL NUMBERS (OR COUNTING NUMBERS)**

**Natural numbers** are those numbers used for counting: $\{1, 2, 3, \ldots\}$.

---

**WHOLE NUMBERS**

**Whole numbers** are the set of natural numbers with 0 included: $\{0, 1, 2, 3, \ldots\}$.

---

**INTEGERS**

**Integers** are the set of whole numbers and their opposites:

$$\{\ldots, -4, -3, -2, -1, 0, 1, 2, 3, 4, \ldots\}.$$

---

The integers can be illustrated on the real-number line as follows.

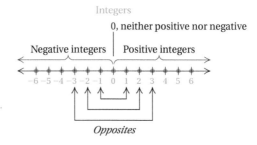

*Opposites*

The set of integers extends infinitely to the left and to the right of 0. The **opposite** of a number is found by reflecting it across the number 0. Thus the opposite of 3 is $-3$. The opposite of $-4$ is 4. The opposite of 0 is 0. We read a symbol like $-3$ as either "the opposite of 3" or "negative 3."

The natural numbers are called **positive integers**. The opposites of the natural numbers (those to the left of 0) are called **negative integers**. Zero is neither positive nor negative.

Do Exercises 1–3 (in the margin at left).

Each point on the number line corresponds to a real number. In order to fill in the remaining numbers on the number line, we must describe two other subsets of the real numbers. And to do that, we need another type of set notation.

**Set-builder notation** is used to specify conditions under which a number is in a set. For example, the set of all odd natural numbers less than 9 can be described as follows:

$$\{x \mid x \text{ is an odd natural number less than } 9\}.$$

The set of ←
all numbers $x$ ←
such that ←
$x$ is an odd natural number less than 9. ←

We can easily write another name for this set using roster notation, as follows:

$$\{1, 3, 5, 7\}.$$

**EXAMPLE 1** Name the set consisting of the first six even whole numbers using both roster notation and set-builder notation.

Roster notation: $\{0, 2, 4, 6, 8, 10\}$

Set-builder notation: $\{x \mid x \text{ is one of the first six even whole numbers}\}$

Do Exercise 4.

**4.** Name the set consisting of the first seven odd whole numbers using both roster notation and set-builder notation.

The advantage of set-builder notation is that we can use it to describe very large sets that may be difficult to describe using roster notation. Such is the case when we try to name the set of **rational numbers**. Rational numbers can be named using fraction notation. The following are examples of rational numbers:

$$\frac{5}{8}, \quad \frac{12}{-7}, \quad \frac{-17}{15}, \quad -\frac{9}{7}, \quad \frac{39}{1}, \quad \frac{0}{6}.$$

We can now describe the set of rational numbers.

---

### RATIONAL NUMBERS

A **rational number** can be expressed as an integer divided by a nonzero integer. The set of rational numbers is

$$\left\{ \frac{p}{q} \,\middle|\, p \text{ is an integer, } q \text{ is an integer, and } q \neq 0 \right\}.$$

Rational numbers are numbers whose decimal representation either terminates or has a repeating block of digits.

---

Each of the following is a rational number:

$$\frac{5}{8} = 0.625 \quad \text{and} \quad \frac{6}{11} = 0.545454\ldots = 0.\overline{54}.$$

Terminating      Repeating

The bar in $0.\overline{54}$ indicates the repeating block of digits in decimal notation.

Note that $\frac{39}{1} = 39$. Thus the set of rational numbers contains the integers.

Do Exercises 5 and 6.

Convert each fraction to decimal notation by long division and determine whether it is terminating or repeating.

**5.** $\dfrac{11}{16}$

**6.** $\dfrac{14}{13}$

*Answers*

**4.** $\{1, 3, 5, 7, 9, 11, 13\}$; $\{x \mid x \text{ is one of the first seven odd whole numbers}\}$   **5.** 0.6875; terminating   **6.** $1.\overline{076923}$; repeating

The real-number line has a point for every rational number.

However, there are many points on the line for which there is no rational number. These points correspond to what are called **irrational numbers**.

Numbers like $\pi$, $\sqrt{2}$, $-\sqrt{10}$, $\sqrt{13}$, and $-1.898898889\ldots$ are examples of irrational numbers. The decimal notation for an irrational number *neither* terminates *nor* repeats. Recall that decimal notation for rational numbers either terminates or has a repeating block of digits.

---

**IRRATIONAL NUMBERS**

**Irrational numbers** are numbers whose decimal representation neither terminates nor has a repeating block of digits. They cannot be represented as the quotient of two integers.

---

The irrational number $\sqrt{2}$ (read "the square root of 2") is the length of the diagonal of a square with sides of length 1. It is also the number that, when multiplied by itself, gives 2. No rational number can be multiplied by itself to get 2, although some approximations come close:

1.4 is an *approximation* of $\sqrt{2}$ because $(1.4)^2 = (1.4)(1.4) = 1.96$;

1.41 is a better approximation because $(1.41)^2 = (1.41)(1.41) = 1.9881$;

1.4142 is an even better approximation because $(1.4142)^2 = (1.4142)(1.4142) = 1.99996164$.

We say that 1.4142 is a rational approximation of $\sqrt{2}$ because

$$(1.4142)^2 = 1.99996164 \approx 2.$$

The symbol $\approx$ means "is approximately equal to." We can find rational approximations for square roots and other irrational numbers using a calculator.

The set of all rational numbers, combined with the set of all irrational numbers, gives us the set of **real numbers**.

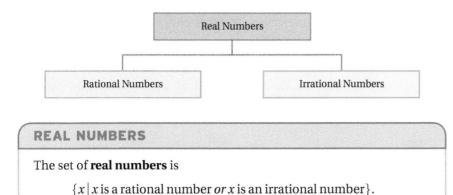

> ## REAL NUMBERS
>
> The set of **real numbers** is
>
> $\{x \mid x \text{ is a rational number } or \text{ } x \text{ is an irrational number}\}$.

Every point on the number line represents some real number and every real number is represented by some point on the number line.

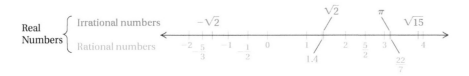

The following figure shows the relationships among various kinds of real numbers.

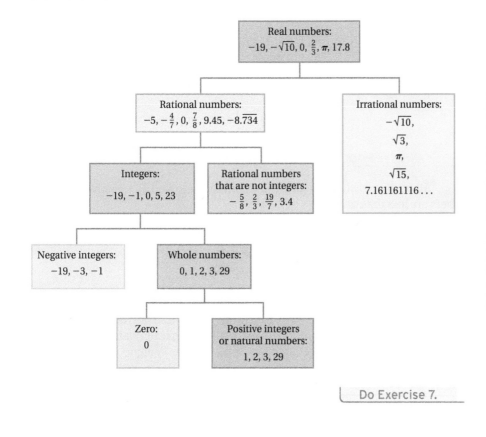

Do Exercise 7.

**7.** Given the numbers

$20,\ -10,\ -5.34,\ 18.999,$

$\dfrac{11}{45},\ \sqrt{7},\ -\sqrt{2},\ \sqrt{16},\ 0,\ -\dfrac{2}{3},$

$9.34334333433334\ldots$ :

a) Name the natural numbers.

b) Name the whole numbers.

c) Name the integers.

d) Name the irrational numbers.

e) Name the rational numbers.

f) Name the real numbers.

*Answer*

**7.** (a) $20, \sqrt{16}$; (b) $20, \sqrt{16}, 0$; (c) $20, -10, \sqrt{16}, 0$; (d) $\sqrt{7}, -\sqrt{2}$, $9.34334333433334\ldots$; (e) $20, -10$, $-5.34, 18.999, \dfrac{11}{45}, \sqrt{16}, 0, -\dfrac{2}{3}$; (f) $20, -10$, $-5.34, 18.999, \dfrac{11}{45}, \sqrt{7}, -\sqrt{2}, \sqrt{16}, 0, -\dfrac{2}{3}$, $9.34334333433334\ldots$

## b  Order for the Real Numbers

Real numbers are named in order on the number line, with larger numbers named further to the right. For any two numbers on the line, the one to the left is less than the one to the right.

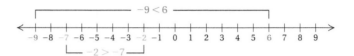

We use the symbol **<** to mean "**is less than.**" The sentence $-9 < 6$ means "$-9$ is less than 6." The symbol **>** means "**is greater than.**" The sentence $-2 > -7$ means "$-2$ is greater than $-7$." A handy mental device is to think of $>$ or $<$ as an arrowhead that points to the smaller number.

**EXAMPLES**  Use either $<$ or $>$ for $\square$ to write a true sentence.

**2.** $4 \square 9$ — Since 4 is to the left of 9, 4 is less than 9, so $4 < 9$.

**3.** $-8 \square 3$ — Since $-8$ is to the left of 3, we have $-8 < 3$.

**4.** $7 \square -12$ — Since 7 is to the right of $-12$, then $7 > -12$.

**5.** $-21 \square -5$ — Since $-21$ is to the left of $-5$, we have $-21 < -5$.

**6.** $-2.7 \square -\dfrac{3}{2}$ — Since $-\dfrac{3}{2} = -1.5$ and $-2.7$ is to the left of $-1.5$, we have $-2.7 < -\dfrac{3}{2}$.

**7.** $1\dfrac{1}{4} \square -2.7$ — The answer is $1\dfrac{1}{4} > -2.7$.

**8.** $4.79 \square 4.97$ — The answer is $4.79 < 4.97$.

**9.** $-8.45 \square 1.32$ — The answer is $-8.45 < 1.32$.

**10.** $\dfrac{5}{8} \square \dfrac{7}{11}$ — We convert to decimal notation $\left(\dfrac{5}{8} = 0.625 \text{ and } \dfrac{7}{11} = 0.6363\ldots\right)$ and compare. Thus, $\dfrac{5}{8} < \dfrac{7}{11}$.

Do Exercises 8–16.

All positive real numbers are greater than zero and all negative real numbers are less than zero.

> If $x$ is a positive real number, then $x > 0$.
> If $x$ is a negative real number, then $x < 0$.

Note that $-8 < 5$ and $5 > -8$ are both true. These are **inequalities**. Every true inequality yields another true inequality if we interchange the numbers or variables and reverse the direction of the inequality sign.

> $a < b$ also has the meaning $b > a$.

Insert $<$ or $>$ for $\square$ to write a true sentence.

**8.** $-5 \square -4$

**9.** $-\dfrac{1}{4} \square -\dfrac{1}{2}$

**10.** $87 \square 67$

**11.** $-9.8 \square -4\dfrac{2}{3}$

**12.** $6.78 \square -6.77$

**13.** $-\dfrac{4}{5} \square -0.86$

**14.** $\dfrac{14}{29} \square \dfrac{17}{32}$

**15.** $-\dfrac{12}{13} \square -\dfrac{14}{15}$

**16.** $1.8 \square 1.08$

*Answers*

8. $<$    9. $>$    10. $>$    11. $<$    12. $>$
13. $>$    14. $<$    15. $>$    16. $>$

**EXAMPLES** Write a different inequality with the same meaning.

**11.** $a < -5$     The inequality $-5 > a$ has the same meaning.

**12.** $-3 > -8$     The inequality $-8 < -3$ has the same meaning.

Do Exercises 17 and 18.

Expressions like $a \leq b$ and $b \geq a$ are also **inequalities**. We read $a \leq b$ as "**$a$ is less than or equal to $b$.**" We read $a \geq b$ as "**$a$ is greater than or equal to $b$.**" If $a$ is nonnegative, then $a \geq 0$.

**EXAMPLES** Write true or false.

**13.** $-8 \leq 5.7$     True since $-8 < 5.7$ is true.

**14.** $-8 \leq -8$     True since $-8 = -8$ is true.

**15.** $-7 \geq 4\frac{1}{3}$     False since neither $-7 > 4\frac{1}{3}$ nor $-7 = 4\frac{1}{3}$ is true.

**16.** $-\frac{2}{3} \geq -\frac{5}{4}$     True since $-\frac{2}{3} = -0.666\ldots$ and $-\frac{5}{4} = -1.25$ and $-0.666\ldots > -1.25$.

Do Exercises 19-22.

### (c) Graphing Inequalities on the Number Line

Some replacements for the variable in an inequality make it true and some make it false. A replacement that makes it true is called a **solution**. The set of all solutions is called the **solution set**. A **graph** of an inequality is a drawing that represents its solution set.

**EXAMPLE 17** Graph the inequality $x > -3$ on the number line.

The solutions consist of all real numbers greater than $-3$, so we shade all numbers greater than $-3$. Note that $-3$ is not a solution. We indicate this by using a parenthesis at $-3$.

The graph represents the solution set $\{x \mid x > -3\}$. Numbers in this set include $-2.6, -1, 0, \pi, \sqrt{2}, 3\frac{7}{8}, 5$, and $123$.

**EXAMPLE 18** Graph the inequality $x \leq 2$ on the number line.

We make a drawing that represents the solution set $\{x \mid x \leq 2\}$. The graph consists of 2 as well as the numbers less than 2. We shade all numbers to the left of 2 and use a bracket at 2 to indicate that it is also a solution.

Do Exercises 23-28. (Exercises 25-28 are on the following page.)

---

Write a different inequality with the same meaning.

**17.** $x > 6$

**18.** $-4 < 7$

Write true or false.

**19.** $6 \geq -9.4$

**20.** $-18 \leq -18$

**21.** $-7.6 \leq -10\frac{4}{5}$

**22.** $-\frac{24}{27} \geq -\frac{25}{28}$

Graph each inequality.

**23.** $x > -1$

**24.** $x \leq 5$

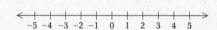

Match each inequality with one of the graphs shown below.

**25.** $x \leq -\dfrac{5}{2}$        **26.** $x > 0$

**27.** $-4 > x$        **28.** $2 \leq x$

a)
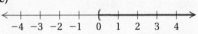

b)
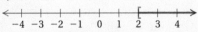

c)
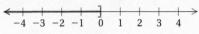

d)

e)
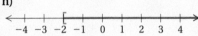

f)

g)

h)

Find the absolute value.

**29.** $\left| -\dfrac{1}{4} \right|$        **30.** $|2|$

**31.** $\left| \dfrac{3}{2} \right|$        **32.** $|-2.3|$

## d) Absolute Value

We see that numbers like $-6$ and $6$ are the same distance from $0$ on the number line. We call the distance of a number from $0$ on the number line the **absolute value** of the number. Since distance is always a nonnegative number, the absolute value of a number is always greater than or equal to $0$.

The distance from $-6$ to $0$ is $6$.
The absolute value of $-6$ is $6$.

The distance from $6$ to $0$ is $6$.
The absolute value of $6$ is $6$.

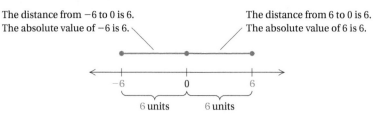

6 units    6 units

**ABSOLUTE VALUE\***

The **absolute value** of a number is its distance from zero on the number line. We use the symbol $|x|$ to represent the absolute value of a number $x$.

To find absolute value:

1. If a number is negative, its absolute value is its opposite.
2. If a number is positive or zero, its absolute value is the same as the number.

**EXAMPLES**  Find the absolute value.

**19.** $|-7|$     The distance of $-7$ from $0$ is $7$, so $|-7|$ is $7$.
**20.** $|12|$     The distance of $12$ from $0$ is $12$, so $|12|$ is $12$.
**21.** $|0|$     The distance of $0$ from $0$ is $0$, so $|0|$ is $0$.
**22.** $\left| \dfrac{4}{5} \right| = \dfrac{4}{5}$
**23.** $|-3.86| = 3.86$

Do Exercises 29–32.

\*A more formal definition of $|x|$ is given in Section R.2.

**a**    Given the numbers $-6, 0, 1, -\frac{1}{2}, -4, \frac{7}{9}, 12, -\frac{6}{5}, 3.45, 5\frac{1}{2}, \sqrt{3}, \sqrt{25}, -\frac{12}{3}, 0.131331333133331\ldots$ :

**1.** Name the natural numbers.

**2.** Name the whole numbers.

**3.** Name the rational numbers.

**4.** Name the integers.

**5.** Name the real numbers.

**6.** Name the irrational numbers.

Given the numbers $-\sqrt{5}, -3.43, -11, 12, 0, \frac{11}{34}, -\frac{7}{13}, \pi, -3.565665666566665\ldots$ :

**7.** Name the whole numbers.

**8.** Name the natural numbers.

**9.** Name the integers.

**10.** Name the rational numbers.

**11.** Name the irrational numbers.

**12.** Name the real numbers.

Use roster notation to name each set.

**13.** The set of all letters in the word "math"

**14.** The set of all letters in the word "solve"

**15.** The set of all positive integers less than 13

**16.** The set of all odd whole numbers less than 13

**17.** The set of all even natural numbers

**18.** The set of all negative integers greater than $-4$

Use set-builder notation to name each set.

**19.** $\{0, 1, 2, 3, 4, 5\}$

**20.** $\{4, 5, 6, 7, 8, 9, 10\}$

**21.** The set of all rational numbers

**22.** The set of all real numbers

**23.** The set of all real numbers greater than $-3$

**24.** The set of all real numbers less than or equal to 21

**b** Use either < or > for ☐ to write a true sentence.

**25.** 13 ☐ 0

**26.** 18 ☐ 0

**27.** −8 ☐ 2

**28.** 7 ☐ −7

**29.** −8 ☐ 8

**30.** 0 ☐ −11

**31.** −8 ☐ −3

**32.** −6 ☐ −3

**33.** −2 ☐ −12

**34.** −7 ☐ −10

**35.** −9.9 ☐ −2.2

**36.** $-13\frac{1}{5}$ ☐ $\frac{11}{250}$

**37.** $37\frac{1}{5}$ ☐ $-1\frac{67}{100}$

**38.** −13.99 ☐ −8.45

**39.** $\frac{6}{13}$ ☐ $\frac{13}{25}$

**40.** $-\frac{14}{15}$ ☐ $-\frac{27}{53}$

Write a different inequality with the same meaning.

**41.** −8 > x

**42.** x < 7

**43.** −12.7 ≤ y

**44.** $10\frac{2}{3} \geq t$

Write true or false.

**45.** 6 ≤ −6

**46.** −7 ≤ −7

**47.** 5 ≥ −8.4

**48.** $-11 \geq -13\frac{1}{2}$

**c** Graph each inequality.

**49.** x < −2

**50.** x < −1

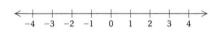

**51.** x ≤ −2

**52.** x ≥ −1

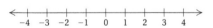

**53.** $x > -3.3$

**54.** $x < 0$

**55.** $x \geq 2$

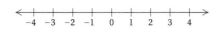

**56.** $x \leq 0$

**d** Find the absolute value.

**57.** $|-6|$  **58.** $|-3|$  **59.** $|28|$  **60.** $|16|$  **61.** $|-35|$

**62.** $|-127|$  **63.** $\left|-\dfrac{2}{3}\right|$  **64.** $\left|-\dfrac{13}{8}\right|$  **65.** $|42.8|$  **66.** $|16.4|$

**67.** $|986|$  **68.** $|465|$  **69.** $\left|\dfrac{0}{-7}\right|$  **70.** $\left|\dfrac{0}{-15}\right|$

## Synthesis

*To the student and the instructor*: The Synthesis exercises found at the end of every exercise set challenge students to combine concepts or skills studied in that section or in preceding parts of the text.

Use either $\leq$ or $\geq$ for ☐ to write a true sentence.

**71.** $|-3|$ ☐ $5$  **72.** $|-5|$ ☐ $|-2|$  **73.** $|4|$ ☐ $|-7|$  **74.** $|-8|$ ☐ $|8|$

**75.** List the following numbers in order from least to greatest.

$$\dfrac{1}{11}, \quad 1.1\%, \quad \dfrac{2}{7}, \quad 0.3\%, \quad 0.11, \quad \dfrac{1}{8}\%, \quad 0.009, \quad \dfrac{99}{1000}, \quad 0.286, \quad \dfrac{1}{8}, \quad 1\%, \quad \dfrac{9}{100}$$

# R.2

# Operations with Real Numbers

## OBJECTIVES

**a** Add real numbers.

**b** Find the opposite, or additive inverse, of a number.

**c** Subtract real numbers.

**d** Multiply real numbers.

**e** Divide real numbers.

We now review addition, subtraction, multiplication, and division of real numbers.

## a Addition

To gain an understanding of addition of real numbers, we first add using the number line.

---

**ADDITION ON THE NUMBER LINE**

To find $a + b$, we start at 0, move to $a$, and then move according to $b$.

- If $b$ is positive, move to the right.
- If $b$ is negative, move to the left.
- If $b$ is 0, stay at $a$.

---

**EXAMPLES**

**1.** $6 + (-8) = -2$:   We begin at 0 and move 6 units right since 6 is positive. Then we move 8 units left since $-8$ is negative. The answer is $-2$.

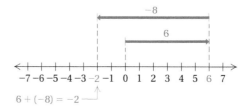

**2.** $-3 + 7 = 4$:   We begin at 0 and move 3 units left since $-3$ is negative. Then we move 7 units right since 7 is positive. The answer is 4.

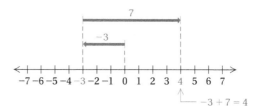

**3.** $-2 + (-5) = -7$:   We begin at 0 and move 2 units left since $-2$ is negative. Then we move 5 units further left since $-5$ is negative. The answer is $-7$.

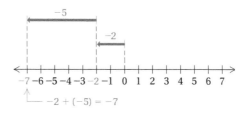

Add using the number line.

**1.** $-5 + 9$

$\longleftarrow | | | | | | | | | | | | \longrightarrow$
$\,-6\,-5\,-4\,-3\,-2\,-1\ \ 0\ \ 1\ \ 2\ \ 3\ \ 4\ \ 5\ \ 6$

**2.** $4 + (-2)$

$\longleftarrow | | | | | | | | | | | | \longrightarrow$
$\,-6\,-5\,-4\,-3\,-2\,-1\ \ 0\ \ 1\ \ 2\ \ 3\ \ 4\ \ 5\ \ 6$

**3.** $3 + (-8)$

$\longleftarrow | | | | | | | | | | | | \longrightarrow$
$\,-6\,-5\,-4\,-3\,-2\,-1\ \ 0\ \ 1\ \ 2\ \ 3\ \ 4\ \ 5\ \ 6$

**4.** $-5 + 5$

$\longleftarrow | | | | | | | | | | | | \longrightarrow$
$\,-6\,-5\,-4\,-3\,-2\,-1\ \ 0\ \ 1\ \ 2\ \ 3\ \ 4\ \ 5\ \ 6$

*Answers*

**1.** 4    **2.** 2    **3.** −5    **4.** 0

Do Exercises 1–4.

You may have noticed some patterns in the preceding examples. These lead us to rules for adding without using the number line.

---

**RULES FOR ADDITION OF REAL NUMBERS**

1. *Positive numbers*: Add the numbers. The result is positive.
2. *Negative numbers*: Add absolute values. Make the answer negative.
3. *A positive and a negative number*:
   - If the numbers have the same absolute value, the answer is 0.
   - If the numbers have different absolute values, subtract the smaller absolute value from the larger. Then:
     a) If the positive number has the greater absolute value, make the answer positive.
     b) If the negative number has the greater absolute value, make the answer negative.
4. *One number is zero*: The sum is the other number.

---

Rule 4 is known as the **identity property of 0.** It says that for any real number $a$, $a + 0 = a$.

**EXAMPLES** Add without using the number line.

**4.** $-13 + (-8) = -21$    Two negatives. Add the absolute values: $|-13| + |-8| = 13 + 8 = 21$. Make the answer *negative*: $-21$.

**5.** $-2.1 + 8.5 = 6.4$    One negative, one positive. Find the absolute values: $|-2.1| = 2.1$; $|8.5| = 8.5$. Subtract the smaller absolute value from the larger: $8.5 - 2.1 = 6.4$. The *positive* number, 8.5, has the larger absolute value, so the answer is *positive*, 6.4.

**6.** $-48 + 31 = -17$    One negative, one positive. Find the absolute values: $|-48| = 48$; $|31| = 31$. Subtract the smaller absolute value from the larger: $48 - 31 = 17$. The *negative* number, $-48$, has the larger absolute value, so the answer is *negative*, $-17$.

**7.** $2.6 + (-2.6) = 0$    One positive, one negative. The numbers have the same absolute value. The sum is 0.

**8.** $-\dfrac{5}{9} + 0 = -\dfrac{5}{9}$    One number is zero. The sum is $-\frac{5}{9}$.

**9.** $-\dfrac{3}{4} + \dfrac{9}{4} = \dfrac{6}{4} = \dfrac{3}{2}$

**10.** $-\dfrac{2}{3} + \dfrac{5}{8} = -\dfrac{16}{24} + \dfrac{15}{24} = -\dfrac{1}{24}$

Do Exercises 5–14.

Add.

**5.** $-7 + (-11)$

**6.** $-8.9 + (-9.7)$

**7.** $-\dfrac{6}{5} + \left(-\dfrac{23}{5}\right)$

**8.** $-\dfrac{3}{10} + \left(-\dfrac{2}{5}\right)$

**9.** $-7 + 7$

**10.** $-7.4 + 0$

**11.** $4 + (-7)$

**12.** $-7.8 + 4.5$

**13.** $\dfrac{3}{8} + \left(-\dfrac{5}{8}\right)$

**14.** $-\dfrac{3}{5} + \dfrac{7}{10}$

*Answers*

**5.** $-18$   **6.** $-18.6$   **7.** $-\dfrac{29}{5}$   **8.** $-\dfrac{7}{10}$
**9.** $0$   **10.** $-7.4$   **11.** $-3$   **12.** $-3.3$
**13.** $-\dfrac{1}{4}$   **14.** $\dfrac{1}{10}$

Find the opposite, or additive inverse, of each number.

**15.** $-14$

**16.** $\dfrac{2}{3}$

**17.** $0$

------- *Caution!* -------

A symbol such as $-8$ is usually read "negative 8." It could be read "the opposite of 8," because the opposite of 8 is $-8$. It could also be read "the additive inverse of 8," because the additive inverse of 8 is $-8$. When a variable is involved, as in a symbol like $-x$, it can be read "the opposite of $x$" or "the additive inverse of $x$" but *not* "negative $x$," because we do not know whether the symbol represents a positive number, a negative number, or 0. It is never correct to read $-8$ as "minus 8."

**18.** Evaluate $-a$ when $a = 9$.

**19.** Evaluate $-a$ when $a = -\dfrac{3}{5}$.

**20.** Evaluate $-(-a)$ when $a = -5.9$.

**21.** Evaluate $-(-a)$ when $a = \dfrac{2}{3}$.

## b  Opposites, or Additive Inverses

Suppose we add two numbers that are **opposites**, such as 4 and $-4$. The result is 0. When opposites are added, the result is always 0. Such numbers are also called **additive inverses**. Every real number has an opposite, or additive inverse.

> **OPPOSITES, OR ADDITIVE INVERSES**
>
> Two numbers whose sum is 0 are called **opposites**, or **additive inverses**, of each other.

**EXAMPLES**  Find the opposite, or additive inverse, of each number.

**11.** $8.6$     The opposite of 8.6 is $-8.6$ because $8.6 + (-8.6) = 0$.
**12.** $0$     The opposite of 0 is $0$ because $0 + 0 = 0$.
**13.** $-\dfrac{7}{9}$     The opposite of $-\dfrac{7}{9}$ is $\dfrac{7}{9}$ because $-\dfrac{7}{9} + \dfrac{7}{9} = 0$.

To name the opposite, or additive inverse, we use the symbol $-$, and read the symbolism $-a$ as "the opposite of $a$" or "the additive inverse of $a$."

Do Exercises 15–17.

**EXAMPLE 14**  Evaluate $-x$ and $-(-x)$ when **(a)** $x = 23$ and **(b)** $x = -5$.

**a)**  If $x = 23$, then $-x = -23 = -23$.       The opposite, or additive inverse, of 23 is $-23$.

If $x = 23$, then $-(-x) = -(-23) = 23$.       The opposite of the opposite of 23 is 23.

**b)**  If $x = -5$, then $-x = -(-5) = 5$.
If $x = -5$, then $-(-x) = -(-(-5)) = -(5) = -5$.

Note in Example 14(b) that an extra set of parentheses is used to show that we are substituting the negative number $-5$ for $x$. Symbolism like $--x$ is not considered meaningful.

Do Exercises 18–21.

We can use the symbolism $-a$ for the opposite of $a$ to restate the definition of opposite.

> **OPPOSITES, OR ADDITIVE INVERSES**
>
> For any real number $a$, the **opposite**, or **additive inverse**, of $a$, which is $-a$, is such that
>
> $$a + (-a) = (-a) + a = 0.$$

**Answers**

15. 14   16. $-\dfrac{2}{3}$   17. 0   18. $-9$

19. $\dfrac{3}{5}$   20. $-5.9$   21. $\dfrac{2}{3}$

### Signs of Numbers

A negative number is sometimes said to have a "negative sign." A positive number is said to have a "positive sign." When we replace a number with its opposite, or additive inverse, we can say that we have "changed its sign."

**EXAMPLES** Change the sign. (Find the opposite, or additive inverse.)

**15.** $-3$ $\quad -(-3) = 3$

**16.** $-\frac{3}{8}$ $\quad -\left(-\frac{3}{8}\right) = \frac{3}{8}$

**17.** $0$ $\quad -0 = 0$

**18.** $14$ $\quad -(14) = -14$

> Do Exercise 22.

We can now use the concept of opposite to give a more formal definition of absolute value.

---

**ABSOLUTE VALUE**

For any real number $a$, the **absolute value** of $a$, denoted $|a|$, is given by

$$|a| = \begin{cases} a, & \text{if } a \geq 0, \\ -a, & \text{if } a < 0. \end{cases}$$
For example, $|8| = 8$ and $|0| = 0$.
For example, $|-5| = -(-5) = 5$.

(The absolute value of $a$ is $a$ if $a$ is nonnegative. The absolute value of $a$ is the opposite of $a$ if $a$ is negative.)

---

## (c) Subtraction

---

**SUBTRACTION**

The difference $a - b$ is the unique number $c$ for which $a = b + c$.
That is, $a - b = c$ if $c$ is the number such that $a = b + c$.

---

For example, $3 - 5 = -2$ because $3 = 5 + (-2)$. That is, $-2$ is the number that when added to 5 gives 3. Although this illustrates the formal definition of subtraction, we generally use the following when we subtract.

---

**SUBTRACTING BY ADDING THE OPPOSITE**

For any real numbers $a$ and $b$,

$$a - b = a + (-b).$$

(We can subtract by adding the opposite (additive inverse) of the number being subtracted.)

---

**EXAMPLES** Subtract.

**19.** $3 - 5 = 3 + (-5) = -2$ $\qquad$ Changing the sign of 5 and adding

**20.** $7 - (-3) = 7 + (3) = 10$ $\qquad$ Changing the sign of $-3$ and adding

**21.** $-19.4 - 5.6 = -19.4 + (-5.6) = -25$

**22.** $-\frac{4}{3} - \left(-\frac{2}{5}\right) = -\frac{4}{3} + \frac{2}{5} = -\frac{20}{15} + \frac{6}{15} = -\frac{14}{15}$

---

**22.** Change the sign.

a) 11

b) $-17$

c) 0

d) $x$

e) $-x$

Subtract.

**23.** $8 - (-9)$

**24.** $-10 - 6$

**25.** $5 - 8$

**26.** $-23.7 - 5.9$

**27.** $-2 - (-5)$

**28.** $-\frac{11}{12} - \left(-\frac{23}{12}\right)$

**29.** $\frac{2}{3} - \left(-\frac{5}{6}\right)$

**30.** a) $17 - 23$

b) $-17 - 23$

c) $-17 - (-23)$

**31.** Look for a pattern and complete.

$$4 \cdot 5 = 20 \qquad -2 \cdot 5 =$$
$$3 \cdot 5 = 15 \qquad -3 \cdot 5 =$$
$$2 \cdot 5 = \qquad -4 \cdot 5 =$$
$$1 \cdot 5 = \qquad -5 \cdot 5 =$$
$$0 \cdot 5 = \qquad -6 \cdot 5 =$$
$$-1 \cdot 5 =$$

Multiply.

**32.** $-4 \cdot 6$

**33.** $(3.5)(-8.1)$

**34.** $-\dfrac{4}{5} \cdot 10$

**35.** Look for a pattern and complete.

$$4(-5) = -20 \qquad -1(-5) =$$
$$3(-5) = -15 \qquad -2(-5) =$$
$$2(-5) = \qquad -3(-5) =$$
$$1(-5) = \qquad -4(-5) =$$
$$0(-5) = \qquad -5(-5) =$$

Multiply.

**36.** $-8(-9)$

**37.** $\left(-\dfrac{4}{5}\right) \cdot \left(-\dfrac{2}{3}\right)$

**38.** $(-4.7)(-9.1)$

Do Exercises 23–30 on the preceding page.

## d Multiplication

We know how to multiply positive numbers. What happens when we multiply a positive number and a negative number?

Do Exercise 31.

> **THE PRODUCT OF A POSITIVE NUMBER AND A NEGATIVE NUMBER**
>
> To multiply a positive number and a negative number, multiply their absolute values. Then make the answer negative.

**EXAMPLES** Multiply.

**23.** $-3 \cdot 5 = -15$

**24.** $6 \cdot (-7) = -42$

**25.** $(-1.2)(4.5) = -5.4$

**26.** $3 \cdot \left(-\tfrac{1}{2}\right) = \tfrac{3}{1} \cdot \left(-\tfrac{1}{2}\right) = -\tfrac{3}{2}$

Note in Example 25 that the parentheses indicate multiplication.

Do Exercises 32–34.

What happens when we multiply two negative numbers?

Do Exercise 35.

> **THE PRODUCT OF TWO NEGATIVE NUMBERS**
>
> To multiply two negative numbers, multiply their absolute values. The answer is positive.

**EXAMPLES** Multiply.

**27.** $-3 \cdot (-5) = 15$

**28.** $-5.2(-10) = 52$

**29.** $(-8.8)(-3.5) = 30.8$

**30.** $\left(-\tfrac{3}{4}\right) \cdot \left(-\tfrac{5}{2}\right) = \tfrac{15}{8}$

Do Exercises 36–38.

## e Division

> **DIVISION**
>
> The quotient $a \div b$, or $\dfrac{a}{b}$, where $b \neq 0$, is that unique real number $c$ for which $a = b \cdot c$.

The definition of division parallels the one for subtraction. Using this definition and the rules for multiplying, we can see how to handle signs when dividing.

*Answers*

**31.** $10, 5, 0, -5, -10, -15, -20, -25, -30$
**32.** $-24$ **33.** $-28.35$ **34.** $-8$ **35.** $-10,$
$-5, 0, 5, 10, 15, 20, 25$ **36.** $72$ **37.** $\dfrac{8}{15}$
**38.** $42.77$

**EXAMPLES** Divide.

**31.** $\dfrac{10}{-2} = -5$, because $-5 \cdot (-2) = 10$

**32.** $\dfrac{-32}{4} = -8$, because $-8 \cdot (4) = -32$

**33.** $\dfrac{-25}{-5} = 5$, because $5 \cdot (-5) = -25$

**34.** $\dfrac{40}{-4} = -10$

**35.** $-10 \div 5 = -2$

**36.** $\dfrac{-10}{-40} = \dfrac{1}{4}$, or $0.25$

**37.** $\dfrac{-10}{-3} = \dfrac{10}{3}$, or $3.\overline{3}$

The rules for division and multiplication are the same.

> To multiply or divide two real numbers:
>
> **1.** Multiply or divide the absolute values.
> **2.** If the signs are the same, then the answer is positive.
> **3.** If the signs are different, then the answer is negative.

Do Exercises 39–42.

## Excluding Division by Zero

We cannot divide a nonzero number $n$ by zero. By the definition of division, $n/0$ would be some number that when multiplied by 0 gives $n$. But when any number is multiplied by 0, the result is 0. Thus the only possibility for $n$ would be 0.

Consider $0/0$. We might say that it is 5 because $5 \cdot 0 = 0$. We might also say that it is $-8$ because $-8 \cdot 0 = 0$. In fact, $0/0$ could be any number at all. So, division by 0 does not make sense. Division by 0 is not defined and is not possible.

**EXAMPLES** Divide, if possible.

**38.** $\dfrac{7}{0}$     Not defined: Division by 0.

**39.** $\dfrac{0}{7} = 0$     The quotient is 0 because $0 \cdot 7 = 0$.

**40.** $\dfrac{4}{x-x}$     Not defined: $x - x = 0$ for any $x$.

Do Exercises 43–46.

## Division and Reciprocals

Two numbers whose product is 1 are called **reciprocals** (or **multiplicative inverses**) of each other.

> **PROPERTIES OF RECIPROCALS**
>
> Every nonzero real number $a$ has a **reciprocal** (or **multiplicative inverse**) $1/a$. The reciprocal of a positive number is positive. The reciprocal of a negative number is negative.

Divide.

**39.** $\dfrac{-28}{-14}$

**40.** $125 \div (-5)$

**41.** $\dfrac{-75}{25}$

**42.** $-4.2 \div (-21)$

Divide, if possible.

**43.** $\dfrac{8}{0}$     **44.** $\dfrac{0}{9}$

**45.** $\dfrac{17}{2x - 2x}$     **46.** $\dfrac{3x - 3x}{x - x}$

Find the reciprocal of each number.

**47.** $\dfrac{3}{8}$     **48.** $-\dfrac{4}{5}$

**49.** $18$     **50.** $-4.3$

**51.** $0.5$

*Answers*

**39.** 2   **40.** $-25$   **41.** $-3$   **42.** 0.2
**43.** Not defined   **44.** 0   **45.** Not defined
**46.** Not defined   **47.** $\dfrac{8}{3}$   **48.** $-\dfrac{5}{4}$   **49.** $\dfrac{1}{18}$
**50.** $-\dfrac{1}{4.3}$, or $-\dfrac{10}{43}$   **51.** $\dfrac{1}{0.5}$, or 2

**52.** Complete the following table.

| NUMBER | OPPOSITE (Additive Inverse) | RECIPROCAL (Multiplicative Inverse) |
|---|---|---|
| $\dfrac{2}{3}$ | $-\dfrac{2}{3}$ | $\dfrac{3}{2}$ |
| $\dfrac{4}{9}$ | | |
| $-\dfrac{3}{4}$ | | |
| $0.25$ | | |
| $8$ | | |
| $-5$ | | |
| $0$ | | |

**EXAMPLES** Find the reciprocal of each number.

**41.** $\dfrac{4}{5}$ The reciprocal is $\dfrac{5}{4}$, because $\dfrac{4}{5} \cdot \dfrac{5}{4} = 1$.

**42.** $8$ The reciprocal is $\dfrac{1}{8}$, because $8 \cdot \dfrac{1}{8} = 1$.

**43.** $-\dfrac{2}{3}$ The reciprocal is $-\dfrac{3}{2}$, because $-\dfrac{2}{3} \cdot \left(-\dfrac{3}{2}\right) = 1$.

**44.** $0.25$ The reciprocal is $\dfrac{1}{0.25}$ or $4$, because $0.25 \cdot 4 = 1$.

Remember that a number and its reciprocal (multiplicative inverse) have the same sign. Do *not* change the sign when taking the reciprocal of a number. On the other hand, when finding an opposite (additive inverse), change the sign.

Do Exercises 47–52. (Exercises 47–51 are on the preceding page.)

We know that we can subtract by adding an opposite, or additive inverse. Similarly, we can divide by multiplying by a reciprocal.

---

**RECIPROCALS AND DIVISION**

For any real numbers $a$ and $b$, $b \neq 0$,

$$a \div b = \frac{a}{b} = a \cdot \frac{1}{b}.$$

(To divide, we can multiply by the reciprocal of the divisor.)

---

Divide by multiplying by the reciprocal of the divisor.

**53.** $-\dfrac{3}{4} \div \dfrac{7}{8}$

**54.** $-\dfrac{12}{5} \div \left(-\dfrac{7}{15}\right)$

**55.** $-\dfrac{3}{8} \div (-5)$

**56.** $\dfrac{4}{5} \div \left(-\dfrac{1}{10}\right)$

We sometimes say that we "invert the divisor and multiply."

**EXAMPLES** Divide by multiplying by the reciprocal of the divisor.

**45.** $\dfrac{1}{4} \div \dfrac{3}{5} = \dfrac{1}{4} \cdot \dfrac{5}{3} = \dfrac{5}{12}$  "Inverting" the divisor, $\dfrac{3}{5}$, and multiplying

**46.** $\dfrac{2}{3} \div \left(-\dfrac{4}{9}\right) = \dfrac{2}{3} \cdot \left(-\dfrac{9}{4}\right) = -\dfrac{18}{12}$, or $-\dfrac{3}{2}$

**47.** $-\dfrac{5}{7} \div 3 = -\dfrac{5}{7} \cdot \dfrac{1}{3} = -\dfrac{5}{21}$

Do Exercises 53–56.

The following properties can be used to make sign changes.

---

**SIGN CHANGES IN FRACTION NOTATION**

For any numbers $a$ and $b$, $b \neq 0$,

$$\frac{-a}{b} = \frac{a}{-b} = -\frac{a}{b} \quad \text{and} \quad \frac{-a}{-b} = \frac{a}{b}.$$

---

*Answers*

**52.** $-\dfrac{4}{9}, \dfrac{9}{4}; \dfrac{3}{4}, -\dfrac{4}{3}; -0.25, \dfrac{1}{0.25},$ or $4; -8, \dfrac{1}{8}; 5,$
$-\dfrac{1}{5}; 0,$ does not exist   **53.** $-\dfrac{6}{7}$   **54.** $\dfrac{36}{7}$

**55.** $\dfrac{3}{40}$   **56.** $-8$

We can illustrate this property with $a = 4$ and $b = 9$:

$$\frac{-4}{9} = \frac{4}{-9} = -\frac{4}{9} \quad \text{and} \quad \frac{-4}{-9} = \frac{4}{9}.$$

**a**  Add.

**1.** $-10 + (-18)$

**2.** $-13 + (-12)$

**3.** $7 + (-2)$

**4.** $7 + (-5)$

**5.** $-8 + (-8)$

**6.** $-6 + (-6)$

**7.** $7 + (-11)$

**8.** $9 + (-12)$

**9.** $-16 + 6$

**10.** $-21 + 11$

**11.** $-26 + 0$

**12.** $0 + (-32)$

**13.** $-8.4 + 9.6$

**14.** $-6.3 + 8.2$

**15.** $-2.62 + (-6.24)$

**16.** $-2.73 + (-8.46)$

**17.** $-\dfrac{5}{9} + \dfrac{2}{9}$

**18.** $-\dfrac{3}{7} + \dfrac{1}{7}$

**19.** $-\dfrac{11}{12} + \left(-\dfrac{5}{12}\right)$

**20.** $-\dfrac{3}{8} + \left(-\dfrac{7}{8}\right)$

**21.** $\dfrac{2}{5} + \left(-\dfrac{3}{10}\right)$

**22.** $-\dfrac{3}{4} + \dfrac{1}{8}$

**23.** $-\dfrac{2}{5} + \dfrac{3}{4}$

**24.** $-\dfrac{5}{6} + \left(-\dfrac{7}{8}\right)$

**b**  Evaluate $-a$ for each of the following.

**25.** $a = -4$

**26.** $a = -9$

**27.** $a = 3.7$

**28.** $a = 0$

Find the opposite (additive inverse).

**29.** 10

**30.** $-\dfrac{2}{3}$

**31.** 0

**32.** $-2x$

**c**  Subtract.

**33.** $3 - 7$

**34.** $8 - 13$

**35.** $-5 - 9$

**36.** $-6 - 14$

**37.** $23 - 23$

**38.** $23 - (-23)$

**39.** $-23 - 23$

**40.** $-23 - (-23)$

**41.** $-6 - (-11)$

**42.** $-7 - (-12)$

**43.** $10 - (-5)$

**44.** $28 - (-16)$

**45.** $15.8 - 27.4$

**46.** $17.2 - 34.9$

**47.** $-18.01 - 11.24$

**48.** $-19.04 - 15.76$

**49.** $-\dfrac{21}{4} - \left(-\dfrac{7}{4}\right)$

**50.** $-\dfrac{16}{5} - \left(-\dfrac{3}{5}\right)$

**51.** $-\dfrac{1}{3} - \left(-\dfrac{1}{12}\right)$

**52.** $-\dfrac{7}{8} - \left(-\dfrac{5}{2}\right)$

**53.** $-\dfrac{3}{4} - \dfrac{5}{6}$

**54.** $-\dfrac{2}{3} - \dfrac{4}{5}$

**55.** $\dfrac{1}{3} - \dfrac{4}{5}$

**56.** $-\dfrac{4}{7} - \left(-\dfrac{5}{9}\right)$

**d** Multiply.

**57.** $3(-7)$

**58.** $5(-8)$

**59.** $-2 \cdot 4$

**60.** $-5 \cdot 9$

**61.** $-8(-3)$

**62.** $-5(-7)$

**63.** $-7 \cdot 16$

**64.** $-8 \cdot 19$

**65.** $-6(-5.7)$

**66.** $-7(-6.1)$

**67.** $-\dfrac{3}{5} \cdot \dfrac{4}{7}$

**68.** $-\dfrac{5}{4} \cdot \dfrac{11}{3}$

**69.** $-3\left(-\dfrac{2}{3}\right)$

**70.** $-5\left(-\dfrac{3}{5}\right)$

**71.** $-3(-4)(5)$

**72.** $-6(-8)(9)$

**73.** $(-4.2)(-6.3)$

**74.** $(-7.4)(-9.6)$

**75.** $-\dfrac{9}{11} \cdot \left(-\dfrac{11}{9}\right)$

**76.** $-\dfrac{13}{7} \cdot \left(-\dfrac{5}{2}\right)$

**77.** $-\dfrac{2}{3} \cdot \left(-\dfrac{2}{3}\right) \cdot \left(-\dfrac{2}{3}\right)$

**78.** $-\dfrac{4}{5} \cdot \left(-\dfrac{4}{5}\right) \cdot \left(-\dfrac{4}{5}\right)$

**e** Divide, if possible.

**79.** $\dfrac{-8}{4}$  **80.** $\dfrac{-16}{2}$  **81.** $\dfrac{56}{-8}$  **82.** $\dfrac{63}{-7}$  **83.** $-77 \div (-11)$

**84.** $-48 \div (-6)$  **85.** $\dfrac{-5.4}{-18}$  **86.** $\dfrac{-8.4}{-12}$  **87.** $\dfrac{5}{0}$  **88.** $\dfrac{92}{0}$

**89.** $\dfrac{0}{32}$  **90.** $\dfrac{0}{17}$  **91.** $\dfrac{9}{y-y}$  **92.** $\dfrac{2x-2x}{2x-2x}$

Find the reciprocal of each number.

**93.** $\dfrac{3}{4}$  **94.** $\dfrac{9}{10}$  **95.** $-\dfrac{7}{8}$  **96.** $-\dfrac{5}{6}$  **97.** $25$

**98.** $-65$  **99.** $0.2$  **100.** $0.8$  **101.** $-\dfrac{a}{b}$  **102.** $\dfrac{1}{8x}$

Divide.

**103.** $\dfrac{2}{7} \div \left(-\dfrac{11}{3}\right)$  **104.** $\dfrac{3}{5} \div \left(-\dfrac{6}{7}\right)$  **105.** $-\dfrac{10}{3} \div \left(-\dfrac{2}{15}\right)$  **106.** $-\dfrac{12}{5} \div \left(-\dfrac{3}{10}\right)$

**107.** $18.6 \div (-3.1)$  **108.** $39.9 \div (-13.3)$  **109.** $(-75.5) \div (-15.1)$  **110.** $(-12.1) \div (-0.11)$

**111.** $-48 \div 0.4$  **112.** $520 \div (-0.13)$  **113.** $\dfrac{3}{4} \div \left(-\dfrac{2}{3}\right)$  **114.** $\dfrac{5}{8} \div \left(-\dfrac{1}{2}\right)$

**115.** $-\dfrac{5}{4} \div \left(-\dfrac{3}{4}\right)$  **116.** $-\dfrac{5}{9} \div \left(-\dfrac{5}{6}\right)$  **117.** $-\dfrac{2}{3} \div \left(-\dfrac{4}{9}\right)$  **118.** $-\dfrac{3}{5} \div \left(-\dfrac{5}{8}\right)$

**119.** $-\dfrac{3}{8} \div \left(-\dfrac{8}{3}\right)$  **120.** $-\dfrac{5}{8} \div \left(-\dfrac{5}{6}\right)$  **121.** $-6.6 \div 3.3$  **122.** $-44.1 \div (-6.3)$

**123.** $\dfrac{-12}{-13}$

**124.** $\dfrac{-1.9}{20}$

**125.** $\dfrac{48.6}{-30}$

**126.** $\dfrac{-17.8}{3.2}$

**127.** $\dfrac{-9}{17-17}$

**128.** $\dfrac{-8}{-6+6}$

**129.** Complete the following table.

| NUMBER | OPPOSITE (Additive Inverse) | RECIPROCAL (Multiplicative Inverse) |
|---|---|---|
| $\dfrac{2}{3}$ | | |
| $-\dfrac{5}{4}$ | | |
| $0$ | | |
| $1$ | | |
| $-4.5$ | | |
| $x, x \neq 0$ | | |

**130.** Complete the following table.

| NUMBER | OPPOSITE (Additive Inverse) | RECIPROCAL (Multiplicative Inverse) |
|---|---|---|
| $-\dfrac{3}{8}$ | | |
| $\dfrac{7}{10}$ | | |
| $-1$ | | |
| $0$ | | |
| $-6.4$ | | |
| $a, a \neq 0$ | | |

## Skill Maintenance

This heading indicates that the exercises that follow are *Skill Maintenance exercises,* which review any skill previously studied in the text. You can expect such exercises in every exercise set. Answers to *all* skill maintenance exercises are found at the back of the book. If you miss an exercise, restudy the objective shown in red.

Given the numbers $\sqrt{3}, -12.47, -13, 26, \pi, 0, -\dfrac{23}{32}, \dfrac{7}{11}, 4.57557555755557\ldots:$   [R.1a]

**131.** Name the whole numbers.

**132.** Name the natural numbers.

**133.** Name the integers.

**134.** Name the irrational numbers.

**135.** Name the rational numbers.

**136.** Name the real numbers.

Use either $<$ or $>$ for $\square$ to write a true sentence.   [R.1b]

**137.** $-7 \,\square\, 8$

**138.** $5 \,\square\, \tfrac{3}{8}$

**139.** $-45.6 \,\square\, -23.8$

**140.** $123 \,\square\, -10$

## Synthesis

**141.** The reciprocal of an electric resistance is called *conductance.* When two resistors are connected in parallel, the conductance is the sum of the conductances,

$$\dfrac{1}{r_1} + \dfrac{1}{r_2}.$$

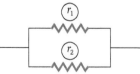

Find the conductance of two resistors of 12 ohms and 6 ohms when connected in parallel.

**142.** What number can be added to 11.7 to obtain $-7\tfrac{3}{4}$?

**143.** What number can be multiplied by $-0.02$ to obtain $-625$?

# R.3 Exponential Notation and Order of Operations

## a Exponential Notation

Exponential notation is a shorthand device. For $3 \cdot 3 \cdot 3 \cdot 3$, we write $3^4$. In the **exponential notation** $3^4$, the number 3 is called the **base** and the number 4 is called the **exponent**.

a Rewrite expressions with whole-number exponents, and evaluate exponential expressions.

b Rewrite expressions with or without negative integers as exponents.

c Simplify expressions using the rules for order of operations.

> **EXPONENTIAL NOTATION**
>
> Exponential notation $a^n$, where $n$ is an integer greater than 1, means
>
> $$\underbrace{a \cdot a \cdot a \cdots a \cdot a.}_{n \text{ factors}}$$
>
> We read "$a^n$" as "$a$ to the $n$th power," or simply "$a$ to the $n$th."
> We can read "$a^2$" as "$a$-squared" and "$a^3$" as "$a$-cubed."

---

### Caution!

$a^n$ does *not* mean to multiply $n$ times $a$. For example, $3^2$ means $3 \cdot 3$, or 9, not $3 \cdot 2$, or 6.

---

**EXAMPLES**   Write exponential notation.

1. $7 \cdot 7 \cdot 7 = 7^3$
2. $xxxxx = x^5$
3. $\dfrac{2}{3} \cdot \dfrac{2}{3} \cdot \dfrac{2}{3} \cdot \dfrac{2}{3} = \left(\dfrac{2}{3}\right)^4$

Write exponential notation.

1. $8 \cdot 8 \cdot 8 \cdot 8$

2. $mmmmmm$

3. $\dfrac{7}{8} \cdot \dfrac{7}{8} \cdot \dfrac{7}{8}$

Do Exercises 1–3.

**EXAMPLES**   Evaluate.

4. $9^2 = 9 \cdot 9 = 81$
5. $\left(\dfrac{1}{2}\right)^3 = \dfrac{1}{2} \cdot \dfrac{1}{2} \cdot \dfrac{1}{2} = \dfrac{1}{8}$
6. $\left(\dfrac{7}{8}\right)^2 = \dfrac{7}{8} \cdot \dfrac{7}{8} = \dfrac{49}{64}$
7. $(0.1)^4 = (0.1)(0.1)(0.1)(0.1) = 0.0001$
8. $(-5)^3 = (-5)(-5)(-5) = -125$
9. $-(5^3) = -(5 \cdot 5 \cdot 5) = -125$
10. $-(10)^4 = -(10 \cdot 10 \cdot 10 \cdot 10) = -10,000$
11. $(-10)^4 = (-10)(-10)(-10)(-10) = 10,000$

Note that $-(10)^4 \neq (-10)^4$, as shown in Examples 10 and 11. In $-(10)^4$, the sign is *outside* the parentheses; in $(-10)^4$, the sign is *inside* the parentheses.

Evaluate.

4. $3^4$          5. $\left(\dfrac{1}{4}\right)^2$

6. $(-10)^6$       7. $(0.2)^3$

8. $(5.8)^4$       9. $-4^4$

10. $(-3)^4$

Do Exercises 4–10.

**Answers**

1. $8^4$   2. $m^6$   3. $\left(\dfrac{7}{8}\right)^3$   4. 81   5. $\dfrac{1}{16}$
6. 1,000,000   7. 0.008   8. 1131.6496
9. $-256$   10. 81

When an exponent is an integer greater than 1, it tells how many times the base occurs as a factor. What happens when the exponent is 1 or 0? We cannot have the base occurring as a factor 1 time or 0 times because there are no products. Look for a pattern below. Think of dividing by 10 on the right.

| On this side, the exponents decrease by 1 at each step. | $10^4 = 10 \cdot 10 \cdot 10 \cdot 10 = 10{,}000$ $10^3 = 10 \cdot 10 \cdot 10 = 1000$ $10^2 = 10 \cdot 10 = 100$ $10^1 = ?$ $10^0 = ?$ | On this side, we divide by 10 at each step. |

In order for the pattern to continue, $10^1$ would have to be 10 and $10^0$ would have to be 1. We will *agree* that exponents of 1 and 0 have that meaning.

---

**EXPONENTS OF 0 AND 1**

For any number $a$, we agree that $a^1$ means $a$.

For any nonzero number $a$, we agree that $a^0$ means 1.

---

**EXAMPLES** Rewrite without an exponent.

**12.** $4^1 = 4$          **13.** $(-97)^1 = -97$

**14.** $6^0 = 1$          **15.** $(-37.4)^0 = 1$

Let's consider a justification for not defining $0^0$. By examining the pattern $3^0 = 1$, $2^0 = 1$, and $1^0 = 1$, we might think that $0^0$ should be 1. However, by examining the pattern $0^3 = 0$, $0^2 = 0$, and $0^1 = 0$, we might think that $0^0$ should be 0. To avoid this confusion, mathematicians agree *not* to define $0^0$.

Do Exercises 11–15.

## b Negative Integers as Exponents

How shall we define negative integers as exponents? Look for a pattern below. Again, think of dividing by 10 on the right.

| On this side, the exponents decrease by 1 at each step. | $10^2 = 100$ $10^1 = 10$ $10^0 = 1$ $10^{-1} = ?$ $10^{-2} = ?$ | On this side, we divide by 10 at each step. |

In order for the pattern to continue, $10^{-1}$ would have to be $\frac{1}{10}$ and $10^{-2}$ would have to be $\frac{1}{100}$. This leads to the following agreement.

---

**NEGATIVE EXPONENTS**

For any real number $a$ that is nonzero and any integer $n$,

$$a^{-n} = \frac{1}{a^n}.$$

---

Rewrite without exponents.

**11.** $8^1$

**12.** $(-31)^1$

**13.** $3^0$

**14.** $(-7)^0$

**15.** $y^0$, where $y \neq 0$

*Answers*

**11.** 8   **12.** −31   **13.** 1   **14.** 1   **15.** 1

**EXAMPLES** Rewrite using a positive exponent. Evaluate, if possible.

**16.** $y^{-5} = \dfrac{1}{y^5}$

**17.** $\dfrac{1}{t^{-4}} = t^4$

**18.** $(-2)^{-3} = \dfrac{1}{(-2)^3} = \dfrac{1}{(-2)(-2)(-2)} = \dfrac{1}{-8} = -\dfrac{1}{8}$

**19.** $\left(\dfrac{1}{2}\right)^{-3} = \dfrac{1}{\left(\frac{1}{2}\right)^3} = \dfrac{1}{\frac{1}{8}} = 1 \cdot \dfrac{8}{1} = 8$

**20.** $\left(\dfrac{2}{5}\right)^{-2} = \dfrac{1}{\left(\frac{2}{5}\right)^2} = \dfrac{1}{\frac{4}{25}} = 1 \cdot \dfrac{25}{4} = \dfrac{25}{4}$

The numbers $a^n$ and $a^{-n}$ are reciprocals because

$$a^n \cdot a^{-n} = a^n \cdot \dfrac{1}{a^n} = \dfrac{a^n}{a^n} = 1.$$

For example, $y^3$ and $y^{-3}$ are reciprocals:

$$y^3 \cdot y^{-3} = y^3 \cdot \dfrac{1}{y^3} = \dfrac{y^3}{y^3} = 1.$$

Rewrite using a positive exponent. Evaluate, if possible.

**16.** $m^{-4}$

**17.** $(-4)^{-3}$

**18.** $\dfrac{1}{x^{-3}}$

**19.** $\left(\dfrac{1}{5}\right)^{-3}$

**20.** $\left(\dfrac{3}{4}\right)^{-2}$

------------------------------- *Caution!* -------------------------------

**A negative exponent does *not* necessarily indicate that an answer is negative!** For example, $3^{-2}$ means $1/3^2$, or $1/9$, not $-9$.

⌐Do Exercises 16–20.⌐

**EXAMPLES** Rewrite using a negative exponent.

**21.** $\dfrac{1}{x^2} = x^{-2}$

**22.** $\dfrac{1}{(-7)^4} = (-7)^{-4}$

Rewrite using a negative exponent.

**21.** $\dfrac{1}{a^3}$

**22.** $\dfrac{1}{(-5)^4}$

⌐Do Exercises 21 and 22.⌐

## (c) Order of Operations

What does $8 + 2 \cdot 5^3$ mean? If we add 8 and 2 and multiply by $5^3$, or 125, we get 1250. If we multiply 2 times 125 and add 8, we get 258. Both results cannot be correct. To avoid such difficulties, we make agreements about which operations should be done first.

---
**RULES FOR ORDER OF OPERATIONS**

1. Do all the calculations within grouping symbols, like parentheses, before operations outside.
2. Evaluate all exponential expressions.
3. Do all multiplications and divisions in order from left to right.
4. Do all additions and subtractions in order from left to right.
---

Most computers and calculators are programmed using these rules.

*Answers*

**16.** $\dfrac{1}{m^4}$   **17.** $-\dfrac{1}{64}$   **18.** $x^3$   **19.** 125

**20.** $\dfrac{16}{9}$   **21.** $a^{-3}$   **22.** $(-5)^{-4}$

**EXAMPLE 23** Simplify: $-43 \cdot 56 - 17$.

There are no parentheses or powers so we start with the third rule.

$$-43 \cdot 56 - 17 = -2408 - 17 \qquad \text{Carrying out all multiplications and divisions in order from left to right}$$

$$= -2425 \qquad \text{Carrying out all additions and subtractions in order from left to right}$$

**EXAMPLE 24** Simplify: $8 + 2 \cdot 5^3$.

$$8 + 2 \cdot 5^3 = 8 + 2 \cdot 125 \qquad \text{Evaluating the exponential expression}$$

$$= 8 + 250 \qquad \text{Doing the multiplication}$$

$$= 258 \qquad \text{Adding}$$

**EXAMPLE 25** Simplify and compare: $(8 - 10)^2$ and $8^2 - 10^2$.

$$(8 - 10)^2 = (-2)^2 = 4;$$

$$8^2 - 10^2 = 64 - 100 = -36$$

We see that $(8 - 10)^2$ and $8^2 - 10^2$ are *not* the same.

**EXAMPLE 26** Simplify: $3^4 + 62 \cdot 8 - 2(29 + 33 \cdot 4)$.

$$3^4 + 62 \cdot 8 - 2(29 + 33 \cdot 4)$$

$$= 3^4 + 62 \cdot 8 - 2(29 + 132) \qquad \text{Carrying out operations inside parentheses first; doing the multiplication}$$

$$= 3^4 + 62 \cdot 8 - 2(161) \qquad \text{Completing the addition inside parentheses}$$

$$= 81 + 62 \cdot 8 - 2(161) \qquad \text{Evaluating the exponential expression}$$

$$= 81 + 496 - 2(161) \left.\begin{array}{l} \\ \\ \end{array}\right\} \text{Doing the multiplication in order from left to right}$$

$$= 81 + 496 - 322$$

$$= 577 - 322 \left.\begin{array}{l} \\ \\ \end{array}\right\} \text{Doing all additions and subtractions in order from left to right}$$

$$= 255$$

Do Exercises 23–26.

When parentheses occur within parentheses, we can make them different shapes, such as [ ] (also called "brackets") and { } (usually called "braces"). Parentheses, brackets, and braces all have the same meaning. When parentheses occur within parentheses, **computations in the *innermost* ones are to be done first**.

**EXAMPLE 27** Simplify: $5 - \{6 - [3 - (7 + 3)]\}$.

$$5 - \{6 - [3 - (7 + 3)]\} = 5 - \{6 - [3 - 10]\} \qquad \text{Adding } 7 + 3$$

$$= 5 - \{6 - [-7]\} \qquad \text{Subtracting } 3 - 10$$

$$= 5 - 13 \qquad \text{Subtracting } 6 - [-7]$$

$$= -8$$

Simplify.

**23.** $43 - 52 \cdot 80$

**24.** $3^5 \div 3^4 \cdot 3^2$

**25.** $62 \cdot 8 + 4^3 - (5^2 - 64 \div 4)$

**26.** Simplify and compare:

$(7 - 4)^2$ and $7^2 - 4^2$.

**EXAMPLE 28** Simplify: $7 - [3(2 - 5) - 4(2 + 3)]$.

$7 - [3(2 - 5) - 4(2 + 3)] = 7 - [3(-3) - 4(5)]$    Doing the calculations in the innermost grouping symbols first

$\qquad\qquad\qquad = 7 - [-9 - 20]$

$\qquad\qquad\qquad = 7 - [-29]$

$\qquad\qquad\qquad = 36$

Do Exercises 27 and 28.

Simplify.

**27.** $6 - \{5 - [2 - (8 + 20)]\}$

**28.** $5 + \{6 - [2 + (5 - 2)]\}$

In addition to the usual grouping symbols—parentheses, brackets, and braces—a fraction bar and absolute-value signs can act as grouping symbols.

**EXAMPLE 29** Calculate: $\dfrac{12|7 - 9| + 8 \cdot 5}{3^2 + 2^3}$.

An equivalent expression with brackets as grouping symbols is

$[12|7 - 9| + 8 \cdot 5] \div [3^2 + 2^3]$.

What this shows, in effect, is that we do the calculations in the numerator and in the denominator separately, and then divide the results:

$\dfrac{12|7 - 9| + 8 \cdot 5}{3^2 + 2^3} = \dfrac{12|-2| + 8 \cdot 5}{9 + 8}$    Subtracting inside the absolute-value signs before taking the absolute value

$\qquad\qquad = \dfrac{12(2) + 8 \cdot 5}{17}$

$\qquad\qquad = \dfrac{24 + 40}{17} = \dfrac{64}{17}$.

Do Exercises 29 and 30.

Simplify.

**29.** $\dfrac{8 \cdot 7 - |6 - 8|}{5^2 + 6^3}$

**30.** $\dfrac{(8 - 3)^2 + (7 - 10)^2}{3^2 - 2^3}$

## Calculator Corner

**Order of Operations**   Computations are usually entered on a graphing calculator in the same way in which we would write them. To calculate $5 + 3 \cdot 4$, for example, we press ⑤ ➕ ③ ✖ ④ **ENTER**. The result is 17.

When an expression contains grouping symbols, we enter them using the ⦅ and ⦆ keys. To calculate $7(11 - 2) - 24$, we press ⑦ ⦅ ① ① ➖ ② ⦆ ➖ ② ④ **ENTER**. The result is 39.

Since a fraction bar acts as a grouping symbol, we must supply parentheses when entering some fraction expressions. To calculate $\dfrac{45 + 135}{2 - 17}$, for example, we enter it as $(45 + 135) \div (2 - 17)$. The result is $-12$.

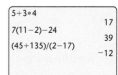

**Exercises:**   Calculate.

**1.** $48 \div 2 \cdot 3 - 4 \cdot 4$

**2.** $48 \div (2 \cdot 3 - 4) \cdot 4$

**3.** $\{(25 \cdot 30) \div [(2 \cdot 16) \div (4 \cdot 2)]\} + 15(45 \div 9)$

**4.** $\dfrac{17^2 - 311}{16 - 7}$

**a**    Write exponential notation.

**1.** $4 \cdot 4 \cdot 4 \cdot 4 \cdot 4$

**2.** $6 \cdot 6 \cdot 6$

**3.** $5 \cdot 5 \cdot 5 \cdot 5 \cdot 5 \cdot 5$

**4.** $x \cdot x \cdot x \cdot x$

**5.** $mmm$

**6.** $ttttt$

**7.** $\dfrac{7}{12} \cdot \dfrac{7}{12} \cdot \dfrac{7}{12} \cdot \dfrac{7}{12}$

**8.** $(3.8)(3.8)(3.8)(3.8)(3.8)$

**9.** $(123.7)(123.7)$

**10.** $\left(-\dfrac{4}{5}\right)\left(-\dfrac{4}{5}\right)\left(-\dfrac{4}{5}\right)$

Evaluate.

**11.** $2^7$

**12.** $9^3$

**13.** $(-2)^5$

**14.** $(-7)^2$

**15.** $\left(\dfrac{1}{3}\right)^4$

**16.** $(0.1)^6$

**17.** $(-4)^3$

**18.** $(-3)^4$

**19.** $(-5.6)^2$

**20.** $\left(\dfrac{2}{3}\right)^4$

**21.** $5^1$

**22.** $\left(\sqrt{6}\right)^1$

**23.** $34^0$

**24.** $\left(\dfrac{5}{2}\right)^1$

**25.** $\left(\sqrt{6}\right)^0$

**26.** $(-4)^0$

**27.** $\left(\dfrac{7}{8}\right)^1$

**28.** $(-87)^0$

**b**    Rewrite using a positive exponent. Evaluate, if possible.

**29.** $\left(\dfrac{1}{4}\right)^{-2}$

**30.** $\left(\dfrac{1}{5}\right)^{-3}$

**31.** $\left(\dfrac{2}{3}\right)^{-3}$

**32.** $\left(\dfrac{5}{2}\right)^{-4}$

**33.** $y^{-5}$

**34.** $x^{-6}$

**35.** $\dfrac{1}{a^{-2}}$

**36.** $\dfrac{1}{y^{-7}}$

**37.** $(-11)^{-1}$

**38.** $(-4)^{-3}$

Rewrite using a negative exponent.

**39.** $\dfrac{1}{3^4}$

**40.** $\dfrac{1}{9^2}$

**41.** $\dfrac{1}{b^3}$

**42.** $\dfrac{1}{n^5}$

**43.** $\dfrac{1}{(-16)^2}$

**44.** $\dfrac{1}{(-8)^6}$

(C) Simplify.

**45.** $12 - 4(5 - 1)$

**46.** $6 - 4(8 - 5)$

**47.** $9[8 - 7(5 - 2)]$

**48.** $10[7 - 4(8 - 5)]$

**49.** $[5(8 - 6) + 12] - [24 - (8 - 4)]$

**50.** $[9(7 - 4) + 19] - [25 - (7 + 3)]$

**51.** $[64 \div (-4)] \div (-2)$

**52.** $[48 \div (-3)] \div \left(-\dfrac{1}{4}\right)$

**53.** $19(-22) + 60$

**54.** $30 \cdot 10 - 18 \cdot 25$

**55.** $(5 + 7)^2;\ \ 5^2 + 7^2$

**56.** $(9 - 12)^2;\ \ 9^2 - 12^2$

**57.** $2^3 + 2^4 - 20 \cdot 30$

**58.** $7 \cdot 8 - 3^2 - 2^3$

**59.** $5^3 + 36 \cdot 72 - (18 + 25 \cdot 4)$

**60.** $4^3 + 20 \cdot 10 + 7^2 - 23$

**61.** $(13 \cdot 2 - 8 \cdot 4)^2$

**62.** $(9 \cdot 8 + 3 \cdot 3)^2$

**63.** $4000 \cdot (1 + 0.12)^3$

**64.** $5000 \cdot (4 + 1.16)^2$

**65.** $(20 \cdot 4 + 13 \cdot 8)^2 - (39 \cdot 15)^3$

**66.** $(43 \cdot 6 - 14 \cdot 7)^3 + (33 \cdot 34)^2$

**67.** $18 - 2 \cdot 3 - 9$

**68.** $18 - (2 \cdot 3 - 9)$

**69.** $(18 - 2 \cdot 3) - 9$

**70.** $(18 - 2)(3 - 9)$

**71.** $[24 \div (-3)] \div \left(-\dfrac{1}{2}\right)$

**72.** $[(-32) \div (-2)] \div (-2)$

**73.** $15 \cdot (-24) + 50$

**74.** $30 \cdot 20 - 15 \cdot 24$

**75.** $4 \div (8 - 10)^2 + 1$

**76.** $16 \div (19 - 15)^2 - 7$

**77.** $6^3 + 25 \cdot 71 - (16 + 25 \cdot 4)$

**78.** $5^3 + 20 \cdot 40 + 8^2 - 29$

**79.** $5000 \cdot (1 + 0.16)^3$

**80.** $4000 \cdot (3 + 1.14)^2$

**81.** $4 \cdot 5 - 2 \cdot 6 + 4$

**82.** $8(7 - 3)/4$

**83.** $4 \cdot (6 + 8)/(4 + 3)$

**84.** $4^3/8$

**85.** $[2 \cdot (5 - 3)]^2$

**86.** $5^3 - 7^2$

**87.** $8(-7) + 6(-5)$

**88.** $10(-5) + 1(-1)$

**89.** $19 - 5(-3) + 3$

**90.** $14 - 2(-6) + 7$

**91.** $9 \div (-3) + 16 \div 8$

**92.** $-32 - 8 \div 4 - (-2)$

**93.** $7 + 10 - (-10 \div 2)$

**94.** $(3 - 8)^2$

**95.** $5^2 - 8^2$

**96.** $28 - 10^3$

**97.** $20 + 4^3 \div (-8)$

**98.** $2 \times 10^3 - 5000$

**99.** $-7(3^4) + 18$

**100.** $6[9 - (3 - 4)]$

**101.** $9[(8 - 11) - 13]$

**102.** $1000 \div (-100) \div 10$

**103.** $256 \div (-32) \div (-4)$

**104.** $\dfrac{20 - 6^2}{9^2 + 3^2}$

**105.** $\dfrac{5^2 - |4^3 - 8|}{9^2 - 2^2 - 1^5}$

**106.** $\dfrac{4|6 - 7| - 5 \cdot 4}{6 \cdot 7 - 8|4 - 1|}$

**107.** $\dfrac{30(8 - 3) - 4(10 - 3)}{10|2 - 6| - 2(5 + 2)}$

**108.** $\dfrac{5^3 - 3^2 + 12 \cdot 5}{-32 \div (-16) \div (-4)}$

## Skill Maintenance

Find the absolute value.   [R.1d]

**109.** $\left| -\dfrac{9}{7} \right|$

**110.** $|2.3|$

**111.** $|0|$

**112.** $|-900|$

Compute.   [R.2a, c, d]

**113.** $23 - 56$

**114.** $-23 - 56$

**115.** $-23 - (-56)$

**116.** $-23 + (-56)$

**117.** $(-10)(2.3)$

**118.** $(-10)(-2.3)$

**119.** $10(-2.3)$

**120.** $\left( -\dfrac{2}{3} \right)\left( -\dfrac{15}{16} \right)$

## Synthesis

Simplify.

**121.** $(-2)^0 - (-2)^3 - (-2)^{-1} + (-2)^4 - (-2)^{-2}$

**122.** $2(6^1 \cdot 6^{-1} - 6^{-1} \cdot 6^0)$

**123.** Place parentheses in this statement to make it true: $9 \cdot 5 + 2 - 8 \cdot 3 + 1 = 22$.

The symbol ⚈ means to use your calculator to work a particular exercise.

**124.** ⚈ Find each of the following.

$12345679 \cdot 9 = ?$

$12345679 \cdot 18 = ?$

$12345679 \cdot 27 = ?$

Then look for a pattern and find $12345679 \cdot 36$ without the use of a calculator.

**125.** ⚈ Find $(0.2)^{(-0.2)^{-1}}$.

**126.** ⚈ Determine which is larger: $(\pi)^{\sqrt{2}}$ or $(\sqrt{2})^{\pi}$.

**127.** Find $(2 + 3)^{-1}$ and $2^{-1} + 3^{-1}$ and determine whether they are equivalent.

# R.4

# Introduction to Algebraic Expressions

## OBJECTIVES

**a** Translate a phrase to an algebraic expression.

**b** Evaluate an algebraic expression by substitution.

The study of algebra involves the use of equations to solve problems. Equations are constructed from algebraic expressions. The purpose of Part 2 of this chapter is to provide a review of the types of expressions encountered in algebra and ways in which we can manipulate them.

### Algebraic Expressions and Their Use

In arithmetic, you worked with expressions such as

$$91 + 76, \quad 26 - 17, \quad 14 \cdot 35, \quad 7 \div 8, \quad \frac{7}{8}, \quad \text{and} \quad 5^2 - 3^2.$$

In algebra, we use these as well as expressions like

$$x + 76, \quad 26 - q, \quad 14 \cdot x, \quad d \div t, \quad \frac{d}{t}, \quad \text{and} \quad x^2 - y^2.$$

When a letter is used to stand for various numbers, it is called a **variable**. Let $t =$ the number of hours that a passenger jet has been flying. Then $t$ is a variable, because $t$ changes as the flight continues. If a letter represents one particular number, it is called a **constant**. Let $d =$ the number of hours in a day. Then $d$ is a constant.

An **algebraic expression** consists of variables, numbers, and operation signs, such as $+, -, \cdot, \div$. All the expressions above are examples of algebraic expressions. When an equals sign, $=$, is placed between two expressions, an **equation** is formed.

We compare algebraic expressions with equations in the table at left. Note that none of the expressions has an equals sign ($=$).

| ALGEBRAIC EXPRESSIONS | EQUATIONS |
|---|---|
| 10 | $t = 10$ |
| $x - 5$ | $x - 5 = 10$ |
| $11x$ | $x - 5 = 11x$ |
| $y^2 + 2y$ | $y^2 + 2y = 1 + y$ |

Do Exercise 1.

Equations can be used to solve applied problems. To illustrate this, consider the bar graph below, which shows farm income for several recent years.

**1.** Which of the following are equations?

a) $3x + 7$

b) $-3x - 7 = 18$

c) $-3(x - 5) + 17$

d) $7 = t - 4$

**Farm Income**

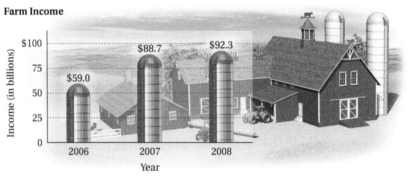

SOURCE: U.S. Department of Agriculture

Suppose we want to determine how much higher farm income was in 2008 than in 2007. We can translate this problem to an equation, as follows:

| Farm income in 2007 | plus | How much more | is | Farm income in 2008 |
|---|---|---|---|---|
| ↓ | ↓ | ↓ | ↓ | ↓ |
| 88.7 | + | $x$ | = | 92.3. |

To find the number that $x$ represents, we subtract 88.7 on both sides of the equation:

$$88.7 + x = 92.3$$
$$88.7 + x - 88.7 = 92.3 - 88.7 \qquad \text{Subtracting } 88.7$$
$$x = 3.6.$$

We see that farm income was \$3.6 billion higher in 2008 than in 2007.

Do Exercise 2.

**2.** Refer to the graph on the preceding page. Translate to an equation and solve: How much higher was farm income in 2008 than in 2006?

## (a) Translating to Algebraic Expressions

To translate problems to equations, we need to know that certain words correspond to certain symbols, as shown in the following table.

**KEY WORDS**

| ADDITION | SUBTRACTION | MULTIPLICATION | DIVISION |
|---|---|---|---|
| add | subtract | multiply | divide |
| sum | difference | product | quotient |
| plus | minus | times | divided by |
| total | decreased by | twice | ratio |
| increased by | less than | of | per |
| more than | | | |

Expressions like $rs$ represent products and can also be written as $r \cdot s$, $r \times s$, $(r)(s)$, or $r(s)$. The multipliers $r$ and $s$ are also called **factors**. A quotient $m \div 5$ can also be represented as $m/5$ or $\dfrac{m}{5}$.

**EXAMPLE 1** Translate to an algebraic expression: Eight less than some number.

We can use any variable we wish, such as $x, y, t, m, n$, and so on. Here we let $t$ represent the number. If we knew the number to be 23, then the translation of "eight less than 23" would be $23 - 8$. If we knew the number to be 345, then the translation of "eight less than 345" would be $345 - 8$. Since we are using a variable for the number, the translation is

$$t - 8. \qquad \textit{Caution!} \; 8 - t \text{ would be incorrect.}$$

**EXAMPLE 2** Translate to an algebraic expression: Twenty-two more than some number.

This time we let $y$ represent the number. If we knew the number to be 47, then the translation would be $47 + 22$, or $22 + 47$. If we knew the number to be 17.95, then the translation would be $17.95 + 22$, or $22 + 17.95$. Since we are using a variable, the translation is

$$y + 22, \quad \text{or} \quad 22 + y.$$

**EXAMPLE 3** Translate to an algebraic expression: Five less than forty-three percent of the quotient of two numbers.

We let $r$ and $s$ represent the two numbers.

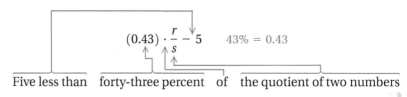

**EXAMPLE 4** Translate each of the following to an algebraic expression.

| PHRASE | ALGEBRAIC EXPRESSION |
|---|---|
| Five *more than* some number | $n + 5$, or $5 + n$ |
| Half *of* a number | $\frac{1}{2}t$, or $\frac{t}{2}$ |
| Five *more than* three *times* some number | $3p + 5$, or $5 + 3p$ |
| The *difference* of two numbers | $x - y$ |
| Six *less than* the *product* of two numbers | $rs - 6$ |
| Seventy-six percent *of* some number | $0.76z$, or $\frac{76}{100}z$ |
| Eight *less than twice* some number | $2x - 8$ |

Do Exercises 3–8.

## b Evaluating Algebraic Expressions

When we replace a variable with a number, we say that we are **substituting** for the variable. Carrying out the resulting calculation is called **evaluating the expression**.

**EXAMPLE 5** Evaluate $x - y$ when $x = 83$ and $y = 49$.

We substitute 83 for $x$ and 49 for $y$ and carry out the subtraction:

$$x - y = 83 - 49 = 34.$$

The number 34 is called the **value** of the expression.

---

Translate to an algebraic expression.

**3.** Sixteen less than some number

**4.** Forty-seven more than some number

**5.** Sixteen minus some number

**6.** One-fourth of some number

**7.** Six more than eight times some number

**8.** Eight less than ninety-nine percent of the quotient of two numbers

*Answers*

**3.** $x - 16$   **4.** $y + 47$, or $47 + y$   **5.** $16 - x$

**6.** $\frac{1}{4}t$   **7.** $8x + 6$, or $6 + 8x$

**8.** $99\% \cdot \frac{a}{b} - 8$, or $(0.99) \cdot \frac{a}{b} - 8$

**EXAMPLE 6**  Evaluate $a/b$ when $a = -63$ and $b = 7$.

We substitute $-63$ for $a$ and 7 for $b$ and carry out the division:

$$\frac{a}{b} = \frac{-63}{7} = -9.$$

**EXAMPLE 7**  Evaluate the expression $3xy + z$ when $x = 2$, $y = -5$, and $z = 7$.

We substitute and carry out the calculations according to the rules for order of operations:

$$3xy + z = 3(2)(-5) + 7 = -30 + 7 = -23.$$

> Do Exercises 9–14.

Geometric formulas must often be evaluated in applied problems. In the next example, we use the formula for the area $A$ of a triangle with a base of length $b$ and a height of length $h$:

$$A = \tfrac{1}{2}bh.$$

**EXAMPLE 8**  *Area of a Triangular Sail.*  The base of a triangular sail is 6.4 m and the height is 8 m. Find the area of the sail.

We substitute 6.4 for $b$ and 8 for $h$ and multiply:

$$A = \tfrac{1}{2}bh = \tfrac{1}{2} \cdot 6.4 \cdot 8$$
$$= 25.6 \text{ m}^2.$$

> Do Exercise 15.

**EXAMPLE 9**  Evaluate $5 + 2(a - 1)^2$ when $a = 4$.

| | |
|---|---|
| $5 + 2(a - 1)^2 = 5 + 2(4 - 1)^2$ | Substituting |
| $= 5 + 2(3)^2$ | Working within parentheses first |
| $= 5 + 2(9)$ | Simplifying $3^2$ |
| $= 5 + 18$ | Multiplying |
| $= 23$ | Adding |

**EXAMPLE 10**  Evaluate $9 - x^3 + 6 \div 2y^2$ when $x = 2$ and $y = 5$.

| | |
|---|---|
| $9 - x^3 + 6 \div 2y^2 = 9 - 2^3 + 6 \div 2(5)^2$ | Substituting |
| $= 9 - 8 + 6 \div 2 \cdot 25$ | Simplifying $2^3$ and $5^2$ |
| $= 9 - 8 + 3 \cdot 25$ | Dividing |
| $= 9 - 8 + 75$ | Multiplying |
| $= 1 + 75$ | Subtracting |
| $= 76$ | Adding |

> Do Exercises 16–18.

9. Evaluate $a + b$ when $a = 48$ and $b = 36$.

10. Evaluate $x - y$ when $x = -97$ and $y = 29$.

11. Evaluate $a/b$ when $a = 400$ and $b = -8$.

12. Evaluate $8t$ when $t = 15$.

13. Evaluate $4x + 5y$ when $x = -2$ and $y = 10$.

14. Evaluate $7ab - c$ when $a = -3$, $b = 4$, and $c = 62$.

15. Find the area of a triangle when $h$ is 24 ft and $b$ is 8 ft.

16. Evaluate $(x - 3)^2$ when $x = 11$.

17. Evaluate $x^2 - 6x + 9$ when $x = 11$.

18. Evaluate $8 - x^3 + 10 \div 5y^2$ when $x = 4$ and $y = 6$.

**a** Translate each phrase to an algebraic expression.

**1.** 8 more than $b$

**2.** 11 more than $t$

**3.** 13.4 less than $c$

**4.** 0.203 less than $d$

**5.** 5 increased by $q$

**6.** 18 increased by $z$

**7.** $b$ more than $a$

**8.** $c$ more than $d$

**9.** $x$ divided by $y$

**10.** $c$ divided by $h$

**11.** $x$ plus $w$

**12.** $s$ added to $t$

**13.** $m$ subtracted from $n$

**14.** $p$ subtracted from $q$

**15.** The sum of $p$ and $q$

**16.** The sum of $a$ and $b$

**17.** Three times $q$

**18.** Twice $z$

**19.** $-18$ multiplied by $m$

**20.** The product of $-6$ and $t$

**21.** The product of 17% and your salary

**22.** 48% of the women attending

**23.** Megan drove at a speed of 75 mph for $t$ hours on an interstate highway in Arizona. How far did Megan travel?

**24.** Joe had $d$ dollars before spending $19.95 on a DVD of the movie *Citizen Kane*. How much did Joe have after the purchase?

**25.** Jennifer had $40 before spending $x$ dollars on a pizza. How much remains?

**26.** Lance drove his pickup truck at a speed of 65 mph for $t$ hours. How far did he travel?

**b** Evaluate.

**27.** $23z$, when $z = -4$

**28.** $57y$, when $y = -8$

**29.** $\dfrac{a}{b}$, when $a = -24$ and $b = -8$

**30.** $\dfrac{x}{y}$, when $x = 30$ and $y = -6$

**31.** $\dfrac{m - n}{8}$, when $m = 36$ and $n = 4$

**32.** $\dfrac{5}{p + q}$, when $p = 20$ and $q = 30$

**33.** $\dfrac{5z}{y}$, when $z = 9$ and $y = 2$

**34.** $\dfrac{18m}{n}$, when $m = 7$ and $n = 18$

**35.** $2c \div 3b$, when $b = 4$ and $c = 6$

**36.** $4x - y$, when $x = 3$ and $y = -2$

**37.** $25 - r^2 + s \div r^2$, when $r = 3$ and $s = 27$

**38.** $n^3 - 2 + p \div n^2$, when $n = 2$ and $p = 12$

**39.** $m + n(5 + n^2)$, when $m = 15$ and $n = 3$

**40.** $a^2 - 3(a - b)$, when $a = 10$ and $b = -8$

*Simple Interest.* The **simple interest** $I$ on a principal of $P$ dollars at interest rate $r$ for $t$ years is given by $I = Prt$.

**41.** Find the simple interest on a principal of $7345 at 6% for 1 year.

**42.** Find the simple interest on a principal of $18,000 at 4.6% for 2 years. (*Hint*: 4.6% = 0.046.)

**43.** *Area of a Dining Table.* The area $A$ of a circle with radius $r$ is given by $A = \pi r^2$. The circumference $C$ of the circle is given by $C = 2\pi r$. The radius of Ray and Mary's round oak dining table is 27 in. Find the area and the circumference of the table. Use 3.14 for $\pi$.

$r = 27$ in.

**44.** *Area of a Parallelogram.* The area $A$ of a parallelogram with base $b$ and height $h$ is given by $A = bh$. Find the area of a flower garden that is shaped like a parallelogram with a height of 1.9 m and a base of 3.6 m.

$h$

$b$

## Skill Maintenance

Evaluate. [R.3a]

**45.** $3^5$

**46.** $(-3)^5$

**47.** $(-10)^2$

**48.** $(-10)^4$

**49.** $(-5.3)^2$

**50.** $\left(\dfrac{3}{5}\right)^2$

**51.** $(4.5)^0$

**52.** $(4.5)^1$

**53.** $(3x)^1$

**54.** $(3x)^0$

## Synthesis

Translate to an equation.

**55.** The distance $d$ that a rapid transit train in the Denver airport travels in time $t$ at a speed $r$ is given by speed times time. Write an equation for $d$.

**56.** Marlana invests $P$ dollars at 2.7% simple interest. Write an equation for the number of dollars $N$ in the account 1 year from now.

Evaluate.

**57.** $\dfrac{x + y}{2} + \dfrac{3y}{2}$, when $x = 2$ and $y = 4$

**58.** $\dfrac{2.56y}{3.2x}$, when $y = 3$ and $x = 4$

# R.5

# Equivalent Algebraic Expressions

## OBJECTIVES

**a** Determine whether two expressions are equivalent by completing a table of values.

**b** Find equivalent fraction expressions by multiplying by 1, and simplify fraction expressions.

**c** Use the commutative laws and the associative laws to find equivalent expressions.

**d** Use the distributive laws to find equivalent expressions by multiplying and factoring.

## a Equivalent Expressions

When solving equations and performing other operations in algebra, we manipulate expressions in various ways. For example, rather than $x + 2x$, we might write $3x$, knowing that the two expressions represent the same number for any allowable replacement of $x$. In that sense, the expressions $x + 2x$ and $3x$ are **equivalent**, as are $5/x$ and $5x/x^2$, even though 0 is not an allowable replacement because division by 0 is not defined.

> **EQUIVALENT EXPRESSIONS**
>
> Two expressions that have the same value for all *allowable* replacements are called **equivalent expressions**.

**EXAMPLE 1** Complete the table by evaluating each of the expressions $x + 2x$, $3x$, and $8x - x$ for the given values. Then look for expressions that are equivalent.

| VALUE | $x + 2x$ | $3x$ | $8x - x$ |
|---|---|---|---|
| $x = -2$ | | | |
| $x = 5$ | | | |
| $x = 0$ | | | |

We substitute and find the value of each expression. For example, for $x = -2$,

$$x + 2x = -2 + 2(-2) = -2 - 4 = -6,$$
$$3x = 3(-2) = -6, \quad \text{and}$$
$$8x - x = 8(-2) - (-2) = -16 + 2 = -14.$$

| VALUE | $x + 2x$ | $3x$ | $8x - x$ |
|---|---|---|---|
| $x = -2$ | | | |
| $x = 5$ | | | |
| $x = 0$ | | | |

Note that the values of $x + 2x$ and $3x$ are the same for the given values of $x$. Indeed, they are the same for any allowable real-number replacement of $x$, though we cannot substitute them all to find out. The expressions $x + 2x$ and $3x$ are **equivalent**. But the expressions $x + 2x$ and $8x - x$ are not equivalent, and the expressions $3x$ and $8x - x$ are not equivalent. Although $3x$ and $8x - x$ have the same value for $x = 0$, they are not equivalent since values are not the same for *all x*.

Complete each table by evaluating each expression for the given values. Then look for expressions that may be equivalent.

**1.**

| VALUE | $6x - x$ | $5x$ | $8x + x$ |
|---|---|---|---|
| $x = -2$ | | | |
| $x = 8$ | | | |
| $x = 0$ | | | |

**2.**

| VALUE | $(x + 3)^2$ | $x^2 + 9$ |
|---|---|---|
| $x = -2$ | | |
| $x = 5$ | | |
| $x = 4.8$ | | |

*Answers*

**1.** $-10, -10, -18$; $40, 40, 72$; $0, 0, 0$; $6x - x$ and $5x$ are equivalent.   **2.** $1, 13$; $64, 34$; $60.84$, $32.04$; the expressions are not equivalent.

Do Exercises 1 and 2.

## b Equivalent Fraction Expressions

For the remainder of this section, we will consider several properties of real numbers that will allow us to find equivalent expressions.

> **THE IDENTITY PROPERTY OF 1**
>
> For any real number $a$,
>
> $$a \cdot 1 = 1 \cdot a = a.$$
>
> (The number 1 is the **multiplicative identity**.)

We will often refer to the use of the identity property of 1 as "multiplying by 1." We can use multiplying by 1 to change from one fraction expression to an equivalent one with a different denominator.

**EXAMPLE 2** Use multiplying by 1 to find an expression equivalent to $\frac{3}{5}$ with a denominator of $10x$.

Because $10x = 5 \cdot 2x$, we multiply by 1, using $2x/(2x)$ as a name for 1:

$$\frac{3}{5} = \frac{3}{5} \cdot 1 = \frac{3}{5} \cdot \frac{2x}{2x} = \frac{3 \cdot 2x}{5 \cdot 2x} = \frac{6x}{10x}.$$

Note that the expressions $3/5$ and $6x/(10x)$ are equivalent. They have the same value for any allowable replacement. Note too that 0 is not an allowable replacement in $6x/(10x)$, but for all nonzero real numbers, the expressions $3/5$ and $6x/(10x)$ have the same value.

Do Exercises 3 and 4.

**3.** Use multiplying by 1 to find an expression equivalent to $\frac{2}{7}$ with a denominator of $7y$.

**4.** Use multiplying by 1 to find an expression equivalent to $\frac{2}{11}$ with a denominator of $44x$.

In algebra, we consider an expression like $3/5$ to be a "simplified" form of $6x/(10x)$. To find such simplified expressions, we reverse the identity property of 1 in order to "remove a factor of 1."

**EXAMPLE 3** Simplify: $\frac{7x}{9x}$.

We do the reverse of what we did in Example 2:

$$\frac{7x}{9x} = \frac{7 \cdot x}{9 \cdot x} \qquad \text{We factor the numerator and the denominator and then look for the largest common factor of both.}$$

$$= \frac{7}{9} \cdot \frac{x}{x} \qquad \text{Factoring the expression}$$

$$= \frac{7}{9} \cdot 1 \qquad \frac{x}{x} = 1$$

$$= \frac{7}{9}. \qquad \text{Removing a factor of 1 using the identity property of 1 in reverse}$$

**EXAMPLE 4** Simplify: $-\dfrac{24y}{16y}$.

$$-\frac{24y}{16y} = -\frac{3 \cdot 8y}{2 \cdot 8y} = -\frac{3}{2} \cdot \frac{8y}{8y} = -\frac{3}{2} \cdot 1 = -\frac{3}{2}$$

Do Exercises 5 and 6.

Simplify.

**5.** $\dfrac{2y}{3y}$

**6.** $-\dfrac{20m}{12m}$

*Answers*

**3.** $\dfrac{2y}{7y}$  **4.** $\dfrac{8x}{44x}$  **5.** $\dfrac{2}{3}$  **6.** $-\dfrac{5}{3}$

## (c) The Commutative Laws and the Associative Laws

Let's examine the expressions $x + y$ and $y + x$, as well as $xy$ and $yx$.

**EXAMPLE 5** Evaluate $x + y$ and $y + x$ when $x = 5$ and $y = 8$.

We substitute 5 for $x$ and 8 for $y$ in both expressions:

$$x + y = 5 + 8 = 13; \qquad y + x = 8 + 5 = 13.$$

**EXAMPLE 6** Evaluate $xy$ and $yx$ when $x = 4$ and $y = 3$.

We substitute 4 for $x$ and 3 for $y$ in both expressions:

$$xy = 4 \cdot 3 = 12; \qquad yx = 3 \cdot 4 = 12.$$

Do Exercises 7 and 8.

**7.** Evaluate $x + y$ and $y + x$ when $x = -3$ and $y = 5$.

**8.** Evaluate $xy$ and $yx$ when $x = -2$ and $y = 7$.

Note that the expressions $x + y$ and $y + x$ have the same values no matter what the variables stand for. Thus they are equivalent. They illustrate that when we add two numbers, the order in which we add does not matter. Similarly, when we multiply two numbers, the order in which we multiply does not matter. Thus the expressions $xy$ and $yx$ are equivalent. They have the same values no matter what the variables stand for. These are examples of general patterns or laws.

---

**THE COMMUTATIVE LAWS**

*Addition.* For any numbers $a$ and $b$,

$$a + b = b + a.$$

(We can change the order when adding without affecting the answer.)

*Multiplication.* For any numbers $a$ and $b$,

$$ab = ba.$$

(We can change the order when multiplying without affecting the answer.)

---

Using a commutative law, we know that $x + 4$ and $4 + x$ are equivalent. Similarly, $5x$ and $x \cdot 5$ are equivalent. Thus, in an algebraic expression, we can replace one with the other and the result will be equivalent to the original expression.

Now let's examine the expressions $a + (b + c)$ and $(a + b) + c$. Note that these expressions use parentheses as grouping symbols, and they also involve three numbers. Calculations within grouping symbols are to be done first.

**EXAMPLE 7** Evaluate $a + (b + c)$ and $(a + b) + c$ when $a = 4$, $b = 8$, and $c = 5$.

$$
\begin{aligned}
a + (b + c) &= 4 + (8 + 5) && \text{Substituting} \\
&= 4 + 13 && \text{Calculating within parentheses first:} \\
&= 17; && \text{adding 8 and 5}
\end{aligned}
$$

$$
\begin{aligned}
(a + b) + c &= (4 + 8) + 5 && \text{Substituting} \\
&= 12 + 5 && \text{Calculating within parentheses first:} \\
&= 17 && \text{adding 4 and 8}
\end{aligned}
$$

*Answers*

**7.** 2; 2    **8.** −14; −14

**EXAMPLE 8**  Evaluate $a \cdot (b \cdot c)$ and $(a \cdot b) \cdot c$ when $a = 7$, $b = 4$, and $c = 2$.

$$a \cdot (b \cdot c) = 7 \cdot (4 \cdot 2) = 7 \cdot 8 = 56;$$
$$(a \cdot b) \cdot c = (7 \cdot 4) \cdot 2 = 28 \cdot 2 = 56$$

Do Exercises 9 and 10.

**9.** Evaluate
$$a + (b + c) \quad \text{and} \quad (a + b) + c$$
when $a = 10$, $b = 9$, and $c = 2$.

**10.** Evaluate
$$a \cdot (b \cdot c) \quad \text{and} \quad (a \cdot b) \cdot c$$
when $a = 11$, $b = 5$, and $c = 8$.

When only addition is involved, grouping symbols can be placed any way we please without affecting the answer. Likewise, when only multiplication is involved, grouping symbols can be placed any way we please without affecting the answer.

---

**THE ASSOCIATIVE LAWS**

*Addition.*  For any numbers $a$, $b$, and $c$,

$$a + (b + c) = (a + b) + c.$$

(Numbers can be grouped in any manner for addition.)

*Multiplication.*  For any numbers $a$, $b$, and $c$,

$$a \cdot (b \cdot c) = (a \cdot b) \cdot c.$$

(Numbers can be grouped in any manner for multiplication.)

---

Since grouping symbols can be placed any way we please when only additions or only multiplications are involved, we often omit them. For example,

$$x + (y + 3) \text{ means } x + y + 3, \quad \text{and} \quad l(wh) \text{ means } lwh.$$

**EXAMPLE 9**  Use the commutative and the associative laws to write at least three expressions equivalent to $(x + 8) + y$.

**a)**  $(x + 8) + y = x + (8 + y)$ ⟶ Using the associative law first and then
$\phantom{(x + 8) + y} = x + (y + 8)$ ⟶ the commutative law

**b)**  $(x + 8) + y = y + (x + 8)$ ⟶ Using the commutative law and then
$\phantom{(x + 8) + y} = y + (8 + x)$ ⟶ the commutative law again

**c)**  $(x + 8) + y = (8 + x) + y$ ⟶ Using the commutative law first and then
$\phantom{(x + 8) + y} = 8 + (x + y)$ ⟶ the associative law

Do Exercises 11 and 12.

**11.** Use the commutative laws to write an expression equivalent to each of $y + 5$, $ab$, and $8 + mn$.

**12.** Use the commutative and the associative laws to write at least three expressions equivalent to $(2 \cdot x) \cdot y$.

### d  The Distributive Laws

Let's now examine two laws, each of which involves two operations. The first involves multiplication and addition.

**EXAMPLE 10**  Evaluate $8(x + y)$ and $8x + 8y$ when $x = 4$ and $y = 5$.

$$8(x + y) = 8(4 + 5) \qquad 8x + 8y = 8 \cdot 4 + 8 \cdot 5$$
$$\phantom{8(x + y)} = 8(9) \phantom{= 8(4 + 5)} \qquad \phantom{8x + 8y} = 32 + 40$$
$$\phantom{8(x + y)} = 72; \phantom{= 8(4 + 5)} \qquad \phantom{8x + 8y} = 72$$

***Answers***

**9.** 21; 21   **10.** 440; 440   **11.** $5 + y$; $ba$; $mn + 8$, or $nm + 8$, or $8 + nm$   **12.** $2 \cdot (x \cdot y)$; $(2 \cdot y) \cdot x$; $(y \cdot 2) \cdot x$; answers may vary

The expressions $8(x + y)$ and $8x + 8y$ in Example 10 are equivalent. This fact is the result of a law called *the distributive law of multiplication over addition*.

---

**THE DISTRIBUTIVE LAW OF MULTIPLICATION OVER ADDITION**

For any numbers $a$, $b$, and $c$,

$$a(b + c) = ab + ac, \quad \text{or} \quad (b + c)a = ba + ca.$$

(We can add and then multiply, or we can multiply and then add.)

---

**13.** Evaluate $10(x + y)$ and $10x + 10y$ when $x = 7$ and $y = 11$.

**14.** Evaluate $9(a + b)$, $(a + b)9$, and $9a + 9b$ when $a = 5$ and $b = -2$.

Do Exercises 13 and 14.

The other distributive law involves multiplication and subtraction.

**EXAMPLE 11** Evaluate $\frac{1}{2}(a - b)$ and $\frac{1}{2}a - \frac{1}{2}b$ when $a = 42$ and $b = 78$.

$$\begin{aligned}
\frac{1}{2}(a - b) &= \frac{1}{2}(42 - 78) & \frac{1}{2}a - \frac{1}{2}b &= \frac{1}{2} \cdot 42 - \frac{1}{2} \cdot 78 \\
&= \frac{1}{2}(-36) & &= 21 - 39 \\
&= -18; & &= -18
\end{aligned}$$

The expressions $\frac{1}{2}(a - b)$ and $\frac{1}{2}a - \frac{1}{2}b$ in Example 11 are equivalent. This fact is the result of a law called *the distributive law of multiplication over subtraction*.

---

**THE DISTRIBUTIVE LAW OF MULTIPLICATION OVER SUBTRACTION**

For any real numbers $a$, $b$, and $c$,

$$a(b - c) = ab - ac, \quad \text{or} \quad (b - c)a = ba - ca.$$

(We can subtract and then multiply, or we can multiply and then subtract.)

---

**15.** Evaluate $5(a - b)$ and $5a - 5b$ when $a = 10$ and $b = 8$.

**16.** Evaluate $\frac{2}{3}(p - q)$ and $\frac{2}{3}p - \frac{2}{3}q$ when $p = 60$ and $q = 24$.

We often refer to "*the* distributive law" when we mean *either* or *both* of these laws.

Do Exercises 15 and 16.

### Multiplying Expressions with Variables

The distributive laws are the basis of multiplication in algebra as well as in arithmetic. In the following examples, note that we multiply each number or letter inside the parentheses by the factor outside.

Multiply.

**17.** $8(y - 10)$      **18.** $a(x + y - z)$

**19.** $10\left(4x - 6y + \frac{1}{2}z\right)$

**EXAMPLES** Multiply.

**12.** $4(x - 2) = 4 \cdot x - 4 \cdot 2 = 4x - 8$

**13.** $b(s - t + f) = bs - bt + bf$

**14.** $-3(y + 4) = -3 \cdot y + (-3) \cdot 4 = -3y - 12$

**15.** $-2x(y - 1) = -2x \cdot y - (-2x) \cdot 1 = -2xy + 2x$

Do Exercises 17–19.

## Factoring Expressions with Variables

The reverse of multiplying is called **factoring**. Factoring an expression involves factoring its *terms*. **Terms** of algebraic expressions are the parts separated by plus signs.

**EXAMPLE 16** List the terms of $3x - 4y - 2z$.

We first find an equivalent expression that uses addition signs:

$3x - 4y - 2z = 3x + (-4y) + (-2z)$.     Using the property $a - b = a + (-b)$

Thus the terms are $3x$, $-4y$, and $-2z$.

Do Exercise 20.

Now we can consider the reverse of multiplying: *factoring*.

> ### FACTORS
>
> To **factor** an expression is to find an equivalent expression that is a product. If $N = ab$, then $a$ and $b$ are **factors** of $N$.

**EXAMPLES** Factor.

**17.** $8x + 8y = 8(x + y)$     8 and $x + y$ are factors.

**18.** $cx - cy = c(x - y)$     $c$ and $x - y$ are factors.

The distributive laws tell us that $8(x + y)$ and $8x + 8y$ are equivalent. We consider $8(x + y)$ to be **factored**. The factors are 8 and $x + y$. Whenever the terms of an expression have a factor in common, we can "remove" that factor, or "factor it out," using the distributive laws. We proceed as in Examples 17 and 18, but we may have to factor some of the terms first in order to display the common factor.

Generally, we try to factor out the largest factor common to all the terms. In the following example, we might factor out 3, but there is a larger factor common to the terms, 9. So we factor out the 9.

**EXAMPLE 19** Factor: $9x + 27y$.

$9x + 27y = 9 \cdot x + 9 \cdot (3y) = 9(x + 3y)$

We often must supply a factor of 1 when factoring out a common factor, as in the next example, which is a formula involving simple interest.

**EXAMPLE 20** Factor: $P + Prt$.

$P + Prt = P \cdot 1 + P \cdot rt$     Writing $P$ as a product of $P$ and 1

$\phantom{P + Prt} = P(1 + rt)$     Using the distributive law

You can always check a factorization by multiplying it out.

Do Exercises 21-25.

**20.** List the terms of
$$-5x - 7y + 67t - \frac{4}{5}.$$

Factor.

**21.** $9x + 9y$

**22.** $ac - ay$

**23.** $6x - 12$

**24.** $35x - 25y + 15w + 5$

**25.** $bs + bt - bw$

**a** Complete each table by evaluating each expression for the given values. Then look for expressions that are equivalent.

**1.**

| VALUE | $2x + 3x$ | $5x$ | $2x - 3x$ |
|---|---|---|---|
| $x = -2$ | | | |
| $x = 5$ | | | |
| $x = 0$ | | | |

**2.**

| VALUE | $7x + 2x$ | $5x$ | $7x - 2x$ |
|---|---|---|---|
| $x = -2$ | | | |
| $x = 5$ | | | |
| $x = 0$ | | | |

**3.**

| VALUE | $4x + 8x$ | $4(x + 3x)$ | $4(x + 2x)$ |
|---|---|---|---|
| $x = -1$ | | | |
| $x = 3.2$ | | | |
| $x = 0$ | | | |

**4.**

| VALUE | $5(x - 2)$ | $5x - 2$ | $5x - 10$ |
|---|---|---|---|
| $x = -1$ | | | |
| $x = 4.6$ | | | |
| $x = 0$ | | | |

**b** Use multiplying by 1 to find an equivalent expression with the given denominator.

**5.** $\dfrac{7}{8}$; $8x$

**6.** $\dfrac{4}{3}$; $3a$

**7.** $\dfrac{3}{4}$; $8a$

**8.** $\dfrac{3}{10}$; $50y$

Simplify.

**9.** $\dfrac{25x}{15x}$

**10.** $\dfrac{36y}{18y}$

**11.** $-\dfrac{100a}{25a}$

**12.** $\dfrac{-625t}{15t}$

**c** Use a commutative law to find an equivalent expression.

**13.** $w + 3$

**14.** $y + 5$

**15.** $rt$

**16.** $cd$

**17.** $4 + cd$

**18.** $pq + 14$

**19.** $yz + x$

**20.** $s + qt$

Use an associative law to find an equivalent expression.

**21.** $m + (n + 2)$

**22.** $5 \cdot (p \cdot q)$

**23.** $(7 \cdot x) \cdot y$

**24.** $(7 + p) + q$

Use the commutative and the associative laws to find three equivalent expressions.

**25.** $(a + b) + 8$

**26.** $(4 + x) + y$

**27.** $7 \cdot (a \cdot b)$

**28.** $(8 \cdot m) \cdot n$

**d** Multiply.

**29.** $4(a + 1)$

**30.** $3(c + 1)$

**31.** $8(x - y)$

**32.** $7(b - c)$

**33.** $-5(2a + 3b)$  **34.** $-2(3c + 5d)$  **35.** $2a(b - c + d)$  **36.** $5x(y - z + w)$

**37.** $2\pi r(h + 1)$  **38.** $P(1 + rt)$  **39.** $\frac{1}{2}h(a + b)$  **40.** $\frac{1}{4}\pi r(1 + s)$

List the terms of each of the following.

**41.** $4a - 5b + 6$  **42.** $5x - 9y + 12$  **43.** $2x - 3y - 2z$  **44.** $5a - 7b - 9c$

Factor.

**45.** $24x + 24y$  **46.** $9a + 9b$  **47.** $7p - 7$  **48.** $22x - 22$

**49.** $7x - 21$  **50.** $6y - 36$  **51.** $xy + x$  **52.** $ab + a$

**53.** $2x - 2y + 2z$  **54.** $3x + 3y - 3z$  **55.** $3x + 6y - 3$  **56.** $4a + 8b - 4$

**57.** $4w - 12z + 8$  **58.** $8m + 4n - 24$  **59.** $20x - 36y - 12$  **60.** $18a - 24b - 48$

**61.** $ab + ac - ad$  **62.** $xy - xz + xw$  **63.** $\frac{1}{4}\pi rr + \frac{1}{4}\pi rs$  **64.** $\frac{1}{2}ah + \frac{1}{2}bh$

## Skill Maintenance

Translate to an algebraic expression.  [R.4a]

**65.** The square of the sum of two numbers

**66.** The sum of the squares of two numbers

Subtract.  [R.2c]

**67.** $-34.2 - 67.8$  **68.** $-\frac{11}{5} - \left(-\frac{17}{10}\right)$  **69.** $-\frac{1}{4}\left(-\frac{1}{2}\right)$  **70.** $0.23(-200)$

## Synthesis

Make substitutions to determine whether each pair of expressions is equivalent.

**71.** $x^2 + y^2$; $(x + y)^2$  **72.** $(a - b)(a + b)$; $a^2 - b^2$  **73.** $x^2 \cdot x^3$; $x^5$  **74.** $\dfrac{x^8}{x^4}$; $x^2$

# R.6

## Simplifying Algebraic Expressions

### OBJECTIVES

**a** Simplify an expression by collecting like terms.

**b** Simplify an expression by removing parentheses and collecting like terms.

There are many situations in algebra in which we want to find either an alternative or a simpler expression equivalent to a given one.

### a Collecting Like Terms

If two terms have the same letter, or letters, we say that they are **like terms**, or **similar terms**. (If powers, or exponents, are involved, then like terms must have the same letters raised to the same powers. We will consider this in Chapter 4.) If two terms have no letters at all but are just numbers, they are also similar terms. We can simplify by **collecting**, or **combining**, **like terms**, using the distributive laws.

**EXAMPLES** Collect like terms.

**1.** $3x + 5x = (3 + 5)x = 8x$    Factoring out the $x$ using the distributive law

**2.** $x - 3x = 1 \cdot x - 3 \cdot x = (1 - 3)x = -2x$

**3.** $2x + 3y - 5x - 2y$

$$= 2x + 3y + (-5x) + (-2y)$$    Subtracting by adding an opposite

$$= 2x + (-5x) + 3y + (-2y)$$    Using a commutative law

$$= (2 - 5)x + (3 - 2)y$$    Using a distributive law

$$= -3x + y$$    Simplifying

**4.** $3x + 2x + 5 + 7 = (3 + 2)x + (5 + 7) = 5x + 12$

**5.** $4.2x - 6.7y - 5.8x + 23y = (4.2 - 5.8)x + (-6.7 + 23)y$

$$= -1.6x + 16.3y$$

**6.** $-\dfrac{1}{4}a + \dfrac{1}{2}b - \dfrac{3}{5}a - \dfrac{2}{5}b = \left(-\dfrac{1}{4} - \dfrac{3}{5}\right)a + \left(\dfrac{1}{2} - \dfrac{2}{5}\right)b$

$$= \left(-\dfrac{5}{20} - \dfrac{12}{20}\right)a + \left(\dfrac{5}{10} - \dfrac{4}{10}\right)b$$

$$= -\dfrac{17}{20}a + \dfrac{1}{10}b$$

You need not write the intervening steps when you can do the computations mentally.

Do Exercises 1–6.

Collect like terms.

**1.** $9x + 11x$

**2.** $5x - 12x$

**3.** $5x + x$

**4.** $x - 7x$

**5.** $22x - 2.5y + 1.4x + 6.4y$

**6.** $\dfrac{2}{3}x - \dfrac{3}{4}y + \dfrac{4}{5}x - \dfrac{5}{6}y + 23$

---

*Answers*

**1.** $20x$    **2.** $-7x$    **3.** $6x$    **4.** $-6x$

**5.** $23.4x + 3.9y$    **6.** $\dfrac{22}{15}x - \dfrac{19}{12}y + 23$

## b Multiplying by −1 and Removing Parentheses

What happens when we multiply a number by −1?

**EXAMPLES**

**7.** $-1 \cdot 9 = -9$      **8.** $-1 \cdot \left(-\dfrac{3}{5}\right) = \dfrac{3}{5}$      **9.** $-1 \cdot 0 = 0$

> Do Exercises 7–9.

---

**THE PROPERTY OF −1**

For any number $a$,

$$-1 \cdot a = -a.$$

(Negative 1 times $a$ is the opposite of $a$. In other words, changing the sign is the same as multiplying by −1.)

---

From the property of −1, we know that we can replace − with −1 or the reverse, in any expression. In that way, we can find an equivalent expression for an opposite.

**EXAMPLES** Find an equivalent expression without parentheses.

**10.** $-(3x) = -1(3x)$    Replacing − with −1 using the property of −1

$\quad\quad\quad = (-1 \cdot 3)x$    Using an associative law

$\quad\quad\quad = -3x$    Multiplying

**11.** $-(-9y) = -1(-9y)$    Replacing − with −1

$\quad\quad\quad\quad = [-1(-9)]y$    Using an associative law

$\quad\quad\quad\quad = 9y$    Multiplying

> Do Exercises 10 and 11.

**EXAMPLES** Find an equivalent expression without parentheses.

**12.** $-(4 + x) = -1(4 + x)$    Replacing − with −1

$\quad\quad\quad\quad = -1 \cdot 4 + (-1) \cdot x$    Multiplying using the distributive law

$\quad\quad\quad\quad = -4 + (-x)$    Replacing $-1 \cdot x$ with $-x$

$\quad\quad\quad\quad = -4 - x$    Adding an opposite is the same as subtracting.

**13.** $-(3x - 2y + 4) = -1(3x - 2y + 4)$

$\quad\quad\quad\quad\quad = -1 \cdot 3x - (-1)2y + (-1)4$    Using the distributive law

$\quad\quad\quad\quad\quad = -3x - (-2y) + (-4)$    Multiplying

$\quad\quad\quad\quad\quad = -3x + [-(-2y)] + (-4)$    Adding an opposite

$\quad\quad\quad\quad\quad = -3x + 2y - 4$

**14.** $-(a - b) = -1(a - b) = -1 \cdot a - (-1) \cdot b$

$\quad\quad\quad\quad = -a + [-(-1)b] = -a + b = b - a$

---

Multiply.

**7.** $-1 \cdot 24$

**8.** $-1 \cdot 0$

**9.** $-1 \cdot (-10)$

Find an equivalent expression without parentheses.

**10.** $-(9x)$

**11.** $-(-24t)$

*Answers*

**7.** $-24$    **8.** 0    **9.** 10    **10.** $-9x$
**11.** $24t$

Example 14 illustrates something that you should remember, because it is a convenient shortcut.

Find an equivalent expression without parentheses.

**12.** $-(7 - y)$

**13.** $-(x - y)$

**14.** $-(9x + 6y + 11)$

**15.** $-(23x - 7y - 2)$

**16.** $-(-3x - 2y - 1)$

---

**THE OPPOSITE OF A DIFFERENCE**

For any real numbers $a$ and $b$,

$$-(a - b) = b - a.$$

(The opposite of $a - b$ is $b - a$.)

---

Do Exercises 12-16.

Examples 10–14 show that we can find an equivalent expression for an opposite by multiplying every term by $-1$. We could also say that we change the sign of every term inside the parentheses. Thus we can skip some steps.

**EXAMPLE 15** Find an equivalent expression without parentheses:

$$-\left(-9t + 7z - \tfrac{1}{4}w\right).$$

We have

$$-\left(-9t + 7z - \tfrac{1}{4}w\right) = 9t - 7z + \tfrac{1}{4}w. \qquad \text{Changing the sign of every term}$$

Do Exercises 17-19.

Find an equivalent expression without parentheses.

**17.** $-(-2x - 5z + 24)$

**18.** $-(3x - 2y)$

**19.** $-\left(\dfrac{1}{4}t + 41w - 5d - 23\right)$

In some expressions commonly encountered in algebra, there are parentheses preceded by subtraction signs. These parentheses can be removed by changing the sign of *every* term inside. In this way, we simplify by finding a less complicated equivalent expression.

**EXAMPLES** Remove parentheses and simplify.

**16.** 
$$
\begin{aligned}
6x - (4x + 2) &= 6x + [-(4x + 2)] && \text{Subtracting by adding the opposite} \\
&= 6x - 4x - 2 && \text{Changing the sign of every term inside} \\
&= 2x - 2 && \text{Collecting like terms}
\end{aligned}
$$

**17.** 
$$
\begin{aligned}
3y - 4 - (9y - 7) &= 3y - 4 - 9y + 7 \\
&= -6y + 3, \text{ or } 3 - 6y
\end{aligned}
$$

In Example 16, we see the reason for the word "simplify." The expression $2x - 2$ is equivalent to $6x - (4x + 2)$ but it is shorter.

If parentheses are preceded by an addition sign, *no* signs are changed when they are removed.

**EXAMPLES** Remove parentheses and simplify.

**18.** 
$$
\begin{aligned}
3y + (3x - 8) - (5 - 12y) &= 3y + 3x - 8 - 5 + 12y \\
&= 15y + 3x - 13
\end{aligned}
$$

**19.** 
$$
\begin{aligned}
\tfrac{1}{3}(15x - 4) - (5x + 2y) + 1 &= \tfrac{1}{3} \cdot 15x - \tfrac{1}{3} \cdot 4 - 5x - 2y + 1 \\
&= 5x - \tfrac{4}{3} - 5x - 2y + 1 \\
&= -2y - \tfrac{1}{3}
\end{aligned}
$$

Do Exercises 20-23.

Remove parentheses and simplify.

**20.** $6x - (3x + 8)$

**21.** $6y - 4 - (2y - 5)$

**22.** $6x - (9y - 4) - (8x + 10)$

**23.** $7x - (-9y - 4) + (8x - 10)$

*Answers*

**12.** $y - 7$   **13.** $y - x$
**14.** $-9x - 6y - 11$   **15.** $-23x + 7y + 2$
**16.** $3x + 2y + 1$   **17.** $2x + 5z - 24$
**18.** $-3x + 2y$   **19.** $-\dfrac{1}{4}t - 41w + 5d + 23$
**20.** $3x - 8$   **21.** $4y + 1$   **22.** $-2x - 9y - 6$
**23.** $15x + 9y - 6$

We now consider subtracting an expression consisting of several terms preceded by a number other than $-1$.

**EXAMPLES**   Remove parentheses and simplify.

**20.** $x - 3(x + y) = x + [-3(x + y)]$   Subtracting by adding the opposite

$\qquad\quad = x - 3x - 3y$   Removing parentheses by multiplying $x + y$ by $-3$

$\qquad\quad = -2x - 3y$   Collecting like terms

---------------------------------- *Caution!* ----------------------------------

A common error is to forget to change this sign. *Remember*: When multiplying by a negative number, change the sign of *every* term inside the parentheses.

---------------------------------------------------------------

**21.** $3y - 2(4y - 5) = 3y - 8y + 10$   Removing parentheses by multiplying $4y - 5$ by $-2$

$\qquad\quad = -5y + 10$   Collecting like terms

> Do Exercises 24–26.

When expressions with grouping symbols contain variables, we still work from the inside out when simplifying, using the rules for order of operations.

**EXAMPLE 22**   Simplify: $[2(x + 7) - 4^2] - (2 - x)$.

$[2(x + 7) - 4^2] - (2 - x)$

$= [2x + 14 - 4^2] - (2 - x)$   Multiplying to remove the innermost grouping symbols using the distributive law

$= [2x + 14 - 16] - (2 - x)$   Evaluating the exponential expression

$= [2x - 2] - (2 - x)$   Collecting like terms inside the brackets

$= 2x - 2 - 2 + x$   Multiplying by $-1$ to remove the parentheses

$= 3x - 4$   Collecting like terms

> Do Exercises 27 and 28.

**EXAMPLE 23**   Simplify: $6y - \{4[3(y - 2) - 4(y + 2)] - 3\}$.

$6y - \{4[3(y - 2) - 4(y + 2)] - 3\}$

$= 6y - \{4[3y - 6 - 4y - 8] - 3\}$   Multiplying to remove the innermost grouping symbols using the distributive law

$= 6y - \{4[-y - 14] - 3\}$   Collecting like terms inside the brackets

$= 6y - \{-4y - 56 - 3\}$   Multiplying to remove the inner brackets using the distributive law

$= 6y - \{-4y - 59\}$   Collecting like terms in the braces

$= 6y + 4y + 59$   Removing braces

$= 10y + 59$   Collecting like terms

> Do Exercises 29 and 30.

Remove parentheses and simplify.

**24.** $x - 2(y + x)$

**25.** $3x - 5(2y - 4x)$

**26.** $(4a - 3b) - \dfrac{1}{4}(4a - 3) + 5$

Simplify.

**27.** $(3x - 5) - [4(x - 1) + 2]$

**28.** $[3 - 2(x + 9)] - 4(3^2 - x)$

Simplify.

**29.** $15x - \{2[2(x - 5) - 6(x + 3)] + 4\}$

**30.** $9a + \{3a - 2[(a - 4) - (a + 2)]\}$

*Answers*

**24.** $-x - 2y$   **25.** $23x - 10y$

**26.** $3a - 3b + \dfrac{23}{4}$   **27.** $-x - 3$

**28.** $2x - 51$   **29.** $23x + 52$

**30.** $12a + 12$

**a** Collect like terms.

**1.** $7x + 5x$

**2.** $6a + 9a$

**3.** $8b - 11b$

**4.** $9c - 12c$

**5.** $14y + y$

**6.** $13x + x$

**7.** $12a - a$

**8.** $15x - x$

**9.** $t - 9t$

**10.** $x - 6x$

**11.** $5x - 3x + 8x$

**12.** $3x - 11x + 2x$

**13.** $3x - 5y + 8x$

**14.** $4a - 9b + 10a$

**15.** $3c + 8d - 7c + 4d$

**16.** $12a + 3b - 5a + 6b$

**17.** $4x - 7 + 18x + 25$

**18.** $13p + 5 - 4p + 7$

**19.** $1.3x + 1.4y - 0.11x - 0.47y$

**20.** $0.17a + 1.7b - 12a - 38b$

**21.** $\frac{2}{3}a + \frac{5}{6}b - 27 - \frac{4}{5}a - \frac{7}{6}b$

**22.** $-\frac{1}{4}x - \frac{1}{2}x + \frac{1}{4}y + \frac{1}{2}y - 34$

The **perimeter** of a rectangle is the distance around it. The perimeter $P$ is given by $P = 2l + 2w$.

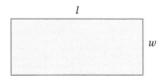

$l$

$w$

**23.** Find an equivalent expression for the perimeter formula $P = 2l + 2w$ by factoring.

**24.** *Perimeter of a Football Field.* The standard football field has $l = 360$ ft and $w = 160$ ft. Evaluate both expressions in Exercise 23 to find the perimeter.

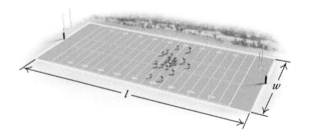

$l$

$w$

**b** Find an equivalent expression without parentheses.

**25.** $-(-2c)$

**26.** $-(-5y)$

**27.** $-(b + 4)$

**28.** $-(a + 9)$

**29.** $-(b - 3)$

**30.** $-(x - 8)$

**31.** $-(t - y)$

**32.** $-(r - s)$

**33.** $-(x + y + z)$

**34.** $-(r + s + t)$

**35.** $-(8x - 6y + 13)$

**36.** $-(9a - 7b + 24)$

**37.** $-(-2c + 5d - 3e + 4f)$

**38.** $-(-4x + 8y - 5w + 9z)$

**39.** $-\left(-1.2x + 56.7y - 34z - \dfrac{1}{4}\right)$

**40.** $-\left(-x + 2y - \dfrac{2}{3}z - 56.3w\right)$

Simplify by removing parentheses and collecting like terms.

**41.** $a + (2a + 5)$

**42.** $x + (5x + 9)$

**43.** $4m - (3m - 1)$

**44.** $5a - (4a - 3)$

**45.** $5d - 9 - (7 - 4d)$

**46.** $6x - 7 - (9 - 3x)$

**47.** $-2(x + 3) - 5(x - 4)$

**48.** $-9(y + 7) - 6(y - 3)$

**49.** $5x - 7(2x - 3) - 4$

**50.** $8y - 4(5y - 6) + 9$

**51.** $8x - (-3y + 7) + (9x - 11)$

**52.** $-5t + (4t - 12) - 2(3t + 7)$

**53.** $\frac{1}{4}(24x - 8) - \frac{1}{2}(-8x + 6) - 14$

**54.** $-\frac{1}{2}(10t - w) + \frac{1}{4}(-28t + 4) + 1$

Simplify.

**55.** $7a - [9 - 3(5a - 2)]$

**56.** $14b - [7 - 3(9b - 4)]$

**57.** $5\{-2 + 3[4 - 2(3 + 5)]\}$

**58.** $7\{-7 + 8[5 - 3(4 + 6)]\}$

**59.** $[10(x + 3) - 4] + [2(x - 1) + 6]$

**60.** $[9(x + 5) - 7] + [4(x - 12) + 9]$

**61.** $[7(x + 5) - 19] - [4(x - 6) + 10]$

**62.** $[6(x + 4) - 12] - [5(x - 8) + 11]$

**63.** $3\{[7(x - 2) + 4] - [2(2x - 5) + 6]\}$

**64.** $4\{[8(x - 3) + 9] - [4(3x - 7) + 2]\}$

**65.** $4\{[5(x - 3) + 2^2] - 3[2(x + 5) - 9^2]\}$

**66.** $3\{[6(x - 4) + 5^2] - 2[5(x + 8) - 10^2]\}$

**67.** $2y + \{8[3(2y - 5) - (8y + 9)] + 6\}$

**68.** $7b - \{5[4(3b - 8) - (9b + 10)] + 14\}$

## Skill Maintenance

Add. [R.2a]

**69.** $17 + (-54)$

**70.** $-17 + (-54)$

**71.** $-13.78 + (-9.32)$

**72.** $-\dfrac{2}{3} + \dfrac{7}{8}$

Divide. [R.2e]

**73.** $-256 \div 16$

**74.** $-256 \div (-16)$

**75.** $256 \div (-16)$

**76.** $-\dfrac{3}{8} \div \dfrac{9}{4}$

Multiply. [R.5d]

**77.** $8(a - b)$

**78.** $-8(2a - 3b + 4)$

**79.** $6x(a - b + 2c)$

**80.** $\dfrac{2}{3}(24x - 12y + 15)$

Factor. [R.5d]

**81.** $24a - 24$

**82.** $24a - 16b$

**83.** $ab - ac + a$

**84.** $15p + 45q - 10$

## Synthesis

Insert one pair of parentheses to convert the false statement into a true statement.

**85.** $3 - 8^2 + 9 = 34$

**86.** $2 \cdot 7 + 3^2 \cdot 5 = 104$

**87.** $5 \cdot 2^3 \div 3 - 4^4 = 40$

**88.** $2 - 7 \cdot 2^2 + 9 = -11$

Simplify.

**89.** $[11(a - 3) + 12a] - \{6[4(3b - 7) - (9b + 10)] + 11\}$

**90.** $-3[9(x - 4) + 5x] - 8\{3[5(3y + 4)] - 12\}$

**91.** $z - \{2z + [3z - (4z + 5x) - 6z] + 7z\} - 8z$

**92.** $\{x + [f - (f + x)] + [x - f]\} + 3x$

**93.** $x - \{x + 1 - [x + 2 - (x - 3 - \{x + 4 - [x - 5 + (x - 6)]\})]\}$

# R.7

## Properties of Exponents and Scientific Notation

## OBJECTIVES

**a** Use exponential notation in multiplication and division.

**b** Use exponential notation in raising a power to a power, and in raising a product or a quotient to a power.

**c** Convert between decimal notation and scientific notation, and use scientific notation with multiplication and division.

We often need to find ways to determine *equivalent exponential expressions*. We do this with several rules or properties regarding exponents.

### a Multiplication and Division

To see how to multiply, or simplify, in an expression such as $a^3 \cdot a^2$, we use the definition of exponential notation:

$$a^3 \cdot a^2 = \underbrace{a \cdot a \cdot a}_{3 \text{ factors}} \cdot \underbrace{a \cdot a}_{2 \text{ factors}} = a^5.$$

The exponent in $a^5$ is the *sum* of those in $a^3 \cdot a^2$. In general, the exponents are added when we multiply, but note that the base must be the same in all factors. This is true for any integer exponents, even those that may be negative or zero.

> **THE PRODUCT RULE**
>
> For any number $a$ and any integers $m$ and $n$,
>
> $$a^m \cdot a^n = a^{m+n}.$$
>
> (When multiplying with exponential notation, add the exponents if the bases are the same.)

**EXAMPLES** Multiply and simplify.

**1.** $x^4 \cdot x^3 = x^{4+3} = x^7$

**2.** $4^5 \cdot 4^{-3} = 4^{5+(-3)} = 4^2 = 16$

**3.** $(-2)^{-3}(-2)^7 = (-2)^{-3+7}$
$= (-2)^4 = 16$

**4.** $(8x^n)(6x^{2n}) = 8 \cdot 6x^{n+2n}$
$= 48x^{3n}$

**5.** $(8x^4y^{-2})(-3x^{-3}y) = 8 \cdot (-3) \cdot x^4 \cdot x^{-3} \cdot y^{-2} \cdot y^1$    Using the associative and the commutative laws

$= -24x^{4-3}y^{-2+1}$    Using the product rule

$= -24xy^{-1} = -\dfrac{24x}{y}$    Using $a^{-n} = \dfrac{1}{a^n}$

Note that we give answers using positive exponents. In some situations, this may not be appropriate, but we do so here.

Do Exercises 1–7.

Consider this division:

$$\frac{8^5}{8^3} = \frac{8 \cdot 8 \cdot 8 \cdot 8 \cdot 8}{8 \cdot 8 \cdot 8} = \frac{8 \cdot 8 \cdot 8}{8 \cdot 8 \cdot 8} \cdot 8 \cdot 8 = 8 \cdot 8 = 8^2.$$

We can obtain the result by subtracting exponents. This is always the case, even if exponents are negative or zero.

---

Multiply and simplify.

**1.** $8^{-3} \cdot 8^7$

**2.** $y^7 \cdot y^{-2}$

**3.** $(9x^{-4})(2x^7)$

**4.** $(-3x^{-4})(25x^{-10})$

**5.** $(-7x^{3n})(6x^{5n})$

**6.** $(5x^{-3}y^4)(-2x^{-9}y^{-2})$

**7.** $(4x^{-2}y^4)(15x^2y^{-3})$

*Answers*

**1.** $8^4$   **2.** $y^5$   **3.** $18x^3$   **4.** $-\dfrac{75}{x^{14}}$

**5.** $-42x^{8n}$   **6.** $-\dfrac{10y^2}{x^{12}}$   **7.** $60y$

## THE QUOTIENT RULE

For any nonzero number $a$ and any integers $m$ and $n$,

$$\frac{a^m}{a^n} = a^{m-n}.$$

(When dividing with exponential notation, subtract the exponent of the denominator from the exponent of the numerator, if the bases are the same.)

**EXAMPLES** Divide and simplify.

**6.** $\dfrac{5^7}{5^3} = 5^{7-3} = 5^4$      Subtracting exponents using the quotient rule

**7.** $\dfrac{5^7}{5^{-3}} = 5^{7-(-3)} = 5^{7+3} = 5^{10}$      Subtracting exponents (adding an opposite)

**8.** $\dfrac{9^{-2}}{9^5} = 9^{-2-5} = 9^{-7} = \dfrac{1}{9^7}$

**9.** $\dfrac{7^{-4}}{7^{-5}} = 7^{-4-(-5)} = 7^{-4+5} = 7^1 = 7$

**10.** $\dfrac{16x^4y^7}{-8x^3y^9} = \dfrac{16}{-8} \cdot \dfrac{x^4}{x^3} \cdot \dfrac{y^7}{y^9} = -2xy^{-2} = -\dfrac{2x}{y^2}$

The answers $\dfrac{-2x}{y^2}$ or $\dfrac{2x}{-y^2}$ would also be correct here.

**11.** $\dfrac{40x^{-2n}}{4x^{5n}} = \dfrac{40}{4}x^{-2n-5n} = 10x^{-7n} = \dfrac{10}{x^{7n}}$

**12.** $\dfrac{14x^7y^{-3}}{4x^5y^{-5}} = \dfrac{14}{4} \cdot \dfrac{x^7}{x^5} \cdot \dfrac{y^{-3}}{y^{-5}} = \dfrac{7}{2}x^{7-5}y^{-3-(-5)} = \dfrac{7}{2}x^2y^2$

In exercises such as Examples 6–12 above, it may help to think as follows: After writing the base, write the top exponent. Then write a subtraction sign. Then write the bottom exponent. Then do the subtraction. For example,

$$\frac{x^{-3}}{x^{-5}} = x^{-3-(-5)}$$

Writing the base and the top exponent    Writing a subtraction sign    Writing the bottom exponent

Do Exercises 8–13.

Divide and simplify.

**8.** $\dfrac{4^8}{4^5}$     **9.** $\dfrac{5^4}{5^{-2}}$

**10.** $\dfrac{10^{-8}}{10^{-2}}$     **11.** $\dfrac{45x^{5n}}{-9x^{3n}}$

**12.** $\dfrac{42y^7x^6}{-21y^{-3}x^{10}}$     **13.** $\dfrac{33a^5b^{-2}}{22a^2b^{-4}}$

*Answers*

**8.** $4^3$   **9.** $5^6$   **10.** $\dfrac{1}{10^6}$   **11.** $-5x^{2n}$

**12.** $-\dfrac{2y^{10}}{x^4}$   **13.** $\dfrac{3}{2}a^3b^2$

## b) Raising Powers to Powers and Products and Quotients to Powers

When an expression inside parentheses is raised to a power, the inside expression is the base. Consider an expression like $(5^2)^4$. In this case, we are raising $5^2$ to the fourth power:

$$(5^2)^4 = (5^2)(5^2)(5^2)(5^2)$$
$$= (5 \cdot 5)(5 \cdot 5)(5 \cdot 5)(5 \cdot 5)$$
$$= 5 \cdot 5 \cdot 5 \cdot 5 \cdot 5 \cdot 5 \cdot 5 \cdot 5 \quad \text{Using an associative law}$$
$$= 5^8.$$

Note that here we could have multiplied the exponents:

$$(5^2)^4 = 5^{2 \cdot 4} = 5^8.$$

Likewise, $(y^8)^3 = (y^8)(y^8)(y^8) = y^{24}$. Once again, we get the same result if we multiply the exponents:

$$(y^8)^3 = y^{8 \cdot 3} = y^{24}.$$

---

**THE POWER RULE**

For any real number $a$ and any integers $m$ and $n$,

$$(a^m)^n = a^{mn}.$$

(To raise a power to a power, multiply the exponents.)

---

**EXAMPLES** Simplify.

**13.** $(x^5)^7 = x^{5 \cdot 7}$     Multiply exponents.
$$= x^{35}$$

**14.** $(y^{-2})^{-2} = y^{(-2)(-2)}$
$$= y^4$$

**15.** $(x^{-5})^4 = x^{-5 \cdot 4}$
$$= x^{-20} = \frac{1}{x^{20}}$$

**16.** $(x^4)^{-2t} = x^{4(-2t)}$
$$= x^{-8t} = \frac{1}{x^{8t}}$$

Do Exercises 14–16.

Let's compare $2a^3$ and $(2a)^3$:

$$2a^3 = 2 \cdot a \cdot a \cdot a \quad \text{The base is } a.$$

and

$$(2a)^3 = (2a)(2a)(2a) \quad \text{The base is } 2a.$$
$$= (2 \cdot 2 \cdot 2)(a \cdot a \cdot a) \quad \text{Using the associative law of multiplication}$$
$$= 2^3 a^3 = 8a^3.$$

We see that $2a^3$ and $(2a)^3$ are *not* equivalent. We also see that we can evaluate the power $(2a)^3$ by raising each factor to the power 3. This leads us to the following rule for raising a product to a power.

Simplify.

**14.** $(3^7)^6$

**15.** $(z^{-4})^{-5}$

**16.** $(t^2)^{-7m}$

*Answers*

**14.** $3^{42}$    **15.** $z^{20}$    **16.** $\dfrac{1}{t^{14m}}$

## RAISING A PRODUCT TO A POWER

For any real numbers $a$ and $b$ and any integer $n$,

$$(ab)^n = a^n b^n.$$

(To raise a product to the $n$th power, raise each factor to the $n$th power.)

**EXAMPLES** Simplify.

**17.** $(3x^2 y^{-2})^3 = 3^3 (x^2)^3 (y^{-2})^3 = 3^3 x^6 y^{-6} = 27 x^6 y^{-6} = \dfrac{27 x^6}{y^6}$

**18.** $(5x^3 y^{-5} z^2)^4 = 5^4 (x^3)^4 (y^{-5})^4 (z^2)^4 = 625 x^{12} y^{-20} z^8 = \dfrac{625 x^{12} z^8}{y^{20}}$

Do Exercises 17-20.

There is a similar rule for raising a quotient to a power.

## RAISING A QUOTIENT TO A POWER

For any real numbers $a$ and $b$, and any integer $n$,

$$\left(\frac{a}{b}\right)^n = \frac{a^n}{b^n}, \, b \neq 0; \quad \text{and} \quad \left(\frac{a}{b}\right)^{-n} = \left(\frac{b}{a}\right)^n = \frac{b^n}{a^n}, \, a \neq 0, b \neq 0.$$

(To raise a quotient to the $n$th power, raise the numerator to the $n$th power and divide by the denominator to the $n$th power.)

**EXAMPLES** Simplify. Write the answer using positive exponents.

**19.** $\left(\dfrac{x^2}{y^{-3}}\right)^{-5} = \dfrac{x^{2 \cdot (-5)}}{y^{-3 \cdot (-5)}} = \dfrac{x^{-10}}{y^{15}} = \dfrac{1}{x^{10} y^{15}}$

**20.** $\left(\dfrac{2x^3 y^{-2}}{3y^4}\right)^5 = \dfrac{(2x^3 y^{-2})^5}{(3y^4)^5} = \dfrac{2^5 (x^3)^5 (y^{-2})^5}{3^5 (y^4)^5} = \dfrac{32 x^{15} y^{-10}}{243 y^{20}}$

$\qquad = \dfrac{32 x^{15} y^{-10-20}}{243} = \dfrac{32 x^{15} y^{-30}}{243} = \dfrac{32 x^{15}}{243 y^{30}}$

**21.** $\left[\dfrac{-3a^{-5} b^3}{2a^{-2} b^{-4}}\right]^{-2} = \dfrac{(-3a^{-5} b^3)^{-2}}{(2a^{-2} b^{-4})^{-2}} = \dfrac{(-3)^{-2} (a^{-5})^{-2} (b^3)^{-2}}{2^{-2} (a^{-2})^{-2} (b^{-4})^{-2}}$

$\qquad = \dfrac{\dfrac{1}{(-3)^2} a^{10} b^{-6}}{\dfrac{1}{2^2} a^4 b^8} = \dfrac{2^2}{(-3)^2} a^{10-4} b^{-6-8}$

$\qquad = \dfrac{4}{9} a^6 b^{-14} = \dfrac{4a^6}{9b^{14}}$

An alternative way to carry out Example 21 is to first write the expression with a positive exponent, as follows:

$\left[\dfrac{-3a^{-5} b^3}{2a^{-2} b^{-4}}\right]^{-2} = \left[\dfrac{2a^{-2} b^{-4}}{-3a^{-5} b^3}\right]^2 = \dfrac{(2a^{-2} b^{-4})^2}{(-3a^{-5} b^3)^2} = \dfrac{2^2 (a^{-2})^2 (b^{-4})^2}{(-3)^2 (a^{-5})^2 (b^3)^2}$

$\qquad = \dfrac{4a^{-4} b^{-8}}{9a^{-10} b^6} = \dfrac{4}{9} a^{-4-(-10)} b^{-8-6} = \dfrac{4}{9} a^6 b^{-14} = \dfrac{4a^6}{9b^{14}}.$

Simplify.

**17.** $(2xy)^3$

**18.** $(4x^{-2} y^7)^2$

**19.** $(-2x^4 y^2)^5$

**20.** $(10x^{-4} y^7 z^{-2})^3$

Simplify.

**21.** $\left(\dfrac{x^{-3}}{y^4}\right)^{-3}$

**22.** $\left(\dfrac{3x^2 y^{-3}}{y^5}\right)^2$

**23.** $\left[\dfrac{-3a^{-5} b^3}{2a^{-2} b^{-4}}\right]^{-3}$

***Answers***

**17.** $8x^3 y^3$ **18.** $\dfrac{16y^{14}}{x^4}$ **19.** $-32x^{20} y^{10}$

**20.** $\dfrac{1000 y^{21}}{x^{12} z^6}$ **21.** $x^9 y^{12}$ **22.** $\dfrac{9x^4}{y^{16}}$

**23.** $-\dfrac{8a^9}{27b^{21}}$

Do Exercises 21-23 on the preceding page.

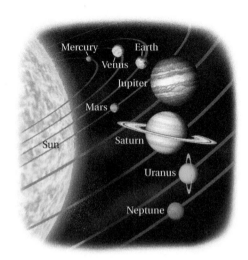

## c  Scientific Notation

There are many kinds of symbolism, or *notation*, for numbers. You are already familiar with fraction notation, decimal notation, and percent notation. Now we study another, **scientific notation**, which is especially useful when representing very large or very small numbers and when estimating.

The following are examples of scientific notation:

- *The distance from the sun to the planet Saturn:*

  $8.908 \times 10^8$ mi $= 890{,}800{,}000$ mi

- *The diameter of a helium atom:*

  $2.2 \times 10^{-8}$ cm $= 0.000000022$ cm

- Americans made $1.1 \times 10^9$ visits to doctors' offices, emergency rooms, and hospital outpatient departments in a recent year. During these visits, $2.6 \times 10^9$ prescriptions were written.

  **Source:** Centers for Disease Control and Prevention

- Americans had $7.2114 \times 10^7$ pet dogs and $8.1721 \times 10^7$ pet cats in a recent year. They spent $\$1.5783 \times 10^{10}$ on food and $\$2.2433 \times 10^{10}$ on veterinary care for these pets during the year.

  **Sources:** American Veterinary Medical Association; Euromonitor International

---

**SCIENTIFIC NOTATION**

**Scientific notation** for a number is an expression of the type

$M \times 10^n$,

where $n$ is an integer, $M$ is greater than or equal to 1 and less than 10 ($1 \le M < 10$), and $M$ is expressed in decimal notation. $10^n$ is also considered to be scientific notation when $M = 1$.

---

You should try to make conversions to scientific notation mentally as much as possible. Here is a handy mental device.

> A positive exponent in scientific notation indicates a large number (greater than or equal to 10) and a negative exponent indicates a small number (between 0 and 1).

**EXAMPLES**  Convert mentally to scientific notation.

**22.** Light travels 9,460,000,000,000 km in one year.

$$9{,}460{,}000{,}000{,}000 = 9.46 \times 10^{12} \qquad 9{.}460{,}000{,}000{,}000.$$

12 places

Large number, so the exponent is positive.

**23.** The mass of a grain of sand is 0.0648 g (grams).

$$0.0648 = 6.48 \times 10^{-2} \qquad 0.06{.}48$$

2 places

Small number, so the exponent is negative.

**EXAMPLES**  Convert mentally to decimal notation.

**24.** $4.893 \times 10^{5} = 489{,}300 \qquad 4.89300.$

5 places

Positive exponent, so the answer is a large number.

**25.** $8.7 \times 10^{-8} = 0.000000087 \qquad 0.00000008.7$

8 places

Negative exponent, so the answer is a small number.

Each of the following is *not* scientific notation.

$$13.95 \times 10^{13}, \qquad\qquad 0.468 \times 10^{-8}$$

This number is greater than 10.     This number is less than 1.

Do Exercises 24–27.

We can use the properties of exponents when we multiply and divide in scientific notation.

**EXAMPLE 26**  Multiply and write scientific notation for the answer: $(3.1 \times 10^{5})(4.5 \times 10^{-3})$.

We apply the commutative and the associative laws to get

$$(3.1 \times 10^{5})(4.5 \times 10^{-3}) = (3.1 \times 4.5)(10^{5} \times 10^{-3}) = 13.95 \times 10^{2}.$$

To find scientific notation for the result, we convert 13.95 to scientific notation and then simplify:

$$13.95 \times 10^{2} = (1.395 \times 10^{1}) \times 10^{2} = 1.395 \times 10^{3}.$$

Do Exercises 28 and 29.

Convert to scientific notation.
**24.** Light travels 5,880,000,000,000 mi in one year.

**25.** 0.000000000257

Convert to decimal notation.
**26.** $4.567 \times 10^{-13}$

**27.** The distance from the earth to the sun is $9.3 \times 10^{7}$ mi.

Multiply and write scientific notation for the answer.
**28.** $(9.1 \times 10^{-17})(8.2 \times 10^{3})$

**29.** $(1.12 \times 10^{-8})(5 \times 10^{-7})$

***Answers***
**24.** $5.88 \times 10^{12}$ mi   **25.** $2.57 \times 10^{-10}$
**26.** 0.0000000000004567   **27.** 93,000,000 mi
**28.** $7.462 \times 10^{-13}$   **29.** $5.6 \times 10^{-15}$

**EXAMPLE 27** Divide and write scientific notation for the answer:

$$\frac{6.4 \times 10^{-7}}{8.0 \times 10^{6}}.$$

$$\frac{6.4 \times 10^{-7}}{8.0 \times 10^{6}} = \frac{6.4}{8.0} \times \frac{10^{-7}}{10^{6}}$$

| Factoring shows two divisions. |

$$= 0.8 \times 10^{-13}$$ ← Doing the divisions separately

| The answer $0.8 \times 10^{-13}$ is not scientific notation because $0.8 < 1$. |

$$= (8.0 \times 10^{-1}) \times 10^{-13}$$  Converting 0.8 to scientific notation

$$= 8.0 \times (10^{-1} \times 10^{-13})$$  Using the associative law of multiplication

$$= 8.0 \times 10^{-14}$$

Do Exercises 30 and 31.

**EXAMPLE 28**  *Light from the Sun to Neptune.*  The planet Neptune is about 2,790,000,000 mi from the sun. Light travels $1.86 \times 10^{5}$ mi in 1 sec. About how many seconds does it take light from the sun to reach Neptune? Write scientific notation for the answer.

Source: *The Handy Science Answer Book*

The time it takes light to travel from the sun to Neptune is

$$\frac{2,790,000,000}{1.86 \times 10^{5}} = \frac{2.79 \times 10^{9}}{1.86 \times 10^{5}} = \frac{2.79}{1.86} \times \frac{10^{9}}{10^{5}} = 1.5 \times 10^{4} \text{ sec.}$$

**EXAMPLE 29**  *Mass of the Sun.*  The mass of Earth is about $5.98 \times 10^{24}$ kg. The mass of the sun is about 333,000 times the mass of Earth. Write scientific notation for the mass of the sun.

Source: *The Handy Science Answer Book*

The mass of the sun is 333,000 times the mass of Earth. We convert to scientific notation and multiply:

$$(333,000)(5.98 \times 10^{24}) = (3.33 \times 10^{5})(5.98 \times 10^{24})$$
$$= (3.33 \times 5.98)(10^{5} \times 10^{24})$$
$$= 19.9134 \times 10^{29}$$
$$= (1.99134 \times 10^{1}) \times 10^{29}$$
$$= 1.99134 \times 10^{30} \text{ kg.}$$

Do Exercises 32 and 33.

---

Divide and write scientific notation for the answer.

**30.** $\dfrac{4.2 \times 10^{5}}{2.1 \times 10^{2}}$  **31.** $\dfrac{1.1 \times 10^{-4}}{2.0 \times 10^{-7}}$

**32. Light from the Sun to Pluto.** The distance from the dwarf planet Pluto to the sun is about 3,647,000,000 mi. Light travels $1.86 \times 10^{5}$ mi in 1 sec. About how many seconds does it take light from the sun to reach Pluto? Write scientific notation for the answer.
Source: *The Handy Science Answer Book*

**33. Mass of Jupiter.** The mass of the planet Jupiter is about 318 times the mass of Earth. Write scientific notation for the mass of Jupiter. See Example 29.

## Calculator Corner

**Scientific Notation**   To enter a number in scientific notation on a graphing calculator, we first type the decimal portion of the number. Then we press **2ND** (EE). (EE is the second operation associated with the ● key.) Finally, we type the exponent, which can be at most two digits. For example, to enter $2.36 \times 10^{-8}$ in scientific notation, we press ②(·)③⑥ **2ND** (EE) (-)⑧ **ENTER**. The decimal portion of the number appears before a small E and the exponent follows the E, as shown on the left below.

The graphing calculator can be used to perform computations using scientific notation. To find the product in Example 26 and express the result in scientific notation, we first set the calculator in Scientific mode by pressing **MODE**, positioning the cursor over Sci on the first line, and pressing **ENTER**. Then we press **2ND** (QUIT) to go to the home screen and enter the computation by pressing ③(·)①(**2ND**)(EE) ⑤(×)④(·)⑤(**2ND**)(EE)(-)③(**ENTER**).

```
2.36E-8
            2.36E-8
```

```
3.1E5*4.5E-3
            1.395E3
```

**Exercises:**   Multiply or divide and express the answer in scientific notation.

**1.** $(5.13 \times 10^8)(2.4 \times 10^{-13})$

**2.** $(3.45 \times 10^{-4})(7.1 \times 10^6)$

**3.** $(7 \times 10^9)(4 \times 10^{-5})$

**4.** $(6 \times 10^6)(9 \times 10^7)$

**5.** $\dfrac{4.8 \times 10^6}{1.6 \times 10^{12}}$

**6.** $\dfrac{7.2 \times 10^{-5}}{1.2 \times 10^{-10}}$

**7.** $\dfrac{6 \times 10^{-10}}{5 \times 10^4}$

**8.** $\dfrac{12 \times 10^9}{4 \times 10^{-3}}$

---

## R.7 Exercise Set

For Extra Help

*MyMathLab* 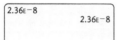   Math XL PRACTICE    WATCH    DOWNLOAD    READ    REVIEW

**a**   Multiply and simplify.

**1.** $3^6 \cdot 3^3$

**2.** $8^2 \cdot 8^6$

**3.** $6^{-6} \cdot 6^2$

**4.** $9^{-5} \cdot 9^3$

**5.** $8^{-2} \cdot 8^{-4}$

**6.** $9^{-1} \cdot 9^{-6}$

**7.** $b^2 \cdot b^{-5}$

**8.** $a^4 \cdot a^{-3}$

**9.** $a^{-3} \cdot a^4 \cdot a^2$

**10.** $x^{-8} \cdot x^5 \cdot x^3$

**11.** $(2x)^3 \cdot (3x)^2$

**12.** $(9y)^2 \cdot (2y)^3$

**13.** $(14m^2n^3)(-2m^3n^2)$

**14.** $(6x^5y^{-2})(-3x^2y^3)$

**15.** $(-2x^{-3})(7x^{-8})$

**16.** $(6x^{-4}y^3)(-4x^{-8}y^{-2})$

**17.** $(15x^{4t})(7x^{-6t})$

**18.** $(9x^{-4n})(-4x^{-8n})$

**19.** $(2y^{3m})(-4y^{-9m})$

**20.** $(-3t^{-4a})(-5t^{-a})$

Divide and simplify.

**21.** $\dfrac{8^9}{8^2}$

**22.** $\dfrac{7^8}{7^2}$

**23.** $\dfrac{6^3}{6^{-2}}$

**24.** $\dfrac{5^{10}}{5^{-3}}$

**25.** $\dfrac{10^{-3}}{10^6}$

**26.** $\dfrac{12^{-4}}{12^8}$

**27.** $\dfrac{9^{-4}}{9^{-6}}$

**28.** $\dfrac{2^{-7}}{2^{-5}}$

**29.** $\dfrac{x^{-4n}}{x^{6n}}$

**30.** $\dfrac{y^{-3t}}{y^{8t}}$

**31.** $\dfrac{w^{-11q}}{w^{-6q}}$

**32.** $\dfrac{m^{-7t}}{m^{-5t}}$

**33.** $\dfrac{a^3}{a^{-2}}$

**34.** $\dfrac{y^4}{y^{-5}}$

**35.** $\dfrac{27x^7z^5}{-9x^2z}$

**36.** $\dfrac{24a^5b^3}{-8a^4b}$

**37.** $\dfrac{-24x^6y^7}{18x^{-3}y^9}$

**38.** $\dfrac{14a^4b^{-3}}{-8a^8b^{-5}}$

**39.** $\dfrac{-18x^{-2}y^3}{-12x^{-5}y^5}$

**40.** $\dfrac{-14a^{14}b^{-5}}{-18a^{-2}b^{-10}}$

**b**   Simplify.

**41.** $(4^3)^2$

**42.** $(5^4)^5$

**43.** $(8^4)^{-3}$

**44.** $(9^3)^{-4}$

**45.** $(6^{-4})^{-3}$

**46.** $(7^{-8})^{-5}$

**47.** $(5a^2b^2)^3$

**48.** $(2x^3y^4)^5$

**49.** $(-3x^3y^{-6})^{-2}$

**50.** $(-3a^2b^{-5})^{-3}$

**51.** $(-6a^{-2}b^3c)^{-2}$

**52.** $(-8x^{-4}y^5z^2)^{-4}$

**53.** $\left(\dfrac{4^{-3}}{3^4}\right)^3$

**54.** $\left(\dfrac{5^2}{4^{-3}}\right)^{-3}$

**55.** $\left(\dfrac{2x^3y^{-2}}{3y^{-3}}\right)^3$

**56.** $\left(\dfrac{-4x^4y^{-2}}{5x^{-1}y^4}\right)^{-4}$

**57.** $\left(\dfrac{125a^2b^{-3}}{5a^4b^{-2}}\right)^{-5}$

**58.** $\left(\dfrac{-200x^3y^{-5}}{8x^5y^{-7}}\right)^{-4}$

**59.** $\left(\dfrac{-6^5y^4z^{-5}}{2^{-2}y^{-2}z^3}\right)^6$

**60.** $\left(\dfrac{9^{-2}x^{-4}y}{3^{-3}x^{-3}y^2}\right)^8$

**61.** $[(-2x^{-4}y^{-2})^{-3}]^{-2}$

**62.** $[(-4a^{-4}b^{-5})^{-3}]^4$

**63.** $\left(\dfrac{3a^{-2}b}{5a^{-7}b^5}\right)^{-7}$

**64.** $\left(\dfrac{2x^2y^{-2}}{3x^8y^7}\right)^9$

**65.** $\dfrac{10^{2a+1}}{10^{a+1}}$

**66.** $\dfrac{11^{b+2}}{11^{3b-3}}$

**67.** $\dfrac{9a^{x-2}}{3a^{2x+2}}$

**68.** $\dfrac{-12x^{a+1}}{4x^{2-a}}$

**69.** $\dfrac{45x^{2a+4}y^{b+1}}{-9x^{a+3}y^{2+b}}$

**70.** $\dfrac{-28x^{b+5}y^{4+c}}{7x^{b-5}y^{c-4}}$

**71.** $(8^x)^{4y}$

**72.** $(7^{2p})^{3q}$

**73.** $(12^{3-a})^{2b}$

**74.** $(x^{a-1})^{3b}$

**75.** $(5x^{a-1}y^{b+1})^{2c}$

**76.** $(4x^{3a}y^{2b})^{5c}$

**77.** $\dfrac{4x^{2a+3}y^{2b-1}}{2x^{a+1}y^{b+1}}$

**78.** $\dfrac{25x^{a+b}y^{b-a}}{-5x^{a-b}y^{b+a}}$

**C**    Convert each number to scientific notation.

**79.** 47,000,000,000

**80.** 2,600,000,000,000

**81.** 0.000000016

**82.** 0.000000263

**83.** *Coupon Redemptions.*   Shoppers redeemed 2,600,000,000 manufacturers' grocery coupons in a recent year. Write scientific notation for the number of coupons redeemed.
**Source:** CMS

**84.** *Cell-Phone Subscribers.*   In 1985, there were 340 thousand cell-phone subscribers. This number increased to 272 million in 2009. Write the number of cell-phone subscribers in 1985 and in 2009 in scientific notation.
**Sources:** *USA Weekend*, December 31, 2004–January 2, 2005; CTIA–The Wireless Association

**85.** *Insect-Eating Lizard.* A gecko is an insect-eating lizard. Its feet will adhere to virtually any surface because they contain millions of miniscule hairs, or setae, that are 200 billionths of a meter wide. Write 200 billionths in scientific notation.

**Source:** *The Proceedings of the National Academy of Sciences*, Dr. Kellar Autumn and Wendy Hansen of Lewis and Clark College, Portland, Oregon

**86.** *Multiple-Birth Rate.* The rate of triplet and higher-order multiple births in the United States is $\frac{161.8}{100,000}$. Write scientific notation for this birth rate.

**Source:** U.S. National Center for Health Statistics

Convert each number to decimal notation.

**87.** $6.73 \times 10^8$

**88.** $9.24 \times 10^7$

**89.** The wavelength of a certain red light is $6.6 \times 10^{-5}$ cm.

**90.** The mass of an electron is $9.11 \times 10^{-28}$ g.

**91.** About $\$2 \times 10^{12}$ is spent on health care annually in the United States.

**Source:** Centers for Medicare and Medicaid Services

**92.** About $1.61 \times 10^7$ Americans are members of labor unions.

**Source:** U.S. Bureau of Labor Statistics

Multiply and write the answer in scientific notation.

**93.** $(2.3 \times 10^6)(4.2 \times 10^{-11})$

**94.** $(6.5 \times 10^3)(5.2 \times 10^{-8})$

**95.** $(2.34 \times 10^{-8})(5.7 \times 10^{-4})$

**96.** $(3.26 \times 10^{-6})(8.2 \times 10^9)$

Divide and write the answer in scientific notation.

**97.** $\dfrac{8.5 \times 10^8}{3.4 \times 10^5}$

**98.** $\dfrac{5.1 \times 10^6}{3.4 \times 10^3}$

**99.** $\dfrac{4.0 \times 10^{-6}}{8.0 \times 10^{-3}}$

**100.** $\dfrac{7.5 \times 10^{-9}}{2.5 \times 10^{-4}}$

Write the answers to Exercises 101–110 in scientific notation.

**101.** *The Dark Knight Opening Weekend.* The movie *The Dark Knight* opened in 4366 theaters and earned an average of $36,283 per theater the weekend it opened. Find the total amount that the movie earned in its opening weekend.

**Source:** Box Office Mojo

**102.** *Orbit of Venus.* Venus has a nearly circular orbit of the sun. The average distance from the sun to Venus is about $6.71 \times 10^7$ mi. How far does Venus travel in one orbit?

**103.** *Seconds in 2000 Years.* About how many seconds are there in 2000 yr? Assume that there are 365 days in one year.

**104.** *Hot Dog Consumption.* Americans consume 818 hot dogs per second in the summer. How many hot dogs are consumed in July? (July has 31 days.)
Source: National Hot Dog & Sausage Council; American Meat Institute

**105.** *Alpha Centauri.* Other than the sun, the star closest to Earth is Alpha Centauri. Its distance from Earth is about $2.4 \times 10^{13}$ mi. One light-year = the distance that light travels in one year = $5.88 \times 10^{12}$ mi. How many light-years is it from Earth to Alpha Centauri?
Source: The Handy Science Answer Book

1 light-year = $5.88 \times 10^{12}$ mi

Earth · Alpha Centauri

$2.4 \times 10^{13}$ mi

**106.** *Amazon River Water Flow.* The average discharge at the mouth of the Amazon River is 4,200,000 cubic feet per second. How much water is discharged from the Amazon River in one hour? in one year?

**107.** *Word Knowledge.* There are 300,000 words in the English language. The average person knows about 10,000 of them. What part of the total number of words does the average person know?

**108.** *Computer Calculations.* Engineers from the Los Alamos National Laboratory and IBM Corporation have developed a supercomputer that can perform 1000 trillion calculations per second. How many calculations can be performed in one minute? in one hour?
Source: The New York Times, June 9, 2008

**109.** *Printing and Engraving.* A ton of five-dollar bills is worth $4,540,000. How many pounds does a five-dollar bill weigh?

**110.** *Astronomy.* The brightest star in the night sky, Sirius, is about $4.704 \times 10^{13}$ mi from Earth. One light-year is $5.88 \times 10^{12}$ mi. How many light-years is it from Earth to Sirius?
Source: The Handy Science Answer Book

## Skill Maintenance

Simplify.  [R.3c], [R.6b]

**111.** $9x - (-4y + 8) + (10x - 12)$

**112.** $-6t - (5t - 13) + 2(4 - 6t)$

**113.** $4^2 + 30 \cdot 10 - 7^3 + 16$

**114.** $5^4 - 38 \cdot 24 - (16 - 4 \cdot 18)$

**115.** $20 - 5 \cdot 4 - 8$

**116.** $20 - (5 \cdot 4 - 8)$

## Synthesis

Simplify.

**117.** $\dfrac{(2^{-2})^{-4} \cdot (2^3)^{-2}}{(2^{-2})^2 \cdot (2^5)^{-3}}$

**118.** $\left[ \dfrac{(-3x^{-2}y^5)^{-3}}{(2x^4y^{-8})^{-2}} \right]^2$

**119.** $\left[ \left( \dfrac{a^{-2}}{b^7} \right)^{-3} \cdot \left( \dfrac{a^4}{b^{-3}} \right)^2 \right]^{-1}$

Simplify. Assume that variables in exponents represent integers.

**120.** $(m^{x-b}n^{x+b})^x(m^b n^{-b})^x$

**121.** $\left[ \dfrac{(2x^a y^b)^3}{(-2x^a y^b)^2} \right]^2$

**122.** $(x^b y^a \cdot x^a y^b)^c$

# Summary and Review

## Key Terms and Properties

natural numbers, p. 2
whole numbers, p. 2
integers, p. 2
set-builder notation, p. 3
rational numbers, p. 3
irrational numbers, p. 4
real numbers, p. 5
inequalities, p. 6
solution, p. 7

solution set, p. 7
absolute value, pp. 8, 15
opposites, or additive inverses, p. 14
reciprocals, or multiplicative
   inverses, p. 17
exponential notation, p. 23
variable, p. 32
constant, p. 32
algebraic expression, p. 32

substituting, p. 34
evaluating, p. 34
equivalent expressions, p. 38
multiplicative identity, p. 39
factor, p. 43
like, or similar, terms, p. 46
scientific notation, p. 58

## Properties of Real Numbers

*Commutative Laws:*    $a + b = b + a, \quad ab = ba$

*Associative Laws:*    $a + (b + c) = (a + b) + c, \quad a(bc) = (ab)c$

*Distributive Laws:*    $a(b + c) = ab + ac, \quad a(b - c) = ab - ac$

*Inverses:*    $a + (-a) = 0, \quad a \cdot \dfrac{1}{a} = 1$

*Identity Property of 0:*   $a + 0 = a$

*Identity Property of 1:*   $1 \cdot a = a$

*Property of −1:*    $-1 \cdot a = -a$

## Properties of Exponents:   $a^1 = a, \quad a^0 = 1, \quad a^{-n} = \dfrac{1}{a^n}, \quad \dfrac{1}{a^{-n}} = a^n$

*Product Rule:*    $a^m \cdot a^n = a^{m+n}$

*Power Rule:*    $(a^m)^n = a^{mn}$

*Quotient Rule:*    $\dfrac{a^m}{a^n} = a^{m-n}$

*Raising a Product to a Power:*    $(ab)^n = a^n b^n$

*Raising a Quotient to a Power:*    $\left(\dfrac{a}{b}\right)^n = \dfrac{a^n}{b^n}, \quad \left(\dfrac{a}{b}\right)^{-n} = \left(\dfrac{b}{a}\right)^n = \dfrac{b^n}{a^n}$

*Scientific Notation:*    $M \times 10^n$, or $10^n$, where $M$ is such that $1 \le M < 10$.

# Concept Reinforcement

Determine whether each statement is true or false.

_____ **1.** For any numbers $a$ and $b$, $a - b = b - a$.   [R.6b]

_____ **2.** Each member of the set of natural numbers is a member of the set of whole numbers.
[R.1a]

_____ **3.** The opposite of $-a$ when $a < 0$ is negative.   [R.2b]

_____ **4.** Zero is both positive and negative.   [R.1a]

_____ **5.** The absolute value of any real number is positive.   [R.1d]

_____ **6.** The reciprocal of a negative number is negative.   [R.2e]

_____ **7.** If $c$ and $d$ are real numbers and $c + d = 0$, then $c$ and $d$ are additive inverses.   [R.2b]

_____ **8.** The number $4.6 \times 10^n$, where $n$ is an integer, is greater than 0 and less than 1 when $n < 0$.   [R.7c]

# Review Exercises

## Part 1

**1.** Which of the following numbers are rational?   [R.1a]

$$2, \sqrt{3}, -\frac{2}{3}, 0.45\overline{45}, -23.788$$

**2.** Use set-builder notation to name the set of all real numbers less than or equal to 46.   [R.1a]

**3.** Use $<$ or $>$ for ☐ to write a true sentence:   [R.1b]
$-3.9$ ☐ $2.9$.

**4.** Write a different inequality with the same meaning as $19 > x$.   [R.1b]

Determine whether each of the following is true or false.
[R.1b]

**5.** $-13 \geq 5$        **6.** $7.01 \leq 7.01$

Graph each inequality on the number line.   [R.1c]

**7.** $x > -4$        **8.** $x \leq 1$

Find the absolute value.   [R.1d]

**9.** $|-7.23|$        **10.** $|9 - 9|$

Add, subtract, multiply, or divide, if possible.   [R.2a, c, d, e]

**11.** $6 + (-8)$        **12.** $-3.8 + (-4.1)$

**13.** $\frac{3}{4} + \left(-\frac{13}{7}\right)$        **14.** $-8 - (-3)$

**15.** $-17.3 - 9.4$        **16.** $\frac{3}{2} - \left(-\frac{13}{4}\right)$

**17.** $(-3.8)(-2.7)$        **18.** $-\frac{2}{3}\left(\frac{9}{14}\right)$

**19.** $-6(-7)(4)$        **20.** $-12 \div 3$

**21.** $\frac{-84}{-4}$        **22.** $\frac{49}{-7}$

**23.** $\dfrac{5}{6} \div \left(-\dfrac{10}{7}\right)$   **24.** $-\dfrac{5}{2} \div \left(-\dfrac{15}{16}\right)$

**25.** $\dfrac{21}{0}$   **26.** $-108 \div 4.5$

Evaluate $-a$ for each of the following.   [R.2b]

**27.** $a = -7$   **28.** $a = 2.3$

**29.** $a = 0$

Write using exponential notation.   [R.3a]

**30.** $a \cdot a \cdot a \cdot a \cdot a$   **31.** $\left(-\dfrac{7}{8}\right)\left(-\dfrac{7}{8}\right)\left(-\dfrac{7}{8}\right)$

**32.** Rewrite using a positive exponent: $a^{-4}$.   [R.3b]

**33.** Rewrite using a negative exponent: $\dfrac{1}{x^8}$.   [R.3b]

Simplify.   [R.3c]

**34.** $2^3 - 3^4 + (13 \cdot 5 + 67)$

**35.** $64 \div (-4) + (-5)(20)$

## Part 2

Translate to an algebraic expression.   [R.4a]

**36.** Five times some number

**37.** Twenty-eight percent of some number

**38.** Nine less than $t$

**39.** Eight less than the quotient of two numbers

Evaluate.   [R.4b]

**40.** $5x - 7$, when $x = -2$

**41.** $\dfrac{x - y}{2}$, when $x = 4$ and $y = 20$

**42.** *Area of a Rug.*   The area $A$ of a rectangle is given by the length $l$ times the width $w$: $A = lw$. Find the area of a rectangular rug that measures 7 ft by 12 ft.   [R.4b]

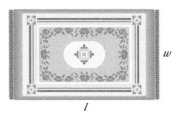

Complete each table by evaluating each expression for the given values. Then look for expressions that are equivalent. [R.5a]

**43.**

|  | $x^2 - 5$ | $(x + 5)^2$ | $(x - 5)^2$ | $x^2 + 5$ |
|---|---|---|---|---|
| $x = -1$ |  |  |  |  |
| $x = 10$ |  |  |  |  |
| $x = 0$ |  |  |  |  |

**44.**

|  | $2x - 14$ | $2x - 7$ | $2(x - 7)$ | $2x + 14$ |
|---|---|---|---|---|
| $x = -1$ |  |  |  |  |
| $x = 10$ |  |  |  |  |
| $x = 0$ |  |  |  |  |

**45.** Use multiplying by 1 to find an equivalent expression with the given denominator: [R.5b]

$$\frac{7}{3}; \quad 9x.$$

**46.** Simplify: $\dfrac{-84x}{7x}$. [R.5b]

Use a commutative law to find an equivalent expression. [R.5c]

**47.** $11 + a$

**48.** $8y$

Use an associative law to find an equivalent expression. [R.5c]

**49.** $(9 + a) + b$

**50.** $8(xy)$

Multiply. [R.5d]

**51.** $-3(2x - y)$

**52.** $4ab(2c + 1)$

Factor. [R.5d]

**53.** $5x + 10y - 5z$

**54.** $ptr + pts$

Collect like terms. [R.6a]

**55.** $2x + 6y - 5x - y$

**56.** $7c - 6 + 9c + 2 - 4c$

**57.** Find an equivalent expression without parentheses: $-(-9c + 4d - 3)$. [R.6b]

Simplify. [R.6b]

**58.** $4(x - 3) - 3(x - 5)$

**59.** $12x - 3(2x - 5)$

**60.** $7x - [4 - 5(3x - 2)]$

**61.** $4m - 3[3(4m - 2) - (5m + 2) + 12]$

Multiply or divide, and simplify. [R.7a]

**62.** $(2x^4y^{-3})(-5x^3y^{-2})$

**63.** $\dfrac{-15x^2y^{-5}}{10x^6y^{-8}}$

Simplify. [R.7b]

**64.** $(-3a^{-4}bc^3)^{-2}$

**65.** $\left[\dfrac{-2x^4y^{-4}}{3x^{-2}y^6}\right]^{-4}$

Multiply or divide, and write scientific notation for the answer. [R.7c]

**66.** $\dfrac{2.2 \times 10^7}{3.2 \times 10^{-3}}$

**67.** $(3.2 \times 10^4)(4.1 \times 10^{-6})$

**68. Finance.** A **mil** is one thousandth of a dollar. The taxation rate in a certain school district is 5.0 mils for every dollar of assessed valuation. The assessed valuation for the district is 13.4 million dollars. How much tax revenue will be raised? [R.7c]

**69. Volume of a Plastic Sheet.** The volume of a rectangular solid is given by the length $l$ times the width $w$ times the height $h$: $V = lwh$. A sheet of plastic has a thickness of 0.00015 m. The sheet is 1.2 m by 79 m. Find the volume of the sheet and express the answer in scientific notation. [R.4b], [R.7c]

**70.** Evaluate $\dfrac{x - 4y}{3}$ when $x = 5$ and $y = -4$. [R.4b]

   **A.** $-8$            **B.** $-7$

   **C.** $-\dfrac{11}{3}$       **D.** $7$

**71.** Use the commutative and the associative laws to determine which expression is *not* equivalent to $2x + y$. [R.5c]

   **A.** $2y + x$           **B.** $x \cdot 2 + y$

   **C.** $y + 2x$           **D.** $y + x \cdot 2$

## Synthesis

**72.** Simplify: $(x^y \cdot x^{3y})^3$. [R.7b]

**73.** If $a = 2^x$ and $b = 2^{x+5}$, find $a^{-1}b$. [R.7a]

**74.** Which of the following expressions are equivalent? [R.5d], [R.7b]

   a) $3x - 3y$          b) $3x - y$

   c) $x^{-2}x^5$          d) $x^{-10}$

   e) $x^{-3}$            f) $(x^{-2})^5$

   g) $x(yz)$           h) $x(y + z)$

   i) $3(x - y)$         j) $xy + xz$

# Understanding Through Discussion and Writing

*To the student and the instructor:* The *Understanding Through Discussion and Writing* exercises are meant to be answered with one or more sentences. They can be discussed and answered collaboratively by the entire class or by small groups.

**1.** List five examples of rational numbers that are not integers and explain why they are not. [R.1a]

**2.** Explain in your own words why $\frac{7}{0}$ is not defined. [R.2e]

**3.** If the base and the height of a triangle are doubled, does its area double? Explain. [R.4b]

**4.** If the base and the height of a parallelogram are doubled, does its area double? Explain. (See Exercise 44 in Exercise Set R.4.) [R.4b]

**5.** A \$20 bill weighs about $2.2 \times 10^{-3}$ lb. A criminal claims to be carrying \$5 million in \$20 bills in his suitcase. Is this possible? Why or why not? [R.7c]

**6.** When a calculator indicates that $5^{17} = 7.629394531 \times 10^{11}$, you know that an approximation is being made. How can you tell? (*Hint:* What should the ones digit be?) [R.7c]

Test   For Extra Help

CHAPTER Test Prep VIDEOS

Step-by-step test solutions are found on the Chapter Test Prep Videos available via the Video Resources on DVD, in *MyMathLab*, and on YouTube (search "BittingerInterAlgPB" and click on "Channels").

## Part 1

**1.** Which of the following numbers are irrational?

$$-43, \quad \sqrt{7}, \quad -\frac{2}{3}, \quad 2.3\overline{76}, \quad \pi$$

**2.** Use set-builder notation to name the set of real numbers greater than 20.

**3.** Use < or > for ☐ to write a true sentence:

$$-4.5 \ \square \ -8.7.$$

**4.** Write a different inequality with the same meaning as $a \leq 5$.

Is each of the following true or false?

**5.** $-6 \geq -6$

**6.** $-8 \leq -6$

**7.** Graph $x > -2$ on the number line.

<---+---+---+---+---+---+---+---+---->
    -4  -3  -2  -1  0   1   2   3   4

Find the absolute value.

**8.** $|0|$

**9.** $\left| -\frac{7}{8} \right|$

Add, subtract, multiply, or divide, if possible.

**10.** $7 + (-9)$

**11.** $-5.3 + (-7.8)$

**12.** $-\frac{5}{2} + \left( -\frac{7}{2} \right)$

**13.** $-6 - (-5)$

**14.** $-18.2 - 11.5$

**15.** $\frac{19}{4} - \left( -\frac{3}{2} \right)$

**16.** $(-4.1)(8.2)$

**17.** $-\frac{4}{5} \left( -\frac{15}{16} \right)$

**18.** $-6(-4)(-11)2$

**19.** $-75 \div (-5)$

**20.** $\frac{-10}{2}$

**21.** $-\frac{5}{2} \div \left( -\frac{15}{16} \right)$

**22.** $-459.2 \div 5.6$

**23.** $\frac{-3}{0}$

Evaluate $-a$ for each of the following.

**24.** $a = -13$

**25.** $a = 0$

**26.** Write exponential notation: $q \cdot q \cdot q \cdot q$.

**27.** Rewrite using a negative exponent: $\frac{1}{a^9}$.

Simplify.

**28.** $1 - (2 - 5)^2 + 5 \div 10 \cdot 4^2$

**29.** $\frac{7(5 - 2 \cdot 3) - 3^2}{4^2 - 3^2}$

## Part 2

Translate to an algebraic expression.

**30.** Nine more than $t$

**31.** Twelve less than the quotient of two numbers

**32.** Evaluate $3x - 3y$ when $x = 2$ and $y = -4$.

**33.** *Area of a Triangular Stamp.* The area $A$ of a triangle is given by $A = \frac{1}{2}bh$. Find the area of a triangular stamp whose base measures 3 cm and whose height measures 2.5 cm.

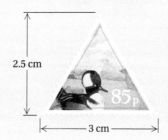

2.5 cm

3 cm

85p

Complete a table by evaluating each expression for $x = -1$, $x = 10$, and $x = 0$. Then determine whether the expressions are equivalent. Answer yes or no.

**34.** $x(x - 3)$; $x^2 - 3x$

**35.** $3x + 5x^2$; $8x^2$

**36.** Use multiplying by 1 to find an equivalent expression with the given denominator.

$$\frac{3}{4}; \ 36x$$

**37.** Simplify:

$$\frac{-54x}{-36x}.$$

Use a commutative law to find an equivalent expression.

**38.** $pq$

**39.** $t + 4$

Use an associative law to find an equivalent expression.

**40.** $3 + (t + w)$

**41.** $(4a)b$

Multiply.

**42.** $-2(3a - 4b)$

**43.** $3\pi r(s + 1)$

Factor.

**44.** $ab - ac + 2ad$

**45.** $2ah + h$

Collect like terms.

**46.** $6y - 8x + 4y + 3x$

**47.** $4a - 7 + 17a + 21$

**48.** Find an equivalent expression without parentheses: $-(-9x + 7y - 22)$.

Simplify.

**49.** $-3(x + 2) - 4(x - 5)$

**50.** $4x - [6 - 3(2x - 5)]$

Multiply or divide, and simplify.

**51.** $\dfrac{-12x^3y^{-4}}{8x^7y^{-6}}$

**52.** $(3a^4b^{-2})(-2a^5b^{-3})$

**53.** $(5a^{4n})(-10a^{5n})$

**54.** $\dfrac{-60x^{3t}}{12x^{7t}}$

Simplify.

**55.** $(-3a^{-3}b^2c)^{-4}$

**56.** $\left[\dfrac{-5a^{-2}b^8}{10a^{10}b^{-4}}\right]^{-4}$

**57.** Convert to scientific notation: 0.0000437.

Multiply or divide, and write scientific notation for the answer.

**58.** $(8.7 \times 10^{-9})(4.3 \times 10^{15})$

**59.** $\dfrac{1.2 \times 10^{-12}}{6.4 \times 10^{-7}}$

**60.** *Mass of Pluto.* The mass of Earth is $5.98 \times 10^{24}$ kg. The mass of the dwarf planet Pluto is about 0.002 times the mass of Earth. Find the mass of Pluto and express the answer in scientific notation.
  **A.** $29.9 \times 10^{26}$ kg      **B.** $2.99 \times 10^{27}$ kg      **C.** $1.196 \times 10^{22}$ kg      **D.** $11.96 \times 10^{21}$ kg

## Synthesis

**61.** Which of the following expressions are equivalent?
  **a)** $x^{-3}x^{-4}$      **b)** $x^{12}$      **c)** $x^{-12}$      **d)** $5x + 5$      **e)** $(x^{-3})^{-4}$
  **f)** $5(x + 1)$      **g)** $5x$      **h)** $5 + 5x$      **i)** $5(xy)$      **j)** $(5x)y$

# Solving Linear Equations and Inequalities

## Real-World Application

Pizza Hut and Domino's Pizza are the top pizza chains in the United States. In 2008, Pizza Hut's sales totaled $10.2 billion. This was $4.8 billion more than the total sales for Domino's. What was the total for Domino's?

*Source:* Directory of Chain Restaurant Operators

*This problem appears as Exercise 30 in the Mid-Chapter Review.*

# 1.1

## Solving Equations

## OBJECTIVES

**a** Determine whether a given number is a solution of a given equation.

**b** Solve equations using the addition principle.

**c** Solve equations using the multiplication principle.

**d** Solve equations using the addition principle and the multiplication principle together, removing parentheses where appropriate.

**SKILL TO REVIEW**
Objective R.2d: Multiply real numbers.

Multiply.

1. $-\dfrac{3}{4}\left(-\dfrac{4}{3}\right)$

2. $\dfrac{2}{3} \cdot \dfrac{15}{8}$

Consider the following equations.

a) $3 + 4 = 7$
b) $5 - 1 = 2$
c) $21 + 2 = 24$
d) $x - 5 = 12$
e) $9 - x = x$
f) $13 + 2 = 15$

1. Which equations are true?

2. Which equations are false?

3. Which equations are neither true nor false?

### a  Equations and Solutions

In order to solve many kinds of problems, we must be able to solve *equations*. Some examples of equations are

$$3 + 5 = 8, \qquad 15 - 10 = 2 + 3,$$
$$x + 8 = 23, \qquad 5x - 2 = 9 - x.$$

---

**EQUATION**

An **equation** is a number sentence that says that the expressions on either side of the equals sign, =, represent the same number.

---

The sentence "$15 - 10 = 2 + 3$" asserts that the expressions $15 - 10$ and $2 + 3$ name the same number. It is a *true* equation because both represent the number 5.

Some equations are true. Some are false. Some are neither true nor false.

**EXAMPLES**  Determine whether the equation is true, false, or neither.

1. $1 + 10 = 11$      Both expressions represent 11. The equation is *true*.
2. $7 - 8 = 9 - 13$      $7 - 8$ represents $-1$ and $9 - 13$ represents $-4$. The equation is *false*.
3. $x - 9 = 3$      The equation is *neither* true nor false, because we do not know what number $x$ represents.

Do Margin Exercises 1–3.

If an equation contains a variable, then some replacements or values of the variable may make it true and some may make it false.

---

**SOLUTION OF AN EQUATION**

The replacements for the variable that make an equation true are called the **solutions** of the equation. The set of all solutions is called the **solution set** of the equation. When we find all the solutions, we say that we have **solved** the equation.

---

To determine whether a number is a solution of an equation, we evaluate the algebraic expression on each side of the equals sign by substitution. If the values are the same, then the number is a solution of the equation. If they are not, then the number is not a solution.

*Answers*

*Skill to Review:*

1. 1  2. $\dfrac{5}{4}$

*Margin Exercises:*
1. (a), (f)  2. (b), (c)  3. (d), (e)

**EXAMPLE 4**  Determine whether 5 is a solution of $x + 6 = 11$.

$$x + 6 = 11 \qquad \text{Writing the equation}$$
$$5 + 6 \;?\; 11 \qquad \text{Substituting 5 for } x$$
$$11 \;|\; \qquad \text{TRUE}$$

Since the left-hand side and the right-hand side are the same, 5 is a solution of the equation.

**EXAMPLE 5**  Determine whether 18 is a solution of $2x - 3 = 5$.

We have

$$2x - 3 = 5 \qquad \text{Writing the equation}$$
$$2 \cdot 18 - 3 \;?\; 5 \qquad \text{Substituting 18 for } x$$
$$36 - 3 \;|\;$$
$$33 \;|\; \qquad \text{FALSE}$$

Since the left-hand side and the right-hand side are not the same, 18 is not a solution of the equation.

> Do Exercises 4–6.

Determine whether the given number is a solution of the given equation.

**4.** 8; $x + 5 = 13$

**5.** $-4$; $7x = 16$

**6.** 5; $2x + 3 = 13$

### Equivalent Equations

Consider the equation

$$x = 5.$$

The solution of this equation is easily "seen" to be 5. If we replace $x$ with 5, we get

$$5 = 5, \quad \text{which is true.}$$

In Example 4, we saw that the solution of the equation $x + 6 = 11$ is also 5, but the fact that 5 is the solution is not so readily apparent. We now consider principles that allow us to start with one equation and end up with an *equivalent equation*, like $x = 5$, in which the variable is alone on one side, and for which the solution is read directly from the equation.

---

**EQUIVALENT EQUATIONS**

Equations with the same solutions are called **equivalent equations**.

---

> Do Exercises 7 and 8.

**7.** Determine whether
$$3x + 2 = 11 \quad \text{and} \quad x = 3$$
are equivalent.

**8.** Determine whether
$$4 - 5x = -11 \quad \text{and} \quad x = -3$$
are equivalent.

## b  The Addition Principle

One of the principles we use in solving equations involves addition. The equation $a = b$ says that $a$ and $b$ represent the same number. Suppose that $a = b$ is true and we then add a number $c$ to $a$. We will get the same result if we add $c$ to $b$, because $a$ and $b$ are the same number.

---

**THE ADDITION PRINCIPLE**

For any real numbers $a$, $b$, and $c$,

$$a = b \quad \text{is equivalent to} \quad a + c = b + c.$$

---

*Answers*

**4.** Yes  **5.** No  **6.** Yes  **7.** Yes  **8.** No

When we use the addition principle, we sometimes say that we "add the same number on both sides of an equation." We can also "subtract the same number on both sides of an equation," because we can express subtraction as the addition of an opposite. That is,

$$a - c = b - c \quad \text{is equivalent to} \quad a + (-c) = b + (-c).$$

To the student:

At the front of the text, you will find a Student Organizer card. This pullout card will help you keep track of important dates and useful contact information. You can also use it to plan time for class, study, work, and relaxation. By managing your time wisely, you will provide yourself the best possible opportunity to be successful in this course.

**EXAMPLE 6**   Solve: $x + 6 = 11$.

$$x + 6 = 11$$

$$\left.\begin{array}{l} x + 6 + (-6) = 11 + (-6) \\ x + 6 - 6 = 11 - 6 \end{array}\right\}$$ Using the addition principle: adding $-6$ on both sides or subtracting 6 on both sides. Note that 6 and $-6$ are opposites.

$$x + 0 = 5 \qquad \text{Simplifying}$$

$$x = 5 \qquad \text{Using the identity property of 0: } x + 0 = x$$

Check:   $\dfrac{x + 6 = 11}{5 + 6 \; ? \; 11}$   Substituting 5 for $x$

$\phantom{5 + 6 \;?} 11 \mid$   TRUE

The solution is 11.

In Example 6, we wanted to get $x$ alone so that we could readily see the solution, so we added the opposite of 6. This eliminated the 6 on the left, giving us the *additive identity* 0, which when added to $x$ is $x$. We began with $x + 6 = 11$. Using the addition principle, we derived a simpler equation, $x = 5$. The equations $x + 6 = 11$ and $x = 5$ are *equivalent*.

**EXAMPLE 7**   Solve: $y - 4.7 = 13.9$.

$$y - 4.7 = 13.9$$

$$y - 4.7 + 4.7 = 13.9 + 4.7 \qquad \text{Using the addition principle: adding 4.7 on both sides. Note that } -4.7 \text{ and } 4.7 \text{ are opposites.}$$

$$y + 0 = 18.6 \qquad \text{Simplifying}$$

$$y = 18.6 \qquad \text{Using the identity property of 0: } y + 0 = y$$

Check:   $\dfrac{y - 4.7 = 13.9}{18.6 - 4.7 \; ? \; 13.9}$   Substituting 18.6 for $y$

$\phantom{18.6 - 4.7 \;?} 13.9 \mid$   TRUE

The solution is 18.6.

**EXAMPLE 8**   Solve: $-\frac{3}{8} + x = -\frac{5}{7}$.

$$-\tfrac{3}{8} + x = -\tfrac{5}{7}$$

$$\tfrac{3}{8} + \left(-\tfrac{3}{8}\right) + x = \tfrac{3}{8} + \left(-\tfrac{5}{7}\right) \qquad \text{Using the addition principle: adding } \tfrac{3}{8}$$

$$0 + x = \tfrac{3}{8} - \tfrac{5}{7}$$

$$x = \tfrac{3}{8} \cdot \tfrac{7}{7} - \tfrac{5}{7} \cdot \tfrac{8}{8} \qquad \text{Multiplying by 1 to obtain the least common denominator}$$

$$x = \tfrac{21}{56} - \tfrac{40}{56}$$

$$x = -\tfrac{19}{56}$$

Check: 
$$-\frac{3}{8} + x = -\frac{5}{7}$$

$$\frac{-\frac{3}{8} + \left(-\frac{19}{56}\right) \ ? \ -\frac{5}{7}}{}$$ Substituting $-\frac{19}{56}$ for $x$

$$-\frac{3}{8} \cdot \frac{7}{7} + \left(-\frac{19}{56}\right)$$

$$-\frac{21}{56} + \left(-\frac{19}{56}\right)$$

$$-\frac{40}{56}$$

$$-\frac{5}{7} \ \bigg| \qquad \text{TRUE}$$

The solution is $-\frac{19}{56}$.

Do Exercises 9-12.

Do Exercises 9-12.

Solve using the addition principle.

**9.** $x + 9 = 2$

**10.** $x + \dfrac{1}{4} = -\dfrac{3}{5}$

**11.** $13 = -25 + y$

**12.** $y - 61.4 = 78.9$

## c The Multiplication Principle

A second principle for solving equations involves multiplication. Suppose that $a = b$ is true and we multiply $a$ by a nonzero number $c$. We get the same result if we multiply $b$ by $c$, because $a$ and $b$ are the same number.

> **THE MULTIPLICATION PRINCIPLE**
>
> For any real numbers $a$, $b$, and $c$, $c \neq 0$,
>
> $$a = b \quad \text{is equivalent to} \quad a \cdot c = b \cdot c.$$

**EXAMPLE 9** Solve: $\frac{4}{5}x = 22$.

$$\frac{4}{5}x = 22$$

$$\frac{5}{4} \cdot \frac{4}{5}x = \frac{5}{4} \cdot 22 \qquad \text{Multiplying by } \tfrac{5}{4}, \text{ the reciprocal of } \tfrac{4}{5}$$

$$1 \cdot x = \frac{55}{2} \qquad \text{Multiplying and simplifying}$$

$$x = \frac{55}{2} \qquad \text{Using the identity property of 1: } 1 \cdot x = x$$

Check: 
$$\frac{4}{5}x = 22$$

$$\frac{\frac{4}{5} \cdot \frac{55}{2} \ ? \ 22}{22 \ \bigg| \qquad \text{TRUE}}$$

The solution is $\frac{55}{2}$.

In Example 9, in order to get $x$ alone, we multiplied by the *multiplicative inverse*, or *reciprocal*, of $\frac{4}{5}$. When we multiplied, we got the *multiplicative identity* 1 times $x$, or $1 \cdot x$, which simplified to $x$. This enabled us to eliminate the $\frac{4}{5}$ on the left.

The multiplication principle also tells us that we can "divide by a nonzero number on both sides" because division is the same as multiplying by a reciprocal. That is,

$$\frac{a}{c} = \frac{b}{c} \quad \text{is equivalent to} \quad a \cdot \frac{1}{c} = b \cdot \frac{1}{c}, \quad \text{when } c \neq 0.$$

In a product like $\frac{4}{5}x$, the number in front of the variable is called the **coefficient**. When this number is in fraction notation, it is usually most convenient to multiply both sides by its reciprocal. If the coefficient is an integer or is in decimal notation, it is usually more convenient to divide by the coefficient.

**EXAMPLE 10** Solve: $4x = 9$.

$$4x = 9$$

$$\frac{4x}{4} = \frac{9}{4}$$    Using the multiplication principle: multiplying on both sides by $\frac{1}{4}$ or dividing on both sides by the coefficient, 4

$$1 \cdot x = \frac{9}{4}$$    Simplifying

$$x = \frac{9}{4}$$    Using the identity property of 1: $1 \cdot x = x$

Check:

$$\frac{4x = 9}{4 \cdot \frac{9}{4} \; ? \; 9}$$
$$9 \; | \quad \text{TRUE}$$

The solution is $\frac{9}{4}$.

Do Exercises 13–15.

---

**EXAMPLE 11** Solve: $5.5 = -0.05y$.

$$5.5 = -0.05y$$

$$\frac{5.5}{-0.05} = \frac{-0.05y}{-0.05}$$    Dividing by $-0.05$ on both sides

$$\frac{5.5}{-0.05} = 1 \cdot y$$

$$-110 = y$$

The check is left to the student. The solution is $-110$.

Note that equations are reversible. That is, $a = b$ is equivalent to $b = a$. Thus, $-110 = y$ and $y = -110$ are equivalent, and the solution of both equations is $-110$.

Do Exercise 16.

---

**EXAMPLE 12** Solve: $-\dfrac{x}{4} = 10$.

$$-\frac{x}{4} = 10$$

$$-\frac{1}{4}x = 10 \qquad\qquad -\frac{x}{4} = -\frac{1}{4} \cdot x$$

$$-4 \cdot \left(-\frac{1}{4}\right)x = -4 \cdot 10 \quad \text{Multiplying by } -4 \text{ on both sides}$$

$$1 \cdot x = -40 \qquad\qquad \text{Simplifying}$$

$$x = -40$$

The check is left to the student. The solution is $-40$.

Do Exercises 17 and 18.

---

Solve using the multiplication principle.

**13.** $8x = 10$

**14.** $-\dfrac{3}{7}y = 21$

**15.** $-4x = -\dfrac{6}{7}$

**16.** Solve: $-12.6 = 4.2y$.

Solve.

**17.** $-\dfrac{x}{8} = 17$

**18.** $-x = -5$

---

*Answers*

**13.** $\dfrac{5}{4}$   **14.** $-49$   **15.** $\dfrac{3}{14}$   **16.** $-3$
**17.** $-136$   **18.** $5$

## d Using the Principles Together

Let's see how we can use the addition and multiplication principles together.

**EXAMPLE 13**  Solve: $3x - 4 = 13$.

$$3x - 4 = 13$$
$$3x - 4 + 4 = 13 + 4 \qquad \text{Using the addition principle: adding 4}$$
$$3x = 17 \qquad \text{Simplifying}$$
$$\frac{3x}{3} = \frac{17}{3} \qquad \text{Dividing by 3}$$
$$x = \frac{17}{3} \qquad \text{Simplifying}$$

Check:
$$\frac{3x - 4 = 13}{3 \cdot \frac{17}{3} - 4 \;?\; 13}$$
$$17 - 4 \;\Big|$$
$$13 \;\Big| \qquad \text{TRUE}$$

The solution is $\frac{17}{3}$, or $5\frac{2}{3}$.

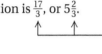

In algebra, "improper" fraction notation, such as $\frac{17}{3}$, is quite "proper." We will generally use such notation rather than $5\frac{2}{3}$.

Do Exercise 19.

**19.** Solve: $-4 + 9x = 8$.

In a situation such as Example 13, it is easier to first use the addition principle. In a situation in which fractions or decimals are involved, it may be easier to use the multiplication principle first to clear them, but it is not mandatory.

**EXAMPLE 14**  Clear the fractions and solve: $\frac{3}{16}x + \frac{1}{2} = \frac{11}{8}$.

We multiply on both sides by the least common multiple of the denominators—in this case, 16:

$$\frac{3}{16}x + \frac{1}{2} = \frac{11}{8} \qquad \text{The LCM of the denominators is 16.}$$
$$16\left(\frac{3}{16}x + \frac{1}{2}\right) = 16\left(\frac{11}{8}\right) \qquad \text{Multiplying by 16}$$
$$16 \cdot \frac{3}{16}x + 16 \cdot \frac{1}{2} = 22 \qquad \begin{array}{l}\text{Carrying out the multiplication. We use}\\ \text{the distributive law on the left, being}\\ \text{careful to multiply \textit{both} terms by 16.}\end{array}$$
$$3x + 8 = 22 \qquad \text{Simplifying. The fractions are cleared.}$$
$$3x + 8 - 8 = 22 - 8 \qquad \text{Subtracting 8}$$
$$3x = 14$$
$$\frac{3x}{3} = \frac{14}{3} \qquad \text{Dividing by 3}$$
$$x = \frac{14}{3}.$$

The number $\frac{14}{3}$ checks and is the solution.

Do Exercise 20.

**20.** Clear the fractions and solve:
$$\frac{2}{3} - \frac{5}{6}y = \frac{1}{3}.$$

*Answers*

**19.** $\frac{4}{3}$    **20.** $4 - 5y = 2; \frac{2}{5}$

**EXAMPLE 15** Clear the decimals and solve: $12.4 - 5.12x = 3.14x$.

We multiply on both sides by a power of ten—10, 100, 1000, and so on—to clear the equation of decimals. In this case, we use $10^2$, or 100, because the greatest number of decimal places is 2.

$$12.4 - 5.12x = 3.14x$$

$$100(12.4 - 5.12x) = 100(3.14x) \qquad \text{Multiplying by 100}$$

$$100(12.4) - 100(5.12x) = 314x \qquad \text{Carrying out the multiplication. We use the distributive law on the left.}$$

$$1240 - 512x = 314x \qquad \text{Simplifying}$$

$$1240 - 512x + 512x = 314x + 512x \qquad \text{Adding } 512x$$

$$1240 = 826x$$

$$\frac{1240}{826} = \frac{826x}{826} \qquad \text{Dividing by 826}$$

$$x = \frac{1240}{826}, \text{ or } \frac{620}{413}$$

The solution is $\frac{620}{413}$.

**21.** Clear the decimals and solve:

$$6.3x - 9.1 = 3x.$$

Do Exercise 21.

When there are like terms on the same side of an equation, we collect them. If there are like terms on opposite sides of an equation, we use the addition principle to get them on the same side of the equation.

**EXAMPLE 16** Solve: $8x + 6 - 2x = -4x - 14$.

$$8x + 6 - 2x = -4x - 14$$

$$6x + 6 = -4x - 14 \qquad \text{Collecting like terms on the left}$$

$$4x + 6x + 6 = 4x - 4x - 14 \qquad \text{Adding } 4x$$

$$10x + 6 = -14 \qquad \text{Collecting like terms}$$

$$10x + 6 - 6 = -14 - 6 \qquad \text{Subtracting 6}$$

$$10x = -20$$

$$\frac{10x}{10} = \frac{-20}{10} \qquad \text{Dividing by 10}$$

$$x = -2$$

Check:

$$\begin{array}{rcl} \underline{8x + 6 - 2x} & = & \underline{-4x - 14} \\ 8(-2) + 6 - 2(-2) & ? & -4(-2) - 14 \\ -16 + 6 + 4 & | & 8 - 14 \\ -6 & | & -6 \qquad \text{TRUE} \end{array}$$

The solution is $-2$.

Solve.

**22.** $\dfrac{5}{2}x + \dfrac{9}{2}x = 21$

**23.** $1.4x - 0.9x + 0.7 = -2.2$

**24.** $-4x + 2 + 5x = 3x - 15$

Do Exercises 22-24.

## Special Cases

Some equations have no solution.

**EXAMPLE 17**  Solve: $-8x + 5 = 14 - 8x$.

We have

$$-8x + 5 = 14 - 8x$$
$$8x - 8x + 5 = 8x + 14 - 8x \qquad \text{Adding } 8x$$
$$5 = 14. \qquad\qquad \text{We get a false equation.}$$

No matter what number we use for $x$, we get a false sentence. Thus the equation has *no* solution.

There are some equations for which any real number is a solution.

**EXAMPLE 18**  Solve: $-8x + 5 = 5 - 8x$.

We have

$$-8x + 5 = 5 - 8x$$
$$8x - 8x + 5 = 8x + 5 - 8x \qquad \text{Adding } 8x$$
$$5 = 5. \qquad\qquad \text{We get a true equation.}$$

Replacing $x$ with any real number gives a true sentence. Thus any real number is a solution. The equation has *infinitely* many solutions.

Do Exercises 25 and 26.

Do Exercises 25 and 26.

Solve.

**25.** $4 + 7x = 7x + 9$

**26.** $3 + 9x = 9x + 3$

## Equations Containing Parentheses

Equations containing parentheses can often be solved by first multiplying to remove parentheses and then proceeding as before.

**EXAMPLE 19**  Solve: $30 + 5(x + 3) = -3 + 5x + 48$.

We have

$$30 + 5(x + 3) = -3 + 5x + 48$$
$$30 + 5x + 15 = -3 + 5x + 48 \qquad \text{Multiplying, using the distributive law, to remove parentheses}$$
$$45 + 5x = 45 + 5x \qquad \text{Collecting like terms on each side}$$
$$45 + 5x - 5x = 45 + 5x - 5x \qquad \text{Subtracting } 5x$$
$$45 = 45. \qquad \text{Simplifying. We get a true equation.}$$

All real numbers are solutions.

Do Exercises 27–29.

Do Exercises 27-29.

Solve.

**27.** $7x - 17 = 4 + 7(x - 3)$

**28.** $3x + 4(x + 2) = 11 + 7x$

**29.** $3x + 8(x + 2) = 11 + 7x$

**EXAMPLE 20** Solve: $3(7 - 2x) = 14 - 8(x - 1)$.

$$3(7 - 2x) = 14 - 8(x - 1)$$

| | |
|---|---|
| $21 - 6x = 14 - 8x + 8$ | Multiplying, using the distributive law, to remove parentheses |
| $21 - 6x = 22 - 8x$ | Collecting like terms |
| $21 - 6x + 8x = 22 - 8x + 8x$ | Adding $8x$ |
| $21 + 2x = 22$ | Collecting like terms |
| $21 + 2x - 21 = 22 - 21$ | Subtracting 21 |
| $2x = 1$ | |
| $\dfrac{2x}{2} = \dfrac{1}{2}$ | Dividing by 2 |
| $x = \dfrac{1}{2}$ | |

Check:

$$\dfrac{3(7 - 2x) = 14 - 8(x - 1)}{}$$

$$3\left(7 - 2 \cdot \tfrac{1}{2}\right) \;?\; 14 - 8\left(\tfrac{1}{2} - 1\right)$$
$$3(7 - 1) \;\Big|\; 14 - 8\left(-\tfrac{1}{2}\right)$$
$$3 \cdot 6 \;\Big|\; 14 + 4$$
$$18 \;\Big|\; 18 \qquad \text{TRUE}$$

The solution is $\frac{1}{2}$.

Do Exercises 30 and 31.

Solve.

**30.** $30 + 7(x - 1) = 3(2x + 7)$

**31.** $3(y - 1) - 1 = 2 - 5(y + 5)$

---

**AN EQUATION-SOLVING PROCEDURE**

1. Clear the equation of fractions or decimals if that is needed.
2. If parentheses occur, multiply to remove them using the distributive law.
3. Collect like terms on each side of the equation, if necessary.
4. Use the addition principle to get all terms with letters on one side and all other terms on the other side.
5. Collect like terms on each side again, if necessary.
6. Use the multiplication principle to solve for the variable.

---

The following table describes the kinds of solutions we have considered.

| EQUIVALENT EQUATION | NUMBER OF SOLUTIONS | SOLUTION(S) |
|---|---|---|
| $x = a$, where $a$ is a real number | One | The number $a$ |
| A true equation, such as $8 = 8$, $-15 = -15$, or $0 = 0$ | Infinitely many | Every real number is a solution. |
| A false equation, such as $3 = 8$, $-4 = 5$, or $0 = -5$ | Zero | There are no solutions. |

*Answers*

**30.** $-2$    **31.** $-\dfrac{19}{8}$

**Checking Possible Solutions**   Although a calculator is *not* required for this textbook, the book contains a series of *optional* discussions on using a graphing calculator. The keystrokes for the TI-84 Plus graphing calculator will be shown throughout. For keystrokes for other models of calculators, consult the user's manual for your particular model.

To check possible solutions of an equation on a calculator, we can substitute and carry out the calculations on each side of the equation just as we do when we check by hand. If the left-hand and the right-hand sides of the equation have the same value, then the number that was substituted is a solution of the equation. To check the possible solution $-2$ in the equation $8x + 6 - 2x = -4x - 14$ in Example 16, for instance, we first substitute $-2$ for $x$ in the expression on the left side of the equation. We press ⑧ ✕ ⟨−⟩ ② ⊕ ⑥ ⊖ ② ✕ ⟨−⟩ ② **ENTER**, and get $-6$. Then we substitute $-2$ for $x$ in the expression on the right side of the equation. We press ⟨−⟩ ④ ✕ ⟨−⟩ ② ⊖ ① ④ **ENTER**. Again, we get $-6$. Since the two sides of the equation have the same value when $x$ is $-2$, we know that $-2$ is the solution of the equation.

```
8*-2+6-2*-2
                    -6
-4*-2-14
                    -6
```

A table can also be used to check possible solutions of equations. First, we press ⟨Y=⟩ to display the equation-editor screen. If an expression for Y1 is currently entered, we place the cursor on it and press **CLEAR** to delete it. We do the same for any other entries that are present.

Next, we position the cursor to the right of Y1 = and enter the left side of the equation by pressing ⑧ **X,T,θ,n** ⊕ ⑥ ⊖ ② **X,T,θ,n**. Then we position the cursor beside Y2 = and enter the right side of the equation by pressing ⟨−⟩ ④ **X,T,θ,n** ⊖ ① ④. Now we press **2ND** ⟨TBLSET⟩ to display the Table Setup screen. (TBLSET is the second operation associated with the ⟨WINDOW⟩ key.) On the INDPNT line, we position the cursor on "Ask" and press **ENTER** to set up a table in ASK mode. (The settings for TblStart and ΔTbl are irrelevant in ASK mode.)

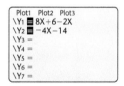

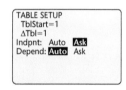

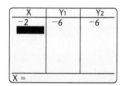

We press **2ND** ⟨TABLE⟩ to display the table. (TABLE is the second operation associated with the ⟨GRAPH⟩ key.) We enter the possible solution, $-2$, by pressing ⟨−⟩ ② **ENTER**, and see that Y1 $= -6 =$ Y2 for this value of $x$. This confirms that the left and right sides of the equation have the same value for $x = -2$, so $-2$ is the solution of the equation.

**Exercises:**

**1.** Use substitution to check the solutions found in Examples 9, 13, and 15.

**2.** Use a table set in ASK mode to check the solutions found in Margin Exercises 24, 30, and 31.

Remember to review the objectives before doing the exercises.

**a**   Determine whether the given number is a solution of the given equation.

**1.** $17; \ x + 23 = 40$

**2.** $24; \ 47 - x = 23$

**3.** $-8; \ 2x - 3 = -18$

**4.** $-10; \ 3x + 14 = -27$

**5.** $45; \ \dfrac{-x}{9} = -2$

**6.** $32; \ \dfrac{-x}{8} = -3$

**7.** $10; \ 2 - 3x = 21$

**8.** $-11; \ 4 - 5x = 59$

**9.** $19; \ 5x + 7 = 102$

**10.** $9; \ 9y + 5 = 86$

**11.** $-11; \ 7(y - 1) = 84$

**12.** $-13; \ x + 5 = 5 + x$

**b**   Solve using the addition principle. Don't forget to check.

**13.** $y + 6 = 13$

**14.** $x + 7 = 14$

**15.** $-20 = x - 12$

**16.** $-27 = y - 17$

**17.** $-8 + x = 19$

**18.** $-8 + r = 17$

**19.** $-12 + z = -51$

**20.** $-37 + x = -89$

**21.** $p - 2.96 = 83.9$

**22.** $z - 14.9 = -5.73$

**23.** $-\dfrac{3}{8} + x = -\dfrac{5}{24}$

**24.** $x + \dfrac{1}{12} = -\dfrac{5}{6}$

**c**   Solve using the multiplication principle. Don't forget to check.

**25.** $3x = 18$

**26.** $5x = 30$

**27.** $-11y = 44$

**28.** $-4x = 124$

**29.** $-\dfrac{x}{7} = 21$

**30.** $-\dfrac{x}{3} = -25$

**31.** $-96 = -3z$

**32.** $-120 = -8y$

**33.** $4.8y = -28.8$

**34.** $0.39t = -2.73$

**35.** $\dfrac{3}{2}t = -\dfrac{1}{4}$

**36.** $-\dfrac{7}{6}y = -\dfrac{7}{8}$

**d** Solve using the principles together. Don't forget to check.

**37.** $6x - 15 = 45$

**38.** $4x - 7 = 81$

**39.** $5x - 10 = 45$

**40.** $6z - 7 = 11$

**41.** $9t + 4 = -104$

**42.** $5x + 7 = -108$

**43.** $-\dfrac{7}{3}x + \dfrac{2}{3} = -18$

**44.** $-\dfrac{9}{2}y + 4 = -\dfrac{91}{2}$

**45.** $\dfrac{6}{5}x + \dfrac{4}{10}x = \dfrac{32}{10}$

**46.** $\dfrac{9}{5}y + \dfrac{4}{10}y = \dfrac{66}{10}$

**47.** $0.9y - 0.7y = 4.2$

**48.** $0.8t - 0.3t = 6.5$

**49.** $8x + 48 = 3x - 12$

**50.** $15x + 40 = 8x - 9$

**51.** $7y - 1 = 27 + 7y$

**52.** $3x - 15 = 15 + 3x$

**53.** $3x - 4 = 5 + 12x$

**54.** $9t - 4 = 14 + 15t$

**55.** $5 - 4a = a - 13$

**56.** $6 - 7x = x - 14$

**57.** $3m - 7 = -7 - 4m - m$

**58.** $5x - 8 = -8 + 3x - x$

**59.** $5x + 3 = 11 - 4x + x$

**60.** $6y + 20 = 10 + 3y + y$

**61.** $-7 + 9x = 9x - 7$

**62.** $-3t + 4 = 5 - 3t$

**63.** $6y - 8 = 9 + 6y$

**64.** $5 - 2y = -2y + 5$

**65.** $2(x + 7) = 4x$

**66.** $3(y + 6) = 9y$

**67.** $80 = 10(3t + 2)$

**68.** $27 = 9(5y - 2)$

**69.** $180(n - 2) = 900$

**70.** $210(x - 3) = 840$

**71.** $5y - (2y - 10) = 25$

**72.** $8x - (3x - 5) = 40$

**73.** $7(3x + 6) = 11 - (x + 2)$

**74.** $3(4 - 2x) = 4 - (6x - 8)$

**75.** $2[9 - 3(-2x - 4)] = 12x + 42$

**76.** $-40x + 45 = 3[7 - 2(7x - 4)]$

**77.** $\frac{1}{8}(16y + 8) - 17 = -\frac{1}{4}(8y - 16)$

**78.** $\frac{1}{6}(12t + 48) - 20 = -\frac{1}{8}(24t - 144)$

**79.** $3[5 - 3(4 - t)] - 2 = 5[3(5t - 4) + 8] - 26$

**80.** $6[4(8 - y) - 5(9 + 3y)] - 21 = -7[3(7 + 4y) - 4]$

**81.** $\dfrac{2}{3}\left(\dfrac{7}{8} + 4x\right) - \dfrac{5}{8} = \dfrac{3}{8}$

**82.** $\dfrac{3}{4}\left(3x - \dfrac{1}{2}\right) + \dfrac{2}{3} = \dfrac{1}{3}$

**83.** $5(4x - 3) - 2(6 - 8x) + 10(-2x + 7) = -4(9 - 12x)$

**84.** $9(4x + 7) - 3(5x - 8) = 6\left(\dfrac{2}{3} - x\right) - 5\left(\dfrac{3}{5} + 2x\right)$

## Skill Maintenance

This heading indicates that the exercises that follow are *Skill Maintenance* exercises, which review any skill previously studied in the text. You will see them in virtually every exercise set. Answers to *all* skill maintenance exercises are found at the back of the book. If you miss an exercise, restudy the objective shown in red.

Multiply or divide, and simplify.   [R.7a]

**85.** $a^{-9} \cdot a^{23}$

**86.** $\dfrac{a^{-9}}{a^{23}}$

**87.** $(6x^5 y^{-4})(-3x^{-3} y^{-7})$

**88.** $\dfrac{6x^5 y^{-4}}{-3x^{-3} y^{-7}}$

Multiply.   [R.5d]

**89.** $2(6 - 10x)$

**90.** $-1(5 - 6x)$

**91.** $-4(3x - 2y + z)$

**92.** $5(-2x + 7y - 4)$

Factor.   [R.5d]

**93.** $2x - 6y$

**94.** $-4x - 24y$

**95.** $4x - 10y + 2$

**96.** $-10x + 35y - 20$

**97.** Name the set consisting of the positive integers less than 10, using both roster notation and set-builder notation.   [R.1a]

**98.** Name the set consisting of the negative integers greater than $-9$ using both roster notation and set-builder notation.   [R.1a]

## Synthesis

*To the student and the instructor*: The Synthesis exercises found at the end of every exercise set challenge students to combine concepts or skills studied in that section or in preceding parts of the text.

Solve. (The symbol ⌐⊾⌐ indicates an exercise designed to be done using a calculator.)

**99.** ⌐⊾⌐ $4.23x - 17.898 = -1.65x - 42.454$

**100.** ⌐⊾⌐ $-0.00458y + 1.7787 = 13.002y - 1.005$

**101.** $\dfrac{3x}{2} + \dfrac{5x}{3} - \dfrac{13x}{6} - \dfrac{2}{3} = \dfrac{5}{6}$

**102.** $\dfrac{2x - 5}{6} + \dfrac{4 - 7x}{8} = \dfrac{10 + 6x}{3}$

**103.** $x - \{3x - [2x - (5x - (7x - 1))]\} = x + 7$

**104.** $23 - 2\{4 + 3(x - 1)\} + 5\{x - 2(x + 3)\} = 7\{x - 2[5 - (2x + 3)]\}$

# 1.2

# Formulas and Applications

## OBJECTIVE

a Evaluate formulas and solve a formula for a specified letter.

### SKILL TO REVIEW
Objective R.4b: Evaluate an algebraic expression by substitution.

1. Evaluate $\dfrac{3a}{b}$ when $a = 8$ and $b = 12$.

2. Evaluate $\dfrac{x - y}{4}$ when $x = 18$ and $y = 2$.

## a Evaluating and Solving Formulas

A **formula** is an equation that represents or models a relationship between two or more quantities. For example, the relationship between the perimeter $P$ of a square and the length $s$ of its sides is given by the formula $P = 4s$. The formula $A = s^2$ represents the relationship between the area $A$ of a square and the length $s$ of its sides.

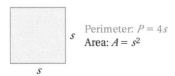

Perimeter: $P = 4s$
Area: $A = s^2$

Other important geometric formulas are $A = \pi r^2$ (for the area $A$ of a circle of radius $r$), $C = \pi d$ (for the circumference $C$ of a circle of diameter $d$), and $A = b \cdot h$ (for the area $A$ of a parallelogram of height $h$ and base $b$). A more complete list of geometric formulas appears on the inside back cover of this text.

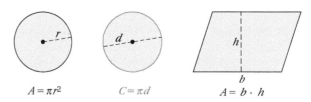

$A = \pi r^2$ $\qquad$ $C = \pi d$ $\qquad$ $A = b \cdot h$

**EXAMPLE 1** *Body Mass Index.* **Body mass index** $I$ can be used to determine whether an individual has a healthy weight for his or her height. An index in the range 18.5–24.9 indicates a normal weight. Body mass index is given by the formula, or model,

$$I = \frac{703\,W}{H^2},$$

where $W$ is weight, in pounds, and $H$ is height, in inches.
Source: Centers for Disease Control and Prevention

a) Lindsay Vonn of the U.S. Ski Team is 5 ft 10 in. tall and weighs 160 lb. What is her body mass index?

b) Professional basketball player Dwight Howard has a body mass index of 27 and a height of 6 ft 11 in. What is his weight?

*Answers*

*Skill to Review:*
1. 2    2. 4

**a)** We substitute 160 lb for $W$ and 5 ft 10 in., or $5 \cdot 12 + 10 = 70$ in., for $H$. Then we have

$$I = \frac{703\,W}{H^2} = \frac{703(160)}{70^2} \approx 23.0.$$

Thus Lindsey Vonn's body mass index is 23.0.

**b)** We substitute 27 for $I$ and 6 ft 11 in., or $6 \cdot 12 + 11 = 83$ in., for $H$ and solve for $W$ using the equation-solving principles introduced in Section 1.1:

$$I = \frac{703\,W}{H^2}$$

$$27 = \frac{703\,W}{83^2} \qquad \text{Substituting}$$

$$27 = \frac{703\,W}{6889}$$

$$6889 \cdot 27 = 6889 \cdot \frac{703\,W}{6889} \qquad \text{Multiplying by 6889}$$

$$186{,}003 = 703\,W \qquad \text{Simplifying}$$

$$\frac{186{,}003}{703} = \frac{703\,W}{703} \qquad \text{Dividing by 703}$$

$$265 \approx W.$$

Dwight Howard weighs about 265 lb.

> Do Exercise 1.

If we want to make repeated calculations of $W$, as in Example 1(b), it might be easier to first solve for $W$, getting it alone on one side of the equation. We "solve" for $W$ as we did above, using the equation-solving principles of Section 1.1.

**EXAMPLE 2** Solve for $W$: $I = \dfrac{703\,W}{H^2}$.

$$I = \frac{703\,W}{H^2} \qquad \text{We want this letter alone.}$$

$$I \cdot H^2 = \frac{703\,W}{H^2} \cdot H^2 \qquad \begin{array}{l}\text{Multiplying by } H^2 \text{ on both}\\ \text{sides to clear the fraction}\end{array}$$

$$IH^2 = 703\,W \qquad \text{Simplifying}$$

$$\frac{IH^2}{703} = \frac{703\,W}{703} \qquad \text{Dividing by 703}$$

$$\frac{IH^2}{703} = W$$

> Do Exercise 2.

---

**1. Body Mass Index.**

**a)** Roland is 6 ft 1 in. tall and weighs 195 lb. What is his body mass index?

**b)** Keisha has a body mass index of 24.5 and a height of 5 ft 8 in. What is her weight?

**c)** Calculate your own body mass index.

**2.** Solve for $m$: $F = \dfrac{mv^2}{r}$.
(This is a physics formula.)

---

*Answers*

**1.** (a) 25.7; (b) 161 lb; (c) Answers will vary.

**2.** $m = \dfrac{rF}{v^2}$

**EXAMPLE 3**  Solve for $r$:  $H = 2r + 3m$.

$$H = 2r + 3m \qquad \text{We want this letter alone.}$$
$$H - 3m = 2r \qquad \text{Subtracting } 3m$$
$$\frac{H - 3m}{2} = r \qquad \text{Dividing by 2}$$

**3.** Solve for $m$:  $H = 2r + 3m$.

Do Exercise 3.

**EXAMPLE 4**  Solve for $b$:  $A = \frac{5}{2}(b - 20)$.

$$A = \frac{5}{2}(b - 20) \qquad \text{We want this letter alone.}$$
$$2A = 5(b - 20) \qquad \text{Multiplying by 2 to clear the fraction}$$
$$2A = 5b - 100 \qquad \text{Removing parentheses}$$
$$2A + 100 = 5b \qquad \text{Adding 100}$$
$$\frac{2A + 100}{5} = b, \quad \text{or} \quad b = \frac{2A}{5} + \frac{100}{5} = \frac{2A}{5} + 20 \qquad \text{Dividing by 5}$$

**4.** Solve for $c$:  $P = \dfrac{3}{5}(c + 10)$.

Do Exercise 4.

**EXAMPLE 5**  *Area of a Trapezoid.*  Solve for $a$:  $A = \frac{1}{2}h(a + b)$. (To find the area of a trapezoid, take half the product of the height, $h$, and the sum of the lengths of the parallel sides, $a$ and $b$.)

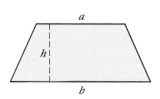

$$A = \frac{1}{2}h(a + b) \qquad \text{We want this letter alone.}$$
$$2A = h(a + b) \qquad \text{Multiplying by 2 to clear the fraction}$$
$$2A = ha + hb \qquad \text{Using the distributive law}$$
$$2A - hb = ha \qquad \text{Subtracting } hb$$
$$\frac{2A - hb}{h} = a, \quad \text{or} \quad a = \frac{2A}{h} - \frac{hb}{h} = \frac{2A}{h} - b \qquad \text{Dividing by } h$$

Note that there is more than one correct form of the answers in Examples 4 and 5. This is a common occurrence when we solve formulas.

**5.** Solve for $b$:  $A = \dfrac{1}{2}h(a + b)$.

Do Exercise 5.

*Answers*

**3.** $m = \dfrac{H - 2r}{3}$  **4.** $c = \dfrac{5}{3}P - 10$, or $\dfrac{5P - 30}{3}$
**5.** $b = \dfrac{2A - ha}{h}$, or $\dfrac{2A}{h} - a$

We used the addition principle and the multiplication principle to solve equations in Section 1.1. In a similar manner, we use the same principles in this section to solve a formula for a given letter.

To solve a formula for a given letter, identify the letter, and:

1. Multiply on both sides to clear the fractions or decimals, if necessary.
2. If parentheses occur, multiply to remove them using the distributive law.
3. Collect like terms on each side, if necessary. This may require factoring if a variable is in more than one term.
4. Using the addition principle, get all terms with the letter to be solved for on one side of the equation and all other terms on the other side.
5. Collect like terms again, if necessary.
6. Solve for the letter in question using the multiplication principle.

As indicated in step (3) above, sometimes we must factor to isolate a letter.

**EXAMPLE 6** *Simple Interest.* Solve for $P$: $A = P + Prt$. (To find the amount $A$ to which principal $P$, in dollars, will grow at simple interest rate $r$, in $t$ years, add the principal $P$ to the interest, $Prt$.)

$A = P + Prt$    We want this letter alone.

$A = P(1 + rt)$    Factoring (or collecting like terms)

$\dfrac{A}{1 + rt} = P$    Dividing by $1 + rt$ on both sides

Do Exercise 6.

**6.** Solve for $Q$: $T = Q + Quy$.

**EXAMPLE 7** *Chess Ratings.* The formula

$$R = r + \frac{400(W - L)}{N}$$

is used to establish a chess player's rating $R$, after he or she has played $N$ games, where $W$ is the number of wins, $L$ is the number of losses, and $r$ is the average rating of the opponents.

**Source:** U.S. Chess Federation

a) Cara plays 8 games in a chess tournament, winning 5 games and losing 3. The average rating of her opponents is 1205. Find Cara's chess rating.

b) Solve the formula for $L$.

a) We substitute 8 for $N$, 5 for $W$, 3 for $L$, and 1205 for $r$ in the formula. Then we calculate $R$:

$$R = r + \frac{400(W - L)}{N} = 1205 + \frac{400(5 - 3)}{8} = 1305.$$

*Answer*

**6.** $Q = \dfrac{T}{1 + uy}$

**b)** We solve as follows:

$$R = r + \frac{400(W - L)}{N}$$     We want this letter alone.

$$NR = N\left[r + \frac{400(W - L)}{N}\right]$$     Multiplying by $N$ to clear the fraction

$$NR = N \cdot r + N \cdot \frac{400(W - L)}{N}$$     Multiplying using the distributive law

$$NR = Nr + 400(W - L)$$     Simplifying

$$NR - Nr = 400(W - L)$$     Subtracting $Nr$

$$NR - Nr = 400W - 400L$$     Using the distributive law

$$NR - Nr - 400W = -400L$$     Subtracting $400W$

$$\frac{NR - Nr - 400W}{-400} = L.$$     Dividing by $-400$

Other correct forms of the answer are

$$L = \frac{Nr + 400W - NR}{400} \quad \text{and} \quad L = W - \frac{NR - Nr}{400}.$$

Do Exercise 7.

**7. Chess Ratings.** Use the formula given in Example 7.

  **a)** Martin plays 6 games in a tournament, winning 2 games and losing 4. The average rating of his opponents is 1384. Find Martin's chess rating.

  **b)** Solve the formula for $W$.

---

## STUDY TIPS

### USING THIS TEXTBOOK

- **Be sure to note the symbols (a), (b), (c), and so on, that correspond to the objectives you are to master.** The first time you see them is in the margin at the beginning of each section; the second time is in the subheadings of each section; and the third time is in the exercise set for the section. You will also find objective references next to the skill maintenance exercises in each exercise set and in the mid-chapter review and end-of-chapter review exercises, as well as in the answers to the chapter tests and the cumulative reviews. These objective symbols allow you to refer to the appropriate place in the text whenever you need to review a topic.

- **Read and study each step of each example.** The examples include important side comments that explain each step. These carefully chosen examples and notes prepare you for success in the exercise set.

- **Stop and do the margin exercises as you study a section.** Doing the margin exercises is one of the most effective ways to enhance your ability to learn mathematics from this text. Don't deprive yourself of its benefits!

- **Note the icons listed at the top of each exercise set.** These refer to the many distinctive multimedia study aids that accompany the book.

- **Odd-numbered exercises.** Often an instructor will assign some odd-numbered exercises. When you complete these, you can check your answers at the back of the book. If you miss any, check your work in the *Student's Solutions Manual* or ask your instructor for help.

- **Even-numbered exercises.** Whether or not your instructor assigns the even-numbered exercises, always do some on your own. Remember, there are no answers given for the class tests, so you need to practice doing exercises without answers. Check your answers later with a friend or your instructor.

---

*Answers*

**7. (a)** About 1251; **(b)** $W = \dfrac{NR - Nr + 400L}{400}$,

or $L + \dfrac{NR - Nr}{400}$

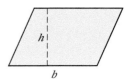
**a** Solve for the given letter.

**1.** *Motion Formula:*

$$d = rt, \text{ for } r$$

(Distance $d$, speed $r$, time $t$)

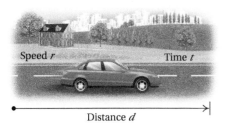

Speed $r$    Time $t$

Distance $d$

**2.** $d = rt$, for $t$

**3.** *Area of a Parallelogram:*

$$A = bh, \text{ for } h$$

(Area $A$, base $b$, height $h$)

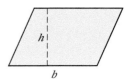

**4.** *Volume of a Sphere:*

$$V = \frac{4}{3}\pi r^3, \text{ for } r^3$$

(Volume $V$, radius $r$)

**5.** *Perimeter of a Rectangle:*

$$P = 2l + 2w, \text{ for } w$$

(Perimeter $P$, length $l$, and width $w$)

**6.** $P = 2l + 2w$, for $l$

**7.** *Area of a Triangle:*

$$A = \frac{1}{2}bh, \text{ for } b$$

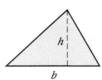

**8.** $A = \frac{1}{2}bh$, for $h$

**9.** *Average of Two Numbers:*

$$A = \frac{a+b}{2}, \text{ for } a$$

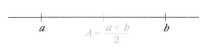

**10.** $A = \frac{a+b}{2}$, for $b$

**11.** *Force:*

$$F = ma, \text{ for } m$$

(Force $F$, mass $m$, acceleration $a$)

**12.** $F = ma$, for $a$

**13.** *Simple Interest:*

$$I = Prt, \text{ for } t$$

(Interest $I$, principal $P$, interest rate $r$, time $t$)

**14.** $I = Prt$, for $P$

**15.** *Relativity:*

$$E = mc^2, \text{ for } c^2$$

(Energy $E$, mass $m$, speed of light $c$)

**16.** $E = mc^2$, for $m$

**17.** $Q = \dfrac{p-q}{2}$, for $p$

**18.** $Q = \dfrac{p-q}{2}$, for $q$

**19.** $Ax + By = c$, for $y$

**20.** $Ax + By = c$, for $x$

**21.** $I = 1.08\dfrac{T}{N}$, for $N$

**22.** $F = \dfrac{mv^2}{r}$, for $v^2$

**23.** $C = \dfrac{3}{4}(m + 5)$, for $m$

**24.** $N = \dfrac{1}{3}M(t + w)$, for $w$

**25.** $n = \dfrac{1}{3}(a + b - c)$, for $b$

**26.** $t = \dfrac{1}{6}(x - y + z)$, for $z$

**27.** $d = R - Rst$, for $R$

**28.** $g = m + mnp$, for $m$

**29.** $T = B + Bqt$, for $B$

**30.** $Z = Q - Qab$, for $Q$

*Basal Metabolic Rate.* An individual's basal metabolic rate is the minimum number of calories required to sustain life when the individual is at rest. It can be thought of as the number of calories burned by an individual who sleeps all day. The Harris–Benedict formula for basal metabolic rate for a man is $R = 66 + 6.23w + 12.7h - 6.8a$. The formula for a woman is $R = 655 + 4.35w + 4.7h - 4.7a$. In each formula, $R$ is in calories, $w$ is weight, in pounds, $h$ is height, in inches, and $a$ is age, in years.

**Source:** Shapefit

**31. a)** Gary weighs 185 lb, is 5 ft 11 in. tall, and is 28 years old. Use the formula for the basal metabolic rate for a man to find Gary's basal metabolic rate.
**b)** Solve the formula for $w$.

**32. a)** Alyssa weighs 145 lb, is 5 ft 6 in. tall, and is 32 years old. Use the formula for the basal metabolic rate for a woman to find Alyssa's basal metabolic rate.
**b)** Solve the formula for $h$.

**33.** *Caloric Requirement.* The number of calories $K$ required each day by a moderately active female who wants to maintain her weight is estimated by the formula

$$K = 1015.25 + 6.74w + 7.29h - 7.29a,$$

where $w$ is weight, in pounds, $h$ is height, in inches, and $a$ is age, in years.

**Source:** Shapefit

a) Serena is a moderately active 25-year-old woman who weighs 150 lb and is 5 ft 8 in. tall. Find the number of calories she requires each day in order to maintain her weight.

b) Solve the formula for $a$.

**34.** *Caloric Requirement.* The number of calories $K$ required each day by a moderately active male who wants to maintain his weight is estimated by the formula

$$K = 102.3 + 9.66w + 19.69h - 10.54a,$$

where $w$ is weight, in pounds, $h$ is height, in inches, and $a$ is age, in years.

**Source:** Shapefit

a) Dan is a moderately active man who weighs 210 lb, is 6 ft 2 in. tall, and is 34 years old. Find the number of calories he requires each day in order to maintain his weight.

b) Solve the formula for $a$.

*Projecting Birth Weight.* Ultrasonic images of 29-week-old fetuses can be used to predict birth weight. One model, or formula, developed by Thurnau, is $P = 9.337da - 299$; a second model, developed by Weiner, is $P = 94.593c + 34.227a - 2134.616$. For both formulas, $P$ is the estimated birth weight, in grams, $d$ is the diameter of the fetal head, in centimeters, $c$ is the circumference of the fetal head, in centimeters, and $a$ is the circumference of the fetal abdomen, in centimeters.

**Sources:** G. R. Thurnau, R. K. Tamura, R. E. Sabbagha, et al. *Am. J. Obstet Gynecol* 1983; **145**:557; C. P. Weiner, R. E. Sabbagha, N. Vaisrub, et al. *Obstet Gynecol* 1985; **65**:812.

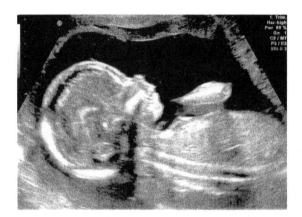

**35. a)** Use Thurnau's model to estimate the birth weight of a 29-week-old fetus when the diameter of the fetal head is 8.5 cm and the circumference of the fetal abdomen is 24.1 cm.

**b)** Solve the formula for $a$.

**36. a)** Use Weiner's model to estimate the birth weight of a 29-week-old fetus when the circumference of the fetal head is 26.7 cm and the circumference of the fetal abdomen is 24.1 cm.

**b)** Solve the formula for $c$.

**37.** *Young's Rule in Medicine.* Young's rule for determining the amount of a medicine dosage for a child is given by

$$c = \frac{ad}{a + 12},$$

where $a$ is the child's age, in years, and $d$ is the usual adult dosage, in milligrams. (*Warning!* Do not apply this formula without checking with a physician!)

**Source:** June Looby Olsen, et al., *Medical Dosage Calculations*, 6th ed. Reading, MA: Addison Wesley Longman, p. A-31

**a)** The usual adult dosage of a particular medication is 250 mg. Find the dosage for a child of age 3.

**b)** Solve the formula for $d$.

**38.** *Full-Time-Equivalent Students.* Colleges accommodate students who need to take different total-credit-hour loads. They determine the number of "full-time-equivalent" students, $F$, using the formula

$$F = \frac{n}{15},$$

where $n$ is the total number of credits students enroll in for a given semester.

**a)** Determine the number of full-time-equivalent students on a campus in which students register for 42,690 credits.

**b)** Solve the formula for $n$.

## Skill Maintenance

Divide. [R.2e]

**39.** $\dfrac{80}{-16}$

**40.** $-2000 \div (-8)$

**41.** $-\dfrac{1}{2} \div \dfrac{1}{4}$

**42.** $120 \div (-4.8)$

**43.** $-\dfrac{2}{3} \div \left(-\dfrac{5}{6}\right)$

**44.** $\dfrac{-90}{-15}$

**45.** $\dfrac{-90}{15}$

**46.** $\dfrac{-80}{16}$

## Synthesis

Solve.

**47.** $A = \pi rs + \pi r^2$, for $s$

**48.** $s = v_1 t + \frac{1}{2}at^2$, for $a$; for $v_1$

**49.** $\dfrac{P_1 V_1}{T_1} = \dfrac{P_2 V_2}{T_2}$, for $V_1$; for $P_2$

**50.** $\dfrac{P_1 V_1}{T_1} = \dfrac{P_2 V_2}{T_2}$, for $T_2$; for $P_1$

**51.** In Exercise 13, you solved the formula $I = Prt$ for $t$. Now use the formula to determine how long it will take a deposit of $75 to earn $3 interest when invested at 5% simple interest.

**52.** The area of the shaded triangle $ABE$ is 20 cm². Find the area of the trapezoid. (See Example 5.)

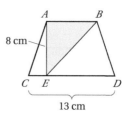

**53.** *Horsepower of an Engine.* The horsepower of an engine can be calculated by the formula

$$H = W\left(\dfrac{v}{234}\right)^3,$$

where $W$ is the weight, in pounds, of the car, including the driver, fluids, and fuel, and $v$ is the maximum velocity, or speed, in miles per hour, of the car attained a quarter mile after beginning acceleration.

**a)** Find the horsepower of a V-6, 2.8-liter engine if $W = 2700$ lb and $v = 83$ mph.

**b)** Find the horsepower of a 4-cylinder, 2.0-liter engine if $W = 3100$ lb and $v = 73$ mph.

# Mid-Chapter Review

## Concept Reinforcement

Determine whether each statement is true or false.

_____ **1.** $2x + 3 = 7$ and $x = 2$ are equivalent equations.   [1.1a]

_____ **2.** It is possible for an equation to be false.   [1.1a]

_____ **3.** Every equation has at least one solution.   [1.1d]

_____ **4.** When we solve an applied problem, we check the possible solution in the equation to which the problem was translated.   [1.3a]

## Guided Solutions

Fill in each box with the number or expression that creates a correct statement or solution.

**5.** Solve: $2x - 5 = 1 - 4x$.   [1.1d]

$$2x - 5 = 1 - 4x$$
$$2x - 5 + 4x = 1 - 4x + \square$$
$$6x - 5 = \square \qquad \text{Collecting like terms}$$
$$6x - 5 + \square = 1 + 5$$
$$6x = \square \qquad \text{Collecting like terms}$$
$$\frac{6x}{6} = \frac{6}{\square}$$
$$x = \square \qquad \text{Simplifying}$$

**6.** Solve for $y$: $Mx + Ny = T$.   [1.2a]

$$Mx + Ny = T$$
$$Mx + Ny - Mx = T - \square$$
$$\square = T - Mx$$
$$y = \frac{T - Mx}{\square}$$

## Mixed Review

Determine whether the given number is a solution of the given equation.   [1.1a]

**7.** 7; $x + 5 = 12$

**8.** $\frac{1}{3}$; $3x - 4 = 5$

**9.** $-24$; $\frac{-x}{8} = -3$

**10.** 9; $6(x - 3) = 36$

Solve.   [1.1b, c, d]

**11.** $x - 7 = -10$

**12.** $-7x = 56$

**13.** $8x - 9 = 23$

**14.** $1 - x = 3x - 7$

**15.** $2 - 4y = -4y + 2$

**16.** $\frac{3}{4}y + 2 = \frac{7}{2}$

**17.** $5t - 9 = 7t - 4$

**18.** $4x - 11 = 11 + 4x$

**19.** $2(y - 4) = 8y$

**20.** $4y - (y - 1) = 16$

**21.** $t - 3(t - 4) = 9$

**22.** $6(2x + 3) = 10 - (4x - 5)$

Solve for the given letter. [1.2a]

**23.** $P = mn$, for $n$

**24.** $z = 3t + 3w$, for $t$

**25.** $N = \dfrac{r + s}{4}$, for $s$

**26.** $T = 1.5\dfrac{A}{B}$, for $B$

**27.** $H = \dfrac{2}{3}(t - 5)$, for $t$

**28.** $f = g + ghm$, for $g$

Solve. [1.3a, b]

**29.** *Falling DVD Sales.* Sales of DVDs totaled $14.5 billion in 2008. This was a decrease of 9% from the 2007 sales total. What was the 2007 sales total?
**Source:** Digital Entertainment Group

**30.** *Pizza Sales.* Pizza Hut and Domino's Pizza are the top pizza chains in the United States. In 2008, Pizza Hut's sales totaled $10.2 billion. This was $4.8 billion more than the total sales for Domino's. What was the total for Domino's?
**Source:** Directory of Chain Restaurant Operators

**31.** *Carpet Dimensions.* The width of an Oriental carpet is 2 ft less than the length. The perimeter of the carpet is 24 ft. Find the dimensions of the carpet.

**32.** *Boating.* Frederick's boat travels at a speed of 9 mph in still water. The Bailey River flows at a speed of 3 mph. How long will it take Frederick to travel 18 mi downstream? 18 mi upstream?

## Understanding Through Discussion and Writing

*To the student and the instructor*: The Discussion and Writing exercises are meant to be answered with one or more sentences. They can be discussed and answered collaboratively by the entire class or by small groups.

**33.** Explain the difference between equivalent expressions and equivalent equations. [R.5a], [1.1a]

**34.** Devise an application in which it would be useful to solve the motion formula $d = rt$ for $r$. [1.2a]

**35.** The equations

$$P = 2l + 2w \quad \text{and} \quad w = \frac{P}{2} - l$$

are equivalent formulas involving the perimeter $P$, length $l$, and width $w$ of a rectangle. Devise a problem for which the second of the two formulas would be more useful. [1.2a]

**36.** Explain why we can use the addition principle to subtract the same number on both sides of an equation and why we can use the multiplication principle to divide by the same nonzero number on both sides of an equation. [1.1b, c]

**37.** How can a guess or an estimate help prepare you for the *Translate* step when solving problems? [1.3a]

**38.** Why is it important to label clearly what a variable represents in an applied problem? [1.3a]

# 1.4 Sets, Inequalities, and Interval Notation

## a Inequalities

We can extend our equation-solving skills to the solving of inequalities. (See Section R.1 for an introduction to inequalities.)

> **INEQUALITY**
>
> An **inequality** is a sentence containing $<, >, \leq, \geq,$ or $\neq$.

Some examples of inequalities are

$$-2 < a, \quad x > 4, \quad x + 3 \leq 6, \quad 6 - 7y \geq 10y - 4, \quad \text{and} \quad 5x \neq 10.$$

> **SOLUTION OF AN INEQUALITY**
>
> Any replacement or value for the variable that makes an inequality true is called a **solution** of the inequality. The set of all solutions is called the **solution set**. When all the solutions of an inequality have been found, we say that we have **solved** the inequality.

**EXAMPLES** Determine whether the given number is a solution of the inequality.

**1.** $x + 3 < 6$; 5

We substitute 5 for $x$ and get $5 + 3 < 6$, or $8 < 6$, a *false* sentence. Therefore, 5 is not a solution.

**2.** $2x - 3 > -3$; 1

We substitute 1 for $x$ and get $2(1) - 3 > -3$, or $-1 > -3$, a *true* sentence. Therefore, 1 is a solution.

**3.** $4x - 1 \leq 3x + 2$; $-3$

We substitute $-3$ for $x$ and get $4(-3) - 1 \leq 3(-3) + 2$, or $-13 \leq -7$, a *true* sentence. Therefore, $-3$ is a solution.

Do Margin Exercises 1–3.

## b Inequalities and Interval Notation

The **graph** of an inequality is a drawing that represents its solutions. An inequality in one variable can be graphed on the number line.

**EXAMPLE 4** Graph $x < 4$ on the number line.

The solutions are all real numbers less than 4, so we shade all numbers less than 4 on the number line. To indicate that 4 is not a solution, we use a right parenthesis ")" at 4.

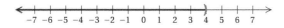

## OBJECTIVES

**a** Determine whether a given number is a solution of an inequality.

**b** Write interval notation for the solution set or the graph of an inequality.

**c** Solve an inequality using the addition principle and the multiplication principle and then graph the inequality.

**d** Solve applied problems by translating to inequalities.

**SKILL TO REVIEW**
Objective R.1c: Graph inequalities on the number line.

Graph each inequality.

**1.** $x > -2$

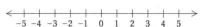

**2.** $x \leq 1$

Determine whether the given number is a solution of the inequality.

**1.** $3 - x < 2$; 8

**2.** $3x + 2 > -1$; $-2$

**3.** $3x + 2 \leq 4x - 3$; 5

**Answers**

*Skill to Review:*

1.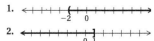

2. 

*Margin Exercises:*
**1.** Yes **2.** No **3.** Yes

We can write the solution set for $x < 4$ using **set-builder notation** (see Section R.1): $\{x \mid x < 4\}$. This is read "The set of all $x$ such that $x$ is less than 4."

Another way to write solutions of an inequality in one variable is to use **interval notation**. Interval notation uses parentheses ( ) and brackets [ ].

If $a$ and $b$ are real numbers such that $a < b$, we define the interval $(a, b)$ as the set of all numbers between but not including $a$ and $b$—that is, the set of all $x$ for which $a < x < b$. Thus,

$$(a, b) = \{x \mid a < x < b\}.$$

The points $a$ and $b$ are the **endpoints** of the interval. The parentheses indicate that the endpoints are *not* included in the graph.

The interval $[a, b]$ is defined as the set of all numbers $x$ for which $a \leq x \leq b$. Thus,

$$[a, b] = \{x \mid a \leq x \leq b\}.$$

The brackets indicate that the endpoints *are* included in the graph.*

---

*Caution!*

Do not confuse the *interval* $(a, b)$ with the *ordered pair* $(a, b)$, which denotes a point in the plane, as we will see in Chapter 2. The context in which the notation appears usually makes the meaning clear.

---

The following intervals include one endpoint and exclude the other:

$(a, b] = \{x \mid a < x \leq b\}$.  The graph excludes $a$ and includes $b$.

$[a, b) = \{x \mid a \leq x < b\}$.  The graph includes $a$ and excludes $b$.

Some intervals extend without bound in one or both directions. We use the symbols $\infty$, read "infinity," and $-\infty$, read "negative infinity," to name these intervals. The notation $(a, \infty)$ represents the set of all numbers greater than $a$—that is,

$$(a, \infty) = \{x \mid x > a\}.$$

Similarly, the notation $(-\infty, a)$ represents the set of all numbers less than $a$—that is,

$$(-\infty, a) = \{x \mid x < a\}.$$

---

*Some books use the representations 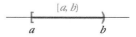 and instead of, respectively,

The notations $[a, \infty)$ and $(-\infty, a]$ are used when we want to include the endpoint $a$. The interval $(-\infty, \infty)$ names the set of all real numbers.

$$(-\infty, \infty) = \{x \mid x \text{ is a real number}\}$$

Interval notation is summarized in the following table.

**INTERVALS: NOTATION AND GRAPHS**

| INTERVAL NOTATION | SET NOTATION | GRAPH |
|---|---|---|
| $(a, b)$ | $\{x \mid a < x < b\}$ | |
| $[a, b]$ | $\{x \mid a \leq x \leq b\}$ | |
| $[a, b)$ | $\{x \mid a \leq x < b\}$ | |
| $(a, b]$ | $\{x \mid a < x \leq b\}$ | |
| $(a, \infty)$ | $\{x \mid x > a\}$ | |
| $[a, \infty)$ | $\{x \mid x \geq a\}$ | |
| $(-\infty, b)$ | $\{x \mid x < b\}$ | |
| $(-\infty, b]$ | $\{x \mid x \leq b\}$ | |
| $(-\infty, \infty)$ | $\{x \mid x \text{ is a real number}\}$ | |

---

*Caution!*

---

Whenever the symbol $\infty$ is included in interval notation, a right parenthesis ")" is used. Similarly, when $-\infty$ is included, a left parenthesis "(" is used.

---

**EXAMPLES**   Write interval notation for the given set or graph.

**5.** $\{x \mid -4 < x < 5\} = (-4, 5)$

**6.** $\{x \mid x \geq -2\} = [-2, \infty)$

**7.** $\{x \mid 7 > x \geq 1\} = \{x \mid 1 \leq x < 7\} = [1, 7)$

**8.**  
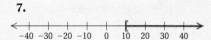
$(-2, 4]$

**9.**
$(-\infty, -1)$

Do Exercises 4-8.

## c Solving Inequalities

Two inequalities are **equivalent** if they have the same solution set. For example, the inequalities $x > 4$ and $4 < x$ are equivalent. Just as the addition principle for equations gives us equivalent equations, the addition principle for inequalities gives us equivalent inequalities.

Write interval notation for the given set or graph.

**4.** $\{x \mid -4 \leq x < 5\}$

**5.** $\{x \mid x \leq -2\}$

**6.** $\{x \mid 6 \geq x > 2\}$

**7.**
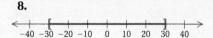

**8.**

*Answers*

**4.** $[-4, 5)$   **5.** $(-\infty, -2]$   **6.** $(2, 6]$
**7.** $[10, \infty)$   **8.** $[-30, 30]$

Since subtracting $c$ is the same as adding $-c$, there is no need for a separate subtraction principle.

**EXAMPLE 10** Solve and graph: $x + 5 > 1$.

We have

$$x + 5 > 1$$
$$x + 5 - 5 > 1 - 5 \qquad \text{Using the addition principle:}$$
$$\text{adding } -5 \text{ or subtracting } 5$$
$$x > -4.$$

We used the addition principle to show that the inequalities $x + 5 > 1$ and $x > -4$ are equivalent. The solution set is $\{x \mid x > -4\}$ and consists of an infinite number of solutions. We cannot possibly check them all. Instead, we can perform a partial check by substituting one member of the solution set (here we use $-1$) into the original inequality:

$$\frac{x + 5 > 1}{-1 + 5 \; ? \; 1}$$
$$4 \; | \qquad \text{TRUE}$$

Since $4 > 1$ is true, we have a partial check. The solution set is $\{x \mid x > -4\}$, or $(-4, \infty)$. The graph is as follows:

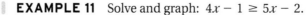

Do Exercises 9 and 10.

**EXAMPLE 11** Solve and graph: $4x - 1 \ge 5x - 2$.

We have

$$4x - 1 \ge 5x - 2$$
$$4x - 1 + 2 \ge 5x - 2 + 2 \qquad \text{Adding 2}$$
$$4x + 1 \ge 5x \qquad \text{Simplifying}$$
$$4x + 1 - 4x \ge 5x - 4x \qquad \text{Subtracting } 4x$$
$$1 \ge x. \qquad \text{Simplifying}$$

The inequalities $1 \ge x$ and $x \le 1$ have the same meaning and the same solutions. The solution set is $\{x \mid 1 \ge x\}$ or, more commonly, $\{x \mid x \le 1\}$. Using interval notation, we write that the solution set is $(-\infty, 1]$. The graph is as follows:

Do Exercise 11.

**Solve and graph.**

**9.** $x + 6 > 9$

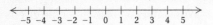

**10.** $x + 4 \le 7$

**11. Solve and graph:**

$$2x - 3 \ge 3x - 1.$$

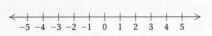

**Answers**

**9.** $\{x \mid x > 3\}$, or $(3, \infty)$;

**10.** $\{x \mid x \le 3\}$, or $(-\infty, 3]$;

**11.** $\{x \mid x \le -2\}$, or $(-\infty, -2]$;

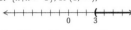

The multiplication principle for inequalities differs from the multiplication principle for equations. Consider the true inequality

$$-4 < 9.$$

If we multiply both numbers by 2, we get another true inequality:

$$-4(2) < 9(2), \quad \text{or} \quad -8 < 18. \qquad \text{True}$$

If we multiply both numbers by $-3$, we get a false inequality:

$$-4(-3) < 9(-3), \quad \text{or} \quad 12 < -27. \qquad \text{False}$$

However, if we now *reverse* the inequality symbol above, we get a true inequality:

$$12 > -27. \qquad \text{True}$$

---

**THE MULTIPLICATION PRINCIPLE FOR INEQUALITIES**

For any real numbers $a$ and $b$, and any *positive* number $c$:

$\qquad a < b$ is equivalent to $ac < bc$;

$\qquad a > b$ is equivalent to $ac > bc$.

For any real numbers $a$ and $b$, and any *negative* number $c$:

$\qquad a < b$ is equivalent to $ac > bc$;

$\qquad a > b$ is equivalent to $ac < bc$.

Similar statements hold for $\leq$ and $\geq$.

---

Since division by $c$ is the same as multiplication by $1/c$, there is no need for a separate division principle.

---

The multiplication principle tells us that when we multiply or divide on both sides of an inequality by a negative number, we must reverse the inequality symbol to obtain an equivalent inequality.

---

**EXAMPLE 12** Solve and graph: $3y < \frac{3}{4}$.

We have

$$3y < \frac{3}{4}$$

$$\frac{1}{3} \cdot 3y < \frac{1}{3} \cdot \frac{3}{4} \qquad \text{Multiplying by } \tfrac{1}{3}. \text{ Since } \tfrac{1}{3} > 0, \text{ the symbol stays the same.}$$

$$y < \frac{1}{4}. \qquad \text{Simplifying}$$

Any number less than $\frac{1}{4}$ is a solution. The solution set is $\left\{ y \,\middle|\, y < \frac{1}{4} \right\}$, or $\left( -\infty, \frac{1}{4} \right)$. The graph is as follows:

Solve and graph.

**12.** $5y \le \dfrac{3}{2}$

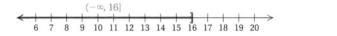

**13.** $-2y > 10$

**14.** $-\dfrac{1}{3}x \le -4$

---

**EXAMPLE 13**  Solve and graph: $-5x \ge -80$.

We have

$$-5x \ge -80$$

$$\dfrac{-5x}{-5} \le \dfrac{-80}{-5} \quad \begin{array}{l}\text{Dividing by } -5. \text{ Since } -5 < 0, \text{ the}\\ \text{inequality symbol must be reversed.}\end{array}$$

$$x \le 16.$$

The solution set is $\{x \mid x \le 16\}$, or $(-\infty, 16]$. The graph is as follows:

Do Exercises 12-14.

We use the addition and multiplication principles together in solving inequalities in much the same way as in solving equations.

**EXAMPLE 14**  Solve: $16 - 7y \ge 10y - 4$.

We have

$$16 - 7y \ge 10y - 4$$

$$-16 + 16 - 7y \ge -16 + 10y - 4 \qquad \text{Adding } -16$$

$$-7y \ge 10y - 20 \qquad \text{Collecting like terms}$$

$$-10y + (-7y) \ge -10y + 10y - 20 \qquad \text{Adding } -10y$$

$$-17y \ge -20 \qquad \text{Collecting like terms}$$

$$\dfrac{-17y}{-17} \le \dfrac{-20}{-17} \qquad \begin{array}{l}\text{Dividing by } -17. \text{ The symbol}\\ \text{must be reversed.}\end{array}$$

$$y \le \dfrac{20}{17}. \qquad \text{Simplifying}$$

The solution set is $\left\{ y \mid y \le \frac{20}{17} \right\}$, or $\left( -\infty, \frac{20}{17} \right]$.

In some cases, we can avoid multiplying or dividing by a negative number by using the addition principle in a different way. Let's rework Example 14 by adding $7y$ instead of $-10y$:

$$16 - 7y \ge 10y - 4$$

$$16 - 7y + 7y \ge 10y - 4 + 7y \qquad \begin{array}{l}\text{Adding } 7y. \text{ This makes the coefficient}\\ \text{of the } y\text{-term positive.}\end{array}$$

$$16 \ge 17y - 4 \qquad \text{Collecting like terms}$$

$$16 + 4 \ge 17y - 4 + 4 \qquad \text{Adding } 4$$

$$20 \ge 17y \qquad \text{Collecting like terms}$$

$$\dfrac{20}{17} \ge \dfrac{17y}{17} \qquad \begin{array}{l}\text{Dividing by } 17. \text{ The symbol}\\ \text{stays the same.}\end{array}$$

$$\dfrac{20}{17} \ge y.$$

Note that $\frac{20}{17} \ge y$ is equivalent to $y \le \frac{20}{17}$.

---

*Answers*

**12.** $\left\{ y \mid y \le \dfrac{3}{10} \right\}$, or $\left( -\infty, \dfrac{3}{10} \right]$

**13.** $\{ y \mid y < -5 \}$, or $(-\infty, -5)$

**14.** $\{ x \mid x \ge 12 \}$, or $[12, \infty)$

**EXAMPLE 15**  Solve: $-3(x + 8) - 5x > 4x - 9$.

We have

$$-3(x + 8) - 5x > 4x - 9$$

$$-3x - 24 - 5x > 4x - 9 \qquad \text{Using the distributive law}$$

$$-24 - 8x > 4x - 9 \qquad \text{Collecting like terms}$$

$$-24 - 8x + 8x > 4x - 9 + 8x \qquad \text{Adding } 8x$$

$$-24 > 12x - 9 \qquad \text{Collecting like terms}$$

$$-24 + 9 > 12x - 9 + 9 \qquad \text{Adding } 9$$

$$-15 > 12x$$

Dividing by 12. The symbol stays the same.

$$\frac{-15}{12} > \frac{12x}{12}$$

$$-\frac{5}{4} > x.$$

The solution set is $\left\{ x \middle| -\frac{5}{4} > x \right\}$, or $\left\{ x \middle| x < -\frac{5}{4} \right\}$, or $\left( -\infty, -\frac{5}{4} \right)$.

> Do Exercises 15–17.

**Solve.**

**15.** $6 - 5y \geq 7$

**16.** $3x + 5x < 4$

**17.** $17 - 5(y - 2) \leq 45y + 8(2y - 3) - 39y$

## d  Applications and Problem Solving

Many problem-solving and applied situations translate to inequalities. In addition to "is less than" and "is more than," other phrases are commonly used.

| IMPORTANT WORDS | SAMPLE SENTENCE | TRANSLATION |
|---|---|---|
| is at least | Max is at least 5 years old. | $m \geq 5$ |
| is at most | At most 6 people could fit in the elevator. | $n \leq 6$ |
| cannot exceed | Total weight in the elevator cannot exceed 2000 pounds. | $w \leq 2000$ |
| must exceed | The speed must exceed 15 mph. | $s > 15$ |
| is between | Heather's income is between $23,000 and $35,000. | $23,000 < h < 35,000$ |
| no more than | Bing weighs no more than 90 pounds. | $w \leq 90$ |
| no less than | Saul would accept no less than $4000 for the piano. | $t \geq 4000$ |

The following phrases deserve special attention.

### TRANSLATING "AT LEAST" AND "AT MOST"

A quantity $x$ is **at least** some amount $q$:  $x \geq q$.
(If $x$ is at least $q$, it cannot be less than $q$.)

A quantity $x$ is **at most** some amount $q$:  $x \leq q$.
(If $x$ is at most $q$, it cannot be more than $q$.)

**Translate.**

**18.** Russell will pay at most $250 for that plane ticket.

**19.** Emma scored at least an 88 on her Spanish test.

**20.** The time of the test was between 50 and 60 min.

**21.** The University of Northern Kentucky is more than 25 mi away.

**22.** Sarah's weight is less than 110 lb.

**23.** That number is greater than $-8$.

**24.** The costs of production of that DVD player cannot exceed $135,000.

> Do Exercises 18–24.

*Answers*

**15.** $\left\{ y \middle| y \leq -\frac{1}{5} \right\}$, or $\left( -\infty, -\frac{1}{5} \right]$

**16.** $\left\{ x \middle| x < \frac{1}{2} \right\}$, or $\left( -\infty, \frac{1}{2} \right)$

**17.** $\left\{ y \middle| y \geq \frac{17}{9} \right\}$, or $\left[ \frac{17}{9}, \infty \right)$

**18.** $t \leq 250$   **19.** $s \geq 88$   **20.** $50 < t < 60$
**21.** $d > 25$   **22.** $w < 110$   **23.** $n > -8$
**24.** $c \leq 135,000$

**EXAMPLE 16** *Cost of Higher Education.* The equation

$$C = 126t + 1293$$

can be used to estimate the average cost of tuition and fees at two-year public institutions of higher education, where $t$ is the number of years after 2000. Determine, in terms of an inequality, the years for which the cost will be more than $3000.

**Source:** National Center for Education Statistics

1. **Familiarize.** We already have a formula. To become more familiar with it, we might make a substitution for $t$. Suppose we want to know the cost 15 yr after 2000, or in 2015. We substitute 15 for $t$:

   $$C = 126(15) + 1293 = \$3183.$$

   We see that in 2015, the cost of tuition and fees at two-year public institutions will be more than $3000. To find all the years in which the cost exceeds $3000, we could make other guesses less than 15, but it is more efficient to proceed to the next step.

2. **Translate.** The cost $C$ is to be *more than* $3000. Thus we have

   $$C > 3000.$$

   We replace $C$ with $126t + 1293$ to find the values of $t$ that are solutions of the inequality:

   $$126t + 1293 > 3000.$$

3. **Solve.** We solve the inequality:

   $$126t + 1293 > 3000$$
   $$126t > 1707 \qquad \text{Subtracting 1293}$$
   $$t > 13.55. \qquad \text{Dividing by 126 and rounding}$$

4. **Check.** A partial check is to substitute a value for $t$ greater than 13.55. We did that in the *Familiarize* step and found that the cost was more than $3000.

5. **State.** The average cost of tuition and fees at two-year public institutions of higher education will be more than $3000 for years more than 13.55 yr after 2000, so we have $\{t \mid t > 13.55\}$.

Do Exercise 25.

**25. Cost of Higher Education.** Refer to Example 16. Determine, in terms of an inequality, the years for which the average cost of tuition and fees is more than $2500.

*Answer*

**25.** More than 9.58 yr after 2000, or $\{t \mid t > 9.58\}$

**EXAMPLE 17** *Salary Plans.* On her new job, Rose can be paid in one of two ways: *Plan A* is a salary of $600 per month, plus a commission of 4% of sales; and *Plan B* is a salary of $800 per month, plus a commission of 6% of sales in excess of $10,000. For what amount of monthly sales is plan A better than plan B, if we assume that sales are always more than $10,000?

1. **Familiarize.** Listing the given information in a table will be helpful.

| PLAN A: MONTHLY INCOME | PLAN B: MONTHLY INCOME |
|---|---|
| $600 salary | $800 salary |
| 4% of sales | 6% of sales over $10,000 |
| *Total:* $600 + 4% of sales | *Total:* $800 + 6% of sales over $10,000 |

Next, suppose that Rose had sales of $12,000 in one month. Which plan would be better? Under plan A, she would earn $600 plus 4% of $12,000, or

$$600 + 0.04(12,000) = \$1080.$$

Since with plan B commissions are paid only on sales in excess of $10,000, Rose would earn $800 plus 6% of ($12,000 − $10,000), or

$$800 + 0.06(12,000 - 10,000) = 800 + 0.06(2000) = \$920.$$

This shows that for monthly sales of $12,000, plan A is better. Similar calculations will show that for sales of $30,000 a month, plan B is better. To determine *all* values for which plan A pays more money, we must solve an inequality that is based on the calculations above.

2. **Translate.** We let $S$ = the amount of monthly sales. If we examine the calculations in the *Familiarize* step, we see that the monthly income from plan A is $600 + 0.04S$ and from plan B is $800 + 0.06(S - 10,000)$. Thus we want to find all values of $S$ for which

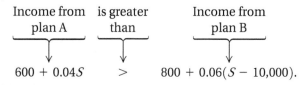

$$600 + 0.04S \quad > \quad 800 + 0.06(S - 10,000).$$

3. **Solve.** We solve the inequality:

$$600 + 0.04S > 800 + 0.06(S - 10,000)$$
$$600 + 0.04S > 800 + 0.06S - 600 \qquad \text{Using the distributive law}$$
$$600 + 0.04S > 200 + 0.06S \qquad \text{Collecting like terms}$$
$$400 > 0.02S \qquad \text{Subtracting 200 and } 0.04S$$
$$20,000 > S, \text{ or } S < 20,000. \qquad \text{Dividing by 0.02}$$

4. **Check.** For $S = 20,000$, the income from plan A is

$$600 + 4\% \cdot 20,000, \text{ or } \$1400.$$

The income from plan B is

$$800 + 6\% \cdot (20,000 - 10,000), \text{ or } \$1400.$$

This confirms that for sales of $20,000, Rose's pay is the same under either plan.

In the *Familiarize* step, we saw that for sales of $12,000, plan A pays more. Since $12,000 < 20,000$, this is a partial check. Since we cannot check all possible values of $S$, we will stop here.

5. **State.** For monthly sales of less than $20,000, plan A is better.

Do Exercise 26.

**26. Salary Plans.** A painter can be paid in one of two ways:

*Plan A:* $500 plus $4 per hour;

*Plan B:* Straight $9 per hour.

Suppose that the job takes $n$ hours. For what values of $n$ is plan A better for the painter?

*Answer*

**26.** For $\{n | n < 100\}$, plan A is better.

# Translating for Success

**1.** *Consecutive Integers.* The sum of two consecutive even integers is 102. Find the integers.

**2.** *Salary Increase.* After Susanna earned a 5% raise, her new salary was $25,750. What was her former salary?

**3.** *Dimensions of a Rectangle.* The length of a rectangle is 6 in. more than the width. The perimeter of the rectangle is 102 in. Find the length and the width.

**4.** *Population.* The population of Doddville is decreasing at a rate of 5% per year. The current population is 25,750. What was the population the previous year?

**5.** *Reading Assignment.* Quinn has 6 days to complete a 150-page reading assignment. How many pages must he read the first day so that he has no more than 102 pages left to read on the 5 remaining days?

The goal of these matching questions is to practice step (2), *Translate*, of the five-step problem-solving process. Translate each word problem to an equation or an inequality and select a correct translation from A–O.

**A.** $0.05(25,750) = x$

**B.** $x + 2x = 102$

**C.** $2x + 2(x + 6) = 102$

**D.** $150 - x \leq 102$

**E.** $x - 0.05x = 25,750$

**F.** $x + (x + 2) = 102$

**G.** $x + (x + 6) > 102$

**H.** $x + 5x = 150$

**I.** $x + 0.05x = 25,750$

**J.** $x + (2x + 6) = 102$

**K.** $x + (x + 1) = 102$

**L.** $102 + x > 150$

**M.** $0.05x = 25,750$

**N.** $102 + 5x > 150$

**O.** $x + (x + 6) = 102$

*Answer on page A-3*

**6.** *Numerical Relationship.* One number is 6 more than twice another. The sum of the numbers is 102. Find the numbers.

**7.** *DVD Collections.* Together Ella and Ken have 102 DVDs. If Ken has 6 more DVDs than Ella, how many does each have?

**8.** *Sales Commissions.* Will earns a commission of 5% on his sales. One year he earned commissions totaling $25,750. What were his total sales for the year?

**9.** *Fencing.* Jess has 102 ft of fencing that he plans to use to enclose two dog runs. The perimeter of one run is to be twice the perimeter of the other. Into what lengths should the fencing be cut?

**10.** *Quiz Scores.* Lupe has a total of 102 points on the first 6 quizzes in her sociology class. How many total points must she earn on the 5 remaining quizzes in order to have more than 150 points for the semester?

**a** Determine whether the given numbers are solutions of the inequality.

**1.** $x - 2 \geq 6$; $-4, 0, 4, 8$

**2.** $3x + 5 \leq -10$; $-5, -10, 0, 27$

**3.** $t - 8 > 2t - 3$; $0, -8, -9, -3, -\frac{7}{8}$

**4.** $5y - 7 < 8 - y$; $2, -3, 0, 3, \frac{2}{3}$

**b** Write interval notation for the given set or graph.

**5.** $\{x \mid x < 5\}$

**6.** $\{t \mid t \geq -5\}$

**7.** $\{x \mid -3 \leq x \leq 3\}$

**8.** $\{t \mid -10 < t \leq 10\}$

**9.** $\{x \mid -4 > x > -8\}$

**10.** $\{x \mid 13 > x \geq 5\}$

**11.**

**12.**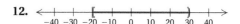

**13.**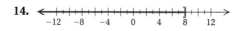

**14.**

**c** Solve and graph.

**15.** $x + 2 > 1$

**16.** $x + 8 > 4$

**17.** $y + 3 < 9$

**18.** $y + 4 < 10$

**19.** $a - 9 \leq -31$

**20.** $a + 6 \leq -14$

**21.** $t + 13 \geq 9$

**22.** $x - 8 \leq 17$

**23.** $y - 8 > -14$

**24.** $y - 9 > -18$

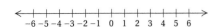

**25.** $x - 11 \leq -2$

**26.** $y - 18 \leq -4$

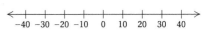

**27.** $8x \geq 24$

**28.** $8t < -56$

**29.** $0.3x < -18$



**30.** $0.6x < 30$



**31.** $\frac{2}{3}x > 2$



**32.** $\frac{3}{5}x > -3$



Solve.

**33.** $-9x \geq -8.1$

**34.** $-5y \leq 3.5$

**35.** $-\frac{3}{4}x \geq -\frac{5}{8}$

**36.** $-\frac{1}{8}y \leq -\frac{9}{8}$

**37.** $2x + 7 < 19$

**38.** $5y + 13 > 28$

**39.** $5y + 2y \leq -21$

**40.** $-9x + 3x \geq -24$

**41.** $2y - 7 < 5y - 9$

**42.** $8x - 9 < 3x - 11$

**43.** $0.4x + 5 \leq 1.2x - 4$

**44.** $0.2y + 1 > 2.4y - 10$

**45.** $5x - \frac{1}{12} \leq \frac{5}{12} + 4x$

**46.** $2x - 3 < \frac{13}{4}x + 10 - 1.25x$

**47.** $4(4y - 3) \geq 9(2y + 7)$

**48.** $2m + 5 \geq 16(m - 4)$

**49.** $3(2 - 5x) + 2x < 2(4 + 2x)$

**50.** $2(0.5 - 3y) + y > (4y - 0.2)8$

**51.** $5[3m - (m + 4)] > -2(m - 4)$

**52.** $[8x - 3(3x + 2)] - 5 \geq 3(x + 4) - 2x$

**53.** $3(r - 6) + 2 > 4(r + 2) - 21$

**54.** $5(t + 3) + 9 < 3(t - 2) + 6$

**55.** $19 - (2x + 3) \leq 2(x + 3) + x$

**56.** $13 - (2c + 2) \geq 2(c + 2) + 3c$

**57.** $\frac{1}{4}(8y + 4) - 17 < -\frac{1}{2}(4y - 8)$

**58.** $\frac{1}{3}(6x + 24) - 20 > -\frac{1}{4}(12x - 72)$

**59.** $2[4 - 2(3 - x)] - 1 \geq 4[2(4x - 3) + 7] - 25$

**60.** $5[3(7 - t) - 4(8 + 2t)] - 20 \leq -6[2(6 + 3t) - 4]$

**61.** $\frac{4}{5}(7x - 6) < 40$

**62.** $\frac{2}{3}(4x - 3) > 30$

**63.** $\frac{3}{4}(3 + 2x) + 1 \geq 13$

**64.** $\frac{7}{8}(5 - 4x) - 17 \geq 38$

**65.** $\frac{3}{4}\left(3x - \frac{1}{2}\right) - \frac{2}{3} < \frac{1}{3}$

**66.** $\frac{2}{3}\left(\frac{7}{8} - 4x\right) - \frac{5}{8} < \frac{3}{8}$

**67.** $0.7(3x + 6) \geq 1.1 - (x + 2)$

**68.** $0.9(2x + 8) < 20 - (x + 5)$

**69.** $a + (a - 3) \leq (a + 2) - (a + 1)$

**70.** $0.8 - 4(b - 1) > 0.2 + 3(4 - b)$

 Solve.

*Body Mass Index.* *Body mass index I* can be used to determine whether an individual has a healthy weight for his or her height. An index in the range 18.5–24.9 indicates a normal weight. Body mass index is given by the formula, or model,

$$I = \frac{703\,W}{H^2},$$

where *W* is weight, in pounds, and *H* is height, in inches. (See Example 1 in Section 1.2.) Use this formula for Exercises 71 and 72.

**Source:** Centers for Disease Control and Prevention

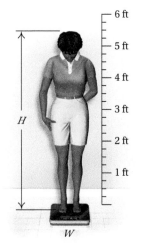

**71.** *Body Mass Index.*   Marv's height is 73 in. Determine, in terms of an inequality, those weights *W* that will keep his body mass index below 25.

**72.** *Body Mass Index.*   Elaine's height is 67 in. Determine, in terms of an inequality, those weights *W* that will keep her body mass index below 25.

**73.** *Grades.*   Morris is taking a European history course in which there will be 4 tests, each worth 100 points. He has scores of 89, 92, and 95 on the first three tests. He must make a total of at least 360 in order to get an A. What scores on the last test will give Morris an A?

**74.** *Grades.*   Eve is taking a literature course in which there will be 5 tests, each worth 100 points. She has scores of 94, 90, and 89 on the first three tests. She must make a total of at least 450 in order to get an A. What scores on the fourth test will keep Eve eligible for an A?

**75.** *Insurance Claims.*   After a serious automobile accident, most insurance companies will replace the damaged car with a new one if repair costs exceed 80% of the N.A.D.A., or "blue-book," value of the car. Miguel's car recently sustained $9200 worth of damage but was not replaced. What was the blue-book value of his car?

**76.** *Delivery Service.*   Jay's Express prices cross-town deliveries at $15 for the first 10 miles plus $1.25 for each additional mile. PDQ, Inc., prices its cross-town deliveries at $25 for the first 10 miles plus $0.75 for each additional mile. For what number of miles is PDQ less expensive?

**77.** *Salary Plans.* Toni can be paid in one of two ways:

*Plan A:* A salary of $400 per month plus a commission of 8% of gross sales;

*Plan B:* A salary of $610 per month, plus a commission of 5% of gross sales.

For what amount of gross sales should Toni select plan A?

**78.** *Salary Plans.* Branford can be paid for his masonry work in one of two ways:

*Plan A:* $300 plus $9.00 per hour;

*Plan B:* Straight $12.50 per hour.

Suppose that the job takes $n$ hours. For what values of $n$ is plan B better for Branford?

**79.** *Checking-Account Rates.* The Hudson Bank offers two checking-account plans. Their Anywhere plan charges 20¢ per check whereas their Acu-checking plan costs $2 per month plus 12¢ per check. For what numbers of checks per month will the Acu-checking plan cost less?

**80.** *Insurance Benefits.* Bayside Insurance offers two plans. Under plan A, Giselle would pay the first $50 of her medical bills and 20% of all bills after that. Under plan B, Giselle would pay the first $250 of bills, but only 10% of the rest. For what amount of medical bills will plan B save Giselle money? (Assume that her bills will exceed $250.)

**81.** *Wedding Costs.* The Arnold Inn offers two plans for wedding parties. Under plan A, the inn charges $30 for each person in attendance. Under plan B, the inn charges $1300 plus $20 for each person in excess of the first 25 who attend. For what size parties will plan B cost less? (Assume that more than 25 guests will attend.)

**82.** *Investing.* Lillian is about to invest $20,000, part at 3% and the rest at 4%. What is the most that she can invest at 3% and still be guaranteed at least $650 in interest per year?

**83.** *Converting Dress Sizes.* The formula

$$I = 2(s + 10)$$

can be used to convert dress sizes $s$ in the United States to dress sizes $I$ in Italy. For what dress sizes in the United States will dress sizes in Italy be larger than 36?

**84.** *Temperatures of Solids.* The formula

$$C = \frac{5}{9}(F - 32)$$

can be used to convert Fahrenheit temperatures $F$ to Celsius temperatures $C$.

a) Gold is a solid at Celsius temperatures less than 1063°C. Find the Fahrenheit temperatures for which gold is a solid.

b) Silver is a solid at Celsius temperatures less than 960.8°C. Find the Fahrenheit temperatures for which silver is a solid.

**85.** *Bottled Water Consumption.* Bottled water consumption has increased steadily in recent years. The number $N$ of gallons, in millions, consumed in the United States $t$ years after 2006 is approximated by the equation

$$N = 0.6t + 8.2.$$

Source: Beverage Marketing Corporation

a) How many gallons of bottled water were consumed in the United States in 2006 ($t = 0$)? in 2008 ($t = 2$)? in 2010 ($t = 4$)?

b) For what years will the amount of bottled water consumed in the United States exceed 12 million gal?

**86.** *Dewpoint Spread.* Pilots use the **dewpoint spread**, or the difference between the current temperature and the dewpoint (the temperature at which dew occurs), to estimate the height of the cloud cover. Each 3° of dewpoint spread corresponds to an increased height of cloud cover of 1000 ft. A plane, flying with limited instruments, must have a cloud cover higher than 3500 ft. What dewpoint spreads will allow the plane to fly?

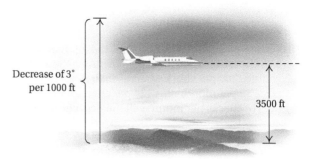

Decrease of 3° per 1000 ft

3500 ft

## Skill Maintenance

Simplify.   [R.6b]

**87.** $3a - 6(2a - 5b)$

**88.** $2(x - y) + 10(3x - 7y)$

**89.** $4(a - 2b) - 6(2a - 5b)$

**90.** $-3(2a - 3b) + 8b$

Factor.   [R.5d]

**91.** $30x - 70y - 40$

**92.** $-12a + 30ab$

**93.** $-8x + 24y - 4$

**94.** $10n - 45mn + 100m$

Add or subtract.   [R.2a, c]

**95.** $-2.3 - 8.9$

**96.** $-2.3 + 8.9$

**97.** $-2.3 + (-8.9)$

**98.** $-2.3 - (-8.9)$

## Synthesis

**99.** *Supply and Demand.* The supply $S$ and demand $D$ for a certain product are given by

$$S = 460 + 94p \quad \text{and} \quad D = 2000 - 60p.$$

a) Find those values of $p$ for which supply exceeds demand.

b) Find those values of $p$ for which supply is less than demand.

Determine whether each statement is true or false. If false, give a counterexample.

**100.** For any real numbers $x$ and $y$, if $x < y$, then $x^2 < y^2$.

**101.** For any real numbers $a$, $b$, $c$, and $d$, if $a < b$ and $c < d$, then $a + c < b + d$.

**102.** Determine whether the inequalities

$$x < 3 \quad \text{and} \quad 0 \cdot x < 0 \cdot 3$$

are equivalent. Give reasons to support your answer.

Solve.

**103.** $x + 5 \leq 5 + x$

**104.** $x + 8 < 3 + x$

**105.** $x^2 + 1 > 0$

# 1.5 Intersections, Unions, and Compound Inequalities

Cholesterol is a substance that is found in every cell of the human body. High levels of cholesterol can cause fatty deposits in the blood vessels that increase the risk of heart attack or stroke. A blood test can be used to measure *total cholesterol*. The following table shows the health risks associated with various cholesterol levels.

| TOTAL CHOLESTEROL | RISK LEVEL |
|---|---|
| Less than 200 | Normal |
| From 200 to 239 | Borderline high |
| 240 or higher | High |

## OBJECTIVES

a Find the intersection of two sets. Solve and graph conjunctions of inequalities.

b Find the union of two sets. Solve and graph disjunctions of inequalities.

c Solve applied problems involving conjunctions and disjunctions of inequalities.

A total-cholesterol level $T$ from 200 to 239 is considered borderline high. We can express this by the sentence

$$200 \leq T \quad and \quad T \leq 239$$

or more simply by

$$200 \leq T \leq 239.$$

This is an example of a *compound inequality*. **Compound inequalities** consist of two or more inequalities joined by the word *and* or the word *or*. We now "solve" such sentences—that is, we find the set of all solutions.

## a Intersections of Sets and Conjunctions of Inequalities

> **INTERSECTION**
>
> The **intersection** of two sets $A$ and $B$ is the set of all members that are common to $A$ and $B$. We denote the intersection of sets $A$ and $B$ as
>
> $$A \cap B.$$

The intersection of two sets is often illustrated as shown at right.

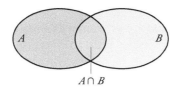

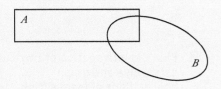
**EXAMPLE 1** Find the intersection: $\{1, 2, 3, 4, 5\} \cap \{-2, -1, 0, 1, 2, 3\}$.

The numbers 1, 2, and 3 are common to the two sets, so the intersection is $\{1, 2, 3\}$.

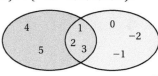

Do Exercises 1 and 2.

## CONJUNCTION

When two or more sentences are joined by the word *and* to make a compound sentence, the new sentence is called a **conjunction** of the sentences.

The following is a conjunction of inequalities:

$$-2 < x \quad and \quad x < 1.$$

A number is a solution of a conjunction if it is a solution of *both* inequalities. For example, 0 is a solution of $-2 < x$ *and* $x < 1$ because $-2 < 0$ *and* $0 < 1$. Shown below is the graph of $-2 < x$, followed by the graph of $x < 1$, and then by the graph of the conjunction $-2 < x$ *and* $x < 1$. As the graphs demonstrate, *the solution set of a conjunction is the intersection of the solution sets of the individual inequalities.*

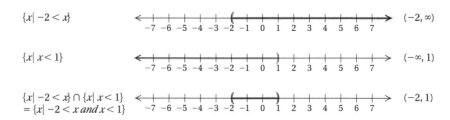

Because there are numbers that are both greater than $-2$ and less than 1, the conjunction $-2 < x$ *and* $x < 1$ can be abbreviated by $-2 < x < 1$. Thus the interval $(-2, 1)$ can be represented as $\{x \mid -2 < x < 1\}$, the set of all numbers that are *simultaneously* greater than $-2$ *and* less than 1. Note that, in general, for $a < b$,

$$a < x \quad and \quad x < b \quad \text{can be abbreviated} \quad a < x < b;$$
$$and \quad b > x \quad and \quad x > a \quad \text{can be abbreviated} \quad b > x > a.$$

### *Caution!*

"$a > x$ *and* $x < b$" cannot be abbreviated as "$a > x < b$".

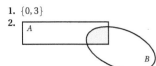

The word **"and"** corresponds to **"intersection"** and to the symbol "∩". In order for a number to be a solution of a conjunction, it must make each part of the conjunction true.

Do Exercise 3.

**3.** Graph and write interval notation:

$$-1 < x \text{ and } x < 4.$$

**EXAMPLE 2** Solve and graph: $-1 \leq 2x + 5 < 13$.

This inequality is an abbreviation for the conjunction

$$-1 \leq 2x + 5 \quad and \quad 2x + 5 < 13.$$

The word *and* corresponds to set *intersection*, ∩. To solve the conjunction, we solve each of the two inequalities separately and then find the intersection of the solution sets:

$$-1 \leq 2x + 5 \quad and \quad 2x + 5 < 13$$
$$-6 \leq 2x \qquad and \qquad 2x < 8 \qquad \text{Subtracting 5}$$
$$-3 \leq x \qquad and \qquad x < 4. \qquad \text{Dividing by 2}$$

We now abbreviate the result:

$$-3 \leq x < 4.$$

The solution set is $\{x | -3 \leq x < 4\}$, or, in interval notation, $[-3, 4)$. The graph is the intersection of the two separate solution sets.

$\{x | -3 \leq x\}$

$[-3, \infty)$

$\{x | x < 4\}$

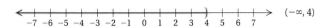

$(-\infty, 4)$

$\{x | -3 \leq x\} \cap \{x | x < 4\}$
$= \{x | -3 \leq x < 4\}$

$[-3, 4)$

The steps above are generally combined as follows:

$$-1 \leq 2x + 5 < 13 \qquad 2x + 5 \text{ appears in both inequalities.}$$
$$-6 \leq 2x < 8 \qquad \text{Subtracting 5}$$
$$-3 \leq x < 4. \qquad \text{Dividing by 2}$$

Such an approach saves some writing and will prove useful in Section 1.6.

Do Exercise 4.

**4.** Solve and graph:

$$-22 < 3x - 7 \leq 23.$$

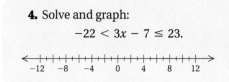

**EXAMPLE 3** Solve and graph: $2x - 5 \geq -3 \text{ and } 5x + 2 \geq 17$.

We first solve each inequality separately:

$$2x - 5 \geq -3 \quad and \quad 5x + 2 \geq 17$$
$$2x \geq 2 \qquad and \qquad 5x \geq 15$$
$$x \geq 1 \qquad and \qquad x \geq 3.$$

**Answers**

**3.**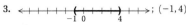

**4.** $\{x | -5 < x \leq 10\}$, or $(-5, 10]$;

Next, we find the intersection of the two separate solution sets:

$\{x\,|\,x \geq 1\}$  $[1, \infty)$

$\{x\,|\,x \geq 3\}$  $[3, \infty)$

$\{x\,|\,x \geq 1\} \cap \{x\,|\,x \geq 3\}$
$= \{x\,|\,x \geq 3\}$ 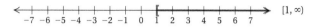 $[3, \infty)$

The numbers common to both sets are those that are greater than or equal to 3. Thus the solution set is $\{x\,|\,x \geq 3\}$, or, in interval notation, $[3, \infty)$. You should check that any number in $[3, \infty)$ satisfies the conjunction whereas numbers outside $[3, \infty)$ do not.

Do Exercise 5.

**5.** Solve and graph:

$3x + 4 < 10$ *and* $2x - 7 < -13$.

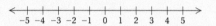

---

## EMPTY SET; DISJOINT SETS

Sometimes two sets have no elements in common. In such a case, we say that the intersection of the two sets is the **empty set**, denoted $\{\ \}$ or $\varnothing$. Two sets with an empty intersection are said to be **disjoint**.

$$A \cap B = \varnothing$$

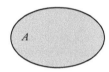 

---

**EXAMPLE 4**  Solve and graph: $2x - 3 > 1$ *and* $3x - 1 < 2$.

We solve each inequality separately:

$$2x - 3 > 1 \quad and \quad 3x - 1 < 2$$
$$2x > 4 \quad and \quad \quad 3x < 3$$
$$x > 2 \quad and \quad \quad x < 1.$$

The solution set is the intersection of the solution sets of the individual inequalities.

$\{x\,|\,x > 2\}$  $(2, \infty)$

$\{x\,|\,x < 1\}$  $(-\infty, 1)$

$\{x\,|\,x > 2\} \cap \{x\,|\,x < 1\}$
$= \{x\,|\,x > 2 \ and \ x < 1\}$
$= \varnothing$  $\varnothing$

Since no number is both greater than 2 and less than 1, the solution set is the empty set, $\varnothing$.

Do Exercise 6.

**6.** Solve and graph:

$3x - 7 \leq -13$ *and* $4x + 3 > 8$.

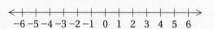

---

*Answers*

**5.** $\{x\,|\,x < -3\}$;

**6.** $\varnothing$

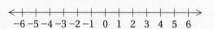

**EXAMPLE 5** Solve: $3 \le 5 - 2x < 7$.

We have

$$3 \le 5 - 2x < 7$$
$$3 - 5 \le 5 - 2x - 5 < 7 - 5 \qquad \text{Subtracting 5}$$
$$-2 \le \quad -2x \quad < 2 \qquad \text{Simplifying}$$
$$\frac{-2}{-2} \ge \frac{-2x}{-2} \quad > \frac{2}{-2} \qquad \text{Dividing by } -2. \text{ The symbols must be reversed.}$$
$$1 \ge x > -1. \qquad \text{Simplifying}$$

The solution set is $\{x | 1 \ge x > -1\}$, or $\{x | -1 < x \le 1\}$, since the inequalities $1 \ge x > -1$ and $-1 < x \le 1$ are equivalent. The solution, in interval notation, is $(-1, 1]$.

Do Exercise 7.

**7.** Solve: $-4 \le 8 - 2x \le 4$.

## b  Unions of Sets and Disjunctions of Inequalities

### UNION

The **union** of two sets $A$ and $B$ is the collection of elements belonging to $A$ and/or $B$. We denote the union of $A$ and $B$ by

$$A \cup B.$$

The union of two sets is often pictured as shown below.

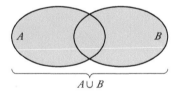

$A \cup B$

**EXAMPLE 6** Find the union: $\{2, 3, 4\} \cup \{3, 5, 7\}$.

The numbers in either or both sets are 2, 3, 4, 5, and 7, so the union is $\{2, 3, 4, 5, 7\}$. We don't list the number 3 twice.

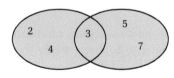

Do Exercises 8 and 9.

**8.** Find the union:
$$\{0, 1, 3, 4\} \cup \{0, 1, 7, 9\}.$$

**9.** Shade the union of sets $A$ and $B$.

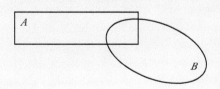

### DISJUNCTION

When two or more sentences are joined by the word *or* to make a compound sentence, the new sentence is called a **disjunction** of the sentences.

*Answers*

**7.** $\{x | 2 \le x \le 6\}$, or $[2, 6]$  **8.** $\{0, 1, 3, 4, 7, 9\}$

**9.**

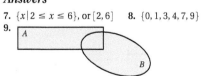

The following is an example of a disjunction:

$$x < -3 \quad or \quad x > 3.$$

A number is a solution of a disjunction if it is a solution of at least one of the individual inequalities. For example, $-7$ is a solution of $x < -3$ or $x > 3$ because $-7 < -3$. Similarly, 5 is also a solution because $5 > 3$.

Shown below is the graph of $x < -3$, followed by the graph of $x > 3$, and then by the graph of the disjunction $x < -3$ or $x > 3$. As the graphs demonstrate, *the solution set of a disjunction is the union of the solution sets of the individual sentences.*

The solution set of

$$x < -3 \quad or \quad x > 3$$

is written $\{x | x < -3 \text{ or } x > 3\}$, or, in interval notation, $(-\infty, -3) \cup (3, \infty)$. This cannot be written in a more condensed form.

> **"OR"; "UNION"**
>
> The word **"or"** corresponds to **"union"** and the symbol "$\cup$". In order for a number to be in the solution set of a disjunction, it must be in *at least one* of the solution sets of the individual sentences.

Do Exercise 10.

**EXAMPLE 7** Solve and graph: $7 + 2x < -1$ *or* $13 - 5x \le 3$.

We solve each inequality separately, retaining the word *or*:

$$7 + 2x < -1 \quad or \quad 13 - 5x \le 3$$
$$2x < -8 \quad or \quad -5x \le -10$$

Dividing by $-5$. The symbol must be reversed.

$$x < -4 \quad or \quad x \ge 2.$$

To find the solution set of the disjunction, we consider the individual graphs. We graph $x < -4$ and then $x \ge 2$. Then we take the union of the graphs.

The solution set is written $\{x | x < -4 \text{ or } x \ge 2\}$, or, in interval notation, $(-\infty, -4) \cup [2, \infty)$.

**10.** Graph and write interval notation:

$$x \le -2 \text{ or } x > 4.$$

---- *Caution!* ----

A compound inequality like

$$x < -4 \quad or \quad x \geq 2,$$

as in Example 7, *cannot* be expressed as $2 \leq x < -4$ because to do so would be to say that $x$ is *simultaneously* less than $-4$ and greater than or equal to 2. No number is both less than $-4$ *and* greater than or equal to 2, but many are less than $-4$ *or* greater than or equal to 2.

Do Exercises 11 and 12.

**EXAMPLE 8**  Solve: $-2x - 5 < -2$ or $x - 3 < -10$.

We solve the individual inequalities separately, retaining the word *or*:

$$-2x - 5 < -2 \quad or \quad x - 3 < -10$$
$$-2x < 3 \quad or \quad x < -7$$

Reversing the symbol

$$x > -\tfrac{3}{2} \quad or \quad x < -7.$$

Keep the word "or."

The solution set is written $\{x \,|\, x < -7 \text{ or } x > -\tfrac{3}{2}\}$, or, in interval notation, $(-\infty, -7) \cup \left(-\tfrac{3}{2}, \infty\right)$.

Do Exercise 13.

**EXAMPLE 9**  Solve: $3x - 11 < 4$ or $4x + 9 \geq 1$.

We solve the individual inequalities separately, retaining the word *or*:

$$3x - 11 < 4 \quad or \quad 4x + 9 \geq 1$$
$$3x < 15 \quad or \quad 4x \geq -8$$
$$x < 5 \quad or \quad x \geq -2.$$

To find the solution set, we first look at the individual graphs.

$\{x \,|\, x < 5\}$      (−∞, 5)

$\{x \,|\, x \geq -2\}$      [−2, ∞)

$\{x \,|\, x < 5\} \cup \{x \,|\, x \geq -2\}$
$= \{x \,|\, x < 5 \text{ or } x \geq -2\}$
$= \{x \,|\, x \text{ is a real number}\}$    (−∞, ∞) = The set of all real numbers

Since any number is either less than 5 or greater than or equal to $-2$, the two sets fill the entire number line. Thus the solution set is the set of all real numbers, $(-\infty, \infty)$.

Do Exercise 14.

Solve and graph.

**11.** $x - 4 < -3$ or $x - 3 \geq 3$

$-10\ -8\ -6\ -4\ -2\ \ 0\ \ 2\ \ 4\ \ 6\ \ 8\ \ 10$

**12.** $-2x + 4 \leq -3$ or $x + 5 < 3$

$-6\,-5\,-4\,-3\,-2\,-1\ \ 0\ \ 1\ \ 2\ \ 3\ \ 4\ \ 5\ \ 6$

**13.** Solve:

$$-3x - 7 < -1 \text{ or } x + 4 < -1.$$

**14.** Solve and graph:

$$5x - 7 \leq 13 \text{ or } 2x - 1 \geq -7.$$

$-6\,-5\,-4\,-3\,-2\,-1\ \ 0\ \ 1\ \ 2\ \ 3\ \ 4\ \ 5\ \ 6$

***Answers***

**11.** $\{x \,|\, x < 1 \text{ or } x \geq 6\}$, or $(-\infty, 1) \cup [6, \infty)$;

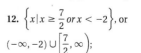

**12.** $\left\{x \,\middle|\, x \geq \tfrac{7}{2} \text{ or } x < -2\right\}$, or

$(-\infty, -2) \cup \left[\tfrac{7}{2}, \infty\right)$;

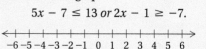

**13.** $\{x \,|\, x < -5 \text{ or } x \,|\, x > -2\}$, or $(-\infty, -5) \cup (-2, \infty)$
**14.** All real numbers;

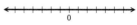

## (c) Applications and Problem Solving

**EXAMPLE 10** *Converting Dress Sizes.* The equation

$$I = 2(s + 10)$$

can be used to convert dress sizes $s$ in the United States to dress sizes $I$ in Italy. Which dress sizes in the United States correspond to dress sizes between 32 and 46 in Italy?

1. **Familiarize.** We have a formula for converting the dress sizes. Thus we can substitute a value into the formula. For a dress of size 6 in the United States, we get the corresponding dress size in Italy as follows:

$$I = 2(6 + 10) = 2 \cdot 16 = 32.$$

This familiarizes us with the formula and also tells us that the United States sizes that we are looking for must be larger than size 6.

2. **Translate.** We want the Italian sizes *between* 32 and 46, so we want to find those values of $s$ for which

$$32 < I < 46 \qquad \text{$I$ is between 32 and 46}$$

or

$$32 < 2(s + 10) < 46. \qquad \text{Substituting $2(s + 10)$ for $I$}$$

Thus we have translated the problem to an inequality.

3. **Solve.** We solve the inequality:

$$32 < 2(s + 10) < 46$$
$$\frac{32}{2} < \frac{2(s + 10)}{2} < \frac{46}{2} \qquad \text{Dividing by 2}$$
$$16 < s + 10 < 23$$
$$6 < s < 13. \qquad \text{Subtracting 10}$$

4. **Check.** We substitute some values as we did in the *Familiarize* step.

5. **State.** Dress sizes between 6 and 13 in the United States correspond to dress sizes between 32 and 46 in Italy.

Do Exercise 15.

---

---

**ⓐ, ⓑ** Find the intersection or union.

**1.** $\{9, 10, 11\} \cap \{9, 11, 13\}$

**2.** $\{1, 5, 10, 15\} \cap \{5, 15, 20\}$

**3.** $\{a, b, c, d\} \cap \{b, f, g\}$

**4.** $\{m, n, o, p\} \cap \{m, o, p\}$

**5.** $\{9, 10, 11\} \cup \{9, 11, 13\}$

**6.** $\{1, 5, 10, 15\} \cup \{5, 15, 20\}$

**7.** $\{a, b, c, d\} \cup \{b, f, g\}$

**8.** $\{m, n, o, p\} \cup \{m, o, p\}$

**9.** $\{2, 5, 7, 9\} \cap \{1, 3, 4\}$

**10.** $\{a, e, i, o, u\} \cap \{m, q, w, s, t\}$

**11.** $\{3, 5, 7\} \cup \varnothing$

**12.** $\{3, 5, 7\} \cap \varnothing$

**ⓐ** Graph and write interval notation.

**13.** $-4 < a$ *and* $a \leq 1$

**14.** $-\frac{5}{2} \leq m$ *and* $m < \frac{3}{2}$

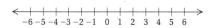

**15.** $1 < x < 6$

**16.** $-3 \leq y \leq 4$

Solve and graph.

**17.** $-10 \leq 3x + 2$ *and* $3x + 2 < 17$

**18.** $-11 < 4x - 3$ *and* $4x - 3 \leq 13$

**19.** $3x + 7 \geq 4$ *and* $2x - 5 \geq -1$

**20.** $4x - 7 < 1$ *and* $7 - 3x > -8$

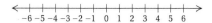

**21.** $4 - 3x \geq 10$ *and* $5x - 2 > 13$

**22.** $5 - 7x > 19$ *and* $2 - 3x < -4$

Solve.

**23.** $-4 < x + 4 < 10$

**24.** $-6 < x + 6 \leq 8$

**25.** $6 > -x \geq -2$

**26.** $3 > -x \geq -5$

**27.** $2 < x + 3 \le 9$

**28.** $-6 \le x + 1 < 9$

**29.** $1 < 3y + 4 \le 19$

**30.** $5 \le 8x + 5 \le 21$

**31.** $-10 \le 3x - 5 \le -1$

**32.** $-6 \le 2x - 3 < 6$

**33.** $-18 \le -2x - 7 < 0$

**34.** $4 > -3m - 7 \ge 2$

**35.** $-\dfrac{1}{2} < \dfrac{1}{4}x - 3 \le \dfrac{1}{2}$

**36.** $-\dfrac{2}{3} \le 4 - \dfrac{1}{4}x < \dfrac{2}{3}$

**37.** $-4 \le \dfrac{7 - 3x}{5} \le 4$

**38.** $-3 < \dfrac{2x - 5}{4} < 8$

**b**  Graph and write interval notation.

**39.** $x < -2 \ or \ x > 1$

**40.** $x < -4 \ or \ x > 0$

**41.** $x \le -3 \ or \ x > 1$

**42.** $x \le -1 \ or \ x > 3$

Solve and graph.

**43.** $x + 3 < -2 \ or \ x + 3 > 2$

**44.** $x - 2 < -1 \ or \ x - 2 > 3$

**45.** $2x - 8 \le -3 \ or \ x - 1 \ge 3$

**46.** $x - 5 \le -4 \ or \ 2x - 7 \ge 3$

**47.** $7x + 4 \ge -17 \ or \ 6x + 5 \ge -7$

**48.** $4x - 4 < -8 \ or \ 4x - 4 < 12$

Solve.

**49.** $7 > -4x + 5 \ or \ 10 \le -4x + 5$

**50.** $6 > 2x - 1 \ or \ -4 \le 2x - 1$

**51.** $3x - 7 > -10$ *or* $5x + 2 \leq 22$

**52.** $3x + 2 < 2$ *or* $4 - 2x < 14$

**53.** $-2x - 2 < -6$ *or* $-2x - 2 > 6$

**54.** $-3m - 7 < -5$ *or* $-3m - 7 > 5$

**55.** $\frac{2}{3}x - 14 < -\frac{5}{6}$ *or* $\frac{2}{3}x - 14 > \frac{5}{6}$

**56.** $\frac{1}{4} - 3x \leq -3.7$ *or* $\frac{1}{4} - 5x \geq 4.8$

**57.** $\frac{2x - 5}{6} \leq -3$ *or* $\frac{2x - 5}{6} \geq 4$

**58.** $\frac{7 - 3x}{5} < -4$ *or* $\frac{7 - 3x}{5} > 4$

**C**    Solve.

**59.** *Pressure at Sea Depth.*   The equation

$$P = 1 + \frac{d}{33}$$

gives the pressure $P$, in atmospheres (atm), at a depth of $d$ feet in the sea. For what depths $d$ is the pressure at least 1 atm and at most 7 atm?

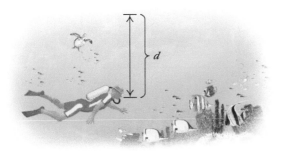

**60.** *Temperatures of Liquids.*   The formula

$$C = \tfrac{5}{9}(F - 32)$$

can be used to convert Fahrenheit temperatures $F$ to Celsius temperatures $C$.

**a)** Gold is a liquid for Celsius temperatures $C$ such that $1063° \leq C < 2660°$. Find such an inequality for the corresponding Fahrenheit temperatures.

**b)** Silver is a liquid for Celsius temperatures $C$ such that $960.8° \leq C < 2180°$. Find such an inequality for the corresponding Fahrenheit temperatures.

**61.** *Aerobic Exercise.*   In order to achieve maximum results from aerobic exercise, one should maintain one's heart rate at a certain level. A 30-year-old woman with a resting heart rate of 60 beats per minute should keep her heart rate between 138 and 162 beats per minute while exercising. She checks her pulse for 10 sec while exercising. What should the number of beats be?

**62.** *Minimizing Tolls.*   A $6.00 toll is charged to cross the bridge from mainland Florida to Sanibel Island. A six-month pass, costing $50.00, reduces the toll to $2.00. A one-year pass, costing $400, allows for free crossings. How many crossings per year does it take, on average, for the two six-month passes to be the most economical choice? Assume a constant number of trips per month.

**Source:** leewayinfo.com

**63.** *Body Mass Index.*   Refer to Exercises 71 and 72 in Exercise Set 1.4. Marv's height is 73 in. What weights $W$ will allow Marv to keep his body mass index $I$ in the 18.5–24.9 range?

**64.** *Body Mass Index.*   Refer to Exercises 71 and 72 in Exercise Set 1.4. Elaine's height is 67 in. What weight $W$ will allow Elaine to keep her body mass index in the 18.5–24.9 range?

**65.** *Young's Rule in Medicine.*   Refer to Exercise 37 in Exercise Set 1.2. The dosage of a medication for an 8-year-old child must stay between 100 mg and 200 mg. Find the equivalent adult dosage.

**66.** *Young's Rule in Medicine.*   Refer to Exercise 37 in Exercise Set 1.2. The dosage of a medication for a 5-year-old child must stay between 50 mg and 100 mg. Find the equivalent adult dosage.

## Skill Maintenance

Find the absolute value.   [R.1d]

**67.** $|-3.2|$

**68.** $|-5| + |7|$

**69.** $|-5 + 7|$

**70.** $|7 - 7|$

Simplify.   [R.7a, b]

**71.** $(-2x^{-4}y^6)^5$

**72.** $(-4a^5b^{-7})(5a^{-12}b^8)$

**73.** $\dfrac{-4a^5b^{-7}}{5a^{-12}b^8}$

**74.** $(5p^6q^{11})^2$

**75.** $\left(\dfrac{56a^5b^{-6}}{28a^7b^{-8}}\right)^{-3}$

**76.** $\left(\dfrac{125p^{11}q^{12}}{25p^6q^8}\right)^2$

## Synthesis

Solve.

**77.** $x - 10 < 5x + 6 \le x + 10$

**78.** $4m - 8 > 6m + 5 \text{ or } 5m - 8 < -2$

**79.** $-\frac{2}{15} \le \frac{2}{3}x - \frac{2}{5} \le \frac{2}{15}$

**80.** $2[5(3 - y) - 2(y - 2)] > y + 4$

**81.** $3x < 4 - 5x < 5 + 3x$

**82.** $2x - \frac{3}{4} < -\frac{1}{10} \text{ or } 2x - \frac{3}{4} > \frac{1}{10}$

**83.** $x + 4 < 2x - 6 \le x + 12$

**84.** $2x + 3 \le x - 6 \text{ or } 3x - 2 \le 4x + 5$

Determine whether each sentence is true or false for all real numbers $a$, $b$, and $c$.

**85.** If $-b < -a$, then $a < b$.

**86.** If $a \le c$ and $c \le b$, then $b \ge a$.

**87.** If $a < c$ and $b < c$, then $a < b$.

**88.** If $-a < c$ and $-c > b$, then $a > b$.

**89.** What is the union of the set of all rational numbers with the set of all irrational numbers? the intersection?

# Summary and Review

## Key Terms and Properties

equation, p. 74
solution, p. 74
solution set, p. 74
equivalent equations, p. 75
formula, p. 88
inequality, p. 113

graph of an inequality, p. 113
set-builder notation, p. 114
interval notation, p. 114
compound inequality, p. 129
intersection of sets, p. 129
conjunction, p. 130

empty set, p. 132
disjoint sets, p. 132
union of sets, p. 133
disjunction, p. 133
absolute value, p. 141

*The Addition Principle for Equations:* For any real numbers $a$, $b$, and $c$: $a = b$ is equivalent to $a + c = b + c$.

*The Multiplication Principle for Equations:* For any real numbers $a$, $b$, and $c$, $c \neq 0$; $a = b$ is equivalent to $a \cdot c = b \cdot c$.

*The Addition Principle for Inequalities:* For any real numbers $a$, $b$, and $c$: $a < b$ is equivalent to $a + c < b + c$; $a > b$ is equivalent to $a + c > b + c$.

*The Multiplication Principle for Inequalities:* For any real numbers $a$ and $b$, and any *positive* number $c$: $a < b$ is equivalent to $ac < bc$; $a > b$ is equivalent to $ac > bc$.

For any real numbers $a$ and $b$, and any *negative* number $c$: $a < b$ is equivalent to $ac > bc$; $a > b$ is equivalent to $ac < bc$.

Similar statements hold for $\leq$ and $\geq$.

*Set Intersection:* $A \cap B = \{x \mid x \text{ is in } A \text{ and } x \text{ is in } B\}$

*Set Union:* $A \cup B = \{x \mid x \text{ is in } A \text{ or } x \text{ is in } B, \text{ or } x \text{ is in both } A \text{ and } B\}$

"$a < x$ *and* $x < b$" is equivalent to "$a < x < b$."

*Properties of Absolute Value*

$|ab| = |a| \cdot |b|$, $\quad \left|\dfrac{a}{b}\right| = \dfrac{|a|}{|b|}$, $\quad |-a| = |a|$, $\quad$ The distance between $a$ and $b$ is $|a - b|$.

*Principles for Solving Equations and Inequalities Involving Absolute Value:*

For any positive number $p$ and any algebraic expression $X$:

**a)** The solutions of $|X| = p$ are those numbers that satisfy $X = -p$ or $X = p$.
**b)** The solutions of $|X| < p$ are those numbers that satisfy $-p < X < p$.
**c)** The solutions of $|X| > p$ are those numbers that satisfy $X < -p$ or $X > p$.

## Concept Reinforcement

Determine whether each statement is true or false.

_____ **1.** For any real numbers $a$, $b$, and $c$, $c \neq 0$, $a = b$ is equivalent to $a \cdot c = b \cdot c$.  [1.1c]

_____ **2.** When we solve $3B = mt + nt$ for $t$, we get $t = \dfrac{3B - mt}{n}$.  [1.2a]

_____ **3.** For any real numbers $a$, $b$, and $c$, $c \neq 0$, $a \leq b$ is equivalent to $ac \leq bc$.  [1.4c]

_____ **4.** The inequalities $x < 2$ and $x \leq 1$ are equivalent.  [1.4c]

_____ **5.** If $x$ is negative, $|x| = -x$.  [1.6a]

_____ **6.** $|x|$ is always positive.  [1.6a]

_____ **7.** $|a - b| = |b - a|$.  [1.6b]

# Important Concepts

**Objective 1.1d**  Solve equations using the addition principle and the multiplication principle together, removing parentheses where appropriate.

**Example**  Solve: $10y - 2(3y + 1) = 6$.

$$10y - 2(3y + 1) = 6$$
$$10y - 6y - 2 = 6 \qquad \text{Removing parentheses}$$
$$4y - 2 = 6 \qquad \text{Collecting like terms}$$
$$4y = 8 \qquad \text{Adding 2}$$
$$y = 2 \qquad \text{Dividing by 4}$$

The solution is 2.

**Practice Exercise**

1. Solve: $2(x + 2) = 5(x - 4)$.

---

**Objective 1.2a**  Evaluate formulas and solve a formula for a specified letter.

**Example**  Solve for $z$:  $T = \dfrac{w + z}{3}$.

$$T = \frac{w + z}{3}$$
$$3 \cdot T = 3\left(\frac{w + z}{3}\right) \qquad \begin{array}{l}\text{Multiplying by 3 to}\\\text{clear the fraction}\end{array}$$
$$3T = w + z \qquad \text{Simplifying}$$
$$3T - w = z \qquad \text{Subtracting } w$$

**Practice Exercise**

2. Solve for $h$:  $F = \dfrac{1}{4}gh$.

---

**Objective 1.4c**  Solve an inequality using the addition principle and the multiplication principle and then graph the inequality.

**Example**  Solve and graph: $6x - 7 \leq 3x + 2$.

$$6x - 7 \leq 3x + 2$$
$$3x - 7 \leq 2 \qquad \text{Subtracting } 3x$$
$$3x \leq 9 \qquad \text{Adding 7}$$
$$x \leq 3 \qquad \text{Dividing by 3}$$

The solution set is $\{x \mid x \leq 3\}$, or $(-\infty, 3]$. We graph the solution set.

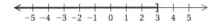

**Practice Exercise**

3. Solve and graph: $5y + 5 < 2y - 1$.

---

**Objective 1.5a**  Find the intersection of two sets. Solve and graph conjunctions of inequalities.

**Example**  Solve and graph: $-5 < 2x - 3 \leq 3$.

$$-5 < 2x - 3 \leq 3$$
$$-2 < 2x \leq 6 \qquad \text{Adding 3}$$
$$-1 < x \leq 3 \qquad \text{Dividing by 2}$$

The solution set is $\{x \mid -1 < x \leq 3\}$, or $(-1, 3]$. We graph the solution set.

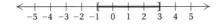

**Practice Exercise**

4. Solve and graph: $-4 \leq 5z + 6 < 11$.

**Objective 1.5b** Find the union of two sets. Solve and graph disjunctions of inequalities.

**Example**  Solve and graph: $2x + 1 \leq -5$ *or* $3x + 1 > 7$.

$$2x + 1 \leq -5 \quad or \quad 3x + 1 > 7$$
$$2x \leq -6 \quad or \quad 3x > 6$$
$$x \leq -3 \quad or \quad x > 2$$

The solution set is $\{x \mid x \leq -3 \ or \ x > 2\}$, or $(-\infty, -3] \cup (2, \infty)$. We graph the solution set.

**Practice Exercise**

**5.** Solve and graph: $z + 4 < 3$ *or* $4z + 1 \geq 5$.

---

**Objective 1.6c**  Solve equations with absolute-value expressions.

**Example**  Solve: $|y - 2| = 1$.

$$y - 2 = -1 \quad or \quad y - 2 = 1$$
$$y = 1 \quad or \quad y = 3$$

The solution set is $\{1, 3\}$.

**Practice Exercise**

**6.** Solve: $|5x - 1| = 9$.

---

**Objective 1.6d**  Solve equations with two absolute-value expressions.

**Example**  Solve: $|4x - 4| = |2x + 8|$.

$$4x - 4 = 2x + 8 \quad or \quad 4x - 4 = -(2x + 8)$$
$$2x - 4 = 8 \quad or \quad 4x - 4 = -2x - 8$$
$$2x = 12 \quad or \quad 6x - 4 = -8$$
$$x = 6 \quad or \quad 6x = -4$$
$$x = 6 \quad or \quad x = -\frac{2}{3}$$

The solution set is $\left\{6, -\frac{2}{3}\right\}$.

**Practice Exercise**

**7.** Solve: $|z + 4| = |3z - 2|$.

---

**Objective 1.6e**  Solve inequalities with absolute-value expressions.

**Example**  Solve: **(a)** $|5x + 3| < 2$; **(b)** $|x + 3| \geq 1$.

**a)** $|5x + 3| < 2$

$$-2 < 5x + 3 < 2$$
$$-5 < 5x < -1$$
$$-1 < x < -\frac{1}{5}$$

The solution set is $\left\{x \mid -1 < x < -\frac{1}{5}\right\}$, or $\left(-1, -\frac{1}{5}\right)$.

**b)** $\qquad |x + 3| \geq 1$

$$x + 3 \leq -1 \quad or \quad x + 3 \geq 1$$
$$x \leq -4 \quad or \quad x \geq -2$$

The solution set is $\{x \mid x \leq -4 \ or \ x \geq -2\}$, or $(-\infty, -4] \cup [-2, \infty)$.

**Practice Exercise**

**8.** Solve: **(a)** $|2x + 3| < 5$; **(b)** $|3x + 2| \geq 8$.

## Review Exercises

Solve. [1.1b, c, d]

**1.** $-11 + y = -3$

**2.** $-7x = -3$

**3.** $-\frac{5}{3}x + \frac{7}{3} = -5$

**4.** $6(2x - 1) = 3 - (x + 10)$

**5.** $2.4x + 1.5 = 1.02$

**6.** $2(3 - x) - 4(x + 1) = 7(1 - x)$

Solve for the indicated letter. [1.2a]

**7.** $C = \frac{4}{11}d + 3$, for $d$

**8.** $A = 2a - 3b$, for $b$

**9.** *Interstate Mile Markers.* If you are traveling on a U.S. interstate highway, you will notice numbered markers every mile to tell your location in case of an accident or other emergency. In many states, the numbers on the markers increase from west to east. The sum of two consecutive mile markers on I-70 in Utah is 371. Find the numbers on the markers. [1.3a]

**Source:** Federal Highway Administration, Ed Rotalewski

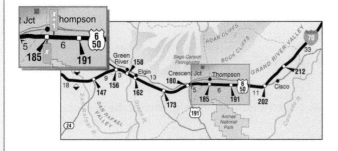

**10.** *Rope Cutting.* A piece of rope 27 m long is cut into two pieces so that one piece is four-fifths as long as the other. Find the length of each piece. [1.3a]

**11.** *Population Growth.* The population of Newcastle grew 12% from one year to the next to a total of 179,200. What was the former population? [1.3a]

**12.** *Moving Walkway.* A moving walkway in an airport is 360 ft long and moves at a speed of 6 ft/sec. If Arnie walks at a speed of 3 ft/sec, how long will it take him to walk the length of the moving walkway? [1.3b]

Write interval notation for the given set or graph. [1.4b]

**13.** $\{x \mid -8 \le x < 9\}$

**14.**
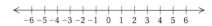

Solve and graph. Write interval notation for the solution set. [1.4c]

**15.** $x - 2 \le -4$

**16.** $x + 5 > 6$

Solve. [1.4c]

**17.** $a + 7 \le -14$

**18.** $y - 5 \ge -12$

**19.** $4y > -16$

**20.** $-0.3y < 9$

**21.** $-6x - 5 < 13$

**22.** $4y + 3 \le -6y - 9$

**23.** $-\frac{1}{2}x - \frac{1}{4} > \frac{1}{2} - \frac{1}{4}x$

**24.** $0.3y - 8 < 2.6y + 15$

**25.** $-2(x - 5) \ge 6(x + 7) - 12$

**26.** *Moving Costs.* Metro Movers charges $85 plus $40 an hour to move households across town. Champion Moving charges $60 an hour for cross-town moves. For what lengths of time is Champion more expensive? [1.4d]

**27.** *Investments.* Joe plans to invest $30,000, part at 3% and part at 4%, for one year. What is the most that can be invested at 3% in order to make at least $1100 interest in one year? [1.4d]

Graph and write interval notation. [1.5a, b]

**28.** $-2 \le x < 5$

**29.** $x \le -2 \text{ or } x > 5$

$$\begin{array}{c} \longleftarrow \!\!\!+\!\!+\!\!+\!\!+\!\!+\!\!+\!\!+\!\!+\!\!+\!\!+\!\!+\!\!+\!\!\! \longrightarrow \\ {\scriptstyle -6\,-5\,-4\,-3\,-2\,-1\ \ 0\ \ 1\ \ 2\ \ 3\ \ 4\ \ 5\ \ 6} \end{array}$$

**30.** Find the intersection: [1.5a]
$$\{1, 2, 5, 6, 9\} \cap \{1, 3, 5, 9\}.$$

**31.** Find the union: [1.5b]
$$\{1, 2, 5, 6, 9\} \cup \{1, 3, 5, 9\}.$$

Solve. [1.5a, b]

**32.** $2x - 5 < -7 \text{ and } 3x + 8 \ge 14$

**33.** $-4 < x + 3 \le 5$

**34.** $-15 < -4x - 5 < 0$

**35.** $3x < -9 \text{ or } -5x < -5$

**36.** $2x + 5 < -17 \text{ or } -4x + 10 \le 34$

**37.** $2x + 7 \le -5 \text{ or } x + 7 \ge 15$

Simplify. [1.6a]

**38.** $\left| -\dfrac{3}{x} \right|$     **39.** $\left| \dfrac{2x}{y^2} \right|$     **40.** $\left| \dfrac{12y}{-3y^2} \right|$

**41.** Find the distance between $-23$ and $39$. [1.6b]

Solve. [1.6c, d]

**42.** $|x| = 6$     **43.** $|x - 2| = 7$

**44.** $|2x + 5| = |x - 9|$     **45.** $|5x + 6| = -8$

Solve. [1.6e]

**46.** $|2x + 5| < 12$     **47.** $|x| \ge 3.5$

**48.** $|3x - 4| \ge 15$     **49.** $|x| < 0$

*Greenhouse Gases.* The equation
$$G = 0.506t + 18.3$$
is used to estimate global carbon dioxide emissions, in billions of metric tons, $t$ years after 1980—that is, $t = 0$ corresponds to 1980, $t = 20$ corresponds to 2000, and so on. Use this equation in Exercises 50 and 51.
**Source:** U.S. Department of Energy

**50.** Estimate global carbon dioxide emissions in 2010.
[1.2a], [1.3a]
   A. 23.36 billion metric tons
   B. 33.48 billion metric tons
   C. 38.54 billion metric tons
   D. 1035.4 billion metric tons

**51.** For what years are global carbon dioxide emissions predicted to be between 35 and 40 billion metric tons? [1.5c]
   A. Between 2013 and 2023
   B. Between 2011 and 2025
   C. Between 2020 and 2025
   D. Years after 2025

## Synthesis

**52.** Solve: $|2x + 5| \le |x + 3|$. [1.6d, e]

# Understanding Through Discussion and Writing

**1.** Explain in your own words why the inequality symbol must be reversed when both sides of an inequality are multiplied or divided by a negative number. [1.4c]

**2.** Explain in your own words why the solutions of the inequality $|x + 5| \le 2$ can be interpreted as "all those numbers $x$ whose distance from $-5$ is at most 2 units." [1.6e]

**3.** Describe the circumstances under which, for intervals, $[a, b] \cup [c, d] = [a, d]$. [1.5b]

**4.** Explain in your own words why the interval $[6, \infty)$ is only part of the solution set of $|x| \ge 6$. [1.6e]

**5.** Find the error or errors in each of the following steps: [1.4c]

$$
\begin{array}{ll}
7 - 9x + 6x < -9(x + 2) + 10x & \\
7 - 9x + 6x < -9x + 2 + 10x & (1) \\
7 + 6x > 2 + 10x & (2) \\
-4x > 8 & (3) \\
x > -2. & (4)
\end{array}
$$

**6.** Explain why the conjunction $3 < x \text{ and } x < 5$ is equivalent to $3 < x < 5$, but the disjunction $3 < x \text{ or } x < 5$ is not. [1.5a, b]

Test

**For Extra Help**

CHAPTER
Test Prep
VIDEOS

Step-by-step test solutions are found on the Chapter Test Prep Videos available via the Video Resources on DVD, in *MyMathLab*, and on You Tube (search "BittingerInterAlgPB" and click on "Channels").

Solve.

**1.** $x + 7 = 5$

**2.** $-12x = -8$

**3.** $x - \frac{3}{5} = \frac{2}{3}$

**4.** $3y - 4 = 8$

**5.** $1.7y - 0.1 = 2.1 - 0.3y$

**6.** $5(3x + 6) = 6 - (x + 8)$

**7.** Solve $A = 3B - C$ for $B$.

**8.** Solve $m = n - nt$ for $n$.

Solve.

**9.** *Room Dimensions.* A rectangular room has a perimeter of 48 ft. The width is two-thirds of the length. What are the dimensions of the room?

**10.** *Copy Budget.* Copy Solutions rents a copier for $240 per month plus 1.5¢ per copy. A law firm needs to lease a copy machine for use during a special case that they anticipate will take 3 months. If they allot a budget of $1500 for copying costs, how many copies can they make?

**11.** *Population Decrease.* The population of Baytown dropped 12% from one year to the next to a total of 158,400. What was the former population?

**12.** *Angles in a Triangle.* The measures of the angles of a triangle are three consecutive integers. Find the measures of the angles.

**13.** *Boating.* A paddleboat moves at a rate of 12 mph in still water. If the river's current moves at a rate of 3 mph, how long will it take the boat to travel 36 mi downstream? 36 mi upstream?

Write interval notation for the given set or graph.

**14.** $\{x \mid -3 < x \leq 2\}$

**15.**

**Solve and graph. Write interval notation for the solution set.**

**16.** $x - 2 \leq 4$

**17.** $-4y - 3 \geq 5$

Solve.

**18.** $x - 4 \geq 6$

**19.** $-0.6y < 30$

**20.** $3a - 5 \leq -2a + 6$

**21.** $-5y - 1 > -9y + 3$

**22.** $4(5 - x) < 2x + 5$

**23.** $-8(2x + 3) + 6(4 - 5x) \geq 2(1 - 7x) - 4(4 + 6x)$

Solve.

**24.** *Moving Costs.* Mitchell Moving Company charges $105 plus $30 an hour to move households across town. Quick-Pak Moving charges $80 an hour for cross-town moves. For what lengths of time is Quick-Pak more expensive?

**25.** *Pressure at Sea Depth.* The equation
$$P = 1 + \frac{d}{33}$$
gives the pressure $P$, in atmospheres (atm), at a depth of $d$ feet in the sea. For what depths $d$ is the pressure at least 2 atm and at most 8 atm?

Graph and write interval notation.

**26.** $-3 \le x \le 4$

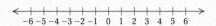

**27.** $x < -3 \, or \, x > 4$

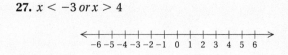

Solve.

**28.** $5 - 2x \le 1 \, and \, 3x + 2 \ge 14$

**29.** $-3 < x - 2 < 4$

**30.** $-11 \le -5x - 2 < 0$

**31.** $-3x > 12 \, or \, 4x > -10$

**32.** $x - 7 \le -5 \, or \, x - 7 \ge -10$

**33.** $3x - 2 < 7 \, or \, x - 2 > 4$

Simplify.

**34.** $\left| \dfrac{7}{x} \right|$

**35.** $\left| \dfrac{-6x^2}{3x} \right|$

**36.** Find the distance between 4.8 and $-3.6$.

**37.** Find the intersection:
$$\{1, 3, 5, 7, 9\} \cap \{3, 5, 11, 13\}.$$

**38.** Find the union:
$$\{1, 3, 5, 7, 9\} \cup \{3, 5, 11, 13\}.$$

Solve.

**39.** $|x| = 9$

**40.** $|x - 3| = 9$

**41.** $|x + 10| = |x - 12|$

**42.** $|2 - 5x| = -10$

**43.** $|4x - 1| < 4.5$

**44.** $|x| > 3$

**45.** $\left| \dfrac{6 - x}{7} \right| \le 15$

**46.** $|-5x - 3| \ge 10$

**47.** The solution of $2(3x - 6) + 5 = 1 - (x - 6)$ is which of the following?

  **A.** Less than 0         **B.** Between 0 and 1
  **C.** Between 1 and 3      **D.** Greater than 3

# Synthesis

Solve.

**48.** $|3x - 4| \le -3$

**49.** $7x < 8 - 3x < 6 + 7x$

# Graphs, Functions, and Applications

# Real-World Application

Amelia's Beads offers a class in designing necklaces. For a necklace made of 6-mm beads, 4.23 beads per inch are needed. The cost of a necklace made of 6-mm gemstone beads that sell for 40¢ each is $7 for the clasp and the crimps and approximately $1.70 per inch. Formulate a linear function that models the total cost of a necklace $C(n)$, where $n$ is the length of the necklace, in inches. Then graph the model and use the model to determine the cost of a 30-in. necklace.

*This problem appears as Example 6 in Section 2.6.*

# 2.1

# Graphs of Equations

Graphs display information in a compact way and can provide a visual approach to problem solving. We often see graphs in newspapers and magazines. Examples of bar, circle, and line graphs are shown below.

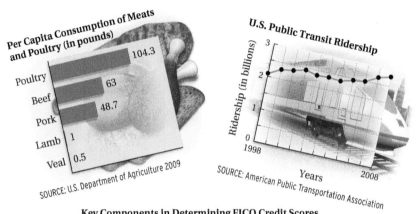

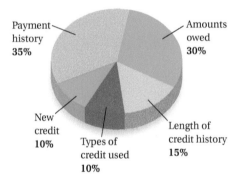

Key Components in Determining FICO Credit Scores

SOURCE: Farmers Market

## a Plotting Ordered Pairs

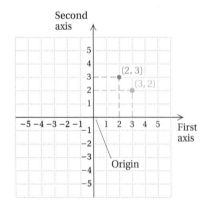

We have already learned to graph numbers and inequalities in one variable on a line. To graph an equation that contains two variables, we graph pairs of numbers on a plane.

On the number line, each point is the graph of a number. On a plane, each point is the graph of a number pair. To locate points on a plane, we use two perpendicular number lines called **axes**. They cross at a point called the **origin**. The arrows show the positive directions on the axes. Consider the **ordered pair** $(2, 3)$. The numbers in an ordered pair are called **coordinates**. In $(2, 3)$, the **first coordinate** is 2 and the **second coordinate** is 3. (The first coordinate is sometimes called the **abscissa** and the second the **ordinate**.) To plot $(2, 3)$, we start at the origin and move 2 units in the positive horizontal direction (2 units to the right). Then we move 3 units in the positive vertical direction (3 units up) and make a dot.

The point $(3, 2)$, is also plotted in the figure. Note that $(3, 2)$ and $(2, 3)$ are different points. The order of the numbers in the pair is indeed important. They are called *ordered pairs* because it makes a difference which number is listed first.

*Answers*

*Skill to Review:*
**1.** No    **2.** Yes

The coordinates of the origin are $(0, 0)$. In general, the first axis is called the *x*-axis and the second axis is called the *y*-axis. We call this the **Cartesian coordinate system** in honor of the great French mathematician and philosopher René Descartes (1596–1650).

**EXAMPLE 1** Plot the points $(-4, 3)$, $(-5, -3)$, $(0, 4)$, and $(2.5, 0)$.

To plot $(-4, 3)$, we note that the first number, $-4$, tells us the distance in the first, or horizontal, direction. We move 4 units in the negative direction, *left*. The second number tells us the distance in the second, or vertical, direction. We move 3 units in the positive direction, *up*. The point $(-4, 3)$ is then marked, or plotted.

The points $(-5, -3)$, $(0, 4)$, and $(2.5, 0)$ are plotted in the same manner.

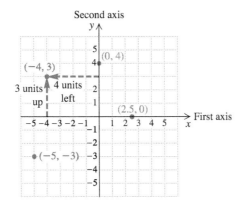

Plot each point on the plane below.

**1.** $(6, 4)$     **2.** $(4, 6)$

**3.** $(-3, 5)$     **4.** $(5, -3)$

**5.** $(-4, -3)$     **6.** $(4, -2)$

**7.** $(0, 3)$     **8.** $(3, 0)$

**9.** $(0, -4)$     **10.** $(-4, 0)$

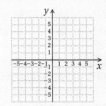

Do Exercises 1–10.

## Quadrants

The axes divide the plane into four regions called **quadrants**, denoted by Roman numerals and numbered counterclockwise starting at the upper right. In region I (the *first* quadrant), both coordinates of a point are positive. In region II (the *second* quadrant), the first coordinate is negative and the second coordinate is positive. In the *third* quadrant, both coordinates are negative, and in the *fourth* quadrant, the first coordinate is positive and the second coordinate is negative.

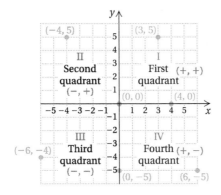

Points with one or more 0's as coordinates, such as $(0, -5)$, $(4, 0)$, and $(0, 0)$ are on axes and *not* in quadrants.

Do Exercises 11 and 12.

**11.** What can you say about the coordinates of a point in the third quadrant?

**12.** What can you say about the coordinates of a point in the fourth quadrant?

*Answers*

**1.–10.**

Second axis

$(-3, 5)$   $(4, 6)$   $(6, 4)$
$(0, 3)$
$(-4, 0)$   $(3, 0)$   First axis
$(4, -2)$
$(-4, -3)$   $(5, -3)$
$(0, -4)$

**11.** Both negative
**12.** First positive, second negative

## b Solutions of Equations

If an equation has two variables, its solutions are pairs of numbers. When such a solution is written as an ordered pair, the first number listed in the pair generally replaces the variable that occurs first alphabetically.

**EXAMPLE 2** Determine whether each of the following pairs is a solution of $5b - 3a = 34$: $(2, 8)$ and $(-1, 6)$.

For the pair $(2, 8)$, we substitute 2 for $a$ and 8 for $b$ (alphabetical order of variables):

$$\frac{5b - 3a = 34}{5 \cdot 8 - 3 \cdot 2 \ ? \ 34}$$
$$\begin{array}{c|c} 40 - 6 & \\ 34 & \text{TRUE} \end{array}$$

Thus, $(2, 8)$ is a solution of the equation.

For $(-1, 6)$, we substitute $-1$ for $a$ and 6 for $b$:

$$\frac{5b - 3a = 34}{5 \cdot 6 - 3 \cdot (-1) \ ? \ 34}$$
$$\begin{array}{c|c} 30 + 3 & \\ 33 & \text{FALSE} \end{array}$$

Thus, $(-1, 6)$ is *not* a solution of the equation.

Do Exercises 13 and 14.

**13.** Determine whether $(2, -4)$ is a solution of $5b - 3a = 34$.

**14.** Determine whether $(2, -4)$ is a solution of $7p + 5q = -6$.

**EXAMPLE 3** Show that the pairs $(-4, 3)$, $(0, 1)$, and $(4, -1)$ are solutions of $y = 1 - \frac{1}{2}x$. Then plot the three points and use them to help determine another pair that is a solution.

We replace $x$ with the first coordinate and $y$ with the second coordinate of each pair:

$$\frac{y = 1 - \frac{1}{2}x}{3 \ ? \ 1 - \frac{1}{2} \cdot (-4)}$$
$$\begin{array}{c|c} 1 + 2 & \\ 3 & \text{TRUE} \end{array}$$

$$\frac{y = 1 - \frac{1}{2}x}{1 \ ? \ 1 - \frac{1}{2} \cdot (0)}$$
$$\begin{array}{c|c} 1 - 0 & \\ 1 & \text{TRUE} \end{array}$$

$$\frac{y = 1 - \frac{1}{2}x}{-1 \ ? \ 1 - \frac{1}{2} \cdot (4)}$$
$$\begin{array}{c|c} 1 - 2 & \\ -1 & \text{TRUE} \end{array}$$

In each case, the substitution results in a true equation. Thus all the pairs are solutions of the equation.

We plot the points as shown at right. Note that the three points appear to "line up." That is, they appear to be on a straight line. We use a ruler and draw a line passing through $(-4, 3)$, $(0, 1)$, and $(4, -1)$.

The line appears to pass through $(2, 0)$ as well. Let's see if this pair is a solution of $y = 1 - \frac{1}{2}x$:

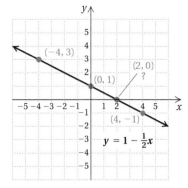

$$\frac{y = 1 - \frac{1}{2}x}{0 \ ? \ 1 - \frac{1}{2} \cdot (2)}$$
$$\begin{array}{c|c} 1 - 1 & \\ 0 & \text{TRUE} \end{array}$$

We see that $(2, 0)$ is another solution of the equation.

Do Exercise 15.

**15.** Use the line in Example 3 to find at least two more points that are solutions.

*Answers*

**13.** No   **14.** Yes
**15.** $(-6, 4)$, $(-2, 2)$; answers may vary

Example 3 leads us to believe that any point on the line that passes through $(-4, 3)$, $(0, 1)$, and $(4, -1)$ represents a solution of $y = 1 - \frac{1}{2}x$. In fact, every solution of $y = 1 - \frac{1}{2}x$ is represented by a point on that line and every point on that line represents a solution. The line is said to be the *graph* of the equation.

---

## GRAPH OF AN EQUATION

The **graph** of an equation is a drawing that represents all its solutions.

---

### c) Graphs of Linear Equations

Equations like $y = 1 - \frac{1}{2}x$ and $2x + 3y = 6$ are said to be **linear** because the graph of their solutions is a line. In general, a linear equation is any equation equivalent to one of the form $y = mx + b$ or $Ax + By = C$, where $m$, $b$, $A$, $B$, and $C$ are constants (that is, they are numbers, not variables) and $A$ and $B$ are not both 0.

**EXAMPLE 4** Graph: $y = 2x$.

We find some ordered pairs that are solutions. This time we list the pairs in a table. To find an ordered pair, we can choose *any* number for $x$ and then determine $y$. For example, if we choose 3 for $x$, then $y = 2 \cdot 3 = 6$ (substituting into the equation $y = 2x$). We choose some negative values for $x$, as well as some positive ones. If a number takes us off the graph paper, we generally do not use it. Next, we plot these points. If we plotted *many* such points, they would appear to make a solid line. We draw the line with a ruler and label it $y = 2x$.

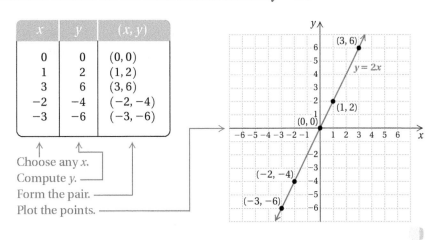

Choose any $x$.
Compute $y$.
Form the pair.
Plot the points.

---

To graph a linear equation:

1. Select a value for one variable and calculate the corresponding value of the other variable. Form an ordered pair using alphabetical order as indicated by the variables.

2. Repeat step (1) to obtain at least two other ordered pairs. Two ordered pairs are essential. A third serves as a check.

3. Plot the ordered pairs and draw a straight line passing through the points.

---

Graph.

**16.** $y = -2x$

| $x$ | $y$ | $(x, y)$ |
|-----|-----|----------|
| $-3$ | | |
| $-1$ | | |
| $0$ | | |
| $1$ | | |
| $3$ | | |

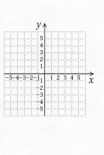

**17.** $y = \frac{1}{2}x$

| $x$ | $y$ | $(x, y)$ |
|-----|-----|----------|
| $4$ | | |
| $2$ | | |
| $0$ | | |
| $-2$ | | |
| $-4$ | | |

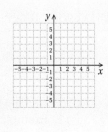

*Answers*

16.
| $x$ | $y$ | $(x, y)$ |
|-----|-----|----------|
| $-3$ | $6$ | $(-3, 6)$ |
| $-1$ | $2$ | $(-1, 2)$ |
| $0$ | $0$ | $(0, 0)$ |
| $1$ | $-2$ | $(1, -2)$ |
| $3$ | $-6$ | $(3, -6)$ |

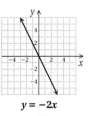

$y = -2x$

17.
| $x$ | $y$ | $(x, y)$ |
|-----|-----|----------|
| $4$ | $2$ | $(4, 2)$ |
| $2$ | $1$ | $(2, 1)$ |
| $0$ | $0$ | $(0, 0)$ |
| $-2$ | $-1$ | $(-2, -1)$ |
| $-4$ | $-2$ | $(-4, -2)$ |

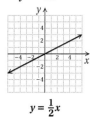

$y = \frac{1}{2}x$

Do Exercises 16 and 17.

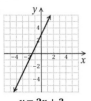
**Finding Solutions of Equations**   A table of values representing ordered pairs that are solutions of an equation can be displayed on a graphing calculator. To do this for the equation in Example 4, $y = 2x$, we first press ⌐Y=⌐ to access the equation-editor screen. Then we clear any equations that are present. (See the Calculator Corner on p. 83 for the procedure for doing this.) Next, we enter the equation by positioning the cursor beside "Y1 =" and pressing ②  X,T,θ,n . Now we press **2ND** ⌐TBLSET⌐ to display the table set-up screen. (TBLSET is the second function associated with the ⌐WINDOW⌐ key.) You can choose to supply the x-values yourself or you can set the calculator to supply them. To supply them yourself, follow the procedure for selecting ASK mode on p. 83. To have the calculator supply the x-values, set "Indpnt" to "Auto" by positioning the cursor over "Auto" and pressing **ENTER**. "Depend" should also be set to "Auto."

When "Indpnt" is set to "Auto," the graphing calculator will supply values of x, beginning with the value specified as TBLSTART and continuing by adding the value of △TBL to the preceding value for x. Below, we show a table of values that starts with $x = -2$ and adds 1 to the preceding x-value. We move to TBLSTART and press ⊙②⊙① or ⊙② **ENTER** ① to select a minimum x-value of $-2$ and an increment of 1. To display the table, we press **2ND** ⌐TABLE⌐. (TABLE is the second operation associated with the ⌐GRAPH⌐ key.) If we are in AUTO mode, we can use the △ and ▽ keys to scroll up and down through the table to see other solutions of the equation.

```
TABLE SETUP
  TblStart=-2
  △Tbl=1
Indpnt: Auto  Ask
Depend: Auto  Ask
```

| X | Y1 | |
|---|----|--|
| -2 | -4 | |
| -1 | -2 | |
| 0 | 0 | |
| 1 | 2 | |
| 2 | 4 | |
| 3 | 6 | |
| 4 | 8 | |
| X = -2 | | |

**Exercises:**   Create a table of ordered pairs that are solutions of the equation.

1. Example 5

2. Example 7

---

**18.** Graph: $y = 2x + 3$.

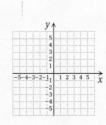

| x | y | $(x, y)$ |
|---|---|----------|
|   |   |          |
|   |   |          |
|   |   |          |

**EXAMPLE 5**   Graph: $y = -\frac{1}{2}x + 3$.

By choosing even integers for x, we can avoid fraction values when calculating y. For example, if we choose 4 for x, we get

$$y = -\frac{1}{2}x + 3 = -\frac{1}{2}(4) + 3 = -2 + 3 = 1.$$

When x is $-6$, we get

$$y = -\frac{1}{2}x + 3 = -\frac{1}{2}(-6) + 3 = 3 + 3 = 6,$$

and when x is 0, we get

$$y = -\frac{1}{2}x + 3 = -\frac{1}{2}(0) + 3 = 0 + 3 = 3.$$

*Answer*

**18.**

$y = 2x + 3$

We list the results in a table. Then we plot the points corresponding to each pair.

| x | y | (x, y) |
|---|---|--------|
| 4 | 1 | (4, 1) |
| −6 | 6 | (−6, 6) |
| 0 | 3 | (0, 3) |

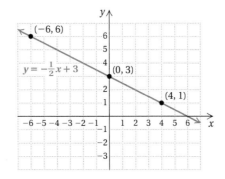

Note that the three points line up. If they did not, we would know that we had made a mistake. When only two points are plotted, an error is harder to detect. We use a ruler or other straightedge to draw a line through the points and then label the graph. Every point on the line represents a solution of $y = -\frac{1}{2}x + 3$.

Do Exercises 18 and 19. (Exercise 18 is on the preceding page.)

Calculating ordered pairs is usually easiest when $y$ is isolated on one side of the equation, as in $y = 2x$ and $y = -\frac{1}{2}x + 3$. To graph an equation in which $y$ is not isolated, we can use the addition principle and the multiplication principle to first solve for $y$. (See Sections 1.1 and 1.2.)

**EXAMPLE 6**  Graph: $3x + 5y = 10$.

We first solve for $y$:

$$3x + 5y = 10$$
$$3x + 5y - 3x = 10 - 3x \qquad \text{Subtracting } 3x$$
$$5y = 10 - 3x \qquad \text{Simplifying}$$
$$\tfrac{1}{5} \cdot 5y = \tfrac{1}{5} \cdot (10 - 3x) \qquad \text{Multiplying by } \tfrac{1}{5}, \text{ or dividing by 5}$$
$$y = \tfrac{1}{5} \cdot (10) - \tfrac{1}{5} \cdot (3x) \qquad \text{Using the distributive law}$$
$$y = 2 - \tfrac{3}{5}x, \text{ or } y = -\tfrac{3}{5}x + 2.$$

Thus the equation $3x + 5y = 10$ is equivalent to $y = -\frac{3}{5}x + 2$. We now find three ordered pairs, using multiples of 5 for $x$ to avoid fractions.

| x | y | (x, y) |
|---|---|--------|
| 0 | 2 | (0, 2) |
| 5 | −1 | (5, −1) |
| −5 | 5 | (−5, 5) |

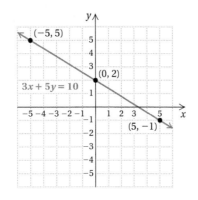

We plot the points, draw the line, and label the graph as shown.

Do Exercises 20 and 21.

**19.** Graph: $y = -\dfrac{1}{2}x - 3$.

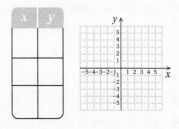

**20.** Graph: $4y - 3x = -8$.

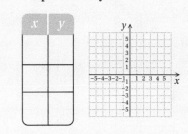

**21.** Graph: $5x + 2y = 4$.

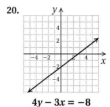

*Answers*

19.
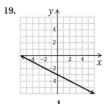
$$y = -\tfrac{1}{2}x - 3$$

20.

$$4y - 3x = -8$$

21.
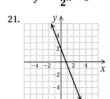
$$5x + 2y = 4$$

## d Graphing Nonlinear Equations

We have seen that equations whose graphs are straight lines are called **linear**. There are many equations whose graphs are not straight lines. Here are some examples.

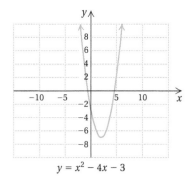

$$y = x^2 - 4x - 3$$

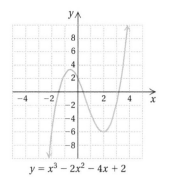

$$y = x^3 - 2x^2 - 4x + 2$$

Let's graph some of these **nonlinear equations**. We usually need to plot more than three points in order to get a good idea of the shape of the graph.

**EXAMPLE 7** Graph: $y = x^2 - 5$.

We select numbers for $x$ and find the corresponding values for $y$. For example, if we choose $-2$ for $x$, we get $y = (-2)^2 - 5 = 4 - 5 = -1$. The table lists several ordered pairs.

| $x$ | $y$ |
|-----|-----|
| 0 | $-5$ |
| $-1$ | $-4$ |
| 1 | $-4$ |
| $-2$ | $-1$ |
| 2 | $-1$ |
| $-3$ | 4 |
| 3 | 4 |

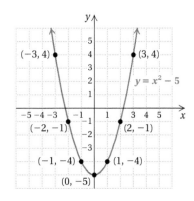

Next, we plot the points. The more points we plot, the more clearly we see the shape of the graph. Since the value of $x^2 - 5$ grows rapidly as $x$ moves away from the origin, the graph rises steeply on either side of the $y$-axis.

Do Exercise 22.

**22.** Graph: $y = 4 - x^2$.

| $x$ | $y$ |
|-----|-----|
| 0 | |
| 1 | |
| $-1$ | |
| 2 | |
| $-2$ | |
| 3 | |
| $-3$ | |

*Answer*

**22.**

| $x$ | $y$ |
|-----|-----|
| 0 | 4 |
| 1 | 3 |
| $-1$ | 3 |
| 2 | 0 |
| $-2$ | 0 |
| 3 | $-5$ |
| $-3$ | $-5$ |

$$y = 4 - x^2$$

**EXAMPLE 8** Graph: $y = 1/x$.

We select $x$-values and find the corresponding $y$-values. The table lists the ordered pairs $\left(3, \frac{1}{3}\right)$, $\left(2, \frac{1}{2}\right)$, $(1, 1)$, and so on.

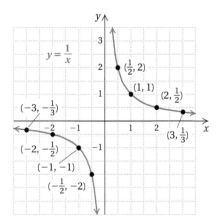

| $x$ | $y$ |
|---|---|
| 3 | $\frac{1}{3}$ |
| 2 | $\frac{1}{2}$ |
| 1 | 1 |
| $\frac{1}{2}$ | 2 |
| $-\frac{1}{2}$ | $-2$ |
| $-1$ | $-1$ |
| $-2$ | $-\frac{1}{2}$ |
| $-3$ | $-\frac{1}{3}$ |

We plot these points, noting that each first coordinate is paired with its reciprocal. Since $1/0$ is undefined, we cannot use 0 as a first coordinate. Thus there are two "branches" to this graph—one on each side of the $y$-axis. Note that for $x$-values far to the right or far to the left of 0, the graph approaches, but does not touch, the $x$-axis; and for $x$-values close to 0, the graph approaches, but does not touch, the $y$-axis.

Do Exercise 23.

**EXAMPLE 9** Graph: $y = |x|$.

We select numbers for $x$ and find the corresponding values for $y$. For example, if we choose $-1$ for $x$, we get $y = |-1| = 1$. Several ordered pairs are listed in the table below.

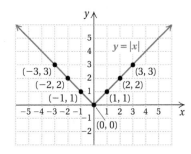

| $x$ | $y$ |
|---|---|
| $-3$ | 3 |
| $-2$ | 2 |
| $-1$ | 1 |
| 0 | 0 |
| 1 | 1 |
| 2 | 2 |
| 3 | 3 |

We plot these points, noting that the absolute value of a positive number is the same as the absolute value of its opposite. Thus the $x$-values 3 and $-3$ both are paired with the $y$-value 3. Note that the graph is V-shaped and centered at the origin.

Do Exercise 24.

With equations like $y = -\frac{1}{2}x + 3$, $y = x^2 - 5$, and $y = |x|$, which we have graphed in this section, it is understood that $y$ is the **dependent variable** and $x$ is the **independent variable**, since $y$ is expressed in terms of $x$ and consequently $y$ is calculated after first choosing $x$.

**23.** Graph: $y = \dfrac{2}{x}$.

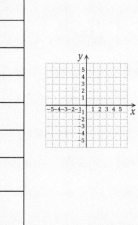

| $x$ | $y$ |
|---|---|
| 1 | |
| 2 | |
| 4 | |
| $-1$ | |
| $-2$ | |
| $-4$ | |
| $\frac{1}{2}$ | |
| $-\frac{1}{2}$ | |

**24.** Graph: $y = 4 - |x|$.

| $x$ | $y$ |
|---|---|
| 0 | |
| 2 | |
| $-2$ | |
| 4 | |
| $-4$ | |
| 5 | |
| $-5$ | |

*Answers*

**23.**

| x | y |
|---|---|
| 1 | 2 |
| 2 | 1 |
| 4 | $\frac{1}{2}$ |
| −1 | −2 |
| −2 | −1 |
| −4 | $-\frac{1}{2}$ |
| $\frac{1}{2}$ | 4 |
| $-\frac{1}{2}$ | −4 |

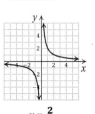

$y = \frac{2}{x}$

**24.**

| x | y |
|---|---|
| 0 | 4 |
| 2 | 2 |
| −2 | 2 |
| 4 | 0 |
| −4 | 0 |
| 5 | −1 |
| −5 | −1 |

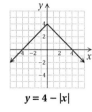

$y = 4 - |x|$

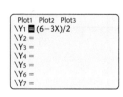
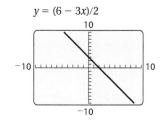
**2.1**   **Exercise Set**

For Extra Help

MyMathLab | Math XL PRACTICE | WATCH | DOWNLOAD | READ | REVIEW

**a**   Plot the following points.

**1.** $A(4, 1)$, $B(2, 5)$, $C(0, 3)$, $D(0, -5)$, $E(6, 0)$, $F(-3, 0)$, $G(-2, -4)$, $H(-5, 1)$, $J(-6, 6)$

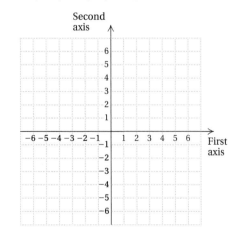

**2.** $A(-3, -5)$, $B(1, 3)$, $C(0, 7)$, $D(0, -2)$, $E(5, 0)$, $F(-4, 0)$, $G(1, -7)$, $H(-6, 4)$, $J(-3, 3)$

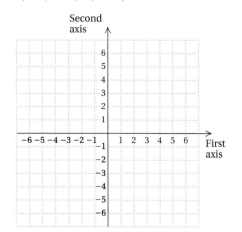

**3.** Plot the points $M(2, 3)$, $N(5, -3)$, and $P(-2, -3)$. Draw $\overline{MN}$, $\overline{NP}$, and $\overline{MP}$. ($\overline{MN}$ means the line segment from $M$ to $N$.) What kind of geometric figure is formed? What is its area?

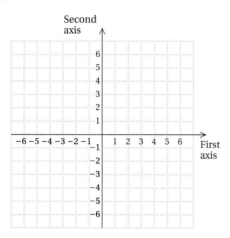

**4.** Plot the points $Q(-4, 3)$, $R(5, 3)$, $S(2, -1)$, and $T(-7, -1)$. Draw $\overline{QR}$, $\overline{RS}$, $\overline{ST}$, and $\overline{TQ}$. What kind of figure is formed? What is its area?

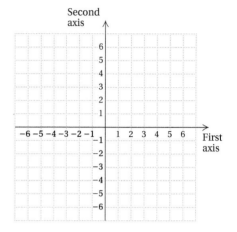

**b**   Determine whether the given point is a solution of the equation.

**5.** $(1, -1)$; $y = 2x - 3$

**6.** $(3, 4)$; $t = 4 - 3s$

**7.** $(3, 5)$; $4x - y = 7$

**8.** $(2, -1)$; $4r + 3s = 5$

**9.** $\left(0, \dfrac{3}{5}\right)$; $2a + 5b = 7$

**10.** $(-5, 1)$; $2p - 3q = -13$

In Exercises 11–16, an equation and two ordered pairs are given. Show that each pair is a solution of the equation. Then graph the equation and use the graph to determine another solution. Answers for solutions may vary, but the graphs do not.

**11.** $y = 4 - x$; $(-1, 5), (3, 1)$

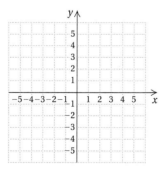

**12.** $y = x - 3$; $(5, 2), (-1, -4)$

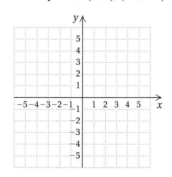

**13.** $3x + y = 7$; $(2, 1), (4, -5)$

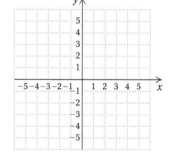

**14.** $y = \dfrac{1}{2}x + 3$; $(4, 5), (-2, 2)$

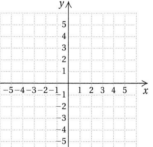

**15.** $6x - 3y = 3$; $(1, 1), (-1, -3)$

**16.** $4x - 2y = 10$; $(0, -5), (4, 3)$

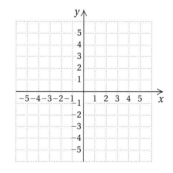

**c** Graph.

**17.** $y = x - 1$

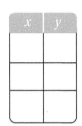

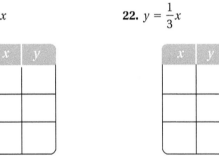

**18.** $y = x + 1$

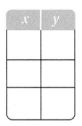

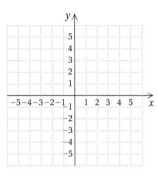

**19.** $y = x$

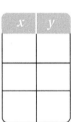

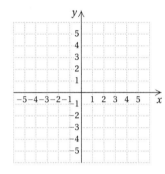

**20.** $y = -3x$

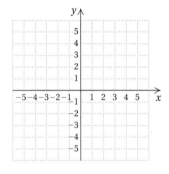

**21.** $y = \frac{1}{4}x$

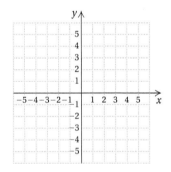

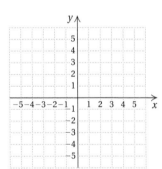

**22.** $y = \frac{1}{3}x$

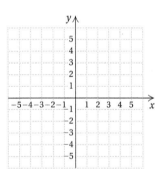

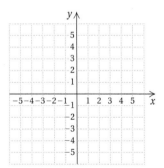

**23.** $y = 3 - x$

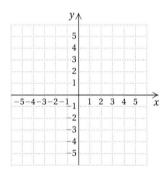

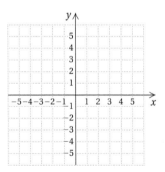

**24.** $y = x + 3$

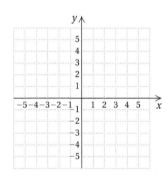

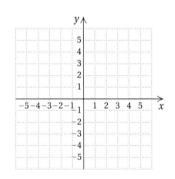

**25.** $y = 5x - 2$

**26.** $y = \frac{1}{4}x + 2$

**27.** $y = \frac{1}{2}x + 1$

**28.** $y = \frac{1}{3}x - 4$

**29.** $x + y = 5$

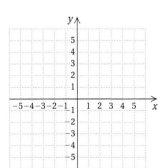

**30.** $x + y = -4$

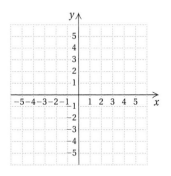

**31.** $y = -\dfrac{5}{3}x - 2$

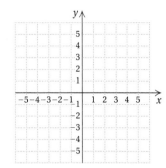

**32.** $y = -\dfrac{5}{2}x + 3$

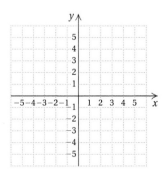

**33.** $x + 2y = 8$

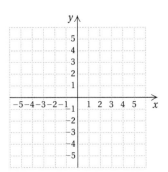

**34.** $x + 2y = -6$

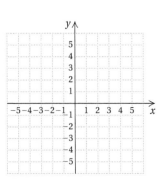

**35.** $y = \dfrac{3}{2}x + 1$

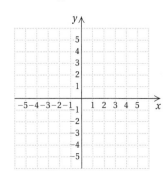

**36.** $y = -\dfrac{1}{2}x - 3$

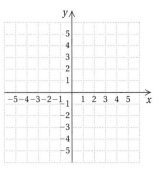

**37.** $8y + 2x = 4$

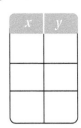

| x | y |
|---|---|
|   |   |
|   |   |

**38.** $6x - 3y = -9$

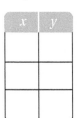

| x | y |
|---|---|
|   |   |
|   |   |

**39.** $8y + 2x = -4$

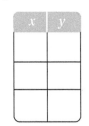

| x | y |
|---|---|
|   |   |
|   |   |

**40.** $6y + 2x = 8$

| x | y |
|---|---|
|   |   |
|   |   |

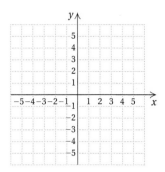

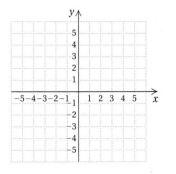

**d** Graph.

**41.** $y = x^2$

| x | y |
|---|---|
|   |   |
|   |   |
|   |   |
|   |   |

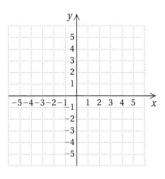

**42.** $y = -x^2$
(*Hint:* $-x^2 = -1 \cdot x^2$.)

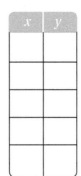

| x | y |
|---|---|
|   |   |
|   |   |
|   |   |
|   |   |

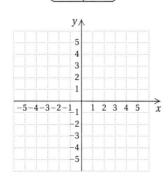

**43.** $y = x^2 + 2$

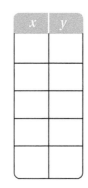

| x | y |
|---|---|
|   |   |
|   |   |
|   |   |
|   |   |

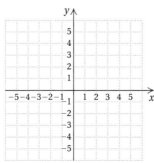

**44.** $y = 3 - x^2$

| x | y |
|---|---|
|   |   |
|   |   |
|   |   |
|   |   |

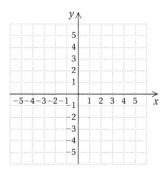

**45.** $y = x^2 - 3$

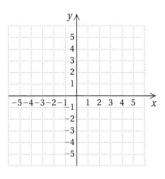

**46.** $y = x^2 - 3x$

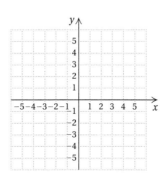

**47.** $y = -\dfrac{1}{x}$

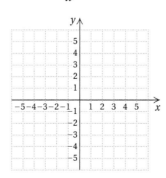

**48.** $y = \dfrac{3}{x}$

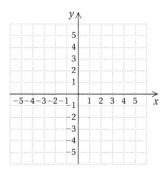

**49.** $y = |x - 2|$

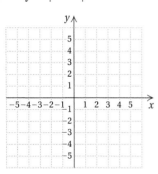

**50.** $y = |x| + 2$

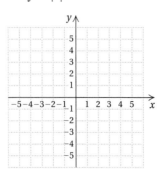

**51.** $y = x^3$

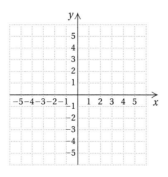

**52.** $y = x^3 - 2$

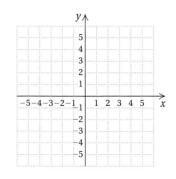

## Skill Maintenance

Solve. [1.5a, b]

**53.** $-3 < 2x - 5 \le 10$

**54.** $2x - 5 \ge -10 \; or$
$-4x - 2 < 10$

**55.** $3x - 5 \le -12 \; or$
$3x - 5 \ge 12$

**56.** $-13 < 3x + 5 < 23$

Solve. [1.3a]

**57.** *Waiting Lists for Organ Transplants.* In the fall of 2008, there were more than 100,000 people on waiting lists for organ transplants. There were 94,018 people waiting for a kidney or a liver, and 62,322 fewer were waiting for a liver than for a kidney. How many were on the waiting list for a kidney? for a liver?

**Source:** Organ Procurement and Transplantation Network

**58.** *Landscaping.* Grass seed is being spread on a triangular traffic island. If the grass seed can cover an area of 200 ft$^2$ and the island's base is 16 ft long, how tall a triangle can the seed fill?

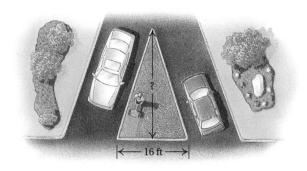

**59.** *Taxi Fare.* The fare for a taxi ride from Jen's office to the South Bay Health Center is $19.85. The driver charges $2.00 for the first $\frac{1}{2}$ mi and $1.05 for each additional $\frac{1}{4}$ mi. How far is it from North Shore Drive to the South Bay Health Center?

**60.** *Real Estate Commission.* The Clines negotiated the following real estate commission on the selling price of their house:

7% for the first $100,000 and

4% for the amount that exceeds $100,000.

The realtor received a commission of $16,200 for selling the house. What was the selling price?

## Synthesis

Use a graphing calculator to graph each of the equations in Exercises 61–64. Use a standard viewing window of $[-10, 10, -10, 10]$, with Xscl $= 1$ and Yscl $= 1$.

**61.** $y = x^3 - 3x + 2$

**62.** $y = x - |x|$

**63.** $y = \dfrac{1}{x - 2}$

**64.** $y = \dfrac{1}{x^2}$

In Exercises 65–68, find an equation for the given graph.

**65.**
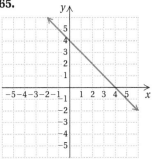

**66.**
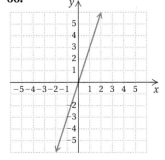

**67.**
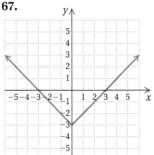

**68.**
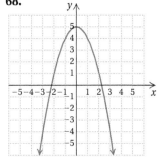

# 2.2

# Functions and Graphs

## OBJECTIVES

**a** Determine whether a correspondence is a function.

**b** Given a function described by an equation, find function values (outputs) for specified values (inputs).

**c** Draw the graph of a function.

**d** Determine whether a graph is that of a function using the vertical-line test.

**e** Solve applied problems involving functions and their graphs.

**SKILL TO REVIEW**
Objective R.4b: Evaluate an algebraic expression by substitution.

Evaluate.

**1.** $-\dfrac{1}{4}x$, when $x = 40$

**2.** $y^2 - 2y + 6$, when $y = -1$

## a Identifying Functions

Consider the equation $y = 2x - 3$. If we substitute a value for $x$—say, 5—we get a value for $y$, 7:

$$y = 2x - 3 = 2(5) - 3 = 10 - 3 = 7.$$

The equation $y = 2x - 3$ is an example of a *function*. We now develop the concept of a *function*, one of the most important concepts in mathematics.

In much the same way that ordered pairs form correspondences between first and second coordinates, a *function* is a correspondence from one set to another. For example:

To each student in a college, there corresponds his or her student ID.

To each item in a store, there corresponds its price.

To each real number, there corresponds the cube of that number.

In each case, the first set is called the **domain** and the second set is called the **range**. Each of these correspondences is a **function**, because given a member of the domain, there is *just one* member of the range to which it corresponds. Given a student, there is *just one* ID. Given an item, there is *just one* price. Given a real number, there is *just one* cube.

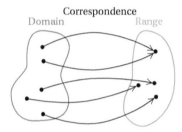
Correspondence
Domain            Range

**EXAMPLE 1** Determine whether the correspondence is a function.

*f*:

| Domain | Range |
|--------|-------|
| 1 ⟶ | $107.40 |
| 2 ⟶ | $ 34.10 |
| 3 ⟶ | $ 29.60 |
| 4 ⟶ | $ 19.60 |

*g*:

| Domain | Range |
|--------|-------|
| 3 ⟶ | 5 |
| 4 ⟶ | 9 |
| 5 ⟶ | −7 |
| 6 ⟶ | |

*h*:

| Domain | Range |
|--------|-------|
| Chicago | Cubs / White Sox |
| Baltimore ⟶ | Orioles |
| San Diego ⟶ | Padres |

*p*:

| Domain | Range |
|--------|-------|
| Cubs | Chicago |
| White Sox ⟶ | Chicago |
| Orioles ⟶ | Baltimore |
| Padres ⟶ | San Diego |

The correspondence *f* is a function because each member of the domain is matched to *only one* member of the range.

The correspondence *g* is a function because each member of the domain is matched to *only one* member of the range. Note that a function allows two or more members of the domain to correspond to the same member of the range.

The correspondence *h is not* a function because one member of the domain, Chicago, is matched to *more than one* member of the range.

The correspondence *p is* a function because each member of the domain is matched to *only one* member of the range.

*Answers*

*Skill to Review:*
**1.** −10   **2.** 9

## FUNCTION; DOMAIN; RANGE

A **function** is a correspondence between a first set, called the **domain**, and a second set, called the **range**, such that each member of the domain corresponds to **exactly one** member of the range.

Do Exercises 1–4.

**EXAMPLE 2**  Determine whether each correspondence is a function.

| *Domain* | *Correspondence* | *Range* |
|---|---|---|
| a) The integers | Each number's square | A set of nonnegative integers |
| b) The set of all states | Each state's members of the U.S. Senate | The set of U.S. Senators |
| c) The set of U.S. Senators | The state that a Senator represents | The set of all states |

a)  The correspondence *is* a function because each integer has *only one* square.

b)  The correspondence *is not* a function because each state has two U.S. Senators.

Richard Burr    Kay R. Hagan

NORTH CAROLINA

c)  The correspondence *is* a function because each Senator represents *only one* state.

Do Exercises 5–7. (Exercise 7 is on the following page.)

When a correspondence between two sets is not a function, it is still an example of a **relation**.

## RELATION

A **relation** is a correspondence between a first set, called the **domain**, and a second set, called the **range**, such that each member of the domain corresponds to **at least one** member of the range.

---

Determine whether each correspondence is a function.

**1.** *Domain*  *Range*

Cheetah ⟶ 70 mph
Human ⟶ 28 mph
Lion ⟶ 50 mph
Chicken ⟶ 9 mph

**2.** *Domain*  *Range*

A ⟶ a
B   b
C   c
D ⟶ d
    e

**3.** *Domain*  *Range*

−2 ⟶
2 ⟶ 4
−3 ⟶
3 ⟶ 9
0 ⟶ 0

**4.** *Domain*  *Range*

4 ⟶ −2
    2
9 ⟶ −3
    3
0 ⟶ 0

Determine whether each correspondence is a function.

**5.** *Domain*
A set of numbers

*Correspondence*
Square each number and subtract 10.

*Range*
A set of numbers

**6.** *Domain*
A set of polygons

*Correspondence*
Find the perimeter of each polygon.

*Range*
A set of numbers

*Answers*
**1.** Yes  **2.** No  **3.** Yes
**4.** No  **5.** Yes  **6.** Yes

**7.** Determine whether the correspondence is a function.

*Domain*
A set of numbers

*Correspondence*
The area of a rectangle

*Range*
A set of rectangles

Thus, although the correspondences of Examples 1 and 2 are not all functions, they *are* all relations. A function is a special type of relation—one in which each member of the domain is paired with *exactly one* member of the range.

## b Finding Function Values

Most functions considered in mathematics are described by equations like $y = 2x + 3$ or $y = 4 - x^2$. We graph the function $y = 2x + 3$ by first performing calculations like the following:

for $x = 4, y = 2x + 3 = 2 \cdot 4 + 3 = 8 + 3 = 11$;

for $x = -5, y = 2x + 3 = 2 \cdot (-5) + 3 = -10 + 3 = -7$;

for $x = 0, y = 2x + 3 = 2 \cdot 0 + 3 = 0 + 3 = 3$;   and so on.

For $y = 2x + 3$, the **inputs** (members of the domain) are values of $x$ substituted into the equation. The **outputs** (members of the range) are the resulting values of $y$. If we call the function $f$, we can use $x$ to represent an arbitrary *input* and $f(x)$—read "$f$ of $x$," or "$f$ at $x$," or "the value of $f$ at $x$"—to represent the corresponding *output*. In this notation, the function given by $y = 2x + 3$ is written as $f(x) = 2x + 3$ and the calculations above can be written more concisely as follows:

$$y = f(4) = 2 \cdot 4 + 3 = 8 + 3 = 11;$$
$$y = f(-5) = 2 \cdot (-5) + 3 = -10 + 3 = -7;$$
$$y = f(0) = 2 \cdot 0 + 3 = 0 + 3 = 3;   \text{and so on.}$$

Thus instead of writing "when $x = 4$, the value of $y$ is 11," we can simply write "$f(4) = 11$," which can also be read as "$f$ of 4 is 11" or "for the input 4, the output of $f$ is 11."

We can think of a function as a machine. Think of $f(4) = 11$ as putting 4, a member of the domain (an input), into the machine. The machine knows the correspondence $f(x) = 2x + 3$, multiplies 4 by 2 and adds 3, and produces 11, a member of the range (the output).

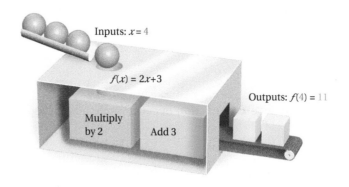

Inputs: $x = 4$

$f(x) = 2x+3$

Outputs: $f(4) = 11$

Multiply by 2

Add 3

-------------------- *Caution!* --------------------

The notation $f(x)$ *does not mean* "$f$ times $x$" and should not be read that way.

--------------------------------------------------------

**EXAMPLE 3**   A function $f$ is given by $f(x) = 3x^2 - 2x + 8$. Find each of the indicated function values.

**a)** $f(0)$          **b)** $f(1)$          **c)** $f(-5)$          **d)** $f(7a)$

One way to find function values when a formula is given is to think of the formula with blanks, or placeholders, replacing the variable as follows:

$$f(\square) = 3\square^2 - 2\square + 8.$$

*Answer*

**7.** No

To find an output for a given input, we think: "Whatever goes in the blank on the left goes in the blank(s) on the right." With this in mind, let's complete the example.

a) $f(0) = 3 \cdot 0^2 - 2 \cdot 0 + 8 = 8$

b) $f(1) = 3 \cdot 1^2 - 2 \cdot 1 + 8 = 3 \cdot 1 - 2 + 8 = 3 - 2 + 8 = 9$

c) $f(-5) = 3(-5)^2 - 2 \cdot (-5) + 8 = 3 \cdot 25 + 10 + 8 = 75 + 10 + 8 = 93$

d) $f(7a) = 3(7a)^2 - 2(7a) + 8 = 3 \cdot 49a^2 - 14a + 8 = 147a^2 - 14a + 8$

> Do Exercise 8.

**EXAMPLE 4** Find the indicated function value.

a) $f(5)$, for $f(x) = 3x + 2$  b) $g(-2)$, for $g(x) = 7$
c) $F(a + 1)$, for $F(x) = 5x - 8$  d) $f(a + h)$, for $f(x) = -2x + 1$

a) $f(5) = 3 \cdot 5 + 2 = 15 + 2 = 17$

b) For the function given by $g(x) = 7$, all inputs share the same output, 7. Thus, $g(-2) = 7$. The function $g$ is an example of a **constant function**.

c) $F(a + 1) = 5(a + 1) - 8 = 5a + 5 - 8 = 5a - 3$

d) $f(a + h) = -2(a + h) + 1 = -2a - 2h + 1$

> Do Exercise 9.

**8.** Find the indicated function values for the following function:

$$f(x) = 2x^2 + 3x - 4.$$

a) $f(0)$  b) $f(8)$
c) $f(-5)$  d) $f(2a)$

**9.** Find the indicated function value.

a) $f(-6)$, for $f(x) = 5x - 3$
b) $g(55)$, for $g(x) = -3$
c) $F(a + 2)$, for $F(x) = -5x + 8$
d) $f(a - h)$, for $f(x) = 6x - 7$

*Answers*

8. (a) $-4$; (b) 148; (c) 31; (d) $8a^2 + 6a - 4$
9. (a) $-33$; (b) $-3$; (c) $-5a - 2$;
(d) $6a - 6h - 7$

---

**Calculator Corner**

**Finding Function Values** We can find function values on a graphing calculator. One method is to substitute inputs directly into the formula. Consider the function $f(x) = x^2 + 3x - 4$. To find $f(-5)$, we press ( (-) 5 ) x² + 3 ( (-) 5 ) − 4 ENTER. We find that $f(-5) = 6$.

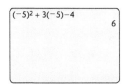
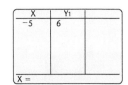
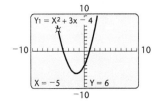

After we have entered the function as $y_1 = x^2 + 3x - 4$ on the equation-editor screen, there are several other methods that we can use to find function values. We can use a table set in ASK mode and enter $x = -5$. (See p. 83.) We see that the function value, $y_1$, is 6. We can also use the VALUE feature to evaluate the function. To do this, we first graph the function. Then we press 2ND CALC 1 to access the VALUE feature. Next, we supply the desired x-value by pressing (-) 5. Finally, we press ENTER to see X $= -5$, Y $= 6$ at the bottom of the screen. Again we see that the function value is 6. Note that when the VALUE feature is used to find a function value, the x-value must be in the viewing window.

A fourth method for finding function values uses the TRACE feature. With the function graphed in a window that includes the x-value $-5$, we press TRACE. The coordinates of the point where the blinking cursor is positioned on the graph are displayed at the bottom of the screen. To move the cursor to the point with x-coordinate $-5$, we press (-) 5 ENTER. Now we see X $= -5$, Y $= 6$ displayed at the bottom of the screen. This tells us that $f(-5) = 6$. The final calculator display for this method is the same as the one shown above for the VALUE feature. There are other ways to find function values, but we will not discuss them here.

**Exercises:** Find each function value.

1. $f(-5.1)$, for $f(x) = 3x + 2$  2. $f(4)$, for $f(x) = -3.6x$
3. $f(-3)$, for $f(x) = x^2 + 5$  4. $f(3)$, for $f(x) = 4x^2 + x - 5$

## (c) Graphs of Functions

To graph a function, we find ordered pairs $(x, y)$ or $(x, f(x))$, plot them, and connect the points. Note that $y$ and $f(x)$ are used interchangeably—that is, $y = f(x)$—when we are working with functions and their graphs.

**EXAMPLE 5**  Graph: $f(x) = x + 2$.

A list of some function values is shown in this table. We plot the points and connect them. The graph is a straight line. The "$y$" on the vertical axis could also be labeled "$f(x)$."

**10.** Graph: $f(x) = x - 4$.

| $x$ | $f(x)$ |
|-----|--------|
|     |        |
|     |        |
|     |        |

| $x$ | $f(x)$ |
|-----|--------|
| $-4$ | $-2$ |
| $-3$ | $-1$ |
| $-2$ | $0$ |
| $-1$ | $1$ |
| $0$ | $2$ |
| $1$ | $3$ |
| $2$ | $4$ |
| $3$ | $5$ |
| $4$ | $6$ |

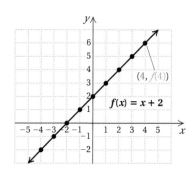

Do Exercise 10.

**11.** Graph: $g(x) = 5 - x^2$.

| $x$ | $g(x)$ |
|-----|--------|
|     |        |
|     |        |
|     |        |
|     |        |
|     |        |
|     |        |
|     |        |

**EXAMPLE 6**  Graph: $g(x) = 4 - x^2$.

We calculate some function values, plot the corresponding points, and draw the curve.

$$g(0) = 4 - 0^2 = 4 - 0 = 4,$$
$$g(-1) = 4 - (-1)^2 = 4 - 1 = 3,$$
$$g(2) = 4 - 2^2 = 4 - 4 = 0,$$
$$g(-3) = 4 - (-3)^2 = 4 - 9 = -5$$

| $x$ | $g(x)$ |
|-----|--------|
| $-3$ | $-5$ |
| $-2$ | $0$ |
| $-1$ | $3$ |
| $0$ | $4$ |
| $1$ | $3$ |
| $2$ | $0$ |
| $3$ | $-5$ |

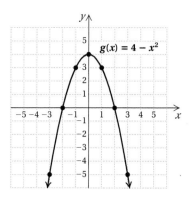

Do Exercise 11.

**Answers**

**10.**

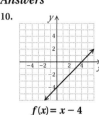

$f(x) = x - 4$

**11.**

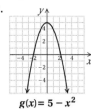

$g(x) = 5 - x^2$

**EXAMPLE 7** Graph: $h(x) = |x|$.

A list of some function values is shown in the following table. We plot the points and connect them. The graph is a V-shaped "curve" that rises on either side of the vertical axis.

| $x$ | $h(x)$ |
|-----|--------|
| $-3$ | 3 |
| $-2$ | 2 |
| $-1$ | 1 |
| 0 | 0 |
| 1 | 1 |
| 2 | 2 |
| 3 | 3 |

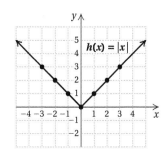

Do Exercise 12.

## d The Vertical-Line Test

Consider the graph of the function $f$ described by $f(x) = x^2 - 5$ shown at right. It is also the graph of the equation $y = x^2 - 5$.

To find a function value, like $f(3)$, from a graph, we locate the input on the horizontal axis, move directly up or down to the graph of the function, and then move left or right to find the output on the vertical axis. Thus, $f(3) = 4$. Keep in mind that members of the domain are found on the horizontal axis, members of the range are found on the vertical axis, and the $y$ on the vertical axis could also be labeled $f(x)$.

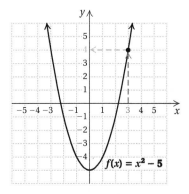

When one member of the domain is paired with two or more different members of the range, the correspondence is not a function. Thus, when a graph contains two or more different points with the same first coordinate, the graph cannot represent a function. Points sharing a common first coordinate are vertically above or below each other. (See the following graph.) This observation leads to the *vertical-line test*.

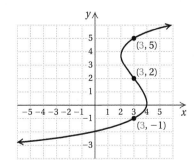

Since 3 is paired with more than one member of the range, the graph does not represent a function.

**THE VERTICAL-LINE TEST**

If it is possible for a vertical line to cross a graph more than once, then the graph is *not* the graph of a function.

**12.** Graph: $t(x) = 3 - |x|$.

| $x$ | $t(x)$ |
|-----|--------|
|  |  |
|  |  |
|  |  |
|  |  |

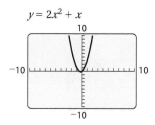
*Answer*

12.

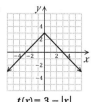

$t(x) = 3 - |x|$

**EXAMPLE 8** Determine whether each of the following is the graph of a function.

a)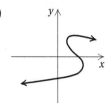

b)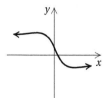

c)

d)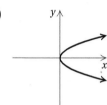

a) The graph *is not* that of a function because a vertical line can cross the graph at more than one point.

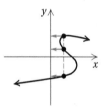

b) The graph *is* that of a function because no vertical line can cross the graph at more than one point. This can be confirmed with a ruler or straightedge.

c) The graph *is* that of a function because no vertical line can cross the graph more than once.

d) The graph *is not* that of a function because a vertical line can cross the graph more than once.

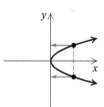

Do Exercises 13–16.

Do Exercises 13–16.

### (e) Applications of Functions and Their Graphs

Functions are often described by graphs, whether or not an equation is given. To use a graph in an application, we note that each point on the graph represents a pair of values.

Determine whether each of the following is the graph of a function.

13.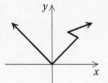

14.

15.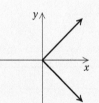

16.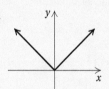

*Answers*

13. Yes   14. No   15. No   16. Yes

**EXAMPLE 9** *World Population.* The following graph represents the world population, in billions. The population is a function of the year. Note that no equation is given for the function.

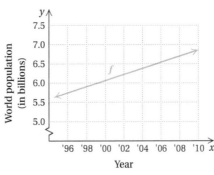

SOURCE: U.S. Census Bureau, Population Division/ International Programs Center

**a)** What was the world population in 1998? That is, find *f*(1998).

**b)** What was the world population in 2008? That is, find *f*(2008).

**a)** To estimate the world population in 1998, we locate 1998 on the horizontal axis and move directly up until we reach the graph. Then we move across to the vertical axis. We come to a point that is about 5.9, so we estimate that the population was about 5.9 billion in 1998.

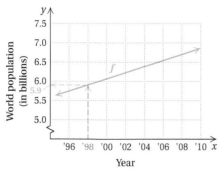

SOURCE: U.S. Census Bureau, Population Division/ International Programs Center

SOURCE: U.S. Census Bureau, Population Division/ International Programs Center

**b)** To estimate the world population in 2008, we locate 2008 on the horizontal axis and move directly up until we reach the graph. Then we move across to the vertical axis. We come to a point that is about 6.7, so we estimate that the population was about 6.7 billion in 2008.

Do Exercises 17 and 18.

Refer to the graph in Example 9 for Margin Exercises 17 and 18.

**17.** What was the world population in 2000?

**18.** What was the world population in 2010?

*Answers*

**17.** About 6.1 billion
**18.** About 6.8 billion

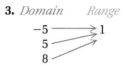 
**a** Determine whether each correspondence is a function.

**1.** Domain    Range

2 ⟶ 9
5 ⟶ 8
19

**2.** Domain    Range

5 ⟶ 3
−3 ⟶ 7
7
−7

**3.** Domain    Range

−5 ⟶ 1
5
8

**4.** Domain    Range

6 ⟶ −6
7 ⟶ −7
3 ⟶ −3

**5.** Domain    Range

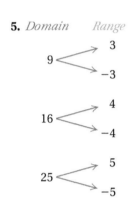

**6.** Domain      Range

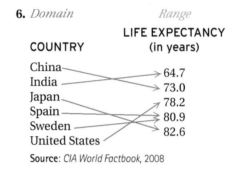

**Source:** *CIA World Factbook*, 2008

**7.** Domain    Range

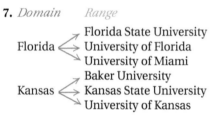

**8.** Domain      Range

**9.** Domain    Range

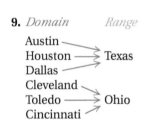

**10.** Domain    Range

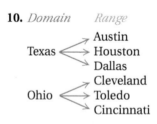

| Domain | Correspondence | Range |
|---|---|---|
| **11.** A set of numbers | The area of a triangle | A set of triangles |
| **12.** A family | Each person's height, in inches | A set of positive numbers |
| **13.** A set of numbers | Square each number and then add 4. | A set of positive numbers |
| **14.** A set of years | A student's year of birth | A first-grade class |

**b** Find the function values.

**15.** $f(x) = x + 5$

   **a)** $f(4)$          **b)** $f(7)$
   **c)** $f(-3)$       **d)** $f(0)$
   **e)** $f(2.4)$      **f)** $f\left(\frac{2}{3}\right)$

**16.** $g(t) = t - 6$

   **a)** $g(0)$        **b)** $g(6)$
   **c)** $g(13)$      **d)** $g(-1)$
   **e)** $g(-1.08)$   **f)** $g\left(\frac{7}{8}\right)$

**17.** $h(p) = 3p$

   **a)** $h(-7)$      **b)** $h(5)$
   **c)** $h\left(\frac{2}{3}\right)$      **d)** $h(0)$
   **e)** $h(6a)$      **f)** $h(a + 1)$

**18.** $f(x) = -4x$

   **a)** $f(6)$         **b)** $f\left(-\frac{1}{2}\right)$
   **c)** $f(0)$         **d)** $f(-1)$
   **e)** $f(3a)$       **f)** $f(a - 1)$

**19.** $g(s) = 3s + 4$

   **a)** $g(1)$        **b)** $g(-7)$
   **c)** $g\left(\frac{2}{3}\right)$      **d)** $g(0)$
   **e)** $g(a - 2)$    **f)** $g(a + h)$

**20.** $h(x) = 19$, a constant function

   **a)** $h(4)$        **b)** $h(-6)$
   **c)** $h(12.5)$    **d)** $h(0)$
   **e)** $h\left(\frac{2}{3}\right)$      **f)** $h(a + 3)$

**21.** $f(x) = 2x^2 - 3x$

   **a)** $f(0)$        **b)** $f(-1)$
   **c)** $f(2)$        **d)** $f(10)$
   **e)** $f(-5)$      **f)** $f(4a)$

**22.** $f(x) = 3x^2 - 2x + 1$

   **a)** $f(0)$        **b)** $f(1)$
   **c)** $f(-1)$      **d)** $f(10)$
   **e)** $f(-3)$      **f)** $f(2a)$

**23.** $f(x) = |x| + 1$

   **a)** $f(0)$        **b)** $f(-2)$
   **c)** $f(2)$        **d)** $f(-10)$
   **e)** $f(a - 1)$    **f)** $f(a + h)$

**24.** $g(t) = |t - 1|$

   **a)** $g(4)$        **b)** $g(-2)$
   **c)** $g(-1)$      **d)** $g(100)$
   **e)** $g(5a)$      **f)** $g(a + 1)$

**25.** $f(x) = x^3$

   **a)** $f(0)$        **b)** $f(-1)$
   **c)** $f(2)$        **d)** $f(10)$
   **e)** $f(-5)$      **f)** $f(-3a)$

**26.** $f(x) = x^4 - 3$

   **a)** $f(1)$        **b)** $f(-1)$
   **c)** $f(0)$        **d)** $f(2)$
   **e)** $f(-2)$      **f)** $f(-a)$

**27.** *Average Age of Senators.* The function $A(s)$ given by

$$A(s) = 0.321s + 54$$

can be used to estimate the average age of senators in the U.S. Senate in the years 1981 to 2009. Let $A(s) =$ the average age of the senators and $s =$ the number of years since 1981—that is, $s = 0$ for 1981 and $s = 9$ for 1990. What was the average age of the U.S. Senators in 2003? in 2009?

**Source:** House and Senate Historical Offices

**28.** *Average Age of House Members.* The function $A(h)$ given by

$$A(h) = 0.314h + 48$$

can be used to estimate the average age of house members in the U.S. House of Representatives in the years 1981 to 2009. Let $A(h) =$ the average age of the house members and $h =$ the number of years since 1981. What is the average age of U.S. House members in 1981? in 2005?

**Source:** House and Senate Historical Offices

**29.** *Pressure at Sea Depth.* The function $P(d) = 1 + (d/33)$ gives the pressure, in *atmospheres* (atm), at a depth of $d$ feet in the sea. Note that $P(0) = 1$ atm, $P(33) = 2$ atm, and so on. Find the pressure at 20 ft, 30 ft, and 100 ft.

**30.** *Temperature as a Function of Depth.* The function $T(d) = 10d + 20$ gives the temperature, in degrees Celsius, inside the earth as a function of the depth $d$, in kilometers. Find the temperature at 5 km, 20 km, and 1000 km.

**31.** *Melting Snow.* The function $W(d) = 0.112d$ approximates the amount, in centimeters, of water that results from $d$ centimeters of snow melting. Find the amount of water that results from snow melting from depths of 16 cm, 25 cm, and 100 cm.

**32.** *Temperature Conversions.* The function $C(F) = \frac{5}{9}(F - 32)$ determines the Celsius temperature that corresponds to $F$ degrees Fahrenheit. Find the Celsius temperature that corresponds to 62°F, 77°F, and 23°F.

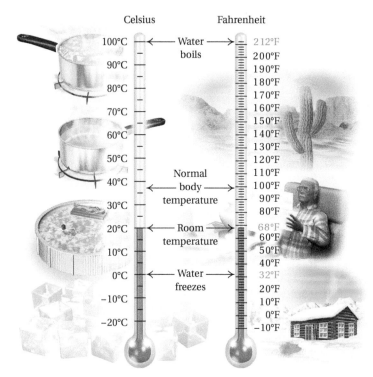

**c** Graph each function.

**33.** $f(x) = -2x$

| x | y |
|---|---|
|   |   |
|   |   |
|   |   |

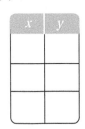

**34.** $g(x) = 3x$

| x | y |
|---|---|
|   |   |
|   |   |
|   |   |

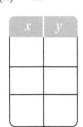

**35.** $f(x) = 3x - 1$

| x | y |
|---|---|
|   |   |
|   |   |
|   |   |

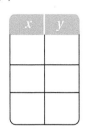

**36.** $g(x) = 2x + 5$

| x | y |
|---|---|
|   |   |
|   |   |
|   |   |

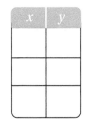

**37.** $g(x) = -2x + 3$

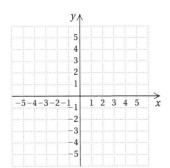

**38.** $f(x) = -\frac{1}{2}x + 2$

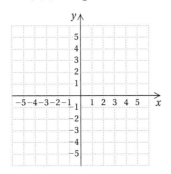

**39.** $f(x) = \frac{1}{2}x + 1$

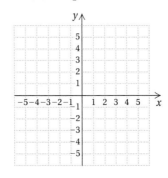

**40.** $f(x) = -\frac{3}{4}x - 2$

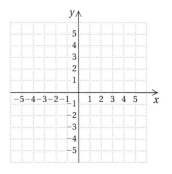

**41.** $f(x) = 2 - |x|$

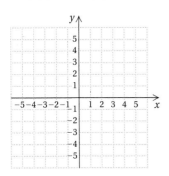

**42.** $f(x) = |x| - 4$

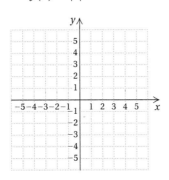

**43.** $g(x) = |x - 1|$

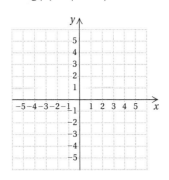

**44.** $g(x) = |x + 3|$

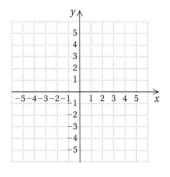

**45.** $f(x) = x^2$

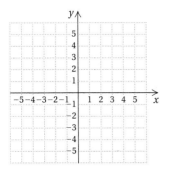

**46.** $f(x) = x^2 - 1$

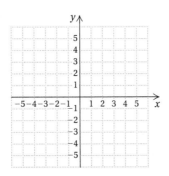

**47.** $f(x) = x^2 - x - 2$

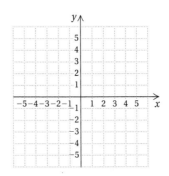

**48.** $f(x) = x^2 + 6x + 5$

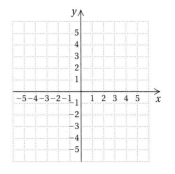

**49.** $f(x) = 2 - x^2$

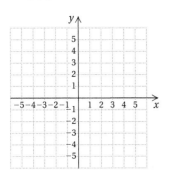

**50.** $f(x) = 1 - x^2$

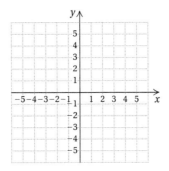

**51.** $f(x) = x^3 + 1$

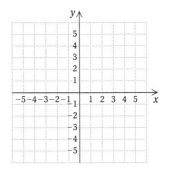

**52.** $f(x) = x^3 - 2$

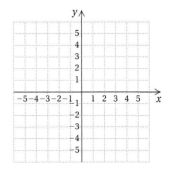

**d** Determine whether each of the following is the graph of a function.

**53.**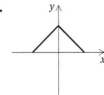

**54.**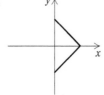

**55.**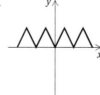

**56.**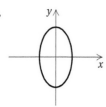

**57.**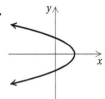

**58.**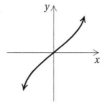

**59.**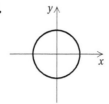

**60.**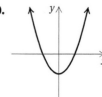

**e** Solve.

*News/Talk Radio Stations.* The following graph approximates the number of U.S. commercial radio stations with a news/talk format. The number of stations is a function *f* of the year *x*.

**61.** Approximate the number of news/talk radio stations in 2000. That is, find $f(2000)$.

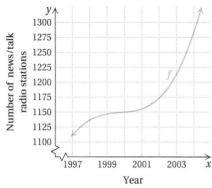

SOURCE: M Street Corporation

**62.** Approximate the number of news/talk radio stations in 2003. That is, find $f(2003)$.

*Digital Photographs.* The following graph approximates the number of digital photos taken but not printed, in billions. The number of photos that are not printed is a function *f* of the year *x*.

**63.** Approximate the number of digital photos taken but not printed in 2000. That is, find $f(2000)$.

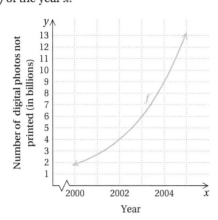

**64.** Approximate the number of digital photos taken but not printed in 2002. That is, find $f(2002)$.

## Skill Maintenance

In each of Exercises 65–72, fill in the blank with the correct term from the given list. Some of the choices may not be used and some may be used more than once.

**65.** The axes divide the plane into four regions called
_____. [2.1a]

**66.** A(n) _____ is a correspondence between two sets such that each member of the first set corresponds to at least one member of the second set. [2.2a]

**67.** A(n) _____ is a correspondence between a first set, called the _____, and a second set, called the _____, such that each member of the _____ corresponds to exactly one member of the _____. [2.2a]

**68.** The _____ of an equation is a drawing that represents all of its solutions. [2.1b]

**69.** Members of the domain of a function are its _____.
[2.2b]

**70.** The replacements for the variable that make an equation true are its _____. [1.1a]

**71.** The _____ states that for any real numbers $a$, $b$, and $c$, $a = b$ is equivalent to $a + c = b + c$. [1.1b]

**72.** The _____ can be used to determine whether a graph represents a function. [2.2d]

axes

coordinates

quadrants

addition principle

multiplication principle

vertical-line test

graph

domain

range

relation

function

inputs

outputs

solutions

values

## Synthesis

**73.** Suppose that for some function $g$, $g(x - 6) = 10x - 1$. Find $g(-2)$.

**74.** Suppose that for some function $h$, $h(x + 5) = x^2 - 4$. Find $h(3)$.

For Exercises 75 and 76, let $f(x) = 3x^2 - 1$ and $g(x) = 2x + 5$.

**75.** Find $f(g(-4))$ and $g(f(-4))$.

**76.** Find $f(g(-1))$ and $g(f(-1))$.

**77.** Suppose that a function $g$ is such that $g(-1) = -7$ and $g(3) = 8$. Find a formula for $g$ if $g(x)$ is of the form $g(x) = mx + b$, where $m$ and $b$ are constants.

# 2.3

# Finding Domain and Range

**SKILL TO REVIEW**
Objective 1.1d: Solve equations using the addition principle and the multiplication principle together, removing parentheses where appropriate.

Solve.

1. $6x - 3 = 51$

2. $15 - 2x = 0$

1. Find the domain and the range of the function $f$ whose graph is shown below.

## a) Finding Domain and Range

The solutions of an equation in two variables consist of a set of ordered pairs. A set of ordered pairs is called a **relation**. When a set of ordered pairs is such that no two different pairs share a common first coordinate, we have a **function**. The **domain** is the set of all first coordinates, and the **range** is the set of all second coordinates.

**EXAMPLE 1** Find the domain and the range of the function $f$ whose graph is shown below.

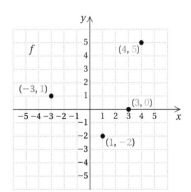

This function contains just four ordered pairs and it can be written as

$$\{(-3, 1), (1, -2), (3, 0), (4, 5)\}.$$

We can determine the domain and the range by reading the $x$- and $y$-values directly from the graph.

The domain is the set of all first coordinates, or $x$-values, $\{-3, 1, 3, 4\}$. The range is the set of all second coordinates, or $y$-values, $\{1, -2, 0, 5\}$.

Do Margin Exercise 1.

**EXAMPLE 2** For the function $f$ whose graph is shown below, determine each of the following.

a) The number in the range that is paired with 1 from the domain. That is, find $f(1)$.

b) The domain of $f$

c) The numbers in the domain that are paired with 1 from the range. That is, find all $x$ such that $f(x) = 1$.

d) The range of $f$

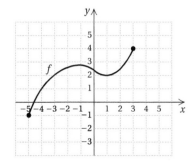

a) To determine which number in the range is paired with 1 in the domain, we locate 1 on the horizontal axis. Next, we find the point on the graph of $f$ for which 1 is the first coordinate. From that point, we can look to the vertical axis to find the corresponding $y$-coordinate, 2. The input 1 has the output 2—that is, $f(1) = 2$.

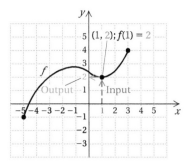

*Answers*

*Skill to Review:*

1. 9   2. $\frac{15}{2}$, or 7.5

*Margin Exercise:*

1. Domain $= \{-3, -2, 0, 2, 5\}$; range $= \{-3, -2, 2, 3\}$

**b)** The domain of the function is the set of all $x$-values, or inputs, of the points on the graph. These extend from $-5$ to $3$ and can be viewed as the curve's shadow, or projection, onto the $x$-axis. Thus the domain is the set $\{x\,|\,-5 \le x \le 3\}$, or, in interval notation, $[-5, 3]$.

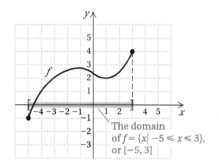

The domain of $f = \{x\,|\,-5 \le x \le 3\}$, or $[-5, 3]$

**c)** To determine which numbers in the domain are paired with 1 in the range, we locate 1 on the vertical axis. From there, we look left and right to the graph of $f$ to find any points for which 1 is the second coordinate (output). One such point exists, $(-4, 1)$. For this function, we note that $x = -4$ is the only member of the domain paired with 1. For other functions, there might be more than one member of the domain paired with a member of the range.

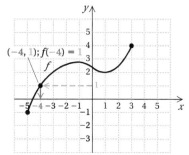

$(-4, 1); f(-4) = 1$

**d)** The range of the function is the set of all $y$-values, or outputs, of the points on the graph. These extend from $-1$ to $4$ and can be viewed as the curve's shadow, or projection, onto the $y$-axis. Thus the range is the set $\{y\,|\,-1 \le y \le 4\}$, or, in interval notation, $[-1, 4]$.

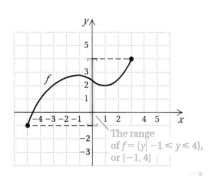

The range of $f = \{y\,|\,-1 \le y \le 4\}$, or $[-1, 4]$

Do Exercise 2.

**2.** For the function $f$ whose graph is shown below, determine each of the following.

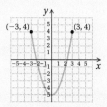

$(-3, 4)$    $(3, 4)$

**a)** The number in the range that is paired with the input 1. That is, find $f(1)$.

**b)** The domain of $f$

**c)** The numbers in the domain that are paired with 4

**d)** The range of $f$

**EXAMPLE 3**  Find the domain and the range of the function $f$ whose graph is shown below.

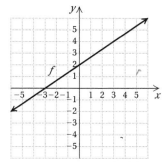

Since no endpoints are indicated, the graph extends indefinitely both horizontally and vertically. Thus the domain is the set of all real numbers. Likewise, the range is the set of all real numbers.

Do Exercise 3.

**3.** Find the domain and the range of the function $f$ whose graph is shown below.

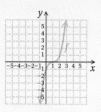

***Answers***

**2.** (a) $-4$; (b) $\{x\,|\,-3 \le x \le 3\}$, or $[-3, 3]$; (c) $-3, 3$; (d) $\{y\,|\,-5 \le y \le 4\}$, or $[-5, 4]$
**3.** Domain: all real numbers; range: all real numbers

When a function is given by an equation or a formula, the domain is understood to be the largest set of real numbers (inputs) for which function values (outputs) can be calculated. That is, the domain is the set of all possible allowable inputs into the formula. To find the domain, think, "What can we substitute?"

**EXAMPLE 4**   Find the domain: $f(x) = |x|$.

We ask, "What can we substitute?" Is there any number $x$ for which we cannot calculate $|x|$? The answer is no. Thus the domain of $f$ is the set of all real numbers.

**EXAMPLE 5**   Find the domain: $f(x) = \dfrac{3}{2x - 5}$.

We ask, "What can we substitute?" Is there any number $x$ for which we cannot calculate $3/(2x - 5)$? Since $3/(2x - 5)$ cannot be calculated when the denominator $2x - 5$ is 0, we solve the following equation to find those real numbers that must be excluded from the domain of $f$:

$$2x - 5 = 0 \qquad \text{Setting the denominator equal to 0}$$
$$2x = 5 \qquad \text{Adding 5}$$
$$x = \tfrac{5}{2}. \qquad \text{Dividing by 2}$$

Thus, $\frac{5}{2}$ is not in the domain, whereas all other real numbers are.

The domain of $f$ is $\left\{x \mid x \text{ is a real number } and \, x \neq \frac{5}{2}\right\}$. In interval notation, the domain is $\left(-\infty, \frac{5}{2}\right) \cup \left(\frac{5}{2}, \infty\right)$.

Do Exercises 4 and 5.

The task of determining the domain and the range of a function is one that we will return to several times as we consider other types of functions in this book.

### Functions: A Review

The following is a review of the function concepts considered in Sections 2.2 and 2.3.

*Function Concepts*

- Formula for $f$: $f(x) = x^2 - 7$
- For every input of $f$, there is exactly one output.
- When 1 is the input, $-6$ is the output.
- $f(1) = -6$
- $(1, -6)$ is on the graph.
- Domain = The set of all inputs
  = The set of all real numbers
- Range = The set of all outputs
  = $\{y \mid y \geq -7\}$
  = $[-7, \infty)$

*Graph*

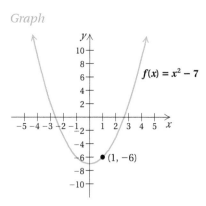

$f(x) = x^2 - 7$

$(1, -6)$

---

Find the domain.

**4.** $f(x) = x^3 - |x|$

**5.** $f(x) = \dfrac{4}{3x + 2}$

*Answers*

**4.** All real numbers

**5.** $\left\{x \mid x \text{ is a real number } and \, x \neq -\dfrac{2}{3}\right\}$, or $\left(-\infty, -\dfrac{2}{3}\right) \cup \left(-\dfrac{2}{3}, \infty\right)$

**a** In Exercises 1–12, the graph is that of a function. Determine for each one **(a)** $f(1)$; **(b)** the domain; **(c)** all $x$-values such that $f(x) = 2$; and **(d)** the range. An open dot indicates that the point does not belong to the graph.

**1.**
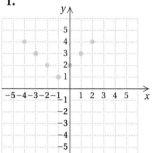

**2.**
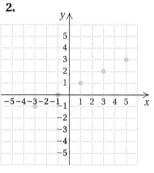

**3.**
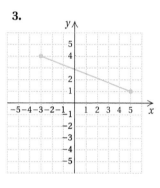

**4.**
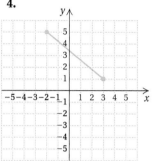

**5.**
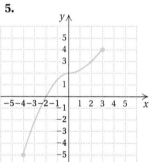

**6.**
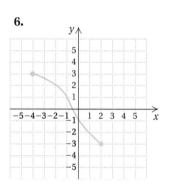

**7.**
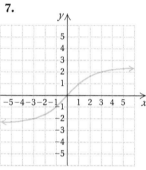

**8.**
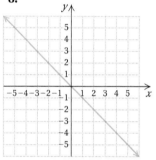

**9.**
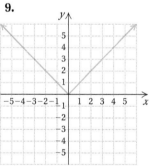

**10.**
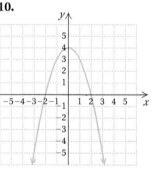

**11.**
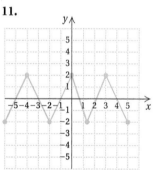

**12.**
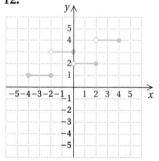

Find the domain.

**13.** $f(x) = \dfrac{2}{x + 3}$

**14.** $f(x) = \dfrac{7}{5 - x}$

**15.** $f(x) = 2x + 1$

**16.** $f(x) = 4 - 5x$

**17.** $f(x) = x^2 + 3$

**18.** $f(x) = x^2 - 2x + 3$

**19.** $f(x) = \dfrac{8}{5x - 14}$

**20.** $f(x) = \dfrac{x - 2}{3x + 4}$

**21.** $f(x) = |x| - 4$

**22.** $f(x) = |x - 4|$

**23.** $f(x) = \dfrac{x^2 - 3x}{|4x - 7|}$

**24.** $f(x) = \dfrac{4}{|2x - 3|}$

**25.** $g(x) = \dfrac{1}{x - 1}$

**26.** $g(x) = \dfrac{-11}{4 + x}$

**27.** $g(x) = x^2 - 2x + 1$

**28.** $g(x) = 8 - x^2$

**29.** $g(x) = x^3 - 1$

**30.** $g(x) = 4x^3 + 5x^2 - 2x$

**31.** $g(x) = \dfrac{7}{20 - 8x}$

**32.** $g(x) = \dfrac{2x - 3}{6x - 12}$

**33.** $g(x) = |x + 7|$

**34.** $g(x) = |x| + 1$

**35.** $g(x) = \dfrac{-2}{|4x + 5|}$

**36.** $g(x) = \dfrac{x^2 + 2x}{|10x - 20|}$

**37.** For the function $f$ whose graph is shown below, find $f(-1), f(0),$ and $f(1)$.

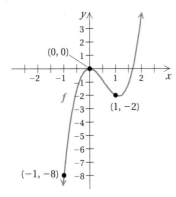

**38.** For the function $g$ whose graph is shown below, find all the $x$-values for which $g(x) = 1$.

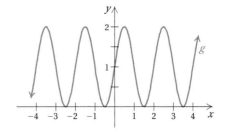

## Skill Maintenance

Solve. [1.4d]

**39.** On a new job, Anthony can be paid in one of two ways:

Plan A:   A salary of $800 per month, plus a commission of 5% of sales;

Plan B:   A salary of $1000 per month, plus a commission of 7% of sales in excess of $15,000.

For what amount of monthly sales is plan B better than plan A, if we assume that sales are always more than $15,000?

**40.** *Test Score.*   You are taking a business course for which there will be 4 tests, each worth 100 points. You have scores of 92, 90, and 88 on the first three tests. You must make a total of at least 360 points in order to get an A. What scores on the fourth test will earn you an A?

Solve. [1.6c, d]

**41.** $|x| = 8$

**42.** $|x| = -8$

**43.** $|x - 7| = 11$

**44.** $|2x + 3| = 13$

**45.** $|3x - 4| = |x + 2|$

**46.** $|5x - 6| = |3 - 8x|$

**47.** $|3x - 8| = -11$

**48.** $|3x - 8| = 0$

## Synthesis

**49.** 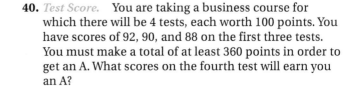 Determine the range of each of the functions in Exercises 13, 18, 21, and 22.

**50.** Determine the range of each of the functions in Exercises 26, 27, 28, and 34.

Find the domain of each function.

**51.** $f(x) = \sqrt[3]{x - 1}$

**52.** $g(x) = \sqrt{2 - x}$

# Mid-Chapter Review

## Concept Reinforcement

Determine whether each statement is true or false.

_____ **1.** Every function is a relation.   [2.2a]

_____ **2.** It is possible for one input of a function to have two or more outputs.   [2.2a]

_____ **3.** It is possible for all the inputs of a function to have the same output.   [2.2a]

_____ **4.** If it is possible for a vertical line to cross a graph more than once, the graph is not the graph of a function.   [2.2d]

_____ **5.** If the domain of a function is the set of real numbers, then the range is the set of real numbers.   [2.3a]

## Guided Solutions

Use the graph to complete the table of ordered pairs that name points on the graph.

**6.** [2.1c]

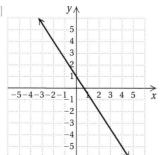

| x | y |
|---|---|
| 0 | ☐ |
| ☐ | −2 |
| −2 | ☐ |
| 4 | ☐ |

**7.** [2.2c]

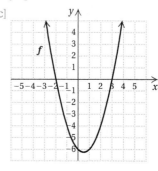

| x | f(x) |
|---|---|
| −2 | ☐ |
| ☐ | 0 |
| 2 | ☐ |
| ☐ | −4 |
| 1 | ☐ |

## Mixed Review

Determine whether the given point is a solution of the equation.   [2.1b]

**8.** $(-2, -1)$;  $5y + 6 = 4x$

**9.** $\left(\dfrac{1}{2}, 0\right)$;  $8a = 4 - b$

Determine whether the correspondence is a function.   [2.2a]

**10.** *Domain*   *Range*

$\begin{array}{c} 7 \\ 9 \end{array} \longrightarrow 11$

**11.** *Domain*   *Range*

**12.** Find the domain and the range.
[2.3a]

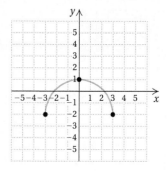

Find the function values.   [2.2b]

**13.** $g(x) = 2 + x$;  $g(-5)$

**14.** $f(x) = x - 7$;  $f(0)$

**15.** $h(x) = 8$;  $h\left(\dfrac{1}{2}\right)$

**16.** $f(x) = 3x^2 - x + 5$;  $f(-1)$

**17.** $g(p) = p^4 - p^3$;  $g(10)$

**18.** $f(t) = \dfrac{1}{2}t + 3$;  $f(-6)$

Determine whether each of the following is the graph of a function. [2.2d]

**19.**

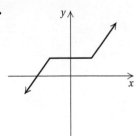

**20.**

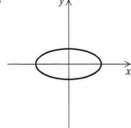

**21.**

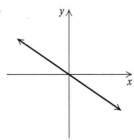

Find the domain. [2.3a]

**22.** $g(x) = \dfrac{3}{12 - 3x}$

**23.** $f(x) = x^2 - 10x + 3$

**24.** $h(x) = \dfrac{x - 2}{x + 2}$

**25.** $f(x) = |x - 4|$

Graph. [2.1c], [2.2c]

**26.** $y = -\dfrac{2}{3}x - 2$

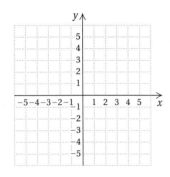

**27.** $f(x) = x - 1$

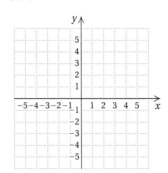

**28.** $h(x) = 2x + \dfrac{1}{2}$

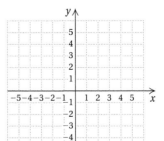

**29.** $g(x) = |x| - 3$

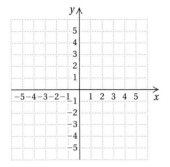

**30.** $y = 1 + x^2$

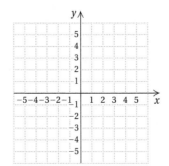

**31.** $f(x) = -\dfrac{1}{4}x$

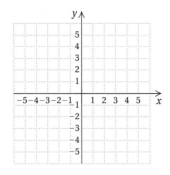

# Understanding Through Discussion and Writing

**32.** Is it possible for a function to have more numbers as outputs than as inputs? Why or why not? [2.2a]

**33.** Without making a drawing, how can you tell that the graph of $y = x - 30$ passes through three quadrants? [2.1c]

**34.** For a given function $f$, it is known that $f(2) = -3$. Give as many interpretations of this fact as you can. [2.2b], [2.3a]

**35.** Explain the difference between the domain and the range of a function. [2.3a]

# 2.4 Linear Functions: Graphs and Slope

We now turn our attention to functions whose graphs are straight lines. Such functions are called **linear** and can be written in the form $f(x) = mx + b$.

> ### LINEAR FUNCTION
>
> A **linear function** $f$ is any function that can be described by $f(x) = mx + b$.

Compare the two equations $7y + 2x = 11$ and $y = 3x + 5$. Both are linear equations because their graphs are straight lines. Each can be expressed in an equivalent form that is a linear function.

The equation $y = 3x + 5$ can be expressed as $f(x) = mx + b$, where $m = 3$ and $b = 5$.

The equation $7y + 2x = 11$ also has an equivalent form $f(x) = mx + b$. To see this, we solve for $y$:

$$7y + 2x = 11$$
$$7y + 2x - 2x = -2x + 11 \qquad \text{Subtracting } 2x$$
$$7y = -2x + 11$$
$$\frac{7y}{7} = \frac{-2x + 11}{7} \qquad \text{Dividing by 7}$$
$$y = -\frac{2}{7}x + \frac{11}{7}. \qquad \text{Simplifying}$$

(It might be helpful to review the discussion on solving formulas in Section 1.2.) We now have an equivalent equation in the form

$$f(x) = -\frac{2}{7}x + \frac{11}{7}, \qquad \text{where} \quad m = -\frac{2}{7} \quad \text{and} \quad b = \frac{11}{7}.$$

In this section, we consider the effects of the constants $m$ and $b$ on the graphs of linear functions.

## (a) The Constant $b$: The $y$-Intercept

Let's first explore the effect of the constant $b$.

**EXAMPLE 1** Graph $y = 2x$ and $y = 2x + 3$ using the same set of axes. Compare the graphs.

We first make a table of solutions of both equations.

| $x$ | $y$<br>$y = 2x$ | $y$<br>$y = 2x + 3$ |
|---|---|---|
| 0 | 0 | 3 |
| 1 | 2 | 5 |
| −1 | −2 | 1 |
| 2 | 4 | 7 |
| −2 | −4 | −1 |

### OBJECTIVES

**a** Find the $y$-intercept of a line from the equation $y = mx + b$ or $f(x) = mx + b$.

**b** Given two points on a line, find the slope. Given a linear equation, derive the equivalent slope-intercept equation and determine the slope and the $y$-intercept.

**c** Solve applied problems involving slope.

---

**SKILL TO REVIEW**
Objective R.2c: Subtract real numbers.

Subtract.
**1.** $11 - (-8)$      **2.** $-6 - (-6)$

**Calculator Corner**

**Exploring b** We can use a graphing calculator to explore the effect of the constant $b$ on the graph of a function of the form $f(x) = mx + b$. Graph $y_1 = x$ in the standard $[-10, 10, -10, 10]$ viewing window. Then graph $y_2 = x + 4$, followed by $y_3 = x - 3$, in the same viewing window.

**Exercises:**

**1.** Compare the graph of $y_2$ with the graph of $y_1$.

**2.** Compare the graph of $y_3$ with the graph of $y_1$.

**3.** Visualize the graphs of $y = x + 8$ and $y = x - 5$. Compare each graph with the graph of $y_1$.

*Answers*

*Skill to Review:*
1. 19    2. 0

**1.** Graph $y = 3x$ and $y = 3x - 6$ using the same set of axes. Compare the graphs.

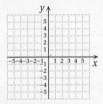

**2.** Graph $y = -2x$ and $y = -2x + 3$ using the same set of axes. Compare the graphs.

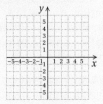

Next, we plot these points. Drawing a red line for $y = 2x$ and a blue line for $y = 2x + 3$, we note that the graph of $y = 2x + 3$ is simply the graph of $y = 2x$ shifted, or *translated*, up 3 units. The lines are parallel.

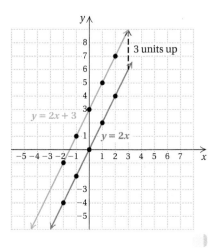

Do Exercises 1 and 2.

**EXAMPLE 2** Graph $f(x) = \frac{1}{3}x$ and $g(x) = \frac{1}{3}x - 2$ using the same set of axes. Compare the graphs.

We first make a table of solutions of both equations. By choosing multiples of 3, we can avoid fractions.

| | $f(x)$ | $g(x)$ |
|---|---|---|
| $x$ | $f(x) = \frac{1}{3}x$ | $g(x) = \frac{1}{3}x - 2$ |
| 0 | 0 | $-2$ |
| 3 | 1 | $-1$ |
| $-3$ | $-1$ | $-3$ |
| 6 | 2 | 0 |

We then plot these points. Drawing a red line for $f(x) = \frac{1}{3}x$ and a blue line for $g(x) = \frac{1}{3}x - 2$, we see that the graph of $g(x) = \frac{1}{3}x - 2$ is simply the graph of $f(x) = \frac{1}{3}x$ shifted, or translated, down 2 units. The lines are parallel.

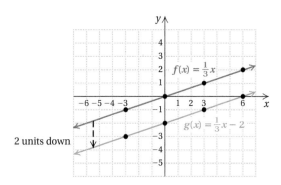

*Answers*

**1.**
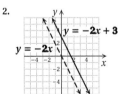
The graph of $y = 3x - 6$ looks just like the graph of $y = 3x$, but it is shifted down 6 units.

**2.**
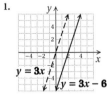
The graph of $y = -2x + 3$ looks just like the graph of $y = -2x$, but it is shifted up 3 units.

In Example 1, we saw that the graph of $y = 2x + 3$ is parallel to the graph of $y = 2x$ and that it passes through the point $(0, 3)$. Similarly, in Example 2, we saw that the graph of $y = \frac{1}{3}x - 2$ is parallel to the graph of $y = \frac{1}{3}x$ and that it passes through the point $(0, -2)$. In general, the graph of $y = mx + b$ is a line parallel to $y = mx$, passing through the point $(0, b)$. The point $(0, b)$ is called the **y-intercept** because it is the point at which the graph crosses the $y$-axis. Often it is convenient to refer to the number $b$ as the $y$-intercept. The constant $b$ has the effect of moving the graph of $y = mx$ up or down $|b|$ units to obtain the graph of $y = mx + b$.

Do Exercise 3.

**3.** Graph $f(x) = \frac{1}{3}x$ and $g(x) = \frac{1}{3}x + 2$ using the same set of axes. Compare the graphs.

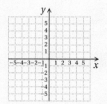

---

### y-INTERCEPT

The $y$-intercept of the graph of $f(x) = mx + b$ is the point $(0, b)$ or, simply, $b$.

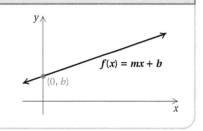

---

**EXAMPLE 3**  Find the $y$-intercept: $y = -5x + 4$.

$$y = -5x + 4 \qquad (0, 4) \text{ is the } y\text{-intercept.}$$

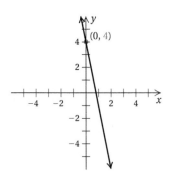

**EXAMPLE 4**  Find the $y$-intercept: $f(x) = 6.3x - 7.8$.

$$f(x) = 6.3x - 7.8 \qquad (0, -7.8) \text{ is the } y\text{-intercept.}$$

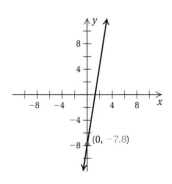

Find the $y$-intercept.

**4.** $y = 7x + 8$

**5.** $f(x) = -6x - \frac{2}{3}$

*Answers*

**3.**

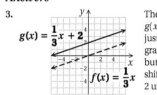

$$g(x) = \frac{1}{3}x + 2$$
$$f(x) = \frac{1}{3}x$$

The graph of $g(x)$ looks just like the graph of $f(x)$, but it is shifted up 2 units.

**4.** $(0, 8)$  **5.** $\left(0, -\frac{2}{3}\right)$

Do Exercises 4 and 5.

## b The Constant *m*: Slope

Look again at the graphs in Examples 1 and 2. Note that the slant of each red line seems to match the slant of each blue line. This leads us to believe that the number *m* in the equation $y = mx + b$ is related to the slant of the line. Let's consider some examples.

**Graphs with *m* < 0:**

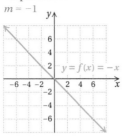

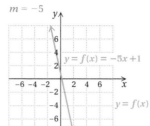

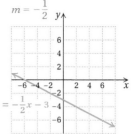

**Graphs with *m* = 0:**

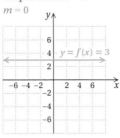

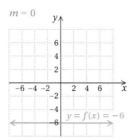

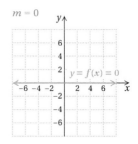

**Graphs with *m* > 0:**

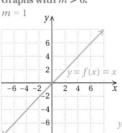

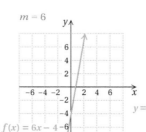

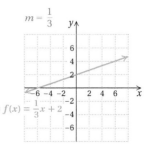

Note that

$m < 0 \rightarrow$ The graph slants down from left to right;

$m = 0 \rightarrow$ the graph is horizontal; and

$m > 0 \rightarrow$ the graph slants up from left to right.

The following definition enables us to visualize the slant and attach a number, a geometric ratio, or *slope*, to the line.

---

**SLOPE**

The **slope** of a line containing points $(x_1, y_1)$ and $(x_2, y_2)$ is given by

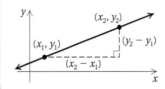

$$m = \frac{\text{rise}}{\text{run}}$$

$$= \frac{\text{change in } y}{\text{change in } x} = \frac{y_2 - y_1}{x_2 - x_1} = \frac{y_1 - y_2}{x_1 - x_2}.$$

---

Consider a line with two points marked $P_1$ and $P_2$, as follows. As we move from $P_1$ to $P_2$, the $y$-coordinate changes from 1 to 3 and the $x$-coordinate changes from 2 to 7. The change in $y$ is $3 - 1$, or 2. The change in $x$ is $7 - 2$, or 5.

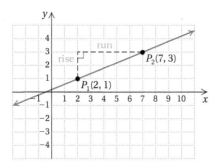

We call the change in $y$ the **rise** and the change in $x$ the **run**. The ratio rise/run is the same for any two points on a line. We call this ratio the **slope**. Slope describes the slant of a line. The slope of the line in the graph above is given by

$$\frac{\text{rise}}{\text{run}}, \quad \text{or} \quad \frac{\text{change in } y}{\text{change in } x}, \quad \text{or} \quad \frac{2}{5}.$$

Whenever $x$ increases by 5 units, $y$ increases by 2 units. Equivalently, whenever $x$ increases by 1 unit, $y$ increases by $\frac{2}{5}$ unit.

**EXAMPLE 5**   Graph the line containing the points $(-4, 3)$ and $(2, -5)$ and find the slope.

The graph is shown below. Going from $(-4, 3)$ to $(2, -5)$, we see that the change in $y$, or the rise, is $-5 - 3$, or $-8$. The change in $x$, or the run, is $2 - (-4)$, or 6.

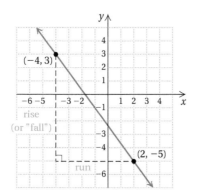

$$\begin{aligned}
\text{Slope} &= \frac{\text{rise}}{\text{run}} = \frac{\text{change in } y}{\text{change in } x} \\
&= \frac{-5 - 3}{2 - (-4)} \\
&= \frac{-8}{6} = -\frac{8}{6}, \text{ or } -\frac{4}{3}
\end{aligned}$$

**Calculator Corner**

**Visualizing Slope**

**Exercises:**   Use the window settings $[-6, 6, -4, 4]$, with Xscl $= 1$ and Yscl $= 1$.

1. Graph $y = x$, $y = 2x$, and $y = 5x$ in the same window. What do you think the graph of $y = 10x$ will look like?

2. Graph $y = x$, $y = \frac{1}{2}x$, and $y = 0.1x$ in the same window. What do you think the graph of $y = 0.005x$ will look like?

3. Graph $y = -x$, $y = -2x$, and $y = -5x$ in the same window. What do you think the graph of $y = -10x$ will look like?

4. Graph $y = -x$, $y = -\frac{1}{2}x$, and $y = -0.1x$ in the same window. What do you think the graph of $y = -0.005x$ will look like?

The formula

$$m = \frac{y_2 - y_1}{x_2 - x_1} = \frac{y_1 - y_2}{x_1 - x_2}$$

tells us that we can subtract in two ways. We must remember, however, to subtract the $x$-coordinates in the same order that we subtract the $y$-coordinates. Let's do Example 5 again:

$$\text{Slope} = \frac{\text{change in } y}{\text{change in } x} = \frac{3 - (-5)}{-4 - 2} = \frac{8}{-6} = -\frac{8}{6} = -\frac{4}{3}.$$

We see that both ways give the same value for the slope.

The slope of a line tells how it slants. A line with positive slope slants up from left to right. The larger the positive number, the steeper the slant. A line with negative slope slants downward from left to right. The smaller the negative number, the steeper the line.

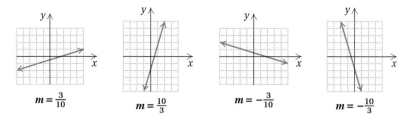

Do Exercises 6 and 7.

How can we find the slope from a given equation? Let's consider the equation $y = 2x + 3$, which is in the form $y = mx + b$. We can find two points by choosing convenient values for $x$—say, 0 and 1—and substituting to find the corresponding $y$-values.

If $x = 0$, $y = 2 \cdot 0 + 3 = 3$.

If $x = 1$, $y = 2 \cdot 1 + 3 = 5$.

We find two points on the line to be

$$(0, 3) \quad \text{and} \quad (1, 5).$$

The slope of the line is found as follows, using the definition of slope:

$$m = \frac{\text{change in } y}{\text{change in } x}$$

$$= \frac{5 - 3}{1 - 0} = \frac{2}{1} = 2.$$

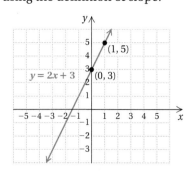

The slope is 2. Note that this is the coefficient of the $x$-term in the equation $y = 2x + 3$.

If we had chosen different points on the line—say, $(-2, -1)$ and $(4, 11)$—the slope would still be 2, as we see in the following calculation:

$$m = \frac{11 - (-1)}{4 - (-2)} = \frac{11 + 1}{4 + 2} = \frac{12}{6} = 2.$$

Do Exercise 8.

---

Graph the line through the given points and find its slope.

**6.** $(-1, -1)$ and $(2, -4)$

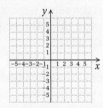

**7.** $(0, 2)$ and $(3, 1)$

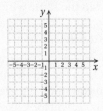

**8.** Find the slope of the line $f(x) = -\frac{2}{3}x + 1$. Use the points $(9, -5)$ and $(3, -1)$.

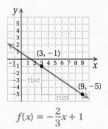

**Answers**

6. 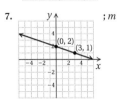 ; $m = -1$

7. 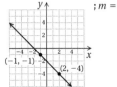 ; $m = -\frac{1}{3}$

8. $m = -\frac{2}{3}$

We see that the slope of the line $y = mx + b$ is indeed the constant $m$, the coefficient of $x$.

> ### SLOPE
>
> The **slope** of the line $y = mx + b$ is $m$.

From a linear equation in the form $y = mx + b$, we can read the slope and the $y$-intercept of the graph directly.

> ### SLOPE-INTERCEPT EQUATION
>
> The equation $y = mx + b$ is called the **slope–intercept equation**. The slope is $m$ and the $y$-intercept is $(0, b)$.

Note that any graph of an equation $y = mx + b$ passes the vertical-line test and thus represents a function.

**EXAMPLE 6** Find the slope and the $y$-intercept of $y = 5x - 4$.

Since the equation is already in the form $y = mx + b$, we simply read the slope and the $y$-intercept from the equation:

$$y = 5x - 4.$$

The slope is $5$.    The $y$-intercept is $(0, -4)$.

**EXAMPLE 7** Find the slope and the $y$-intercept of $2x + 3y = 8$.

We first solve for $y$ so we can easily read the slope and the $y$-intercept:

$$2x + 3y = 8$$
$$3y = -2x + 8 \qquad \text{Subtracting } 2x$$
$$\frac{3y}{3} = \frac{-2x + 8}{3} \qquad \text{Dividing by 3}$$
$$y = -\frac{2}{3}x + \frac{8}{3}. \qquad \text{Finding the form } y = mx + b$$

The slope is $-\frac{2}{3}$.    The $y$-intercept is $\left(0, \frac{8}{3}\right)$.

Do Exercises 9 and 10.

Find the slope and the $y$-intercept.

**9.** $f(x) = -8x + 23$

**10.** $5x - 10y = 25$

### (c) Applications

Slope has many real-world applications. For example, numbers like 2%, 3%, and 6% are often used to represent the *grade* of a road, a measure of how steep a road on a hill or mountain is. A 3% grade $\left(3\% = \frac{3}{100}\right)$ means that for every horizontal distance of 100 ft that the road runs, the road rises 3 ft, and a −3% grade means that for every horizontal distance of 100 ft, the road drops 3 ft. (Normally, the road signs do not include negative signs, since it is obvious

*Answers*

**9.** Slope: $-8$; $y$-intercept: $(0, 23)$

**10.** Slope: $\frac{1}{2}$; $y$-intercept: $\left(0, -\frac{5}{2}\right)$

whether you are climbing or descending.) An athlete might change the grade of a treadmill during a workout. An escape ramp on an airliner might have a slope of about −0.6.

Architects and carpenters use slope when designing and building stairs, ramps, or roof pitches. Another application occurs in hydrology. The strength or force of a river depends on how far the river falls vertically compared to how far it flows horizontally. Slope can also be considered as a **rate of change**.

**EXAMPLE 8**   *Health Insurance.*   Premiums for family health insurance plans have increased steadily in recent years. In 2000, the average premium was $6438 per year. By 2008, this amount had increased to $12,680 per year. Find the rate of change of the average yearly family health insurance premium with respect to time, in years.

**Cost of Yearly Family Health Insurance Premiums**

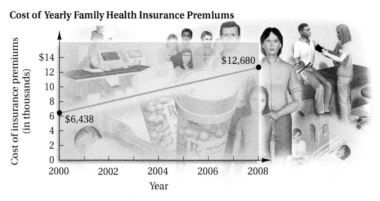

SOURCE: The Kaiser Family Foundation

The rate of change with respect to time, in years, is given by

$$\text{Rate of change} = \frac{\$12{,}680 - \$6438}{2008 - 2000}$$

$$= \frac{\$6242}{8 \text{ yr}}$$

$$= \$780.25.$$

The average yearly family health insurance premium is increasing at a rate of about $780.25 per year.

> Do Exercise 11.

**EXAMPLE 9** *Volume of Mail.* The volume of mail through the U.S. Postal Service has been dropping since 2006, as shown in the graph below.

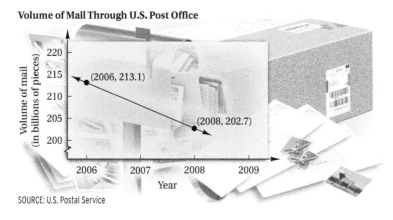

**Volume of Mail Through U.S. Post Office**

SOURCE: U.S. Postal Service

Since the graph is linear, we can use any pair of points to determine the rate of change:

$$\text{Rate of change} = \frac{202.7 \text{ billion} - 213.1 \text{ billion}}{2008 - 2006}$$

$$= \frac{-10.4 \text{ billion}}{2 \text{ yr}} = -5.2 \text{ billion per year.}$$

The volume of mail through the U.S. Postal Service is decreasing at a rate of about 5.2 billion pieces per year.

> Do Exercise 12.

**11. Haircutting.** The graph below displays data from a day's work at Lee's Barbershop. At 2:00, 8 haircuts had been completed. At 4:00, 14 haircuts had been done. Use the graph to determine the rate of change of the number of haircuts with respect to time.

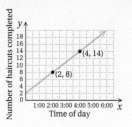

**12. Newspaper Circulation.** Daily newspaper circulation has decreased in recent years. The graph below shows the circulation of daily newspapers, in millions, for three years. Find the rate of change of the circulation of daily newspapers per year.

**Circulation of Daily Newspapers**

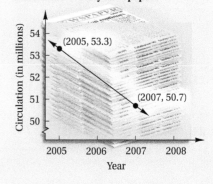

**a**, **b** Find the slope and the *y*-intercept.

**1.** $y = 4x + 5$

**2.** $y = -5x + 10$

**3.** $f(x) = -2x - 6$

**4.** $g(x) = -5x + 7$

**5.** $y = -\frac{3}{8}x - \frac{1}{5}$

**6.** $y = \frac{15}{7}x + \frac{16}{5}$

**7.** $g(x) = 0.5x - 9$

**8.** $f(x) = -3.1x + 5$

**9.** $2x - 3y = 8$

**10.** $-8x - 7y = 24$

**11.** $9x = 3y + 6$

**12.** $9y + 36 - 4x = 0$

**13.** $3 - \frac{1}{4}y = 2x$

**14.** $5x = \frac{2}{3}y - 10$

**15.** $17y + 4x + 3 = 7 + 4x$

**16.** $3y - 2x = 5 + 9y - 2x$

**b** Find the slope of each line.

**17.**

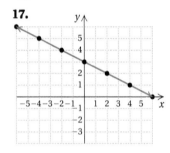

**18.**

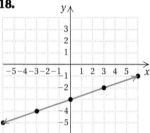

**19.**

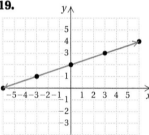

**20.**

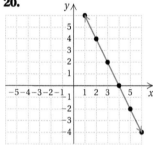

Find the slope of the line containing the given pair of points.

**21.** $(6, 9)$ and $(4, 5)$

**22.** $(8, 7)$ and $(2, -1)$

**23.** $(9, -4)$ and $(3, -8)$

**24.** $(17, -12)$ and $(-9, -15)$

**25.** $(-16.3, 12.4)$ and $(-5.2, 8.7)$

**26.** $(14.4, -7.8)$ and $(-12.5, -17.6)$

**c** Find the slope (or rate of change).

**27.** Find the slope (or grade) of the treadmill.

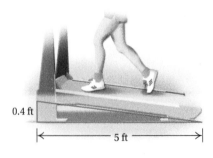

0.4 ft

5 ft

**28.** Find the slope (or head) of the river.

43.33 ft

1238 ft

**29.** Find the slope (or pitch) of the roof.

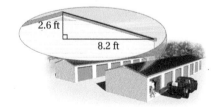

2.6 ft

8.2 ft

**30.** Public buildings regularly include steps with 7-in. risers and 11-in. treads. Find the grade of such a stairway.

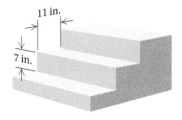

**31.** *Mine Deaths.* Find the rate of change of the number of mine deaths in the United States with respect to time, in years.

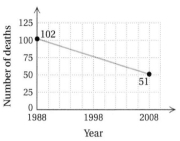

SOURCE: U.S. Mine Safety and Health Administration

**32.** Find the rate of change of the cost of a formal wedding.

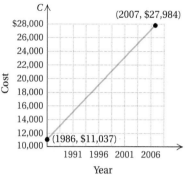

SOURCE: Modern Bride Magazine

Find the rate of change.

**33.**

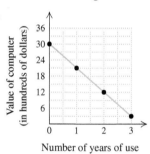

**34.**

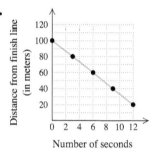

**35.**

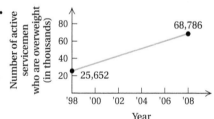

SOURCE: U.S. Department of Defense

**36.**

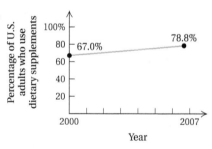

## Skill Maintenance

Simplify.  [R.3c], [R.6b]

**37.** $3^2 - 24 \cdot 56 + 144 \div 12$

**38.** $9\{2x - 3[5x + 2(-3x + y^0 - 2)]\}$

**39.** $10\{2x + 3[5x - 2(-3x + y^1 - 2)]\}$

**40.** $5^4 \div 625 \div 5^2 \cdot 5^7 \div 5^3$

Solve.  [1.3a]

**41.** One side of a square is 5 yd less than a side of an equilateral triangle. If the perimeter of the square is the same as the perimeter of the triangle, what is the length of a side of the square? of the triangle?

Solve.  [1.6c, e]

**42.** $|5x - 8| \geq 32$

**43.** $|5x - 8| < 32$

**44.** $|5x - 8| = 32$

**45.** $|5x - 8| = -32$

# 2.5

# More on Graphing Linear Equations

## OBJECTIVES

**a** Graph linear equations using intercepts.

**b** Given a linear equation in slope–intercept form, use the slope and the y-intercept to graph the line.

**c** Graph linear equations of the form $x = a$ or $y = b$.

**d** Given the equations of two lines, determine whether their graphs are parallel or whether they are perpendicular.

### SKILL TO REVIEW
Objective 2.1a: Plot points associated with ordered pairs of numbers.

1. Plot the following points:
$A(0, 4)$, $B(0, -1)$, $C(0, 0)$, $D(3, 0)$, and $E\left(-\frac{7}{2}, 0\right)$.

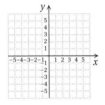

## a Graphing Using Intercepts

The **x-intercept** of the graph of a linear equation or function is the point at which the graph crosses the x-axis. The **y-intercept** is the point at which the graph crosses the y-axis. We know from geometry that only one line can be drawn through two given points. Thus, if we know the intercepts, we can graph the line. To ensure that a computation error has not been made, it is a good idea to calculate a third point as a check.

Many equations of the type $Ax + By = C$ can be graphed conveniently using intercepts.

---

**x- AND y-INTERCEPTS**

A **y-intercept** is a point $(0, b)$. To find $b$, let $x = 0$ and solve for $y$.

An **x-intercept** is a point $(a, 0)$. To find $a$, let $y = 0$ and solve for $x$.

---

**EXAMPLE 1** Find the intercepts of $3x + 2y = 12$ and then graph the line.

*y-intercept:* To find the y-intercept, we let $x = 0$ and solve for $y$:

$$3x + 2y = 12$$
$$3 \cdot 0 + 2y = 12 \qquad \text{Substituting 0 for } x$$
$$2y = 12$$
$$y = 6.$$

The y-intercept is $(0, 6)$.

*x-intercept:* To find the x-intercept, we let $y = 0$ and solve for $x$:

$$3x + 2y = 12$$
$$3x + 2 \cdot 0 = 12 \qquad \text{Substituting 0 for } y$$
$$3x = 12$$
$$x = 4.$$

The x-intercept is $(4, 0)$.

We plot these points and draw the line, using a third point as a check. We choose $x = 6$ and solve for $y$:

$$3(6) + 2y = 12$$
$$18 + 2y = 12$$
$$2y = -6$$
$$y = -3.$$

We plot $(6, -3)$ and note that it is on the line.

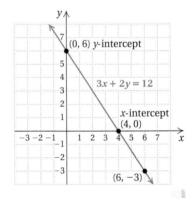

---

*Answer*

*Skill to Review:*

1.

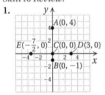

When both the $x$-intercept and the $y$-intercept are $(0, 0)$, as is the case with an equation such as $y = 2x$, whose graph passes through the origin, another point would have to be calculated and a third point used as a check.

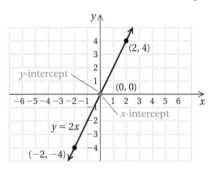

1. Find the intercepts of $4y - 12 = -6x$ and then graph the line.

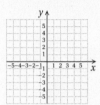

Do Exercise 1.

## Calculator Corner

**Viewing the Intercepts**  Knowing the intercepts of a linear equation helps us determine a good viewing window for the graph of the equation. For example, when we graph the equation $y = -x + 15$ in the standard window, we see only a small portion of the graph in the upper right-hand corner of the screen, as shown on the left below.

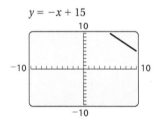

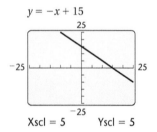

Using algebra, as we did in Example 1, we can find that the intercepts of the graph of this equation are $(0, 15)$ and $(15, 0)$. This tells us that, if we are to see a portion of the graph that includes the intercepts, both Xmax and Ymax should be greater than 15. We can try different window settings until we find one that suits us. One good choice, shown on the right above, is $[-25, 25, -25, 25]$, with Xscl $= 5$ and Yscl $= 5$.

**Exercises:**  Find the intercepts of the equation algebraically. Then graph the equation on a graphing calculator, choosing window settings that allow the intercepts to be seen clearly. (Settings may vary.)

1. $y = -3.2x - 16$

2. $y - 4.25x = 85$

3. $6x + 5y = 90$

4. $5x - 6y = 30$

5. $8x + 3y = 9$

6. $y = 0.4x - 5$

7. $y = 1.2x - 12$

8. $4x - 5y = 2$

*Answer*

1.
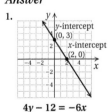

$4y - 12 = -6x$

Graph using the slope and the
*y*-intercept.

**2.** $y = \dfrac{3}{2}x + 1$

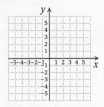

**3.** $f(x) = \dfrac{3}{4}x - 2$

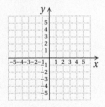

**4.** $g(x) = -\dfrac{3}{5}x + 5$

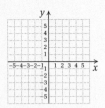

**5.** $y = -\dfrac{5}{3}x - 4$

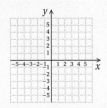

# **b** Graphing Using the Slope and the *y*-Intercept

We can also graph a line using its slope and *y*-intercept.

**EXAMPLE 2**  Graph: $y = -\dfrac{2}{3}x + 1$.

This equation is in slope–intercept form, $y = mx + b$. The *y*-intercept is $(0, 1)$. We plot $(0, 1)$. We can think of the slope $\left(m = -\dfrac{2}{3}\right)$ as $\dfrac{-2}{3}$.

$$m = \frac{\text{Rise}}{\text{Run}} = \frac{-2}{3} \qquad \begin{array}{l}\text{Move 2 units down.}\\ \text{Move 3 units right.}\end{array}$$

Starting at the *y*-intercept and using the slope, we find another point by moving down 2 units (since the numerator is *negative* and corresponds to the change in *y*) and to the right 3 units (since the denominator is *positive* and corresponds to the change in *x*). We get to a new point, $(3, -1)$. In a similar manner, we can move from the point $(3, -1)$ to find another point, $(6, -3)$.

We could also think of the slope $\left(m = -\dfrac{2}{3}\right)$ as $\dfrac{2}{-3}$.

$$m = \frac{\text{Rise}}{\text{Run}} = \frac{2}{-3} \qquad \begin{array}{l}\text{Move 2 units up.}\\ \text{Move 3 units left.}\end{array}$$

Then we can start again at $(0, 1)$, but this time we move up 2 units (since the numerator is *positive* and corresponds to the change in *y*) and to the left 3 units (since the denominator is *negative* and corresponds to the change in *x*). We get another point on the graph, $(-3, 3)$, and from it we can obtain $(-6, 5)$ and others in a similar manner. We plot the points and draw the line.

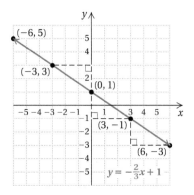

**EXAMPLE 3**  Graph: $f(x) = \dfrac{2}{5}x + 4$.

First, we plot the *y*-intercept, $(0, 4)$. We then consider the slope $\dfrac{2}{5}$. A slope of $\dfrac{2}{5}$ tells us that, for every 2 units that the graph rises, it runs 5 units horizontally in the positive direction, or to the right. Thus, starting at the *y*-intercept and using the slope, we find another point by moving up 2 units (since the numerator is *positive* and corresponds to the change in *y*) and to the right 5 units (since the denominator is *positive* and corresponds to the change in *x*). We get to a new point, $(5, 6)$.

*Answers*

**2.**
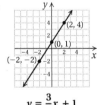
$$y = \frac{3}{2}x + 1$$

**3.**

$$f(x) = \frac{3}{4}x - 2$$

**4.**

$$g(x) = -\frac{3}{5}x + 5$$

**5.**
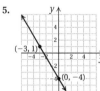
$$y = -\frac{5}{3}x - 4$$

We can also think of the slope $\frac{2}{5}$ as $\frac{-2}{-5}$. A slope of $\frac{-2}{-5}$ tells us that, for every 2 units that the graph drops, it runs 5 units horizontally in the negative direction, or to the left. We again start at the $y$-intercept, $(0, 4)$. We move down 2 units (since the numerator is *negative* and corresponds to the change in $y$) and to the left 5 units (since the denominator is *negative* and corresponds to the change in $x$). We get to another new point, $(-5, 2)$. We plot the points and draw the line.

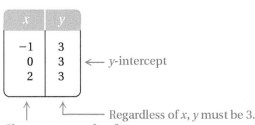

Do Exercises 2–5 on the preceding page.

## c  Horizontal and Vertical Lines

Some equations have graphs that are parallel to one of the axes. This happens when either $A$ or $B$ is 0 in $Ax + By = C$. These equations have a missing variable; that is, there is only one variable in the equation. In the following example, $x$ is missing.

**EXAMPLE 4**  Graph: $y = 3$.

Since $x$ is missing, any number for $x$ will do. Thus all ordered pairs $(x, 3)$ are solutions. The graph is a **horizontal line** parallel to the $x$-axis.

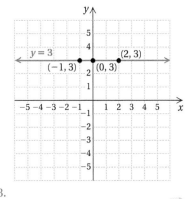

| $x$ | $y$ | |
|-----|-----|-----|
| $-1$ | 3 | |
| 0 | 3 | ← $y$-intercept |
| 2 | 3 | |

↑ Choose *any* number for $x$.  ↑ Regardless of $x$, $y$ must be 3.

What about the slope of a horizontal line? In Example 4, consider the points $(-1, 3)$ and $(2, 3)$, which are on the line $y = 3$. The change in $y$ is $3 - 3$, or 0. The change in $x$ is $-1 - 2$, or $-3$. Thus,

$$m = \frac{3 - 3}{-1 - 2} = \frac{0}{-3} = 0.$$

Any two points on a horizontal line have the same $y$-coordinate. Thus the change in $y$ is always 0, so the slope is 0.

Do Exercises 6 and 7.

Graph and determine the slope.

**6.** $f(x) = -4$

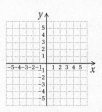

**7.** $y = 3.6$

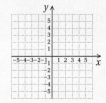

***Answers***

**6.** $m = 0$

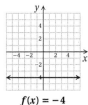

$f(x) = -4$

**7.** $m = 0$

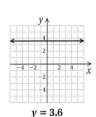

$y = 3.6$

We can also determine the slope by noting that $y = 3$ can be written in slope–intercept form as $y = 0x + 3$, or $f(x) = 0x + 3$. From this equation, we read that the slope is 0. A function of this type is called a **constant function**. We can express it in the form $y = b$, or $f(x) = b$. Its graph is a horizontal line that crosses the $y$-axis at $(0, b)$.

In the following example, $y$ is missing and the graph is parallel to the $y$-axis.

**EXAMPLE 5**   Graph: $x = -2$.

Since $y$ is missing, any number for $y$ will do. Thus all ordered pairs $(-2, y)$ are solutions. The graph is a **vertical line** parallel to the $y$-axis.

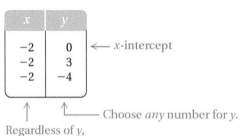

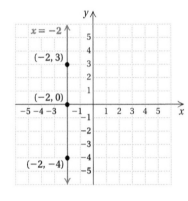

This graph is not the graph of a function because it fails the vertical-line test. The vertical line itself crosses the graph more than once.

Do Exercises 8 and 9.

What about the slope of a vertical line? In Example 5, consider the points $(-2, 3)$ and $(-2, -4)$, which are on the line $x = -2$. The change in $y$ is $3 - (-4)$, or 7. The change in $x$ is $-2 - (-2)$, or 0. Thus,

$$m = \frac{3 - (-4)}{-2 - (-2)} = \frac{7}{0}. \qquad \text{Not defined}$$

Since division by 0 is not defined, the slope of this line is not defined. Any two points on a vertical line have the same $x$-coordinate. Thus the change in $x$ is always 0, so the slope of any vertical line is not defined.

The following summarizes horizontal and vertical lines and their equations.

---

**HORIZONTAL LINE; VERTICAL LINE**

The graph of $y = b$, or $f(x) = b$, is a **horizontal line** with $y$-intercept $(0, b)$. It is the graph of a constant function with slope 0.

The graph of $x = a$ is a **vertical line** through the point $(a, 0)$. The slope is not defined. It is not the graph of a function.

---

Do Exercise 10.

Graph.

**8.** $x = -5$

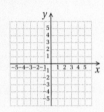

**9.** $8x - 5 = 19$ (*Hint*: Solve for $x$.)

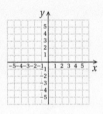

**10.** Determine, if possible, the slope of each line.

a) $x = -12$    b) $y = 6$

c) $2y + 7 = 11$    d) $x = 0$

e) $y = -\frac{3}{4}$    f) $10 - 5x = 15$

*Answers*

**8.**

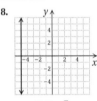

$x = -5$

**9.**

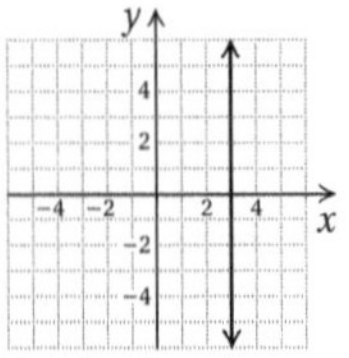

$8x - 5 = 19$

**10.** (a) Not defined; (b) $m = 0$; (c) $m = 0$; (d) not defined; (e) $m = 0$; (f) not defined

We have graphed linear equations in several ways in this chapter. Although, in general, you can use any method that works best for you, we list some guidelines in the margin at right.

###  d  Parallel and Perpendicular Lines

#### Parallel Lines

Parallel lines extend indefinitely without intersecting. If two lines are vertical, they are parallel. How can we tell whether nonvertical lines are parallel? We examine their slopes and $y$-intercepts.

> **PARALLEL LINES**
>
> Two nonvertical lines are **parallel** if they have the *same* slope and *different* $y$-intercepts.

**EXAMPLE 6**  Determine whether the graphs of

$$y - 3x = 1 \quad \text{and} \quad 3x + 2y = -2$$

are parallel.

To determine whether lines are parallel, we first find their slopes. To do this, we find the slope–intercept form of each equation by solving for $y$:

$$
\begin{aligned}
y - 3x &= 1 & 3x + 2y &= -2 \\
y &= 3x + 1; & 2y &= -3x - 2 \\
& & y &= \tfrac{1}{2}(-3x - 2) \\
& & y &= -\tfrac{3}{2}x - 1.
\end{aligned}
$$

The slopes, 3 and $-\frac{3}{2}$, are different. Thus the lines are not parallel, as the graphs at right confirm.

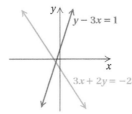

**EXAMPLE 7**  Determine whether the graphs of

$$3x - y = -5 \quad \text{and} \quad y - 3x = -2$$

are parallel.

We first find the slope–intercept form of each equation by solving for $y$:

$$
\begin{aligned}
3x - y &= -5 & y - 3x &= -2 \\
-y &= -3x - 5 & y &= 3x - 2. \\
-1(-y) &= -1(-3x - 5) \\
y &= 3x + 5;
\end{aligned}
$$

The slopes, 3, are the same. The $y$-intercepts, $(0, 5)$ and $(0, -2)$, are different. Thus the lines are parallel, as the graphs appear to confirm.

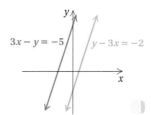

Do Exercises 11–13.

**To graph a linear equation:**

1. Is the equation of the type $x = a$ or $y = b$? If so, the graph will be a line parallel to an axis; $x = a$ is vertical and $y = b$ is horizontal.

2. If the line is of the type $y = mx$, both intercepts are the origin, $(0, 0)$. Plot $(0, 0)$ and one other point.

3. If the line is of the type $y = mx + b$, plot the $y$-intercept and one other point.

4. If the equation is of the form $Ax + By = C$, graph using intercepts. If the intercepts are too close together, choose another point farther from the origin.

5. In all cases, use a third point as a check.

Determine whether the graphs of the given pair of lines are parallel.

11. $x + 4 = y,$
    $y - x = -3$

12. $y + 4 = 3x,$
    $4x - y = -7$

13. $y = 4x + 5,$
    $2y = 8x + 10$

*Answers*

**11.** Yes   **12.** No   **13.** No; they are the same line.

## Perpendicular Lines

If one line is vertical and another is horizontal, they are perpendicular. For example, the lines $x = 5$ and $y = -3$ are perpendicular. Otherwise, how can we tell whether two lines are perpendicular?

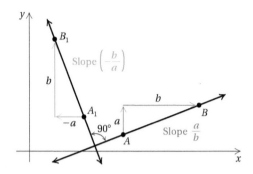

Consider a line $\overleftrightarrow{AB}$, as shown in the figure above, with slope $a/b$. Then think of rotating the line 90° to get a line $\overleftrightarrow{A_1B_1}$ perpendicular to $\overleftrightarrow{AB}$. For the new line, the rise and the run are interchanged, but the run is now negative. Thus the slope of the new line is $-b/a$, which is the opposite of the reciprocal of the slope of the first line. Also note that when we multiply the slopes, we get

$$\frac{a}{b}\left(-\frac{b}{a}\right) = -1.$$

This is the condition under which lines will be perpendicular.

---

### PERPENDICULAR LINES

Two nonvertical lines are **perpendicular** if the product of their slopes is $-1$. (If one line has slope $m$, the slope of a line perpendicular to it is $-1/m$. That is, to find the slope of a line perpendicular to a given line, we take the reciprocal of the given slope and change the sign.)

Lines are also perpendicular if one of them is vertical ($x = a$) and one of them is horizontal ($y = b$).

---

**EXAMPLE 8**   Determine whether the graphs of $5y = 4x + 10$ and $4y = -5x + 4$ are perpendicular.

To determine whether the lines are perpendicular, we determine whether the product of their slopes is $-1$. We first find the slope–intercept form of each equation by solving for $y$.

We have

$$5y = 4x + 10 \qquad\qquad 4y = -5x + 4$$
$$y = \tfrac{1}{5}(4x + 10) \qquad\quad y = \tfrac{1}{4}(-5x + 4)$$
$$= \tfrac{1}{5}(4x) + \tfrac{1}{5}(10) \qquad = \tfrac{1}{4}(-5x) + \tfrac{1}{4}(4)$$
$$= \tfrac{4}{5}x + 2; \qquad\qquad = -\tfrac{5}{4}x + 1.$$

The slope of the first line is $\frac{4}{5}$, and the slope of the second line is $-\frac{5}{4}$. The product of the slopes is $\frac{4}{5} \cdot \left(-\frac{5}{4}\right) = -1$. Thus the lines are perpendicular.

Do Exercises 14 and 15.

---

Determine whether the graphs of the given pair of lines are perpendicular.

**14.** $2y - x = 2,$
     $y + 2x = 4$

**15.** $3y = 2x + 15,$
     $2y = 3x + 10$

*Answers*

**14.** Yes   **15.** No

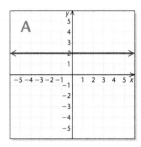

A

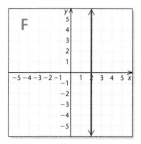

F

# Visualizing for Success

Match each equation with its graph.

1. $y = 2 - x$

2. $x - y = 2$

3. $x + 2y = 2$

4. $2x - 3y = 6$

5. $x = 2$

6. $y = 2$

7. $y = |x + 2|$

8. $y = |x| + 2$

9. $y = x^2 - 2$

10. $y = 2 - x^2$

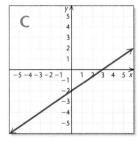

B

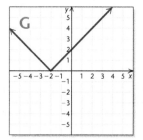

G

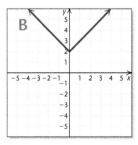

C

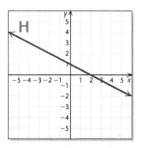

H

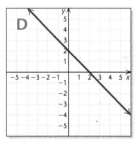

D

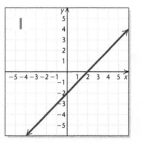

I

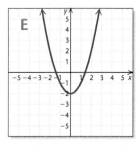

E

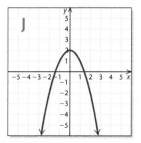

J

*Answers on page A-8*

**a** Find the intercepts and then graph the line.

**1.** $x - 2 = y$

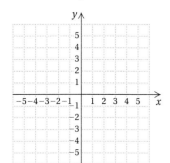

**2.** $x + 3 = y$

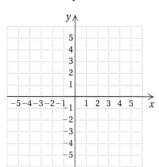

**3.** $x + 3y = 6$

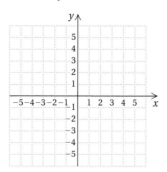

**4.** $x - 2y = 4$

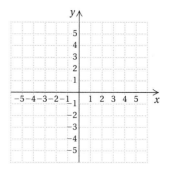

**5.** $2x + 3y = 6$

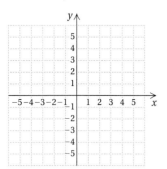

**6.** $5x - 2y = 10$

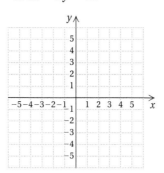

**7.** $f(x) = -2 - 2x$

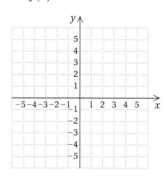

**8.** $g(x) = 5x - 5$

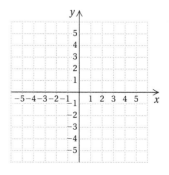

**9.** $5y = -15 + 3x$

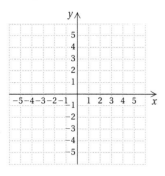

**10.** $5x - 10 = 5y$

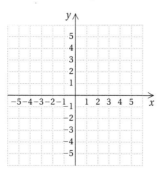

**11.** $2x - 3y = 6$

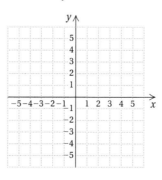

**12.** $4x + 5y = 20$

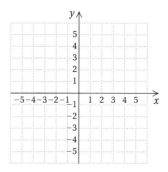

**13.** $2.8y - 3.5x = -9.8$

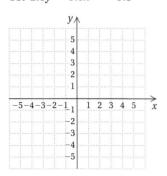

**14.** $10.8x - 22.68 = 4.2y$

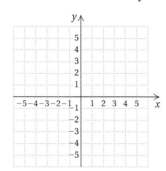

**15.** $5x + 2y = 7$

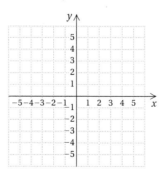

**16.** $3x - 4y = 10$

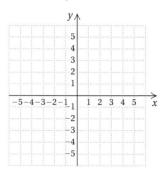

**b** Graph using the slope and the y-intercept.

**17.** $y = \dfrac{5}{2}x + 1$

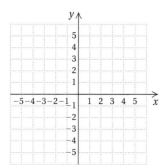

**18.** $y = \dfrac{2}{5}x - 4$

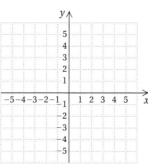

**19.** $f(x) = -\dfrac{5}{2}x - 4$

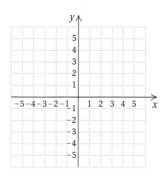

**20.** $f(x) = \dfrac{2}{5}x + 3$

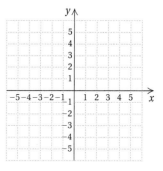

**21.** $x + 2y = 4$

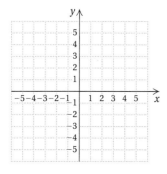

**22.** $x - 3y = 6$

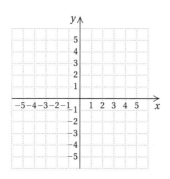

**23.** $4x - 3y = 12$

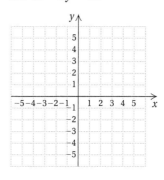

**24.** $2x + 6y = 12$

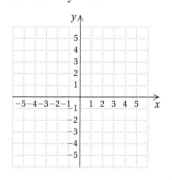

**25.** $f(x) = \dfrac{1}{3}x - 4$

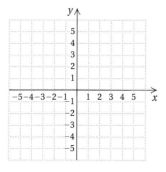

**26.** $g(x) = -0.25x + 2$

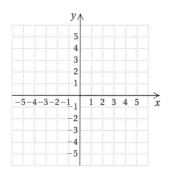

**27.** $5x + 4 \cdot f(x) = 4$
(*Hint*: Solve for $f(x)$.)

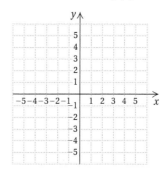

**28.** $3 \cdot f(x) = 4x + 6$

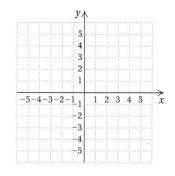

**c** Graph and, if possible, determine the slope.

**29.** $x = 1$

**30.** $x = -4$

**31.** $y = -1$

**32.** $y = \dfrac{3}{2}$

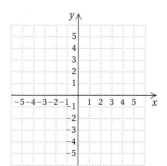

**33.** $f(x) = -6$

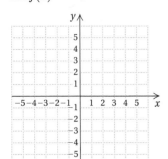

**34.** $f(x) = 2$

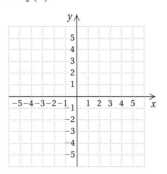

**35.** $y = 0$

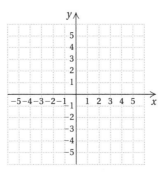

**36.** $x = 0$

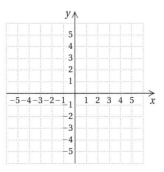

**37.** $2 \cdot f(x) + 5 = 0$

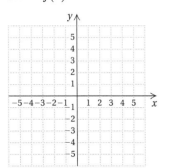

**38.** $4 \cdot g(x) + 3x = 12 + 3x$

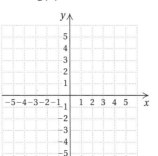

**39.** $7 - 3x = 4 + 2x$

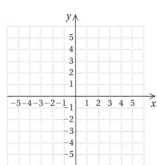

**40.** $3 - f(x) = 2$

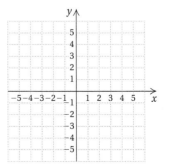

**d**    Determine whether the graphs of the given pair of lines are parallel.

**41.** $x + 6 = y,$
    $y - x = -2$

**42.** $2x - 7 = y,$
    $y - 2x = 8$

**43.** $y + 3 = 5x,$
    $3x - y = -2$

**44.** $y + 8 = -6x,$
    $-2x + y = 5$

**45.** $y = 3x + 9,$
    $2y = 6x - 2$

**46.** $y + 7x = -9,$
    $-3y = 21x + 7$

**47.** $12x = 3,$
    $-7x = 10$

**48.** $5y = -2,$
    $\frac{3}{4}x = 16$

Determine whether the graphs of the given pair of lines are perpendicular.

**49.** $y = 4x - 5,$
    $4y = 8 - x$

**50.** $2x - 5y = -3,$
    $2x + 5y = 4$

**51.** $x + 2y = 5,$
    $2x + 4y = 8$

**52.** $y = -x + 7,$
    $y = x + 3$

**53.** $2x - 3y = 7,$
    $2y - 3x = 10$

**54.** $x = y,$
    $y = -x$

**55.** $2x = 3,$
    $-3y = 6$

**56.** $-5y = 10,$
    $y = -\frac{4}{9}$

## Skill Maintenance

Write in scientific notation.  [R.7c]

**57.** 53,000,000,000

**58.** 0.000047

**59.** 0.018

**60.** 99,902,000

Write in decimal notation.  [R.7c]

**61.** $2.13 \times 10^{-5}$

**62.** $9.01 \times 10^{8}$

**63.** $2 \times 10^{4}$

**64.** $8.5677 \times 10^{-2}$

Factor.  [R.5d]

**65.** $9x - 15y$

**66.** $12a + 21ab$

**67.** $21p - 7pq + 14p$

**68.** $64x - 128y + 256$

## Synthesis

**69.** Find an equation of a horizontal line that passes through the point $(-2, 3)$.

**70.** Find an equation of a vertical line that passes through the point $(-2, 3)$.

**71.** Find the value of $a$ such that the graphs of $5y = ax + 5$ and $\frac{1}{4}y = \frac{1}{10}x - 1$ are parallel.

**72.** Find the value of $k$ such that the graphs of $x + 7y = 70$ and $y + 3 = kx$ are perpendicular.

**73.** Write an equation of the line that has $x$-intercept $(-3, 0)$ and $y$-intercept $\left(0, \frac{2}{5}\right)$.

**74.** Find the coordinates of the point of intersection of the graphs of the equations $x = -4$ and $y = 5$.

**75.** Write an equation for the $x$-axis. Is this equation a function?

**76.** Write an equation for the $y$-axis. Is this equation a function?

**77.** Find the value of $m$ in $y = mx + 3$ so that the $x$-intercept of its graph will be $(4, 0)$.

**78.** Find the value of $b$ in $2y = -7x + 3b$ so that the $y$-intercept of its graph will be $(0, -13)$.

**79.** Match each sentence with the most appropriate graph from those at right.

   **a)** The rate at which fluids were given intravenously was doubled after 3 hr.

   **b)** The rate at which fluids were given intravenously was gradually reduced to 0.

   **c)** The rate at which fluids were given intravenously remained constant for 5 hr.

   **d)** The rate at which fluids were given intravenously was gradually increased.

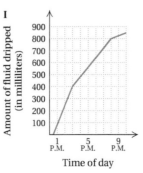

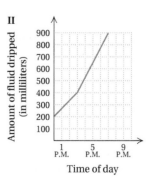

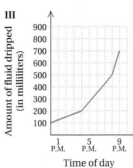

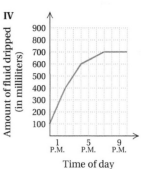

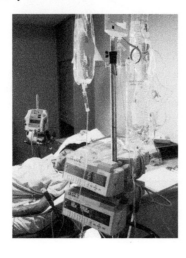

# 2.6

# Finding Equations of Lines; Applications

## OBJECTIVES

**a** Find an equation of a line when the slope and the y-intercept are given.

**b** Find an equation of a line when the slope and a point are given.

**c** Find an equation of a line when two points are given.

**d** Given a line and a point not on the given line, find an equation of the line parallel to the line and containing the point, and find an equation of the line perpendicular to the line and containing the point.

**e** Solve applied problems involving linear functions.

**SKILL TO REVIEW**
Objective R.2e: Divide real numbers.

Find the reciprocal of the number.
**1.** 3

**2.** $-\dfrac{4}{9}$

**1.** A line has slope 3.4 and y-intercept $(0, -8)$. Find an equation of the line.

In this section, we will learn to find an equation of a line for which we have been given two pieces of information.

## a Finding an Equation of a Line When the Slope and the y-Intercept Are Given

If we know the slope and the y-intercept of a line, we can find an equation of the line using the slope–intercept equation $y = mx + b$.

**EXAMPLE 1**  A line has slope $-0.7$ and y-intercept $(0, 13)$. Find an equation of the line.

We use the slope–intercept equation and substitute $-0.7$ for $m$ and 13 for $b$:

$$y = mx + b$$
$$y = -0.7x + 13.$$

Do Margin Exercise 1.

## b Finding an Equation of a Line When the Slope and a Point Are Given

Suppose we know the slope of a line and the coordinates of one point on the line. We can use the slope–intercept equation to find an equation of the line. Or, we can use the **point–slope equation**. We first develop a formula for such a line.

Suppose that a line of slope $m$ passes through the point $(x_1, y_1)$. For any other point $(x, y)$ on this line, we must have

$$\frac{y - y_1}{x - x_1} = m.$$

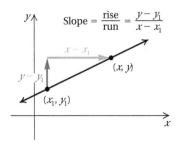

$$\text{Slope} = \frac{\text{rise}}{\text{run}} = \frac{y - y_1}{x - x_1}$$

It is tempting to use this last equation as an equation of the line of slope $m$ that passes through $(x_1, y_1)$. The only problem with this form is that when $x$ and $y$ are replaced with $x_1$ and $y_1$, we have $\frac{0}{0} = m$, a false equation. To avoid this difficulty, we multiply by $x - x_1$ on both sides and simplify:

$$\frac{y - y_1}{x - x_1}(x - x_1) = m(x - x_1) \qquad \text{Multiplying by } x - x_1 \text{ on both sides}$$

$$y - y_1 = m(x - x_1). \qquad \text{Removing a factor of 1: } \frac{x - x_1}{x - x_1} = 1$$

This is the *point–slope* form of a linear equation.

## POINT-SLOPE EQUATION

The **point–slope equation** of a line with slope $m$, passing through $(x_1, y_1)$, is

$$y - y_1 = m(x - x_1).$$

If we know the slope of a line and a certain point on the line, we can find an equation of the line using either the point–slope equation,

$$y - y_1 = m(x - x_1),$$

or the slope–intercept equation,

$$y = mx + b.$$

**EXAMPLE 2**   Find an equation of the line with slope 5 and containing the point $\left(\frac{1}{2}, -1\right)$.

**Using the Point–Slope Equation:**   We consider $\left(\frac{1}{2}, -1\right)$ to be $(x_1, y_1)$ and 5 to be the slope $m$, and substitute:

$$
\begin{aligned}
y - y_1 &= m(x - x_1) &&\text{Point–slope equation} \\
y - (-1) &= 5\left(x - \tfrac{1}{2}\right) &&\text{Substituting} \\
y + 1 &= 5x - \tfrac{5}{2} &&\text{Simplifying} \\
y &= 5x - \tfrac{5}{2} - 1 \\
y &= 5x - \tfrac{5}{2} - \tfrac{2}{2} \\
y &= 5x - \tfrac{7}{2}.
\end{aligned}
$$

**Using the Slope–Intercept Equation:**   The point $\left(\frac{1}{2}, -1\right)$ is on the line, so it is a solution. Thus we can substitute $\frac{1}{2}$ for $x$ and $-1$ for $y$ in $y = mx + b$. We also substitute 5 for $m$, the slope. Then we solve for $b$:

$$
\begin{aligned}
y &= mx + b &&\text{Slope–intercept equation} \\
-1 &= 5 \cdot \left(\tfrac{1}{2}\right) + b &&\text{Substituting} \\
-1 &= \tfrac{5}{2} + b \\
-1 - \tfrac{5}{2} &= b \\
-\tfrac{2}{2} - \tfrac{5}{2} &= b \\
-\tfrac{7}{2} &= b. &&\text{Solving for } b
\end{aligned}
$$

We then use the slope–intercept equation $y = mx + b$ again and substitute 5 for $m$ and $-\frac{7}{2}$ for $b$:

$$y = 5x - \tfrac{7}{2}.$$

Do Exercises 2–5.

Find an equation of the line with the given slope and containing the given point.

**2.** $m = -5$, $(-4, 2)$

**3.** $m = 3$, $(1, -2)$

**4.** $m = 8$, $(3, 5)$

**5.** $m = -\dfrac{2}{3}$, $(1, 4)$

*Answers*

**2.** $y = -5x - 18$   **3.** $y = 3x - 5$

**4.** $y = 8x - 19$   **5.** $y = -\dfrac{2}{3}x + \dfrac{14}{3}$

## (c) Finding an Equation of a Line When Two Points Are Given

We can also use the slope–intercept equation or the point–slope equation to find an equation of a line when two points are given.

**EXAMPLE 3** Find an equation of the line containing the points $(2, 3)$ and $(-6, 1)$.

First, we find the slope:

$$m = \frac{3 - 1}{2 - (-6)} = \frac{2}{8}, \text{ or } \frac{1}{4}.$$

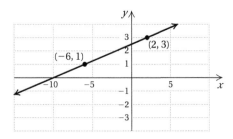

Now we have the slope and two points. We then proceed as we did in Example 2, using either point, and either the point–slope equation or the slope–intercept equation.

**Using the Point–Slope Equation:** We choose $(2, 3)$ and substitute 2 for $x_1$, 3 for $y_1$, and $\frac{1}{4}$ for $m$:

$$y - y_1 = m(x - x_1) \qquad \text{Point–slope equation}$$
$$y - 3 = \tfrac{1}{4}(x - 2) \qquad \text{Substituting}$$
$$y - 3 = \tfrac{1}{4}x - \tfrac{1}{2}$$
$$y = \tfrac{1}{4}x - \tfrac{1}{2} + 3$$
$$y = \tfrac{1}{4}x - \tfrac{1}{2} + \tfrac{6}{2}$$
$$y = \tfrac{1}{4}x + \tfrac{5}{2}.$$

**Using the Slope–Intercept Equation:** We choose $(2, 3)$ and substitute 2 for $x$, 3 for $y$, and $\frac{1}{4}$ for $m$:

$$y = mx + b \qquad \text{Slope–intercept equation}$$
$$3 = \tfrac{1}{4} \cdot 2 + b \qquad \text{Substituting}$$
$$3 = \tfrac{1}{2} + b$$
$$3 - \tfrac{1}{2} = \tfrac{1}{2} + b - \tfrac{1}{2}$$
$$\tfrac{6}{2} - \tfrac{1}{2} = b$$
$$\tfrac{5}{2} = b. \qquad \text{Solving for } b$$

Finally, we use the slope–intercept equation $y = mx + b$ again and substitute $\frac{1}{4}$ for $m$ and $\frac{5}{2}$ for $b$:

$$y = \tfrac{1}{4}x + \tfrac{5}{2}.$$

Do Exercises 6 and 7.

**6.** Find an equation of the line containing the points $(4, -3)$ and $(1, 2)$.

**7.** Find an equation of the line containing the points $(-3, -5)$ and $(-4, 12)$.

*Answers*

**6.** $y = -\frac{5}{3}x + \frac{11}{3}$   **7.** $y = -17x - 56$

## (d) Finding an Equation of a Line Parallel or Perpendicular to a Given Line Through a Point Off the Line

We can also use the methods of Example 2 to find an equation of a line through a point off the line parallel or perpendicular to a given line.

**EXAMPLE 4**  Find an equation of the line containing the point $(-1, 3)$ and parallel to the line $2x + y = 10$.

A line parallel to the given line $2x + y = 10$ must have the same slope as the given line. To find that slope, we first find the slope–intercept equation by solving for $y$:

$$2x + y = 10$$
$$y = -2x + 10.$$

Thus the line we want to find through $(-1, 3)$ must also have slope $-2$.

**Using the Point–Slope Equation:**  We use the point $(-1, 3)$ and the slope $-2$, substituting $-1$ for $x_1$, 3 for $y_1$, and $-2$ for $m$:

$$y - y_1 = m(x - x_1)$$
$$y - 3 = -2(x - (-1)) \qquad \text{Substituting}$$
$$y - 3 = -2(x + 1) \qquad \text{Simplifying}$$
$$y - 3 = -2x - 2$$
$$y = -2x - 2 + 3$$
$$y = -2x + 1.$$

**Using the Slope–Intercept Equation:**  We substitute $-1$ for $x$ and 3 for $y$ in $y = mx + b$, and $-2$ for $m$, the slope. Then we solve for $b$:

$$y = mx + b$$
$$3 = -2(-1) + b \qquad \text{Substituting}$$
$$3 = 2 + b$$
$$1 = b. \qquad \text{Solving for } b$$

We then use the equation $y = mx + b$ again and substitute $-2$ for $m$ and 1 for $b$:

$$y = -2x + 1.$$

The given line $2x + y = 10$, or $y = -2x + 10$, and the line $y = -2x + 1$ have the same slope but different $y$-intercepts. Thus their graphs are parallel.

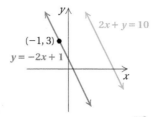

Do Exercise 8.

**8.** Find an equation of the line containing the point $(2, -1)$ and parallel to the line $9x - 3y = 5$.

*Answer*

**8.** $y = 3x - 7$

**EXAMPLE 5**  Find an equation of the line containing the point $(2, -3)$ and perpendicular to the line $4y - x = 20$.

To find the slope of the given line, we first find its slope–intercept form by solving for $y$:

$$4y - x = 20$$
$$4y = x + 20$$
$$\frac{4y}{4} = \frac{x + 20}{4} \quad \text{Dividing by 4}$$
$$y = \tfrac{1}{4}x + 5.$$

We know that the slope of the perpendicular line must be the opposite of the reciprocal of $\tfrac{1}{4}$. Thus the new line through $(2, -3)$ must have slope $-4$.

**Using the Point–Slope Equation:**  We use the point $(2, -3)$ and the slope $-4$, substituting 2 for $x_1$, $-3$ for $y_1$, and $-4$ for $m$:

$$y - y_1 = m(x - x_1)$$
$$y - (-3) = -4(x - 2) \quad \text{Substituting}$$
$$y + 3 = -4(x - 2) \quad \text{Simplifying}$$
$$y + 3 = -4x + 8$$
$$y = -4x + 8 - 3$$
$$y = -4x + 5.$$

**Using the Slope–Intercept Equation:**  We now substitute 2 for $x$ and $-3$ for $y$ in $y = mx + b$. We also substitute $-4$ for $m$, the slope. Then we solve for $b$:

$$y = mx + b$$
$$-3 = -4(2) + b \quad \text{Substituting}$$
$$-3 = -8 + b$$
$$5 = b. \quad \text{Solving for } b$$

Finally, we use the equation $y = mx + b$ again and substitute $-4$ for $m$ and 5 for $b$:

$$y = -4x + 5.$$

The product of the slopes of the lines $4y - x = 20$ and $y = -4x + 5$ is $\tfrac{1}{4} \cdot (-4) = -1$. Thus their graphs are perpendicular.

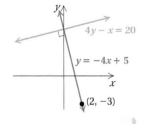

**9.** Find an equation of the line containing the point $(5, 4)$ and perpendicular to the line $2x - 4y = 9$.

Do Exercise 9.

## e Applications of Linear Functions

When the essential parts of a problem are described in mathematical language, we say that we have a **mathematical model**. We have already studied many kinds of mathematical models in this text—for example, the formulas in Section 1.2 and the functions in Section 2.2. Here we study linear functions as models.

**EXAMPLE 6** *Cost of a Necklace.* Amelia's Beads offers a class in designing necklaces. For a necklace made of 6-mm beads, 4.23 beads per inch are needed. The cost of a necklace of 6-mm gemstone beads that sell for 40¢ each is $7 for the clasp and the crimps and approximately $1.70 per inch.

a) Formulate a linear function that models the total cost of a necklace $C(n)$, where $n$ is the length of the necklace, in inches.

b) Graph the model.

c) Use the model to determine the cost of a 30-in. necklace.

a) The problem describes a situation in which cost per inch is charged in addition to the fixed cost of the clasp and the crimps. The total cost of a 16-in. necklace is

$$\$7 + \$1.70 \cdot 16 = \$34.20.$$

For a 17-in. necklace, the total cost is

$$\$7 + \$1.70 \cdot 17 = \$35.90.$$

These calculations lead us to generalize that for a necklace that is $n$ inches long, the total cost is given by $C(n) = 7 + 1.7n$, where $n \geq 0$ since the length of the necklace cannot be negative. (Actually most necklaces are at least 14 in. long.) The notation $C(n)$ indicates that the cost $C$ is a function of the length $n$.

b) Before we draw the graph, we rewrite the model in slope–intercept form:

$$C(n) = 1.7n + 7.$$

The $y$-intercept is $(0, 7)$ and the slope, or rate of change, is $1.70 per inch, or $\frac{17}{10}$. We first plot $(0, 7)$; from that point, we move up 17 units and to the right 10 units to the point $(10, 24)$. We then draw a line through these points. We also calculate a third value as a check:

$$C(20) = 1.7 \cdot 20 + 7 = 41.$$

The point $(20, 41)$ lines up with the other two points so the graph is correct.

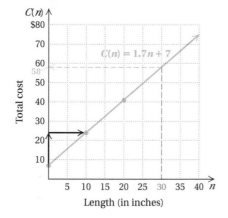

**10. Cost of a Service Call.** For a service call, Belmont Heating and Air Conditioning charges a $65 trip fee and $80 per hour for labor.

a) Formulate a linear function for the total cost of the service call $C(t)$, where $t$ is the length of the call, in hours.

b) Graph the model.

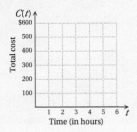

Time (in hours)

c) Use the model to determine the cost of a $2\frac{1}{2}$-hr service call.

c) To determine the total cost of a 30-in. necklace, we find $C(30)$:

$$C(30) = 1.7 \cdot 30 + 7 = 58.$$

From the graph, we see that the input 30 corresponds to the output 58. Thus we see that a 30-in. necklace costs $58.

Do Exercise 10.

In the following example, we use two points and find an equation for the linear function through these points. Then we use the equation to make a prediction.

**EXAMPLE 7** *Retail Trade.* Sales at warehouse clubs and superstores have increased steadily in recent years. The table below lists data regarding the correspondence between the year and the total sales at warehouses and superstores, in billions of dollars.

| YEAR, $x$ (in years since 2000) | TOTAL SALES (in billions) |
|---|---|
| 2000, 0 | $139.6 |
| 2007, 7 | 323.3 |

SOURCE: U.S. Census Bureau

a) Assuming a constant rate of change, use the two data points to find a linear function that fits the data.

b) Use the function to determine the total sales in 2005.

c) In which year will the total sales reach $400 billion?

a) We let $x =$ the number of years since 2000 and $S =$ total sales. The table gives us two ordered pairs, $(0, 139.6)$ and $(7, 323.3)$. We use them to find a linear function that fits the data. First, we find the slope:

$$m = \frac{323.3 - 139.6}{7 - 0} = \frac{183.7}{7} \approx 26.24.$$

Next, we find an equation $S = mx + b$ that fits the data. We can use either the point–slope equation or the slope–intercept equation to do this.

*Answer*

10. (a) $C(t) = 80t + 65$;
(b)

Time (in hours)

(c) $265

**Using the Point–Slope Equation:** We substitute one of the points—say, $(0, 139.6)$—and the slope, $26.24$, in the point–slope equation:

$$S - S_1 = m(x - x_1) \qquad \text{Point–slope equation}$$
$$S - 139.6 = 26.24(x - 0) \qquad \text{Substituting}$$
$$S - 139.6 = 26.24x - 0$$
$$S = 26.24x + 139.6.$$

**Using the Slope–Intercept Equation:** One of the data points $(0, 139.6)$ is the $y$-intercept. Thus we know $b$ in the slope–intercept equation, $y = mx + b$. We use the equation $S = mx + b$ and substitute $26.24$ for $m$ and $139.6$ for $b$:

$$S = 26.24x + 139.6.$$

Using function notation, we have

$$S(x) = 26.24x + 139.6.$$

**b)** To determine the total sales in 2005, we substitute 5 for $x$ (2005 is 5 yr since 2000) in the function $S(x) = 26.24x + 139.6$:

$$S(x) = 26.24x + 139.6$$
$$S(5) = 26.24 \cdot 5 + 139.6 \qquad \text{Substituting}$$
$$= 131.2 + 139.6$$
$$= 270.8.$$

The total sales in 2005 were $270.8 billion.

**c)** To find the year in which total sales will reach $400 billion, we substitute 400 for $S(x)$ and solve for $x$:

$$S(x) = 26.24x + 139.6$$
$$400 = 26.24x + 139.6 \qquad \text{Substituting}$$
$$260.4 = 26.24x \qquad \text{Subtracting 139.6}$$
$$10 \approx x. \qquad \text{Dividing by 26.24}$$

Total sales will reach $400 billion about 10 yr after 2000, or in 2010.

Do Exercise 11.

**11. Hat Size as a Function of Head Circumference.** The table below lists data relating hat size to head circumference.

| HEAD CIRCUMFERENCE, $C$ (in inches) | HAT SIZE, $H$ |
|---|---|
| 21.2 | $6\frac{3}{4}$ |
| 22 | 7 |

SOURCE: Shushan's New Oreleans

**a)** Assuming a constant rate of change, use the two data points to find a linear function that fits the data.

**b)** Use the function to determine the hat size of a person whose head has a circumference of 24.8 in.

**c)** Jerome's hat size is 8. What is the circumference of his head?

**a**   Find an equation of the line having the given slope and $y$-intercept.

**1.** Slope: $-8$;   $y$-intercept: $(0, 4)$

**2.** Slope: $5$;   $y$-intercept: $(0, -3)$

**3.** Slope: $2.3$;   $y$-intercept: $(0, -1)$

**4.** Slope: $-9.1$;   $y$-intercept: $(0, 2)$

Find a linear function $f(x) = mx + b$ whose graph has the given slope and $y$-intercept.

**5.** Slope: $-\frac{7}{3}$;   $y$-intercept: $(0, -5)$

**6.** Slope: $\frac{4}{5}$;   $y$-intercept: $(0, 28)$

**7.** Slope: $\frac{2}{3}$;   $y$-intercept: $\left(0, \frac{5}{8}\right)$

**8.** Slope: $-\frac{7}{8}$;   $y$-intercept: $\left(0, -\frac{7}{11}\right)$

**b**   Find an equation of the line having the given slope and containing the given point.

**9.** $m = 5$,   $(4, 3)$

**10.** $m = 4$,   $(5, 2)$

**11.** $m = -3$,   $(9, 6)$

**12.** $m = -2$,   $(2, 8)$

**13.** $m = 1$,   $(-1, -7)$

**14.** $m = 3$,   $(-2, -2)$

**15.** $m = -2$,   $(8, 0)$

**16.** $m = -3$,   $(-2, 0)$

**17.** $m = 0$,   $(0, -7)$

**18.** $m = 0$,   $(0, 4)$

**19.** $m = \frac{2}{3}$,   $(1, -2)$

**20.** $m = -\frac{4}{5}$,   $(2, 3)$

**c**   Find an equation of the line containing the given pair of points.

**21.** $(1, 4)$ and $(5, 6)$

**22.** $(2, 5)$ and $(4, 7)$

**23.** $(-3, -3)$ and $(2, 2)$

**24.** $(-1, -1)$ and $(9, 9)$

**25.** $(-4, 0)$ and $(0, 7)$

**26.** $(0, -5)$ and $(3, 0)$

**27.** $(-2, -3)$ and $(-4, -6)$

**28.** $(-4, -7)$ and $(-2, -1)$

**29.** $(0, 0)$ and $(6, 1)$

**30.** $(0, 0)$ and $(-4, 7)$

**31.** $\left(\frac{1}{4}, -\frac{1}{2}\right)$ and $\left(\frac{3}{4}, 6\right)$

**32.** $\left(\frac{2}{3}, \frac{3}{2}\right)$ and $\left(-3, \frac{5}{6}\right)$

**d** Write an equation of the line containing the given point and parallel to the given line.

**33.** $(3, 7)$; $x + 2y = 6$

**34.** $(0, 3)$; $2x - y = 7$

**35.** $(2, -1)$; $5x - 7y = 8$

**36.** $(-4, -5)$; $2x + y = -3$

**37.** $(-6, 2)$; $3x = 9y + 2$

**38.** $(-7, 0)$; $2y + 5x = 6$

Write an equation of the line containing the given point and perpendicular to the given line.

**39.** $(2, 5)$; $2x + y = 3$

**40.** $(4, 1)$; $x - 3y = 9$

**41.** $(3, -2)$; $3x + 4y = 5$

**42.** $(-3, -5)$; $5x - 2y = 4$

**43.** $(0, 9)$; $2x + 5y = 7$

**44.** $(-3, -4)$; $6y - 3x = 2$

 **e** Solve.

**45.** *Moving Costs.* Metro Movers charges $85 plus $40 an hour to move households across town.
  **a)** Formulate a linear function for the total cost $C(t)$ of $t$ hours of moving.
  **b)** Graph the model.
  **c)** Use the model to determine the cost of $6\frac{1}{2}$ hr of moving service.

**46.** *Deluxe Cable TV Service.* Vista Cable TV Service charges a $35 installation fee and $20 per month for basic service.
  **a)** Formulate a linear function for the total cost $C(t)$ of $t$ months of cable TV service.
  **b)** Graph the model.
  **c)** Use the model to determine the cost of 9 months of service.

**47.** *Value of a Fax Machine.* Melton Corporation bought a multifunction fax machine for $750. The value $V(t)$ of the machine depreciates (declines) at a rate of $25 per month.
  **a)** Formulate a linear function for the value $V(t)$ of the machine after $t$ months.
  **b)** Graph the model.
  **c)** Use the model to determine the value of the machine after 13 months.

**48.** *Value of a Computer.* True Tone Graphics bought a computer for $3800. The value $V(t)$ of the computer depreciates at a rate of $50 per month.
  **a)** Formulate a linear function for the value $V(t)$ of the computer after $t$ months.
  **b)** Graph the model.
  **c)** Use the model to determine the value of the computer after $10\frac{1}{2}$ months.

In Exercises 49–54, assume that a constant rate of change exists for each model formed.

**49.** *Whooping Cough.* The table below lists data regarding the number of cases of whooping cough in 1987 and in 2007.

| YEAR, x (in years since 1987) | NUMBER OF CASES |
| --- | --- |
| 1987, 0 | 2,862 |
| 2007, 20 | 10,454 |

SOURCE: Centers for Disease Control and Prevention

**a)** Use the two data points to find a linear function that fits the data. Let $x$ = the number of years since 1987 and $W(x)$ = the number of cases of whooping cough.

**b)** Use the function of part (a) to estimate and predict the number of cases of whooping cough in 1990 and in 2012.

**50.** *Lobbying Expenses.* The table below lists data regarding spending, in billions of dollars, on lobbying Congress and the federal government in 2004 and in 2008.

| YEAR, x (in years since 2004) | AMOUNT SPENT ON LOBBYING (in billions) |
| --- | --- |
| 2004, 0 | $1.5 |
| 2008, 4 | $3.3 |

SOURCE: CQ MoneyLine

**a)** Use the two data points to find a linear function that fits the data. Let $x$ = the number of years since 2004 and $L(x)$ = the amount spent, in billions of dollars, on lobbying Congress and the federal government.

**b)** Use the function of part (a) to estimate the amount spent on lobbying in 2005 and in 2010.

**51.** *Auto Dealers.* At the close of 1991, there were 24,026 auto dealers in the United States. By the end of 2008, this number had dropped to 20,084. Let $D(x)$ = the number of auto dealerships and $x$ = the number of years since 1991.

Source: Urban Science Automotive Dealer Census

**a)** Find a linear function that fits the data.

**b)** Use the function of part (a) to estimate the number of auto dealerships in 2000.

**c)** At this rate of decrease, when will the number of auto dealerships be 18,000?

**52.** *Records in the 400-Meter Run.* In 1930, the record for the 400-m run was 46.8 sec. In 1970, it was 43.8 sec. Let $R(t)$ = the record in the 400-m run and $t$ = the number of years since 1930.

**a)** Find a linear function that fits the data.

**b)** Use the function of part (a) to estimate the record in 2003; in 2006.

**c)** When will the record be 40 sec?

**53.** *Life Expectancy of Males in the United States.* In 1990, the life expectancy of males was 71.8 yr. In 2001, it was 74.4 yr. Let $M(t)$ = life expectancy and $t$ = the number of years since 1990.

Source: U.S. National Center for Health Statistics

**a)** Find a linear function that fits the data.

**b)** Use the function of part (a) to estimate the life expectancy of males in 2007.

**54.** *Life Expectancy of Females in the United States.* In 1990, the life expectancy of females was 78.8 yr. In 2001, it was 79.8 yr. Let $F(t)$ = life expectancy and $t$ = the number of years since 1990.

Source: U.S. National Center for Health Statistics

**a)** Find a linear function that fits the data.

**b)** Use the function of part (a) to estimate the life expectancy of females in 2010.

## Skill Maintenance

Solve. [1.4c], [1.5a], [1.6c, d, e]

**55.** $2x + 3 > 51$

**56.** $|2x + 3| = 51$

**57.** $2x + 3 \le 51$

**58.** $2x + 3 \le 5x - 4$

**59.** $|2x + 3| \le 13$

**60.** $|2x + 3| = |x - 4|$

**61.** $|5x - 4| = -8$

**62.** $-12 \le 2x + 3 < 51$

## Key Terms, Properties, and Formulas

| | | |
|---|---|---|
| axes, p. 160 | dependent variable, p. 167 | run, p. 199 |
| origin, p. 160 | independent variable, p. 167 | slope–intercept equation, p. 201 |
| ordered pair, p. 160 | function, p. 174 | grade, p. 201 |
| coordinates, p. 160 | domain, p. 174 | rate of change, p. 202 |
| first coordinate, p. 160 | range, p. 174 | $y$-intercept, pp. 197, 206 |
| second coordinate, p. 160 | relation, p. 175 | $x$-intercept, p. 206 |
| abscissa, p. 160 | inputs, p. 176 | horizontal line, p. 209 |
| ordinate, p. 160 | outputs, p. 176 | vertical line, p. 209 |
| Cartesian coordinate system, p. 161 | constant function, p. 177 | parallel lines, p. 211 |
| quadrants, p. 161 | vertical-line test, p. 179 | perpendicular lines, p. 212 |
| graph of an equation, p. 163 | linear function, p. 195 | point–slope equation, p. 218 |
| linear equation, p. 163 | slope, p. 198 | mathematical model, p. 223 |
| nonlinear equation, p. 166 | rise, p. 199 | |

$$\text{Slope} = m = \frac{y_2 - y_1}{x_2 - x_1}, \text{ or } \frac{y_1 - y_2}{x_1 - x_2}$$

*Slope–Intercept Equation*: $f(x) = mx + b$, or $y = mx + b$

*Point–Slope Equation*: $y - y_1 = m(x - x_1)$

*Horizontal Line*: $f(x) = b$, or $y = b$; slope $= 0$

*Vertical Line*: $x = a$, slope is not defined.

*Parallel Lines*: $m_1 = m_2, b_1 \neq b_2$

*Perpendicular Lines*: $m_1 = -\dfrac{1}{m_2}, m_1, m_2 \neq 0$

## Concept Reinforcement

Determine whether each statement is true or false.

_____ **1.** The slope of a vertical line is 0.   [2.5c]

_____ **2.** A line with slope 1 slants less steeply than a line with slope −5.   [2.4b]

_____ **3.** Parallel lines have the same slope and $y$-intercept.   [2.5d]

## Important Concepts

**Objective 2.1c**   Graph linear equations using tables.

**Example**   Graph: $y = -\dfrac{2}{3}x + 2$.

By choosing multiples of 3 for $x$, we can avoid fraction values for $y$. If $x = -3$, then $y = -\frac{2}{3} \cdot (-3) + 2 = 2 + 2 = 4$. We list three ordered pairs in a table, plot the points, draw the line, and label the graph.

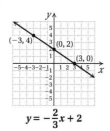

$$y = -\frac{2}{3}x + 2$$

**Practice Exercise**

**1.** Graph: $y = \dfrac{2}{5}x - 3$.

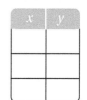

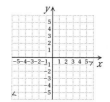

**Objective 2.2a** Determine whether a correspondence is a function.

**Example** Determine whether each correspondence is a function.

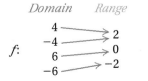

The correspondence *f* is a function because each member of the domain is matched to *only one* member of the range. The correspondence *g* is *not* a function because one member of the domain, *Q*, is matched to more than one member of the range.

**Practice Exercise**

2. Determine whether the correspondence is a function.

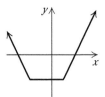

---

**Objective 2.2b** Given a function described by an equation, find function values (outputs) for specified values (inputs).

**Example** Find the indicated function value.

**a)** $f(0)$, for $f(x) = -x + 6$    **b)** $g(5)$, for $g(x) = -10$

**c)** $h(-1)$, for $h(x) = 4x^2 + x$

**a)** $f(x) = -x + 6$: $f(0) = -0 + 6 = 6$

**b)** $g(x) = -10$: $g(5) = -10$

**c)** $h(x) = 4x^2 + x$: $h(-1) = 4(-1)^2 + (-1) = 4 \cdot 1 - 1 = 3$

**Practice Exercise**

3. Find $g(0)$, $g(-2)$, and $g(6)$ for $g(x) = \frac{1}{2}x - 2$.

---

**Objective 2.2d** Determine whether a graph is that of a function using the vertical-line test.

**Example** Determine whether each of the following is the graph of a function.

**a)**

**b)**
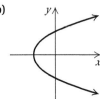

**a)** The graph is that of a function because no vertical line can cross the graph at more than one point.

**b)** The graph is not that of a function because a vertical line can cross the graph more than once.

**Practice Exercise**

4. Determine whether the graph is the graph of a function.

---

**Objective 2.3a** Find the domain and the range of a function.

**Example** For the function *f* whose graph is shown below, determine the domain and the range.

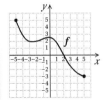 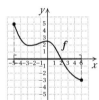 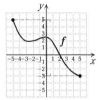

Domain: $[-5, 5]$; range: $[-3, 5]$

**Practice Exercises**

5. For the function *g* whose graph is shown below, determine the domain and the range.

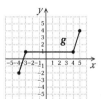

**Example** Find the domain of $g(x) = \dfrac{x+1}{2x-6}$.

Since $(x+1)/(2x-6)$ cannot be calculated when the denominator $2x-6$ is 0, we solve $2x-6=0$ to find the real numbers that must be excluded from the domain of $g$:

$$2x - 6 = 0$$
$$2x = 6$$
$$x = 3.$$

Thus, 3 is not in the domain. The domain of $g$ is $\{x \mid x$ is a real number $and\ x \neq 3\}$, or $(-\infty, 3) \cup (3, \infty)$.

**6.** Find the domain of

$$h(x) = \dfrac{x-3}{3x+9}.$$

---

**Objective 2.4b** Given two points on a line, find the slope. Given a linear equation, derive the equivalent slope–intercept equation and determine the slope and the $y$-intercept.

**Example** Find the slope of the line containing $(-5, 6)$ and $(-1, -4)$.

$$m = \dfrac{\text{change in } y}{\text{change in } x} = \dfrac{6 - (-4)}{-5 - (-1)} = \dfrac{6 + 4}{-5 + 1} = \dfrac{10}{-4} = -\dfrac{5}{2}$$

**Example** Find the slope and the $y$-intercept of

$$4x - 2y = 20.$$

We first solve for $y$:

$$4x - 2y = 20$$
$$-2y = -4x + 20 \qquad \text{Subtracting } 4x$$
$$y = 2x - 10. \qquad \text{Dividing by } -2$$

The slope is 2, and the $y$-intercept is $(0, -10)$.

**Practice Exercises**

**7.** Find the slope of the line containing $(2, -8)$ and $(-3, 2)$.

**8.** Find the slope and the $y$-intercept of

$$3x = -6y + 12.$$

---

**Objective 2.5a** Graph linear equations using intercepts.

**Example** Find the intercepts of $x - 2y = 6$ and then graph the line.

To find the $y$-intercept, we let $x = 0$ and solve for $y$:

$$0 - 2y = 6 \qquad \text{Substituting 0 for } x$$
$$-2y = 6$$
$$y = -3.$$

The $y$-intercept is $(0, -3)$.

To find the $x$-intercept, we let $y = 0$ and solve for $x$:

$$x - 2 \cdot 0 = 6 \qquad \text{Substituting 0 for } y$$
$$x - 0 = 6$$
$$x = 6.$$

The $x$-intercept is $(6, 0)$.

We plot these points and draw the line, using a third point as a check. We let $x = -2$ and solve for $y$:

$$-2 - 2y = 6$$
$$-2y = 8$$
$$y = -4.$$

We plot $(-2, -4)$ and note that it is on the line.

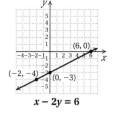

**Practice Exercise**

**9.** Find the intercepts of $3y - 3 = x$ and then graph the line.

**Objective 2.5b**  Given a linear equation in slope–intercept form, use the slope and the $y$-intercept to graph the line.

**Example**  Graph using the slope and the $y$-intercept:

$$y = -\frac{3}{2}x + 5.$$

This equation is in slope–intercept form, $y = mx + b$. The $y$-intercept is $(0, 5)$. We plot $(0, 5)$. We can think of the slope $\left(m = -\frac{3}{2}\right)$ as $\frac{-3}{2}$.

Starting at the $y$-intercept, we use the slope to find another point on the graph. We move down 3 units and to the right 2 units. We get a new point: $(2, 2)$.

To get a third point for a check, we start at $(2, 2)$ and move down 3 units and to the right 2 units to the point $(4, -1)$. We plot the points and draw the line.

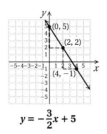

$$y = -\frac{3}{2}x + 5$$

**Practice Exercise**

**10.** Graph using the slope and the $y$-intercept: $y = \frac{1}{4}x - 3$.

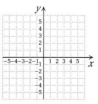

---

**Objective 2.5c**  Graph linear equations of the form $x = a$ or $y = b$.

**Example**  Graph: $y = -1$.

All ordered pairs $(x, -1)$ are solutions; $y$ is $-1$ at each point. The graph is a horizontal line that intersects the $y$-axis at $(0, -1)$.

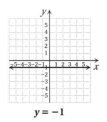

$$y = -1$$

**Example**  Graph: $x = 2$.

All ordered pairs $(2, y)$ are solutions; $x$ is 2 at each point. The graph is a vertical line that intersects the $x$-axis at $(2, 0)$.

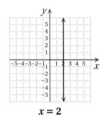

$$x = 2$$

**Practice Exercises**

**11.** Graph: $y = 3$.

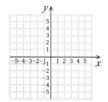

**12.** Graph: $x = -\frac{5}{2}$.

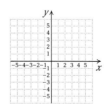

**Objective 2.5d**   Given the equations of two lines, determine whether their graphs are parallel or whether they are perpendicular.

**Example**   Determine whether the graphs of the given pair of lines are parallel, perpendicular, or neither.

a) $2y - x = 16$,
   $x + \frac{1}{2}y = 4$

b) $5x - 3 = 2y$,
   $2y + 12 = 5x$

a) Writing each equation in slope–intercept form, we have $y = \frac{1}{2}x + 8$ and $y = -2x + 8$. The slopes are $\frac{1}{2}$ and $-2$. The product of the slopes is $-1$: $\frac{1}{2} \cdot (-2) = -1$. The graphs are perpendicular.

b) Writing each equation in slope–intercept form, we have $y = \frac{5}{2}x - \frac{3}{2}$ and $y = \frac{5}{2}x - 6$. The slopes are the same, $\frac{5}{2}$, and the $y$-intercepts are different. The graphs are parallel.

**Practice Exercises**

Determine whether the graphs of the given pair of lines are parallel, perpendicular, or neither.

13. $-3x + 8y = -8$,
    $8y = 3x + 40$

14. $5x - 2y = -8$,
    $2x + 5y = 15$

---

**Objective 2.6a**   Find an equation of a line when the slope and the $y$-intercept are given.

**Example**   A line has slope 0.8 and $y$-intercept $(0, -17)$. Find an equation of the line.

We use the slope–intercept equation and substitute 0.8 for $m$ and $-17$ for $b$:

$y = mx + b$   Slope–intercept equation

$y = 0.8x - 17$.

**Practice Exercise**

15. A line has slope $-8$ and $y$-intercept $(0, 0.3)$. Find an equation of the line.

---

**Objective 2.6b**   Find an equation of a line when the slope and a point are given.

**Example**   Find an equation of the line with slope $-2$ and containing the point $\left(\frac{1}{3}, -1\right)$.

Using the *point–slope equation*, we substitute $-2$ for $m$, $\frac{1}{3}$ for $x_1$, and $-1$ for $y_1$:

$y - (-1) = -2\left(x - \frac{1}{3}\right)$   Using $y - y_1 = m(x - x_1)$

$y + 1 = -2x + \frac{2}{3}$

$y = -2x - \frac{1}{3}$.

Using the *slope–intercept equation*, we substitute $-2$ for $m$, $\frac{1}{3}$ for $x$, and $-1$ for $y$, and then solve for $b$:

$-1 = -2 \cdot \frac{1}{3} + b$   Using $y = mx + b$

$-1 = -\frac{2}{3} + b$

$-\frac{1}{3} = b$.

Then, substituting $-2$ for $m$ and $-\frac{1}{3}$ for $b$ in the slope–intercept equation $y = mx + b$, we have $y = -2x - \frac{1}{3}$.

**Practice Exercise**

16. Find an equation of the line with slope $-4$ and containing the point $\left(\frac{1}{2}, -3\right)$.

**Objective 2.6c**    Find an equation of a line when two points are given.

**Example**    Find an equation of the line containing the points $(-3, 9)$ and $(1, -2)$.

We first find the slope:

$$\frac{9 - (-2)}{-3 - 1} = \frac{11}{-4} = -\frac{11}{4}.$$

Using the slope–intercept equation and point $(1, -2)$, we substitute $-\frac{11}{4}$ for $m$, 1 for $x$, and $-2$ for $y$, and then solve for $b$. We could also have used the point $(-3, 9)$.

$$y = mx + b$$
$$-2 = -\frac{11}{4} \cdot 1 + b$$
$$-\frac{8}{4} = -\frac{11}{4} + b$$
$$\frac{3}{4} = b$$

Then substituting $-\frac{11}{4}$ for $m$ and $\frac{3}{4}$ for $b$ in $y = mx + b$, we have $y = -\frac{11}{4}x + \frac{3}{4}$.

**Practice Exercise**

17. Find an equation of the line containing the points $(-2, 7)$ and $(4, -3)$.

---

**Objective 2.6d**    Given a line and a point not on the given line, find an equation of the line parallel to the line and containing the point, and find an equation of the line perpendicular to the line and containing the point.

**Example**    Write an equation of the line containing $(-1, 1)$ and parallel to $3y - 6x = 5$.

Solving $3y - 6x = 5$ for $y$, we get $y = 2x + \frac{5}{3}$. The slope of the given line is 2.

A line parallel to the given line must have the same slope, 2. We substitute 2 for $m$, $-1$ for $x_1$, and 1 for $y_1$ in the point–slope equation:

$$y - 1 = 2[x - (-1)] \quad \text{Using } y - y_1 = m(x - x_1)$$
$$y - 1 = 2(x + 1)$$
$$y - 1 = 2x + 2$$
$$y = 2x + 3. \quad \text{Line parallel to the given line and passing through } (-1, 1)$$

**Example**    Write an equation of the line containing the point $(2, -4)$ and perpendicular to $6x + 2y = 13$.

Solving $6x + 2y = 13$ for $y$, we get $y = -3x + \frac{13}{2}$. The slope of the given line is $-3$.

The slope of a line perpendicular to the given line is the opposite of the reciprocal of $-3$, or $\frac{1}{3}$. We substitute $\frac{1}{3}$ for $m$, 2 for $x_1$, and $-4$ for $y_1$ in the point–slope equation:

$$y - (-4) = \frac{1}{3}(x - 2) \quad \text{Using } y - y_1 = m(x - x_1)$$
$$y + 4 = \frac{1}{3}x - \frac{2}{3}$$
$$y = \frac{1}{3}x - \frac{14}{3}. \quad \text{Line perpendicular to the given line and passing through } (2, -4)$$

**Practice Exercises**

18. Write an equation of the line containing the point $(2, -5)$ and parallel to $4x - 3y = 6$.

19. Write an equation of the line containing $(2, -5)$ and perpendicular to $4x - 3y = 6$.

## Review Exercises

1. Show that the ordered pairs $(0, -2)$ and $(-1, -5)$ are solutions of the equation $3x - y = 2$. Then use the graph of the two points to determine another solution. Answers may vary. Show your work.   [2.1a, b]

Graph.   [2.1c, d]

2. $y = -3x + 2$

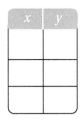
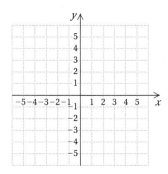

3. $y = \frac{5}{2}x - 3$

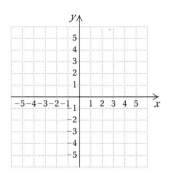

4. $y = |x - 3|$

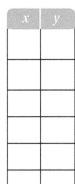
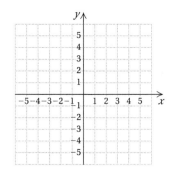

5. $y = 3 - x^2$

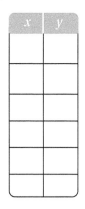
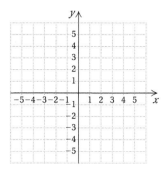

Determine whether each correspondence is a function. [2.2a]

6.

7.

Find the function values.   [2.2b]

8. $g(x) = -2x + 5$;  $g(0)$ and $g(-1)$

9. $f(x) = 3x^2 - 2x + 7$;  $f(0)$ and $f(-1)$

10. *Tuition Cost.*   The function $C(t) = 309.2t + 3717.7$ can be used to approximate the average cost of tuition and fees for in-state students at public four-year colleges, where $t$ is the number of years after 2000. Estimate the average cost of tuition and fees in 2010. That is, find $C(10)$.   [2.2b]
**Source:** U.S. National Center for Education Statistics

Determine whether each of the following is the graph of a function.   [2.2d]

11.

12.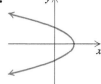

**13.** For the following graph of a function $f$, determine **(a)** $f(2)$; **(b)** the domain; **(c)** all $x$-values such that $f(x) = 2$; and **(d)** the range. [2.3a]

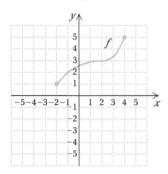

Find the domain. [2.3a]

**14.** $f(x) = \dfrac{5}{x - 4}$          **15.** $g(x) = x - x^2$

Find the slope and the $y$-intercept. [2.4a, b]

**16.** $y = -3x + 2$          **17.** $4y + 2x = 8$

**18.** Find the slope, if it exists, of the line containing the points $(13, 7)$ and $(10, -4)$. [2.4b]

Find the intercepts. Then graph the equation. [2.5a]

**19.** $2y + x = 4$

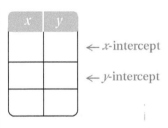

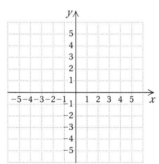

**20.** $2y = 6 - 3x$

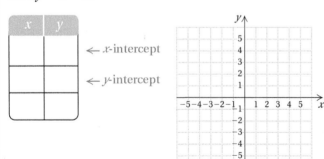

Graph using the slope and the $y$-intercept. [2.5b]

**21.** $g(x) = -\frac{2}{3}x - 4$          **22.** $f(x) = \frac{5}{2}x + 3$

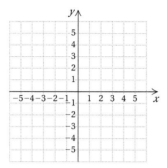 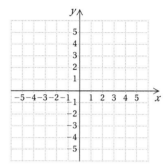

Graph. [2.5c]

**23.** $x = -3$          **24.** $f(x) = 4$

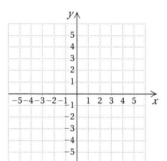 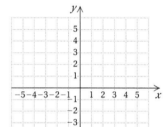

Determine whether the graphs of the given pair of lines are parallel or perpendicular. [2.5d]

**25.** $y + 5 = -x,$          **26.** $3x - 5 = 7y,$
     $x - y = 2$                $7y - 3x = 7$

**27.** $4y + x = 3,$          **28.** $x = 4,$
     $2x + 8y = 5$               $y = -3$

**29.** Find a linear function $f(x) = mx + b$ whose graph has the given slope and $y$-intercept: [2.6a]

        slope: 4.7;    $y$-intercept: $(0, -23)$.

**30.** Find an equation of the line having the given slope and containing the given point: [2.6b]

        $m = -3;$    $(3, -5)$.

**31.** Find an equation of the line containing the given pair of points:   [2.6c]

$(-2,3)$   and   $(-4,6)$.

**32.** Find an equation of the line containing the given point and parallel to the given line:   [2.6d]

$(14,-1)$;   $5x + 7y = 8$.

**33.** Find an equation of the line containing the given point and perpendicular to the given line:   [2.6d]

$(5,2)$;   $3x + y = 5$.

**34.** *Records in the 400-Meter Run.*   The table below shows data regarding the world indoor records in the men's 400-m run.   [2.6e]

| YEAR | RECORDS IN THE 400-M RUN (in seconds) |
|------|----------------------------------------|
| 1970 | 46.8 |
| 2004 | 44.63 |

**a)** Use the two data points to find a linear function that fits the data. Let $x$ = the number of years since 1970 and $R(x)$ = the world record $x$ years from 1970.

**b)** Use the function to estimate the world record in the men's 400-m run in 2008 and in 2010.

**35.** What is the domain of $f(x) = \dfrac{x + 3}{x - 2}$?   [2.3a]

**A.** $[-3,\infty)$       **B.** $(-\infty,0) \cup (0,2) \cup (2,\infty)$
**C.** $(-\infty,2) \cup (2,\infty)$       **D.** $(-3,\infty)$

**36.** Find an equation of the line containing the point $(-2,1)$ and perpendicular to $3y - \frac{1}{2}x = 0$.   [2.6d]

**A.** $6x + y = -11$       **B.** $y = -\dfrac{1}{6}x - 11$

**C.** $y = -2x - 3$       **D.** $2x + \dfrac{1}{3} = 0$

## Synthesis

**37.** Homespun Jellies charges $2.49 for each jar of preserves. Shipping charges are $3.75 for handling, plus $0.60 per jar. Find a linear function for determining the cost of buying and shipping $x$ jars of preserves.   [2.6e]

# Understanding Through Discussion and Writing

**1.** Under what conditions will the $x$-intercept and the $y$-intercept of a line be the same? What would the equation for such a line look like?   [2.5a]

**2.** Explain the usefulness of the concept of slope when describing a line.   [2.4b, c], [2.5b], [2.6a, b, c, d]

**3.** A student makes a mistake when using a graphing calculator to draw $4x + 5y = 12$ and the following screen appears. Use algebra to show that a mistake has been made. What do you think the mistake was?   [2.4b]

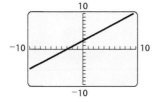

**4.** *Computer Repair.*   The cost $R(t)$, in dollars, of computer repair at PC Pros is given by

$$R(t) = 50t + 35,$$

where $t$ is the number of hours that the repair requires. Determine $m$ and $b$ in this application and explain their meaning.   [2.6e]

**5.** Explain why the slope of a vertical line is not defined but the slope of a horizontal line is 0.   [2.5c]

**6.** A student makes a mistake when using a graphing calculator to draw $5x - 2y = 3$ and the following screen appears. Use algebra to show that a mistake has been made. What do you think the mistake was?   [2.4b]

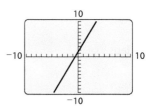

**CHAPTER**

**2**

**Test**

For Extra Help

CHAPTER
Test Prep
VIDEOS

Step-by-step test solutions are found on the Chapter Test Prep Videos available via the Video Resources on DVD, in *MyMathLab*, and on YouTube (search "BittingerInterAlgPB" and click on "Channels").

Determine whether the given points are solutions of the equation.

**1.** $(2, -3)$; $\quad y = 5 - 4x$

**2.** $(2, -3)$; $\quad 5b - 7a = 10$

Graph.

**3.** $y = -2x - 5$

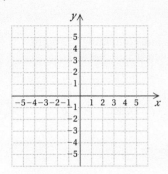

**4.** $f(x) = -\dfrac{3}{5}x$

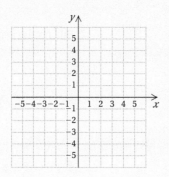

**5.** $g(x) = 2 - |x|$

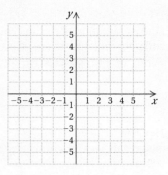

**6.** $y = \dfrac{4}{x}$

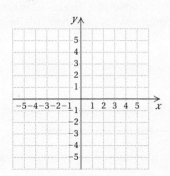

**7.** $y = f(x) = -3$

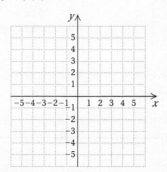

**8.** $2x = -4$

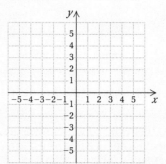

**9.** *Median Age of Cars.* The function

$$A(t) = 0.233t + 5.87$$

can be used to estimate the median age of cars in the United States $t$ years after 1990. (In this context, we mean that if the median age of cars is 3 yr, then half the cars are older than 3 yr and half are younger.)

**Source:** The Polk Co.

**a)** Find the median age of cars in 2002.
**b)** In what year was the median age of cars 7.734 yr?

Determine whether each correspondence is a function.

**10.** cat     dog
fish     worm
dog     cat
tiger     fish
teacher ⟶ student

**11.** Lake Placid     1980
Oslo     1976
Squaw Valley     1960
Innsbruck     1952
    1932

Find the function values.

**12.** $f(x) = -3x - 4$; $\quad f(0)$ and $f(-2)$

**13.** $g(x) = x^2 + 7$; $\quad g(0)$ and $g(-1)$

Determine whether each of the following is the graph of a function.

**14.**

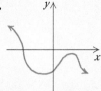

**15.**

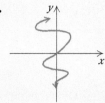

Find the domain.

**16.** $f(x) = \dfrac{8}{2x + 3}$

**17.** $g(x) = 5 - x^2$

**18.** For the following graph of function $f$, determine **(a)** $f(1)$; **(b)** the domain; **(c)** all $x$-values such that $f(x) = 2$; and **(d)** the range.

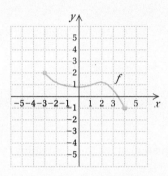

Find the slope and the $y$-intercept.

**19.** $f(x) = -\frac{3}{5}x + 12$

**20.** $-5y - 2x = 7$

Find the slope, if it exists, of the line containing the following points.

**21.** $(-2, -2)$ and $(6, 3)$

**22.** $(-3.1, 5.2)$ and $(-4.4, 5.2)$

**23.** Find the slope, or rate of change, of the graph at right.

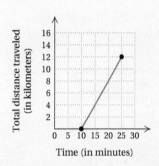

**24.** Find the intercepts. Then graph the equation.

$$2x + 3y = 6$$

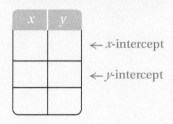

**25.** Graph using the slope and the $y$-intercept:

$$f(x) = -\frac{2}{3}x - 1.$$

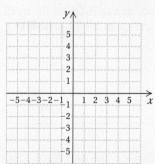

Determine whether the graphs of the given pair of lines are parallel or perpendicular.

**26.** $4y + 2 = 3x$,
  $-3x + 4y = -12$

**27.** $y = -2x + 5$,
  $2y - x = 6$

**28.** Find an equation of the line that has the given characteristics:
  slope: $-3$;  $y$-intercept: $(0, 4.8)$.

**29.** Find a linear function $f(x) = mx + b$ whose graph has the given slope and $y$-intercept:
  slope: $5.2$;  $y$-intercept: $\left(0, -\frac{5}{8}\right)$.

**30.** Find an equation of the line having the given slope and containing the given point:
  $m = -4$;  $(1, -2)$.

**31.** Find an equation of the line containing the given pair of points:
  $(4, -6)$  and  $(-10, 15)$.

**32.** Find an equation of the line containing the given point and parallel to the given line:
  $(4, -1)$;  $x - 2y = 5$.

**33.** Find an equation of the line containing the given point and perpendicular to the given line:
  $(2, 5)$;  $x + 3y = 2$.

**34.** *Median Age of Men at First Marriage.* The table below lists data regarding the median age of men at first marriage in 1970 and in 2007.

| YEAR | MEDIAN AGE OF MEN AT FIRST MARRIAGE |
|------|-------------------------------------|
| 1970 | 23.2 |
| 2007 | 27.7 |

SOURCE: U.S. Census Bureau

**a)** Use the two data points to find a linear function that fits the data. Let $x$ = the number of years since 1970 and $A$ = the median age at first marriage $x$ years from 1970.

**b)** Use the function to estimate the median age of men at first marriage in 2008 and in 2015.

**35.** Find an equation of the line having slope $-2$ and containing the point $(3, 1)$.
  **A.** $y - 1 = 2(x - 3)$      **B.** $y - 1 = -2(x - 3)$
  **C.** $x - 1 = -2(y - 3)$      **D.** $x - 1 = 2(y - 3)$

## Synthesis

**36.** Find $k$ such that the line $3x + ky = 17$ is perpendicular to the line $8x - 5y = 26$.

**37.** Find a formula for a function $f$ for which $f(-2) = 3$.

# Cumulative Review

1. *Records in the 1500-Meter Run.* The table below lists data regarding the world indoor records in the men's 1500-m run in 1950 and in 2004.

| YEAR | RECORDS IN THE 1500-M RUN (in minutes) |
|------|------|
| 1950 | 3.85 |
| 2004 | 3.50 |

**a)** Use the two data points to find a linear function that fits the data. Let $x$ = the number of years since 1950 and $R(x)$ = the world record $x$ years from 1950.

**b)** Use the function to estimate the world record in the 1500-m run in 2008 and in 2010.

2. For the graph of function $f$ shown below, determine
**(a)** $f(15)$; **(b)** the domain; **(c)** all $x$-values such that $f(x) = 14$; and **(d)** the range.

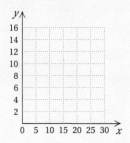

Solve.

3. $x + 9.4 = -12.6$

4. $\frac{2}{3}x - \frac{1}{4} = -\frac{4}{5}x$

5. $-2.4t = -48$

6. $4x + 7 = -14$

7. $3n - (4n - 2) = 7$

8. $5y - 10 = 10 + 5y$

9. Solve $W = Ax + By$ for $x$.

10. Solve $M = A + 4AB$ for $A$.

Solve.

11. $y - 12 \le -5$

12. $6x - 7 < 2x - 13$

13. $5(1 - 2x) + x < 2(3 + x)$

14. $x + 3 < -1 \ or \ x + 9 \ge 1$

15. $-3 < x + 4 \le 8$

16. $-8 \le 2x - 4 \le -1$

17. $|x| = 8$

18. $|y| > 4$

19. $|4x - 1| \le 7$

20. Find an equation of the line containing the point $(-4, -6)$ and perpendicular to the line whose equation is $4y - x = 3$.

21. Find an equation of the line containing the point $(-4, -6)$ and parallel to the line whose equation is $4y - x = 3$.

Graph on a plane.

**22.** $y = -2x + 3$

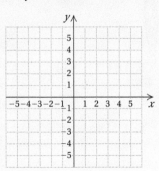

**23.** $3x = 2y + 6$

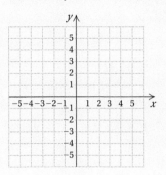

**24.** $4x + 16 = 0$

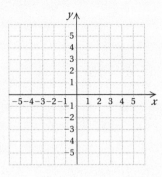

**25.** $-2y = -6$

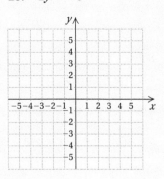

**26.** $f(x) = \dfrac{2}{3}x + 1$

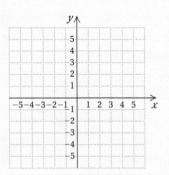

**27.** $g(x) = 5 - |x|$

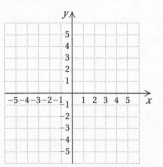

**28.** Find the slope and the $y$-intercept of $-4y + 9x = 12$.

**29.** Find the slope, if it exists, of the line containing the points $(2, 7)$ and $(-1, 3)$.

**30.** Find an equation of the line with slope $-3$ and containing the point $(2, -11)$.

**31.** Find an equation of the line containing the points $(-6, 3)$ and $(4, 2)$.

Solve.

**32.** *Lot Dimensions.* The perimeter of a lot is 80 m. The length exceeds the width by 6 m. Find the dimensions.

**33.** *Salary Raise.* After David receives a 20% raise in salary, his new salary is $27,000. What was the old salary?

## Synthesis

**34.** Which pairs of the following four equations represent perpendicular lines?
   **(1)** $7y - 3x = 21$
   **(2)** $-3x - 7y = 12$
   **(3)** $7y + 3x = 21$
   **(4)** $3y + 7x = 12$

**35.** *Radio Advertising.* Wayside Auto Sales discovers that when $1000 is spent on radio advertising, weekly sales increase by $101,000. When $1250 is spent on radio advertising, weekly sales increase by $126,000. Assuming that sales increase according to a linear equation, by what would sales increase when $1500 is spent on radio advertising?

**36.** Solve: $x + 5 < 3x - 7 \le x + 13$.

# Systems of Equations

## Real-World Application

To stimulate the economy in his town of Brewton, Alabama, in 2009, Danny Cottrell, co-owner of The Medical Center Pharmacy, gave each of his full-time employees $700 and each part-time employee $300. He asked that each person donate 15% to a charity of his or her choice and spend the rest locally. The money was paid in $2 bills, a rarely used currency, so that the business community could easily see how the money circulated. Cottrell gave away a total of $16,000 to his 24 employees. How many full-time employees and how many part-time employees were there?

*This problem appears as Example 7 in Section 3.3.*

# 3.1

# Systems of Equations in Two Variables

## OBJECTIVE

**a** Solve a system of two linear equations or two functions by graphing and determine whether a system is consistent or inconsistent and whether the equations in a system are dependent or independent.

**SKILL TO REVIEW**
Objective 2.1c: Graph linear equations using tables.

Graph.

**1.** $x + y = 3$    **2.** $y = x - 2$

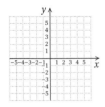 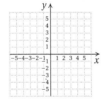

We can solve many applied problems more easily by translating them to two or more equations in two or more variables than by translating to a single equation. Let's look at such a problem.

*Mother's Day Spending.*   Mother's Day ranks fourth in spending in the United States behind the winter holidays, back-to-school buying, and Valentine's Day. About $15.8 billion was spent to celebrate Mother's Day in 2008. Of this amount, a total of $5 billion was spent on meals in restaurants and flowers. The amount spent on restaurant meals was $1 billion more than the amount spent on flowers. How much was spent on each?

Source: National Retail Association

To solve, we first let

$x =$ the amount spent on restaurant meals,   and

$y =$ the amount spent on flowers,

where $x$ and $y$ are in billions of dollars. The problem gives us two statements that can be translated to equations.

First, we consider the total amount spent on meals and flowers:

| Amount spent on meals | plus | Amount spent on flowers | is | Total amount spent |
|:---:|:---:|:---:|:---:|:---:|
| $x$ | $+$ | $y$ | $=$ | 5. |

The second statement compares the two different amounts spent:

| Amount spent on meals | is | $1 billion more than amount spent on flowers |
|:---:|:---:|:---:|
| $x$ | $=$ | $y + 1.$ |

We have now translated the problem to a pair, or **system, of equations**:

$$x + y = 5,$$
$$x = y + 1.$$

A **solution** of a system of two equations in two variables is an ordered pair that makes *both* equations true. If we graph a system of equations, the point at which the graphs intersect will be a solution of *both* equations.

*Answers*

*Skill to Review:*

**1.**

$x + y = 3$

**2.**

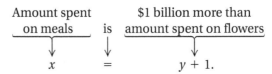

$y = x - 2$

We graph the equations listed on the preceding page.

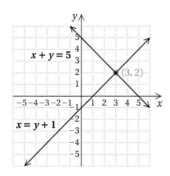

We see that the graphs intersect at the point $(3, 2)$—that is, $x = 3$ and $y = 2$. These numbers check in the statement of the original problem. This tells us that $3 billion was spent on restaurant meals and $2 billion was spent on flowers.

## a  Solving Systems of Equations Graphically

As we have just seen, we can solve systems of equations graphically.

### One Solution

**EXAMPLE 1**   Solve this system graphically:

$$y - x = 1,$$
$$y + x = 3.$$

We draw the graph of each equation using any method studied in Chapter 2 and find the coordinates of the point of intersection.

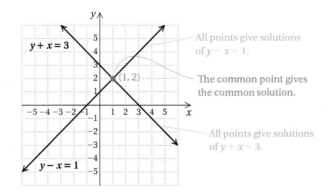

The point of intersection has coordinates that make *both* equations true. The solution seems to be the point $(1, 2)$. However, solving by graphing may give only approximate answers. Thus we check the pair $(1, 2)$ in both equations.

Check:
$$\begin{array}{c|c} y - x = 1 & y + x = 3 \\ \hline 2 - 1 \;?\; 1 & 2 + 1 \;?\; 3 \\ 1 \;\mid\; \text{TRUE} & 3 \;\mid\; \text{TRUE} \end{array}$$

The solution is $(1, 2)$.

Do Exercises 1 and 2.

Solve each system graphically.

**1.** $-2x + y = 1,$
$\quad 3x + y = 1$

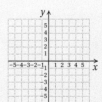

**2.** $y = \frac{1}{2}x,$
$\quad y = -\frac{1}{4}x + \frac{3}{2}$

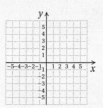

*Answers*

**1.** $(0, 1)$    **2.** $(2, 1)$

**Solving Systems of Equations**   We can solve a system of two equations in two variables using a graphing calculator. Consider the system of equations in Example 1:

$$y - x = 1,$$
$$y + x = 3.$$

First, we solve the equations for $y$, obtaining $y = x + 1$ and $y = -x + 3$. Next, we enter $y_1 = x + 1$ and $y_2 = -x + 3$ on the equation-editor screen and graph the equations. We can use the standard viewing window, $[-10, 10, -10, 10]$.

We will use the INTERSECT feature to find the coordinates of the point of intersection of the lines. To access this feature, we press **2ND** **CALC** **5**. (CALC is the second operation associated with the **TRACE** key.) The query "First curve?" appears on the graph screen. The blinking cursor is positioned on the graph of $y_1$. We press **ENTER** to indicate that this is the first curve involved in the intersection. Next, the query "Second curve?" appears and the blinking cursor is positioned on the graph of $y_2$. We press **ENTER** to indicate that this is the second curve. Now the query "Guess?" appears. We use the ▷ and ◁ keys to move the cursor close to the point of intersection or we enter an $x$-value close to the first coordinate of the point of intersection. Then we press **ENTER**. The coordinates of the point of intersection of the graphs, $x = 1$, $y = 2$, appear at the bottom of the screen. Thus the solution of the system of equations is $(1, 2)$.

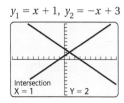

$$y_1 = x + 1, \quad y_2 = -x + 3$$

Intersection
X = 1        Y = 2

**Exercises:**   Use a graphing calculator to solve each system of equations.

**1.** $x + y = 5,$
$\quad y = x + 1$

**2.** $y = x + 3,$
$\quad 2x - y = -7$

**3.** $x - y = -6,$
$\quad y = 2x + 7$

**4.** $x + 4y = -1,$
$\quad x - y = 4$

## No Solution

Sometimes the equations in a system have graphs that are parallel lines.

**EXAMPLE 2**   Solve graphically:

$$f(x) = -3x + 5,$$
$$g(x) = -3x - 2.$$

Note that this system is written using function notation. We graph the functions. The graphs have the same slope, $-3$, and different $y$-intercepts, so they are parallel. There is no point at which they cross, so the system has no solution. No matter what point we try, it will *not* check in *both* equations. The solution set is thus the empty set, denoted $\varnothing$ or $\{\ \}$.

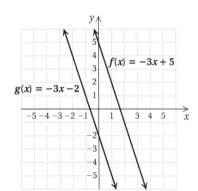

$f(x) = -3x + 5$

$g(x) = -3x - 2$

> **CONSISTENT SYSTEMS AND**
> **INCONSISTENT SYSTEMS**
>
> If a system of equations has at least one solution, it is **consistent**.
>
> If a system of equations has no solution, it is **inconsistent**.

The system in Example 1 is consistent. The system in Example 2 is inconsistent.

> Do Exercises 3 and 4.

### Infinitely Many Solutions

Sometimes the equations in a system have the same graph. In such a case, the equations have an *infinite* number of solutions in common.

**EXAMPLE 3**  Solve graphically:

$$3y - 2x = 6,$$
$$-12y + 8x = -24.$$

We graph the equations and see that the graphs are the same. Thus any solution of one of the equations is a solution of the other. Each equation has an infinite number of solutions, two of which are shown on the graph.

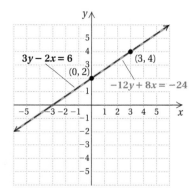

We check one such solution, $(0, 2)$, which is the $y$-intercept of each equation.

Check:

| $3y - 2x = 6$ | | $-12y + 8x = -24$ | |
|---|---|---|---|
| $3(2) - 2(0)$ ? 6 | | $-12(2) + 8(0)$ ? $-24$ | |
| $6 - 0$ | | $-24 + 0$ | |
| 6 | TRUE | $-24$ | TRUE |

On your own, check that $(3, 4)$ is a solution of both equations. If $(0, 2)$ and $(3, 4)$ are solutions, then all points on the line containing them will be solutions. The system has an infinite number of solutions.

**3.** Solve graphically:

$$y + 2x = 3,$$
$$y + 2x = -4.$$

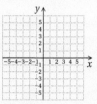

**4.** Classify each of the systems in Margin Exercises 1–3 as consistent or inconsistent.

*Answers*

**3.** No solution     **4.** Consistent: Margin Exercises 1 and 2; inconsistent: Margin Exercise 3

If a system of two equations in two variables:

has infinitely many solutions, the equations are **dependent**.

has one solution or no solutions, the equations are **independent**.

When we graph a system of two equations, one of the following three things can happen.

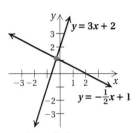

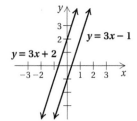

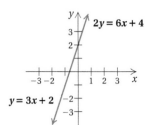

**One solution.**
Graphs intersect.
*The system is* consistent
and *the equations are*
independent.

**No solution.**
Graphs are parallel.
*The system is* inconsistent
and *the equations are*
independent.

**Infinitely many solutions.**
Equations have the same
graph. *The system is* consistent
and *the equations are*
dependent.

Let's summarize what we know about the systems of equations in Examples 1–3. The system in Example 1 has exactly one solution, and the system in Example 3 has an infinite number of solutions. Since each system has at least one solution, both systems are *consistent*. The system of equations in Example 2 has no solution, so it is *inconsistent*.

The system of equations in Example 1 has exactly one solution, and the system in Example 2 has no solutions. Thus the equations in each of these systems are *independent*. In a system of equations with infinitely many solutions, the equations are dependent. This tells us that the equations in Example 3 are *dependent*. In a system with dependent equations, one equation can be obtained by multiplying the other equation by a constant.

Do Exercises 5 and 6.

**5.** Solve graphically:
$$2x - 5y = 10,$$
$$-6x + 15y = -30.$$

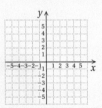

**6.** Classify the equations in Margin Exercises 1, 2, 3, and 5 as dependent or independent.

### ✕ Algebraic-Graphical Connection

To bring together the concepts of Chapters 1–3, let's look at equation solving from both algebraic and graphical viewpoints.

Consider the equation $-2x + 13 = 4x - 17$. Let's solve it algebraically as we did in Chapter 1:

$$-2x + 13 = 4x - 17$$
$$13 = 6x - 17 \qquad \text{Adding } 2x$$
$$30 = 6x \qquad \text{Adding } 17$$
$$5 = x. \qquad \text{Dividing by } 6$$

*Answers*

**5.** Infinitely many solutions
**6.** Independent: Margin Exercises 1, 2, and 3;
dependent: Margin Exercise 5

Could we also solve the equation graphically? The answer is yes, as we see in the following two methods.

METHOD 1: Solve $-2x + 13 = 4x - 17$ graphically.

We let $f(x) = -2x + 13$ and $g(x) = 4x - 17$. Graphing the system of equations, we get the graph shown below.

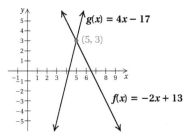

The point of intersection of the two graphs is $(5, 3)$. Note that the $x$-coordinate of this point is 5. This is the value of $x$ for which $-2x + 13 = 4x - 17$, so it is the solution of the equation.

Do Exercises 7 and 8.

METHOD 2: Solve $-2x + 13 = 4x - 17$ graphically.

Adding $-4x$ and 17 on both sides, we obtain an equation with 0 on one side: $-6x + 30 = 0$. This time we let $f(x) = -6x + 30$ and $g(x) = 0$. Since the graph of $g(x) = 0$, or $y = 0$, is the $x$-axis, we need only graph $f(x) = -6x + 30$ and see where it crosses the $x$-axis.

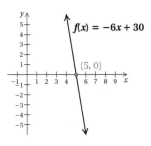

Note that the $x$-intercept of $f(x) = -6x + 30$ is $(5, 0)$, or just 5. This $x$-value is the solution of the equation $-2x + 13 = 4x - 17$.

Do Exercise 9.

Let's compare the two methods. Using Method 1, we graph two functions. The solution of the original equation is the $x$-coordinate of the point of intersection. Using Method 2, we graph one function. The solution of the original equation is the $x$-coordinate of the $x$-intercept of the graph.

Do Exercise 10.

7. a) Solve $x + 1 = \frac{2}{3}x$ algebraically.

   b) Solve $x + 1 = \frac{2}{3}x$ graphically using Method 1.

8. Solve $\frac{1}{2}x + 3 = 2$ graphically using Method 1.

9. a) Solve $x + 1 = \frac{2}{3}x$ graphically using Method 2.

   b) Compare your answers to Margin Exercises 7(a), 7(b), and 9(a).

10. Solve $\frac{1}{2}x + 3 = 2$ graphically using Method 2.

*Answers*

7. (a) $-3$; (b) the same: $-3$    8. $-2$
9. (a) $-3$; (b) All are $-3$.    10. $-2$

For Extra Help

**MyMathLab**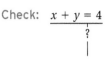

Math XL  PRACTICE  WATCH  DOWNLOAD  READ  REVIEW

**a** Solve each system of equations graphically. Then classify the system as consistent or inconsistent and the equations as dependent or independent. Complete the check for Exercises 1–4.

**1.** $x + y = 4,$
$\quad x - y = 2$

Check: $\begin{array}{c} x + y = 4 \\ \hline ? \\ \\ x - y = 2 \\ \hline ? \end{array}$

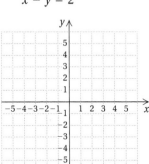

**2.** $x - y = 3,$
$\quad x + y = 5$

Check: $\begin{array}{c} x - y = 3 \\ \hline ? \\ \\ x + y = 5 \\ \hline ? \end{array}$

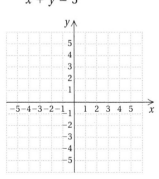

**3.** $2x - y = 4,$
$\quad 2x + 3y = -4$

Check: $\begin{array}{c} 2x - y = 4 \\ \hline ? \\ \\ 2x + 3y = -4 \\ \hline ? \end{array}$

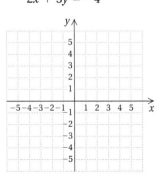

**4.** $3x + y = 5,$
$\quad x - 2y = 4$

Check: $\begin{array}{c} 3x + y = 5 \\ \hline ? \\ \\ x - 2y = 4 \\ \hline ? \end{array}$

**5.** $2x + y = 6,$
$\quad 3x + 4y = 4$

**6.** $2y = 6 - x,$
$\quad 3x - 2y = 6$

**7.** $f(x) = x - 1,$
$\quad g(x) = -2x + 5$

**8.** $f(x) = x + 1,$
$\quad g(x) = \frac{2}{3}x$

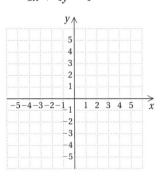

**9.** $2u + v = 3,$
  $2u = v + 7$

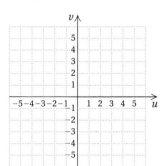

**10.** $2b + a = 11,$
  $a - b = 5$

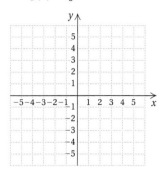

**11.** $f(x) = -\frac{1}{3}x - 1,$
  $g(x) = \frac{4}{3}x - 6$

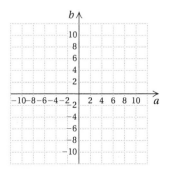

**12.** $f(x) = -\frac{1}{4}x + 1,$
  $g(x) = \frac{1}{2}x - 2$

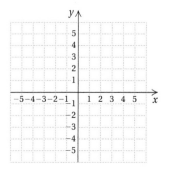

**13.** $6x - 2y = 2,$
  $9x - 3y = 1$

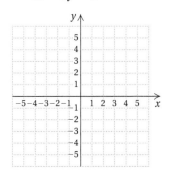

**14.** $y - x = 5,$
  $2x - 2y = 10$

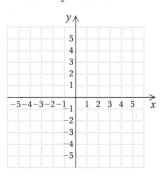

**15.** $2x - 3y = 6,$
  $3y - 2x = -6$

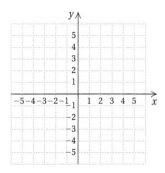

**16.** $y = 3 - x,$
  $2x + 2y = 6$

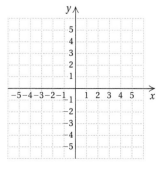

**17.** $x = 4,$
  $y = -5$

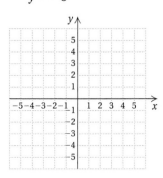

**18.** $x = -3,$
  $y = 2$

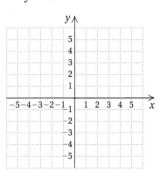

**19.** $y = -x - 1,$
  $4x - 3y = 17$

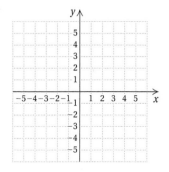

**20.** $a + 2b = -3,$
  $b - a = 6$

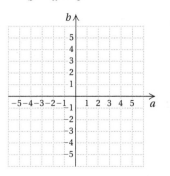

*Matching.* Each of Exercises 21–26 shows the graph of a system of equations and its solution. First, classify the system as consistent or inconsistent and the equations as dependent or independent. Then match it with one of the appropriate systems of equations (A)–(F), which follow.

**21.** Solution: $(3, 3)$

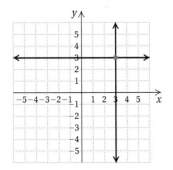

**22.** Solution: $(1, 1)$

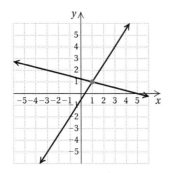

**23.** Solutions: Infinitely many

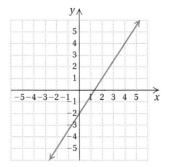

**24.** Solution: $(4, -3)$

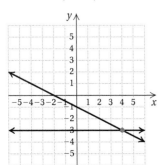

**25.** Solution: No solution

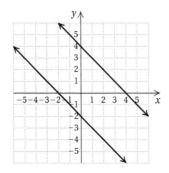

**26.** Solution: $(-1, 3)$

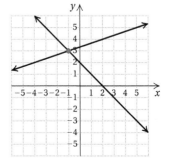

**A.** $3y - x = 10,$
$x = -y + 2$

**B.** $9x - 6y = 12,$
$y = \frac{3}{2}x - 2$

**C.** $2y - 3x = -1,$
$x + 4y = 5$

**D.** $x + y = 4,$
$y = -x - 2$

**E.** $\frac{1}{2}x + y = -1,$
$y = -3$

**F.** $x = 3,$
$y = 3$

## Skill Maintenance

Solve. [1.1d]

**27.** $3x + 4 = x - 2$

**28.** $\frac{3}{4}x + 2 = \frac{2}{5}x - 5$

**29.** $4x - 5x = 8x - 9 + 11x$

**30.** $5(10 - 4x) = -3(7x - 4)$

## Synthesis

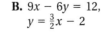 Use a graphing calculator to solve each system of equations. Round all answers to the nearest hundredth. You may need to solve for $y$ first.

**31.** $2.18x + 7.81y = 13.78,$
$5.79x - 3.45y = 8.94$

**32.** $f(x) = 123.52x + 89.32,$
$g(x) = -89.22x + 33.76$

Solve graphically.

**33.** $y = |x|,$
$x + 4y = 15$

**34.** $x - y = 0,$
$y = x^2$

# 3.2 Solving by Substitution

Consider this system of equations:

$$5x + 9y = 2,$$
$$4x - 9y = 10.$$

What is the solution? It is rather difficult to tell exactly by graphing. It would appear that fractions are involved. It turns out that the solution is

$$\left(\frac{4}{3}, -\frac{14}{27}\right).$$

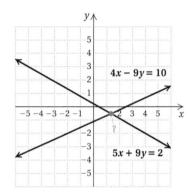

## OBJECTIVES

**a** Solve systems of equations in two variables by the substitution method.

**b** Solve applied problems by solving systems of two equations using substitution.

Solving by graphing, though useful in many applied situations, is not always fast or accurate in cases where solutions are not integers. We need techniques involving algebra to determine the solution exactly. Because they use algebra, they are called **algebraic methods**.

## a The Substitution Method

One nongraphical method for solving systems is known as the **substitution method**.

 **EXAMPLE 1** Solve this system:

$$x + y = 4, \quad (1)$$
$$x = y + 1. \quad (2)$$

Equation (2) says that $x$ and $y + 1$ name the same number. Thus we can substitute $y + 1$ for $x$ in equation (1):

$$x + y = 4 \quad \text{Equation (1)}$$
$$(y + 1) + y = 4. \quad \text{Substituting } y + 1 \text{ for } x$$

Since this equation has only one variable, we can solve for $y$ using methods learned earlier:

$$(y + 1) + y = 4$$
$$2y + 1 = 4 \quad \text{Removing parentheses and collecting like terms}$$
$$2y = 3 \quad \text{Subtracting 1}$$
$$y = \tfrac{3}{2}. \quad \text{Dividing by 2}$$

We return to the original pair of equations and substitute $\frac{3}{2}$ for $y$ in *either* equation so that we can solve for $x$. Calculation will be easier if we choose equation (2) since it is already solved for $x$:

$$x = y + 1 \quad \text{Equation (2)}$$
$$x = \tfrac{3}{2} + 1 \quad \text{Substituting } \tfrac{3}{2} \text{ for } y$$
$$x = \tfrac{3}{2} + \tfrac{2}{2} = \tfrac{5}{2}.$$

We obtain the ordered pair $\left(\frac{5}{2}, \frac{3}{2}\right)$. Even though we solved for *y first*, it is still the *second* coordinate since $x$ is before $y$ alphabetically. We check to be sure that the ordered pair is a solution.

*Answers*

*Skill to Review:*
**1.** 2  **2.** −3

Check: 

$$\frac{x + y = 4}{\frac{5}{2} + \frac{3}{2} \;?\; 4}$$
$$\frac{8}{2}$$
$$4 \quad \text{TRUE}$$

$$\frac{x = y + 1}{\frac{5}{2} \;?\; \frac{3}{2} + 1}$$
$$\frac{3}{2} + \frac{2}{2}$$
$$\frac{5}{2} \quad \text{TRUE}$$

Since $\left(\frac{5}{2}, \frac{3}{2}\right)$ checks, it is the solution. Even though exact fraction solutions are difficult to determine graphically, a graph can help us to visualize whether the solution is reasonable.

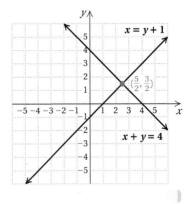

Do Exercises 1 and 2.

Suppose neither equation of a pair has a variable alone on one side. We then solve one equation for one of the variables.

**EXAMPLE 2** Solve this system:

$$2x + y = 6, \quad \textbf{(1)}$$
$$3x + 4y = 4. \quad \textbf{(2)}$$

First, we solve one equation for one variable. Since the coefficient of $y$ is 1 in equation (1), it is the easier one to solve for $y$:

$$y = 6 - 2x. \quad \textbf{(3)}$$

Next, we substitute $6 - 2x$ for $y$ in equation (2) and solve for $x$:

| | |
|---|---|
| $3x + 4(6 - 2x) = 4$ | Substituting $6 - 2x$ for $y$ |
| $3x + 24 - 8x = 4$ | Multiplying to remove parentheses |
| $24 - 5x = 4$ | Collecting like terms |
| $-5x = -20$ | Subtracting 24 |
| $x = 4.$ | Dividing by $-5$ |

-------- *Caution!* --------

Remember to use parentheses when you substitute. Then remove them properly.

In order to find $y$, we return to either of the original equations, (1) or (2), or equation (3), which we solved for $y$. It is generally easier to use an equation like (3), where we have solved for the specific variable. We substitute 4 for $x$ in equation (3) and solve for $y$:

$$y = 6 - 2x = 6 - 2(4) = 6 - 8 = -2.$$

We obtain the ordered pair $(4, -2)$.

Check: 

$$\frac{2x + y = 6}{2(4) + (-2) \;?\; 6}$$
$$8 - 2$$
$$6 \quad \text{TRUE}$$

$$\frac{3x + 4y = 4}{3(4) + 4(-2) \;?\; 4}$$
$$12 - 8$$
$$4 \quad \text{TRUE}$$

Since $(4, -2)$ checks, it is the solution.

Do Exercises 3 and 4.

---

Solve by the substitution method.

**1.** $x + y = 6,$
$\quad y = x + 2$

**2.** $y = 7 - x,$
$\quad 2x - y = 8$

(*Caution*: Use parentheses when you substitute, being careful about removing them. Remember to solve for both variables.)

---

Solve by the substitution method.

**3.** $2y + x = 1,$
$\quad y - 2x = 8$

**4.** $8x - 5y = 12,$
$\quad x - y = 3$

---

**Calculator Corner**

**Solving Systems of Equations** Use the INTERSECT feature to solve the systems of equations in Margin Exercises 1–4. (See the Calculator Corner on p. 246 for the procedure.)

---

*Answers*

**1.** $(2, 4)$ **2.** $(5, 2)$ **3.** $(-3, 2)$
**4.** $(-1, -4)$

**EXAMPLE 3**  Solve this system of equations:

$$y = -3x + 5, \quad \textbf{(1)}$$
$$y = -3x - 2. \quad \textbf{(2)}$$

We solved this system graphically in Example 2 of Section 3.1. We found that the graphs are parallel and the system has no solution. Let's try to solve this system algebraically using substitution.

We substitute $-3x - 2$ for $y$ in equation (1):

$$-3x - 2 = -3x + 5 \qquad \text{Substituting } -3x - 2 \text{ for } y$$
$$-2 = 5. \qquad \text{Adding } 3x$$

We have a false equation. The equation has no solution. (See also Example 17 of Section 1.1.)

> Do Exercise 5.

**5. a)** Solve this system of equations algebraically using substitution:

$$y + 2x = 3,$$
$$y + 2x = -4.$$

**b)** Check your answer in part (a) with the one you found graphically in Margin Exercise 3 of Section 3.1.

## (b) Solving Applied Problems Involving Two Equations

Many applied problems are easier to solve if we first translate to a system of two equations rather than to a single equation. Here we will solve a few problems that can be solved using substitution. Section 3.4 is devoted entirely to applied problems.

**EXAMPLE 4**  *Architecture.*  The architects who designed the John Hancock Building in Chicago created a visually appealing building that slants on the sides. The ground floor is a rectangle that is larger than the rectangle formed by the top floor. The ground floor has a perimeter of 860 ft. The length is 100 ft more than the width. Find the length and the width.

1. **Familiarize.**  We first make a drawing and label it, using $l$ for length and $w$ for width. We recall or look up the formula for perimeter: $P = 2l + 2w$. This formula can be found at the back of this book.

$l = w + 100$      $w$

2. **Translate.**  We translate as follows:

$$\underbrace{\text{The perimeter}}_{2l + 2w} \quad \underset{=}{\text{is}} \quad \underset{860}{860 \text{ ft.}}$$

We can also write a second equation:

$$\underbrace{\text{The length}}_{l} \quad \underset{=}{\text{is}} \quad \underbrace{\overset{100 \text{ ft more than}}{\text{the width.}}}_{w + 100.}$$

We now have a system of equations:

$$2l + 2w = 860, \quad \textbf{(1)}$$
$$l = w + 100. \quad \textbf{(2)}$$

***Answers***

**5. (a)** No solution; **(b)** the same—no solution

**6. Architecture.** The top floor of the John Hancock Building is also a rectangle, but its perimeter is 520 ft. The width is 60 ft less than the length. Find the length and the width.

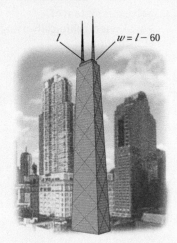

$l$      $w = l - 60$

**3. Solve.** We substitute $w + 100$ for $l$ in equation (1):

| | |
|---|---|
| $2(w + 100) + 2w = 860$ | Substituting in equation (1) |
| $2w + 200 + 2w = 860$ | Multiplying to remove parentheses on the left |
| $4w + 200 = 860$ | Collecting like terms |
| $\left.\begin{array}{r} 4w = 660 \\ w = 165. \end{array}\right\}$ | Solving for $w$ |

Next, we substitute 165 for $w$ in equation (2) and solve for $l$:

$$l = 165 + 100 = 265.$$

**4. Check.** Consider the dimensions 265 ft and 165 ft. The length is 100 ft more than the width. The perimeter is $2(265\text{ ft}) + 2(165\text{ ft})$, or 860 ft. The dimensions 265 ft and 165 ft check in the original problem.

**5. State.** The length is 265 ft, and the width is 165 ft.

Do Exercise 6.

---

---

*Answer*

**6.** Length: 160 ft; width: 100 ft

**a**    Solve each system of equations by the substitution method.

**1.** $y = 5 - 4x,$
$2x - 3y = 13$

**2.** $x = 8 - 4y,$
$3x + 5y = 3$

**3.** $2y + x = 9,$
$x = 3y - 3$

**4.** $9x - 2y = 3,$
$3x - 6 = y$

**5.** $3s - 4t = 14,$
$5s + t = 8$

**6.** $m - 2n = 3,$
$4m + n = 1$

**7.** $9x - 2y = -6,$
$7x + 8 = y$

**8.** $t = 4 - 2s,$
$t + 2s = 6$

**9.** $-5s + t = 11,$
$4s + 12t = 4$

**10.** $5x + 6y = 14,$
$-3y + x = 7$

**11.** $2x + 2y = 2,$
$3x - y = 1$

**12.** $4p - 2q = 16,$
$5p + 7q = 1$

**13.** $3a - b = 7,$
$2a + 2b = 5$

**14.** $5x + 3y = 4,$
$x - 4y = 3$

**15.** $2x - 3 = y,$
$y - 2x = 1$

**16.** $4x + 13y = 5,$
$-6x + y = 13$

**b**    Solve.

**17.** *Racquetball Court.*    A regulation racquetball court has a perimeter of 120 ft, with a length that is twice the width. Find the length and the width of such a court.

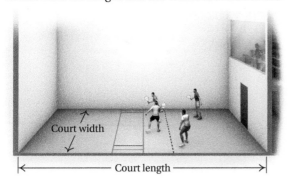

Court width

Court length

**18.** *Soccer Field.*    The perimeter of a soccer field is 340 m. The length exceeds the width by 50 m. Find the length and the width.

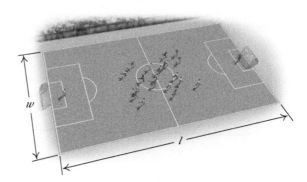

$w$

$l$

**19.** *Supplementary Angles.* **Supplementary angles** are angles whose sum is 180°. Two supplementary angles are such that one angle is 12° less than three times the other. Find the measures of the angles.

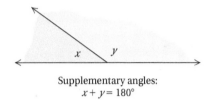

Supplementary angles:
$x + y = 180°$

**20.** *Complementary Angles.* **Complementary angles** are angles whose sum is 90°. Two complementary angles are such that one angle is 6° more than five times the other. Find the measures of the angles.

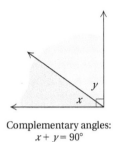

Complementary angles:
$x + y = 90°$

**21.** *Hockey Points.* At one time, hockey teams received two points when they won a game and one point when they tied. One season, a team won a championship with 60 points. They won 9 more games than they tied. How many wins and how many ties did the team have?

**22.** *Airplane Seating.* An airplane has a total of 152 seats. The number of coach-class seats is 5 more than six times the number of first-class seats. How many of each type of seat are there on the plane?

## Skill Maintenance

**23.** Find the slope of the line $y = 1.3x - 7$. [2.4b]

**24.** Simplify: $-9(y + 7) - 6(y - 4)$. [R.6b]

**25.** Solve $A = \dfrac{pq}{7}$ for $p$. [1.2a]

**26.** Find the slope of the line containing the points $(-2, 3)$ and $(-5, -4)$. [2.4b]

Solve. [1.1d]

**27.** $-4x + 5(x - 7) = 8x - 6(x + 2)$

**28.** $-12(2x - 3) = 16(4x - 5)$

## Synthesis

**29.** Two solutions of $y = mx + b$ are $(1, 2)$ and $(-3, 4)$. Find $m$ and $b$.

**30.** Solve for $x$ and $y$ in terms of $a$ and $b$:

$$5x + 2y = a,$$
$$x - y = b.$$

**31.** *Design.* A piece of posterboard has a perimeter of 156 in. If you cut 6 in. off the width, the length becomes four times the width. What are the dimensions of the original piece of posterboard?

**32.** *Nontoxic Scouring Powder.* A nontoxic scouring powder is made up of 4 parts baking soda and 1 part vinegar. How much of each ingredient is needed for a 16-oz mixture?

$P = 156$ in.

# 3.3 Solving by Elimination

## a The Elimination Method

The **elimination method** for solving systems of equations makes use of the *addition principle* for equations. Some systems are much easier to solve using the elimination method rather than the substitution method.

**EXAMPLE 1** Solve this system:

$$2x - 3y = 0, \qquad \textbf{(1)}$$
$$-4x + 3y = -1. \qquad \textbf{(2)}$$

The key to the advantage of the elimination method in this case is the $-3y$ in one equation and the $3y$ in the other. These terms are opposites. If we add them, these terms will add to 0, and in effect, the variable $y$ will have been "eliminated."

We will use the addition principle for equations, adding the same number on both sides of the equation. According to equation (2), $-4x + 3y$ and $-1$ are the same number. Thus we can use a vertical form and add $-4x + 3y$ to the left side of equation (1) and $-1$ to the right side:

$$\begin{array}{ll} 2x - 3y = 0 & \textbf{(1)} \\ \underline{-4x + 3y = -1} & \textbf{(2)} \\ -2x + 0y = -1 & \text{Adding} \\ -2x + \phantom{0}0 = -1 \\ \phantom{-2x + 0}-2x = -1. \end{array}$$

We have eliminated the variable $y$, which is why we call this the *elimination method*.* We now have an equation with just one variable, which we solve for $x$:

$$-2x = -1$$
$$x = \tfrac{1}{2}.$$

Next, we substitute $\tfrac{1}{2}$ for $x$ in either equation and solve for $y$:

$$\begin{array}{ll} 2 \cdot \tfrac{1}{2} - 3y = 0 & \text{Substituting in equation (1)} \\ 1 - 3y = 0 \\ -3y = -1 & \text{Subtracting 1} \\ y = \tfrac{1}{3}. & \text{Dividing by } -3 \end{array}$$

We obtain the ordered pair $\left(\tfrac{1}{2}, \tfrac{1}{3}\right)$.

Check:
$$\begin{array}{c|c}
\begin{array}{c} 2x - 3y = 0 \\ \hline 2\left(\tfrac{1}{2}\right) - 3\left(\tfrac{1}{3}\right) \overset{?}{=} 0 \\ 1 - 1 \\ 0 \quad \text{TRUE} \end{array}
&
\begin{array}{c} -4x + 3y = -1 \\ \hline -4\left(\tfrac{1}{2}\right) + 3\left(\tfrac{1}{3}\right) \overset{?}{=} -1 \\ -2 + 1 \\ -1 \quad \text{TRUE} \end{array}
\end{array}$$

*This method is also called the *addition method*.

## OBJECTIVES

**a** Solve systems of equations in two variables by the elimination method.

**b** Solve applied problems by solving systems of two equations using elimination.

**SKILL TO REVIEW**
Objective 1.1d: Solve equations using the addition principle and the multiplication principle together, removing parentheses where appropriate.

Solve. Clear the fractions or decimals first.

**1.** $\tfrac{1}{2}x + \tfrac{3}{4}y = 2,$
$\tfrac{4}{3}x + \tfrac{1}{6}y = -2$

**2.** $0.5x - 0.3y = 3.4,$
$0.3x + 0.4y = 0.3$

*Answers*

*Skill to Review:*
**1.** $(-2, 4)$ **2.** $(5, -3)$

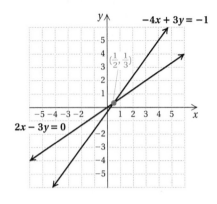

$-4x + 3y = -1$

$2x - 3y = 0$

Solve by the elimination method.

**1.** $5x + 3y = 17,$
$-5x + 2y = 3$

**2.** $-3a + 2b = 0,$
$3a - 4b = -1$

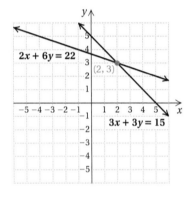

$2x + 6y = 22$

$(2, 3)$

$3x + 3y = 15$

**3.** Solve by the elimination method:

$$2y + 3x = 12,$$
$$-4y + 5x = -2.$$

Since $\left(\frac{1}{2}, \frac{1}{3}\right)$ checks, it is the solution. We can also see this in the graph shown at left.

Do Exercises 1 and 2.

In order to eliminate a variable, we sometimes use the multiplication principle to multiply one or both of the equations by a particular number before adding.

**EXAMPLE 2** Solve this system:

$$3x + 3y = 15, \quad \textbf{(1)}$$
$$2x + 6y = 22. \quad \textbf{(2)}$$

If we add directly, we get $5x + 9y = 37$, and we have not eliminated a variable. However, note that if the $3y$ in equation (1) were $-6y$, we could eliminate $y$. Thus we multiply by $-2$ on both sides of equation (1) and add:

$$
\begin{array}{ll}
-6x - 6y = -30 & \text{Multiplying by } -2 \text{ on both sides of equation (1)} \\
\underline{\phantom{-}2x + 6y = \phantom{-}22} & \text{Equation (2)} \\
-4x + \phantom{6}0 = \phantom{-}-8 & \text{Adding} \\
\phantom{-4x +}-4x = \phantom{-}-8 & \\
\phantom{-4x +}x = 2. & \text{Solving for } x
\end{array}
$$

Then

$$
\begin{array}{ll}
2 \cdot 2 + 6y = 22 & \text{Substituting 2 for } x \text{ in equation (2)} \\
4 + 6y = 22 & \\
6y = 18 & \text{Solving for } y \\
y = 3. &
\end{array}
$$

We obtain $(2, 3)$, or $x = 2$, $y = 3$. This checks, so it is the solution. We can also see this in the graph at left.

Do Exercise 3.

Sometimes we must multiply twice in order to make two terms opposites.

**EXAMPLE 3** Solve this system:

$$2x + 3y = 17, \quad \textbf{(1)}$$
$$5x + 7y = 29. \quad \textbf{(2)}$$

We must first multiply in order to make one pair of terms with the same variable opposites. We decide to do this with the $x$-terms in each equation. We multiply equation (1) by 5 and equation (2) by $-2$. Then we get $10x$ and $-10x$, which are opposites.

$$
\begin{array}{lll}
\textit{From equation (1):} & 10x + 15y = \phantom{-}85 & \text{Multiplying by 5} \\
\textit{From equation (2):} & \underline{-10x - 14y = -58} & \text{Multiplying by } -2 \\
& 0 + \phantom{1}y = \phantom{-}27 & \text{Adding} \\
& \phantom{0 + 1}y = 27 & \text{Solving for } y
\end{array}
$$

Then

$$2x + 3 \cdot 27 = 17 \qquad \text{Substituting 27 for } y \text{ in equation (1)}$$

$$\left. \begin{aligned} 2x + 81 &= 17 \\ 2x &= -64 \\ x &= -32. \end{aligned} \right\} \quad \text{Solving for } x$$

We check the ordered pair $(-32, 27)$.

Check:

$$\begin{array}{c|c} 2x + 3y = 17 \\ \hline 2(-32) + 3(27) \ ? \ 17 \\ -64 + 81 \ \Big| \\ 17 \ \Big| \qquad \text{TRUE} \end{array}$$

$$\begin{array}{c|c} 5x + 7y = 29 \\ \hline 5(-32) + 7(27) \ ? \ 29 \\ -160 + 189 \ \Big| \\ 29 \ \Big| \qquad \text{TRUE} \end{array}$$

We obtain $(-32, 27)$, or $x = -32$, $y = 27$, as the solution.

Do Exercises 4 and 5.

Some systems have no solution, as we saw graphically in Section 3.1 and algebraically in Example 3 of Section 3.2. How do we recognize such systems if we are solving using elimination?

**EXAMPLE 4**  Solve this system:

$$y + 3x = 5, \qquad \textbf{(1)}$$
$$y + 3x = -2. \qquad \textbf{(2)}$$

If we find the slope–intercept equations for this system, we get

$$y = -3x + 5,$$
$$y = -3x - 2.$$

The graphs are parallel lines.
The system has no solution.

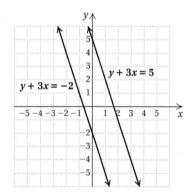

Let's see what happens if we attempt to solve the system by the elimination method. We multiply by $-1$ on both sides of equation (2) and add:

$$\begin{array}{ll} y + 3x = 5 & \text{Equation (1)} \\ \underline{-y - 3x = 2} & \text{Multiplying equation (2) by } -1 \\ \quad\ 0 = 7. & \text{Adding, we obtain a false equation.} \end{array}$$

The $x$-terms and the $y$-terms are eliminated and we have a *false* equation. Thus, if we obtain a false equation, such as $0 = 7$, when solving algebraically, we know that the system has no solution. The system is inconsistent, and the equations are independent.

Do Exercise 6.

Solve by the elimination method.

**4.** $4x + 5y = -8,$
     $7x + 9y = 11$

**5.** $4x - 5y = 38,$
     $7x - 8y = -22$

**6.** Solve by the elimination method:

$$y + 2x = 3,$$
$$y + 2x = -1.$$

***Answers***

**4.** $(-127, 100)$  **5.** $(-138, -118)$
**6.** No solution

Some systems have infinitely many solutions. How can we recognize such a situation when we are solving systems using an algebraic method?

**EXAMPLE 5**  Solve this system:

$$3y - 2x = 6, \quad \text{(1)}$$
$$-12y + 8x = -24. \quad \text{(2)}$$

We see from the figure at left that the graphs are the same line. The system has an infinite number of solutions.

Suppose we try to solve this system by the elimination method:

$$\begin{array}{ll} 12y - 8x = \phantom{-}24 & \text{Multiplying equation (1) by 4} \\ \underline{-12y + 8x = -24} & \text{Equation (2)} \\ \phantom{-12y + 8x =} 0 = 0. & \text{Adding, we obtain a true equation.} \end{array}$$

We have eliminated both variables, and what remains is a true equation, $0 = 0$. It can be expressed as $0 \cdot x + 0 \cdot y = 0$, and is true for all numbers $x$ and $y$. If an ordered pair is a solution of one of the original equations, then it will be a solution of the other. The system has an infinite number of solutions. The system is consistent, and the equations are dependent.

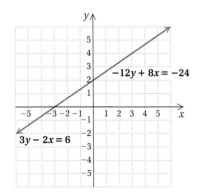

$-12y + 8x = -24$

$3y - 2x = 6$

---

### SPECIAL CASES

When solving a system of two linear equations in two variables:

1. If a false equation is obtained, such as $0 = 7$, then the system has no solution. The system is *inconsistent*, and the equations are *independent*.

2. If a true equation is obtained, such as $0 = 0$, then the system has an infinite number of solutions. The system is *consistent*, and the equations are *dependent*.

---

**7.** Solve by the elimination method:

$$2x - 5y = 10,$$
$$-6x + 15y = -30.$$

Do Exercise 7.

When solving a system of equations using the elimination method, it helps to first write the equations in the form $Ax + By = C$. When decimals or fractions occur, it also helps to *clear* before solving.

**EXAMPLE 6**  Solve this system:

$$0.2x + 0.3y = 1.7,$$
$$\tfrac{1}{7}x + \tfrac{1}{5}y = \tfrac{29}{35}.$$

We have

$$0.2x + 0.3y = 1.7, \xrightarrow[\text{to clear decimals}]{\text{Multiplying by 10}} 2x + 3y = 17,$$
$$\tfrac{1}{7}x + \tfrac{1}{5}y = \tfrac{29}{35} \xrightarrow[\text{to clear fractions}]{\text{Multiplying by 35}} 5x + 7y = 29.$$

We multiplied by 10 to clear the decimals. Multiplication by 35, the least common denominator, clears the fractions. The problem is now identical to Example 3. The solution is $(-32, 27)$, or $x = -32, y = 27$.

**8.** Clear the decimals. Then solve.

$$0.02x + 0.03y = 0.01,$$
$$0.3x - 0.1y = 0.7$$

(*Hint*: Multiply the first equation by 100 and the second one by 10.)

**9.** Clear the fractions. Then solve.

$$\frac{3}{5}x + \frac{2}{3}y = \frac{1}{3},$$
$$\frac{3}{4}x - \frac{1}{3}y = \frac{1}{4}$$

Do Exercises 8 and 9.

*Answers*

**7.** Infinitely many solutions
**8.** $2x + 3y = 1,$
$\phantom{2}3x - \phantom{2}y = 7; (2, -1)$
**9.** $9x + 10y = 5,$
$9x - \phantom{1}4y = 3; \left(\dfrac{25}{63}, \dfrac{1}{7}\right)$

To use the elimination method to solve systems of two equations:

1. Write both equations in the form $Ax + By = C$.
2. Clear any decimals or fractions.
3. Choose a variable to eliminate.
4. Make the chosen variable's terms opposites by multiplying one or both equations by appropriate numbers if necessary.
5. Eliminate a variable by adding the respective sides of the equations and then solve for the remaining variable.
6. Substitute in either of the original equations to find the value of the other variable.

## Comparing Methods

When deciding which method to use, consider this table and directions from your instructor. The situation is analogous to having a piece of wood to cut and three different types of saws available. Although all three saws can cut the wood, the "best" choice depends on the particular piece of wood, the type of cut being made, and your level of skill with each saw.

| METHOD | STRENGTHS | WEAKNESSES |
|---|---|---|
| Graphical | Can "see" solutions. | Inexact when solutions involve numbers that are not integers. Solutions may not appear on the part of the graph drawn. |
| Substitution | Yields exact solutions. Convenient to use when a variable has a coefficient of 1. | Can introduce extensive computations with fractions. Cannot "see" solutions quickly. |
| Elimination | Yields exact solutions. Convenient to use when no variable has a coefficient of 1. The preferred method for systems of 3 or more equations in 3 or more variables. (See Section 3.5.) | Cannot "see" solutions quickly. |

## b) Solving Applied Problems Using Elimination

Let's now solve an applied problem using the elimination method. (We will solve many more problems in Section 3.4, which is devoted entirely to applied problems.)

**EXAMPLE 7** *Stimulating the Hometown Economy.* To stimulate the economy in his town of Brewton, Alabama, in 2009, Danny Cottrell, co-owner of The Medical Center Pharmacy, gave each of his full-time employees $700 and each part-time employee $300. He asked that each person donate 15% to a charity of his or her choice and spend the rest locally. The money was paid in $2 bills, a rarely used currency, so that the business community could easily see how the money circulated. Cottrell gave away a total of $16,000 to his 24 employees. How many full-time employees and how many part-time employees were there?

Source: *The Press-Register*, March 4, 2009

1. **Familiarize.** We let $f$ = the number of full-time employees and $p$ = the number of part-time employees. Each full-time employee received $700, so a total of $700f$ was paid to them. Similarly, the part-time employees received a total of $300p$. Thus a total of $700f + 300p$ was given away.

2. **Translate.** We translate to two equations.

Total amount given away is $16,000.

$$700f + 300p = 16,000$$

Total number of employees is 24.

$$f + p = 24$$

We now have a system of equations:

$$700f + 300p = 16,000, \quad \text{(1)}$$
$$f + p = 24. \quad \text{(2)}$$

3. **Solve.** First, we multiply by $-300$ on both sides of equation (2) and add:

| | |
|---|---|
| $700f + 300p = 16,000$ | Equation (1) |
| $-300f - 300p = -7200$ | Multiplying by $-300$ on both sides of equation (2) |
| $400f = 8800$ | Adding |
| $f = 22.$ | Solving for $f$ |

Next, we substitute 22 for $f$ in equation (2) and solve for $p$:

$$22 + p = 24$$
$$p = 2.$$

4. **Check.** If there are 22 full-time employees and 2 part-time employees, there is a total of $22 + 2$, or 24, employees. The 22 full-time employees received a total of $\$700 \cdot 22$, or $15,400, and the 2 part-time employees received a total of $\$300 \cdot 2$, or $600. Then a total of $15,400 + $600, or $16,000, was given away. The numbers check in the original problem.

5. **State.** There were 22 full-time employees and 2 part-time employees.

**10. Bonuses.** Monica gave each of the full-time employees in her small business a year-end bonus of $500 while each part-time employee received $250. She gave a total of $4000 in bonuses to her 10 employees. How many full-time employees and how many part-time employees did Monica have?

*Answer*

10. Full-time: 6; part-time: 4

Do Exercise 10.

**a** Solve each system of equations by the elimination method.

**1.** $x + 3y = 7,$
$-x + 4y = 7$

**2.** $x + y = 9,$
$2x - y = -3$

**3.** $9x + 5y = 6,$
$2x - 5y = -17$

**4.** $2x - 3y = 18,$
$2x + 3y = -6$

**5.** $5x + 3y = -11,$
$3x - y = -1$

**6.** $2x + 3y = -9,$
$5x - 6y = -9$

**7.** $5r - 3s = 19,$
$2r - 6s = -2$

**8.** $2a + 3b = 11,$
$4a - 5b = -11$

**9.** $2x + 3y = 1,$
$4x + 6y = 2$

**10.** $3x - 2y = 1,$
$-6x + 4y = -2$

**11.** $5x - 9y = 7,$
$7y - 3x = -5$

**12.** $5x + 4y = 2,$
$2x - 8y = 4$

**13.** $3x + 2y = 24,$
$2x + 3y = 26$

**14.** $5x + 3y = 25,$
$3x + 4y = 26$

**15.** $2x - 4y = 5,$
$2x - 4y = 6$

**16.** $3x - 5y = -2,$
$5y - 3x = 7$

**17.** $2a + b = 12,$
$a + 2b = -6$

**18.** $10x + y = 306,$
$10y + x = 90$

**19.** $\frac{1}{3}x + \frac{1}{5}y = 7,$
$\frac{1}{6}x - \frac{2}{5}y = -4$

**20.** $\frac{2}{3}x + \frac{1}{7}y = -11,$
$\frac{1}{7}x - \frac{1}{3}y = -10$

**21.** $\frac{1}{5}x + \frac{1}{2}y = 6,$
$\frac{2}{5}x - \frac{3}{2}y = -8$

**22.** $\frac{2}{3}x + \frac{3}{5}y = -17,$
$\frac{1}{2}x - \frac{1}{3}y = -1$

**23.** $\frac{1}{2}x - \frac{1}{3}y = -4,$
$\frac{1}{4}x + \frac{5}{6}y = 4$

**24.** $\frac{4}{3}x + \frac{3}{2}y = 4,$
$\frac{5}{6}x - \frac{1}{8}y = -6$

**25.** $0.3x - 0.2y = 4,$
$0.2x + 0.3y = 0.5$

**26.** $0.7x - 0.3y = 0.5,$
$-0.4x + 0.7y = 1.3$

**27.** $0.05x + 0.25y = 22,$
$0.15x + 0.05y = 24$

**28.** $1.3x - 0.2y = 12,$
$0.4x + 17y = 89$

 Solve. Use the elimination method when solving the translated system.

**29.** *Finding Numbers.*  The sum of two numbers is 63. The larger number minus the smaller number is 9. Find the numbers.

**30.** *Finding Numbers.*  The sum of two numbers is 2. The larger number minus the smaller number is 20. Find the numbers.

**31.** *Finding Numbers.*  The sum of two numbers is 3. Three times the larger number plus two times the smaller number is 24. Find the numbers.

**32.** *Finding Numbers.*  The sum of two numbers is 9. Two times the larger number plus three times the smaller number is 2. Find the numbers.

**33.** *Complementary Angles.*  Two angles are complementary. (**Complementary angles** are angles whose sum is 90°.) Their difference is 6°. Find the angles.

**34.** *Supplementary Angles.*  Two angles are supplementary. (**Supplementary angles** are angles whose sum is 180°.) Their difference is 22°. Find the angles.

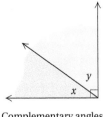

Complementary angles:
$x + y = 90°$

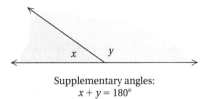

Supplementary angles:
$x + y = 180°$

**35.** *Basketball Scoring.*  Jared's Youth League basketball team scored on 27 shots, some two-point field goals and the rest one-point free throws. The team scored a total of 48 points in the game. How many of each kind of shot was made?

**36.** *Hockey Scoring.*  At one time, hockey teams received two points when they won a game and one point when they tied. One season, a team won a championship with 65 points. They played 35 games. How many wins and how many ties did the team have?

**37.** *Sales Promotion.* Rick's Sporting Goods ran a promotion offering either a free rechargeable lantern or a free portable propane grill to each customer who bought a deluxe family tent. The store's cost for each lantern was $20, and its cost for each grill was $25. At the end of the promotion, 12 tents had been sold. The store's total cost for the items given away was $280. How many of each type of free item did the customers choose?

**38.** *Sales Promotion.* The Serenity Yoga Center offered patrons who bought a 24-class pass either a free eye pillow or a free yoga DVD. The center's cost for each eye pillow was $10, and its cost for each DVD was $8. A total of 15 people took advantage of the offer. The center's total cost for the promotional items was $136. How many of each item did the patrons choose?

## Skill Maintenance

Given the function $f(x) = 3x^2 - x + 1$, find each of the following function values.   [2.2b]

**39.** $f(0)$

**40.** $f(-1)$

**41.** $f(1)$

**42.** $f(10)$

**43.** $f(-2)$

**44.** $f(2a)$

**45.** $f(-4)$

**46.** $f(1.8)$

**47.** Find the domain of the function
$$f(x) = \frac{x - 5}{x + 7}.  \quad [2.3a]$$

**48.** Find the domain and the range of the function
$$g(x) = 5 - x^2.  \quad [2.3a]$$

**49.** Find an equation of the line with slope $-\frac{3}{5}$ and $y$-intercept $(0, -7)$.   [2.6a]

**50.** Simplify: $\dfrac{(a^2b^3)^5}{a^7b^{16}}.$   [R.7b]

## Synthesis

**51.** Use the INTERSECT feature to solve the following system of equations. You may need to first solve for $y$. Round answers to the nearest hundredth.
$$3.5x - 2.1y = 106.2,$$
$$4.1x + 16.7y = -106.28$$

**52.** Solve:
$$\frac{x + y}{2} - \frac{x - y}{5} = 1,$$
$$\frac{x - y}{2} + \frac{x + y}{6} = -2.$$

**53.** The solution of this system is $(-5, -1)$. Find $A$ and $B$.
$$Ax - 7y = -3,$$
$$x - By = -1$$

**54.** Find an equation to pair with $6x + 7y = -4$ such that $(-3, 2)$ is a solution of the system.

**55.** The points $(0, -3)$ and $\left(-\frac{3}{2}, 6\right)$ are two of the solutions of the equation $px - qy = -1$. Find $p$ and $q$.

**56.** Determine $a$ and $b$ for which $(-4, -3)$ will be a solution of the system
$$ax + by = -26,$$
$$bx - ay = 7.$$

# Mid-Chapter Review

## Concept Reinforcement

Determine whether each statement is true or false.

_____ **1.** If, when solving a system of two linear equations in two variables, a false equation is obtained, the system has infinitely many solutions.  [3.2a], [3.3a]

_____ **2.** Every system of equations has at least one solution.  [3.1a]

_____ **3.** If the graphs of two linear equations intersect, then the system is consistent.  [3.1a]

_____ **4.** The intersection of the graphs of the lines $x = a$ and $y = b$ is $(a, b)$.  [3.1a]

## Guided Solutions

Fill in each box with the number, variable, or expression that creates a correct statement or solution.

Solve.  [3.2a], [3.3a]

**5.** $x + 2y = 3,$ **(1)**
$\quad y = x - 6$ **(2)**

$x + 2(\square) = 3$     Substituting for $y$ in equation (1)

$x + \square x - \square = 3$     Removing parentheses

$\square x - 12 = 3$     Collecting like terms

$3x = \square$

$x = \square$

$y = \square - 6$     Substituting in equation (2)

$y = \square$     Subtracting

The solution is $(\square, \square)$.

**6.** $3x - 2y = 5,$ **(1)**
$\quad 2x + 4y = 14$ **(2)**

$\square x - \square y = \square$     Multiplying equation (1) by 2

$\underline{2x + \phantom{0}4y = 14}$     Equation (2)

$\square x \phantom{xxxx} = \square$     Adding

$x = \square$

$2 \cdot \square + 4y = 14$     Substituting for $x$ in equation (2)

$\square + 4y = 14$     Multiplying

$4y = \square$

$y = \square$

The solution is $(\square, \square)$.

## Mixed Review

Solve each system of equations graphically. Then classify the system as consistent or inconsistent and the equations as dependent or independent.  [3.1a]

**7.** $y = x - 6,$
$\quad y = 4 - x$

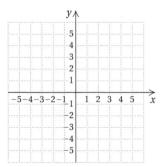

**8.** $x + y = 3,$
$\quad 3x + y = 3$

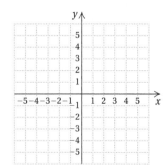

**9.** $y = 2x - 3,$
$\quad 4x - 2y = 6$

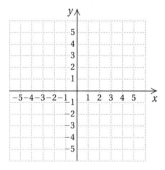

**10.** $x - y = 3,$
$\quad 2y - 2x = 6$

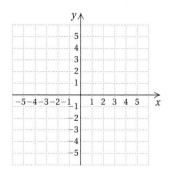

Solve using the substitution method.

**11.** $x = y + 2,$
$\quad 2x - 3y = -2$

**12.** $y = x - 5,$
$\quad x - 2y = 8$

**13.** $4x + 3y = 3,$
$\quad y = x + 8$

**14.** $3x - 2y = 1,$
$\quad x = y + 1$

Solve using the elimination method. [3.3a]

**15.** $2x + y = 2,$
$\quad x - y = 4$

**16.** $x - 2y = 13,$
$\quad x + 2y = -3$

**17.** $3x - 4y = 5,$
$\quad 5x - 2y = -1$

**18.** $3x + 2y = 11,$
$\quad 2x + 3y = 9$

**19.** $x - 2y = 5,$
$\quad 3x - 6y = 10$

**20.** $4x - 6y = 2,$
$\quad -2x + 3y = -1$

**21.** $\dfrac{1}{2}x + \dfrac{1}{3}y = 1,$
$\quad \dfrac{1}{5}x - \dfrac{3}{4}y = 11$

**22.** $0.2x + 0.3y = 0.6,$
$\quad 0.1x - 0.2y = -2.5$

Solve.

**23.** *Garden Dimensions.* A landscape architect designs a garden with a perimeter of 44 ft. The width is 2 ft less than the length. Find the length and the width. [3.2b]

**24.** *Investments.* Sandy made two investments totaling $5000. Part of the money was invested at 2% and the rest at 3%. In one year, these investments earned $129 in simple interest. How much was invested at each rate? [3.4a]

**25.** *Mixing Solutions.* A lab technician wants to mix a solution that is 20% acid with a second solution that is 50% acid in order to get 84 L of a solution that is 30% acid. How many liters of each solution should be used? [3.4a]

**26.** *Boating.* Monica's motorboat took 5 hr to make a trip downstream with a 6-mph current. The return trip against the same current took 8 hr. Find the speed of the boat in still water. [3.4b]

## Understanding Through Discussion and Writing

**27.** Explain how to find the solution of $\frac{3}{4}x + 2 = \frac{2}{5}x - 5$ in two ways graphically and in two ways algebraically. [3.1a], [3.2a], [3.3a]

**28.** Write a system of equations with the given solution. Answers may vary. [3.1a], [3.2a], [3.3a]
   **a)** $(4, -3)$      **b)** No solution
   **c)** Infinitely many solutions

**29.** Describe a method that could be used to create an inconsistent system of equations. [3.1a], [3.2a], [3.3a]

**30.** Describe a method that could be used to create a system of equations with dependent equations. [3.1a], [3.2a], [3.3a]

# Summary and Review

## Key Terms and Formulas

system of equations, p. 244
solutions of a system of equations, p. 244
consistent system of equations, p. 247
inconsistent system of equations, p. 247
dependent equations, p. 248

independent equations, p. 248
substitution method, p. 253
elimination method, p. 259
linear equation in three variables, p. 284
linear inequality, p. 299

system of linear inequalities, p. 303
solution of a system of linear
    inequalities, p. 303

Motion formula:  $d = rt$

## Concept Reinforcement

Determine whether each statement is true or false.

_____ 1. A system of equations with infinitely many solutions is inconsistent.  [3.1a]

_____ 2. It is not possible for the equations in an inconsistent system of two equations to be
dependent.  [3.1a]

_____ 3. If one point in a half-plane is a solution of a linear inequality, then all points in that
half-plane are solutions.  [3.7b]

_____ 4. Every system of linear inequalities has at least one solution.  [3.7c]

## Important Concepts

**Objective 3.1a**  Solve a system of two linear equations or two functions by graphing and determine
whether a system is consistent or inconsistent and whether the equations in a system are
dependent or independent.

**Example**  Solve this system of equations graphically. Then
classify the system as consistent or inconsistent and the
equations as dependent or independent.

$$x - y = 3,$$
$$y = 2x - 4$$

We graph the equations.

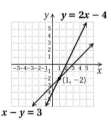

The point of intersection appears to be $(1, -2)$. This checks
in both equations, so it is the solution. The system has one
solution, so it is consistent and the equations are
independent.

**Practice Exercise**

1. Solve this system of equations graphically. Then
classify the system as consistent or inconsistent and
the equations as dependent or independent.

$$x + 3y = 1,$$
$$x + \phantom{3}y = 3$$

**Objective 3.2a**  Solve systems of equations in two variables by the substitution method.

**Example**  Solve the system

$$x - 2y = 1, \quad \textbf{(1)}$$
$$2x - 3y = 3. \quad \textbf{(2)}$$

We solve equation (1) for $x$, since the coefficient of $x$ is 1 in that equation:

$$x - 2y = 1$$
$$x = 2y + 1. \quad \textbf{(3)}$$

Next, we substitute for $x$ in equation (2) and solve for $y$:

$$2x - 3y = 3$$
$$2(2y + 1) - 3y = 3$$
$$4y + 2 - 3y = 3$$
$$y + 2 = 3$$
$$y = 1.$$

Then we substitute 1 for $y$ in equation (1), (2), or (3) and find $x$. We choose equation (3) since it is already solved for $x$:

$$x = 2y + 1 = 2 \cdot 1 + 1 = 2 + 1 = 3.$$

Check:

$$\frac{x - 2y = 1}{3 - 2 \cdot 1 \ ? \ 1}$$
$$3 - 2 \ \Big|$$
$$1 \ \Big| \quad \text{TRUE}$$

$$\frac{2x - 3y = 3}{2 \cdot 3 - 3 \cdot 1 \ ? \ 3}$$
$$6 - 3 \ \Big|$$
$$3 \ \Big| \quad \text{TRUE}$$

The ordered pair (3, 1) checks in both equations, so it is the solution of the system of equations.

**Practice Exercise**

2. Solve the system

$$2x + \ y = 2,$$
$$3x + 2y = 5.$$

---

**Objective 3.3a**  Solve systems of equations in two variables by the elimination method.

**Example**  Solve the system

$$2a + 3b = -1, \quad \textbf{(1)}$$
$$3a + 2b = 6. \quad \textbf{(2)}$$

We could eliminate either $a$ or $b$. In this case, we decide to eliminate the $a$-terms. We multiply equation (1) by 3 and equation (2) by $-2$ and then add and solve for $b$:

$$6a + 9b = -3$$
$$\underline{-6a - 4b = -12}$$
$$5b = -15$$
$$b = -3.$$

Next, we substitute $-3$ for $b$ in either of the original equations:

$$2a + 3b = -1 \quad \textbf{(1)}$$
$$2a + 3(-3) = -1$$
$$2a - 9 = -1$$
$$2a = 8$$
$$a = 4.$$

The ordered pair $(4, -3)$ checks in both equations, so it is a solution of the system of equations.

**Practice Exercise**

3. Solve the system

$$2x + 3y = 5,$$
$$3x + 4y = 6.$$

---

**Objective 3.5a** Solve systems of three equations in three variables.

**Example** Solve:

$$x - y - z = -2, \quad (1)$$
$$2x + 3y + z = 3, \quad (2)$$
$$5x - 2y - 2z = -1. \quad (3)$$

The equations are in standard form and do not contain decimals or fractions. We choose to eliminate $z$ since the $z$-terms in equations (1) and (2) are opposites. First, we add these two equations:

$$\begin{array}{r} x - y - z = -2 \\ 2x + 3y + z = 3 \\ \hline 3x + 2y \quad\quad = 1. \quad (4) \end{array}$$

Next, we multiply equation (2) by 2 and add it to equation (3) to eliminate $z$ from another pair of equations:

$$\begin{array}{r} 4x + 6y + 2z = 6 \\ 5x - 2y - 2z = -1 \\ \hline 9x + 4y \quad\quad = 5. \quad (5) \end{array}$$

Now we solve the system consisting of equations (4) and (5). We multiply equation (4) by $-2$ and add:

$$\begin{array}{r} -6x - 4y = -2 \\ 9x + 4y = 5 \\ \hline 3x \quad\quad = 3 \\ x = 1. \end{array}$$

Then we use either equation (4) or (5) to find $y$:

$$3x + 2y = 1 \quad (4)$$
$$3 \cdot 1 + 2y = 1$$
$$3 + 2y = 1$$
$$2y = -2$$
$$y = -1.$$

Finally, we use one of the original equations to find $z$:

$$2x + 3y + z = 3 \quad (2)$$
$$2 \cdot 1 + 3(-1) + z = 3$$
$$-1 + z = 3$$
$$z = 4.$$

Check:

$$\begin{array}{c|c} \underline{x - y - z = -2} \\ 1 - (-1) - 4 \;?\; -2 \\ 1 + 1 - 4 \;\Big| \\ -2 \;\Big|\quad \text{TRUE} \end{array} \qquad \begin{array}{c|c} \underline{2x + 3y + z = 3} \\ 2 \cdot 1 + 3(-1) + 4 \;?\; 3 \\ 2 - 3 + 4 \;\Big| \\ 3 \;\Big|\quad \text{TRUE} \end{array}$$

$$\begin{array}{c|c} \underline{5x - 2y - 2z = -1} \\ 5 \cdot 1 - 2(-1) - 2 \cdot 4 \;?\; -1 \\ 5 + 2 - 8 \;\Big| \\ -1 \;\Big|\quad \text{TRUE} \end{array}$$

The ordered triple $(1, -1, 4)$ checks in all three equations, so it is the solution of the system of equations.

**Practice Exercise**

**4.** Solve:

$$x - y + z = 9,$$
$$2x + y + 2z = 3,$$
$$4x + 2y - 3z = -1.$$

**Objective 3.7b**   Graph linear inequalities in two variables.

**Example**   Graph: $2x + y \le 4$.

First, we graph the line $2x + y = 4$. The intercepts are $(0, 4)$ and $(2, 0)$. We draw the line solid since the inequality symbol is $\le$. Next, we choose a test point not on the line and determine whether it is a solution of the inequality. We choose $(0, 0)$, since it is usually an easy point to use.

$$\frac{2x + y \le 4}{2 \cdot 0 + 0 \; ? \; 4}$$
$$0 \quad | \quad \text{TRUE}$$

Since $(0, 0)$ is a solution, we shade the half-plane that contains $(0, 0)$.

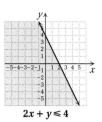

$$2x + y \le 4$$

**Practice Exercise**

**5.** Graph: $3x - 2y > 6$.

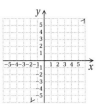

---

**Objective 3.7c**   Graph systems of linear inequalities and find coordinates of any vertices.

**Example**   Graph this system of inequalities and find the coordinates of any vertices formed:

$$x - 2y \ge -2, \quad \textbf{(1)}$$
$$3x - y \le 4, \quad \textbf{(2)}$$
$$y \ge -1. \quad \textbf{(3)}$$

We graph the related equations using solid lines. Then we indicate the region for each inequality by arrows at the ends of the line. Next, we shade the region of overlap.

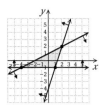

To find the vertices, we solve three different systems of related equations. From (1) and (2), we solve

$$x - 2y = -2,$$
$$3x - y = 4$$

to find the vertex $(2, 2)$. From (1) and (3), we solve

$$x - 2y = -2,$$
$$y = -1$$

to find the vertex $(-4, -1)$. From (2) and (3), we solve

$$3x - y = 4,$$
$$y = -1$$

to find the vertex $(1, -1)$.

**Practice Exercise**

**6.** Graph this system of inequalities and find the coordinates of any vertices found:

$$x - 2y \le 4,$$
$$x + y \le 4,$$
$$x - 1 \ge 0.$$

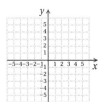

# Review Exercises

Solve graphically. Then classify the system as consistent or inconsistent and the equations as dependent or independent. [3.1a]

**1.** $4x - y = -9,$
$\quad x - y = -3$

**2.** $15x + 10y = -20,$
$\quad 3x + 2y = -4$

**3.** $y - 2x = 4,$
$\quad y - 2x = 5$

Solve by the substitution method. [3.2a]

**4.** $2x - 3y = 5,$
$\quad x = 4y + 5$

**5.** $y = x + 2,$
$\quad y - x = 8$

**6.** $7x - 4y = 6,$
$\quad y - 3x = -2$

Solve by the elimination method. [3.3a]

**7.** $x + 3y = -3,$
$\quad 2x - 3y = 21$

**8.** $3x - 5y = -4,$
$\quad 5x - 3y = 4$

**9.** $\dfrac{1}{3}x + \dfrac{2}{9}y = 1,$
$\quad \dfrac{3}{2}x + \dfrac{1}{2}y = 6$

**10.** $1.5x - 3 = -2y,$
$\quad 3x + 4y = 6$

**11.** *Spending Choices.* Sean has $86 to spend. He can spend all of it on one CD and two DVDs, or he can buy two CDs and one DVD and have $16 left over. What is the price of a CD? of a DVD? [3.4a]

**12.** *Orange Drink Mixtures.* "Orange Thirst" is 15% orange juice and "Quencho" is 5% orange juice. How many liters of each should be combined in order to get 10 L of a mixture that is 10% orange juice? [3.4a]

**13.** *Train Travel.* A train leaves Watsonville at noon traveling north at 44 mph. One hour later, another train, going 52 mph, travels north on a parallel track. How many hours will the second train travel before it overtakes the first train? [3.4b]

Solve. [3.5a]

**14.** $x + 2y + z = 10,$
$\quad 2x - y + z = 8,$
$\quad 3x + y + 4z = 2$

**15.** $3x + 2y + z = 1,$
$\quad 2x - y - 3z = 1,$
$\quad -x + 3y + 2z = 6$

**16.** $2x - 5y - 2z = -4,$
$\quad 7x + 2y - 5z = -6,$
$\quad -2x + 3y + 2z = 4$

**17.** $x + y + 2z = 1,$
$\quad x - y + z = 1,$
$\quad x + 2y + z = 2$

**18.** *Triangle Measure.* In triangle $ABC$, the measure of angle $A$ is four times the measure of angle $C$, and the measure of angle $B$ is 45° more than the measure of angle $C$. What are the measures of the angles of the triangle? [3.6a]

**19.** *Money Mixtures.* Elaine has $194, consisting of $20, $5, and $1 bills. The number of $1 bills is 1 less than the total number of $20 and $5 bills. If she has 39 bills in her purse, how many of each denomination does she have? [3.6a]

Graph. [3.7b]

**20.** $2x + 3y < 12$

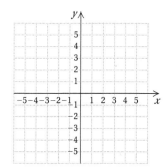

**21.** $y \leq 0$

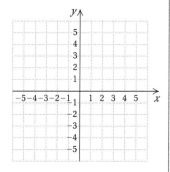

**22.** $x + y \geq 1$

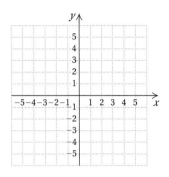

Graph. Find the coordinates of any vertices formed.    [3.7c]

**23.** $y \geq -3$,
$\quad\; x \geq 2$

**24.** $x + 3y \geq -1$,
$\quad\;\; x + 3y \leq 4$

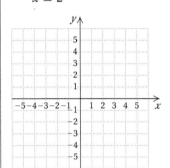 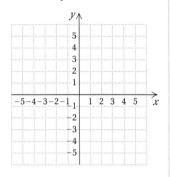

**25.** $x - y \leq 3$,
$\quad\; x + y \geq -1$,
$\quad\quad\;\; y \leq 2$

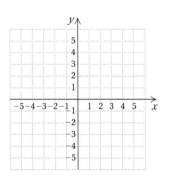

**26.** The sum of two numbers is $-2$. The sum of twice one number and the other is 4. One number is which of the following?    [3.3b]

**A.** $-6$                  **B.** 2

**C.** 6                   **D.** 8

**27.** *Distance Traveled.*   Two cars leave Martinsville traveling in opposite directions. One car travels at a speed of 50 mph and the other at 60 mph. In how many hours will they be 275 mi apart?    [3.4b]

**A.** 2.5 hr            **B.** 3 hr

**C.** 3.5 hr            **D.** 4 hr

## Synthesis

**28.** Solve graphically:    [2.1d], [3.1a]

$$y = x + 2,$$
$$y = x^2 + 2.$$

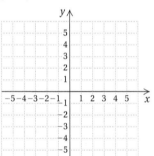

# Understanding Through Discussion and Writing

**1.** Write a problem for a classmate to solve. Design the problem so the answer is "The florist sold 14 hanging baskets and 9 flats of petunias."    [3.4a]

**2.** Exercise 14 in Exercise Set 3.6 can be solved mentally after a careful reading of the problem. Explain how this can be done.    [3.6a]

**3.** *Ticket Revenue.*   A pops-concert audience of 100 people consists of adults, senior citizens, and children. The ticket prices are $10 each for adults, $3 each for senior citizens, and $0.50 each for children. The total amount of money taken in is $100. How many adults, senior citizens, and children are in attendance? Does there seem to be some information missing? Do some careful reasoning and explain.    [3.6a]

**4.** When graphing linear inequalities, Ron always shades above the line when he sees a $\geq$ symbol. Is this wise? Why or why not?    [3.7a]

CHAPTER
3
Test   For Extra Help
CHAPTER
Test Prep
VIDEOS
Step-by-step test solutions are found on the Chapter Test Prep Videos available via the Video Resources on DVD, in *MyMathLab* , and on You Tube (search "BittingerInterAlgPB" and click on "Channels").

Solve graphically. Then classify the system as consistent or inconsistent and the equations as dependent or independent.

**1.** $y = 3x + 7,$
  $3x + 2y = -4$

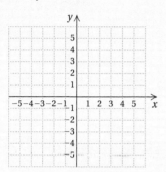

**2.** $y = 3x + 4,$
  $y = 3x - 2$

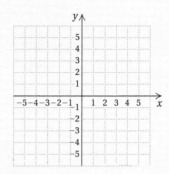

**3.** $y - 3x = 6,$
  $6x - 2y = -12$

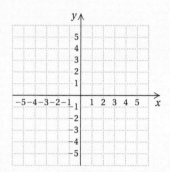

Solve by the substitution method.

**4.** $4x + 3y = -1,$
  $y = 2x - 7$

**5.** $x = 3y + 2,$
  $2x - 6y = 4$

**6.** $x + 2y = 6,$
  $2x + 3y = 7$

Solve by the elimination method.

**7.** $2x + 5y = 3,$
  $-2x + 3y = 5$

**8.** $x + y = -2,$
  $4x - 6y = -3$

**9.** $\frac{2}{3}x - \frac{4}{5}y = 1,$

  $\frac{1}{3}x - \frac{2}{5}y = 2$

Solve.

**10.** *Tennis Court.*  The perimeter of a standard tennis court used for playing doubles is 288 ft. The width of the court is 42 ft less than the length. Find the length and the width.

**11.** *Air Travel.*  An airplane flew for 5 hr with a 20-km/h tailwind and returned in 7 hr against the same wind. Find the speed of the plane in still air.

**12.** *Chicken Dinners.*  High Flyin' Wings charges $12 for a bucket of chicken wings and $7 for a chicken dinner. After filling 28 orders for buckets and dinners during a football game, the waiters had collected $281. How many buckets and how many dinners did they sell?

**13.** *Mixing Solutions.*  A chemist has one solution that is 20% salt and a second solution that is 45% salt. How many liters of each should be used in order to get 20 L of a solution that is 30% salt?

**14.** Solve:

$$6x + 2y - 4z = 15,$$
$$-3x - 4y + 2z = -6,$$
$$4x - 6y + 3z = 8.$$

**15.** *Repair Rates.* An electrician, a carpenter, and a plumber are hired to work on a house. The electrician earns $21 per hour, the carpenter $19.50 per hour, and the plumber $24 per hour. The first day on the job, they worked a total of 21.5 hr and earned a total of $469.50. If the plumber worked 2 hr more than the carpenter did, how many hours did the electrician work?

Graph. Find the coordinates of any vertices formed.

**16.** $y \geq x - 2$

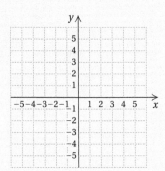

**17.** $x - 6y < -6$

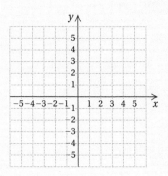

**18.** $x + y \geq 3,$
    $x - y \geq 5$

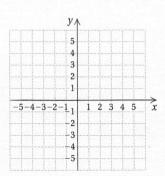

**19.** $2y - x \geq -4,$
    $2y + 3x \leq -6,$
    $y \leq 0,$
    $x \leq 0$

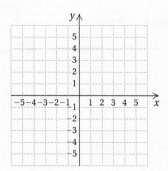

**20.** A business class divided an imaginary $30,000 investment among three funds. The first fund grew 2%, the second grew 3%, and the third grew 5%. Total earnings were $990. The earnings from the third fund were $280 more than the earnings from the first. How much was invested at 5%?

**A.** $9000              **B.** $10,000              **C.** $11,000              **D.** $12,000

## Synthesis

**21.** The graph of the function $f(x) = mx + b$ contains the points $(-1, 3)$ and $(-2, -4)$. Find $m$ and $b$.

# Cumulative Review

Solve.

**1.** $6y - 5(3y - 4) = 10$

**2.** $-3 + 5x = 2x + 15$

**3.** $A = \pi r^2 h$, for $h$

**4.** $L = \dfrac{1}{3}m(k + p)$, for $p$

**5.** $5x + 8 > 2x + 5$

**6.** $-12 \leq -3x + 1 < 0$

**7.** $2x - 10 \leq -4$ or $x - 4 \geq 3$

**8.** $|x + 1| = 4$

**9.** $|8y - 3| \geq 15$

**10.** $|2x + 1| = |x - 4|$

**11.** Find the distance between $-18$ and $-7$ on the number line.

Graph on a plane.

**12.** $3y = 9$

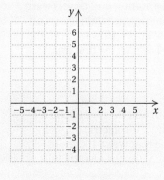

**13.** $f(x) = -\dfrac{1}{2}x - 3$

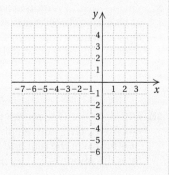

**14.** $3x - 1 = y$

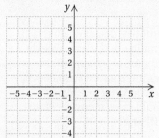

**15.** $3x + 5y = 15$

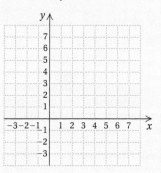

**16.** $y > 3x - 4$

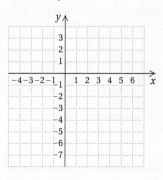

**17.** $2x - y \leq 6$

**18.** Solve graphically. Then classify the system as consistent or inconsistent and the equations as dependent or independent.

$$2x - \ \ y = 7,$$
$$x + 3y = 0$$

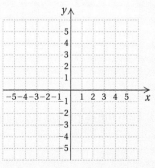

Solve.

**19.** $3x + 4y = 4,$
$\ \ \ x = 2y + 2$

**20.** $3x + y = 2,$
$\ \ \ 6x - y = 7$

**21.** $4x + 3y = 5,$
$\ \ \ 3x + 2y = 3$

**22.** $\ \ x - y + \ \ z = 1,$
$\ \ 2x + y + \ \ z = 3,$
$\ \ \ x + y - 2z = 4$

Graph. Find the coordinates of any vertices formed.

**23.** $x + y \leq -3,$
$\ \ \ x - y \leq 1$

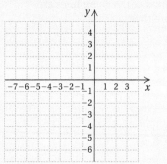

**24.** $4y - 3x \geq -12,$
$\ \ \ 4y + 3x \geq -36,$
$\ \ \ \ \ \ \ \ \ y \leq 0,$
$\ \ \ \ \ \ \ \ \ x \leq 0$

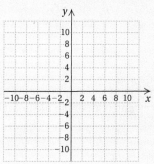

**25.** For the function *f* whose graph is shown below, determine **(a)** the domain, **(b)** the range, **(c)** $f(-3)$, and **(d)** any input for which $f(x) = 5$.

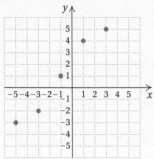

**26.** Find the domain of the function given by

$$f(x) = \frac{7}{2x - 1}.$$

**27.** Given $g(x) = 1 - 2x^2$, find $g(-1)$, $g(0)$, and $g(3)$.

**28.** Find the slope and the *y*-intercept of $5y - 4x = 20$.

**29.** Find an equation of the line with slope $-3$ and containing the point $(5, 2)$.

**30.** Find an equation of the line containing the points $(-1, -3)$ and $(-3, 5)$.

**31.** Determine whether the graphs of the given lines are parallel, perpendicular, or neither.
$$x - 2y = 4,$$
$$4x + 2y = 1$$

**32.** Find an equation of the line parallel to $3x - 9y = 2$ and containing the point $(-6, 2)$.

Solve.

**33.** *Wire Cutting.* Rolly's Electric wants to cut a piece of copper wire 10 m long into two pieces, one of them two-thirds as long as the other. How should the wire be cut?

**34.** *Test Scores.* Adam is taking a geology course in which there will be 4 tests, each worth 100 points. He has scores of 87, 94, and 91 on the first three tests. He must have a total of at least 360 in order to get an A. What scores on the last test will give Adam an A?

**35.** *Inventory.* The Everton College store paid $2268 for an order of 45 calculators. The store paid $9 for each scientific calculator. The others, all graphing calculators, cost the store $78 each. How many of each type of calculator was ordered?

**36.** *Mixing Solutions.* A technician wants to mix one solution that is 15% alcohol with another solution that is 25% alcohol in order to get 30 L of a solution that is 18% alcohol. How much of each solution should be used?

**37.** *Train Travel.* A train leaves a station and travels west at 80 km/h. Three hours later, a second train leaves on a parallel track and travels 120 km/h. How far from the station will the second train overtake the first train?

**38.** *Utility Cost.* One month Ladi and Bo spent $680 for electricity, rent, and telephone. The electric bill was one-fourth of the rent and the rent was $400 more than the phone bill. How much was the electric bill?

## Synthesis

**39.** *Radio Advertising.* An automotive dealer discovers that when $1000 is spent on radio advertising, weekly sales increase by $101,000. When $1250 is spent on radio advertising, weekly sales increase by $126,000. Assuming that sales increase according to a linear function, by what amount would sales increase when $1500 is spent on radio advertising?

**40.** Given that $f(x) = mx + b$ and that $f(5) = -3$ when $f(-4) = 2$, find *m* and *b*.

# Polynomials and Polynomial Functions

## Real-World Application

In filming a movie, a stunt double on a motorcycle must jump over a group of trucks that are lined up side by side. The height $h(t)$, in feet, of the airborne bike $t$ seconds after leaving the ramp can be approximated by $h(t) = -16t^2 + 60t$. After how long will the bike reach the ground?

*This problem appears as Margin Exercise 9 in Section 4.8.*

# 4.1

# Introduction to Polynomials and Polynomial Functions

A **polynomial** is a particular type of algebraic expression. Let's examine an application before we consider definitions and manipulations involving polynomials.

*Stack of Apples.* The stack of apples shown below is formed by square layers of apples. The number $N$ of apples in the stack is given by the polynomial function

$$N(x) = \tfrac{1}{3}x^3 + \tfrac{1}{2}x^2 + \tfrac{1}{6}x,$$

where $x$ is the number of layers. The graph of the function is shown below.

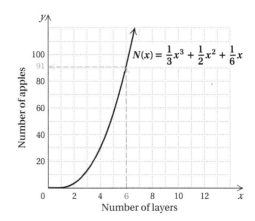

For a stack with 6 layers, there is a total of 91 apples, as we can see from the graph and from substituting 6 for $x$ in the polynomial function:

$$N(x) = \tfrac{1}{3}x^3 + \tfrac{1}{2}x^2 + \tfrac{1}{6}x$$
$$N(6) = \tfrac{1}{3} \cdot 6^3 + \tfrac{1}{2} \cdot 6^2 + \tfrac{1}{6} \cdot 6 = 72 + 18 + 1 = 91.$$

Although we will not be considering graphs of polynomial functions in detail in this chapter (other than in Calculator Corners), this situation gives us an idea of how polynomial functions can occur in applied problems.

## **a** Polynomial Expressions

The following are examples of *monomials*:

$$0, \quad -3, \quad z, \quad 8x, \quad -7y^2, \quad 4a^2b^3, \quad 1.3p^4q^5r^7.$$

> **MONOMIAL**
>
> A **monomial** is a one-term expression like $ax^n y^m z^q$, where $a$ is a real number and $n$, $m$, and $q$ are nonnegative integers. More specifically, a monomial is a constant or a constant times some variable or variables raised to powers that are nonnegative integers.

Expressions like these are called **polynomials in one variable:**

$$5x^2, \quad 8a, \quad 2, \quad 2x + 3,$$
$$-7x + 5, \quad 2y^2 + 5y - 3,$$
$$5a^4 - 3a^2 + \tfrac{1}{4}a - 8, \quad b^6 + 3b^5 - 8b + 7b^4 + \tfrac{1}{2}.$$

Expressions like these are called **polynomials in several variables:**

$$15x^3y^2,$$
$$5a - ab^2 + 7b + 2,$$
$$9xy^2z - 4x^3z - 14x^4y^2 + 9.$$

---

### POLYNOMIAL

A **polynomial** is a monomial or a combination of sums and/or differences of monomials.

---

The following are algebraic expressions that are not polynomials:

$$(1)\ \frac{y^2 - 3}{y^2 + 4}, \qquad (2)\ 8x^4 - 2x^3 + \frac{1}{x}, \qquad (3)\ \frac{2xy}{x^3 - y^3}.$$

Expressions (1) and (3) are not polynomials because they represent quotients. Expression (2) is not a polynomial because

$$\frac{1}{x} = x^{-1};$$

this is not a monomial because the exponent is negative.

The polynomial $5x^3y - 7xy^2 - y^3 + 2$ has four **terms:**

$$5x^3y, \quad -7xy^2, \quad -y^3, \quad \text{and} \quad 2.$$

The **coefficients** of the terms are 5, $-7$, $-1$, and 2. The term 2 is called a **constant term**.

The **degree of a term** is the sum of the exponents of the variables, if there are variables. For example,

the degree of the term $9x^5$ is 5  and

the degree of the term $0.6a^2b^7$ is 9.

The degree of a nonzero constant term, such as 2, is 0. We can express 2 as $2x^0$. Mathematicians agree that the polynomial 0 has *no* degree. This is because we can express 0 as

$$0 = 0x^5 = 0x^{12},$$

and so on, using any exponent we wish.

The **degree of a polynomial** is the same as the degree of its term of highest degree. For example,

the degree of the polynomial $4 - x^3 + 5x^2 - x^6$ is 6.

The **leading term** of a polynomial is the term of highest degree. Its coefficient is called the **leading coefficient**. For example,

the leading term of $9x^2 - 5x^3 + x - 10$ is $-5x^3$  and

the leading coefficient is $-5$.

**EXAMPLE 1** Identify the terms, the degree of each term, and the degree of the polynomial. Then identify the leading term, the leading coefficient, and the constant term.

$$2x^3 + 8x^2 - 17x - 3$$

| TERM | $2x^3$ | $8x^2$ | $-17x$ | $-3$ |
|---|---|---|---|---|
| DEGREE OF TERM | 3 | 2 | 1 | 0 |
| DEGREE OF POLYNOMIAL | 3 | | | |
| LEADING TERM | $2x^3$ | | | |
| LEADING COEFFICIENT | 2 | | | |
| CONSTANT TERM | $-3$ | | | |

1. Identify the terms and the leading term:
   $-92x^5 - 8x^4 + x^2 + 5.$

2. Identify the coefficient of each term and the leading coefficient:
   $5x^3y - 4xy^2 - 2x^3 + xy - y - 5.$

3. Identify the terms, the degree of each term, and the degree of the polynomial. Then identify the leading term, the leading coefficient, and the constant term.
   a) $6x^2 - 5x^3 + 2x - 7$
   b) $2y - 4 - 5x + 9x^2y^3z^2 + 5xy^2$

**EXAMPLE 2** Identify the terms, the degree of each term, and the degree of the polynomial. Then identify the leading term, the leading coefficient, and the constant term.

$$6x^2 + 8x^2y^3 - 17xy - 24xy^2z^4 + 2y + 3$$

| TERM | $6x^2$ | $8x^2y^3$ | $-17xy$ | $-24xy^2z^4$ | $2y$ | $3$ |
|---|---|---|---|---|---|---|
| DEGREE OF TERM | 2 | 5 | 2 | 7 | 1 | 0 |
| DEGREE OF POLYNOMIAL | 7 | | | | | |
| LEADING TERM | $-24xy^2z^4$ | | | | | |
| LEADING COEFFICIENT | $-24$ | | | | | |
| CONSTANT TERM | 3 | | | | | |

Do Exercises 1–3.

The following are some names for certain types of polynomials.

| TYPE | DEFINITION: POLYNOMIAL OF | EXAMPLES | | | |
|---|---|---|---|---|---|
| Monomial | One term | 4, | $-3p$, | $-7a^2b^3$, | 0,    $xyz$ |
| Binomial | Two terms | $2x + 7$, | $a^2 - 3b$, | $5x^3 + 8x$ | |
| Trinomial | Three terms | $x^2 - 7x + 12$, | $4a^2 + 2ab + b^2$ | | |

4. Consider the following polynomials.
   a) $3x^2 - 2$
   b) $5x^3 + 9x - 3$
   c) $4x^2$
   d) $-7y$
   e) $-3$
   f) $8x^3 - 2x^2$
   g) $-4y^2 - 5 - 5y$
   h) $5 - 3x$

   Identify the monomials, the binomials, and the trinomials.

Do Exercise 4.

We generally arrange polynomials in one variable so that the exponents *decrease* from left to right, which is **descending order**. Sometimes they may be written so that the exponents *increase* from left to right, which is **ascending order**. In general, if an exercise is written in a particular order, we write the answer in that same order.

*Answers*

1. $-92x^5, -8x^4, x^2, 5; -92x^5$
2. $5, -4, -2, 1, -1, -5; 5$     3. (a) $6x^2, -5x^3,$ $2x, -7; 2, 3, 1, 0; 3; -5x^3; -5; -7;$
(b) $2y, -4, -5x, 9x^2y^3z^2, 5xy^2; 1, 0, 1, 7, 3; 7;$ $9x^2y^3z^2; 9; -4$     4. Monomials: (c), (d), (e); binomials: (a), (f), (h); trinomials: (b), (g)

**EXAMPLE 3**  Consider $12 + x^2 - 7x$. Arrange in descending order and then in ascending order.

$$\textit{Descending order:} \quad x^2 - 7x + 12 \qquad \textit{Ascending order:} \quad 12 - 7x + x^2$$

**EXAMPLE 4**  Consider $x^4 + 2 - 5x^2 + 3x^3y + 7xy^2$. Arrange in descending powers of $x$ and then in ascending powers of $x$.

$$\textit{Descending powers of } x: \quad x^4 + 3x^3y - 5x^2 + 7xy^2 + 2$$
$$\textit{Ascending powers of } x: \quad 2 + 7xy^2 - 5x^2 + 3x^3y + x^4$$

> Do Exercises 5 and 6.

**5. a)** Arrange in ascending order:
$5 - 6x^2 + 7x^3 - x^4 + 10x$.

**b)** Arrange in descending order:
$5 - 6x^2 + 7x^3 - x^4 + 10x$.

**6. a)** Arrange in ascending powers of $y$:
$5x^4y - 3y^2 + 3x^2y^3 + x^3 - 5$.

**b)** Arrange in descending powers of $y$:
$5x^4y - 3y^2 + 3x^2y^3 + x^3 - 5$.

## b  Evaluating Polynomial Functions

A polynomial function is one like

$$P(x) = 5x^7 + 3x^5 - 4x^2 - 5,$$

where the algebraic expression used to describe the function is a polynomial. To find the outputs of a polynomial function for a given input, we substitute the input for each occurrence of the variable as we did in Section 2.2.

**EXAMPLE 5**  For the polynomial function $P(x) = -x^2 + 4x - 1$, find $P(2)$, $P(10)$, and $P(-10)$.

$$P(2) = -2^2 + 4(2) - 1 = -4 + 8 - 1 = 3;$$
$$P(10) = -10^2 + 4(10) - 1 = -100 + 40 - 1 = -61;$$
$$P(-10) = -(-10)^2 + 4(-10) - 1 = -100 - 40 - 1 = -141$$

**7.** For the polynomial function
$$P(x) = x^2 - 2x + 5,$$
find $P(0)$, $P(4)$, and $P(-2)$.

> Do Exercise 7.

**EXAMPLE 6**  *Veterinary Medicine.*  Gentamicin is an antibiotic frequently used by veterinarians. The concentration $C$, in micrograms per milliliter (mcg/mL), of Gentamicin in a horse's bloodstream $t$ hours after injection can be approximated by the polynomial function

$$C(t) = -0.005t^4 + 0.003t^3 + 0.35t^2 + 0.5t.$$

**a)** Evaluate $C(2)$ to find the concentration 2 hr after injection.

**b)** Use only the graph below to estimate $C(4)$.

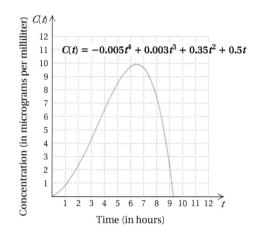

Concentration (in micrograms per milliliter)

$C(t) = -0.005t^4 + 0.003t^3 + 0.35t^2 + 0.5t$

Time (in hours)

***Answers***

**5. (a)** $5 + 10x - 6x^2 + 7x^3 - x^4$;
**(b)** $-x^4 + 7x^3 - 6x^2 + 10x + 5$
**6. (a)** $-5 + x^3 + 5x^4y - 3y^2 + 3x^2y^3$;
**(b)** $3x^2y^3 - 3y^2 + 5x^4y + x^3 - 5$
**7.** $5; 13; 13$

a) We evaluate the function when $t = 2$:

$$C(2) = -0.005(2)^4 + 0.003(2)^3 + 0.35(2)^2 + 0.5(2)$$
$$= -0.005(16) + 0.003(8) + 0.35(4) + 0.5(2)$$
$$= -0.08 + 0.024 + 1.4 + 1 = 2.344.$$

We carry out the calculation using the rules for order of operations.

The concentration after 2 hr is about 2.344 mcg/mL.

b) To estimate $C(4)$, the concentration after 4 hr, we locate 4 on the horizontal axis. From there we move vertically to the graph of the function and then horizontally to the $C(t)$-axis. This locates a value of about 6.5. Thus,

$$C(4) \approx 6.5.$$

The concentration after 4 hr is about 6.5 mcg/mL.

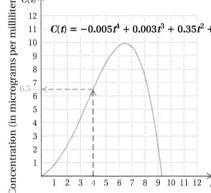

**8. Veterinary Medicine.** Refer to the function and the graph of Example 6.

a) Evaluate $C(3)$ to find the concentration 3 hr after injection.

b) Use only the graph at right to estimate $C(9)$.

Do Exercise 8.

## (c) Adding Polynomials

When two terms have the same variable(s) raised to the same power(s), they are called **like terms**, or **similar terms**, and they can be "collected," or "combined," using the distributive laws, adding or subtracting the coefficients as follows.

**EXAMPLES** Collect like terms.

**7.** $3x^2 - 4y + 2x^2 = 3x^2 + 2x^2 - 4y$    Rearranging using the commutative law for addition

$$= (3 + 2)x^2 - 4y$$    Using the distributive law
$$= 5x^2 - 4y$$

**8.** $9x^3 + 5x - 4x^2 - 2x^3 + 5x^2 = 7x^3 + x^2 + 5x$

**9.** $3x^2y + 5xy^2 - 3x^2y - xy^2 = 4xy^2$

Do Exercises 9 and 10.

Collect like terms.

**9.** $3y - 4x + 6xy^2 - 2xy^2$

**10.** $3xy^3 + 2x^3y + 5xy^3 - 8x + 15 - 3x^2y - 6x^2y + 11x - 8$

The sum of two polynomials can be found by writing a plus sign between them and then collecting like terms to simplify the expression.

**EXAMPLE 10**   Add: $(-3x^3 + 2x - 4) + (4x^3 + 3x^2 + 2)$.

$$(-3x^3 + 2x - 4) + (4x^3 + 3x^2 + 2) = x^3 + 3x^2 + 2x - 2$$

*Answers*

**8.** (a) $C(3) = 4.326$ mcg/mL;
(b) $C(9) \approx 2$ mcg/mL    **9.** $3y - 4x + 4xy^2$
**10.** $8xy^3 + 2x^3y + 3x + 7 - 9x^2y$

**EXAMPLE 11**  Add: $13x^3y + 3x^2y - 5y$ and $x^3y + 4x^2y - 3xy$.

$$(13x^3y + 3x^2y - 5y) + (x^3y + 4x^2y - 3xy) = 14x^3y + 7x^2y - 3xy - 5y$$

Do Exercises 11-13.

Using columns to add is sometimes helpful. To do so, we write the polynomials one under the other, listing like terms under one another and leaving spaces for missing terms.

**EXAMPLE 12**  Add: $4ax^2 + 4bx - 5$ and $-6ax^2 + 8$.

$$
\begin{array}{r}
4ax^2 + 4bx - 5 \\
-6ax^2 \qquad + 8 \\
\hline
-2ax^2 + 4bx + 3
\end{array}
$$

## (d) Subtracting Polynomials

If the sum of two polynomials is 0, they are called **opposites**, or **additive inverses**, of each other. For example,

$$(3x^2 - 5x + 2) + (-3x^2 + 5x - 2) = 0,$$

so the opposite of $3x^2 - 5x + 2$ is $-3x^2 + 5x - 2$. We can say the same thing using algebraic symbolism, as follows:

The opposite of   $(3x^2 - 5x + 2)$   is   $(-3x^2 + 5x - 2)$.

$$-\qquad (3x^2 - 5x + 2) \quad = \quad -3x^2 + 5x - 2$$

Thus, $-(3x^2 - 5x + 2)$ and $-3x^2 + 5x - 2$ are equivalent.

The *opposite* of a polynomial $P$ can be symbolized by $-P$ or by replacing each term with its opposite. The two expressions for the opposite are equivalent.

**EXAMPLE 13**  Write two equivalent expressions for the opposite of

$$7xy^2 - 6xy - 4y + 3.$$

*First expression:*   $-(7xy^2 - 6xy - 4y + 3)$   Writing an inverse sign in front

*Second expression:*   $-7xy^2 + 6xy + 4y - 3$   Writing the opposite of each term (see also Section R.6)

Do Exercises 14-16.

To subtract a polynomial, we add its opposite.

**EXAMPLE 14**  Subtract: $(-5x^2 + 4) - (2x^2 + 3x - 1)$.

We have

$(-5x^2 + 4) - (2x^2 + 3x - 1)$

$= (-5x^2 + 4) + [-(2x^2 + 3x - 1)]$   Adding the opposite

$= (-5x^2 + 4) + (-2x^2 - 3x + 1)$   $-2x^2 - 3x + 1$ is equivalent to $-(2x^2 + 3x - 1)$.

$= -7x^2 - 3x + 5.$   Adding

---

Add.

**11.** $(3x^3 + 4x^2 - 7x - 2) +$
$(-7x^3 - 2x^2 + 3x + 4)$

**12.** $(7y^5 - 5) + (3y^5 - 4y^2 + 10)$

**13.** $(5p^2q^4 - 2p^2q^2 - 3q) +$
$(-6p^2q^2 + 3q + 5)$

Write two equivalent expressions for the opposite, or additive inverse.

**14.** $4x^3 - 5x^2 + \dfrac{1}{4}x - 10$

**15.** $8xy^2 - 4x^3y^2 - 9x - \dfrac{1}{5}$

**16.** $-9y^5 - 8y^4 + \dfrac{1}{2}y^3 - y^2 + y - 1$

*Answers*
**11.** $-4x^3 + 2x^2 - 4x + 2$
**12.** $10y^5 - 4y^2 + 5$   **13.** $5p^2q^4 - 8p^2q^2 + 5$
**14.** $-(4x^3 - 5x^2 + \frac{1}{4}x - 10)$;
$-4x^3 + 5x^2 - \frac{1}{4}x + 10$
**15.** $-(8xy^2 - 4x^3y^2 - 9x - \frac{1}{5})$;
$-8xy^2 + 4x^3y^2 + 9x + \frac{1}{5}$
**16.** $-(-9y^5 - 8y^4 + \frac{1}{2}y^3 - y^2 + y - 1)$;
$9y^5 + 8y^4 - \frac{1}{2}y^3 + y^2 - y + 1$

With practice, you may find that you can skip some steps, by mentally taking the opposite of each term and then combining like terms. Eventually, all you will write is the answer.

$$(-5x^2 + 4) - (2x^2 + 3x - 1)$$
$$= -7x^2 - 3x + 5$$

*Think:*
$$-5x^2 - 2x^2 = -5x^2 + (-2x^2) = -7x^2,$$
$$0x - 3x = 0x + (-3x) = -3x,$$
$$4 - (-1) = 4 + 1 = 5.$$

Do Exercises 17–19.

Subtract.

**17.** $(6x^2 + 4) - (3x^2 - 1)$

**18.** $(9y^3 - 2y - 4) - (-5y^3 - 8)$

**19.** $(-3p^2 + 5p - 4) -$
$(-4p^2 + 11p - 2)$

To use columns for subtraction, we mentally change the signs of the terms being subtracted.

**EXAMPLE 15** Subtract:
$$(4x^2y - 6x^3y^2 + x^2y^2) - (4x^2y + x^3y^2 + 3x^2y^3 - 8x^2y^2).$$

*Write:* (Subtract)

$$4x^2y - 6x^3y^2 \qquad + x^2y^2$$
$$-(4x^2y + x^3y^2 + 3x^2y^3 - 8x^2y^2) \longleftrightarrow$$

*Think:* (Add)

$$4x^2y - 6x^3y^2 \qquad + x^2y^2$$
$$-4x^2y - x^3y^2 - 3x^2y^3 + 8x^2y^2$$
$$-7x^3y^2 - 3x^2y^3 + 9x^2y^2$$

Take the opposite of each term mentally and add.

Subtract.

**20.** $(2y^5 - y^4 + 3y^3 - y^2 - y - 7) -$
$(-y^5 + 2y^4 - 2y^3 + y^2 - y - 4)$

**21.** $(4p^4q - 5p^3q^2 + p^2q^3 + 2q^4) -$
$(-5p^4q + 5p^3q^2 - 3p^2q^3 - 7q^4)$

**22.** $\left(\dfrac{3}{2}y^3 - \dfrac{1}{2}y^2 + 0.3\right) -$
$\left(\dfrac{1}{2}y^3 + \dfrac{1}{2}y^2 - \dfrac{4}{3}y + 0.2\right)$

Do Exercises 20–22.

## Calculator Corner

**Checking Addition and Subtraction of Polynomials** A table set in AUTO mode can be used to perform a partial check that polynomials in a single variable have been added or subtracted correctly. To check Example 10, we enter $y_1 = (-3x^3 + 2x - 4) + (4x^3 + 3x^2 + 2)$ and $y_2 = x^3 + 3x^2 + 2x - 2$. If the addition has been done correctly, the values of $y_1$ and $y_2$ will be the same regardless of the table settings used.

| X | Y₁ | Y₂ |
|---|---|---|
| -2 | -2 | -2 |
| -1 | -2 | -2 |
| 0 | -2 | -2 |
| 1 | 4 | 4 |
| 2 | 22 | 22 |
| 3 | 58 | 58 |
| 4 | 118 | 118 |

X=−2

Graphs can also be used to check addition and subtraction. See the Calculator Corner on p. 339 for the procedure. Keep in mind that these procedures provide only a partial check since we can neither view all possible values of $x$ in a table nor see the entire graph.

**Exercises:** Use a table to determine whether the sum or difference is correct.

**1.** $(x^3 - 2x^2 + 3x - 7) + (3x^2 - 4x + 5) = x^3 + x^2 - x - 2$

**2.** $(2x^2 + 3x - 6) + (5x^2 - 7x + 4) = 7x^2 + 4x - 2$

**3.** $(4x^3 + 3x^2 + 2) + (-3x^3 + 2x - 4) = x^3 + 3x^2 + 2x - 2$

**4.** $(7x^5 + 2x^4 - 5x) - (-x^5 - 2x^4 + 3) = 8x^5 + 4x^4 - 5x - 3$

**5.** $(-2x^3 + 3x^2 - 4x + 5) - (3x^2 + 2x - 8) = -2x^3 - 6x - 3$

**6.** $(3x^4 - 2x^2 - 1) - (2x^4 - 3x^2 - 4) = x^4 + x^2 - 5$

*Answers*
**17.** $3x^2 + 5$    **18.** $14y^3 - 2y + 4$
**19.** $p^2 - 6p - 2$
**20.** $3y^5 - 3y^4 + 5y^3 - 2y^2 - 3$
**21.** $9p^4q - 10p^3q^2 + 4p^2q^3 + 9q^4$
**22.** $y^3 - y^2 + \frac{4}{3}y + 0.1$

**a**  Identify the terms, the degree of each term, and the degree of the polynomial. Then identify the leading term, the leading coefficient, and the constant term.

**1.** $-9x^4 - x^3 + 7x^2 + 6x - 8$

**2.** $y^3 - 5y^2 + y + 1$

**3.** $t^3 + 4t^7 + s^2t^4 - 2$

**4.** $a^2 + 9b^5 - a^4b^3 - 11$

**5.** $u^7 + 8u^2v^6 + 3uv + 4u - 1$

**6.** $2p^6 + 5p^4w^4 - 13p^3w + 7p^2 - 10$

Arrange in descending powers of $y$.

**7.** $23 - 4y^3 + 7y - 6y^2$

**8.** $5 - 8y + 6y^2 + 11y^3 - 18y^4$

**9.** $x^2y^2 + x^3y - xy^3 + 1$

**10.** $x^3y - x^2y^2 + xy^3 + 6$

**11.** $2by - 9b^5y^5 - 8b^2y^3$

**12.** $dy^6 - 2d^7y^2 + 3cy^5 - 7y - 2d$

Arrange in ascending powers of $x$.

**13.** $12x + 5 + 8x^5 - 4x^3$

**14.** $-3x^2 + 8x + 2$

**15.** $-9x^3y + 3xy^3 + x^2y^2 + 2x^4$

**16.** $5x^2y^2 - 9xy + 8x^3y^2 - 5x^4$

**17.** $4ax - 7ab + 4x^6 - 7ax^2$

**18.** $5xy^8 - 3ax^5 + 4ax^3 - 12a + 5x^5$

**b**  Evaluate each polynomial function for the given values of the variable.

**19.** $P(x) = 3x^2 - 2x + 5$;  $P(4), P(-2), P(0)$

**20.** $f(x) = -7x^3 + 10x^2 - 13$;  $f(4), f(-1), f(0)$

**21.** $p(x) = 9x^3 + 8x^2 - 4x - 9$;  $p(-3), p(0), p(1), p\left(\frac{1}{2}\right)$

**22.** $Q(x) = 6x^3 - 11x - 4$;  $Q(-2), Q\left(\frac{1}{3}\right), Q(0), Q(10)$

**23.** *Falling Distance.*  The distance $s(t)$, in feet, traveled by an object falling freely from rest in $t$ seconds is approximated by the function given by
$$s(t) = 16t^2.$$
**a)** A paintbrush falls from a scaffold and takes 3 sec to hit the ground. How high is the scaffold?
**b)** A stone is dropped from a cliff and takes 8 sec to hit the ground. How high is the cliff?

$s(t) = 16 t^2$

**24.** *Golf Ball Stacks.*  Each stack of golf balls pictured below is formed by square layers of golf balls. The number $N$ of balls in the stack is given by the polynomial function
$$N(x) = \tfrac{1}{3}x^3 + \tfrac{1}{2}x^2 + \tfrac{1}{6}x,$$
where $x$ is the number of layers. How many golf balls are in each of the stacks?

**25.** *Medicine.* Ibuprofen is a medication used to relieve pain. The polynomial function

$$M(t) = 0.5t^4 + 3.45t^3 - 96.65t^2 + 347.7t,$$
$$0 \le t \le 6,$$

can be used to estimate the number of milligrams of ibuprofen in the bloodstream $t$ hours after 400 mg of the medication has been swallowed.

**Source:** Based on data from Dr. P. Carey, Burlington, VT

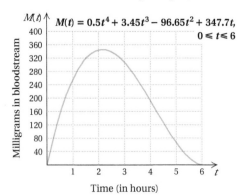

**a)** Use the graph above to estimate the number of milligrams of ibuprofen in the bloodstream 2 hr after 400 mg has been swallowed.
**b)** Use the graph above to estimate the number of milligrams of ibuprofen in the bloodstream 4 hr after 400 mg has been swallowed.
**c)** Approximate $M(5)$.
**d)** Approximate $M(3)$.

**27.** *Total Revenue.* A firm is marketing a new style of sunglasses. The firm determines that when it sells $x$ pairs of sunglasses, its total revenue is

$$R(x) = 240x - 0.5x^2 \text{ dollars.}$$

**a)** What is the total revenue from the sale of 50 pairs of sunglasses?
**b)** What is the total revenue from the sale of 95 pairs of sunglasses?

**26.** *Median Income by Age.* The polynomial function

$$I(x) = -0.0560x^4 + 7.9980x^3 - 436.1840x^2$$
$$+ 11{,}627.8376x - 90{,}625.0001,$$
$$13 \le x \le 65,$$

can be used to approximate the median income $I$ by age $x$ of a person living in the United States. The graph is shown below.

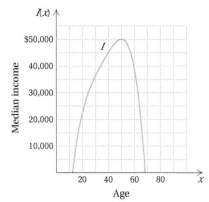

**SOURCE:** U.S. Census Bureau;
The Conference Board: Simmons Bureau of Labor Statistics

**a)** Evaluate $I(22)$ to estimate the median income of a 22-year-old.
**b)** Use only the graph to estimate $I(40)$.

**28.** *Total Cost.* A firm determines that the total cost, in dollars, of producing $x$ pairs of sunglasses is given by

$$C(x) = 5000 + 0.4x^2.$$

**a)** What is the total cost of producing 50 pairs of sunglasses?
**b)** What is the total cost of producing 95 pairs of sunglasses?

*Total Profit.* **Total profit $P$** is defined as total revenue $R$ minus total cost $C$, and is given by the function

$$P(x) = R(x) - C(x).$$

For each of the following, find the total profit $P(x)$.

**29.** $R(x) = 280x - 0.4x^2$, $C(x) = 7000 + 0.6x^2$

**30.** $R(x) = 280x - 0.7x^2$, $C(x) = 8000 + 0.5x^2$

*Magic Number.* In a recent season, the Arizona Diamondbacks were leading the San Francisco Giants for the Western Division championship of the National League. In the table below, the number in parentheses, 18, was the **magic number**. It means that any combination of Diamondbacks wins and Giants losses that totals 18 would ensure the championship for the Diamondbacks. The magic number $M$ is given by the polynomial

$$M = G - W_1 - L_2 + 1,$$

where $W_1$ is the number of wins for the first-place team, $L_2$ is the number of losses for the second-place team, and $G$ is the total number of games in the season, which is 162 in the major leagues. When the magic number reaches 1, a tie for the championship is clinched. When the magic number reaches 0, the championship is clinched. For the situation shown below, $G = 162$, $W_1 = 81$, and $L_2 = 64$. Then the magic number is

$$M = G - W_1 - L_2 + 1$$
$$= 162 - 81 - 64 + 1$$
$$= 18.$$

| WEST | W | L | Pct. | GB |
|---|---|---|---|---|
| Arizona (18) | 81 | 62 | .566 | – |
| San Francisco | 80 | 64 | .556 | 1½ |
| Los Angeles | 78 | 65 | .545 | 3 |
| San Diego | 70 | 73 | .490 | 11 |
| Colorado | 62 | 80 | .437 | 18½ |

Magic number in parentheses

**31.** Compute the magic number for Atlanta.

| EAST | W | L | PCT. | GB |
|---|---|---|---|---|
| Atlanta (?) | 78 | 64 | .549 | — |
| Philadelphia | 75 | 68 | .524 | $3\frac{1}{2}$ |
| New York | 71 | 73 | .493 | 8 |
| Florida | 66 | 77 | .462 | $12\frac{1}{2}$ |
| Montreal | 61 | 82 | .427 | $17\frac{1}{2}$ |

**32.** Compute the magic number for Houston.

| CENTRAL | W | L | PCT. | GB |
|---|---|---|---|---|
| Houston (?) | 84 | 59 | .587 | — |
| St. Louis | 78 | 64 | .549 | $5\frac{1}{2}$ |
| Chicago | 78 | 65 | .545 | 6 |
| Milwaukee | 63 | 80 | .441 | 21 |
| Cincinnati | 58 | 86 | .403 | $26\frac{1}{2}$ |
| Pittsburgh | 55 | 88 | .385 | 29 |

**33.** Compute the magic number for New York.

| EAST | W | L | PCT. | GB |
|---|---|---|---|---|
| New York (?) | 86 | 57 | .601 | — |
| Boston | 72 | 69 | .511 | 13 |
| Toronto | 70 | 73 | .490 | 16 |
| Baltimore | 55 | 87 | .387 | $30\frac{1}{2}$ |
| Tampa Bay | 50 | 93 | .350 | 36 |

**34.** Compute the magic number for Cleveland.

| CENTRAL | W | L | PCT. | GB |
|---|---|---|---|---|
| Cleveland (?) | 82 | 62 | .569 | — |
| Minnesota | 76 | 68 | .528 | 6 |
| Chicago | 74 | 70 | .514 | 8 |
| Detroit | 57 | 86 | .399 | $24\frac{1}{2}$ |
| Kansas City | 57 | 86 | .399 | $24\frac{1}{2}$ |

**C** Collect like terms.

**35.** $6x^2 - 7x^2 + 3x^2$

**36.** $-2y^2 - 7y^2 + 5y^2$

**37.** $7x - 2y - 4x + 6y$

**38.** $a - 8b - 5a + 7b$

**39.** $3a + 9 - 2 + 8a - 4a + 7$

**40.** $13x + 14 - 6 - 7x + 3x + 5$

**41.** $3a^2b + 4b^2 - 9a^2b - 6b^2$

**42.** $5x^2y^2 + 4x^3 - 8x^2y^2 - 12x^3$

**43.** $8x^2 - 3xy + 12y^2 + x^2 - y^2 + 5xy + 4y^2$

**44.** $a^2 - 2ab + b^2 + 9a^2 + 5ab - 4b^2 + a^2$

**45.** $4x^2y - 3y + 2xy^2 - 5x^2y + 7y + 7xy^2$

**46.** $3xy^2 + 4xy - 7xy^2 + 7xy + x^2y$

Add.

**47.** $(3x^2 + 5y^2 + 6) + (2x^2 - 3y^2 - 1)$

**48.** $(11y^2 + 6y - 3) + (9y^2 - 2y + 9)$

**49.** $(2a - c + 3b) + (4a - 2b + 2c)$

**50.** $(8x + z - 7y) + (5x + 10y - 4z)$

**51.** $(a^2 - 3b^2 + 4c^2) + (-5a^2 + 2b^2 - c^2)$

**52.** $(x^2 - 5y^2 - 9z^2) + (-6x^2 + 9y^2 - 2z^2)$

**53.** $(x^2 + 3x - 2xy - 3) + (-4x^2 - x + 3xy + 2)$

**54.** $(5a^2 - 3b + ab + 6) + (-a^2 + 8b - 8ab - 4)$

**55.** $(7x^2y - 3xy^2 + 4xy) + (-2x^2y - xy^2 + xy)$

**56.** $(7ab - 3ac + 5bc) + (13ab - 15ac - 8bc)$

**57.** $(2r^2 + 12r - 11) + (6r^2 - 2r + 4) + (r^2 - r - 2)$

**58.** $(5x^2 + 19x - 23) + (-7x^2 - 11x + 12) + (-x^2 - 9x + 8)$

**59.** $\left(\frac{2}{3}xy + \frac{5}{6}xy^2 + 5.1x^2y\right) + \left(-\frac{4}{5}xy + \frac{3}{4}xy^2 - 3.4x^2y\right)$

**60.** $\left(\frac{1}{8}xy - \frac{3}{5}x^3y^2 + 4.3y^3\right) + \left(-\frac{1}{3}xy - \frac{3}{4}x^3y^2 - 2.9y^3\right)$

**d** Write two equivalent expressions for the opposite of the polynomial.

**61.** $5x^3 - 7x^2 + 3x - 6$

**62.** $-8y^4 - 18y^3 + 4y - 9$

**63.** $-13y^2 + 6ay^4 - 5by^2$

**64.** $9ax^5y^3 - 8by^5 - abx - 16ay$

Subtract.

**65.** $(7x - 2) - (-4x + 5)$

**66.** $(8y + 1) - (-5y - 2)$

**67.** $(-3x^2 + 2x + 9) - (x^2 + 5x - 4)$

**68.** $(-9y^2 + 4y + 8) - (4y^2 + 2y - 3)$

**69.** $(5a + c - 2b) - (3a + 2b - 2c)$

**70.** $(z + 8x - 4y) - (4x + 6y - 3z)$

**71.** $(3x^2 - 2x - x^3) - (5x^2 - x^3 - 8x)$

**72.** $(8y^2 - 4y^3 - 3y) - (3y^2 - 9y - 7y^3)$

**73.** $(5a^2 + 4ab - 3b^2) - (9a^2 - 4ab + 2b^2)$

**74.** $(9y^2 - 14yz - 8z^2) - (12y^2 - 8yz + 4z^2)$

**75.** $(6ab - 4a^2b + 6ab^2) - (3ab^2 - 10ab - 12a^2b)$

**76.** $(10xy - 4x^2y^2 - 3y^3) - (-9x^2y^2 + 4y^3 - 7xy)$

**77.** $(0.09y^4 - 0.052y^3 + 0.93) - (0.03y^4 - 0.084y^3 + 0.94y^2)$

**78.** $(1.23x^4 - 3.122x^3 + 1.11x) - (0.79x^4 - 8.734x^3 + 0.04x^2 + 6.71x)$

**79.** $\left(\frac{5}{8}x^4 - \frac{1}{4}x^2 - \frac{1}{2}\right) - \left(-\frac{3}{8}x^4 + \frac{3}{4}x^2 + \frac{1}{2}\right)$

**80.** $\left(\frac{5}{6}y^4 - \frac{1}{2}y^2 - 7.8y + \frac{1}{3}\right) - \left(-\frac{3}{8}y^4 + \frac{3}{4}y^2 + 3.4y - \frac{1}{5}\right)$

## Skill Maintenance

Graph.  [2.1c, d], [2.2c]

**81.** $f(x) = \frac{2}{3}x - 1$

**82.** $g(x) = |x| - 1$

**83.** $g(x) = \dfrac{4}{x - 3}$

**84.** $f(x) = 1 - x^2$

Multiply.  [R.5d]

**85.** $3(y - 2)$

**86.** $-10(x + 2y - 7)$

**87.** $-14(3p - 2q - 10)$

**88.** $\frac{2}{3}(12w - 9t + 30)$

Graph using the slope and the $y$-intercept.  [2.5b]

**89.** $y = \frac{4}{3}x + 2$

**90.** $y = -0.4x + 1$

**91.** $y = 0.4x - 3$

**92.** $y = -\frac{2}{3}x - 4$

## Synthesis

**93.** *Triangular Layers.* The number of spheres in a triangular pyramid with $x$ triangular layers is given by the function
$$N(x) = \frac{1}{6}x^3 + \frac{1}{2}x^2 + \frac{1}{3}x.$$
The volume of a sphere of radius $r$ is given by the function
$$V(r) = \frac{4}{3}\pi r^3,$$
where $\pi$ can be approximated as 3.14.

   Chocolate Heaven has a window display of truffles piled in triangular pyramid formations, each 5 layers deep. If the diameter of each truffle is 3 cm, find the volume of chocolate in each triangular pyramid in the display.

**94.** *Surface Area.* Find a polynomial function that gives the outside surface area of a box like this one, with dimensions as shown.

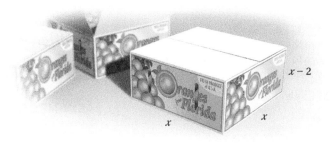

Perform the indicated operations. Assume that the exponents are natural numbers.

**95.** $(47x^{4a} + 3x^{3a} + 22x^{2a} + x^a + 1) + (37x^{3a} + 8x^{2a} + 3)$

**96.** $(3x^{6a} - 5x^{5a} + 4x^{3a} + 8) - (2x^{6a} + 4x^{4a} + 3x^{3a} + 2x^{2a})$

**97.** 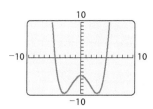 Use the TABLE and GRAPH features of a graphing calculator to check your answers to Exercises 57, 65, and 67.

**98.** A student who is trying to graph $f(x) = 0.05x^4 - x^2 + 5$ gets the following screen. How can the student tell at a glance that a mistake has been made?

# 4.2

# Multiplication of Polynomials

## OBJECTIVES

**a** Multiply any two polynomials.

**b** Use the FOIL method to multiply two binomials.

**c** Use a rule to square a binomial.

**d** Use a rule to multiply a sum and a difference of the same two terms.

**e** For functions $f$ described by second-degree polynomials, find and simplify notation like $f(a + h)$ and $f(a + h) - f(a)$.

## **a** Multiplication of Any Two Polynomials

### Multiplying Monomials

Monomials are expressions like $10x^2$, $8x^5$, and $-7a^2b^3$. To multiply monomials, we first multiply their coefficients. Then we multiply the variables using the commutative and associative laws and the rules for exponents that we studied in Chapter R.

**EXAMPLES**  Multiply and simplify.

**1.** $(10x^2)(8x^5) = (10 \cdot 8)(x^2 \cdot x^5)$
$$= 80x^{2+5} \quad \text{Adding exponents}$$
$$= 80x^7$$

**2.** $(-8x^4y^7)(5x^3y^2) = (-8 \cdot 5)(x^4 \cdot x^3)(y^7 \cdot y^2)$
$$= -40x^{4+3}y^{7+2} \quad \text{Adding exponents}$$
$$= -40x^7y^9$$

Do Margin Exercises 1–3.

### Multiplying Monomials and Binomials

The distributive law is the basis for multiplying polynomials other than monomials. We first multiply a monomial and a binomial.

**EXAMPLE 3**  Multiply: $2x(3x - 5)$.

$$2x \cdot (3x - 5) = 2x \cdot 3x - 2x \cdot 5 \quad \text{Using the distributive law}$$
$$= 6x^2 - 10x \quad \text{Multiplying monomials}$$

**EXAMPLE 4**  Multiply: $3a^2b(a^2 - b^2)$.

$$3a^2b \cdot (a^2 - b^2) = 3a^2b \cdot a^2 - 3a^2b \cdot b^2 \quad \text{Using the distributive law}$$
$$= 3a^4b - 3a^2b^3$$

Do Exercises 4 and 5.

### Multiplying Binomials

Next, we multiply two binomials. To do so, we use the distributive law twice, first considering one of the binomials as a single expression and multiplying it by each term of the other binomial.

### SKILL TO REVIEW
Objective R.5d: Use the distributive laws to find equivalent expressions by multiplying.

Multiply.

**1.** $3(x - y)$

**2.** $-\dfrac{1}{2}(6a - 10b)$

Multiply.

**1.** $(9y^2)(-2y)$

**2.** $(4x^3y)(6x^5y^2)$

**3.** $(-5xy^7z^4)(18x^3y^2z^8)$

Multiply.

**4.** $(-3y)(2y + 6)$

**5.** $(2xy)(4y^2 - 5)$

### Answers

*Skill to Review:*
**1.** $3x - 3y$  **2.** $-3a + 5b$

*Margin Exercises:*
**1.** $-18y^3$  **2.** $24x^8y^3$  **3.** $-90x^4y^9z^{12}$
**4.** $-6y^2 - 18y$  **5.** $8xy^3 - 10xy$

**EXAMPLE 5** Multiply: $(3y^2 + 4)(y^2 - 2)$.

$(3y^2 + 4)(y^2 - 2) = (3y^2 + 4) \cdot y^2 - (3y^2 + 4) \cdot 2$     Using the distributive law

$\qquad = [3y^2 \cdot y^2 + 4 \cdot y^2] - [3y^2 \cdot 2 + 4 \cdot 2]$    Using the distributive law

$\qquad = 3y^2 \cdot y^2 + 4 \cdot y^2 - 3y^2 \cdot 2 - 4 \cdot 2$    Removing parentheses

$\qquad = 3y^4 + 4y^2 - 6y^2 - 8$    Multiplying the monomials

$\qquad = 3y^4 - 2y^2 - 8$    Collecting like terms

Do Exercises 6 and 7.

**Multiply.**

**6.** $(5x^2 - 4)(x + 3)$

**7.** $(2y + 3)(3y - 4)$

## Multiplying Any Two Polynomials

To find a quick way to multiply any two polynomials, let's consider another example.

**EXAMPLE 6** Multiply: $(p + 2)(p^4 - 2p^3 + 3)$.

By the distributive law, we have

$(p + 2)(p^4 - 2p^3 + 3)$

$\qquad = (p + 2)(p^4) - (p + 2)(2p^3) + (p + 2)(3)$

$\qquad = p(p^4) + 2(p^4) - p(2p^3) - 2(2p^3) + p(3) + 2(3)$

$\qquad = p^5 + 2p^4 - 2p^4 - 4p^3 + 3p + 6$

$\qquad = p^5 - 4p^3 + 3p + 6.$    Collecting like terms

Do Exercises 8 and 9.

**Multiply.**

**8.** $(p - 3)(p^3 + 4p^2 - 5)$

**9.** $(2x^3 + 4x - 5)(x - 4)$

From the preceding examples, we can see how to multiply any two polynomials.

> **PRODUCT OF TWO POLYNOMIALS**
>
> To multiply two polynomials $P$ and $Q$, select one of the polynomials, say $P$. Then multiply each term of $P$ by every term of $Q$ and collect like terms.

We can use columns when doing long multiplications. We multiply each term at the top by every term at the bottom, keeping like terms in columns and *adding spaces for missing terms*. Then we add.

**EXAMPLE 7** Multiply: $(5x^3 + 3x^2 + x - 4)(-2x^2 + 3x + 6)$.

$$\begin{array}{r}
5x^3 + 3x^2 + x - 4 \\
-2x^2 + 3x + 6 \\
\hline
30x^3 + 18x^2 + 6x - 24 \\
15x^4 + 9x^3 + 3x^2 - 12x \\
-10x^5 - 6x^4 - 2x^3 + 8x^2 \\
\hline
-10x^5 + 9x^4 + 37x^3 + 29x^2 - 6x - 24
\end{array}$$

Multiplying by 6

Multiplying by $3x$

Multiplying by $-2x^2$

*Answers*

**6.** $5x^3 + 15x^2 - 4x - 12$
**7.** $6y^2 + y - 12$
**8.** $p^4 + p^3 - 12p^2 - 5p + 15$
**9.** $2x^4 - 8x^3 + 4x^2 - 21x + 20$

Multiply. Use columns.

10. $(-4x^3 + 5x^2 - 2x + 1) \times$
    $(-2x^2 - 3x + 6)$

11. $(-4x^3 - 2x + 1) \times$
    $(-2x^2 - 3x + 6)$

12. $(a^2 - 2ab + b^2) \times$
    $(a^3 + 3ab - b^2)$

**EXAMPLE 8** Multiply: $(5x^3 + x - 4)(-2x^2 + 3x + 6)$.

$$
\begin{array}{r}
5x^3 \quad\quad + \quad x - 4 \\
-2x^2 + \ 3x + \ 6 \\
\hline
30x^3 \quad\quad + \ 6x - 24 \\
15x^4 \quad\quad + \ 3x^2 - 12x \\
-10x^5 \quad\quad - \ 2x^3 + \ 8x^2 \\
\hline
-10x^5 + 15x^4 + 28x^3 + 11x^2 - \ 6x - 24
\end{array}
$$

Multiplying by 6
Multiplying by $3x$
Multiplying by $-2x^2$

Do Exercises 10–12.

## b Product of Two Binomials Using the FOIL Method

We now consider some **special products**. There are rules for faster multiplication in certain situations.

Let's find a faster special-product rule for the product of two binomials. Consider $(x + 7)(x + 4)$. We multiply each term of $(x + 7)$ by each term of $(x + 4)$:

$$(x + 7)(x + 4) = x \cdot x + x \cdot 4 + 7 \cdot x + 7 \cdot 4.$$

This multiplication illustrates a pattern that occurs whenever two binomials are multiplied:

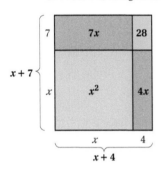

A visualization of $(x + 7)(x + 4)$ using areas

$$
\begin{array}{cccc}
\text{First} & \text{Outside} & \text{Inside} & \text{Last} \\
\text{terms} & \text{terms} & \text{terms} & \text{terms}
\end{array}
$$

$$(x + 7)(x + 4) = x \cdot x \ + \ 4x \ + \ 7x \ + \ 7(4) = x^2 + 11x + 28.$$

This special method of multiplying is called the **FOIL method**. Keep in mind that this method is based on the distributive law.

---

**THE FOIL METHOD**

To multiply two binomials, $A + B$ and $C + D$, multiply the **F**irst terms $AC$, the **O**utside terms $AD$, the **I**nside terms $BC$, and then the **L**ast terms $BD$. Then collect like terms, if possible.

$$(A + B)(C + D) = AC + AD + BC + BD$$

1. Multiply **F**irst terms: $AC$.

2. Multiply **O**utside terms: $AD$.

3. Multiply **I**nside terms: $BC$.

4. Multiply **L**ast terms: $BD$.

$$\downarrow$$

FOIL

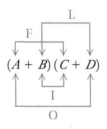

---

**EXAMPLES** Multiply.

$$\overset{F\quad O\quad I\quad L}{9.\ (x+5)(x-8)} = x^2 - 8x + 5x - 40$$
$$= x^2 - 3x - 40 \qquad \text{Collecting like terms}$$

We write the result in descending order since the original binomials are in descending order.

$$\overset{F\qquad O\qquad I\qquad L}{10.\ (3xy+2x)(x^2+2xy^2)} = 3x^3y + 6x^2y^3 + 2x^3 + 4x^2y^2$$

**11.** $(2x-3)(y+2) = 2xy + 4x - 3y - 6$

**12.** $(2x+3y)(x-4y) = 2x^2 - 8xy + 3xy - 12y^2$
$$= 2x^2 - 5xy - 12y^2 \qquad \text{Collecting like terms}$$

Do Exercises 13–15.

Multiply.

**13.** $(y-4)(y+10)$

**14.** $(p+5q)(2p-3q)$

**15.** $(x^2y+2x)(xy^2+y^2)$

---

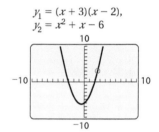

**Calculator Corner**

**Checking Multiplication of Polynomials**   A partial check of multiplication of polynomials can be performed graphically. Consider the product $(x+3)(x-2) = x^2 + x - 6$. We will use two graph styles to determine whether this product is correct. First, we press **MODE** to determine if SEQUENTIAL mode is selected. If it is not, we position the blinking cursor over SEQUENTIAL and then press **ENTER**. Next, on the Y= screen, we enter $y_1 = (x+3)(x-2)$ and $y_2 = x^2 + x - 6$. We will select the line-graph style for $y_1$ and the path style for $y_2$. To select these graph styles, we use ◁ to position the cursor over the icon to the left of the equation and press **ENTER** repeatedly until the desired style of icon appears, as shown below.

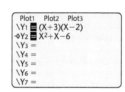

$$y_1 = (x+3)(x-2),$$
$$y_2 = x^2 + x - 6$$

The graphing calculator will graph $y_1$ first as a solid curve. Then it will graph $y_2$ as the circular cursor traces the leading edge of the graph, allowing us to determine visually whether the graphs coincide. In this case, the graphs appear to coincide, so the multiplication is probably correct.

A table can also be used to perform a partial check of a product. See the Calculator Corner on p. 330 for the procedure. Remember that these procedures provide only a partial check since we can neither see the entire graph nor view all possible values of $x$ in a table.

**Exercises:**   Determine graphically whether each product is correct.

**1.** $(x+4)(x+3) = x^2 + 7x + 12$

**2.** $(3x+2)(x-1) = 3x^2 + x - 2$

**3.** $(4x-1)(x-5) = 4x^2 - 21x + 5$

**4.** $(2x-1)(3x-4) = 6x^2 - 11x - 4$

**5.** $(x-1)(x-1) = x^2 + 1$

**6.** $(x-2)(x+2) = x^2 - 4$

## c Squares of Binomials

We can use the FOIL method to develop special products for the square of a binomial:

$$(A + B)^2 = (A + B)(A + B)$$
$$= A^2 + AB + AB + B^2$$
$$= A^2 + 2AB + B^2;$$

$$(A - B)^2 = (A - B)(A - B)$$
$$= A^2 - AB - AB + B^2$$
$$= A^2 - 2AB + B^2.$$

**A visualization of $(A + B)^2$ using areas**

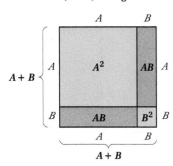

---

### SQUARE OF A BINOMIAL

The **square of a binomial** is the square of the first term, plus twice the product of the two terms, plus the square of the last term.

$$(A + B)^2 = A^2 + 2AB + B^2;$$
$$(A - B)^2 = A^2 - 2AB + B^2$$

---

-------- *Caution!* --------

In general,

$$(AB)^2 = A^2 B^2, \quad \text{but} \quad (A + B)^2 \neq A^2 + B^2.$$

-----------------------------

**EXAMPLES** Multiply.

$$(A - B)^2 = A^2 - 2 \, A \, B + B^2$$

**13.** $(y - 5)^2 = y^2 - 2(y)(5) + 5^2$
$$= y^2 - 10y + 25$$

$$(A + B)^2 = A^2 + 2 \, A \, B + B^2$$

**14.** $(2x + 3y)^2 = (2x)^2 + 2(2x)(3y) + (3y)^2$
$$= 4x^2 + 12xy + 9y^2$$

**15.** $(3x^2 + 5xy^2)^2 = (3x^2)^2 + 2(3x^2)(5xy^2) + (5xy^2)^2$
$$= 9x^4 + 30x^3 y^2 + 25x^2 y^4$$

**16.** $\left(\frac{1}{2}a^2 - b^3\right)^2 = \left(\frac{1}{2}a^2\right)^2 - 2\left(\frac{1}{2}a^2\right)(b^3) + (b^3)^2$
$$= \frac{1}{4}a^4 - a^2 b^3 + b^6$$

Do Exercises 16–19.

## d Products of Sums and Differences

Another special case of a product of two binomials is the product of a sum and a difference. Note the following:

$$\begin{array}{cccc} \text{F} & \text{O} & \text{I} & \text{L} \\ \downarrow & \downarrow & \downarrow & \downarrow \end{array}$$
$$(A + B)(A - B) = A^2 - AB + AB - B^2 = A^2 - B^2.$$

Multiply.

**16.** $(a - b)^2$

**17.** $(x + 8)^2$

**18.** $(3x - 7)^2$

**19.** $\left(m^3 + \frac{1}{4}n\right)^2$

## PRODUCT OF A SUM AND A DIFFERENCE

The product of the sum and the difference of the same two terms is the square of the first term minus the square of the second term (the difference of their squares).

$$(A + B)(A - B) = A^2 - B^2$$ This is called a **difference of squares**.

**EXAMPLES** Multiply. (Say the rule as you work.)

$$(A + B)(A - B) = A^2 - B^2$$

**17.** $(y + 5)(y - 5) = y^2 - 5^2 = y^2 - 25$

**18.** $(2xy^2 + 3x)(2xy^2 - 3x) = (2xy^2)^2 - (3x)^2 = 4x^2y^4 - 9x^2$

**19.** $(0.2t - 1.4m)(0.2t + 1.4m) = (0.2t)^2 - (1.4m)^2 = 0.04t^2 - 1.96m^2$

**20.** $\left(\frac{2}{3}n - m^2\right)\left(\frac{2}{3}n + m^2\right) = \left(\frac{2}{3}n\right)^2 - (m^2)^2 = \frac{4}{9}n^2 - m^4$

> Do Exercises 20–23.

Multiply.

**20.** $(x + 8)(x - 8)$

**21.** $(4y - 7)(4y + 7)$

**22.** $(2.8a + 4.1b)(2.8a - 4.1b)$

**23.** $\left(3w - \frac{3}{5}q^2\right)\left(3w + \frac{3}{5}q^2\right)$

**EXAMPLES** Multiply.

**21.** $(5y + 4 + 3x)(5y + 4 - 3x) = (5y + 4)^2 - (3x)^2$

$$= 25y^2 + 40y + 16 - 9x^2$$

> Here we treat the binomial $5y + 4$ as the first expression, $A$, and $3x$ as the second, $B$.

**22.** $(3xy^2 + 4y)(-3xy^2 + 4y) = (4y + 3xy^2)(4y - 3xy^2)$

$$= (4y)^2 - (3xy^2)^2$$

$$= 16y^2 - 9x^2y^4$$

> Do Exercises 24 and 25.

Multiply.

**24.** $(2x + 3 - 5y)(2x + 3 + 5y)$

**25.** $(7x^2y + 2y)(-2y + 7x^2y)$

Try to multiply polynomials mentally, even when several types are mixed. First, check to see what types of polynomials are to be multiplied. Then use the quickest method. Sometimes we might use more than one method. Remember that FOIL *always* works for multiplying binomials!

**EXAMPLE 23** Multiply: $(s - 5t)(s + 5t)(s^2 - 25t^2)$.

We first note that $s - 5t$ and $s + 5t$ can be multiplied using the rule $(A - B)(A + B) = A^2 - B^2$. Then we have the product of two identical binomials, so we square, using $(A - B)^2 = A^2 - 2AB + B^2$.

$(s - 5t)(s + 5t)(s^2 - 25t^2)$

$= (s^2 - 25t^2)(s^2 - 25t^2)$      Using $(A - B)(A + B) = A^2 - B^2$

$= (s^2 - 25t^2)^2$

$= (s^2)^2 - 2(s^2)(25t^2) + (25t^2)^2$      Using $(A - B)^2 = A^2 - 2AB + B^2$

$= s^4 - 50s^2t^2 + 625t^4$

*Answers*

**20.** $x^2 - 64$    **21.** $16y^2 - 49$

**22.** $7.84a^2 - 16.81b^2$    **23.** $9w^2 - \frac{9}{25}q^4$

**24.** $4x^2 + 12x + 9 - 25y^2$

**25.** $49x^4y^2 - 4y^2$

**26.** Multiply:

$(3x + 2y)(3x - 2y)(9x^2 + 4y^2)$.

Do Exercise 26.

## e Using Function Notation

### ✖ Algebraic–Graphical Connection

Let's stop for a moment and look back at what we have done in this section. We have shown, for example, that

$$(x - 2)(x + 2) = x^2 - 4,$$

that is, $x^2 - 4$ and $(x - 2)(x + 2)$ are equivalent expressions.

From the viewpoint of functions, if

$$f(x) = (x - 2)(x + 2)$$

and

$$g(x) = x^2 - 4,$$

then for any given input $x$, the outputs $f(x)$ and $g(x)$ are identical. Thus the graphs of these functions are identical and we say that $f$ and $g$ represent the same function. Functions like these are graphed in detail in Chapter 7.

| $x$ | $f(x)$ | $g(x)$ |
|---|---|---|
| 3 | 5 | 5 |
| 2 | 0 | 0 |
| 1 | −3 | −3 |
| 0 | −4 | −4 |
| −1 | −3 | −3 |
| −2 | 0 | 0 |
| −3 | 5 | 5 |

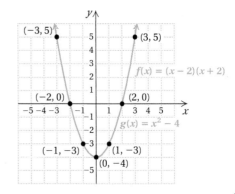

Our work with multiplying can be used when manipulating functions.

**EXAMPLE 24** Given $f(x) = x^2 - 4x + 5$, find and simplify $f(a + 3)$ and $f(a + h) - f(a)$.

To find $f(a + 3)$, we replace $x$ with $a + 3$. Then we simplify:

$$f(a + 3) = (a + 3)^2 - 4(a + 3) + 5$$
$$= a^2 + 6a + 9 - 4a - 12 + 5 = a^2 + 2a + 2.$$

To find $f(a + h) - f(a)$, we replace $x$ with $a + h$ for $f(a + h)$ and $x$ with $a$ for $f(a)$. Then we simplify:

$$f(a + h) - f(a) = [(a + h)^2 - 4(a + h) + 5] - [a^2 - 4a + 5]$$
$$= a^2 + 2ah + h^2 - 4a - 4h + 5 - a^2 + 4a - 5$$
$$= 2ah + h^2 - 4h.$$

Do Exercise 27.

**27.** Given $f(x) = x^2 + 2x - 7$, find and simplify $f(a + 1)$ and $f(a + h) - f(a)$.

**Answers**

**26.** $81x^4 - 16y^4$
**27.** $f(a + 1) = a^2 + 4a - 4;$
  $f(a + h) - f(a) = 2ah + h^2 + 2h$

**a** Multiply.

**1.** $8y^2 \cdot 3y$

**2.** $-5x^2 \cdot 6xy$

**3.** $2x(-10x^2y)$

**4.** $-7ab^2(4a^2b^2)$

**5.** $(5x^5y^4)(-2xy^3)$

**6.** $(2a^2bc^2)(-3ab^5c^4)$

**7.** $2z(7 - x)$

**8.** $4a(a^2 - 3a)$

**9.** $6ab(a + b)$

**10.** $2xy(2x - 3y)$

**11.** $5cd(3c^2d - 5cd^2)$

**12.** $a^2(2a^2 - 5a^3)$

**13.** $(5x + 2)(3x - 1)$

**14.** $(2a - 3b)(4a - b)$

**15.** $(s + 3t)(s - 3t)$

**16.** $(y + 4)(y - 4)$

**17.** $(x - y)(x - y)$

**18.** $(a + 2b)(a + 2b)$

**19.** $(x^3 + 8)(x^3 - 5)$

**20.** $(2x^4 - 7)(3x^3 + 5)$

**21.** $(a^2 - 2b^2)(a^2 - 3b^2)$

**22.** $(2m^2 - n^2)(3m^2 - 5n^2)$

**23.** $(x - 4)(x^2 + 4x + 16)$

**24.** $(y + 3)(y^2 - 3y + 9)$

**25.** $(x + y)(x^2 - xy + y^2)$

**26.** $(a - b)(a^2 + ab + b^2)$

**27.** $(a^2 + a - 1)(a^2 + 4a - 5)$

**28.** $(x^2 - 2x + 1)(x^2 + x + 2)$

**29.** $(4a^2b - 2ab + 3b^2)(ab - 2b + a)$

**30.** $(2x^2 + y^2 - 2xy)(x^2 - 2y^2 - xy)$

**31.** $\left(x + \frac{1}{4}\right)\left(x + \frac{1}{4}\right)$

**32.** $\left(b - \frac{1}{3}\right)\left(b - \frac{1}{3}\right)$

**33.** $\left(\frac{1}{2}x - \frac{2}{3}\right)\left(\frac{1}{4}x + \frac{1}{3}\right)$

**34.** $\left(\frac{2}{3}a + \frac{1}{6}b\right)\left(\frac{1}{3}a - \frac{5}{6}b\right)$

**35.** $(1.3x - 4y)(2.5x + 7y)$

**36.** $(40a - 0.24b)(0.3a + 10b)$

**b** , **c**   Multiply.

**37.** $(a + 8)(a + 5)$

**38.** $(x + 2)(x + 3)$

**39.** $(y + 7)(y - 4)$

**40.** $(y - 2)(y + 3)$

**41.** $\left(3a + \frac{1}{2}\right)^2$

**42.** $\left(2x - \frac{1}{3}\right)^2$

**43.** $(x - 2y)^2$

**44.** $(2s + 3t)^2$

**45.** $\left(b - \frac{1}{3}\right)\left(b - \frac{1}{2}\right)$

**46.** $\left(x - \frac{1}{2}\right)\left(x - \frac{1}{4}\right)$

**47.** $(2x + 9)(x + 2)$

**48.** $(3b + 2)(2b - 5)$

**49.** $(20a - 0.16b)^2$

**50.** $(10p^2 + 2.3q)^2$

**51.** $(2x - 3y)(2x + y)$

**52.** $(2a - 3b)(2a - b)$

**53.** $(x^3 + 2)^2$

**54.** $(y^A - 7)^2$

**55.** $(2x^2 - 3y^2)^2$

**56.** $(3s^2 + 4t^2)^2$

**57.** $(a^3b^2 + 1)^2$

**58.** $(x^2y - xy^3)^2$

**59.** $(0.1a^2 - 5b)^2$

**60.** $(6p + 0.45q^2)^2$

**61.** *Compound Interest.*   Suppose that $P$ dollars is invested in a savings account at interest rate $i$, compounded annually, for 2 years. The amount $A$ in the account after 2 years is given by
$$A = P(1 + i)^2.$$
Find an equivalent expression for $A$ without parentheses.

**62.** *Compound Interest.*   Suppose that $P$ dollars is invested in a savings account at interest rate $i$, compounded semiannually, for 1 year. The amount $A$ in the account after 1 year is given by
$$A = P\left(1 + \frac{i}{2}\right)^2.$$
Find an equivalent expression for $A$ without parentheses.

Multiply.

**63.** $(d + 8)(d - 8)$

**64.** $(y - 3)(y + 3)$

**65.** $(2c + 3)(2c - 3)$

**66.** $(1 - 2x)(1 + 2x)$

**67.** $(6m - 5n)(6m + 5n)$

**68.** $(3x + 7y)(3x - 7y)$

**69.** $(x^2 + yz)(x^2 - yz)$

**70.** $(2a^2 + 5ab)(2a^2 - 5ab)$

**71.** $(-mn + m^2)(mn + m^2)$

**72.** $(1.6 + pq)(-1.6 + pq)$

**73.** $(-3pq + 4p^2)(4p^2 + 3pq)$

**74.** $(-10xy + 5x^2)(5x^2 + 10xy)$

**75.** $\left(\frac{1}{2}p - \frac{2}{3}q\right)\left(\frac{1}{2}p + \frac{2}{3}q\right)$

**76.** $\left(\frac{3}{5}ab + 4c\right)\left(\frac{3}{5}ab - 4c\right)$

**77.** $(x + 1)(x - 1)(x^2 + 1)$

**78.** $(y - 2)(y + 2)(y^2 + 4)$

**79.** $(a - b)(a + b)(a^2 - b^2)$

**80.** $(2x - y)(2x + y)(4x^2 - y^2)$

**81.** $(a + b + 1)(a + b - 1)$

**82.** $(m + n + 2)(m + n - 2)$

**83.** $(2x + 3y + 4)(2x + 3y - 4)$

**84.** $(3a - 2b + c)(3a - 2b - c)$

**e**    For each of the following functions, find $f(t - 1), f(p + 1), f(a + h) - f(a), f(t - 2) + c$, and $f(a) + 5$.

**85.** $f(x) = 5x + x^2$

**86.** $f(x) = 4x + 2x^2$

**87.** $f(x) = 3x^2 - 7x + 8$

**88.** $f(x) = 3x^2 - 4x + 7$

**89.** $f(x) = 5x - x^2$

**90.** $f(x) = 4x - 2x^2$

**91.** $f(x) = 4 + 3x - x^2$

**92.** $f(x) = 2 - 4x - 3x^2$

## Skill Maintenance

Solve.    [3.4b]

**93.** *Auto Travel.*    Rachel leaves on a business trip, forgetting her laptop computer. Her sister discovers Rachel's laptop 2 hr later, and knowing that Rachel needs it for her sales presentation and that Rachel normally travels at a speed of 55 mph, she decides to follow her at a speed of 75 mph. After how long will Rachel's sister catch up with her?

**94.** *Air Travel.*    An airplane flew for 5 hr against a 20-mph headwind. The return trip with the wind took 4 hr. Find the speed of the plane in still air.

Solve.    [3.2a], [3.3a]

**95.** $5x + 9y = 2,$
$4x - 9y = 10$

**96.** $x + 4y = 13,$
$5x - 7y = -16$

**97.** $2x - 3y = 1,$
$4x - 6y = 2$

**98.** $9x - 8y = -2,$
$3x + 2y = 3$

## Synthesis

**99.** Use the TABLE and GRAPH features of a graphing calculator to check your answers to Exercises 28, 40, and 77.

**100.** Use the TABLE and GRAPH features of a graphing calculator to determine whether each of the following is correct.
  **a)** $(x - 1)^2 = x^2 - 1$
  **b)** $(x - 2)(x + 3) = x^2 + x - 6$
  **c)** $(x - 1)^3 = x^3 - 3x^2 + 3x - 1$
  **d)** $(x + 1)^4 = x^4 + 1$

Multiply. Assume that variables in exponents represent natural numbers.

**101.** $(z^{r^2})^{n^3}(z^{4n^3})^{r^2}$

**102.** $y^3 z^n (y^{3n} z^3 - 4yz^{2n})$

**103.** $(r^2 + s^2)^2 (r^2 + 2rs + s^2)(r^2 - 2rs + s^2)$

**104.** $(y - 1)^6 (y + 1)^6$

**105.** $\left(3x^5 - \frac{5}{11}\right)^2$

**106.** $(4x^2 + 2xy + y^2)(4x^2 - 2xy + y^2)$

**107.** $(x^a + y^b)(x^a - y^b)(x^{2a} + y^{2b})$

**108.** $\left(x - \frac{1}{7}\right)\left(x^2 + \frac{1}{7}x + \frac{1}{49}\right)$

**109.** $(x - 1)(x^2 + x + 1)(x^3 + 1)$

**110.** $(x^{a-b})^{a+b}$

# 4.3 Introduction to Factoring

Factoring is the reverse of multiplication. To **factor** an expression is to find an equivalent expression that is a product. For example, reversing a type of multiplication we have considered, we know that

$$x^2 - 9 = (x + 3)(x - 3).$$

We say that $x + 3$ and $x - 3$ are **factors** of $x^2 - 9$ and that $(x + 3)(x - 3)$ is a **factorization**.

> ### FACTOR
>
> To **factor** a polynomial is to express it as a product.
>
> A **factor** of a polynomial $P$ is a polynomial that can be used to express $P$ as a product.

> ### FACTORIZATION
>
> A **factorization** of a polynomial $P$ is an expression that names $P$ as a product of factors.

---

*Caution!*

Be careful not to confuse terms with factors! The terms of $x^2 - 9$ are $x^2$ and $-9$. Terms are used to form sums. Factors of $x^2 - 9$ are $x - 3$ and $x + 3$. Factors are used to form products.

---

> Do Margin Exercise 1.

## a Terms with Common Factors

To multiply a monomial and a polynomial with more than one term, we multiply each term by the monomial using the distributive laws. To factor, we do the reverse. We express a polynomial as a product using the distributive laws in reverse. Compare.

*Multiply*

$5x(x^2 - 3x + 1)$

$= 5x \cdot x^2 - 5x \cdot 3x + 5x \cdot 1$

$= 5x^3 - 15x^2 + 5x$

*Factor*

$5x^3 - 15x^2 + 5x$

$= 5x \cdot x^2 - 5x \cdot 3x + 5x \cdot 1$

$= 5x(x^2 - 3x + 1)$

**EXAMPLE 1** Factor: $4y^2 - 8$.

$4y^2 - 8 = 4 \cdot y^2 - 4 \cdot 2$     4 is the largest common factor.

$= 4(y^2 - 2)$     Factoring out the common factor 4

## OBJECTIVES

**a** Factor polynomials whose terms have a common factor.

**b** Factor certain polynomials with four terms by grouping.

**SKILL TO REVIEW**
Objective R.5d: Use the distributive laws to find equivalent expressions by factoring.

Factor.

1. $2y - 2$

2. $15y - 10x + 25$

1. Consider
$x^2 - 4x - 5 = (x - 5)(x + 1)$.

   **a)** What are the factors of $x^2 - 4x - 5$?

   **b)** What are the terms of $x^2 - 4x - 5$?

*Answers*

*Skill to Review:*
1. $2(y - 1)$    2. $5(3y - 2x + 5)$

*Margin Exercise:*
1. **(a)** $x - 5$ and $x + 1$; **(b)** $x^2$, $-4x$, and $-5$

In some cases, there is more than one common factor. In Example 2 below, for instance, 5 is a common factor, $x^3$ is a common factor, and $5x^3$ is a common factor. If there is more than one common factor, we generally choose the one with the largest coefficient and the largest exponent.

**EXAMPLES**  Factor.

**2.** $5x^4 - 20x^3 = 5x^3 \cdot x - 5x^3 \cdot 4$
$$= 5x^3(x - 4) \quad \text{Multiply mentally to check your answer.}$$

**3.** $12x^2y - 20x^3y = 4x^2y(3 - 5x)$

**EXAMPLE 4**  Factor: $10p^6q^2 - 4p^5q^3 + 2p^4q^4$.

First, we look for the greatest positive common factor in the coefficients:

$$10, -4, 2 \quad \longrightarrow \quad \text{Greatest common factor} = 2.$$

Second, we look for the greatest common factor in the powers of $p$:

$$p^6, \ p^5, \ p^4 \quad \longrightarrow \quad \text{Greatest common factor} = p^4.$$

Third, we look for the greatest common factor in the powers of $q$:

$$q^2, \ q^3, \ q^4 \quad \longrightarrow \quad \text{Greatest common factor} = q^2.$$

Thus, $2p^4q^2$ is the greatest common factor of the given polynomial. Then
$$10p^6q^2 - 4p^5q^3 + 2p^4q^4 = 2p^4q^2 \cdot 5p^2 - 2p^4q^2 \cdot 2pq + 2p^4q^2 \cdot q^2$$
$$= 2p^4q^2(5p^2 - 2pq + q^2).$$

The polynomials in Examples 1–4 have been **factored completely**. They cannot be factored further. The factors in the resulting factorization are said to be **prime polynomials**.

Do Exercises 2–5.

When the leading coefficient is a negative number, we generally factor out the negative coefficient.

**EXAMPLES**  Factor out a common factor with a negative coefficient.

**5.** $-4x - 24 = -4(x + 6)$

**6.** $-2x^2 + 6x - 10 = -2(x^2 - 3x + 5)$

Do Exercises 6 and 7.

**EXAMPLE 7** *Height of a Thrown Object.*  Suppose that a softball is thrown upward with an initial velocity of 64 ft/sec. Its height $h$, in feet, after $t$ seconds is given by the function

$$h(t) = -16t^2 + 64t.$$

**a)** Find an equivalent expression for $h(t)$ by factoring out a common factor with a negative coefficient.

**b)** Check your factoring by evaluating both expressions for $h(t)$ at $t = 1$.

Factor.

**2.** $3x^2 - 6$

**3.** $4x^5 - 8x^3$

**4.** $9y^4 - 15y^3 + 3y^2$

**5.** $6x^2y - 21x^3y^2 + 3x^2y^3$

Factor out a common factor with a negative coefficient.

**6.** $-8x + 32$

**7.** $-3x^2 - 15x + 9$

*Answers*

**2.** $3(x^2 - 2)$   **3.** $4x^3(x^2 - 2)$
**4.** $3y^2(3y^2 - 5y + 1)$
**5.** $3x^2y(2 - 7xy + y^2)$   **6.** $-8(x - 4)$
**7.** $-3(x^2 + 5x - 3)$

**a)** We factor out $-16t$ as follows:

$$h(t) = -16t^2 + 64t = -16t(t - 4).$$

**b)** We check as follows:

$$h(1) = -16 \cdot 1^2 + 64 \cdot 1 = 48;$$
$$h(1) = -16 \cdot 1(1 - 4) = 48. \quad \text{Using the factorization}$$

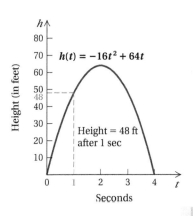

$h(t) = -16t^2 + 64t$

Height = 48 ft after 1 sec

Height (in feet)

Seconds

Do Exercise 8.

## b Factoring by Grouping

In expressions of four or more terms, there may be a *common binomial factor*. We proceed as in the following examples.

**EXAMPLE 8** Factor: $(a - b)(x + 5) + (a - b)(x - y^2)$.

$$(a - b)(x + 5) + (a - b)(x - y^2) = (a - b)[(x + 5) + (x - y^2)]$$
$$= (a - b)(2x + 5 - y^2)$$

Do Exercises 9 and 10.

In Example 9, we factor two parts of the expression. Then we factor as in Example 8.

**EXAMPLE 9** Factor: $y^3 + 3y^2 + 4y + 12$.

$$y^3 + 3y^2 + 4y + 12 = (y^3 + 3y^2) + (4y + 12) \qquad \text{Grouping}$$
$$= y^2(y + 3) + 4(y + 3) \qquad \text{Factoring each binomial}$$
$$= (y + 3)(y^2 + 4) \qquad \text{Factoring out the common factor } y + 3$$

**EXAMPLE 10** Factor: $3x^3 - 6x^2 - x + 2$.

First, we consider the first two terms and factor out the greatest common factor:

$$3x^3 - 6x^2 = 3x^2(x - 2).$$

Next, we look at the third and fourth terms to see if we can factor them in order to have $x - 2$ as a factor. We see that if we factor out $-1$, we get $x - 2$:

$$-x + 2 = -1 \cdot (x - 2).$$

---

**8. Height of a Rocket.** A model rocket is launched upward with an initial velocity of 96 ft/sec. Its height $h$, in feet, after $t$ seconds is given by the function

$$h(t) = -16t^2 + 96t.$$

**a)** Find an equivalent expression for $h(t)$ by factoring out a common factor with a negative coefficient.

**b)** Check your factoring by evaluating both expressions for $h(t)$ at $t = 2$.

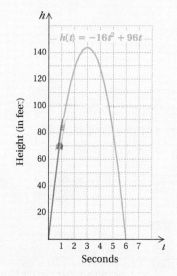

$h(t) = -16t^2 + 96t$

Height (in feet)

Seconds

Factor.

**9.** $(p + q)(x + 2) + (p + q)(x + y)$

**10.** $(y + 3)(y - 21) + (y + 3)(y + 10)$

*Answers*

**8. (a)** $h(t) = -16t(t - 6)$; **(b)** $h(2) = 128$ in each   **9.** $(p + q)(2x + y + 2)$
**10.** $(y + 3)(2y - 11)$

Finally, we factor out the common factor $x - 2$:

$$3x^3 - 6x^2 - x + 2 = (3x^3 - 6x^2) + (-x + 2)$$
$$= 3x^2(x - 2) + (-x + 2)$$
$$= 3x^2(x - 2) - 1(x - 2) \qquad \textit{Check: } -1(x - 2) = -x + 2$$
$$= (x - 2)(3x^2 - 1). \qquad \text{Factoring out the common factor } x - 2$$

**EXAMPLE 11** Factor: $4x^3 - 15 + 20x^2 - 3x$.

$$4x^3 - 15 + 20x^2 - 3x = 4x^3 + 20x^2 - 3x - 15 \qquad \text{Rearranging}$$
$$= 4x^2(x + 5) - 3(x + 5) \qquad \textit{Check:}$$
$$\qquad\qquad\qquad -3(x + 5) = -3x - 15$$
$$= (x + 5)(4x^2 - 3) \qquad \text{Factoring out } x + 5$$

Not all polynomials with four terms can be factored by grouping. An example is

$$x^3 + x^2 + 3x - 3.$$

Note that in a grouping like $x^2(x + 1) + 3(x - 1)$, the expressions $x + 1$ and $x - 1$ are not the same. No grouping allows us to factor out a common binomial.

Factor by grouping, if possible.

**11.** $5y^3 + 2y^2 - 10y - 4$

**12.** $x^3 + 5x^2 + 4x - 20$

Do Exercises 11 and 12.

---

## Calculator Corner

**Checking Factorizations**   A partial check of a factorization can be performed using a table or a graph. To check the factorization $3x^3 - 6x^2 - x + 2 = (x - 2)(3x^2 - 1)$, for example, we enter $y_1 = 3x^3 - 6x^2 - x + 2$ and $y_2 = (x - 2)(3x^2 - 1)$ on the equation-editor screen (see p. 83). Then we set up a table in AUTO mode (see p. 164). If the factorization is correct, the values of $y_1$ and $y_2$ will be the same regardless of the table settings used. We can also graph $y_1 = 3x^3 - 6x^2 - x + 2$ and $y_2 = (x - 2)(3x^2 - 1)$. If the graphs appear to coincide, the factorization is probably correct. Keep in mind that these procedures provide only a partial check since we cannot view all possible values of $x$ in a table nor can we see the entire graph.

$$y_1 = 3x^3 - 6x^2 - x + 2,$$
$$y_2 = (x - 2)(3x^2 - 1)$$

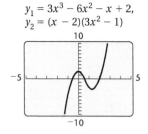

**Exercises:**   Use a table or a graph to determine whether the factorization is correct.

**1.** $18x^2 + 3x - 6 = 3(2x - 1)(3x + 2)$     **2.** $3x^2 - 11x - 20 = (3x + 4)(x - 5)$

**3.** $2x^2 + 5x - 12 = (2x + 3)(x - 4)$     **4.** $20x^2 - 13x - 2 = (4x + 1)(5x - 2)$

**5.** $6x^2 + 13x + 6 = (6x + 1)(x + 6)$     **6.** $6x^2 + 13x + 6 = (3x + 2)(2x + 3)$

**7.** $x^2 + 16 = (x - 4)(x - 4)$     **8.** $x^2 - 16 = (x + 4)(x - 4)$

---

*Answers*

**11.** $(5y + 2)(y^2 - 2)$   **12.** Cannot be factored by grouping

**a** Factor.

**1.** $6a^2 + 3a$

**2.** $4x^2 + 2x$

**3.** $x^3 + 9x^2$

**4.** $y^3 + 8y^2$

**5.** $8x^2 - 4x^4$

**6.** $6x^2 + 3x^4$

**7.** $4x^2y - 12xy^2$

**8.** $5x^2y^3 + 15x^3y^2$

**9.** $3y^2 - 3y - 9$

**10.** $5x^2 - 5x + 15$

**11.** $4ab - 6ac + 12ad$

**12.** $8xy + 10xz - 14xw$

**13.** $10a^4 + 15a^2 - 25a - 30$

**14.** $12t^5 - 20t^4 + 8t^2 - 16$

**15.** $15x^2y^5z^3 - 12x^4y^4z^7$

**16.** $21a^3b^5c^7 - 14a^7b^6c^2$

**17.** $14a^4b^3c^5 + 21a^3b^5c^4 - 35a^4b^4c^3$

**18.** $9x^3y^6z^2 - 12x^4y^4z^4 + 15x^2y^5z^3$

Factor out a common factor with a negative coefficient.

**19.** $-5x - 45$

**20.** $-3t + 18$

**21.** $-6a - 84$

**22.** $-8t + 40$

**23.** $-2x^2 + 2x - 24$

**24.** $-2x^2 + 16x - 20$

**25.** $-3y^2 + 24y$

**26.** $-7x^2 - 56y$

**27.** $-a^4 + 2a^3 - 13a^2 - 1$

**28.** $-m^3 - m^2 + m - 2$

**29.** $-3y^3 + 12y^2 - 15y + 24$

**30.** $-4m^4 - 32m^3 + 64m - 12$

**31.** *Volume of Propane Gas Tank.* A propane gas tank is shaped like a circular cylinder with half of a sphere at each end. The volume of the tank with length $h$ and radius $r$ of the cylindrical section is given by the polynomial
$$\pi r^2 h + \tfrac{4}{3}\pi r^3.$$
Find an equivalent expression by factoring out a common factor.

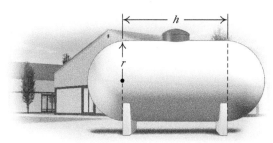

**32.** *Triangular Layers.* The stack of truffles shown below is formed by triangular layers of truffles. The number $N$ of truffles in the stack is given by the polynomial function
$$N(x) = \tfrac{1}{6}x^3 + \tfrac{1}{2}x^2 + \tfrac{1}{3}x,$$
where $x$ is the number of layers. Find an equivalent expression for $N(x)$ by factoring out a common factor.

**33.** *Height of a Baseball.* A baseball is popped up with an upward velocity of 72 ft/sec. Its height $h$, in feet, after $t$ seconds is given by

$$h(t) = -16t^2 + 72t.$$

**a)** Find an equivalent expression for $h(t)$ by factoring out a common factor with a negative coefficient.
**b)** Perform a partial check of part (a) by evaluating both expressions for $h(t)$ at $t = 2$.

**34.** *Number of Diagonals.* The number of diagonals of a polygon having $n$ sides is given by the polynomial function

$$P(n) = \tfrac{1}{2}n^2 - \tfrac{3}{2}n.$$

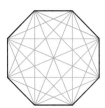

Find an equivalent expression for $P(n)$ by factoring out a common factor.

**35.** *Total Revenue.* Perfect Sound is marketing a new kind of home theater chair. The firm determines that when it sells $x$ chairs, the total revenue $R$ is given by the polynomial function

$$R(x) = 280x + 0.4x^2 \text{ dollars.}$$

Find an equivalent expression for $R(x)$ by factoring out $0.4x$.

**36.** *Total Cost.* Perfect Sound determines that the total cost $C$ of producing $x$ home theater chairs is given by the polynomial function

$$C(x) = 0.18x + 0.6x^2.$$

Find an equivalent expression for $C(x)$ by factoring out $0.6x$.

 Factor.

**37.** $a(b - 2) + c(b - 2)$

**38.** $a(x^2 - 3) - 2(x^2 - 3)$

**39.** $(x - 2)(x + 5) + (x - 2)(x + 8)$

**40.** $(m - 4)(m + 3) + (m - 4)(m - 3)$

**41.** $y^8 - 7y^7 + y - 7$

**42.** $b^5 - 3b^4 + b - 3$

**43.** $ac + ad + bc + bd$

**44.** $xy + xz + wy + wz$

**45.** $b^3 - b^2 + 2b - 2$

**46.** $y^3 - y^2 + 3y - 3$

**47.** $y^3 + 8y^2 - 5y - 40$

**48.** $t^3 + 6t^2 - 2t - 12$

**49.** $24x^3 + 72x - 36x^2 - 108$

**50.** $10a^3 + 50a - 15a^2 - 75$

**51.** $a^4 - a^3 + a^2 + a$

**52.** $p^6 + p^5 - p^3 + p^2$

**53.** $2y^4 + 6y^2 - 5y^2 - 15$

**54.** $2xy + x^2y - 6 - 3x$

## Skill Maintenance

In each of Exercises 55–62, fill in the blank with the correct term from the given list. Some of the choices may not be used.

55. The equation $y = mx + b$ is called the _____ equation of the line with slope $m$ and $y$-intercept $(0, b)$. [2.4b]

56. Equations with the same solutions are called _____ equations. [1.1a]

57. If the slope of a line is less than 0, the graph slants _____ from left to right. [2.4b]

58. A(n) _____ system of equations has no solution. [3.1a]

59. The equation $y - y_1 = m(x - x_1)$, where $m$ is the slope of the line and $(x_1, y_1)$ is a point on the line, is called the _____ equation. [2.6b]

60. _____ angles are angles whose sum is 180°. [3.2b]

61. When the terms of a polynomial are written such that the exponents increase from left to right, we say the polynomial is written in _____ order. [4.1a]

62. The function $h(x) = 5$ is an example of a(n) _____ function. [2.2b]

point–slope
slope–intercept
complementary
supplementary
consistent
inconsistent
equivalent
ascending
descending
up
down
constant
increasing
decreasing

## Synthesis

Complete each of the following.

63. $x^5y^4 + $ _____ $ = x^3y($ _____ $ + xy^5)$

64. $a^3b^7 - $ _____ $ = $ _____ $(ab^4 - c^2)$

Factor.

65. $rx^2 - rx + 5r + sx^2 - sx + 5s$

66. $3a^2 + 6a + 30 + 7a^2b + 14ab + 70b$

67. $a^4x^4 + a^4x^2 + 5a^4 + a^2x^4 + a^2x^2 + 5a^2 + 5x^4 + 5x^2 + 25$   (*Hint*: Use three groups of three.)

Factor out the smallest power of $x$ in each of the following.

68. $x^{1/2} + 5x^{3/2}$

69. $x^{1/3} - 7x^{4/3}$

70. $x^{3/4} + x^{1/2} - x^{1/4}$

71. $x^{1/3} - 5x^{1/2} + 3x^{3/4}$

Factor. Assume that all exponents are natural numbers.

72. $2x^{3a} + 8x^a + 4x^{2a}$

73. $3a^{n+1} + 6a^n - 15a^{n+2}$

74. $4x^{a+b} + 7x^{a-b}$

75. $7y^{2a+b} - 5y^{a+b} + 3y^{a+2b}$

# 4.4

## Factoring Trinomials: $x^2 + bx + c$

### OBJECTIVE

**a** Factor trinomials of the type $x^2 + bx + c$.

---

**SKILL TO REVIEW**
Objective R.2a: Add real numbers.

Add.
1. $-5 + 11$     2. $18 + (-3)$
3. $-7 + (-2)$     4. $9 + (-9)$

---

**a** Factoring Trinomials: $x^2 + bx + c$

We now consider factoring trinomials of the type $x^2 + bx + c$. We use a refined trial-and-error process that is based on the FOIL method.

### Constant Term Positive

Recall the FOIL method of multiplying two binomials:

$$(x + 3)(x + 5) = x^2 + \underbrace{5x + 3x}_{} + 15$$
$$= x^2 + 8x + 15.$$

The product is a trinomial. In this example, the leading term has a coefficient of 1. The constant term is positive. To factor $x^2 + 8x + 15$, we think of FOIL in reverse. We multiplied $x$ times $x$ to get the first term of the trinomial. Thus the first term of each binomial factor is $x$. We want to find numbers $p$ and $q$ such that

$$x^2 + 8x + 15 = (x + p)(x + q).$$

To get the middle term and the last term of the trinomial, we look for two numbers whose product is 15 and whose sum is 8. Those numbers are 3 and 5. Thus the factorization is

$$(x + 3)(x + 5), \quad \text{or} \quad (x + 5)(x + 3)$$

by the commutative law of multiplication. In general,

$$(x + p)(x + q) = x^2 + (p + q)x + pq.$$

To factor, we can use this equation in reverse.

**EXAMPLE 1** Factor: $x^2 + 9x + 8$.

Think of FOIL in reverse. The first term of each factor is $x$. We are looking for numbers $p$ and $q$ such that

$$x^2 + 9x + 8 = (x + p)(x + q) = x^2 + (p + q)x + pq.$$

We look for two numbers $p$ and $q$ whose product is 8 and whose sum is 9. Since both 8 and 9 are positive, we need consider only positive factors.

| PAIRS OF FACTORS | SUMS OF FACTORS |
|---|---|
| 2, 4 | 6 |
| 1, 8 | 9 ← |

The numbers we need are 1 and 8.

The factorization is $(x + 1)(x + 8)$. We can check by multiplying:

$$(x + 1)(x + 8) = x^2 + 9x + 8.$$

Do Margin Exercises 1 and 2.

---

Factor. Check by multiplying.
1. $x^2 + 5x + 6$

2. $y^2 + 7y + 10$

---

**Answers**

*Skill to Review:*
1. 6   2. 15   3. $-9$   4. 0

*Margin Exercises:*
1. $(x + 2)(x + 3)$   2. $(y + 2)(y + 5)$

When the constant term of a trinomial is positive, we look for two factors with the same sign (both positive or both negative). The sign is that of the middle term.

**EXAMPLE 2** Factor: $y^2 - 9y + 20$.

Since the constant term, 20, is positive and the coefficient of the middle term, $-9$, is negative, we look for a factorization of 20 in which both factors are negative. Their sum must be $-9$.

| PAIRS OF FACTORS | SUMS OF FACTORS |
|---|---|
| $-1, -20$ | $-21$ |
| $-2, -10$ | $-12$ |
| $-4, -5$ | $-9$ ← The numbers we need are $-4$ and $-5$. |

The factorization is $(y - 4)(y - 5)$.

Do Exercises 3 and 4.

Factor.

**3.** $m^2 - 8m + 12$

**4.** $24 - 11t + t^2$

## Constant Term Negative

When the constant term of a trinomial is negative, we look for two factors whose product is negative. One of them must be positive and the other negative. Their sum must be the coefficient of the middle term.

**5. a)** Factor: $x^2 - x - 20$.

**b)** Explain why you would not consider these pairs of factors in factoring $x^2 - x - 20$.

| PAIRS OF FACTORS | PRODUCTS OF FACTORS |
|---|---|
| $1, \quad 20$ | |
| $2, \quad 10$ | |
| $4, \quad 5$ | |
| $-1, -20$ | |
| $-2, -10$ | |
| $-4, \quad -5$ | |

**EXAMPLE 3** Factor: $x^3 - x^2 - 30x$.

*Always* look first for the largest common factor. This time $x$ is the common factor. We first factor it out:

$$x^3 - x^2 - 30x = x(x^2 - x - 30).$$

Now consider $x^2 - x - 30$. Since the constant term, $-30$, is negative, we look for a factorization of $-30$ in which one factor is positive and one factor is negative. The sum of the factors must be $-1$, the coefficient of the middle term, so the negative factor must have the larger absolute value. Thus we consider only pairs of factors in which the negative factor has the larger absolute value.

| PAIRS OF FACTORS | SUMS OF FACTORS |
|---|---|
| $1, -30$ | $-29$ |
| $2, -15$ | $-13$ |
| $3, -10$ | $-7$ |
| $5, -6$ | $-1$ ← The numbers we want are $5$ and $-6$. |

Factor.

**6.** $x^3 - 3x^2 - 54x$

**7.** $2x^3 - 2x^2 - 84x$

The factorization of $x^2 - x - 30$ is $(x + 5)(x - 6)$. But do not forget the common factor! The factorization of the original trinomial is

$$x(x + 5)(x - 6).$$

Do Exercises 5-7.

*Answers*

**3.** $(m - 2)(m - 6)$  **4.** $(t - 3)(t - 8)$, or $(3 - t)(8 - t)$  **5.** **(a)** $(x - 5)(x + 4)$; **(b)** The product of each pair is positive. **6.** $x(x - 9)(x + 6)$  **7.** $2x(x - 7)(x + 6)$

**EXAMPLE 4** Factor: $x^2 + 17x - 110$.

Since the constant term, $-110$, is negative, we look for a factorization of $-110$ in which one factor is positive and one factor is negative. Their sum must be 17, so the positive factor must have the larger absolute value.

| PAIRS OF FACTORS | SUMS OF FACTORS |
|------------------|-----------------|
| $-1,\ 110$ | 109 |
| $-2,\ 55$ | 53 |
| $-5,\ 22$ | 17 ← |
| $-10,\ 11$ | 1 |

We consider only pairs of factors in which the positive term has the larger absolute value.

The numbers we need are $-5$ and 22.

The factorization is $(x - 5)(x + 22)$.

Do Exercises 8–10.

Some trinomials are not factorable.

**EXAMPLE 5** Factor: $x^2 - x - 7$.

There are no factors of $-7$ whose sum is $-1$. This trinomial is *not* factorable into binomials.

Do Exercise 11.

> To factor $x^2 + bx + c$:
>
> 1. First arrange in descending order.
>
> 2. Use a trial-and-error procedure that looks for factors of $c$ whose sum is $b$.
>    - If $c$ is positive, then the signs of the factors are the same as the sign of $b$.
>    - If $c$ is negative, then one factor is positive and the other is negative. (If the sum of the two factors is the opposite of $b$, changing the signs of each factor will give the desired factors whose sum is $b$.)
>
> 3. Check your result by multiplying.

The procedure considered here can also be applied to a trinomial with more than one variable.

**EXAMPLE 6** Factor: $x^2 - 2xy - 48y^2$.

We look for numbers $p$ and $q$ such that

$$x^2 - 2xy - 48y^2 = (x + py)(x + qy).$$

Our thinking is much the same as if we were factoring $x^2 - 2x - 48$. We look for factors of $-48$ whose sum is $-2$. Those factors are 6 and $-8$. Then

$$x^2 - 2xy - 48y^2 = (x + 6y)(x - 8y).$$

We can check by multiplying.

Do Exercises 12 and 13.

Factor.

**8.** $x^3 + 4x^2 - 12x$

**9.** $y^2 - 4y - 12$

**10.** $x^2 - 110 - x$

**11.** Factor: $x^2 + x - 5$.

Factor.

**12.** $x^2 - 5xy + 6y^2$

**13.** $p^2 - 6pq - 16q^2$

*Answers*

**8.** $x(x + 6)(x - 2)$ **9.** $(y - 6)(y + 2)$
**10.** $(x + 10)(x - 11)$ **11.** Not factorable
**12.** $(x - 2y)(x - 3y)$ **13.** $(p - 8q)(p + 2q)$

Sometimes a trinomial like $x^4 + 2x^2 - 15$ can be factored using the following method. We can first think of the trinomial as $(x^2)^2 + 2x^2 - 15$, or we can make a substitution (perhaps just mentally), letting $u = x^2$. Then the trinomial becomes

$$u^2 + 2u - 15.$$

As we see in Example 7, we factor this trinomial and if a factorization is found, we replace each occurrence of $u$ with $x^2$.

**EXAMPLE 7** Factor: $x^4 + 2x^2 - 15$.

We let $u = x^2$. Then consider $u^2 + 2u - 15$. The constant term is negative and the middle term is positive. Thus we look for pairs of factors of $-15$, one positive and one negative, such that the positive factor has the larger absolute value and the sum of the factors is 2.

| PAIRS OF FACTORS | SUMS OF FACTORS |
|---|---|
| $-1,\ 15$ | $14$ |
| $-3,\ 5$ | $2 \longleftarrow$ |

The numbers we need are $-3$ and $5$.

The desired factorization of $u^2 + 2u - 15$ is

$$(u - 3)(u + 5).$$

Replacing $u$ with $x^2$, we obtain the following factorization of the original trinomial:

$$(x^2 - 3)(x^2 + 5).$$

Do Exercises 14 and 15.

Factor.

**14.** $x^4 - 9x^2 + 14$

**15.** $p^6 + p^3 - 6$

## Leading Coefficient of $-1$

**EXAMPLE 8** Factor: $14 + 5x - x^2$.

Note that this trinomial is written in ascending order. When we rewrite it in descending order, we get

$$-x^2 + 5x + 14,$$

which has a leading coefficient of $-1$. Before factoring, in such a case, we can factor out a $-1$:

$$-x^2 + 5x + 14 = -1(x^2 - 5x - 14).$$

Then we proceed to factor $x^2 - 5x - 14$. We get

$$-x^2 + 5x + 14 = -1(x^2 - 5x - 14) = -1(x - 7)(x + 2).$$

We can also express this answer two other ways by multiplying through either binomial by $-1$. Thus each of the following is a correct answer:

$$\begin{aligned} -x^2 + 5x + 14 &= -1(x - 7)(x + 2); \\ &= (-x + 7)(x + 2); \quad \text{Multiplying } x - 7 \text{ by } -1 \\ &= (x - 7)(-x - 2). \quad \text{Multiplying } x + 2 \text{ by } -1 \end{aligned}$$

Factor.

**16.** $10 - 3x - x^2$

**17.** $-x^2 + 8x - 16$

Do Exercises 16 and 17.

*Answers*

**14.** $(x^2 - 2)(x^2 - 7)$
**15.** $(p^3 + 3)(p^3 - 2)$
**16.** $-(x + 5)(x - 2)$, or $(-x - 5)(x - 2)$, or $(x + 5)(-x + 2)$    **17.** $-(x - 4)(x - 4)$, or $(-x + 4)(x - 4)$

4.4

**Exercise Set**

For Extra Help

*MyMathLab*

Math XL

PRACTICE   WATCH   DOWNLOAD   READ   REVIEW

**a** Factor.

**1.** $x^2 + 13x + 36$

**2.** $x^2 + 9x + 18$

**3.** $t^2 - 8t + 15$

**4.** $y^2 - 10y + 21$

**5.** $x^2 - 8x - 33$

**6.** $t^2 - 15 - 2t$

**7.** $2y^2 - 16y + 32$

**8.** $2a^2 - 20a + 50$

**9.** $p^2 + 3p - 54$

**10.** $m^2 + m - 72$

**11.** $12x + x^2 + 27$

**12.** $10y + y^2 + 24$

**13.** $y^2 - \frac{2}{3}y + \frac{1}{9}$

**14.** $p^2 + \frac{2}{5}p + \frac{1}{25}$

**15.** $t^2 - 4t + 3$

**16.** $y^2 - 14y + 45$

**17.** $5x + x^2 - 14$

**18.** $x + x^2 - 90$

**19.** $x^2 + 5x + 6$

**20.** $y^2 + 8y + 7$

**21.** $56 + x - x^2$

**22.** $32 + 4y - y^2$

**23.** $32y + 4y^2 - y^3$

**24.** $56x + x^2 - x^3$

**25.** $x^4 + 11x^2 - 80$

**26.** $y^4 + 5y^2 - 84$

**27.** $x^2 - 3x + 7$

**28.** $x^2 + 12x + 13$

**29.** $x^2 + 12xy + 27y^2$

**30.** $p^2 - 5pq - 24q^2$

**31.** $2x^2 - 8x - 90$

**32.** $3x^2 - 21x - 90$

**33.** $-z^2 + 36 - 9z$

**34.** $24 - a^2 - 10a$

**35.** $x^4 + 50x^2 + 49$

**36.** $p^4 + 80p^2 + 79$

**37.** $x^6 + 11x^3 + 18$

**38.** $x^6 - x^3 - 42$

**39.** $x^8 - 11x^4 + 24$

**40.** $x^8 - 7x^4 + 10$

**41.** $y^2 - 0.8y + 0.16$

**42.** $a^2 + 1.4a + 0.49$

**43.** $12 - b^{10} - b^{20}$

**44.** $8 - 7t^{15} - t^{30}$

## Skill Maintenance

Solve.  [3.4a]

**45.** *Mixing Rice.* Countryside Rice is 90% white rice and 10% wild rice. Mystic Rice is 50% wild rice. How much of each type should be used to create a 25-lb batch of rice that is 35% wild rice?

**46.** *Wages.* Takako worked a total of 17 days last month at her father's restaurant. She earned $50 per day during the week and $60 per day during the weekend. Last month Takako earned $940. How many weekdays did she work?

Determine whether each of the following is the graph of a function.  [2.2d]

**47.**

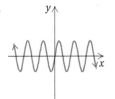

**48.**

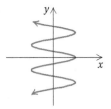

**49.**

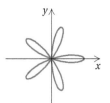

**50.**

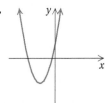

Find the domain of $f$.  [2.3a]

**51.** $f(x) = x^2 - 2$

**52.** $f(x) = 3 - 2x$

**53.** $f(x) = \dfrac{3}{4x - 7}$

**54.** $f(x) = 3 - |x|$

## Synthesis

**55.** Find all integers $m$ for which $x^2 + mx + 75$ can be factored.

**56.** Find all integers $q$ for which $x^2 + qx - 32$ can be factored.

**57.** One of the factors of $x^2 - 345x - 7300$ is $x + 20$. Find the other factor.

**58.**  Use the TABLE and GRAPH features of a graphing calculator to check your answers to Exercises 1–6.

# Mid-Chapter Review

## Concept Reinforcement

Determine whether each statement is true or false.

_____ **1.** The polynomial $5x + 2x^2 - 4x^3$ can be factored.   [4.3a]

_____ **2.** The expression $17x^{-2}y^3$ is a monomial.   [4.1a]

_____ **3.** The degree of a polynomial is the same as the degree of the leading term.   [4.1a]

_____ **4.** The opposite of $-x^2 + x$ is $x - x^2$.   [4.1d]

_____ **5.** The binomial $144 - x^2$ is a difference of squares.   [4.2d]

## Guided Solutions

Fill in each blank with the number or expression that creates a correct solution.

**6.** Multiply: $(8w - 3)(w - 5)$.   [4.2b]

$$
\begin{array}{cccc}
\quad\quad F & \quad\quad O & \quad\quad I & \quad\quad L
\end{array}
$$

$$(8w - 3)(w - 5) = (8w)(\square) + (\square)(-5) + (\square)(w) + (-3)(\square)$$

$$= 8w^{\square} - \square w - \square w + \square$$

$$= \square w^2 - \square w + \square$$

**7.** Factor: $c^3 - 8c^2 - 48c$.   [4.3a], [4.4a]

$$c^3 - 8c^2 - 48c = c \cdot \square - c \cdot \square - c \cdot \square$$

$$= \square(c^2 - \square - 48) = c(c + \square)(c - \square)$$

**8.** Factor: $x^{20} + 8x^{10} - 9$.   [4.4a]

$$x^{20} + 8x^{10} - 9 = (\square)^2 + 8(\square) - 9 = (\square + 9)(\square - 1)$$

**9.** Factor by grouping: $5y^3 + 20y^2 - y - 4$.   [4.3b]

$$5y^3 + 20y^2 - y - 4 = 5y^{\square}(\square + \square) + \square(\square + \square)$$

$$= (y + \square)(5y^2 - \square)$$

## Mixed Review

For each polynomial, identify the terms, the degree of each term, and the degree of the polynomial. Then identify the leading term, the leading coefficient, and the constant term.   [4.1a]

**10.** $-a^7 + a^4 - a + 8$

**11.** $3x^4 + 2x^3w^5 - 12x^2w + 4x^2 - 1$

**12.** Arrange in ascending powers of $y$: $-2y + 5 - y^3 + y^9 - 2y^4$.   [4.1a]

**13.** Arrange in descending powers of $x$: $2qx - 9qr + 2x^5 - 4qx^2$.   [4.1a]

Evaluate each polynomial function for the given values of the variable.   [4.1b]

**14.** $h(x) = -x^3 - 4x + 5$; $h(0), h(-2)$, and $h\left(\dfrac{1}{2}\right)$

**15.** $f(x) = \dfrac{1}{2}x^4 - x^3$; $f(-1), f(1)$, and $f(0)$

**16.** Given $f(x) = x^2 + 2x - 9$, find and simplify $f(a - 2)$ and $f(a + h) - f(a)$.   [4.2e]

Add, subtract, or multiply,

**17.** $(3a^2 - 7b + ab + 2) + (-5a^2 + 4b - 5ab - 3)$   [4.1c]

**18.** $(x^2 + 10x - 4) + (9x^2 - 2x + 1) + (x^2 - x - 5)$   [4.1c]

**19.** $(b - 12)(b + 1)$   [4.2b]

**20.** $c^2(3c^2 - c^3)$   [4.2a]

**21.** $(y^4 - 6)(y^4 + 3)$   [4.2b]

**22.** $(7y^2 - 2y^3 - 5y) - (y^2 - 3y - 6y^3)$   [4.1d]

**23.** $(8x - 11) - (-x + 1)$   [4.1d]

**24.** $(4x - 5)^2$   [4.2c]

**25.** $(2x + 5)^2$   [4.2c]

**26.** $(0.01x - 0.5y) - (2.5y - 0.1x)$   [4.1d]

**27.** $-13x^2 \cdot 10xy$   [4.2a]

**28.** $(x + y)(x^2 - 2xy + 3y^2)$   [4.2a]

**29.** $(5x - 7)(2x + 9)$   [4.2b]

**30.** $(9x - 4)(9x + 4)$   [4.2d]

Factor.

**31.** $5h^2 + 7h$   [4.3a]

**32.** $x^2 + 8x - 20$   [4.4a]

**33.** $21 - 4b - b^2$   [4.4a]

**34.** $m^2 + \dfrac{2}{7}m + \dfrac{1}{49}$   [4.4a]

**35.** $2xy - x^2y - 5x + 10$   [4.3b]

**36.** $3w^2 - 6w + 3$   [4.4a]

**37.** $t^3 + 3t^2 + t + 3$   [4.3b]

**38.** $24xy^6z^4 - 16x^4y^3z$   [4.3a]

**39.** $x^2 + 8x + 6$   [4.4a]

## Understanding Through Discussion and Writing

**40.** Explain in your own words why $-(a - b) = b - a$.
[4.1d], [4.3a]

**41.** Is the sum of two binomials always a binomial? Why or why not?   [4.1c]

**42.** Is it true that if a polynomial's coefficients and exponents are all prime numbers, then the polynomial itself is prime? Why or why not?   [4.3a]

**43.** Under what conditions would it be easier to evaluate a polynomial function after it has been factored?
[4.1b], [4.4a]

**44.** Explain the error in each of the following.
 **a)** $(a + 3)^2 = a^2 + 9$   [4.2c]
 **b)** $(a - b)(a - b) = a^2 - b^2$   [4.2c]
 **c)** $(x + 3)(x - 4) = x^2 - 12$   [4.2b]
 **d)** $(p + 7)(p - 7) = p^2 + 49$   [4.2d]
 **e)** $(t - 3)^2 = t^2 - 9$   [4.2c]

**45.** Checking the factorization of a second-degree polynomial by making a single replacement is only a *partial* check. Write an *incorrect* factorization and explain how evaluating both the polynomial and the factorization might catch a possible error.   [4.4a]

## OBJECTIVES

**a** Factor trinomials of the type $ax^2 + bx + c, a \neq 1$, by the FOIL method.

**b** Factor trinomials of the type $ax^2 + bx + c, a \neq 1$, by the ac-method.

**SKILL TO REVIEW**
Objective 4.2b: Use the FOIL method to multiply two binomials.

Multiply.

**1.** $(8x - 7)(2x + 1)$

**2.** $(6a - b)(3a + 5b)$

Now we learn to factor trinomials of the type $ax^2 + bx + c, a \neq 1$. We use two methods: the FOIL method and the ac-method.* Although one is discussed before the other, this should not be taken as a recommendation of one form over the other.

## **a** The FOIL Method

We first consider the **FOIL method** for factoring trinomials of the type $ax^2 + bx + c, a \neq 1$. Consider the following multiplication.

$$\begin{array}{cccc} \text{F} & \text{O} & \text{I} & \text{L} \\ \downarrow & \downarrow & \downarrow & \downarrow \end{array}$$

$$(3x + 2)(4x + 5) = 12x^2 + 15x + 8x + 10$$

$$= 12x^2 + 23x + 10$$

To factor $12x^2 + 23x + 10$, we must reverse what we just did. We look for two binomials whose product is this trinomial. The product of the First terms must be $12x^2$. The product of the Outside terms plus the product of the Inside terms must be $23x$. The product of the Last terms must be 10. We know from the preceding discussion that the answer is $(3x + 2)(4x + 5)$. In general, however, finding such an answer involves trial and error. We use the following method.

---

**THE FOIL METHOD**

To factor trinomials of the type $ax^2 + bx + c, a \neq 1$, using the **FOIL method**:

**1.** Factor out the largest common factor.

**2.** Find two First terms whose product is $ax^2$:

$$(\square x + \quad)(\square x + \quad) = ax^2 + bx + c.$$

$$\text{FOIL}$$

**3.** Find two Last terms whose product is $c$:

$$(\quad x + \square)(\quad x + \square) = ax^2 + bx + c.$$

$$\text{FOIL}$$

**4.** Repeat steps (2) and (3) until a combination is found for which the sum of the Outside and Inside products is $bx$:

$$(\square x + \square)(\square x + \square) = ax^2 + bx + c.$$

$$\text{I} \qquad \text{FOIL}$$

$$\text{O}$$

**5.** Always check by multiplying.

---

*Answers*

*Skill to Review:*
**1.** $16x^2 - 6x - 7$    **2.** $18a^2 + 27ab - 5b^2$

---

*To the instructor*: Here we present two ways to factor general trinomials: the FOIL method and the ac-method. You can teach both methods and let the student use the one he or she prefers or you can select just one for the student.

**EXAMPLE 1** Factor: $3x^2 + 10x - 8$.

1. First, we factor out the largest common factor, if any. There is none (other than 1 or $-1$).

2. Next, we factor the first term, $3x^2$. The only possibility is $3x \cdot x$. The desired factorization is then of the form $(3x + \square)(x + \square)$.

3. We then factor the last term, $-8$, which is negative. The possibilities are $(-8)(1)$, $8(-1)$, $2(-4)$, and $(-2)(4)$. They can be written in either order.

4. We look for combinations of factors from steps (2) and (3) such that the sum of the outside and the inside products is the middle term, $10x$:

$$\overset{3x}{(3x - 8)(x + 1)} = 3x^2 \underset{-8x}{-5x} - 8; \quad \overset{-3x}{(3x + 8)(x - 1)} = 3x^2 \underset{8x}{+5x} - 8;$$
Wrong middle term          Wrong middle term

$$\overset{-12x}{(3x + 2)(x - 4)} = 3x^2 \underset{2x}{-10x} - 8; \quad \overset{12x}{(3x - 2)(x + 4)} = 3x^2 \underset{-2x}{+10x} - 8.$$
Wrong middle term          Correct middle term!

There are four other possibilities that we could try, but we have a factorization: $(3x - 2)(x + 4)$.

5. *Check*:  $(3x - 2)(x + 4) = 3x^2 + 10x - 8$.

Do Exercises 1 and 2.

Factor by the FOIL method.

1. $3x^2 - 13x - 56$

2. $3x^2 + 5x + 2$

**EXAMPLE 2** Factor: $18x^6 - 57x^5 + 30x^4$.

1. First, we factor out the largest common factor, if any. The expression $3x^4$ is common to all terms, so we factor it out: $3x^4(6x^2 - 19x + 10)$.

2. Next, we factor the trinomial $6x^2 - 19x + 10$. We factor the first term, $6x^2$, and get $6x \cdot x$, or $3x \cdot 2x$. We then have these as possibilities for factorizations: $(3x + \square)(2x + \square)$ or $(6x + \square)(x + \square)$.

3. We then factor the last term, 10, which is positive. The possibilities are $(10)(1)$, $(-10)(-1)$, $(5)(2)$, and $(-5)(-2)$. They can be written in either order.

4. We look for combinations of factors from steps (2) and (3) such that the sum of the outside and the inside products is the middle term, $-19x$. The sign of the middle term is negative, but the sign of the last term, 10, is positive. Thus the signs of both factors of the last term, 10, must be negative. From our list of factors in step (3), we can use only $-10$, $-1$ and $-5$, $-2$ as possibilities. This reduces the possibilities for factorizations by half. We begin by using these factors with $(3x + \square)(2x + \square)$. Should we not find the correct factorization, we will consider $(6x + \square)(x + \square)$.

$$\overbrace{\quad\quad}^{-3x} \\ (3x - 10)(2x - 1) = 6x^2 - 23x + 10;$$
$$\underbrace{\quad\quad}_{-20x} \quad \text{Wrong middle term}$$

$$\overbrace{\quad\quad}^{-30x} \\ (3x - 1)(2x - 10) = 6x^2 - 32x + 10;$$
$$\underbrace{\quad\quad}_{-2x} \quad \text{Wrong middle term}$$

$$\overbrace{\quad\quad}^{-6x} \\ (3x - 5)(2x - 2) = 6x^2 - 16x + 10;$$
$$\underbrace{\quad\quad}_{-10x} \quad \text{Wrong middle term}$$

$$\overbrace{\quad\quad}^{-15x} \\ (3x - 2)(2x - 5) = 6x^2 - 19x + 10$$
$$\underbrace{\quad\quad}_{-4x} \quad \text{Correct middle term!}$$

We have a correct answer. We need not consider $(6x + \square)(x + \square)$.

Look again at the possibility $(3x - 1)(2x - 10)$. Without multiplying, we can reject such a possibility, noting that

$$(3x - 1)(2x - 10) = 2(3x - 1)(x - 5).$$

The expression $2x - 10$ has a common factor, 2. But we removed the largest common factor before we began. If this expression were a factorization, then 2 would have to be a common factor along with $3x^4$. Thus, as we saw when we multiplied, $(3x - 1)(2x - 10)$ cannot be part of the factorization of the original trinomial. Given that we factored out the largest common factor at the outset, we can now eliminate factorizations that have a common factor.

The factorization of $6x^2 - 19x + 10$ is $(3x - 2)(2x - 5)$. But do not forget the common factor! We must include it in order to get a complete factorization of the original trinomial:

$$18x^6 - 57x^5 + 30x^4 = 3x^4(3x - 2)(2x - 5).$$

**5.** *Check*: $3x^4(3x - 2)(2x - 5) = 3x^4(6x^2 - 19x + 10)$
$$= 18x^6 - 57x^5 + 30x^4.$$

Here is another tip that might speed up your factoring. Suppose in Example 2 that we considered the possibility

$$(3x + 2)(2x + 5) = 6x^2 + 19x + 10.$$

We might have tried this before noting that using all plus signs would give us a plus sign for the middle term. If we change *both* signs, however, we get the correct answer before including the common factor:

$$(3x - 2)(2x - 5) = 6x^2 - 19x + 10.$$

Do Exercises 3 and 4.

Factor.

**3.** $24y^2 - 46y + 10$

**4.** $20x^5 - 46x^4 + 24x^3$

*Answers*

**3.** $2(4y - 1)(3y - 5)$
**4.** $2x^3(2x - 3)(5x - 4)$

1. If the largest common factor has been factored out of the original trinomial, then no binomial factor can have a common factor (other than 1 or $-1$).

2. a) If the signs of all the terms are positive, then the signs of all the terms of the binomial factors are positive.

   b) If $a$ and $c$ are positive and $b$ is negative, then the signs of the factors of $c$ are negative.

   c) If $a$ is positive and $c$ is negative, then the factors of $c$ will have opposite signs.

3. Be systematic about your trials. Keep track of those you have tried and those you have not.

4. Changing the signs of the factors of $c$ will change the sign of the middle term.

Keep in mind that this method of factoring trinomials of the type $ax^2 + bx + c$ involves trial and error. As you practice, you will find that you will need fewer trials to arrive at the factorization.

Factor.

**5.** $3x^2 + 19x + 20$

| Do Exercises 5 and 6.

**6.** $16x^2 - 12 + 16x$

The procedure considered here can also be applied to a trinomial with more than one variable.

**EXAMPLE 3**  Factor: $30m^2 + 23mn - 11n^2$.

1. First, we factor out the largest common factor, if any. In this polynomial, there is no common factor (other than 1 or $-1$).

2. Next, we factor the first term, $30m^2$, and get the following possibilities:

   $30m \cdot m, \quad 15m \cdot 2m, \quad 10m \cdot 3m, \quad \text{and} \quad 6m \cdot 5m.$

   We then have these as possibilities for factorizations:

   $(30m + \square)(m + \square), \qquad (15m + \square)(2m + \square),$
   $(10m + \square)(3m + \square), \qquad (6m + \square)(5m + \square).$

3. We then factor the last term, $-11n^2$, which is negative. The possibilities are $-11n \cdot n$ and $11n \cdot (-n)$.

4. We look for combinations of factors from steps (2) and (3) such that the sum of the outside and the inside products is the middle term, $23mn$. Since the coefficient of the middle term is positive, let's begin our search using $11n \cdot (-n)$. Should we not find the correct factorization, we will consider $-11n \cdot n$.

$(30m + 11n)(m - n) = 30m^2 - 19mn - 11n^2;$ ⎫
$(30m - n)(m + 11n) = 30m^2 + 329mn - 11n^2;$ ⎬
$(15m + 11n)(2m - n) = 30m^2 + 7mn - 11n^2;$
$(15m - n)(2m + 11n) = 30m^2 + 163mn - 11n^2;$
$(10m + 11n)(3m - n) = 30m^2 + 23mn - 11n^2$ ⟵—— Correct middle term

Note that changing the order of $11n$ and $-n$ changes the middle term.

Factor.

**7.** $21x^2 - 5xy - 4y^2$

**8.** $60a^2 + 123ab - 27b^2$

We have a correct answer: $30m^2 + 23mn - 11n^2$. The factorization of $30m^2 + 23mn - 11n^2$ is $(10m + 11n)(3m - n)$.

**5.** *Check*: $(10m + 11n)(3m - n) = 30m^2 + 23mn - 11n^2$.

Do Exercises 7 and 8.

## (b) The *ac*-Method

The second method of factoring trinomials of the type $ax^2 + bx + c$, $a \neq 1$, is known as the **ac-method**, or the **grouping method**. It involves not only trial and error and FOIL, but also factoring by grouping. This method can cut down on the guesswork of the trials.

We can factor $x^2 + 7x + 10$ by "splitting" the middle term, $7x$, and using factoring by grouping:

$$x^2 + 7x + 10 = x^2 + 2x + 5x + 10$$
$$= x(x + 2) + 5(x + 2)$$
$$= (x + 2)(x + 5).$$

If the leading coefficient is not 1, as in $6x^2 + 23x + 20$, we use a method for factoring similar to what we just did with $x^2 + 7x + 10$.

**THE *ac*-METHOD**

To factor $ax^2 + bx + c$, $a \neq 1$, using the *ac*-method:

1. Factor out the largest common factor.
2. Multiply the leading coefficient $a$ and the constant $c$.
3. Try to factor the product $ac$ so that the sum of the factors is $b$. That is, find integers $p$ and $q$ such that $pq = ac$ and $p + q = b$.
4. Split the middle term. That is, write it as a sum using the factors found in step (3).
5. Factor by grouping.
6. Always check by multiplying.

**EXAMPLE 4**   Factor: $6x^2 + 23x + 20$.

1. First, factor out a common factor, if any. There is none (other than 1 or $-1$).
2. Multiply the leading coefficient, 6, and the constant, 20: $6 \cdot 20 = 120$.
3. Then look for a factorization of 120 in which the sum of the factors is the coefficient of the middle term, 23. Since both 120 and 23 are positive, we need consider only positive factors of 120.

| PAIRS OF FACTORS | SUMS OF FACTORS | | PAIRS OF FACTORS | SUMS OF FACTORS |
|---|---|---|---|---|
| 1, 120 | 121 | | 5, 24 | 29 |
| 2, 60 | 62 | | 6, 20 | 26 |
| 3, 40 | 43 | | 8, 15 | 23 |
| 4, 30 | 34 | | 10, 12 | 22 |

*Answers*

**7.** $(7x - 4y)(3x + y)$
**8.** $3(4a + 9b)(5a - b)$

**4.** Next, split the middle term as a sum or a difference using the factors found in step (3):

$$6x^2 + 23x + 20 = 6x^2 + 8x + 15x + 20.$$   Substituting $8x + 15x$ for $23x$

**5.** Factor by grouping as follows:

$$6x^2 + 23x + 20 = 6x^2 + 8x + 15x + 20$$
$$= 2x(3x + 4) + 5(3x + 4)$$   Factoring by grouping; see Section 4.3
$$= (3x + 4)(2x + 5).$$

We could also split the middle term as $15x + 8x$. We still get the same factorization, although the factors are in a different order:

$$6x^2 + 23x + 20 = 6x^2 + 15x + 8x + 20$$
$$= 3x(2x + 5) + 4(2x + 5)$$
$$= (2x + 5)(3x + 4).$$

**6.** *Check*:  $(3x + 4)(2x + 5) = 6x^2 + 23x + 20.$

Do Exercises 9 and 10.

Do Exercises 9 and 10.

Factor by the *ac*-method.

**9.** $4x^2 + 4x - 3$

**10.** $4x^2 + 37x + 9$

**EXAMPLE 5**  Factor: $6x^4 - 116x^3 - 80x^2.$

**1.** First, factor out the largest common factor, if any. The expression $2x^2$ is common to all three terms: $2x^2(3x^2 - 58x - 40).$

**2.** Now, factor the trinomial $3x^2 - 58x - 40$. Multiply the leading coefficient, 3, and the constant, $-40$: $3(-40) = -120.$

**3.** Next, try to factor $-120$ so that the sum of the factors is $-58$. Since the coefficient of the middle term, $-58$, is negative, the negative factor of $-120$ must have the larger absolute value.

| PAIRS OF FACTORS | SUMS OF FACTORS |
|---|---|
| 1, −120 | −119 |
| 2, −60 | −58 |
| 3, −40 | −37 |
| 4, −30 | −26 |

| PAIRS OF FACTORS | SUMS OF FACTORS |
|---|---|
| 5, −24 | −19 |
| 6, −20 | −14 |
| 8, −15 | −7 |
| 10, −12 | −2 |

**4.** Split the middle term, $-58x$, as follows: $-58x = 2x - 60x.$

**5.** Factor by grouping:

$$3x^2 - 58x - 40 = 3x^2 + 2x - 60x - 40$$   Substituting $2x - 60x$ for $-58x$
$$= x(3x + 2) - 20(3x + 2)$$   Factoring by grouping
$$= (3x + 2)(x - 20).$$

The factorization of $3x^2 - 58x - 40$ is $(3x + 2)(x - 20)$. But don't forget the common factor! We must include it to get a factorization of the original trinomial:

$$6x^4 - 116x^3 - 80x^2 = 2x^2(3x + 2)(x - 20).$$

**6.** *Check*:  $2x^2(3x + 2)(x - 20) = 2x^2(3x^2 - 58x - 40)$
$$= 6x^4 - 116x^3 - 80x^2.$$

Do Exercises 11 and 12.

Do Exercises 11 and 12.

Factor by the *ac*-method.

**11.** $10y^4 - 7y^3 - 12y^2$

**12.** $6a^3 - 7a^2 - 5a$

*Answers*

**9.** $(2x + 3)(2x - 1)$   **10.** $(4x + 1)(x + 9)$
**11.** $y^2(5y + 4)(2y - 3)$
**12.** $a(3a - 5)(2a + 1)$

For Extra Help

*MyMathLab*  Math XL
PRACTICE   WATCH   DOWNLOAD   READ   REVIEW

**a** , **b**   Factor.

**1.** $3x^2 - 14x - 5$

**2.** $8x^2 - 6x - 9$

**3.** $10y^3 + y^2 - 21y$

**4.** $6x^3 + x^2 - 12x$

**5.** $3c^2 - 20c + 32$

**6.** $12b^2 - 8b + 1$

**7.** $35y^2 + 34y + 8$

**8.** $9a^2 + 18a + 8$

**9.** $4t + 10t^2 - 6$

**10.** $8x + 30x^2 - 6$

**11.** $8x^2 - 16 - 28x$

**12.** $18x^2 - 24 - 6x$

**13.** $18a^2 - 51a + 15$

**14.** $30a^2 - 85a + 25$

**15.** $30t^2 + 85t + 25$

**16.** $18y^2 + 51y + 15$

**17.** $12x^3 - 31x^2 + 20x$

**18.** $15x^3 - 19x^2 - 10x$

**19.** $14x^4 - 19x^3 - 3x^2$

**20.** $70x^4 - 68x^3 + 16x^2$

**21.** $3a^2 - a - 4$

**22.** $6a^2 - 7a - 10$

**23.** $9x^2 + 15x + 4$

**24.** $6y^2 - y - 2$

**25.** $3 + 35z - 12z^2$

**26.** $8 - 6a - 9a^2$

**27.** $-4t^2 - 4t + 15$

**28.** $-12a^2 + 7a - 1$

**29.** $3x^3 - 5x^2 - 2x$

**30.** $18y^3 - 3y^2 - 10y$

**31.** $24x^2 - 2 - 47x$

**32.** $15y^2 - 10 - 15y$

**33.** $-8t^3 - 8t^2 + 30t$

**34.** $-36a^3 + 21a^2 - 3a$

**35.** $-24x^3 + 2x + 47x^2$

**36.** $-15y^3 + 10y + 47y^2$

**37.** $21x^2 + 37x + 12$

**38.** $10y^2 + 23y + 12$

**39.** $40x^4 + 16x^2 - 12$

**40.** $24y^4 + 2y^2 - 15$

**41.** $12a^2 - 17ab + 6b^2$

**42.** $20p^2 - 23pq + 6q^2$

**43.** $2x^2 + xy - 6y^2$

**44.** $8m^2 - 6mn - 9n^2$

**45.** $12x^2 - 58xy + 56y^2$

**46.** $30p^2 + 21pq - 36q^2$

**47.** $9x^2 - 30xy + 25y^2$

**48.** $4p^2 + 12pq + 9q^2$

**49.** $3x^6 + 4x^3 - 4$

**50.** $2p^8 + 11p^4 + 15$

**51.** *Height of a Thrown Baseball.* Suppose that a baseball is thrown upward with an initial velocity of 80 ft/sec from a height of 224 ft. Its height $h$ after $t$ seconds is given by the function

$$h(t) = -16t^2 + 80t + 224.$$

**a)** What is the height of the ball after 0 sec? 1 sec? 3 sec? 4 sec? 6 sec?

**b)** Find an equivalent expression for $h(t)$ by factoring.

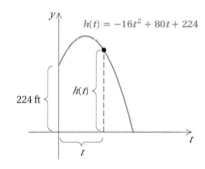

**52.** *Fireworks.* Suppose that a bottle rocket is launched upward with an initial velocity of 96 ft/sec and from a height of 880 ft. Its height $h$ after $t$ seconds is given by the function

$$h(t) = -16t^2 + 96t + 880.$$

**a)** What is the height of the bottle rocket after 0 sec? 1 sec? 3 sec? 8 sec? 10 sec?

**b)** Find an equivalent expression for $h(t)$ by factoring.

## Skill Maintenance

Solve.  [3.5a]

**53.** $\begin{aligned} x + 2y - z &= 0, \\ 4x + 2y + 5z &= 6, \\ 2x - y + z &= 5 \end{aligned}$

**54.** $\begin{aligned} 2x + y + 2z &= 5, \\ 4x - 2y - 3z &= 5, \\ -8x - y + z &= -5 \end{aligned}$

**55.** $\begin{aligned} 2x + 9y + 6z &= 5, \\ x - y + z &= 4, \\ 3x + 2y + 3z &= 7 \end{aligned}$

**56.** $\begin{aligned} x - 3y + 2z &= -8, \\ 2x + 3y + z &= 17, \\ 5x - 2y + 3z &= 5 \end{aligned}$

Determine whether the graphs of the given pairs of lines are parallel or perpendicular.  [2.5d]

**57.** $\begin{aligned} y - 2x &= 18, \\ 2x - 7 &= y \end{aligned}$

**58.** $\begin{aligned} 21x + 7 &= -3y, \\ y + 7x &= -9 \end{aligned}$

**59.** $\begin{aligned} 2x + 5y &= 4, \\ 2x - 5y &= -3 \end{aligned}$

**60.** $\begin{aligned} y + x &= 7, \\ y - x &= 3 \end{aligned}$

Find an equation of the line containing the given pair of points.  [2.6c]

**61.** $(-2, -3)$ and $(5, -4)$

**62.** $(2, -3)$ and $(5, -4)$

**63.** $(-10, 3)$ and $(7, -4)$

**64.** $\left(-\frac{2}{3}, 1\right)$ and $\left(\frac{4}{3}, -4\right)$

## Synthesis

**65.**  Use the TABLE and GRAPH features of a graphing calculator to check your answers to Exercises 2, 17, and 28.

**66.** Use the TABLE and GRAPH features of a graphing calculator to check your answers to Exercises 4, 11, and 32.

Factor. Assume that variables in exponents represent positive integers.

**67.** $7a^2b^2 + 6 + 13ab$

**68.** $2x^4y^6 - 3x^2y^3 - 20$

**69.** $9x^2y^2 - 4 + 5xy$

**70.** $\frac{1}{4}p^2 - \frac{2}{5}p + \frac{4}{25}$

**71.** $x^{2a} + 5x^a - 24$

**72.** $4x^{2a} - 4x^a - 3$

# 4.6

## Special Factoring

### OBJECTIVES

**a** Factor trinomial squares.

**b** Factor differences of squares.

**c** Factor certain polynomials with four terms by grouping and possibly using the factoring of a trinomial square or the difference of squares.

**d** Factor sums and differences of cubes.

In this section, we consider some special factoring methods.

### a Trinomial Squares

Consider the trinomial $x^2 + 6x + 9$. To factor it, we can use the method considered in Section 4.4. We look for factors of 9 whose sum is 6. We see that these factors are 3 and 3 and the factorization is

$$x^2 + 6x + 9 = (x + 3)(x + 3) = (x + 3)^2.$$

Note that the result is the square of a binomial. We also call $x^2 + 6x + 9$ a **trinomial square**, or **perfect-square trinomial**. We can certainly use the procedures of Sections 4.4 and 4.5 to factor trinomial squares, but we want to develop an even faster procedure.

How can we recognize when an expression to be factored is a trinomial square? Look at $A^2 + 2AB + B^2$ and $A^2 - 2AB + B^2$.

How to recognize a **trinomial square**:

a) The two expressions $A^2$ and $B^2$ must be squares.

b) There must be no minus sign before either $A^2$ or $B^2$.

c) Multiplying $A$ and $B$ (expressions whose squares are $A^2$ and $B^2$) and doubling the result, $2 \cdot AB$, gives either the remaining term or its opposite, $-2AB$.

**EXAMPLES** Determine whether the polynomial is a trinomial square.

**1.** $x^2 + 10x + 25$

a) Two terms are squares: $x^2$ and 25.

b) There is no minus sign before either $x^2$ or 25.

c) If we multiply the expressions whose squares are $x^2$ and 25, $x$ and 5, and double the product, we get $10x$, the remaining term.

Thus this is a trinomial square.

**2.** $4x + 16 + 3x^2$

a) Only one term, 16, is a square ($3x^2$ is not a square because 3 is not a perfect square and $4x$ is not a square because $x$ is not a square).

Thus this is not a trinomial square.

**3.** $100y^2 + 81 - 180y$

(It can help to first write this in descending order: $100y^2 - 180y + 81$.)

a) Two of the terms, $100y^2$ and 81, are squares.

b) There is no minus sign before either $100y^2$ or 81.

c) If we multiply the expressions whose squares are $100y^2$ and 81, $10y$ and 9, and double the product, we get the opposite of the remaining term: $2(10y)(9) = 180y$, which is the opposite of $-180y$.

Thus this is a trinomial square.

Do Margin Exercise 1.

### SKILL TO REVIEW

Objective 4.2d: Use a rule to multiply a sum and a difference of the same two terms.

Multiply.

**1.** $(y - 3)(y + 3)$

**2.** $(5x - 7)(5x + 7)$

**1.** Which of the following are trinomial squares?

a) $x^2 + 6x + 9$

b) $x^2 - 8x + 16$

c) $x^2 + 6x + 11$

d) $4x^2 + 25 - 20x$

e) $16x^2 - 20x + 25$

f) $16 + 14x + 5x^2$

g) $x^2 + 8x - 16$

h) $x^2 - 8x - 16$

*Answers*

*Skill to Review:*

**1.** $y^2 - 9$  **2.** $25x^2 - 49$

*Margin Exercise:*

**1.** (a), (b), (d)

The factors of a trinomial square are two identical binomials. We use the following equations.

### TRINOMIAL SQUARES

$$A^2 + 2AB + B^2 = (A + B)^2;$$
$$A^2 - 2AB + B^2 = (A - B)^2$$

**EXAMPLE 4**  Factor: $x^2 - 10x + 25$.

$$x^2 - 10x + 25 = (x - 5)^2$$

Note the sign!

We find the square terms and write their square roots with a minus sign between them.

**EXAMPLE 5**  Factor: $16y^2 + 49 + 56y$.

$$16y^2 + 49 + 56y = 16y^2 + 56y + 49 \quad \text{Rewriting in descending order}$$

$$= (4y + 7)^2 \quad \text{We find the square terms and write their square roots with a plus sign between them.}$$

**EXAMPLE 6**  Factor: $-20xy + 4y^2 + 25x^2$.

We have

$$-20xy + 4y^2 + 25x^2 = 4y^2 - 20xy + 25x^2 \quad \text{Writing descending order in } y$$

$$= (2y - 5x)^2.$$

This square can also be expressed as

$$25x^2 - 20xy + 4y^2 = (5x - 2y)^2.$$

Do Exercises 2–5.

In factoring, we must always remember to look *first* for the largest factor common to all the terms.

**EXAMPLE 7**  Factor: $2x^2 - 12xy + 18y^2$.

Always remember to look first for a common factor. This time the largest common factor is 2.

$$2x^2 - 12xy + 18y^2 = 2(x^2 - 6xy + 9y^2) \quad \text{Factoring out the common factor 2}$$

$$= 2(x - 3y)^2 \quad \text{Factoring the trinomial square}$$

**EXAMPLE 8**  Factor: $-4y^2 - 144y^8 + 48y^5$.

$$-4y^2 - 144y^8 + 48y^5$$

$$= -4y^2(1 + 36y^6 - 12y^3) \quad \text{Factoring out the common factor } -4y^2$$

$$= -4y^2(1 - 12y^3 + 36y^6) \quad \text{Changing order}$$

$$= -4y^2(1 - 6y^3)^2 \quad \text{Factoring the trinomial square}$$

Do Exercises 6 and 7.

Factor.

**2.** $x^2 + 14x + 49$

**3.** $9y^2 - 30y + 25$

**4.** $16x^2 + 72xy + 81y^2$

**5.** $16x^4 - 40x^2y^3 + 25y^6$

Factor.

**6.** $-8a^2 + 24ab - 18b^2$

**7.** $3a^2 - 30ab + 75b^2$

*Answers*

**2.** $(x + 7)^2$   **3.** $(3y - 5)^2$   **4.** $(4x + 9y)^2$
**5.** $(4x^2 - 5y^3)^2$   **6.** $-2(2a - 3b)^2$
**7.** $3(a - 5b)^2$

## b Differences of Squares

The following are *differences of squares:*

$$x^2 - 9, \quad 49 - 4y^2, \quad a^2 - 49b^2.$$

To factor a difference of squares such as $x^2 - 9$, think about the formula we used in Section 4.2:

$$(A + B)(A - B) = A^2 - B^2.$$

Equations are reversible, so we also know the following.

> **FACTORING A DIFFERENCE OF SQUARES**
>
> $$A^2 - B^2 = (A + B)(A - B)$$

To factor a difference of squares $A^2 - B^2$, we find $A$ and $B$, which are square roots of the expressions $A^2$ and $B^2$. We then use $A$ and $B$ to form two factors. One is the sum $A + B$, and the other is the difference $A - B$.

**EXAMPLE 9** Factor: $x^2 - 9$.

$$
\begin{array}{cccccc}
A^2 & - & B^2 & = & (A + B) & (A - B) \\
\downarrow & & \downarrow & & \downarrow \quad \downarrow & \downarrow \quad \downarrow
\end{array}
$$
$$x^2 - 9 = x^2 - 3^2 = (x + 3)(x - 3)$$

**EXAMPLE 10** Factor: $25y^6 - 49x^2$.

$$
\begin{array}{cccccc}
A^2 & - & B^2 & = & (A + B)(A & - B) \\
\downarrow & & \downarrow & & \downarrow \quad \downarrow \quad \downarrow & \downarrow
\end{array}
$$
$$25y^6 - 49x^2 = (5y^3)^2 - (7x)^2 = (5y^3 + 7x)(5y^3 - 7x)$$

**Factor.**

**8.** $y^2 - 4$

**9.** $49x^4 - 25y^{10}$

**10.** $m^2 - \dfrac{1}{9}$

**EXAMPLE 11** Factor: $x^2 - \frac{1}{16}$.

$$x^2 - \tfrac{1}{16} = x^2 - \left(\tfrac{1}{4}\right)^2 = \left(x + \tfrac{1}{4}\right)\left(x - \tfrac{1}{4}\right)$$

> Do Exercises 8–10.

Common factors should always be factored out. Factoring out common factors actually eases the factoring process because the type of factoring to be done becomes clearer.

**EXAMPLE 12** Factor: $5 - 5x^2y^6$.

There is a common factor, 5.

$$
\begin{aligned}
5 - 5x^2y^6 &= 5(1 - x^2y^6) && \text{Factoring out the common factor 5} \\
&= 5[1^2 - (xy^3)^2] && \text{Recognizing the difference of squares;} \\
& && \quad x^2y^6 = (x^1y^3)^2 = (xy^3)^2 \\
&= 5(1 + xy^3)(1 - xy^3) && \text{Factoring the difference of squares}
\end{aligned}
$$

**EXAMPLE 13** Factor: $2x^4 - 8y^4$.

There is a common factor, 2.

$$
\begin{aligned}
2x^4 - 8y^4 &= 2(x^4 - 4y^4) && \text{Factoring out the common factor 2} \\
&= 2[(x^2)^2 - (2y^2)^2] && \text{Recognizing the difference of squares} \\
&= 2(x^2 + 2y^2)(x^2 - 2y^2) && \text{Factoring the difference of squares}
\end{aligned}
$$

**Answers**

**8.** $(y + 2)(y - 2)$
**9.** $(7x^2 + 5y^5)(7x^2 - 5y^5)$
**10.** $\left(m + \tfrac{1}{3}\right)\left(m - \tfrac{1}{3}\right)$

**EXAMPLE 14** Factor: $16x^4y - 81y$.

There is a common factor, $y$.

$$16x^4y - 81y = y(16x^4 - 81)$$ \qquad Factoring out the common factor $y$
$$= y[(4x^2)^2 - 9^2]$$
$$= y(4x^2 + 9)(4x^2 - 9)$$ \qquad Factoring the difference of squares
$$= y(4x^2 + 9)(2x + 3)(2x - 3)$$ \qquad Factoring $4x^2 - 9$, which is also a difference of squares

In Example 14, it may be tempting to try to factor $4x^2 + 9$. Note that it is a sum of two expressions that are squares, but it cannot be factored further. Also note that one of the factors, $4x^2 - 9$, could be factored further. Whenever that is possible, you should do so. That way you will be factoring *completely*.

---

### Caution!

We cannot factor a sum of squares as the square of a binomial. In particular,

$$A^2 + B^2 \neq (A + B)^2.$$

Consider $25x^2 + 225$. This is a case in which we have a sum of squares, but there is a common factor, 25. Factoring, we get $25(x^2 + 9)$. Now $x^2 + 9$ cannot be factored further.

---

Do Exercises 11-14.

Factor.

**11.** $25x^2y^2 - 4a^2$

**12.** $9x^2 - 16y^2$

**13.** $20x^2 - 5y^2$

**14.** $81x^4y^2 - 16y^2$

## c  More Factoring by Grouping

Sometimes when factoring a polynomial with four terms completely, we might get a factor that can be factored further using other methods we have learned.

**EXAMPLE 15** Factor completely: $x^3 + 3x^2 - 4x - 12$.

$$x^3 + 3x^2 - 4x - 12 = x^2(x + 3) - 4(x + 3)$$
$$= (x + 3)(x^2 - 4)$$
$$= (x + 3)(x + 2)(x - 2)$$

Do Exercise 15.

**15.** Factor: $a^3 + a^2 - 16a - 16$.

A difference of squares can have more than two terms. For example, one of the squares may be a trinomial. We can factor by a type of grouping.

**EXAMPLE 16** Factor completely: $x^2 + 6x + 9 - y^2$.

$$x^2 + 6x + 9 - y^2 = (x^2 + 6x + 9) - y^2$$ \qquad Grouping as a trinomial minus $y^2$ to show a difference of squares
$$= (x + 3)^2 - y^2$$
$$= (x + 3 + y)(x + 3 - y)$$

Do Exercises 16-19.

Factor completely.

**16.** $x^2 + 2x + 1 - p^2$

**17.** $y^2 - 8y + 16 - 9m^2$

**18.** $x^2 + 8x + 16 - 100t^2$

**19.** $64p^2 - (x^2 + 8x + 16)$

***Answers***

**11.** $(5xy + 2a)(5xy - 2a)$
**12.** $(3x + 4y)(3x - 4y)$
**13.** $5(2x + y)(2x - y)$
**14.** $y^2(9x^2 + 4)(3x + 2)(3x - 2)$
**15.** $(a + 1)(a + 4)(a - 4)$
**16.** $(x + 1 + p)(x + 1 - p)$
**17.** $(y - 4 + 3m)(y - 4 - 3m)$
**18.** $(x + 4 + 10t)(x + 4 - 10t)$
**19.** $[8p + (x + 4)][8p - (x + 4)]$, or $(8p + x + 4)(8p - x - 4)$

## d) Sums or Differences of Cubes

We can factor the sum or the difference of two expressions that are cubes. Consider the following products:

$$(A + B)(A^2 - AB + B^2) = A(A^2 - AB + B^2) + B(A^2 - AB + B^2)$$
$$= A^3 - A^2B + AB^2 + A^2B - AB^2 + B^3$$
$$= A^3 + B^3$$

and

$$(A - B)(A^2 + AB + B^2) = A(A^2 + AB + B^2) - B(A^2 + AB + B^2)$$
$$= A^3 + A^2B + AB^2 - A^2B - AB^2 - B^3$$
$$= A^3 - B^3.$$

The above equations (reversed) show how we can factor a sum or a difference of two cubes. Each factors as a product of a binomial and a trinomial.

| $N$ | $N^3$ |
|-----|-------|
| 0.2 | 0.008 |
| 0.1 | 0.001 |
| 0 | 0 |
| 1 | 1 |
| 2 | 8 |
| 3 | 27 |
| 4 | 64 |
| 5 | 125 |
| 6 | 216 |
| 7 | 343 |
| 8 | 512 |
| 9 | 729 |
| 10 | 1000 |

> **SUM OR DIFFERENCE OF CUBES**
>
> $$A^3 + B^3 = (A + B)(A^2 - AB + B^2);$$
> $$A^3 - B^3 = (A - B)(A^2 + AB + B^2)$$

Note that what we are considering here is a sum or a difference of cubes. We are not cubing a binomial. For example, $(A + B)^3$ is *not* the same as $A^3 + B^3$. The table of cubes in the margin is helpful.

**EXAMPLE 17**  Factor: $x^3 - 27$.

We have

$$\overset{A^3 \quad - \quad B^3}{\underset{\downarrow \qquad \downarrow}{x^3 - 27 = x^3 - 3^3}}.$$

In one set of parentheses, we write the cube root of the first term, $x$. Then we write the cube root of the second term, $-3$. This gives us the expression $x - 3$:

$$(x - 3)(\qquad\qquad).$$

To get the next factor, we think of $x - 3$ and do the following:

- Square the first term: $x \cdot x = x^2$.
- Multiply the terms, $x(-3) = -3x$, and then change the sign: $3x$.
- Square the second term: $(-3)^2 = 9$.

$$(x - 3)(x^2 + 3x + 9).$$
$$(A - B)(A^2 + AB + B^2)$$

Note that we cannot factor $x^2 + 3x + 9$. It is not a trinomial square nor can it be factored by trial and error. Check this on your own.

Do Exercises 20 and 21.

Factor.

**20.** $x^3 - 8$

**21.** $64 - y^3$

*Answers*

**20.** $(x - 2)(x^2 + 2x + 4)$
**21.** $(4 - y)(16 + 4y + y^2)$

**EXAMPLE 18** Factor: $125x^3 + y^3$.

We have

$$125x^3 + y^3 = (5x)^3 + y^3.$$

In one set of parentheses, we write the cube root of the first term, $5x$. Then we write a plus sign, and then the cube root of the second term, $y$. This gives us the expression $5x + y$:

$$(5x + y)(\qquad).$$

To get the next factor, we think of $5x + y$ and do the following:

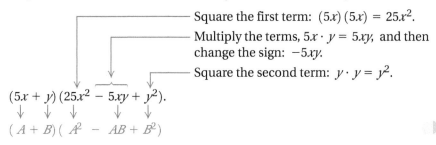

Square the first term: $(5x)(5x) = 25x^2$.

Multiply the terms, $5x \cdot y = 5xy$, and then change the sign: $-5xy$.

Square the second term: $y \cdot y = y^2$.

$$(5x + y)(25x^2 - 5xy + y^2).$$
$$(A + B)(A^2 - AB + B^2)$$

Do Exercises 22 and 23.

Factor.

**22.** $27x^3 + y^3$

**23.** $8y^3 + z^3$

**EXAMPLE 19** Factor: $128y^7 - 250x^6y$.

We first look for the largest common factor:

$$\begin{aligned} 128y^7 - 250x^6y &= 2y(64y^6 - 125x^6) \\ &= 2y[(4y^2)^3 - (5x^2)^3] \\ &= 2y(4y^2 - 5x^2)(16y^4 + 20x^2y^2 + 25x^4). \end{aligned}$$

**EXAMPLE 20** Factor: $a^6 - b^6$.

We can express this polynomial as a difference of squares:

$$a^6 - b^6 = (a^3)^2 - (b^3)^2.$$

We factor as follows:

$$a^6 - b^6 = (a^3 + b^3)(a^3 - b^3).$$

One factor is a sum of two cubes, and the other factor is a difference of two cubes. We factor them:

$$a^6 - b^6 = (a + b)(a^2 - ab + b^2)(a - b)(a^2 + ab + b^2).$$

We have now factored completely.

In Example 20, had we thought of factoring first as a difference of two cubes, we would have had

$$\begin{aligned} (a^2)^3 - (b^2)^3 &= (a^2 - b^2)(a^4 + a^2b^2 + b^4) \\ &= (a + b)(a - b)(a^4 + a^2b^2 + b^4). \end{aligned}$$

In this case, we might have missed some factors; $a^4 + a^2b^2 + b^4$ can be factored as $(a^2 - ab + b^2)(a^2 + ab + b^2)$, but we probably would not have known to do such factoring.

When you can factor as a difference of squares or a difference of cubes, factor as a difference of squares first.

*Answers*

**22.** $(3x + y)(9x^2 - 3xy + y^2)$
**23.** $(2y + z)(4y^2 - 2yz + z^2)$

**EXAMPLE 21**   Factor: $64a^6 - 729b^6$.

We have

$$64a^6 - 729b^6 = (8a^3)^2 - (27b^3)^2$$
$$= (8a^3 - 27b^3)(8a^3 + 27b^3) \quad \text{Factoring a difference of squares}$$
$$= [(2a)^3 - (3b)^3][(2a)^3 + (3b)^3].$$

Each factor is a sum or a difference of cubes. We factor each:

$$= (2a - 3b)(4a^2 + 6ab + 9b^2)(2a + 3b)(4a^2 - 6ab + 9b^2).$$

Factor.

**24.** $m^6 - n^6$

**25.** $16x^7y + 54xy^7$

**26.** $729x^6 - 64y^6$

**27.** $x^3 - 0.027$

**FACTORING SUMMARY**

Sum of cubes:          $A^3 + B^3 = (A + B)(A^2 - AB + B^2)$;

Difference of cubes:   $A^3 - B^3 = (A - B)(A^2 + AB + B^2)$;

Difference of squares: $A^2 - B^2 = (A + B)(A - B)$;

Sum of squares:        $A^2 + B^2$ cannot be factored as the square of a binomial: $A^2 + B^2 \neq (A + B)^2$.

Do Exercises 24–27.

**1**

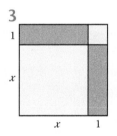

**2**

**3**

**4**

**5**

# Visualizing
# for Success

In each of Exercises 1–10, find two
algebraic expressions from the list
below for the shaded area of the figure.

**A.** $(5x + 2)^2$

**B.** $13x$

**C.** $400 - 4x^2$

**D.** $x^2 - (x - 2y)^2$

**E.** $25x^2 + 20x + 4$

**F.** $\frac{1}{2}(x^2 - y^2)$

**G.** $(x + 1)^2$

**H.** $4y(x - y)$

**I.** $4(10 - x)(10 + x)$

**J.** $\frac{1}{2}(x - y)(x + y)$

**K.** $x^2 + 2x + 1$

**L.** $6x(14x - 5) - 3x(3x + 5)$

**M.** $x^2 + 9x + 20$

**N.** $(x - 2)^2$

**O.** $(x + 4)(x + 5)$

**P.**
$8(x - 5) + (x - 5)(x - 8) + 5(x - 8)$

**Q.** $x^2 - 40$

**R.** $5x + 8x$

**S.** $15x(5x - 3)$

**T.** $x^2 - 4x + 4$

*Answers on page A-15*

**6**

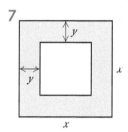

**7**

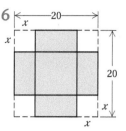

**8**

**9**

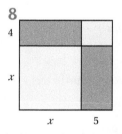

**10**

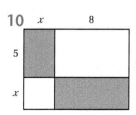

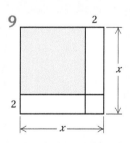

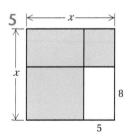

For Extra Help

*MyMathLab*   MathXL   WATCH   DOWNLOAD   READ   REVIEW
PRACTICE

**a**  Factor.

**1.** $x^2 - 4x + 4$

**2.** $y^2 - 16y + 64$

**3.** $y^2 + 18y + 81$

**4.** $x^2 + 8x + 16$

**5.** $x^2 + 1 + 2x$

**6.** $x^2 + 1 - 2x$

**7.** $9y^2 + 12y + 4$

**8.** $25x^2 - 60x + 36$

**9.** $-18y^2 + y^3 + 81y$

**10.** $24a^2 + a^3 + 144a$

**11.** $12a^2 + 36a + 27$

**12.** $20y^2 + 100y + 125$

**13.** $2x^2 - 40x + 200$

**14.** $32x^2 + 48x + 18$

**15.** $1 - 8d + 16d^2$

**16.** $64 + 25y^2 - 80y$

**17.** $3a^3 - 6a^2 + 3a$

**18.** $5c^3 + 20c^2 + 20c$

**19.** $0.25x^2 + 0.30x + 0.09$

**20.** $0.04x^2 - 0.28x + 0.49$

**21.** $p^2 - 2pq + q^2$

**22.** $m^2 + 2mn + n^2$

**23.** $a^2 + 4ab + 4b^2$

**24.** $49p^2 - 14pq + q^2$

**25.** $25a^2 - 30ab + 9b^2$

**26.** $49p^2 - 84pq + 36q^2$

**27.** $y^6 + 26y^3 + 169$

**28.** $p^6 - 10p^3 + 25$

**29.** $16x^{10} - 8x^5 + 1$

**30.** $9x^{10} + 12x^5 + 4$

**31.** $x^4 + 2x^2y^2 + y^4$

**32.** $p^6 - 2p^3q^4 + q^8$

**b**  Factor.

**33.** $p^2 - 49$

**34.** $m^2 - 64$

**35.** $y^4 - 8y^2 + 16$

**36.** $y^4 - 18y^2 + 81$

**37.** $p^2q^2 - 25$

**38.** $a^2b^2 - 81$

**39.** $6x^2 - 6y^2$

**40.** $8x^2 - 8y^2$

**41.** $4xy^4 - 4xz^4$

**42.** $25ab^4 - 25az^4$

**43.** $4a^3 - 49a$

**44.** $9x^3 - 25x$

**45.** $3x^8 - 3y^8$  **46.** $2a^9 - 32a$  **47.** $9a^4 - 25a^2b^4$  **48.** $16x^6 - 121x^2y^4$

**49.** $\frac{1}{36} - z^2$  **50.** $\frac{1}{100} - y^2$  **51.** $0.04x^2 - 0.09y^2$  **52.** $0.01x^2 - 0.04y^2$

**c** Factor.

**53.** $m^3 - 7m^2 - 4m + 28$  **54.** $x^3 + 8x^2 - x - 8$  **55.** $a^3 - ab^2 - 2a^2 + 2b^2$

**56.** $p^2q - 25q + 3p^2 - 75$  **57.** $(a + b)^2 - 100$  **58.** $(p - 7)^2 - 144$

**59.** $144 - (p - 8)^2$  **60.** $100 - (x - 4)^2$  **61.** $a^2 + 2ab + b^2 - 9$

**62.** $x^2 - 2xy + y^2 - 25$  **63.** $r^2 - 2r + 1 - 4s^2$  **64.** $c^2 + 4cd + 4d^2 - 9p^2$

**65.** $2m^2 + 4mn + 2n^2 - 50b^2$  **66.** $12x^2 + 12x + 3 - 3y^2$

**67.** $9 - (a^2 + 2ab + b^2)$  **68.** $16 - (x^2 - 2xy + y^2)$

**d** Factor.

**69.** $z^3 + 27$  **70.** $a^3 + 8$  **71.** $x^3 - 1$  **72.** $c^3 - 64$

**73.** $y^3 + 125$  **74.** $x^3 + 1$  **75.** $8a^3 + 1$  **76.** $27x^3 + 1$

**77.** $y^3 - 8$

**78.** $p^3 - 27$

**79.** $8 - 27b^3$

**80.** $64 - 125x^3$

**81.** $64y^3 + 1$

**82.** $125x^3 + 1$

**83.** $8x^3 + 27$

**84.** $27y^3 + 64$

**85.** $a^3 - b^3$

**86.** $x^3 - y^3$

**87.** $a^3 + \frac{1}{8}$

**88.** $b^3 + \frac{1}{27}$

**89.** $2y^3 - 128$

**90.** $3z^3 - 3$

**91.** $24a^3 + 3$

**92.** $54x^3 + 2$

**93.** $rs^3 + 64r$

**94.** $ab^3 + 125a$

**95.** $5x^3 - 40z^3$

**96.** $2y^3 - 54z^3$

**97.** $x^3 + 0.001$

**98.** $y^3 + 0.125$

**99.** $64x^6 - 8t^6$

**100.** $125c^6 - 8d^6$

**101.** $2y^4 - 128y$

**102.** $3z^5 - 3z^2$

**103.** $z^6 - 1$

**104.** $t^6 + 1$

**105.** $t^6 + 64y^6$

**106.** $p^6 - q^6$

**107.** $8w^9 - z^9$

**108.** $a^9 + 64b^9$

**109.** $\frac{1}{8}c^3 + d^3$

**110.** $\frac{27}{125}x^3 - y^3$

**111.** $0.001x^3 - 0.008y^3$

**112.** $0.125r^3 - 0.216s^3$

## Skill Maintenance

Solve.   [3.2a], [3.3a]

**113.** $7x - 2y = -11,$
$2x + 7y = 18$

**114.** $y = 3x - 8,$
$4x - 6y = 100$

**115.** $x - y = -12,$
$x + y = 14$

**116.** $7x - 2y = -11,$
$2y - 7x = -18$

Graph the given system of inequalities and determine coordinates of any vertices formed.   [3.7c]

**117.** $x - y \leq 5,$
$x + y \geq 3$

**118.** $x - y \leq 5,$
$x + y \geq 3,$
$x \leq 6$

**119.** $x - y \geq 5,$
$x + y \leq 3,$
$x \geq 1$

**120.** $x - y \geq 5,$
$x + y \leq 3$

Given the line and a point not on the line, find an equation through the point parallel to the given line, and find an equation through the point perpendicular to the given line.   [2.6d]

**121.** $x - y = 5; (-2, -4)$

**122.** $2x - 3y = 6; (1, -7)$

**123.** $y = -\frac{1}{2}x + 3; (4, 5)$

**124.** $x - 4y = -10; (6, 0)$

## Synthesis

**125.** Given that $P(x) = x^3$, use factoring to simplify $P(a + h) - P(a)$.

**126.** Given that $P(x) = x^4$, use factoring to simplify $P(a + h) - P(a)$.

**127.** *Volume of Carpeting.*   The volume of a carpet that is rolled up can be estimated by the polynomial $\pi R^2 h - \pi r^2 h.$

**a)** Factor the polynomial.
**b)** Use both the original form and the factored form to find the volume of a roll for which $R = 50$ cm, $r = 10$ cm, and $h = 4$ m. Use 3.14 for $\pi$.

**128.** Show how the geometric model below can be used to verify the formula for factoring $a^3 - b^3$.

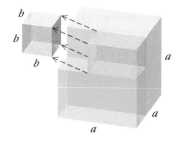

Factor. Assume that variables in exponents represent positive integers.

**129.** $5c^{100} - 80d^{100}$

**130.** $9x^{2n} - 6x^n + 1$

**131.** $x^{6a} + y^{3b}$

**132.** $a^3x^3 - b^3y^3$

**133.** $3x^{3a} + 24y^{3b}$

**134.** $\frac{8}{27}x^3 + \frac{1}{64}y^3$

**135.** $\frac{1}{24}x^3y^3 + \frac{1}{3}z^3$

**136.** $7x^3 - \frac{7}{8}$

**137.** $(x + y)^3 - x^3$

**138.** $(1 - x)^3 + (x - 1)^6$

**139.** $(a + 2)^3 - (a - 2)^3$

**140.** $y^4 - 8y^3 - y + 8$

# 4.7

# Factoring: A General Strategy

## a  A General Factoring Strategy

Factoring is an important algebraic skill, used for solving equations and many other manipulations of algebraic symbolism. We now consider polynomials of many types and learn to use a general strategy for factoring. The key is to recognize the type of polynomial to be factored.

> **A STRATEGY FOR FACTORING**
>
> a)  Always look for a *common factor* (other than 1 or −1). If there are any, factor out the largest one.
>
> b)  Then look at the number of terms.
>
>   *Two terms*: Try factoring as a difference of squares first. Next, try factoring as a sum or a difference of cubes. Do *not* try to factor a *sum* of squares: $A^2 + B^2$.
>
>   *Three terms*: Determine whether the expression is a trinomial square. If it is, you know how to factor. If not, try the trial-and-error method or the *ac*–method.
>
>   *Four or more terms*: Try factoring by grouping and removing a common binomial factor. Next, try grouping into a difference of squares, one of which is a trinomial.
>
> c)  Always *factor completely*. If a factor with more than one term can be factored, you should factor it.
>
> d)  Always *check* by multiplying.

**STUDY TIPS**

**READING EXAMPLES**

A careful study of the examples in these sections on factoring is critical. *Read them carefully* to ensure success!

**EXAMPLE 1**  Factor: $10a^2x - 40b^2x$.

a)  We look first for a common factor:

$$10x(a^2 - 4b^2). \qquad \text{Factoring out the largest common factor}$$

b)  The factor $a^2 - 4b^2$ has only two terms. It is a difference of squares. We factor it, keeping the common factor:  $10x(a + 2b)(a - 2b)$.

c)  Have we factored completely? Yes, because none of the factors with more than one term can be factored further using polynomials of smaller degree.

d)  *Check*:  $10x(a + 2b)(a - 2b) = 10x(a^2 - 4b^2) = 10xa^2 - 40xb^2$, or $10a^2x - 40b^2x$.

**EXAMPLE 2**  Factor: $x^6 - y^6$.

a)  We look for a common factor. There isn't one (other than 1 or −1).

b)  There are only two terms. It is a difference of squares:  $(x^3)^2 - (y^3)^2$. We factor it:  $(x^3 + y^3)(x^3 - y^3)$. One factor is a sum of two cubes, and the other factor is a difference of two cubes. We factor them:

$$x^6 - y^6 = (x^3 + y^3)(x^3 - y^3)$$

$$= (x + y)(x^2 - xy + y^2)(x - y)(x^2 + xy + y^2).$$

c) We have factored completely because none of the factors can be factored further using polynomials of smaller degree.

d) *Check:* $(x + y)(x^2 - xy + y^2)(x - y)(x^2 + xy + y^2)$
$$= (x^3 + y^3)(x^3 - y^3)$$
$$= (x^3)^2 - (y^3)^2 = x^6 - y^6.$$

Do Exercises 1–3.

Factor completely.

**1.** $3y^3 - 12x^2y$

**2.** $7a^3 - 7$

**3.** $64x^6 - 729y^6$

**EXAMPLE 3** Factor: $10x^6 + 40y^2$.

a) We remove the largest common factor: $10(x^6 + 4y^2)$.

b) In the parentheses, there are two terms, a sum of squares, which cannot be factored.

c) We have factored $10x^6 + 40y^2$ completely as $10(x^6 + 4y^2)$.

d) *Check:* $10(x^6 + 4y^2) = 10x^6 + 40y^2$.

**EXAMPLE 4** Factor: $2x^2 + 50a^2 - 20ax$.

a) We remove the largest common factor: $2(x^2 + 25a^2 - 10ax)$.

b) In the parentheses, there are three terms. The trinomial is a square. We factor it: $2(x - 5a)^2$.

c) None of the factors with more than one term can be factored further.

d) *Check:* $2(x - 5a)^2 = 2(x^2 - 10ax + 25a^2) = 2x^2 - 20ax + 50a^2$, or $2x^2 + 50a^2 - 20ax$.

**EXAMPLE 5** Factor: $6x^2 - 20x - 16$.

a) We remove the largest common factor: $2(3x^2 - 10x - 8)$.

b) In the parentheses, there are three terms. The trinomial is not a square. We factor: $2(x - 4)(3x + 2)$.

c) We cannot factor further.

d) *Check:* $2(x - 4)(3x + 2) = 2(3x^2 - 10x - 8) = 6x^2 - 20x - 16$.

**EXAMPLE 6** Factor: $3x + 12 + ax^2 + 4ax$.

a) There is no common factor (other than 1 or $-1$).

b) There are four terms. We try grouping to remove a common binomial factor:

$$3(x + 4) + ax(x + 4) \qquad \text{Factoring two grouped binomials}$$
$$= (x + 4)(3 + ax). \qquad \text{Factoring out the common binomial factor}$$

c) None of the factors with more than one term can be factored further.

d) *Check:* $(x + 4)(3 + ax) = 3x + ax^2 + 12 + 4ax$, or $3x + 12 + ax^2 + 4ax$.

**EXAMPLE 7** Factor: $y^2 - 9a^2 + 12y + 36$.

a) There is no common factor (other than 1 or $-1$).

b) There are four terms. We try grouping to remove a common binomial factor, but that is not possible. We try grouping as a difference of squares:

$$(y^2 + 12y + 36) - 9a^2 = (y + 6)^2 - (3a)^2$$
$$= (y + 6 + 3a)(y + 6 - 3a). \quad \text{Factoring the difference of squares}$$

c) No factor with more than one term can be factored further.

d) *Check*: $(y + 6 + 3a)(y + 6 - 3a) = [(y + 6) + 3a][(y + 6) - 3a]$
$$= (y + 6)^2 - (3a)^2$$
$$= y^2 + 12y + 36 - 9a^2, \text{ or}$$
$$y^2 - 9a^2 + 12y + 36.$$

**EXAMPLE 8** Factor: $x^3 - xy^2 + x^2y - y^3$.

a) There is no common factor (other than 1 or $-1$).

b) There are four terms. We try grouping to remove a common binomial factor:

$$x(x^2 - y^2) + y(x^2 - y^2) \quad \text{Factoring two grouped binomials}$$
$$= (x^2 - y^2)(x + y). \quad \text{Factoring out the common binomial factor}$$

c) The factor $x^2 - y^2$ can be factored further, giving

$$(x + y)(x - y)(x + y). \quad \text{Factoring a difference of squares}$$

None of the factors with more than one term can be factored further, so we have factored completely.

d) *Check*: $(x + y)(x - y)(x + y) = (x^2 - y^2)(x + y)$
$$= x^3 + x^2y - y^2x - y^3, \text{ or}$$
$$x^3 - xy^2 + x^2y - y^3.$$

Do Exercises 4–9.

Factor.

**4.** $3x - 6 - bx^2 + 2bx$

**5.** $5y^4 + 20x^6$

**6.** $6x^2 - 3x - 18$

**7.** $a^3 - ab^2 - a^2b + b^3$

**8.** $3x^2 + 18ax + 27a^2$

**9.** $2x^2 - 20x + 50 - 18b^2$

*Answers*

**4.** $(x - 2)(3 - bx)$     **5.** $5(y^4 + 4x^6)$
**6.** $3(x - 2)(2x + 3)$     **7.** $(a - b)^2(a + b)$
**8.** $3(x + 3a)^2$     **9.** $2(x - 5 + 3b)(x - 5 - 3b)$

**a**    Factor completely.

**1.** $y^2 - 225$

**2.** $x^2 - 400$

**3.** $2x^2 + 11x + 12$

**4.** $8a^2 + 18a - 5$

**5.** $5x^4 - 20$

**6.** $3xy^2 - 75x$

**7.** $p^2 + 36 + 12p$

**8.** $a^2 + 49 + 14a$

**9.** $2x^2 - 10x - 132$

**10.** $3y^2 - 15y - 252$

**11.** $9x^2 - 25y^2$

**12.** $16a^2 - 81b^2$

**13.** $4m^4 - 100$

**14.** $2x^2 - 288$

**15.** $6w^2 + 12w - 18$

**16.** $8z^2 - 8z - 16$

**17.** $2xy^2 - 50x$

**18.** $3a^3b - 108ab$

**19.** $225 - (a - 3)^2$

**20.** $625 - (t - 10)^2$

**21.** $m^6 - 1$

**22.** $64t^6 - 1$

**23.** $x^2 + 6x - y^2 + 9$

**24.** $t^2 + 10t - p^2 + 25$

**25.** $250x^3 - 128y^3$

**26.** $27a^3 - 343b^3$

**27.** $8m^3 + m^6 - 20$

**28.** $-37x^2 + x^4 + 36$

**29.** $ac + cd - ab - bd$

**30.** $xw - yw + xz - yz$

**31.** $50b^2 - 5ab - a^2$

**32.** $9c^2 + 12cd - 5d^2$

**33.** $-7x^2 + 2x^3 + 4x - 14$

**34.** $9m^2 + 3m^3 + 8m + 24$

**35.** $2x^3 + 6x^2 - 8x - 24$

**36.** $3x^3 + 6x^2 - 27x - 54$

**37.** $16x^3 + 54y^3$

**38.** $250a^3 + 54b^3$

**39.** $6y - 60x^2y - 9xy$

**40.** $2b - 28a^2b + 10ab$

**41.** $a^8 - b^8$

**42.** $2x^4 - 32$

**43.** $a^3b - 16ab^3$

**44.** $x^3y - 25xy^3$

**45.** $\frac{1}{16}x^2 - \frac{1}{6}xy^2 + \frac{1}{9}y^4$

**46.** $36x^2 + 15x + \frac{25}{16}$

**47.** $5x^3 - 5x^2y - 5xy^2 + 5y^3$

**48.** $a^3 - ab^2 + a^2b - b^3$

**49.** $42ab + 27a^2b^2 + 8$

**50.** $-23xy + 20x^2y^2 + 6$

**51.** $8y^4 - 125y$

**52.** $64p^4 - p$

**53.** $a^2 - b^2 - 6b - 9$

**54.** $m^2 - n^2 - 8n - 16$

**55.** $q^2 - 10q + 25 - r^2$

**56.** $y^2 - 14y + 49 - z^2$

## Skill Maintenance

Solve. [3.2b]

**57.** *Exam Scores.* There are 75 questions on a college entrance examination. Two points are awarded for each correct answer, and one half point is deducted for each incorrect answer. A score of 100 indicates how many correct and how many incorrect answers, assuming that all questions are answered?

**58.** *Perimeter.* A pentagon with all five sides the same length has the same perimeter as an octagon with all eight sides the same length. One side of the pentagon is 2 less than three times the length of one side of the octagon. Find the perimeters.

## Synthesis

Factor. Assume that variables in exponents represent natural numbers.

**59.** $30y^4 - 97xy^2 + 60x^2$

**60.** $3x^2y^2z + 25xyz^2 + 28z^3$

**61.** $5x^3 - \frac{5}{27}$

**62.** $9y^3 - \frac{9}{1000}$

**63.** $(x - p)^2 - p^2$

**64.** $s^6 - 729t^6$

**65.** $(y - 1)^4 - (y - 1)^2$

**66.** $27x^{6s} + 64y^{3t}$

**67.** $4x^2 + 4xy + y^2 - r^2 + 6rs - 9s^2$

**68.** $c^4d^4 - a^{16}$

**69.** $c^{2w+1} + 2c^{w+1} + c$

**70.** $24x^{2a} - 6$

**71.** $3(x + 1)^2 + 9(x + 1) - 12$

**72.** $8(a - 3)^2 - 64(a - 3) + 128$

**73.** $x^6 - 2x^5 + x^4 - x^2 + 2x - 1$

**74.** $1 - \dfrac{x^{27}}{1000}$

**75.** $y^9 - y$

**76.** $(m - 1)^3 - (m + 1)^3$

# 4.8 Applications of Polynomial Equations and Functions

Whenever two polynomials are set equal to each other, we have a **polynomial equation**. Some examples of polynomial equations are

$$4x^3 + x^2 + 5x = 6x - 3,$$
$$x^2 - x = 6,$$

and $\quad 3y^4 + 2y^2 + 2 = 0.$

A second-degree polynomial equation in one variable is often called a **quadratic equation**. Of the equations listed above, only $x^2 - x = 6$ is a quadratic equation.

Polynomial equations, and quadratic equations in particular, occur frequently in applications, so the ability to solve them is an important skill. One way of solving certain polynomial equations involves factoring.

## a The Principle of Zero Products

When we multiply two or more numbers, if either factor is 0, then the product is 0. Conversely, if a product is 0, then at least one of the factors must be 0. This property of 0 gives us a new principle for solving equations.

> **THE PRINCIPLE OF ZERO PRODUCTS**
>
> For any real numbers $a$ and $b$:
> If $ab = 0$, then $a = 0$ or $b = 0$ (or both).
> If $a = 0$ or $b = 0$, then $ab = 0$.

To solve an equation using the principle of zero products, we first write it in *standard form*: with 0 on one side of the equation and the leading coefficient positive.

**EXAMPLE 1** Solve: $x^2 - x = 6$.

In order to use the principle of zero products, we must have 0 on one side of the equation, so we subtract 6 on both sides:

$$x^2 - x - 6 = 0. \qquad \text{Getting 0 on one side}$$

We need a factorization on the other side, so we factor the polynomial:

$$(x - 3)(x + 2) = 0. \qquad \text{Factoring}$$

We now have two expressions, $x - 3$ and $x + 2$, whose product is 0. Using the principle of zero products, we set each expression or factor equal to 0:

$$x - 3 = 0 \quad or \quad x + 2 = 0. \qquad \text{Using the principle of zero products}$$

This gives us two simple linear equations. We solve them separately,

$$x = 3 \quad or \quad x = -2,$$

and check in the original equation as follows.

**OBJECTIVES**

**a** Solve quadratic and other polynomial equations by first factoring and then using the principle of zero products.

**b** Solve applied problems involving quadratic and other polynomial equations that can be solved by factoring.

**SKILL TO REVIEW**
Objective 4.3a: Factor polynomials whose terms have a common factor.

Factor.
**1.** $x^2 + 20x$
**2.** $3y^2 - 6y$

*Answers*
*Skill to Review:*
**1.** $x(x + 20)$ **2.** $3y(y - 2)$

Check:   $\dfrac{x^2 - x = 6}{\begin{array}{c} 3^2 - 3 \ ?\ 6 \\ 9 - 3\ \big| \\ 6\ \big|\ \text{TRUE} \end{array}}$     $\dfrac{x^2 - x = 6}{\begin{array}{c} (-2)^2 - (-2)\ ?\ 6 \\ 4 + 2\ \big| \\ 6\ \big|\ \text{TRUE} \end{array}}$

The numbers 3 and $-2$ are both solutions.

> To solve an equation using the principle of zero products:
>
> **1.** Obtain a 0 on one side of the equation.
> **2.** Factor the other side.
> **3.** Set each factor equal to 0.
> **4.** Solve the resulting equations.

**1.** Solve: $x^2 + 8 = 6x$.

Do Exercise 1.

When you solve an equation using the principle of zero products, you may wish to check by substitution as we did in Example 1. Such a check will detect errors in solving.

--------- *Caution!* ---------

When we are using the principle of zero products, it is important that there is a 0 on one side of the equation. If neither side of the equation is 0, the procedure will not work.

For example, consider $x^2 - x = 6$ in Example 1 as

$$x(x - 1) = 6.$$

Suppose we reasoned as follows, setting factors equal to 6:

$$x = 6 \quad or \quad x - 1 = 6 \qquad \text{This step is incorrect!}$$
$$x = 7.$$

Neither 6 nor 7 checks, as shown below:

$\dfrac{x(x - 1) = 6}{\begin{array}{c} 6(6 - 1)\ ?\ 6 \\ 6(5)\ \big| \\ 30\ \big|\ \text{FALSE} \end{array}}$     $\dfrac{x(x - 1) = 6}{\begin{array}{c} 7(7 - 1)\ ?\ 6 \\ 7(6)\ \big| \\ 42\ \big|\ \text{FALSE} \end{array}}$

**EXAMPLE 2**   Solve: $7y + 3y^2 = -2$.

Since there must be a 0 on one side of the equation, we add 2 to get 0 on the right-hand side and arrange in descending order. Then we factor and use the principle of zero products.

$$7y + 3y^2 = -2$$
$$3y^2 + 7y + 2 = 0 \qquad \text{Getting 0 on one side}$$
$$(3y + 1)(y + 2) = 0 \qquad \text{Factoring}$$
$$3y + 1 = 0 \quad or \quad y + 2 = 0 \qquad \text{Using the principle of zero products}$$
$$y = -\tfrac{1}{3} \quad or \qquad y = -2$$

**2.** Solve: $5y + 2y^2 = 3$.

The solutions are $-\tfrac{1}{3}$ and $-2$.

Do Exercise 2.

*Answers*

1. 4, 2   2. $\dfrac{1}{2}, -3$

**EXAMPLE 3**  Solve: $5b^2 = 10b$.

$$5b^2 = 10b$$
$$5b^2 - 10b = 0 \qquad \text{Getting 0 on one side}$$
$$5b(b - 2) = 0 \qquad \text{Factoring}$$
$$5b = 0 \quad or \quad b - 2 = 0 \qquad \text{Using the principle of zero products}$$
$$b = 0 \quad or \qquad b = 2$$

The solutions are 0 and 2.

Do Exercise 3.

**3.** Solve: $8b^2 = 16b$.

**EXAMPLE 4**  Solve: $x^2 - 6x + 9 = 0$.

$$x^2 - 6x + 9 = 0 \qquad \text{Getting 0 on one side}$$
$$(x - 3)(x - 3) = 0 \qquad \text{Factoring}$$
$$x - 3 = 0 \quad or \quad x - 3 = 0 \qquad \text{Using the principle of zero products}$$
$$x = 3 \quad or \qquad x = 3$$

There is only one solution, 3.

Do Exercise 4.

**4.** Solve: $25 + x^2 = -10x$.

**EXAMPLE 5**  Solve: $3x^3 - 9x^2 = 30x$.

$$3x^3 - 9x^2 = 30x$$
$$3x^3 - 9x^2 - 30x = 0 \qquad \text{Getting 0 on one side}$$
$$3x(x^2 - 3x - 10) = 0 \qquad \text{Factoring out a common factor}$$
$$3x(x + 2)(x - 5) = 0 \qquad \text{Factoring the trinomial}$$
$$3x = 0 \quad or \quad x + 2 = 0 \quad or \quad x - 5 = 0 \qquad \text{Using the principle of zero products}$$
$$x = 0 \quad or \qquad x = -2 \quad or \qquad x = 5$$

The solutions are 0, −2, and 5.

Do Exercise 5.

**5.** Solve: $x^3 + x^2 = 6x$.

**EXAMPLE 6**  Given that $f(x) = 3x^2 - 4x$, find all values of $x$ for which $f(x) = 4$.

We want all numbers $x$ for which $f(x) = 4$. Since $f(x) = 3x^2 - 4x$, we must have

$$3x^2 - 4x = 4 \qquad \text{Setting } f(x) \text{ equal to 4}$$
$$3x^2 - 4x - 4 = 0 \qquad \text{Getting 0 on one side}$$
$$(3x + 2)(x - 2) = 0 \qquad \text{Factoring}$$
$$3x + 2 = 0 \quad or \quad x - 2 = 0$$
$$x = -\tfrac{2}{3} \quad or \qquad x = 2.$$

We can check as follows.

$$f\left(-\tfrac{2}{3}\right) = 3\left(-\tfrac{2}{3}\right)^2 - 4\left(-\tfrac{2}{3}\right) = 3 \cdot \tfrac{4}{9} + \tfrac{8}{3} = \tfrac{4}{3} + \tfrac{8}{3} = \tfrac{12}{3} = 4;$$
$$f(2) = 3(2)^2 - 4(2) = 3 \cdot 4 - 8 = 12 - 8 = 4$$

To have $f(x) = 4$, we must have $x = -\tfrac{2}{3}$ or $x = 2$.

**6.** Given that $f(x) = 10x^2 + 13x$, find all values of $x$ for which $f(x) = 3$.

Do Exercise 6.

*Answers*

**3.** $0, 2$   **4.** $-5$   **5.** $0, 2, -3$   **6.** $-\dfrac{3}{2}, \dfrac{1}{5}$

**EXAMPLE 7** Find the domain of $F$ if $F(x) = \dfrac{x - 2}{x^2 + 2x - 15}$.

The domain of $F$ is the set of all values for which

$$\frac{x - 2}{x^2 + 2x - 15}$$

is a real number. Since division by 0 is undefined, $F(x)$ cannot be calculated for any $x$-value for which the denominator, $x^2 + 2x - 15$, is 0. To make sure these values are *excluded*, we solve:

$$\begin{aligned}
x^2 + 2x - 15 &= 0 && \text{Setting the denominator equal to 0} \\
(x - 3)(x + 5) &= 0 && \text{Factoring} \\
x - 3 = 0 \;\; &or \;\; x + 5 = 0 \\
x = 3 \;\; &or \;\;\;\;\;\;\; x = -5. && \text{These are the values to } \textit{exclude.}
\end{aligned}$$

The domain of $F$ is $\{x \mid x \text{ is a real number } and\ x \neq -5\ and\ x \neq 3\}$.

Do Exercise 7.

**7.** Find the domain of the function $G$ if

$$G(x) = \frac{2x - 9}{x^2 - 3x - 28}.$$

---

## ✖ Algebraic-Graphical Connection

We now consider graphical connections with the algebraic equation-solving concepts.

In Chapter 2, we briefly considered the graph of a quadratic function $f(x) = ax^2 + bx + c,\ a \neq 0$. For example, the graph of the function $f(x) = x^2 + 6x + 8$ and its $x$-intercepts are shown below.

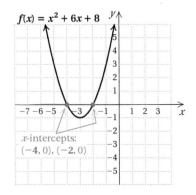

The $x$-intercepts are $(-4, 0)$ and $(-2, 0)$. These pairs are also the points of intersection of the graphs of $f(x) = x^2 + 6x + 8$ and $g(x) = 0$ (the $x$-axis).

In this section, we began studying how to solve quadratic equations like $x^2 + 6x + 8 = 0$ using factoring:

$$\begin{aligned}
x^2 + 6x + 8 &= 0 \\
(x + 4)(x + 2) &= 0 && \text{Factoring} \\
x + 4 = 0 \;\; &or \;\; x + 2 = 0 && \text{Principle of zero products} \\
x = -4 \;\; &or \;\;\;\;\;\;\; x = -2.
\end{aligned}$$

We see that the solutions of $0 = x^2 + 6x + 8$, $-4$ and $-2$, are the first coordinates of the $x$-intercepts, $(-4, 0)$ and $(-2, 0)$, of the graph of $f(x) = x^2 + 6x + 8$.

**8.** Consider solving the equation

$$x^2 - 6x + 8 = 0$$

graphically.

**a)** Below is the graph of

$$f(x) = x^2 - 6x + 8.$$

Use *only* the graph to find the $x$-intercepts of the graph.

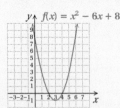

**b)** Use *only* the graph to find the solutions of $x^2 - 6x + 8 = 0$.

**c)** Compare your answers to parts (a) and (b).

---

*Answers*

**7.** $\{x \mid x \text{ is a real number } and\ x \neq -4\ and\ x \neq 7\}$
**8. (a)** $(2, 0)$ and $(4, 0)$; **(b)** 2, 4; **(c)** The solutions of $x^2 - 6x + 8 = 0$, 2 and 4, are the first coordinates of the $x$-intercepts, $(2, 0)$ and $(4, 0)$, of the graph of $f(x) = x^2 - 6x + 8$.

Do Exercise 8.

**Solving Quadratic Equations**   We can solve quadratic equations graphically. Consider the equation $x^2 - x = 6$. First, we must write the equation with 0 on one side. To do this, we subtract 6 on both sides of the equation. We get $x^2 - x - 6 = 0$. Next, we graph $y = x^2 - x - 6$ in a window that shows the $x$-intercepts. The standard window works well in this case.

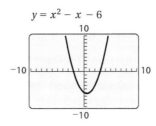

The solutions of the equation are the values of $x$ for which $x^2 - x - 6 = 0$. These are also the first coordinates of the $x$-intercepts of the graph. We use the ZERO feature from the CALC menu to find these numbers. To find the solution corresponding to the leftmost $x$-intercept, we first press **2ND** **CALC** **2** to select the ZERO feature. The prompt "Left Bound?" appears. We use the ◁ or the ▷ key to move the cursor to the left of the intercept and press **ENTER**. Now, the prompt "Right Bound?" appears. We move the cursor to the right of the intercept and press **ENTER**. Next, the prompt "Guess?" appears. We move the cursor close to the intercept and press **ENTER** again. We now see the cursor positioned at the leftmost $x$-intercept and the coordinates of that point, $x = -2$, $y = 0$, are displayed. Thus, $x^2 - x - 6 = 0$ when $x = -2$. This is one solution of the equation.

We repeat this procedure to find the first coordinate of the other $x$-intercept. We see that $x = 3$ at that point. Thus the solutions of the equation are $-2$ and 3.

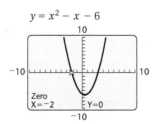

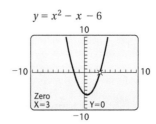

This equation could also be solved by entering $y_1 = x^2 - x$ and $y_2 = 6$ and finding the first coordinate of the points of intersection using the INTERSECT feature as described on p. 246.

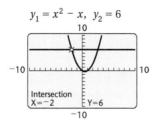

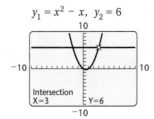

**Exercise:**

**1.** Solve the equations in Examples 2–5 graphically. Note that, regardless of the variable used in an example, each equation should be entered on the equation-editor screen in terms of $x$.

## b Applications and Problem Solving

Some problems can be translated to quadratic equations. The problem-solving process is the same one we use for other kinds of applied problems.

**EXAMPLE 8**   *Prize Tee Shirts.*   During intermission at sporting events, team mascots commonly use a powerful slingshot to launch tightly rolled tee shirts into the stands. The height $h(t)$, in feet, of an airborne tee shirt $t$ seconds after being launched can be approximated by

$$h(t) = -15t^2 + 75t + 10.$$

After peaking, a rolled-up tee shirt is caught by a fan 70 ft above ground level. How long was the tee shirt in the air?

1. **Familiarize.**   We make a drawing and label it, using the information provided (see the figure). We could evaluate $h(t)$ for a few values of $t$. Note that $t$ cannot be negative, since it represents time from launch.

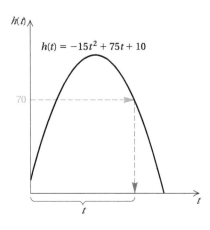

2. **Translate.**   The function is given. Since we are asked to determine how long it will take for the shirt to reach someone 70 ft above ground level, we are interested in the value of $t$ for which $h(t) = 70$:

$$-15t^2 + 75t + 10 = 70.$$

3. **Solve.**   We solve by factoring:

$$\begin{aligned}
-15t^2 + 75t + 10 &= 70 \\
-15t^2 + 75t - 60 &= 0 \qquad \text{Subtracting 70} \\
\left.\begin{aligned}-15(t^2 - 5t + 4) &= 0 \\ -15(t - 4)(t - 1) &= 0\end{aligned}\right\} \quad &\text{Factoring} \\
t - 4 = 0 \quad &or \quad t - 1 = 0 \\
t = 4 \quad &or \qquad t = 1.
\end{aligned}$$

The solutions appear to be 4 and 1.

**4. Check.** We have

$$h(4) = -15 \cdot 4^2 + 75 \cdot 4 + 10 = -240 + 300 + 10 = 70 \text{ ft};$$
$$h(1) = -15 \cdot 1^2 + 75 \cdot 1 + 10 = -15 + 75 + 10 = 70 \text{ ft}.$$

Both 1 and 4 check, as we can also see from the graph below.

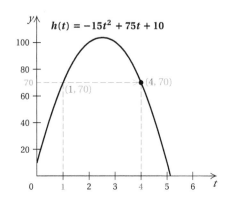

However, the problem states that the tee shirt is caught on the way down from its peak height. Thus we reject the solution 1 since that would indicate when the height of the tee shirt was 70 ft on the way up.

**5. State.** The tee shirt was in the air for 4 sec.

Do Exercise 9.

The following example involves the **Pythagorean theorem**, which relates the lengths of the sides of a right triangle. A **right triangle** has a 90°, or right, angle, which is denoted by a symbol like ⌐. The longest side, opposite the 90° angle, is called the **hypotenuse**. The other sides, called **legs**, form the two sides of the right angle.

---

**THE PYTHAGOREAN THEOREM**

The sum of the squares of the lengths of the legs of a right triangle is equal to the square of the length of the hypotenuse:

$$a^2 + b^2 = c^2.$$

---

**9. Motorcycle Stunt.** In filming a movie, a stunt double on a motorcycle must jump over a group of trucks that are lined up side by side. The height $h(t)$, in feet, of the airborne bike $t$ seconds after leaving the ramp can be approximated by

$$h(t) = -16t^2 + 60t.$$

After how long will the bike reach the ground?

**EXAMPLE 9**   *Carpentry.*   In order to build a deck at a right angle to her lake house, Geri decides to plant a stake in the ground a precise distance from the back wall of her house. This stake will combine with two marks on the house to form a right triangle. From a course in geometry, Geri remembers that there are three consecutive integers that can work as sides of a right triangle. Find the measurements of that triangle.

1. **Familiarize.**   Recall that $x, x + 1$, and $x + 2$ can be used to represent three unknown consecutive integers. Since $x + 2$ is the largest number, it must represent the hypotenuse. The legs serve as the sides of the right angle, so one leg must be formed by the marks on the house. We make a drawing in which

$$x = \text{the distance between the marks on the house,}$$
$$x + 1 = \text{the length of the other leg,}$$

and

$$x + 2 = \text{the length of the hypotenuse.}$$

2. **Translate.**   Applying the Pythagorean theorem, we translate as follows:
$$a^2 + b^2 = c^2$$
$$x^2 + (x + 1)^2 = (x + 2)^2.$$

3. **Solve.**   We solve the equation as follows:

| | |
|---|---|
| $x^2 + (x^2 + 2x + 1) = x^2 + 4x + 4$ | Squaring the binomials |
| $2x^2 + 2x + 1 = x^2 + 4x + 4$ | Collecting like terms |
| $x^2 - 2x - 3 = 0$ | Subtracting $x^2 + 4x + 4$ |
| $(x - 3)(x + 1) = 0$ | Factoring |
| $x - 3 = 0 \quad or \quad x + 1 = 0$ | |
| $x = 3 \quad or \qquad x = -1.$ | |

4. **Check.**   The integer $-1$ cannot be a length of a side because it is negative. For $x = 3$, we have $x + 1 = 4$, and $x + 2 = 5$. Since $3^2 + 4^2 = 5^2$, the lengths 3, 4, and 5 determine a right triangle. Thus, 3, 4, and 5 check.

5. **State.**   Geri should use a triangle with sides having a ratio of $3 : 4 : 5$. Thus, if the marks on the house are 3 yd apart, she should locate the stake at the point in the yard that is precisely 4 yd from one mark and 5 yd from the other mark.

---

Do Exercise 10.

**10. Child's Block.**   The lengths of the sides of a right triangle formed by a child's wooden block are such that one leg has length 5 cm. The lengths of the other sides are consecutive integers. Find the lengths of the other sides of the triangle.

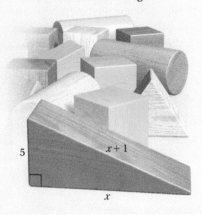

*Answer*

**10.** 12 cm and 13 cm

# Translating for Success

**1.** *Car Travel.* Two cars leave town at the same time going in different directions. One travels 50 mph and the other travels 55 mph. In how many hours will they be 200 mi apart?

**2.** *Mixture of Solutions.* Solution A is 27% alcohol and solution B is 55% alcohol. How much of each should be used in order to make 10 L of a solution that is 48% alcohol?

**3.** *Triangle Dimensions.* The base of a triangle is 3 cm less than the height. The area is 27 cm². Find the height and the base.

**4.** *Three Numbers.* The sum of three numbers is 38. The first number is 3 less than twice the second number. The second number minus the third number is −7. What are the numbers?

**5.** *Supplementary Angles.* Two angles are supplementary. One angle measures 27° more than three times the measure of the other. Find the measure of each angle.

---

Translate each word problem to an equation or a system of equations and select a correct translation from equations A– Q.

**A.** $x + y + z = 38,$
$x = 2y - 3,$
$y - z = -7$

**B.** $\frac{1}{2}x(x - 3) = 27$

**C.** $x + y = 180,$
$x = 3y - 27$

**D.** $x^2 + 36 = (x + 4)^2$

**E.** $x^2 + (x + 4)^2 = 36$

**F.** $x + y = 10,$
$0.27x + 0.55y = 4.8$

**G.** $x + y = 45,$
$10x - 7y = 402$

**H.** $x + y + z = 180,$
$y - 3x - 38 = 0,$
$x - z = 7$

**I.** $x + y = 90,$
$x = 3y + 10$

**J.** $x + 29.3\%x = 77.2$

**K.** $x + y + z = 38,$
$x - 2y = 3,$
$x - z = -7$

**L.** $x + y = 10,$
$27x + 55y = 4.8$

**M.** $55x - 50x = 200$

**N.** $x^2 - 3x = 27$

**O.** $x + y = 45,$
$7x + 10y = 402$

**P.** $x + y = 180,$
$x = 3y + 27$

**Q.** $50x + 55x = 200$

*Answers on page A-16*

---

**6.** *Triangle Dimensions.* The length of one leg of a right triangle is 6 m. The length of the hypotenuse is 4 m longer than the length of the other leg. Find the lengths of the hypotenuse and the other leg.

**7.** *Pizza Sales.* Todd's fraternity sold 45 pizzas over a football weekend. Small pizzas sold for $7 each and large pizzas for $10 each. The total amount of the sales was $402. How many of each size pizza were sold?

**8.** *Angle Measures.* The second angle of a triangle measures 38° more than three times the measure of the first. The measure of the third angle is 7° less than the first. Find the measures of each angle of the triangle.

**9.** *Complementary Angles.* Two angles are complementary. One angle measures 10° more than three times the measure of the other. Find the measure of each angle.

**10.** *Life Expectancy.* Life expectancy in the United States was 77.2 yr in 2002. This was a 29.3% increase from the life expectancy in 1930. What was the life expectancy in 1930?

**Source:** National Center for Health Statistics

**a**   Solve.

**1.** $x^2 + 3x = 28$

**2.** $y^2 - 4y = 45$

**3.** $y^2 + 9 = 6y$

**4.** $r^2 + 4 = 4r$

**5.** $x^2 + 20x + 100 = 0$

**6.** $y^2 + 10y + 25 = 0$

**7.** $9x + x^2 + 20 = 0$

**8.** $8y + y^2 + 15 = 0$

**9.** $x^2 + 8x = 0$

**10.** $t^2 + 9t = 0$

**11.** $x^2 - 25 = 0$

**12.** $p^2 - 49 = 0$

**13.** $z^2 = 144$

**14.** $y^2 = 64$

**15.** $y^2 + 2y = 63$

**16.** $a^2 + 3a = 40$

**17.** $32 + 4x - x^2 = 0$

**18.** $27 + 6t - t^2 = 0$

**19.** $3b^2 + 8b + 4 = 0$

**20.** $9y^2 + 15y + 4 = 0$

**21.** $8y^2 - 10y + 3 = 0$

**22.** $4x^2 + 11x + 6 = 0$

**23.** $6z - z^2 = 0$

**24.** $8y - y^2 = 0$

**25.** $12z^2 + z = 6$

**26.** $6x^2 - 7x = 10$

**27.** $7x^2 - 7 = 0$

**28.** $4y^2 - 36 = 0$

**29.** $10 - r - 21r^2 = 0$

**30.** $28 + 5a - 12a^2 = 0$

**31.** $15y^2 = 3y$

**32.** $18x^2 = 9x$

**33.** $14 = x(x - 5)$

**34.** $x(x - 5) = 24$

**35.** $2x^3 - 2x^2 = 12x$

**36.** $50y + 5y^3 = 35y^2$

**37.** $2x^3 = 128x$

**38.** $147y = 3y^3$

**39.** $t^4 - 26t^2 + 25 = 0$

**40.** $x^4 - 13x^2 + 36 = 0$

**41.** $(a - 4)(a + 4) = 20$

**42.** $(t - 6)(t + 6) = 45$

**43.** $x(5 + 12x) = 28$

**44.** $a(1 + 21a) = 10$

**45.** Given that $f(x) = x^2 + 12x + 40$, find all values of $x$ such that $f(x) = 8$.

**46.** Given that $f(x) = x^2 + 14x + 50$, find all values of $x$ such that $f(x) = 5$.

**47.** Given that $g(x) = 2x^2 + 5x$, find all values of $x$ such that $g(x) = 12$.

**48.** Given that $g(x) = 2x^2 - 15x$, find all values of $x$ such that $g(x) = -7$.

**49.** Given that $h(x) = 12x + x^2$, find all values of $x$ such that $h(x) = -27$.

**50.** Given that $h(x) = 4x - x^2$, find all values of $x$ such that $h(x) = -32$.

Find the domain of the function $f$ given by each of the following.

**51.** $f(x) = \dfrac{3}{x^2 - 4x - 5}$

**52.** $f(x) = \dfrac{2}{x^2 - 7x + 6}$

**53.** $f(x) = \dfrac{x}{6x^2 - 54}$

**54.** $f(x) = \dfrac{2x}{5x^2 - 20}$

**55.** $f(x) = \dfrac{x - 5}{25x^2 - 10x + 1}$

**56.** $f(x) = \dfrac{1 + x}{9x^2 + 30x + 25}$

**57.** $f(x) = \dfrac{7}{5x^3 - 35x^2 + 50x}$

**58.** $f(x) = \dfrac{3}{2x^3 - 2x^2 - 12x}$

In each of Exercises 59–62, an equation $ax^2 + bx + c = 0$ is given. Use *only* the graph of $f(x) = ax^2 + bx + c$ to find the $x$-intercepts of the graph and the solutions of the equation $ax^2 + bx + c = 0$.

**59.** $x^2 - 4x - 45 = 0$

**60.** $-x^2 - 3x + 40 = 0$

**61.** $32 + 4x - x^2 = 0$

**62.** $3x^2 - 12x = 0$

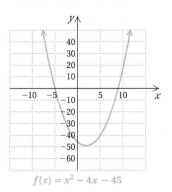

$f(x) = x^2 - 4x - 45$

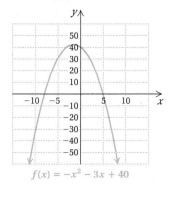

$f(x) = -x^2 - 3x + 40$

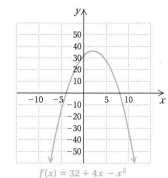

$f(x) = 32 + 4x - x^2$

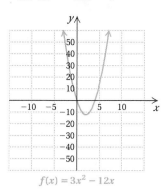

$f(x) = 3x^2 - 12x$

**b**    Solve.

**63.** *Book Area.*   A book is 5 cm longer than it is wide. The area is 84 cm$^2$. Find the length and the width.

**64.** *Area of an Envelope.*   An envelope is 4 cm longer than it is wide. The area is 96 cm$^2$. Find the length and the width.

**65.** *Tent Design.*   The triangular entrance to a tent is 2 ft taller than it is wide. The area of the entrance is 12 ft$^2$. Find the height and the base.

**66.** *Sailing.*   A triangular sail is 9 m taller than it is wide. The area is 56 m$^2$. Find the height and the base of the sail.

Area = 56 m$^2$

**67.** *Geometry.*   If each of the sides of a square is lengthened by 6 cm, the area becomes 144 cm$^2$. Find the length of a side of the original square.

**68.** *Geometry.*   If each of the sides of a square is lengthened by 4 m, the area becomes 49 m$^2$. Find the length of a side of the original square.

**69.** *Antenna Wires.*   A wire is stretched from the ground to the top of an antenna tower, as shown. The wire is 20 ft long. The height of the tower is 4 ft greater than the distance $d$ from the tower's base to the end of the wire. Find the distance $d$ and the height of the tower.

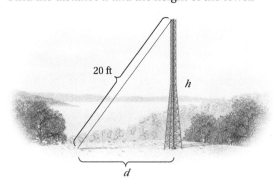

20 ft

$h$

$d$

**70.** *Ladder Location.*   The foot of an extension ladder is 9 ft from a wall. The height that the ladder reaches on the wall and the length of the ladder are consecutive integers. How long is the ladder?

9 ft

**71.** *Consecutive Even Integers.*   Three consecutive even integers are such that the square of the third is 76 more than the square of the second. Find the three integers.

**72.** *Consecutive Even Integers.*   Three consecutive even integers are such that the square of the first plus the square of the third is 136. Find the three integers.

**73.** *Workbench Design.* The length of the top of a workbench is 4 ft greater than the width. The area is 96 ft². Find the length and the width.

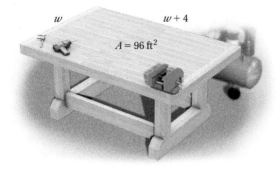

$w$   $w + 4$

$A = 96 \text{ ft}^2$

**74.** *Flower Bed Design.* A rectangular flower bed is to be 3 m longer than it is wide. The flower bed will have an area of 108 m². What will its dimensions be?

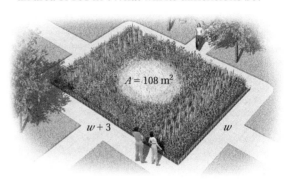

$A = 108 \text{ m}^2$

$w + 3$   $w$

**75.** *Framing a Picture.* A picture frame measures 12 cm by 20 cm, and 84 cm² of picture shows. Find the width of the frame.

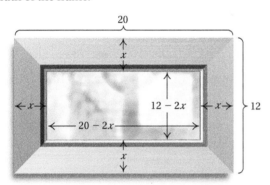

20

$x$

$12 - 2x$   $x$   12

$x$

$20 - 2x$

$x$

**76.** *Enclosure Dimensions.* The number of *square units* in the area of the square base of a walled enclosure is 12 more than the number of *units* in its perimeter. Find the length of a side.

**77.** *Parking Lot Design.* A rectangular parking lot is 50 ft longer than it is wide. Determine the dimensions of the parking lot if it measures 250 ft diagonally.

**78.** *Framing a Picture.* A picture frame measures 14 cm by 20 cm, and 160 cm² of picture shows. Find the width of the frame.

**79.** *Triangle Dimensions.* One leg of a right triangle has length 7 m. The other sides have lengths that are consecutive integers. Find these lengths.

**80.** *Triangle Dimensions.* One leg of a right triangle has length 10 cm. The other sides have lengths that are consecutive even integers. Find these lengths.

**81.** *Triangle Dimensions.* The lengths of the hypotenuse and one leg of a right triangle are consecutive integers. The length of the other leg is 7 ft. Find the missing lengths.

**82.** *Triangle Dimensions.* The lengths of the hypotenuse and one leg of a right triangle are consecutive odd integers. The length of the other leg is 8 ft. Find the missing lengths.

**83.** *Fireworks.* Suppose that a bottle rocket is launched upward with an initial velocity of 96 ft/sec and from a height of 880 ft. Its height $h$, in feet, after $t$ seconds is given by

$$h(t) = -16t^2 + 96t + 880.$$

After how long will the rocket reach the ground?

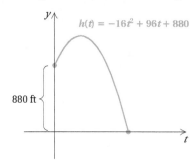

**84.** *Safety Flares.* Suppose that a flare is launched upward with an initial velocity of 80 ft/sec and from a height of 224 ft. Its height $h$, in feet, after $t$ seconds is given by

$$h(t) = -16t^2 + 80t + 224.$$

After how long will the flare reach the ground?

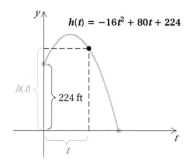

## Skill Maintenance

Find the distance between the given pair of points on the number line.　[1.6b]

**85.** $-3, 4$

**86.** $-3, -4$

**87.** $3, -4$

**88.** $-7.8, -10.3$

**89.** $3.6, 4.9$

**90.** $-\frac{3}{5}, \frac{2}{3}$

**91.** $-123, 568$

**92.** $0, -1023$

Find an equation of the line containing the given pair of points.　[2.6c]

**93.** $(-2, 7)$ and $(-8, -4)$

**94.** $(-2, 7)$ and $(8, -4)$

**95.** $(-2, 7)$ and $(8, 4)$

**96.** $(-24, 10)$ and $(-86, -42)$

## Synthesis

**97.** Following is the graph of $f(x) = -x^2 - 2x + 3$. Use *only* the graph to solve $-x^2 - 2x + 3 = 0$ and $-x^2 - 2x + 3 \geq -5$.

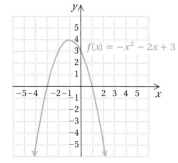

**98.** Following is the graph of $f(x) = x^4 - 3x^3$. Use *only* the graph to solve $x^4 - 3x^3 = 0$, $x^4 - 3x^3 \leq 0$, and $x^4 - 3x^3 > 0$.

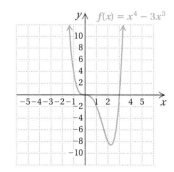

**99.** 📟 Use the TABLE feature of a graphing calculator to check that $-5$ and $3$ are not in the domain of $F$, as given in Example 7.

**100.** 📟 Use the TABLE feature of a graphing calculator to check your answers to Exercises 51, 54, and 57.

**101.** 📟 Use a graphing calculator to solve each equation.
  **a)** $x^4 - 3x^3 - x^2 + 5 = 0$
  **b)** $x^4 - 3x^3 - x^2 + 5 = 5$
  **c)** $x^4 - 3x^3 - x^2 + 5 = -8$
  **d)** $x^4 = 1 + 3x^3 + x^2$

**102.** Solve each of the following equations.
  **a)** $(8x + 11)(12x^2 - 5x - 2) = 0$
  **b)** $(3x^2 - 7x - 20)(x - 5) = 0$
  **c)** $3x^3 + 6x^2 - 27x - 54 = 0$
   (*Hint*: Factor by grouping.)
  **d)** $2x^3 + 6x^2 = 8x + 24$

# Summary and Review

## Key Terms, Properties, and Formulas

monomial, p. 324
polynomial, p. 325
term, p. 325
coefficient, p. 325
constant term, p. 325
degree of a term, p. 325
degree of a polynomial, p. 325
leading term, p. 325
leading coefficient, p. 325
binomial, p. 326
trinomial, p. 326

descending order, p. 326
ascending order, p. 326
like terms, p. 328
similar terms, p. 328
opposites, p. 329
additive inverses, p. 329
FOIL method, p. 338
square of a binomial, p. 340
difference of squares, p. 341
factor (verb), p. 347
factor (noun), p. 347

factorization, p. 347
prime polynomials, p. 348
*ac*-method, p. 366
grouping method, p. 366
trinomial square, p. 370
quadratic equation, p. 387
principle of zero products, p. 387
Pythagorean theorem, p. 393
right triangle, p. 393
hypotenuse, p. 393
legs, p. 393

*Factoring Formulas:* $A^2 - B^2 = (A + B)(A - B)$, $A^2 + 2AB + B^2 = (A + B)^2$, $A^2 - 2AB + B^2 = (A - B)^2$,
$A^3 + B^3 = (A + B)(A^2 - AB + B^2)$, $A^3 - B^3 = (A - B)(A^2 + AB + B^2)$

*The Principle of
Zero Products:* For any real numbers $a$ and $b$: If $ab = 0$, then $a = 0$ or $b = 0$. If $a = 0$ or $b = 0$, then $ab = 0$.

## Concept Reinforcement

Determine whether each statement is true or false.

_____ **1.** According to the principle of zero products, if $ab = 0$, then $a = 0$ and $b = 0$. [4.8a]

_____ **2.** The binomial $27 - t^3$ is a difference of cubes. [4.6d]

_____ **3.** The expression $5x^2 - 6y^{-1}$ is a binomial. [4.1a]

## Important Concepts

**Objective 4.1a** Identify the degree of each term and the degree of a polynomial; identify terms, coefficients, monomials, binomials, and trinomials; arrange polynomials in ascending order or descending order; and identify the leading term, the leading coefficient, and the constant term.

**Example** Identify the terms, the degree of each term, and the degree of the polynomial. Then identify the leading term, the leading coefficient, and the constant term:

$$-x^5 + 3x^4 - 7x^3 - 2x^2 + x - 10.$$

Terms:                      $-x^5, 3x^4, -7x^3, -2x^2, x, -10$

Degree of each term:    5, 4, 3, 2, 1, 0

Degree of polynomial:   5        Leading term:    $-x^5$

Leading coefficient:      $-1$     Constant term:  $-10$

**Example** Arrange in descending order and then in ascending order: $y - 3y^3 + 7y^2 - 4 + 16y^4$.

Descending:  $16y^4 - 3y^3 + 7y^2 + y - 4$

Ascending:     $-4 + y + 7y^2 - 3y^3 + 16y^4$

**Practice Exercises**

**1.** Identify the terms, the degree of each term, and the degree of the polynomial. Then identify the leading term, the leading coefficient, and the constant term:

$$-6x^4 + 5x^3 - x^2 + 10x - 1.$$

**2.** Arrange in descending order and then in ascending order:

$$8x^2 - 7 + 2x^3 - x^4 - 3x.$$

**Objective 4.1d**    Find the opposite of a polynomial and subtract polynomials.

**Example**    Subtract: $(4t^2 - t - t^3) - (7t^2 - t^3 - 5t)$.

$$(4t^2 - t - t^3) - (7t^2 - t^3 - 5t)$$
$$= (4t^2 - t - t^3) + (-7t^2 + t^3 + 5t)$$
$$= 4t^2 - t - t^3 - 7t^2 + t^3 + 5t$$
$$= -3t^2 + 4t$$

**Practice Exercise**

3. Subtract:
$$(3y^2 - 6y^3 + 7y) - (y^2 - 10y - 8y^3 + 8).$$

---

**Objective 4.2b**    Use the FOIL method to multiply two binomials.

**Example**    Multiply: $(7a - b)(4a + 9b)$.

$$\qquad\qquad\qquad\quad \text{F}\qquad\text{O}\qquad\text{I}\qquad\text{L}$$
$$(7a - b)(4a + 9b) = 28a^2 + 63ab - 4ab - 9b^2$$
$$= 28a^2 + 59ab - 9b^2$$

**Practice Exercise**

4. Multiply: $(3x - 5y)(x + 2y)$.

---

**Objective 4.2c**    Use a rule to square a binomial.

**Example**    Multiply: $(3q - 4)^2$.

$$(A - B)^2 = A^2 - 2AB + B^2$$
$$(3q - 4)^2 = (3q)^2 - 2(3q)(4) + 4^2$$
$$= 9q^2 - 24q + 16$$

**Practice Exercise**

5. Multiply: $(2y + 7)^2$.

---

**Objective 4.2d**    Use a rule to multiply a sum and a difference of the same two terms.

**Example**    Multiply: $(8x + 5)(8x - 5)$.

$$(A + B)(A - B) = A^2 - B^2$$
$$(8x + 5)(8x - 5) = (8x)^2 - 5^2$$
$$= 64x^2 - 25$$

**Practice Exercise**

6. Multiply: $(5d + 10)(5d - 10)$.

---

**Objective 4.2e**    For functions $f$ described by second-degree polynomials, find and simplify notation like $f(a + h)$ and $f(a + h) - f(a)$.

**Example**    Given $f(x) = 2x - x^2$, find $f(x - 1)$ and $f(a + h) - f(a)$.

$$f(x - 1) = 2(x - 1) - (x - 1)^2 = 2(x - 1) - (x^2 - 2x + 1)$$
$$= 2x - 2 - x^2 + 2x - 1 = -x^2 + 4x - 3;$$
$$f(a + h) - f(a) = [2(a + h) - (a + h)^2] - [2a - a^2]$$
$$= [2(a + h) - (a^2 + 2ah + h^2)] - [2a - a^2]$$
$$= 2a + 2h - a^2 - 2ah - h^2 - 2a + a^2$$
$$= -h^2 - 2ah + 2h$$

**Practice Exercise**

7. Given $f(x) = 3x^2 - x + 2$, find $f(x + 1)$ and $f(a + h) - f(a)$.

---

**Objective 4.3b**    Factor certain polynomials with four terms by grouping.

**Example**    Factor: $x^3 - 6x^2 + 3x - 18$.

$$x^3 - 6x^2 + 3x - 18 = (x^3 - 6x^2) + (3x - 18)$$
$$= x^2(x - 6) + 3(x - 6)$$
$$= (x - 6)(x^2 + 3)$$

**Practice Exercise**

9. Factor: $y^3 + 3y^2 - 8y - 24$.

---

**Objective 4.5a** Factor trinomials of the type $ax^2 + bx + c, a \neq 1$, by the FOIL method.

**Example** Factor $15x^2 - 4x - 3$ by the FOIL method.

The terms of $15x^2 - 4x - 3$ do not have a common factor. We factor the first term, $15x^2$, and get $15x \cdot x$ and $5x \cdot 3x$. We then have

$$(15x + \Box)(x + \Box) \quad \text{and} \quad (5x + \Box)(3x + \Box)$$

as possible factorizations. We then factor the last term, $-3$. The possibilities are $(-3)(1)$ and $(3)(-1)$. We look for combinations of factors such that the sum of the outside product and the inside product is the middle term, $-4x$.

$(15x - 3)(x + 1)$;    $(5x - 3)(3x + 1)$; $\rightarrow$ Correct middle
                                                                term, $-4x$

$(15x + 3)(x - 1)$;    $(5x + 3)(3x - 1)$;
$(15x + 1)(x - 3)$;    $(5x + 1)(3x - 3)$;
$(15x - 1)(x + 3)$;    $(5x - 1)(3x + 3)$

Thus, $15x^2 - 4x - 3 = (5x - 3)(3x + 1)$.

**Practice Exercise**

**10.** Factor $3x^2 + 19x - 72$ by the FOIL method.

---

**Objective 4.5b** Factor trinomials of the type $ax^2 + bx + c, a \neq 1$, by the $ac$-method.

**Example** Factor $6x^2 - 19x - 36$ by the $ac$-method.

Note that there are no common factors. We multiply the leading coefficient, 6, and the constant, $-36$: $6(-36) = -216$. Next, we try to factor $-216$ so that the sum of the factors is $-19$. Since $-19$ is negative, the negative factor of $-216$ must have the larger absolute value.

| PAIRS OF FACTORS | SUM | PAIRS OF FACTORS | SUM |
|---|---|---|---|
| 1, $-216$ | $-215$ | 6, $-36$ | $-30$ |
| 2, $-108$ | $-106$ | 8, $-27$ | $-19$ |
| 3, $-72$ | $-69$ | 9, $-24$ | $-15$ |
| 4, $-54$ | $-50$ | 12, $-18$ | $-6$ |

Next, we split the middle term using the factors 8 and $-27$:

$$6x^2 - 19x - 36 = 6x^2 + 8x - 27x - 36$$
$$= 2x(3x + 4) - 9(3x + 4)$$
$$= (3x + 4)(2x - 9).$$

**Practice Exercise**

**11.** Factor $10x^2 - 33x - 7$ by the $ac$-method.

---

**Objective 4.6a** Factor trinomial squares.

**Example** Factor: $4x^2 - 44x + 121$.

$A^2 - 2AB + B^2 = (A - B)^2$

$4x^2 - 44x + 121 = (2x)^2 - 44x + 11^2 = (2x - 11)^2$

**Practice Exercise**

**12.** Factor: $81x^2 - 72x + 16$.

---

**Objective 4.6b** Factor differences of squares.

**Example** Factor: $64y^2 - 9$.

$A^2 - B^2 = (A + B)(A - B)$

$64y^2 - 9 = (8y)^2 - 3^2 = (8y + 3)(8y - 3)$

**Practice Exercise**

**13.** Factor: $100t^2 - 1$.

**Objective 4.6d**  Factor sums and differences of cubes.

**Example**  Factor: $8w^3 + 125$.

$A^3 + B^3 = (A + B)(A^2 - AB + B^2)$

$8w^3 + 125 = (2w)^3 + 5^3 = (2w + 5)(4w^2 - 10w + 25)$

**Example**  Factor: $125x^3 - 8$.

$A^3 - B^3 = (A - B)(A^2 + AB + B^2)$

$125x^3 - 8 = (5x)^3 - 2^3 = (5x - 2)(25x^2 + 10x + 4)$

**Practice Exercises**

**14.** Factor: $216x^3 + 1$.

**15.** Factor: $1000y^3 - 27$.

---

**Objective 4.8a**  Solve quadratic and other polynomial equations by first factoring and then using the principle of zero products.

**Example**  Solve: $5x^2 + 11x = 12$.

$5x^2 + 11x - 12 = 0$     Getting 0 on one side

$(5x - 4)(x + 3) = 0$     Factoring

$5x - 4 = 0$  *or*  $x + 3 = 0$     Using the principle of zero products

$5x = 4$  *or*  $x = -3$

$x = \frac{4}{5}$  *or*  $x = -3$

The solutions are $-3$ and $\frac{4}{5}$.

**Practice Exercise**

**16.** Solve: $3x^2 - x = 14$.

---

## Review Exercises

**1.** Given the polynomial  [4.1a]

$3x^6y - 7x^8y^3 + 2x^3 - 3x^2$:

**a)** Identify the degree of each term and the degree of the polynomial.

**b)** Identify the leading term and the leading coefficient.

**c)** Arrange in ascending powers of $x$.

**d)** Arrange in descending powers of $y$.

Evaluate the polynomial function for the given values.
[4.1b]

**2.** $P(x) = x^3 - x^2 + 4x$;  $P(0)$ and $P(-1)$

**3.** $P(x) = 4 - 2x - x^2$;  $P(-2)$ and $P(5)$

Collect like terms.  [4.1c]

**4.** $8x + 13y - 15x + 10y$

**5.** $3ab - 10 + 5ab^2 - 2ab + 7ab^2 + 14$

**6.** *Emergency-Room Visits.*  The number $E$, in thousands, of hospital emergency-room visits involving narcotic painkillers can be estimated by the polynomial function given by

$E(t) = 1.55t^2 + 2.71t + 47.04$,

where $t$ is the number of years since 1996.  [4.1b]

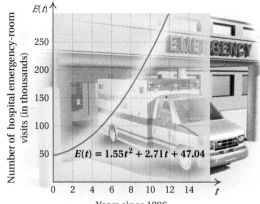

Years since 1996

SOURCE: Data from Substance Abuse and Mental Health Services Administration, Drug Abuse Warning Network

**a)** Use this graph to predict the number of hospital emergency visits involving narcotic painkillers in 2006.

**b)** Use the function to predict the number of hospital emergency visits involving narcotic painkillers in 2010.

Add, subtract, or multiply.   [4.1c, d], [4.2a, b, c, d]

**7.** $(-6x^3 - 4x^2 + 3x + 1) + (5x^3 + 2x + 6x^2 + 1)$

**8.** $(4x^3 - 2x^2 - 7x + 5) + (8x^2 - 3x^3 - 9 + 6x)$

**9.** $(-9xy^2 - xy + 6x^2y) + (-5x^2y - xy + 4xy^2) + (12x^2y - 3xy^2 + 6xy)$

**10.** $(3x - 5) - (-6x + 2)$

**11.** $(4a - b + 3c) - (6a - 7b - 4c)$

**12.** $(9p^2 - 4p + 4) - (-7p^2 + 4p + 4)$

**13.** $(6x^2 - 4xy + y^2) - (2x^2 + 3xy - 2y^2)$

**14.** $(3x^2y)(-6xy^3)$

**15.** $(x^4 - 2x^2 + 3)(x^4 + x^2 - 1)$

**16.** $(4ab + 3c)(2ab - c)$

**17.** $(2x + 5y)(2x - 5y)$

**18.** $(2x - 5y)^2$

**19.** $(5x^2 - 7x + 3)(4x^2 + 2x - 9)$

**20.** $(x^2 + 4y^3)^2$

**21.** $(x - 5)(x^2 + 5x + 25)$

**22.** $\left(x - \frac{1}{3}\right)\left(x - \frac{1}{6}\right)$

**23.** Given that $f(x) = x^2 - 2x - 7$, find and simplify $f(a - 1)$ and $f(a + h) - f(a)$.   [4.2e]

Factor.   [4.3a, b], [4.4a], [4.5a, b], [4.6a, b, c, d], [4.7a]

**24.** $9y^4 - 3y^2$

**25.** $15x^4 - 18x^3 + 21x^2 - 9x$

**26.** $a^2 - 12a + 27$

**27.** $3m^2 + 14m + 8$

**28.** $25x^2 + 20x + 4$

**29.** $4y^2 - 16$

**30.** $ax + 2bx - ay - 2by$

**31.** $4x^4 + 4x^2 + 20$

**32.** $27x^3 - 8$

**33.** $0.064b^3 - 0.125c^3$

**34.** $y^5 - y$      **35.** $2z^8 - 16z^6$

**36.** $54x^6y - 2y$      **37.** $1 + a^3$

**38.** $36x^2 - 120x + 100$      **39.** $6t^2 + 17pt + 5p^2$

**40.** $x^3 + 2x^2 - 9x - 18$      **41.** $a^2 - 2ab + b^2 - 4t^2$

Solve.   [4.8a]

**42.** $x^2 - 20x = -100$      **43.** $6b^2 - 13b + 6 = 0$

**44.** $8y^2 = 14y$      **45.** $r^2 = 16$

**46.** Given that $f(x) = x^2 - 7x - 40$, find all values of $x$ such that $f(x) = 4$.   [4.8a]

**47.** Find the domain of the function $f$ given by

$$f(x) = \frac{x - 3}{3x^2 + 19x - 14}.   \text{[4.8a]}$$

Solve.  [4.8b]

**48.** *Photograph Dimensions.*  A photograph is 3 in. longer than it is wide. When a 2-in. matte border is placed around the photograph, the total area of the photograph and the border is 108 in². Find the dimensions of the photograph.

**49.** The sum of the squares of three consecutive odd integers is 83. Find the integers.

**50.** *Area.*  The number of *square units* in the area of a square is 7 more than six times the number of *units* in the length of a side. What is the length of a side of the square?

**51.** Which of the following is a factor of $t^3 - 64$?  [4.6d]
  **A.** $t - 4$            **B.** $t^2 - 4t + 16$
  **C.** $t^2 + 8t + 16$    **D.** $t + 4$

**52.** Which of the following is a factor of
$$hm + 5hn - gm - 5gn?$$  [4.3b]
  **A.** $m - n$            **B.** $h + g$
  **C.** $m + 5n$           **D.** $m - 5n$

## Synthesis

Factor.  [4.6d]

**53.** $128x^6 - 2y^6$

**54.** $(x + 1)^3 - (x - 1)^3$

**55.** Multiply: $[a - (b - 1)][(b - 1)^2 + a(b - 1) + a^2]$.
  [4.6d]

**56.** Solve: $64x^3 = x$.  [4.8a]

# Understanding Through Discussion and Writing

**1.** Under what conditions, if any, can the sum of two squares be factored? Explain.  [4.3a], [4.6b]

**2.** Explain how to use the *ac*-method to factor trinomials of the type $ax^2 + bx + c, a \neq 1$.  [4.5b]

**3.** Annie claims that she can add any two polynomials but finds subtraction difficult. What advice would you offer her?  [4.1d]

**4.** Suppose that you are given a detailed graph of $y = P(x)$, where $P(x)$ is a polynomial. How could you use the graph to solve the equation $P(x) = 0$? $P(x) = 4$?  [4.8a]

**5.** Explain how you could use factoring or graphing to explain why $x^3 - 8 \neq (x - 2)^3$.  [4.6d]

**6.** Emily has factored a particular polynomial as $(a - b)(x - y)$. George factors the same polynomial and gets $(b - a)(y - x)$. Who is correct and why?  [4.3a], [4.7a]

**7.** Explain how one could write a quadratic equation that has 5 and $-3$ as solutions. Can the number of solutions of a quadratic equation exceed two? Why or why not?  [4.8a]

**8.** In this chapter, we learned to solve equations that we could not have solved before. Describe these new equations and the way we go about solving them. How is the procedure different from those we have used before now?  [4.8a]

Test

For Extra Help

CHAPTER
Test Prep
VIDEOS

Step-by-step test solutions are found on the Chapter Test Prep Videos available via the Video Resources on DVD, in *MyMathLab*, and on You Tube (search "BittingerInterAlgPB" and click on "Channels").

**1.** Given the polynomial
$$3xy^3 - 4x^2y + 5x^5y^4 - 2x^4y:$$

  **a)** Identify the degree of each term and the degree of the polynomial.

  **b)** Identify the leading term and the leading coefficient.

  **c)** Arrange in ascending powers of $x$.

  **d)** Arrange in descending powers of $y$.

**2.** Given that $P(x) = 2x^3 + 3x^2 - x + 4$, find $P(0)$ and $P(-2)$.

**3.** *Video-Game Sales.* Projected sales $S$ of video games, in billions of dollars, can be estimated by the polynomial function given by
$$S(t) = 0.0496t^4 - 0.6705t^3 + 2.6367t^2 - 2.3880t + 1.6123,$$
  where $t$ is the number of years since 2004.

**Source:** Jupiter Research

  **a)** Use the graph to predict the sales of video games, in billions of dollars, in 2010.

  **b)** Use the function to predict the sales of video games, in billions of dollars, in 2009.

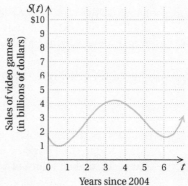

$S(t) = 0.0496t^4 - 0.6705t^3 + 2.6367t^2 - 2.3880t + 1.6123$

**4.** Collect like terms: $5xy - 2xy^2 - 2xy + 5xy^2$.

Add, subtract, or multiply.

**5.** $(-6x^3 + 3x^2 - 4y) + (3x^3 - 2y - 7y^2)$

**6.** $(4a^3 - 2a^2 + 6a - 5) + (3a^3 - 3a + 2 - 4a^2)$

**7.** $(5m^3 - 4m^2n - 6mn^2 - 3n^3) +$ $(9mn^2 - 4n^3 + 2m^3 + 6m^2n)$

**8.** $(9a - 4b) - (3a + 4b)$

**9.** $(4x^2 - 3x + 7) - (-3x^2 + 4x - 6)$

**10.** $(6y^2 - 2y - 5y^3) - (4y^2 - 7y - 6y^3)$

**11.** $(-4x^2y)(-16xy^2)$

**12.** $(6a - 5b)(2a + b)$

**13.** $(x - y)(x^2 - xy - y^2)$

**14.** $(3m^2 + 4m - 2)(-m^2 - 3m + 5)$

**15.** $(4y - 9)^2$

**16.** $(x - 2y)(x + 2y)$

**17.** Given that $f(x) = x^2 - 5x$, find and simplify $f(a + 10)$ and $f(a + h) - f(a)$.

Factor.

**18.** $9x^2 + 7x$

**19.** $24y^3 + 16y^2$

**20.** $y^3 + 5y^2 - 4y - 20$

**21.** $p^2 - 12p - 28$

**22.** $12m^2 + 20m + 3$

**23.** $9y^2 - 25$

**24.** $3r^3 - 3$

**25.** $9x^2 + 25 - 30x$

**26.** $(z + 1)^2 - b^2$

**27.** $x^8 - y^8$

**28.** $y^2 + 8y + 16 - 100t^2$

**29.** $20a^2 - 5b^2$

**30.** $24x^2 - 46x + 10$

**31.** $16a^7b + 54ab^7$

Solve.

**32.** $x^2 - 18 = 3x$

**33.** $5y^2 - 125 = 0$

**34.** $2x^2 + 21 = -17x$

**35.** Given that $f(x) = 3x^2 - 15x + 11$, find all values of $x$ such that $f(x) = 11$.

**36.** Find the domain of the function $f$ given by
$$f(x) = \frac{3 - x}{x^2 + 2x + 1}.$$

Solve.

**37.** *Photograph Dimensions.* A photograph is 3 cm longer than it is wide. Its area is 40 cm$^2$. Find its length and its width.

**38.** *Ladder Location.* The foot of an extension ladder is 10 ft from a wall. The ladder is 2 ft longer than the distance that it reaches up the wall. How far up the wall does the ladder reach?

**39.** *Area.* The number of *square units* in the area of a square is 5 more than four times the number of *units* in the length of a side. What is the length of a side of the square?

**40.** *Number of Games in a League.* If there are $n$ teams in a league and each team plays every other team once, the total number of games played is given by the polynomial function $f(n) = \frac{1}{2}n^2 - \frac{1}{2}n$. Find an equivalent expression for $f(n)$ by factoring completely.

**41.** Factor: $8x^3 - 1$.
   **A.** $(2x - 1)(2x - 1)(2x - 1)$
   **B.** $(2x - 1)(2x + 1)$
   **C.** $(2x - 1)(4x^2 + 2x + 1)$
   **D.** $(2x + 1)(4x^2 - 2x + 1)$

## Synthesis

**42.** Factor: $6x^{2n} - 7x^n - 20$.

**43.** If $pq = 5$ and $(p + q)^2 = 29$, find the value of $p^2 + q^2$.

# Cumulative Review

Simplify.

**1.** $(x^2 + 4x - xy - 9) + (-3x^2 - 3x + 8)$

**2.** $(6x^2 - 3x + 2x^3) - (8x^2 - 9x + 2x^3)$

**3.** $(a^2 - a - 3) \cdot (a^2 + 2a - 3)$

**4.** $(x + 4)(x + 9)$

Solve.

**5.** $8 - 3x = 6x - 10$

**6.** $\frac{1}{2}x - 3 = \frac{7}{2}$

**7.** $A = \frac{1}{2}h(a + b)$, for $b$

**8.** $6x - 1 \leq 3(5x + 2)$

**9.** $4x - 3 < 2$ or $x - 3 > 1$

**10.** $|2x - 3| < 7$

**11.** $x + y + z = -5$,
$x - z = 10$,
$y - z = 12$

**12.** $2x + 5y = -2$,
$5x + 3y = 14$

**13.** $3x - y = 7$,
$2x + 2y = 5$

**14.** $x + 2y - z = 0$,
$3x + y - 2z = -1$,
$x - 4y + z = -2$

**15.** $11x + x^2 + 24 = 0$

**16.** $2x^2 - 15x = -7$

**17.** Given that $f(x) = 3x^2 + 4x$, find all values of $x$ such that $f(x) = 4$.

**18.** Find the domain of the function $F$ given by
$$F(x) = \frac{x + 7}{x^2 - 2x - 15}.$$

Factor.

**19.** $3x^3 - 12x^2$

**20.** $2x^4 + x^3 + 2x + 1$

**21.** $x^2 + 5x - 14$

**22.** $20a^2 - 23a + 6$

**23.** $4x^2 - 25$

**24.** $2x^2 - 28x + 98$

**25.** $a^3 + 64$

**26.** $64x^3 - 1$

**27.** $4a^3 + a^6 - 12$

**28.** $4x^4y^2 - x^2y^4$

**29.** *Producing Bearings.* A factory has three bearing presses, A, B, and C. When all three of them are working, 5700 bearings can be made in one week. When only A and B are working, 3400 bearings can be made in one week. When only B and C are working, 4200 can be made in one week. How many bearings can be made in a week by each machine?

Graph.

**30.** $x < 1$ *or* $x \geq 2$

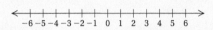

**31.** $y = -2x$　　　　**32.** $6y + 24 = 0$

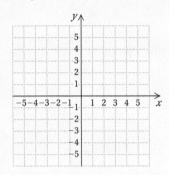

**33.** $y > x + 6$　　　　**34.** $f(x) = x^2 - 3$

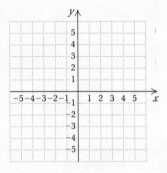

**35.** $g(x) = 4 - |x|$

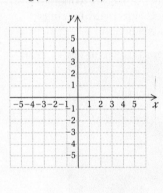

**36.** $2x + 3y \leq 6$,
$5x - 5y \leq 15$,
$x \geq 0$
Label the vertices.

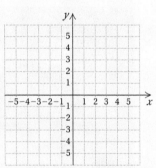

**37.** Find an equation of the line containing the point $(3, 7)$ and parallel to the line $x + 2y = 6$.

**38.** Find an equation of the line containing the point $(3, -2)$ and perpendicular to the line $3x + 4y = 5$.

**39.** Find an equation of the line containing the points $(-1, 4)$ and $(-2, 0)$.

**40.** Find an equation of the line with slope $-3$ and through the point $(2, 1)$.

**41.** *Wild Horses.* The federal government rounds up wild horses and puts them in holding facilities while offering them for adoption to horse lovers who agree not to sell them for slaughter. In 2001, there were 9807 wild horses in holding facilities. This number increased to 30,088 in 2008. Find the rate of change of the number of wild horses in holding facilities with respect to time, in years.

Source: *Washington Post*, "A Dramatic Rescue for Doomed Wild Horses of the West," by Lyndsey Layton, November 18, 2008, p. A01.

**42.** *Games in a Sports League.* In a sports league of $n$ teams in which each team plays every other team twice, the total number $N$ of games to be played is given by the function

$$N(n) = n^2 - n.$$

**a)** A women's college volleyball league has 6 teams. If we assume that each team plays every other team twice, what is the total number of games to be played?

**b)** Another volleyball league plays a total of 72 games. If we assume that each team plays every other team twice, how many teams are in the league?

**43.** *Display of a Sports Card.* A valuable sports card is 4 cm wide and 5 cm long. The card is to be sandwiched by two pieces of Lucite, each of which is $5\frac{1}{2}$ times the area of the card. Determine the dimensions of the Lucite that will ensure a uniform border.

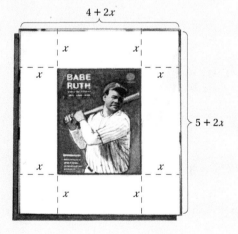

## Synthesis

**44.** Solve: $|x + 1| \leq |x - 3|$.

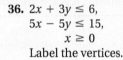

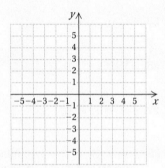

Copyright © 2011 Pearson Education, Inc.

# Rational Expressions, Equations, and Functions

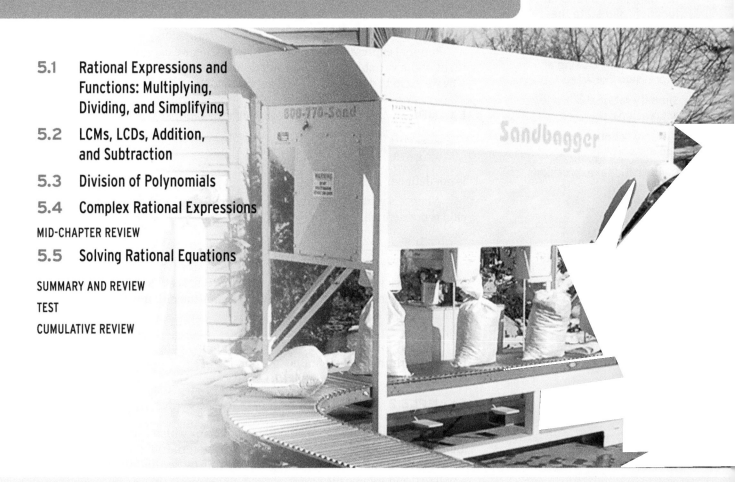

## Real-World Application

The Sandbagger Corporation sells machines that fill sandbags at a job site. The Sandbagger™ can fill an order of 8000 sandbags in 5 hr. The MultiBagger™ can fill the same order in 8 hr. Using both machines together, how long would it take to fill an order of 8000 sandbags?

*Source:* The Sandbagger Corporation

*This problem appears as Example 1 in Section 5.6.*

# Rational Expressions and Functions: Multiplying, Dividing, and Simplifying

## OBJECTIVES

**a** Find all numbers for which a rational expression is not defined or that are not in the domain of a rational function, and state the domain of the function.

**b** Multiply a rational expression by 1, using an expression like $A/A$.

**c** Simplify rational expressions.

**d** Multiply rational expressions and simplify.

**e** Divide rational expressions and simplify.

**SKILL TO REVIEW**

Objective 2.3a: Find the domain and the range of a function.

Find the domain.

**1.** $f(x) = 3x + 7$

**2.** $f(x) = \dfrac{x - 7}{2x + 3}$

## **a** Rational Expressions and Functions

An expression that consists of the quotient of two polynomials, where the polynomial in the denominator is nonzero, is called a **rational expression**. The following are examples of rational expressions:

$$\frac{7}{8}, \quad \frac{z}{-6}, \quad \frac{a}{b}, \quad \frac{8}{y + 5}, \quad \frac{t^4 - 5t}{t^2 - 3t - 28}, \quad \frac{x^2 + 7xy - 4}{x^3 - y^3}.$$

Note that every rational number is a rational expression.

Rational expressions indicate division. Thus we cannot make a replacement of the variable that allows a denominator to be 0. (For a discussion of why we exclude division by 0, see Section R.2.)

**EXAMPLE 1** Find all numbers for which the rational expression

$$\frac{2x + 1}{x - 3}$$

is not defined.

When $x$ is replaced with 3, the denominator is 0, and the rational expression is not defined:

$$\frac{2x + 1}{x - 3} = \frac{2 \cdot 3 + 1}{3 - 3} = \frac{7}{0}. \leftarrow \text{Division by 0 is not defined.}$$

You can check some replacements other than 3 to see that it appears that 3 is the only replacement that is not allowable. Thus the rational expression is not defined for the number 3.

You may have noticed that the procedure in Example 1 is similar to one we have performed when finding the domain of a function.

**EXAMPLE 2** Find the domain of $f$ if $f(x) = \dfrac{2x + 1}{x - 3}$.

The domain is the set of all replacements for which the rational expression is defined (see Section 2.3). We begin by determining the replacements that make the denominator 0. We can do this by setting the denominator equal to 0 and solving for $x$:

$$x - 3 = 0$$
$$x = 3.$$

The domain of $f$ is $\{x | x \text{ is a real number } and\ x \neq 3\}$, or, in interval notation, $(-\infty, 3) \cup (3, \infty)$.

*Answers*

Do Exercises 1 and 2.

## ✖ Algebraic-Graphical Connection

Let's make a visual check of Example 2 by looking at the following graph.

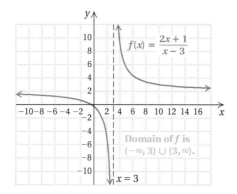

Note that the graph consists of two unconnected "branches." If a vertical line were drawn at $x = 3$, shown dashed here, it would not touch the graph of $f$. Thus 3 is not in the domain of $f$.

---

**EXAMPLE 3** Find all numbers for which the rational expression

$$\frac{t^4 - 5t}{t^2 - 3t - 28}$$

is not defined.

The rational expression is not defined for a replacement that makes the denominator 0. To determine those replacements to exclude, we set the denominator equal to 0 and solve:

| | |
|---|---|
| $t^2 - 3t - 28 = 0$ | Setting the denominator equal to 0 |
| $(t - 7)(t + 4) = 0$ | Factoring |
| $t - 7 = 0 \quad or \quad t + 4 = 0$ | Using the principle of zero products |
| $t = 7 \quad or \qquad t = -4.$ | |

Thus the expression is not defined for the replacements 7 and $-4$.

**EXAMPLE 4** Find the domain of $g$ if

$$g(t) = \frac{t^4 - 5t}{t^2 - 3t - 28}.$$

We proceed as we did in Example 3. The expression is not defined for the replacements 7 and $-4$. Thus the domain is $\{t \mid t$ is a real number $and\ t \neq 7$ $and\ t \neq -4\}$, or, in interval notation, $(-\infty, -4) \cup (-4, 7) \cup (7, \infty)$.

Do Exercises 3 and 4.

**1.** Find all numbers for which the rational expression
$$\frac{x^2 - 4x + 9}{2x + 5}$$
is not defined.

**2.** Find the domain of $f$ if
$$f(x) = \frac{x^2 - 4x + 9}{2x + 5}.$$
Write both set-builder notation and interval notation for the answer.

**3.** Find all numbers for which the rational expression
$$\frac{t^2 - 9}{t^2 - 7t + 10}$$
is not defined.

**4.** Find the domain of $g$ if
$$g(t) = \frac{t^2 - 9}{t^2 - 7t + 10}.$$
Write both set-builder notation and interval notation for the answer.

*Answers*

**1.** $-\dfrac{5}{2}$

**2.** $\left\{ x \mid x \text{ is a real number } and\ x \neq -\dfrac{5}{2} \right\}$,
or $\left( -\infty, -\dfrac{5}{2} \right) \cup \left( -\dfrac{5}{2}, \infty \right)$

**3.** $2, 5$

**4.** $\{t \mid t \text{ is a real number } and\ t \neq 2 \ and\ t \neq 5\}$,
or $(-\infty, 2) \cup (2, 5) \cup (5, \infty)$

## b Finding Equivalent Rational Expressions

Calculations with rational expressions are similar to those with rational numbers.

---

**MULTIPLYING RATIONAL EXPRESSIONS**

To multiply rational expressions, multiply numerators and multiply denominators:

$$\frac{A}{B} \cdot \frac{C}{D} = \frac{AC}{BD}.$$

---

For example, we have the following:

$$\frac{3}{5} \cdot \frac{2}{7} = \frac{3 \cdot 2}{5 \cdot 7} = \frac{6}{35}, \qquad \frac{3x}{4} \cdot \frac{5x}{7} = \frac{(3x)(5x)}{4 \cdot 7} = \frac{15x^2}{28},$$

and $\dfrac{x+3}{y-4} \cdot \dfrac{x^3}{y+5} = \dfrac{(x+3)x^3}{(y-4)(y+5)}.$    Multiplying numerators and multiplying denominators

For purposes of our work in this chapter, it is better in the example above to leave the numerator $(x+3)x^3$ and the denominator $(y-4)(y+5)$ in factored form because it is easier to simplify if we do not multiply.

Before discussing simplifying rational expressions, we first consider multiplying by 1.

---

Any rational expression with the same numerator and denominator is a symbol for 1:

$$\frac{73}{73} = 1, \qquad \frac{x-y}{x-y} = 1, \qquad \frac{4x^2 - 5}{4x^2 - 5} = 1, \qquad \frac{-1}{-1} = 1, \qquad \frac{x+5}{x+5} = 1.$$

---

We can multiply by 1 to get equivalent expressions—for example,

$$\frac{7}{9} \cdot \frac{4}{4} = \frac{7 \cdot 4}{9 \cdot 4} = \frac{28}{36} \quad \text{and} \quad \frac{5}{6} \cdot \frac{x}{x} = \frac{5 \cdot x}{6 \cdot x} = \frac{5x}{6x}.$$

As another example, let's multiply $(x + y)/5$ by 1, using the symbol $(x - y)/(x - y)$:

$$\frac{x+y}{5} \cdot \frac{x-y}{x-y} = \frac{(x+y)(x-y)}{5(x-y)}. \qquad \text{Multiplying by } \frac{x-y}{x-y}, \text{ which is 1}$$

We know that the expressions

$$\frac{x+y}{5} \quad \text{and} \quad \frac{(x+y)(x-y)}{5(x-y)}$$

are equivalent. This means that they will name the same number for all replacements that do not make a denominator 0.

**EXAMPLES** Multiply to obtain an equivalent expression.

**5.** $\dfrac{x^2+3}{x-1}\cdot 1 = \dfrac{x^2+3}{x-1}\cdot\dfrac{x+1}{x+1} = \dfrac{(x^2+3)(x+1)}{(x-1)(x+1)}$  Using $\dfrac{x+1}{x+1}$ for 1

**6.** $1\cdot\dfrac{x-4}{x-y} = \dfrac{-1}{-1}\cdot\dfrac{x-4}{x-y} = \dfrac{-1\cdot(x-4)}{-1\cdot(x-y)}$  Using $\dfrac{-1}{-1}$ for 1

$$= \dfrac{-x+4}{-x+y} = \dfrac{4-x}{y-x}$$

Do Exercises 5–7.

Multiply.

**5.** $\dfrac{3x+2y}{5x+4y}\cdot\dfrac{x}{x}$

**6.** $\dfrac{2x^2-y}{3x+4}\cdot\dfrac{3x+2}{3x+2}$

**7.** $\dfrac{-1}{-1}\cdot\dfrac{2a-5}{a-b}$

## (c) Simplifying Rational Expressions

We simplify rational expressions using the identity property of 1 (see Section R.5b) in reverse. That is, we "remove" factors that are equal to 1. We first factor the numerator and the denominator and then factor the rational expression, so that a factor is equal to 1. We also say, accordingly, that we "remove a factor of 1."

**EXAMPLE 7** Simplify: $\dfrac{120}{320}$.

$$\dfrac{120}{320} = \dfrac{40\cdot 3}{40\cdot 8}$$  Factoring the numerator and the denominator, looking for common factors

$$= \dfrac{40}{40}\cdot\dfrac{3}{8}$$  Factoring the rational expression; $\dfrac{40}{40}$ is a factor of 1

$$= 1\cdot\dfrac{3}{8} \qquad \dfrac{40}{40} = 1$$

$$= \dfrac{3}{8}$$  Removing a factor of 1

Do Exercise 8.

**8.** Simplify: $\dfrac{128}{160}$.

**EXAMPLES** Simplify.

**8.** $\dfrac{5x^2}{x} = \dfrac{5x\cdot x}{1\cdot x}$  Factoring the numerator and the denominator

$$= \dfrac{5x}{1}\cdot\dfrac{x}{x}$$  Factoring the rational expression; $\dfrac{x}{x}$ is a factor of 1

$$= 5x\cdot 1 \qquad \dfrac{x}{x} = 1$$

$$= 5x$$  Removing a factor of 1

In this example, we supplied a 1 in the denominator. This can always be done, but it is not necessary.

**9.** $\dfrac{4a+8}{2} = \dfrac{2(2a+4)}{2\cdot 1}$  Factoring the numerator and the denominator

$$= \dfrac{2}{2}\cdot\dfrac{2a+4}{1}$$  Factoring the rational expression; $\dfrac{2}{2}$ is a factor of 1

$$= \dfrac{2a+4}{1}$$  Removing a factor of 1

$$= 2a+4$$

Simplify.

**9.** $\dfrac{7x^2}{x}$

**10.** $\dfrac{6a+9}{3}$

***Answers***

**5.** $\dfrac{(3x+2y)x}{(5x+4y)x}$  **6.** $\dfrac{(2x^2-y)(3x+2)}{(3x+4)(3x+2)}$

**7.** $\dfrac{-2a+5}{-a+b}$, or $\dfrac{5-2a}{b-a}$  **8.** $\dfrac{4}{5}$  **9.** $7x$

**10.** $2a+3$

Do Exercises 9 and 10.

**EXAMPLES** Simplify.

10. $\dfrac{2x^2 + 4x}{6x^2 + 2x} = \dfrac{2x(x + 2)}{2x(3x + 1)}$    Factoring the numerator and the denominator

$= \dfrac{2x}{2x} \cdot \dfrac{x + 2}{3x + 1}$    Factoring the rational expression

$= \dfrac{x + 2}{3x + 1}$    Removing a factor of 1

11. $\dfrac{x^2 - 1}{2x^2 - x - 1} = \dfrac{(x - 1)(x + 1)}{(2x + 1)(x - 1)}$    Factoring the numerator and the denominator

$= \dfrac{x + 1}{2x + 1} \cdot \dfrac{x - 1}{x - 1}$    Factoring the rational expression

$= \dfrac{x + 1}{2x + 1}$    Removing a factor of 1

12. $\dfrac{9x^2 + 6xy - 3y^2}{12x^2 - 12y^2} = \dfrac{3(x + y)(3x - y)}{3(4)(x + y)(x - y)}$    Factoring the numerator and the denominator

$= \dfrac{3(x + y)}{3(x + y)} \cdot \dfrac{3x - y}{4(x - y)}$    Factoring the rational expression

$= \dfrac{3x - y}{4(x - y)}$    Removing a factor of 1

For purposes of later work, we generally do not multiply out the numerator and the denominator after simplifying rational expressions.

## Canceling

Canceling is a shortcut that you may have used for removing a factor of 1 when working with fraction notation or rational expressions. With great concern, we mention it here as a possible way to speed up your work. **Canceling may be done for removing factors of 1 only in products.** It *cannot* be done in sums or when adding expressions together. Our concern is that canceling be done with care and understanding. Example 12 might have been done faster as follows:

$$\dfrac{9x^2 + 6xy - 3y^2}{12x^2 - 12y^2} = \dfrac{\cancel{3}\cancel{(x + y)}(3x - y)}{\cancel{3}(4)\cancel{(x + y)}(x - y)}$$    When a factor of 1 is noted, it is "canceled" as shown.

$$= \dfrac{3x - y}{4(x - y)}.$$    Removing a factor of 1: $\dfrac{3(x + y)}{3(x + y)} = 1$

-------- *Caution!* --------

The difficulty with canceling is that it can be applied incorrectly in situations such as the following:

$$\dfrac{\cancel{2} + 3}{\cancel{2}} = 3, \qquad \dfrac{\cancel{4} + 1}{\cancel{4} + 2} = \dfrac{1}{2}, \qquad \dfrac{1\cancel{3}}{\cancel{3}4} = \dfrac{1}{4}.$$

Wrong!      Wrong!      Wrong!

In each of these situations, the expressions canceled are *not* factors of 1. Factors are parts of products. For example, in $2 \cdot 3$, 2 and 3 are factors, but in $2 + 3$, 2 and 3 are *not* factors. **If you can't factor, you can't cancel! If in doubt, don't cancel!**

Do Exercises 11–13.

## Opposites in Rational Expressions

Expressions of the form $a - b$ and $b - a$ are opposites, or additive inverses, of each other. When either of these binomials is multiplied by $-1$, the result is the other binomial:

$$-1(a - b) = -a + b = b - a;$$
$$-1(b - a) = -b + a = a - b.$$

Multiplication by $-1$ reverses the order in which subtraction occurs.

Consider

$$\frac{x - 8}{8 - x}.$$

At first glance, the numerator and the denominator do not appear to have any common factors other than 1. But $x - 8$ and $8 - x$ are opposites of each other. Therefore, we can rewrite one as the opposite of the other by factoring out a $-1$.

**EXAMPLE 13** Simplify: $\dfrac{x - 8}{8 - x}$.

$$\frac{x - 8}{8 - x} = \frac{x - 8}{-(x - 8)}$$ Rewriting $8 - x$ as $-(x - 8)$. See Section R.6.

$$= \frac{1(x - 8)}{-1(x - 8)}$$

$$= \frac{1}{-1} \cdot \frac{x - 8}{x - 8}$$

$$= -1 \cdot 1$$ Note that $\dfrac{1}{-1} = -1$, not 1.

$$= -1$$

Do Exercises 14–16.

## d Multiplying and Simplifying

After multiplying, we generally simplify, if possible. That is one reason why we leave the numerator and the denominator in factored form. Even so, we might need to factor them further in order to simplify.

**EXAMPLES** Multiply and simplify.

**14.** $\dfrac{x + 2}{x - 3} \cdot \dfrac{x^2 - 4}{x^2 + x - 2} = \dfrac{(x + 2)(x^2 - 4)}{(x - 3)(x^2 + x - 2)}$ Multiplying the numerators and the denominators

$$= \frac{(x + 2)(x + 2)(x - 2)}{(x - 3)(x + 2)(x - 1)}$$ Factoring the numerator and the denominator

$$= \frac{(x + 2)(x + 2)(x - 2)}{(x - 3)(x + 2)(x - 1)}$$ Removing a factor of 1: $\dfrac{x + 2}{x + 2} = 1$

$$= \frac{(x + 2)(x - 2)}{(x - 3)(x - 1)}$$ Simplifying

**Simplify.**

**11.** $\dfrac{6x^2 + 4x}{4x^2 + 8x}$

**12.** $\dfrac{2y^2 + 6y + 4}{y^2 - 1}$

**13.** $\dfrac{20a^2 - 80b^2}{16a^2 - 64ab + 64b^2}$

**Simplify.**

**14.** $\dfrac{y - 3}{3 - y}$

**15.** $\dfrac{p - q}{q - p}$

**16.** $\dfrac{t + 8}{-t - 8}$

***Answers***

**11.** $\dfrac{3x + 2}{2(x + 2)}$  **12.** $\dfrac{2(y + 2)}{y - 1}$
**13.** $\dfrac{5(a + 2b)}{4(a - 2b)}$  **14.** $-1$  **15.** $-1$  **16.** $-1$

**15.** $\dfrac{a^3 - b^3}{a^2 - b^2} \cdot \dfrac{a^2 + 2ab + b^2}{a^2 + ab + b^2}$

$$= \dfrac{(a^3 - b^3)(a^2 + 2ab + b^2)}{(a^2 - b^2)(a^2 + ab + b^2)}$$

$$= \dfrac{(a - b)(a^2 + ab + b^2)(a + b)(a + b)}{(a - b)(a + b)(a^2 + ab + b^2) \cdot 1} \quad \text{Factoring the numerator and the denominator}$$

$$= \dfrac{\cancel{(a - b)}\,\cancel{(a^2 + ab + b^2)}\,\cancel{(a + b)}\,(a + b)}{\cancel{(a - b)}\,\cancel{(a + b)}\,\cancel{(a^2 + ab + b^2)} \cdot 1}$$

Removing a factor of 1: $\dfrac{(a - b)(a^2 + ab + b^2)(a + b)}{(a - b)(a^2 + ab + b^2)(a + b)} = 1$

$$= \dfrac{a + b}{1} \quad \text{Simplifying}$$

$$= a + b$$

Do Exercises 17 and 18.

**Multiply and simplify.**

**17.** $\dfrac{(x - y)^3}{x + y} \cdot \dfrac{3x + 3y}{x^2 - y^2}$

**18.** $\dfrac{a^3 + b^3}{a^2 - b^2} \cdot \dfrac{a^2 - 2ab + b^2}{a^2 - ab + b^2}$

## e Dividing and Simplifying

Two expressions are reciprocals (or multiplicative inverses) of each other if their product is 1. To find the reciprocal of a rational expression, we interchange the numerator and the denominator.

The reciprocal of $\dfrac{3}{7}$ is $\dfrac{7}{3}$.

The reciprocal of $\dfrac{x + 2y}{x + y - 1}$ is $\dfrac{x + y - 1}{x + 2y}$.

The reciprocal of $y - 8$ is $\dfrac{1}{y - 8}$.

**Find the reciprocal.**

**19.** $\dfrac{x + 3}{x - 5}$

**20.** $x + 7$

**21.** $\dfrac{1}{y^3 - 9}$

Do Exercises 19-21.

We divide rational expressions in the same way that we divide fraction notation in arithmetic. For a review, see Section R.2.

---

**DIVIDING RATIONAL EXPRESSIONS**

To divide by a rational expression, multiply by its reciprocal:

$$\frac{A}{B} \div \frac{C}{D} = \frac{A}{B} \cdot \frac{D}{C} = \frac{AD}{BC}.$$

Then factor and simplify if possible.

---

For example,

$$\frac{2}{3} \div \frac{4}{5} = \frac{2}{3} \cdot \frac{5}{4} = \frac{2 \cdot 5}{3 \cdot 2 \cdot 2} = \frac{5}{3 \cdot 2} \cdot \frac{2}{2} = \frac{5}{6} \cdot 1 = \frac{5}{6}.$$

**Answers**

**17.** $\dfrac{3(x - y)(x - y)}{x + y}$ **18.** $a - b$ **19.** $\dfrac{x - 5}{x + 3}$

**20.** $\dfrac{1}{x + 7}$ **21.** $y^3 - 9$

**EXAMPLES** Divide and simplify.

**16.** $\dfrac{x-2}{x+1} \div \dfrac{x+5}{x-3} = \dfrac{x-2}{x+1} \cdot \dfrac{x-3}{x+5}$    Multiplying by the reciprocal of the divisor

$$= \dfrac{(x-2)(x-3)}{(x+1)(x+5)}$$

**17.** $\dfrac{a^2-1}{a-1} \div \dfrac{a^2-2a+1}{a+1}$

$$= \dfrac{a^2-1}{a-1} \cdot \dfrac{a+1}{a^2-2a+1}$$    Multiplying by the reciprocal of the divisor

$$= \dfrac{(a^2-1)(a+1)}{(a-1)(a^2-2a+1)}$$    Multiplying the numerators and the denominators

$$= \dfrac{(a+1)(a-1)(a+1)}{(a-1)(a-1)(a-1)}$$    Factoring the numerator and the denominator

$$= \dfrac{(a+1)\cancel{(a-1)}(a+1)}{(a-1)\cancel{(a-1)}(a-1)}$$    Removing a factor of 1: $\dfrac{a-1}{a-1} = 1$

$$= \dfrac{(a+1)(a+1)}{(a-1)(a-1)}$$    Simplifying

Do Exercises 22 and 23.

**Calculator Corner**

**Checking Division**  Use the TABLE feature, as described on p. 416, to check the divisions in Examples 16 and 17. Then check your answers to Margin Exercises 22 and 24.

Divide and simplify.

**22.** $\dfrac{x^2+7x+10}{2x-4} \div \dfrac{x^2-3x-10}{x-2}$

**23.** $\dfrac{a^2-b^2}{ab} \div \dfrac{a^2-2ab+b^2}{2a^2b^2}$

**EXAMPLE 18**  Perform the indicated operations and simplify:

$$\dfrac{c^3-d^3}{(c+d)^2} \div (c-d) \cdot (c+d).$$

Using the rules for order of operations, we do the division first:

$$\dfrac{c^3-d^3}{(c+d)^2} \div (c-d) \cdot (c+d)$$

$$= \dfrac{c^3-d^3}{(c+d)^2} \cdot \dfrac{1}{c-d} \cdot (c+d)$$

$$= \dfrac{(c-d)(c^2+cd+d^2)(c+d)}{(c+d)(c+d)(c-d)}$$

$$= \dfrac{\cancel{(c-d)}(c^2+cd+d^2)\cancel{(c+d)}}{(c+d)\cancel{(c+d)}\cancel{(c-d)}}$$    Removing a factor of 1: $\dfrac{(c-d)(c+d)}{(c-d)(c+d)} = 1$

$$= \dfrac{c^2+cd+d^2}{c+d}.$$

Do Exercise 24.

**24.** Perform the indicated operations and simplify:

$$\dfrac{a^3+8}{a-2} \div (a^2-2a+4) \cdot (a-2)^2.$$

**a**   Find all numbers for which the rational expression is not defined.

**1.** $\dfrac{5t^2 - 64}{3t + 17}$

**2.** $\dfrac{x^2 + x + 105}{5x - 45}$

**3.** $\dfrac{x^3 - x^2 + x + 2}{x^2 + 12x + 35}$

**4.** $\dfrac{x^2 - 3x - 4}{x^2 - 18x + 77}$

Find the domain. Write both set-builder notation and interval notation for the answer.

**5.** $f(x) = \dfrac{4x - 5}{x + 7}$

**6.** $f(r) = \dfrac{5r + 3}{r - 6}$

**7.** $g(x) = \dfrac{7}{3x - x^2}$

**8.** $g(x) = \dfrac{9}{8x + x^2}$

**9.** $f(t) = \dfrac{5t^2 - 64}{3t + 17}$

**10.** $f(x) = \dfrac{x^2 + x + 105}{5x - 45}$

**11.** $f(x) = \dfrac{x^3 - x^2 + x + 2}{x^2 + 12x + 35}$

**12.** $f(x) = \dfrac{x^2 - 3x - 4}{x^2 - 18x + 77}$

**b**   Multiply to obtain an equivalent expression. Do not simplify.

**13.** $\dfrac{7x}{7x} \cdot \dfrac{x + 2}{x + 8}$

**14.** $\dfrac{2 - y^2}{8 - y} \cdot \dfrac{-1}{-1}$

**15.** $\dfrac{q - 5}{q + 3} \cdot \dfrac{q + 5}{q + 5}$

**16.** $\dfrac{p + 1}{p + 4} \cdot \dfrac{p - 4}{p - 4}$

**c**   Simplify.

**17.** $\dfrac{15y^5}{5y^4}$

**18.** $\dfrac{7w^3}{28w^2}$

**19.** $\dfrac{16p^3}{24p^7}$

**20.** $\dfrac{48t^5}{56t^{11}}$

**21.** $\dfrac{9a - 27}{9}$

**22.** $\dfrac{6a - 30}{6}$

**23.** $\dfrac{12x - 15}{21}$

**24.** $\dfrac{18a - 2}{22}$

**25.** $\dfrac{4y - 12}{4y + 12}$

**26.** $\dfrac{8x + 16}{8x - 16}$

**27.** $\dfrac{t^2 - 16}{t^2 - 8t + 16}$

**28.** $\dfrac{p^2 - 25}{p^2 + 10p + 25}$

**29.** $\dfrac{x^2 - 9x + 8}{x^2 + 3x - 4}$

**30.** $\dfrac{y^2 + 8y - 9}{y^2 - 5y + 4}$

**31.** $\dfrac{w^3 - z^3}{w^2 - z^2}$

**32.** $\dfrac{a^2 - b^2}{a^3 + b^3}$

**d**    Multiply and simplify.

**33.** $\dfrac{x^4}{3x + 6} \cdot \dfrac{5x + 10}{5x^7}$

**34.** $\dfrac{10t}{6t - 12} \cdot \dfrac{20t - 40}{30t^3}$

**35.** $\dfrac{x^2 - 16}{x^2} \cdot \dfrac{x^2 - 4x}{x^2 - x - 12}$

**36.** $\dfrac{y^2 + 10y + 25}{y^2 - 9} \cdot \dfrac{y^2 - 3y}{y + 5}$

**37.** $\dfrac{y^2 - 16}{2y + 6} \cdot \dfrac{y + 3}{y - 4}$

**38.** $\dfrac{m^2 - n^2}{4m + 4n} \cdot \dfrac{m + n}{m - n}$

**39.** $\dfrac{x^2 - 2x - 35}{2x^3 - 3x^2} \cdot \dfrac{4x^3 - 9x}{7x - 49}$

**40.** $\dfrac{y^2 - 10y + 9}{y^2 - 1} \cdot \dfrac{y + 4}{y^2 - 5y - 36}$

**41.** $\dfrac{c^3 + 8}{c^2 - 4} \cdot \dfrac{c^2 - 4c + 4}{c^2 - 2c + 4}$

**42.** $\dfrac{x^3 - 27}{x^2 - 9} \cdot \dfrac{x^2 - 6x + 9}{x^2 + 3x + 9}$

**43.** $\dfrac{x^2 - y^2}{x^3 - y^3} \cdot \dfrac{x^2 + xy + y^2}{x^2 + 2xy + y^2}$

**44.** $\dfrac{4x^2 - 9y^2}{8x^3 - 27y^3} \cdot \dfrac{4x^2 + 6xy + 9y^2}{4x^2 + 12xy + 9y^2}$

Divide and simplify.

**45.** $\dfrac{12x^8}{3y^4} \div \dfrac{16x^3}{6y}$

**46.** $\dfrac{9a^7}{8b^2} \div \dfrac{12a^2}{24b^7}$

**47.** $\dfrac{3y + 15}{y} \div \dfrac{y + 5}{y}$

**48.** $\dfrac{6x + 12}{x} \div \dfrac{x + 2}{x^3}$

**49.** $\dfrac{y^2 - 9}{y} \div \dfrac{y + 3}{y + 2}$

**50.** $\dfrac{x^2 - 4}{x} \div \dfrac{x - 2}{x + 4}$

**51.** $\dfrac{4a^2 - 1}{a^2 - 4} \div \dfrac{2a - 1}{a - 2}$

**52.** $\dfrac{25x^2 - 4}{x^2 - 9} \div \dfrac{5x - 2}{x + 3}$

**53.** $\dfrac{x^2 - 16}{x^2 - 10x + 25} \div \dfrac{3x - 12}{x^2 - 3x - 10}$

**54.** $\dfrac{y^2 - 36}{y^2 - 8y + 16} \div \dfrac{3y - 18}{y^2 - y - 12}$

**55.** $\dfrac{y^3 + 3y}{y^2 - 9} \div \dfrac{y^2 + 5y - 14}{y^2 + 4y - 21}$

**56.** $\dfrac{a^3 + 4a}{a^2 - 16} \div \dfrac{a^2 + 8a + 15}{a^2 + a - 20}$

**57.** $\dfrac{x^3 - 64}{x^3 + 64} \div \dfrac{x^2 - 16}{x^2 - 4x + 16}$

**58.** $\dfrac{8y^3 + 27}{64y^3 - 1} \div \dfrac{4y^2 - 9}{16y^2 + 4y + 1}$

**59.** $\dfrac{8x^3y^3 + 27x^3}{64x^3y^3 - x^3} \div \dfrac{4x^2y^2 - 9x^2}{16x^2y^2 + 4x^2y + x^2}$

**60.** $\dfrac{x^3y - 64y}{x^3y + 64y} \div \dfrac{x^2y^2 - 16y^2}{x^2y^2 - 4xy^2 + 16y^2}$

Perform the indicated operations and simplify.

**61.** $\dfrac{r^2 - 4s^2}{r + 2s} \div (r + 2s) \cdot \dfrac{2s}{r - 2s}$

**62.** $\dfrac{d^2 - d}{d^2 - 6d + 8} \cdot \dfrac{d - 2}{d^2 + 5d} \div \dfrac{5d}{d^2 - 9d + 20}$

**63.** $\dfrac{y^2 - 2y}{y^2 + y - 2} \cdot \dfrac{y - 1}{y^2 + 4y + 4} \div \dfrac{y^2 + 2y - 8}{y^4}$

**64.** $\dfrac{9x^2}{x^2 - 16y^2} \div \dfrac{1}{x^2 + 4xy} \cdot \dfrac{x - 4y}{3x}$

## Skill Maintenance

In Exercises 65–68, the graph is that of a function. Determine the domain and the range.  [2.3a]

**65.**

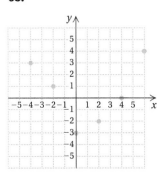

**66.**

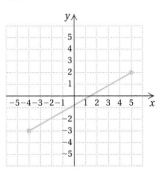

**67.**

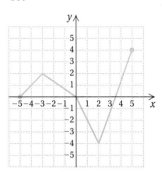

**68.**

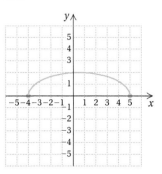

Factor.  [4.7a]

**69.** $6a^2 + 5ab - 25b^2$

**70.** $9a^2 - 30ab + 25b^2$

**71.** $10x^2 - 80x + 70$

**72.** $10x^2 - 13x + 4$

**73.** $21p^2 + p - 10$

**74.** $12m^2 - 26m - 10$

**75.** $2x^3 - 16x^2 - 66x$

**76.** $10y^2 + 80y - 650$

**77.** Find an equation of the line with slope $-\frac{2}{3}$ and $y$-intercept $(0, -5)$.  [2.6a]

**78.** Find an equation of the line having slope $-\frac{2}{7}$ and containing the point $(-4, 8)$.  [2.6b]

## Synthesis

Simplify.

**79.** $\dfrac{x(x + 1) - 2(x + 3)}{(x + 1)(x + 2)(x + 3)}$

**80.** $\dfrac{2x - 5(x + 2) - (x - 2)}{x^2 - 4}$

**81.** $\dfrac{m^2 - t^2}{m^2 + t^2 + m + t + 2mt}$

**82.** $\dfrac{a^3 - 2a^2 + 2a - 4}{a^3 - 2a^2 - 3a + 6}$

**83.** Let
$$g(x) = \frac{2x + 3}{4x - 1}.$$
Find $g(5)$, $g(0)$, $g\left(\frac{1}{4}\right)$, and $g(a + h)$.

# 5.2

# LCMs, LCDs, Addition, and Subtraction

## OBJECTIVES

**a** Find the LCM of several algebraic expressions by factoring.

**b** Add and subtract rational expressions.

**c** Simplify combined additions and subtractions of rational expressions.

**SKILL TO REVIEW**
Objective 4.1d: Find the opposite of a polynomial and subtract polynomials.

Subtract.

1. $(2y - 5) - (y - 6)$
2. $(3x^2 + x - 4) - (5x^2 - x + 10)$

Find the LCM by factoring.

1. 18, 30

2. 12, 18, 24

## a Finding LCMs by Factoring

To add rational expressions when denominators are different, we first find a common denominator. Let's review the procedure used in arithmetic first. To do the addition

$$\frac{5}{42} + \frac{7}{12},$$

we find a common denominator. We look for the least common multiple (LCM) of 42 and 12. That number becomes the least common denominator (LCD).

To find the LCM, we factor both numbers completely (into primes).

$42 = 2 \cdot 3 \cdot 7 \longleftarrow$ Any multiple of 42 has these factors.

$12 = 2 \cdot 2 \cdot 3 \longleftarrow$ Any multiple of 12 has these factors.

The LCM is the number that has 2 as a factor twice, 3 as a factor once, and 7 as a factor once: LCM $= 2 \cdot 2 \cdot 3 \cdot 7$, or 84.

> **FINDING LCMs**
>
> To find the LCM, use each factor the greatest number of times that it occurs in any one prime factorization.

**EXAMPLE 1** Find the LCM of 18 and 24.

$$18 = 3 \cdot 3 \cdot 2$$
$$24 = 2 \cdot 2 \cdot 2 \cdot 3$$

The LCM is $3 \cdot 3 \cdot 2 \cdot 2 \cdot 2$, or 72.

Do Margin Exercises 1 and 2.

Now let's return to adding $\frac{5}{42}$ and $\frac{7}{12}$:

$$\frac{5}{42} + \frac{7}{12} = \frac{5}{2 \cdot 3 \cdot 7} + \frac{7}{2 \cdot 2 \cdot 3}. \qquad \text{Factoring the denominators}$$

The LCD is the LCM of the denominators, $2 \cdot 2 \cdot 3 \cdot 7$. To get this LCD in the first denominator, we need a factor of 2. In the second denominator, we need a factor of 7. We multiply by 1, as follows:

$$\frac{5}{2 \cdot 3 \cdot 7} \cdot \frac{2}{2} + \frac{7}{2 \cdot 2 \cdot 3} \cdot \frac{7}{7} = \frac{10}{2 \cdot 2 \cdot 3 \cdot 7} + \frac{49}{2 \cdot 2 \cdot 3 \cdot 7}$$

$$= \frac{59}{2 \cdot 2 \cdot 3 \cdot 7} = \frac{59}{84}.$$

*Answers*

*Skill to Review:*
1. $y + 1$   2. $-2x^2 + 2x - 14$

*Margin Exercises:*
1. 90   2. 72

Multiplying the first fraction by $\frac{2}{2}$ gave us an equivalent fraction with a denominator that is the LCD. Multiplying the second fraction by $\frac{7}{7}$ also gave us an equivalent fraction with a denominator that is the LCD. Once we had a common denominator, we added the numerators.

Do Exercises 3 and 4.

We find the LCM of algebraic expressions in the same way that we find the LCM of natural numbers.

Our reasoning for learning how to find LCMs is so that we will be able to add rational expressions. For example, to do the addition

$$\frac{7}{12xy^2} + \frac{8}{15x^3y},$$

we first need to find the LCM of $12xy^2$ and $15x^3y$, which is $60x^3y^2$.

## EXAMPLES

**2.** Find the LCM of $12xy^2$ and $15x^3y$.

We factor each expression completely. To find the LCM, we use each factor the greatest number of times that it occurs in any one prime factorization.

$$12xy^2 = 2 \cdot 2 \cdot 3 \cdot x \cdot y \cdot y \ ;$$
$$15x^3y = 3 \cdot 5 \cdot x \cdot x \cdot x \cdot y$$

Factoring

$12xy^2$ is a factor.

$$\text{LCM} = 2 \cdot 2 \cdot 3 \cdot 5 \cdot x \cdot x \cdot x \cdot y \cdot y = 60x^3y^2$$

$15x^3y$ is a factor.

The LCM of $12xy^2$ and $15x^3y$ is $60x^3y^2$.

**3.** Find the LCM of $x^2 + 2x + 1$, $5x^2 - 5x$, and $x^2 - 1$.

$$x^2 + 2x + 1 = (x + 1)(x + 1) \ ;$$
$$5x^2 - 5x = 5x(x - 1) \ ;$$
$$x^2 - 1 = (x + 1)(x - 1)$$

Factoring

Both factors of $x^2 - 1$ are already present in the previous factorizations.

$$\text{LCM} = 5x(x + 1)(x + 1)(x - 1)$$

**4.** Find the LCM of $x^2 - y^2$, $x^3 + y^3$, and $x^2 + 2xy + y^2$.

$$x^2 - y^2 = (x - y)(x + y);$$
$$x^3 + y^3 = (x + y)(x^2 - xy + y^2) \ ;$$
$$x^2 + 2xy + y^2 = (x + y)(x + y) = (x + y)^2$$

Factoring

$$\text{LCM} = (x - y)(x + y)^2(x^2 - xy + y^2)$$

Add, first finding the LCD of the denominators.

**3.** $\dfrac{5}{12} + \dfrac{11}{30}$

**4.** $\dfrac{7}{12} + \dfrac{13}{18} + \dfrac{1}{24}$

Recall that $-(x - 3) = -1(x - 3) = 3 - x$. If $(x - 3)(x + 2)$ is an LCM, then $-1(x - 3)(x + 2) = (3 - x)(x + 2)$ is also an LCM.

If, when we are finding LCMs, factors that are opposites occur, we do not use both of them. For example, if $a - b$ occurs in one factorization and $b - a$ occurs in another, we do not use both, since they are opposites.

**EXAMPLE 5** Find the LCM of $x^2 - y^2$ and $3y - 3x$.

Find the LCM.

**5.** $a^2b^2$, $5a^3b$

**6.** $y^2 + 7y + 12$, $y^2 + 8y + 16$, $y + 4$

**7.** $x^2 - 9$, $x^3 - x^2 - 6x$, $2x^2$

**8.** $a^2 - b^2$, $2b - 2a$

$$x^2 - y^2 = (x + y)(x - y)$$

We can use $(x - y)$ or $(y - x)$, but we do not use both.

$$3y - 3x = 3(y - x), \text{ or } -3(x - y)$$

$$\text{LCM} = 3(x + y)(x - y), \text{ or } 3(x + y)(y - x), \text{ or } -3(x + y)(x - y)$$

In most cases, we would use the form $3(x + y)(x - y)$.

Do Exercises 5-8.

## b  Adding and Subtracting Rational Expressions

> **ADDITION AND SUBTRACTION WITH LIKE DENOMINATORS**
>
> To add or subtract when denominators are the same, add or subtract the numerators and keep the same denominator.
>
> $$\frac{A}{C} + \frac{B}{C} = \frac{A + B}{C} \quad \text{and} \quad \frac{A}{C} - \frac{B}{C} = \frac{A - B}{C}, \quad \text{where } C \neq 0.$$
>
> Then factor and simplify if possible.

**EXAMPLE 6** Add: $\frac{3 + x}{x} + \frac{4}{x}$.

$$\frac{3 + x}{x} + \frac{4}{x} = \frac{3 + x + 4}{x}$$
Adding numerators and keeping the same denominator

----- *Caution!* -----

$$= \frac{7 + x}{x}$$

This expression does *not* simplify to 7: $\frac{7 + x}{x} \neq 7$.

Example 6 shows that

$$\frac{3 + x}{x} + \frac{4}{x} \quad \text{and} \quad \frac{7 + x}{x}$$

are equivalent expressions. They name the same number for all replacements for which the rational expressions are defined.

*Answers*

**5.** $5a^3b^2$  **6.** $(y + 3)(y + 4)(y + 4)$
**7.** $2x^2(x - 3)(x + 3)(x + 2)$
**8.** $2(a + b)(a - b)$, or $2(a + b)(b - a)$

**EXAMPLE 7** Add: $\dfrac{4x^2 - 5xy}{x^2 - y^2} + \dfrac{2xy - y^2}{x^2 - y^2}$.

$$\dfrac{4x^2 - 5xy}{x^2 - y^2} + \dfrac{2xy - y^2}{x^2 - y^2} = \dfrac{4x^2 - 3xy - y^2}{x^2 - y^2}$$     Adding the numerators

$$= \dfrac{(4x + y)(x - y)}{(x + y)(x - y)}$$     Factoring the numerator and the denominator

$$= \dfrac{(4x + y)\cancel{(x - y)}}{(x + y)\cancel{(x - y)}}$$     Removing a factor of 1: $\dfrac{x - y}{x - y} = 1$

$$= \dfrac{4x + y}{x + y}$$

Do Exercises 9 and 10.

Add.

**9.** $\dfrac{5 + y}{y} + \dfrac{7}{y}$

**10.** $\dfrac{2x^2 + 5x - 9}{x - 5} + \dfrac{x^2 - 19x + 4}{x - 5}$

**EXAMPLE 8** Subtract: $\dfrac{4x + 5}{x + 3} - \dfrac{x - 2}{x + 3}$.

$$\dfrac{4x + 5}{x + 3} - \dfrac{x - 2}{x + 3} = \dfrac{4x + 5 - (x - 2)}{x + 3}$$     Subtracting numerators

$$= \dfrac{4x + 5 - x + 2}{x + 3}$$

A common error: forgetting these parentheses. If you forget them, you will be subtracting only *part* of the numerator, $x - 2$.

$$= \dfrac{3x + 7}{x + 3}$$

Do Exercises 11 and 12.

Subtract.

**11.** $\dfrac{a}{b + 2} - \dfrac{b}{b + 2}$

**12.** $\dfrac{4y + 7}{x^2 + y^2} - \dfrac{3y - 5}{x^2 + y^2}$

When denominators are different, we find the least common denominator, LCD. The procedure we will use is as follows.

> **ADDITION AND SUBTRACTION WITH DIFFERENT DENOMINATORS**
>
> To add or subtract rational expressions with different denominators:
>
> **1.** Find the LCM of the denominators. This is the least common denominator (LCD).
>
> **2.** For each rational expression, find an equivalent expression with the LCD. To do so, multiply by 1 using an expression for 1 made up of factors of the LCD that are missing from the original denominator.
>
> **3.** Add or subtract the numerators. Write the result over the LCD.
>
> **4.** Simplify, if possible.

**EXAMPLE 9** Add: $\dfrac{2a}{5} + \dfrac{3b}{2a}$.

We first find the LCD: $\left.\begin{array}{l} 5 \\ 2a \end{array}\right\}$    LCD $= 5 \cdot 2a$, or $10a$.

Now we multiply each expression by 1. We choose symbols for 1 that will give us the LCD in each denominator. In this case, we use $2a/(2a)$ and $5/5$:

$$\dfrac{2a}{5} \cdot \dfrac{2a}{2a} + \dfrac{3b}{2a} \cdot \dfrac{5}{5} = \dfrac{4a^2}{10a} + \dfrac{15b}{10a} = \dfrac{4a^2 + 15b}{10a}.$$

Multiplying the first term by $2a/(2a)$ gave us a denominator of $10a$. Multiplying the second term by $\frac{5}{5}$ also gave us a denominator of $10a$.

*Answers*

**9.** $\dfrac{12 + y}{y}$    **10.** $3x + 1$

**11.** $\dfrac{a - b}{b + 2}$    **12.** $\dfrac{y + 12}{x^2 + y^2}$

**EXAMPLE 10** Add: $\dfrac{3x^2 + 3xy}{x^2 - y^2} + \dfrac{2 - 3x}{x - y}$.

We first find the LCD of the denominators. To do so, we first factor:

$$\left. \begin{array}{l} x^2 - y^2 = (x + y)(x - y) \\ x - y = x - y \end{array} \right\} \quad \text{LCD} = (x + y)(x - y).$$

The first expression already has the LCD. We multiply by 1 to get the LCD in the second expression. Then we add and simplify if possible.

$$\dfrac{3x^2 + 3xy}{(x + y)(x - y)} + \dfrac{2 - 3x}{x - y} \cdot \dfrac{x + y}{x + y} \quad \text{Multiplying by 1 to get the LCD}$$

$$= \dfrac{3x^2 + 3xy}{(x + y)(x - y)} + \dfrac{(2 - 3x)(x + y)}{(x - y)(x + y)}$$

$$= \dfrac{3x^2 + 3xy}{(x + y)(x - y)} + \dfrac{2x + 2y - 3x^2 - 3xy}{(x - y)(x + y)} \quad \text{Multiplying in the numerator}$$

$$= \dfrac{3x^2 + 3xy + 2x + 2y - 3x^2 - 3xy}{(x + y)(x - y)} \quad \text{Adding the numerators}$$

$$= \dfrac{2x + 2y}{(x + y)(x - y)} \quad \text{Combining like terms}$$

$$= \dfrac{2(x + y)}{(x + y)(x - y)} \quad \text{Factoring the numerator}$$

$$= \dfrac{2\cancel{(x + y)}}{\cancel{(x + y)}(x - y)} \quad \text{Removing a factor of 1: } \dfrac{x + y}{x + y} = 1$$

$$= \dfrac{2}{x - y}$$

Do Exercises 13 and 14.

**EXAMPLE 11** Subtract: $\dfrac{2y + 1}{y^2 - 7y + 6} - \dfrac{y + 3}{y^2 - 5y - 6}$.

$$\dfrac{2y + 1}{y^2 - 7y + 6} - \dfrac{y + 3}{y^2 - 5y - 6}$$

$$= \dfrac{2y + 1}{(y - 6)(y - 1)} - \dfrac{y + 3}{(y - 6)(y + 1)} \quad \text{LCD} = (y - 6)(y - 1)(y + 1)$$

$$= \dfrac{2y + 1}{(y - 6)(y - 1)} \cdot \dfrac{y + 1}{y + 1} - \dfrac{y + 3}{(y - 6)(y + 1)} \cdot \dfrac{y - 1}{y - 1} \quad \begin{array}{l}\text{Multiplying by 1} \\ \text{to get the LCD}\end{array}$$

$$= \dfrac{(2y + 1)(y + 1) - (y + 3)(y - 1)}{(y - 6)(y - 1)(y + 1)} \quad \text{Subtracting the numerators}$$

$$= \dfrac{(2y^2 + 3y + 1) - (y^2 + 2y - 3)}{(y - 6)(y - 1)(y + 1)} \quad \begin{array}{l}\text{Multiplying. Note the use} \\ \text{of parentheses.}\end{array}$$

$$= \dfrac{2y^2 + 3y + 1 - y^2 - 2y + 3}{(y - 6)(y - 1)(y + 1)}$$

$$= \dfrac{y^2 + y + 4}{(y - 6)(y - 1)(y + 1)} \quad \begin{array}{l}\text{The numerator cannot be factored.} \\ \text{The rational expression is simplified.}\end{array}$$

We generally do not multiply out a numerator or a denominator if it has three or more factors (other than monomials). This will be helpful when we solve equations.

Do Exercises 15 and 16.

Add.

**13.** $\dfrac{3x}{7} + \dfrac{4y}{3x}$

**14.** $\dfrac{2xy - 2x^2}{x^2 - y^2} + \dfrac{2x + 3}{x + y}$

Subtract.

**15.** $\dfrac{a}{a + 3} - \dfrac{a - 4}{a}$

**16.** $\dfrac{4y - 5}{y^2 - 7y + 12} - \dfrac{y + 7}{y^2 + 2y - 15}$

*Answers*

**13.** $\dfrac{9x^2 + 28y}{21x}$ **14.** $\dfrac{3}{x + y}$ **15.** $\dfrac{a + 12}{a(a + 3)}$

**16.** $\dfrac{3(y^2 + 4y + 1)}{(y - 4)(y - 3)(y + 5)}$

## Denominators That Are Opposites

When one denominator is the opposite of the other, we can first multiply either expression by 1 using $-1/-1$.

**EXAMPLE 12** Add: $\dfrac{a}{2a} + \dfrac{a^3}{-2a}$.

$$\frac{a}{2a} + \frac{a^3}{-2a} = \frac{a}{2a} + \frac{a^3}{-2a} \cdot \frac{-1}{-1} \quad \text{Multiplying by 1, using } \frac{-1}{-1}$$

$\boxed{\text{This is equal to 1 (not } -1).}$

$$= \frac{a}{2a} + \frac{-a^3}{2a}$$

$$= \frac{a - a^3}{2a} \quad \text{Adding numerators}$$

$$= \frac{a(1+a)(1-a)}{2a} \quad \text{Factoring}$$

$$= \frac{\cancel{a}(1+a)(1-a)}{2\cancel{a}} \quad \text{Removing a factor of 1: } \frac{a}{a} = 1$$

$$= \frac{(1+a)(1-a)}{2}$$

Do Exercises 17 and 18.

**Add.**

**17.** $\dfrac{b}{3b} + \dfrac{b^3}{-3b}$

**18.** $\dfrac{3x^2 + 4}{x - 5} + \dfrac{x^2 - 7}{5 - x}$

**EXAMPLE 13** Subtract: $\dfrac{x^2}{5y} - \dfrac{x^3}{-5y}$.

$$\frac{x^2}{5y} - \frac{x^3}{-5y} = \frac{x^2}{5y} - \frac{x^3}{-5y} \cdot \frac{-1}{-1} \quad \text{Multiplying by } \frac{-1}{-1}$$

$$= \frac{x^2}{5y} - \frac{-x^3}{5y}$$

$$= \frac{x^2 - (-x^3)}{5y} \quad \boxed{\text{Don't forget these parentheses!}}$$

$$= \frac{x^2 + x^3}{5y}, \text{ or } \frac{x^2(1+x)}{5y}$$

**EXAMPLE 14** Subtract: $\dfrac{5x}{x - 2y} - \dfrac{3y - 7}{2y - x}$.

$$\frac{5x}{x - 2y} - \frac{3y - 7}{2y - x} = \frac{5x}{x - 2y} - \frac{3y - 7}{2y - x} \cdot \frac{-1}{-1}$$

$$= \frac{5x}{x - 2y} - \frac{-3y + 7}{x - 2y} \quad \boxed{\text{Remember: } (2y - x)(-1) = -2y + x = x - 2y.}$$

$$= \frac{5x - (-3y + 7)}{x - 2y} \quad \text{Subtracting numerators}$$

$$= \frac{5x + 3y - 7}{x - 2y}$$

Do Exercises 19 and 20.

**Subtract.**

**19.** $\dfrac{3}{4y} - \dfrac{7x}{-4y}$

**20.** $\dfrac{4x^2}{2x - y} - \dfrac{7x^2}{y - 2x}$

***Answers***

**17.** $\dfrac{(1 + b)(1 - b)}{3}$  **18.** $\dfrac{2x^2 + 11}{x - 5}$

**19.** $\dfrac{3 + 7x}{4y}$  **20.** $\dfrac{11x^2}{2x - y}$

## c Combined Additions and Subtractions

**EXAMPLE 15** Perform the indicated operations and simplify.

$$\frac{2x}{x^2 - 4} + \frac{5}{2 - x} - \frac{1}{2 + x}$$

$$= \frac{2x}{(x - 2)(x + 2)} + \frac{5}{2 - x} - \frac{1}{2 + x}$$

$$= \frac{2x}{(x - 2)(x + 2)} + \frac{5}{2 - x} \cdot \frac{-1}{-1} - \frac{1}{x + 2} \qquad \text{Multiplying by } \frac{-1}{-1}$$

$$= \frac{2x}{(x - 2)(x + 2)} + \frac{-5}{x - 2} - \frac{1}{x + 2} \qquad \text{LCD} = (x - 2)(x + 2)$$

$$= \frac{2x}{(x - 2)(x + 2)} + \frac{-5}{x - 2} \cdot \frac{x + 2}{x + 2} - \frac{1}{x + 2} \cdot \frac{x - 2}{x - 2} \qquad \begin{array}{l}\text{Multiplying by 1}\\ \text{to get the LCD}\end{array}$$

$$= \frac{2x - 5(x + 2) - (x - 2)}{(x - 2)(x + 2)} \qquad \text{Adding and subtracting the numerators}$$

$$= \frac{2x - 5x - 10 - x + 2}{(x - 2)(x + 2)} \qquad \text{Removing parentheses}$$

$$= \frac{-4x - 8}{(x - 2)(x + 2)}$$

$$= \frac{-4\cancel{(x + 2)}}{(x - 2)\cancel{(x + 2)}} \qquad \text{Removing a factor of 1: } \frac{x + 2}{x + 2} = 1$$

$$= \frac{-4}{x - 2}, \text{ or } -\frac{4}{x - 2}$$

Another correct form of the answer is

$$\frac{4}{2 - x}.$$

It is found by multiplying by $-1/-1$.

Do Exercise 21.

**21.** Perform the indicated operations and simplify:

$$\frac{8x}{x^2 - 1} + \frac{2}{1 - x} - \frac{4}{x + 1}.$$

**Calculator Corner**

**Checking Addition and Subtraction** Use the TABLE feature, as described on p. 416, to check the sums and differences in Examples 6, 8, 11, and 15. Then check your answers to Margin Exercises 15 and 21.

*Answer*

**21.** $\dfrac{2}{x - 1}$

**a** Find the LCM by factoring.

**1.** 15, 40

**2.** 12, 32

**3.** 18, 48

**4.** 45, 54

**5.** 30, 105

**6.** 24, 60

**7.** 9, 15, 5

**8.** 27, 35, 63

Add. Find the LCD first.

**9.** $\dfrac{5}{6} + \dfrac{4}{15}$

**10.** $\dfrac{5}{12} + \dfrac{13}{18}$

**11.** $\dfrac{7}{36} + \dfrac{1}{24}$

**12.** $\dfrac{11}{30} + \dfrac{19}{75}$

**13.** $\dfrac{3}{4} + \dfrac{7}{30} + \dfrac{1}{16}$

**14.** $\dfrac{5}{8} + \dfrac{7}{12} + \dfrac{11}{40}$

Find the LCM.

**15.** $21x^2y,\ 7xy$

**16.** $18a^2b,\ 50ab^3$

**17.** $y^2 - 100,\ 10y + 100$

**18.** $r^2 - s^2,\ rs + s^2$

**19.** $15ab^2,\ 3ab,\ 10a^3b$

**20.** $6x^2y^2,\ 9x^3y,\ 15y^3$

**21.** $5y - 15,\ y^2 - 6y + 9$

**22.** $x^2 + 10x + 25,\ x^2 + 2x - 15$

**23.** $y^2 - 25,\ 5 - y$

**24.** $x^2 - 36,\ 6 - x$

**25.** $2r^2 - 5r - 12,\ 3r^2 - 13r + 4,\ r^2 - 16$

**26.** $2x^2 - 5x - 3,\ 2x^2 - x - 1,\ x^2 - 6x + 9$

**27.** $x^5 + 4x^3,\ x^3 - 4x^2 + 4x$

**28.** $9x^3 + 9x^2 - 18x,\ 6x^5 + 24x^4 + 24x^3$

**29.** $x^5 - 2x^4 + x^3,\ 2x^3 + 2x,\ 5x + 5$

**30.** $x^5 - 4x^4 + 4x^3,\ 3x^2 - 12,\ 2x + 4$

Add or subtract. Then simplify. If a denominator has three or more factors (other than monomials), leave it in factored form.

**31.** $\dfrac{x - 2y}{x + y} + \dfrac{x + 9y}{x + y}$

**32.** $\dfrac{a - 8b}{a + b} + \dfrac{a + 13b}{a + b}$

**33.** $\dfrac{4y + 3}{y - 2} - \dfrac{y - 2}{y - 2}$

**34.** $\dfrac{3t + 2}{t - 4} - \dfrac{t - 4}{t - 4}$

**35.** $\dfrac{a^2}{a - b} + \dfrac{b^2}{b - a}$

**36.** $\dfrac{r^2}{r - s} + \dfrac{s^2}{s - r}$

**37.** $\dfrac{6}{y} - \dfrac{7}{-y}$

**38.** $\dfrac{4}{x} - \dfrac{9}{-x}$

**39.** $\dfrac{4a - 2}{a^2 - 49} + \dfrac{5 + 3a}{49 - a^2}$

**40.** $\dfrac{2y - 3}{y^2 - 1} - \dfrac{4 - y}{1 - y^2}$

**41.** $\dfrac{a^3}{a - b} + \dfrac{b^3}{b - a}$

**42.** $\dfrac{x^3}{x^2 - y^2} + \dfrac{y^3}{y^2 - x^2}$

**43.** $\dfrac{y - 2}{y + 4} + \dfrac{y + 3}{y - 5}$

**44.** $\dfrac{x - 2}{x + 3} + \dfrac{x + 2}{x - 4}$

**45.** $\dfrac{4xy}{x^2 - y^2} + \dfrac{x - y}{x + y}$

**46.** $\dfrac{5ab}{a^2 - b^2} + \dfrac{a + b}{a - b}$

**47.** $\dfrac{9x + 2}{3x^2 - 2x - 8} + \dfrac{7}{3x^2 + x - 4}$

**48.** $\dfrac{3y + 2}{2y^2 - y - 10} + \dfrac{8}{2y^2 - 7y + 5}$

**49.** $\dfrac{4}{x + 1} + \dfrac{x + 2}{x^2 - 1} + \dfrac{3}{x - 1}$

**50.** $\dfrac{-2}{y + 2} + \dfrac{5}{y - 2} + \dfrac{y + 3}{y^2 - 4}$

**51.** $\dfrac{x-1}{3x+15} - \dfrac{x+3}{5x+25}$

**52.** $\dfrac{y-2}{4y+8} - \dfrac{y+6}{5y+10}$

**53.** $\dfrac{5ab}{a^2-b^2} - \dfrac{a-b}{a+b}$

**54.** $\dfrac{6xy}{x^2-y^2} - \dfrac{x+y}{x-y}$

**55.** $\dfrac{3y}{y^2-7y+10} - \dfrac{2y}{y^2-8y+15}$

**56.** $\dfrac{5x}{x^2-6x+8} - \dfrac{3x}{x^2-x-12}$

**57.** $\dfrac{y}{y^2-y-20} + \dfrac{2}{y+4}$

**58.** $\dfrac{6}{y^2+6y+9} + \dfrac{5}{y^2-9}$

**59.** $\dfrac{3y+2}{y^2+5y-24} + \dfrac{7}{y^2+4y-32}$

**60.** $\dfrac{3y+2}{y^2-7y+10} + \dfrac{2y}{y^2-8y+15}$

**61.** $\dfrac{3x-1}{x^2+2x-3} - \dfrac{x+4}{x^2-9}$

**62.** $\dfrac{3p-2}{p^2+2p-24} - \dfrac{p-3}{p^2-16}$

**C**  Perform the indicated operations and simplify.

**63.** $\dfrac{1}{x+1} - \dfrac{x}{x-2} + \dfrac{x^2+2}{x^2-x-2}$

**64.** $\dfrac{2}{y+3} - \dfrac{y}{y-1} + \dfrac{y^2+2}{y^2+2y-3}$

**65.** $\dfrac{y-3}{y-4} - \dfrac{y+2}{y+4} + \dfrac{y-7}{y^2-16}$

**66.** $\dfrac{x-1}{x-2} - \dfrac{x+1}{x+2} + \dfrac{x-6}{x^2-4}$

**67.** $\dfrac{y+2}{y+4} + \dfrac{y-7}{y^2-16} - \dfrac{y-3}{y-4}$

**68.** $\dfrac{x-6}{x^2-4} - \dfrac{x-1}{x-2} - \dfrac{x+1}{x+2}$

**69.** $\dfrac{4x}{x^2-1} + \dfrac{3x}{1-x} - \dfrac{4}{x-1}$

**70.** $\dfrac{5y}{1-2y} - \dfrac{2y}{2y+1} + \dfrac{3}{4y^2-1}$

**71.** $\dfrac{1}{x+y} + \dfrac{1}{y-x} - \dfrac{2x}{x^2-y^2}$

**72.** $\dfrac{1}{b-a} + \dfrac{1}{a+b} - \dfrac{2b}{a^2-b^2}$

**73.** $\dfrac{x+5}{x-3} - \dfrac{x+2}{x+1} - \dfrac{6x+10}{x^2-2x-3}$

**74.** $\dfrac{13x+2}{x^2+3x-10} - \dfrac{x+2}{x-2} + \dfrac{x-3}{x+5}$

## Skill Maintenance

Graph.   [3.7b]

**75.** $2x - 3y > 6$

**76.** $y - x > 3$

**77.** $5x + 3y \le 15$

**78.** $5x - 3y \le 15$

Factor.   [4.6d]

**79.** $t^3 - 8$

**80.** $q^3 + 125$

**81.** $23x^4 + 23x$

**82.** $64a^3 - 27b^3$

**83.** Find an equation of the line that passes through the point $(4, -6)$ and is parallel to the line $3y + 8x = 10$.   [2.6d]

**84.** Find an equation of the line that passes through the point $(-2, 3)$ and is perpendicular to the line $5y + 4x = 7$.   [2.6d]

## Synthesis

**85.** Determine the domain and the range of the function graphed below.

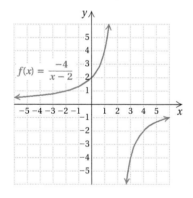

$f(x) = \dfrac{-4}{x-2}$

**86.** 18, 42, 82, 120, 300, 700

Find the LCM.

**87.** $x^8 - x^4,\ x^5 - x^2,\ x^5 - x^3,\ x^5 + x^2$

**88.** The LCM of two expressions is $8a^4b^7$. One of the expressions is $2a^3b^7$. List all possibilities for the other expression.

Perform the indicated operations and simplify.

**89.** $\dfrac{x+y+1}{y-(x+1)} + \dfrac{x+y-1}{x-(y-1)} - \dfrac{x-y-1}{1-(y-x)}$

**90.** $\dfrac{b-c}{a-(b-c)} - \dfrac{b-a}{(b-a)-c}$

**91.** $\dfrac{x}{x^4-y^4} - \dfrac{1}{x^2+2xy+y^2}$

**92.** $\dfrac{x^2}{3x^2-5x-2} - \dfrac{2x}{3x+1} \cdot \dfrac{1}{x-2}$

# 5.3

## Division of Polynomials

A rational expression represents division. "Long" division of polynomials, like division of real numbers, relies on our multiplication and subtraction skills.

### a  Divisor a Monomial

We first consider division by a monomial (a term like $45x^{10}$ or $48a^2b^5$). When we are dividing a monomial by a monomial, we can use the rules of exponents and subtract exponents when the bases are the same. (We studied this in Section R.7.) For example,

$$\frac{45x^{10}}{3x^4} = \frac{45}{3}x^{10-4} = 15x^6 \quad \text{and} \quad \frac{48a^2b^5}{-3ab^2} = \frac{48}{-3}a^{2-1}b^{5-2} = -16ab^3.$$

When we divide a polynomial by a monomial, we break up the division into a sum of quotients of monomials. To do so, we reverse the rule for adding fractions. That is, since

$$\frac{A}{C} + \frac{B}{C} = \frac{A+B}{C}, \quad \text{we know that} \quad \frac{A+B}{C} = \frac{A}{C} + \frac{B}{C}.$$

**EXAMPLE 1**  Divide $12x^3 + 8x^2 + x + 4$ by $4x$.

$$\frac{12x^3 + 8x^2 + x + 4}{4x} \qquad \text{Writing a fraction expression}$$

$$= \frac{12x^3}{4x} + \frac{8x^2}{4x} + \frac{x}{4x} + \frac{4}{4x} \qquad \text{Dividing each term of the numerator by the monomial}$$

$$= 3x^2 + 2x + \frac{1}{4} + \frac{1}{x} \qquad \text{Doing the four indicated divisions}$$

Do Margin Exercise 1.

**EXAMPLE 2**  Divide: $(8x^4y^5 - 3x^3y^4 + 5x^2y^3) \div (x^2y^3)$.

$$\frac{8x^4y^5 - 3x^3y^4 + 5x^2y^3}{x^2y^3} = \frac{8x^4y^5}{x^2y^3} - \frac{3x^3y^4}{x^2y^3} + \frac{5x^2y^3}{x^2y^3}$$

$$= 8x^2y^2 - 3xy + 5$$

> **DIVIDING BY A MONOMIAL**
>
> To divide a polynomial by a monomial, divide each term by the monomial.

Do Exercises 2 and 3.

### b  Divisor Not a Monomial

When the divisor is not a monomial, we use a procedure very much like long division in arithmetic.

---

**SKILL TO REVIEW**
Objective R.7a: Use exponential notation in division.

Divide and simplify.

1. $\dfrac{15w^6}{3w^4}$

2. $\dfrac{36x^8y^{15}}{-4x^3y^{10}}$

1. Divide: $\dfrac{x^3 + 16x^2 + 6x}{2x}$.

Divide.

2. $(15y^5 - 6y^4 + 18y^3) \div (3y^2)$

3. $(x^4y^3 + 10x^3y^2 + 16x^2y) \div (2x^2y)$

*Answers*

*Skill to Review:*
1. $5w^2$  2. $-9x^5y^5$

*Margin Exercises:*
1. $\dfrac{x^2}{2} + 8x + 3$  2. $5y^3 - 2y^2 + 6y$

3. $\dfrac{x^2y^2}{2} + 5xy + 8$

**EXAMPLE 3** Divide $x^2 + 5x + 8$ by $x + 3$.

We have

$$
\begin{array}{r}
x \\
x + 3 \overline{\smash{)}x^2 + 5x + 8} \\
x^2 + 3x \\
\hline
2x
\end{array}
$$

— Divide the first term by the first term: $x^2/x = x$.

— Multiply $x$ above by the divisor, $x + 3$.

— Subtract: $(x^2 + 5x) - (x^2 + 3x) = x^2 + 5x - x^2 - 3x$
  $= 2x$.

We now "bring down" the other terms of the dividend—in this case, 8.

$$
\begin{array}{r}
x + 2 \\
x + 3 \overline{\smash{)}x^2 + 5x + 8} \\
x^2 + 3x \\
\hline
2x + 8 \\
2x + 6 \\
\hline
2
\end{array}
$$

— Divide the first term by the first term: $2x/x = 2$.

— The 8 has been "brought down."

— Multiply 2 above by the divisor, $x + 3$.

— Subtract: $(2x + 8) - (2x + 6) = 2x + 8 - 2x - 6 = 2$.

The answer is $x + 2$, R 2; or

$$x + 2 + \frac{2}{x + 3}.$$

This expression is the remainder over the divisor.

Note that the answer is not a polynomial unless the remainder is 0.

To check, we multiply the quotient by the divisor and add the remainder to see if we get the dividend:

| Divisor | Quotient | Remainder | Dividend |
|---|---|---|---|
| $(x + 3)$ · | $(x + 2)$ + | 2 | $= (x^2 + 5x + 6) + 2$ |
| | | | $= x^2 + 5x + 8$. |

The answer checks.

**EXAMPLE 4** Divide: $(5x^4 + x^3 - 3x^2 - 6x - 8) \div (x - 1)$.

$$
\begin{array}{r}
5x^3 + 6x^2 + 3x - 3 \\
x - 1 \overline{\smash{)}5x^4 + \phantom{0}x^3 - 3x^2 - 6x - 8} \\
5x^4 - 5x^3 \\
\hline
6x^3 - 3x^2 \\
6x^3 - 6x^2 \\
\hline
3x^2 - 6x \\
3x^2 - 3x \\
\hline
-3x - 8 \\
-3x + 3 \\
\hline
-11
\end{array}
$$

— Subtract:
  $(5x^4 + x^3) - (5x^4 - 5x^3) = 6x^3$.

— Subtract:
  $(6x^3 - 3x^2) - (6x^3 - 6x^2) = 3x^2$.

— Subtract:
  $(3x^2 - 6x) - (3x^2 - 3x) = -3x$.

— Subtract:
  $(-3x - 8) - (-3x + 3) = -11$.

The answer is $5x^3 + 6x^2 + 3x - 3$, R $-11$; or

$$5x^3 + 6x^2 + 3x - 3 + \frac{-11}{x - 1}.$$

Do Exercises 4 and 5.

**4.** Divide and check:

$$x - 2 \overline{\smash{)}x^2 + 3x - 10}.$$

**5.** Divide and check:

$(2x^4 + 3x^3 - x^2 - 7x + 9) \div (x + 4)$.

*Answers*

**4.** $x + 5$  **5.** $2x^3 - 5x^2 + 19x - 83$, R 341;

or $2x^3 - 5x^2 + 19x - 83 + \dfrac{341}{x + 4}$

When dividing polynomials, remember to always arrange the polynomials in descending order. In a polynomial division, if there are *missing* terms in the dividend, either write them with 0 coefficients or leave space for them. For example, in $125y^3 - 8$, we say that "the $y^2$- and $y$-terms are **missing**." We could write them in as follows: $125y^3 + 0y^2 + 0y - 8$.

**EXAMPLE 5**   Divide: $(125y^3 - 8) \div (5y - 2)$.

$$
\begin{array}{r}
25y^2 + 10y + 4 \phantom{-8} \\
5y - 2 \overline{)\ 125y^3 + 0y^2 + 0y - 8} \\
\underline{125y^3 - 50y^2} \phantom{+ 0y - 8} \\
50y^2 + 0y \phantom{- 8} \\
\underline{50y^2 - 20y} \phantom{- 8} \\
20y - 8 \\
\underline{20y - 8} \\
0
\end{array}
$$

When there are missing terms, we can write them in.

Subtract: $125y^3 - (125y^3 - 50y^2) = 50y^2$.

Subtract: $50y^2 - (50y^2 - 20y) = 20y$.

Subtract: $(20y - 8) - (20y - 8) = 0$.

The answer is $25y^2 + 10y + 4$.

Do Exercise 6.

Another way to deal with missing terms is to leave space for them, as we see in Example 6.

**EXAMPLE 6**   Divide: $(x^4 - 9x^2 - 5) \div (x - 2)$.

Note that the $x^3$- and $x$-terms are missing in the dividend.

$$
\begin{array}{r}
x^3 + 2x^2 - 5x - 10 \phantom{-5} \\
x - 2 \overline{)\ x^4 \phantom{+ 2x^3} - 9x^2 \phantom{- 5x} - 5} \\
\underline{x^4 - 2x^3} \phantom{- 9x^2 - 5} \\
2x^3 - 9x^2 \phantom{- 5} \\
\underline{2x^3 - 4x^2} \phantom{- 5} \\
-5x^2 \phantom{- 5} \\
\underline{-5x^2 + 10x} \phantom{- 5} \\
-10x - 5 \\
\underline{-10x + 20} \\
-25
\end{array}
$$

We leave spaces for missing terms.

Subtract: $x^4 - (x^4 - 2x^3) = 2x^3$.

Subtract: $(2x^3 - 9x^2) - (2x^3 - 4x^2) = -5x^2$.

Subtract: $-5x^2 - (-5x^2 + 10x) = -10x$.

Subtract: $(-10x - 5) - (-10x + 20) = -25$.

The answer is $x^3 + 2x^2 - 5x - 10$, R $-25$; or

$$x^3 + 2x^2 - 5x - 10 + \frac{-25}{x - 2}.$$

Do Exercises 7 and 8.

**6.** Divide and check:
$$(9y^4 + 14y^2 - 8) \div (3y + 2).$$

Divide and check.

**7.** $(y^3 - 11y^2 + 6) \div (y - 3)$

**8.** $(x^3 + 9x^2 - 5) \div (x - 1)$

When dividing, we may "come out even" (have a remainder of 0) or we may not. If not, how long should we keep working? We continue until the degree of the remainder is less than the degree of the divisor, as in the next example.

**EXAMPLE 7** Divide: $(6x^3 + 9x^2 - 5) \div (x^2 - 2x)$.

$$
\begin{array}{r}
6x + 21 \\
x^2 - 2x \overline{\smash{)}6x^3 + \phantom{0}9x^2 + \phantom{0}0x - 5} \\
\underline{6x^3 - 12x^2} \\
21x^2 + \phantom{0}0x \\
\underline{21x^2 - 42x} \\
42x - 5
\end{array}
$$

We have a missing term.
We can write it in.

The degree of the remainder, 1, is less than the degree of the divisor, 2, so we are finished.

The answer is $6x + 21$, R $(42x - 5)$; or

$$6x + 21 + \frac{42x - 5}{x^2 - 2x}.$$

**9.** Divide and check:

$(y^3 - 11y^2 + 6) \div (y^2 - 3).$

Do Exercise 9.

## c  Synthetic Division

To divide a polynomial by a binomial of the type $x - a$, we can streamline the general procedure by a process called **synthetic division**.

Compare the following. In **A**, we perform a division. In **B**, we also divide but we do not write the variables.

**A.**
$$
\begin{array}{r}
4x^2 + 5x + 11 \\
x - 2 \overline{\smash{)}4x^3 - 3x^2 + \phantom{0}x + 7} \\
\underline{4x^3 - 8x^2} \\
5x^2 + \phantom{0}x \\
\underline{5x^2 - 10x} \\
11x + \phantom{0}7 \\
\underline{11x - 22} \\
29
\end{array}
$$

**B.**
$$
\begin{array}{r}
4 + 5 + 11 \\
1 - 2 \overline{\smash{)}4 - 3 + \phantom{0}1 + 7} \\
\underline{4 - 8} \\
5 + \phantom{0}1 \\
\underline{5 - 10} \\
11 + \phantom{0}7 \\
\underline{11 - 22} \\
29
\end{array}
$$

In **B**, there is still some duplication of writing. Also, since we can subtract by adding the opposite, we can use 2 instead of $-2$ and then add instead of subtracting.

*Answer*

**9.** $y - 11$, R $(3y - 27)$; or $y - 11 + \dfrac{3y - 27}{y^2 - 3}$

**C.** *Synthetic Division*

a) $\underline{2}|4 \quad -3 \quad 1 \quad 7$

$\overline{\phantom{2|4 \quad -3 \quad 1 \quad 7}}$

$\phantom{2|}4$

Write the 2, the opposite of −2 in the divisor $x - 2$, and the coefficients of the dividend.

Bring down the first coefficient.

b)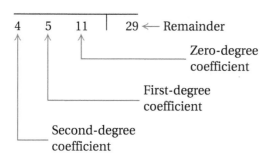

Multiply 4 by 2 to get 8. Add 8 and −3.

c) $\underline{2}|4 \quad -3 \quad 1 \quad 7$

$\phantom{2|4 \quad}8 \quad 10$

$\overline{\phantom{2|}4 \quad \phantom{-}5 \quad 11}$

Multiply 5 by 2 to get 10. Add 10 and 1.

d) $\underline{2}|4 \quad -3 \quad 1 \quad 7$

$\phantom{2|4 \quad}8 \quad 10 \quad 22$

$\overline{\phantom{2|}4 \quad \phantom{-}5 \quad 11\,|\,29}$

Multiply 11 by 2 to get 22. Add 22 and 7.

Quotient  Remainder

The last number, 29, is the remainder. The other numbers are the coefficients of the quotient with that of the term of highest degree first, as follows. Note that the degree of the term of highest degree is 1 less than the degree of the dividend.

$$4 \qquad 5 \qquad 11 \quad | \quad 29 \leftarrow \text{Remainder}$$

Zero-degree coefficient

First-degree coefficient

Second-degree coefficient

The answer is $4x^2 + 5x + 11$, R 29; or $4x^2 + 5x + 11 + \dfrac{29}{x - 2}$.

> It is important to remember that in order for synthetic division to work, the divisor must be of the form $x - a$, that is, a variable minus a constant. The coefficient of the variable must be 1.

**EXAMPLE 8** Use synthetic division to divide:

$$(x^3 + 6x^2 - x - 30) \div (x - 2).$$

We have

$\underline{2}|1 \quad 6 \quad -1 \quad -30$

$\phantom{2|1 \quad}2 \quad 16 \quad 30$

$\overline{\phantom{2|}1 \quad 8 \quad 15\,|\,\phantom{-3}0}$

The answer is $x^2 + 8x + 15$, R 0; or just $x^2 + 8x + 15$.

Do Exercise 10.

**10.** Use synthetic division to divide:
$$(2x^3 - 4x^2 + 8x - 8) \div (x - 3).$$

**Answer**

**10.** $2x^2 + 2x + 14$, R 34;

or $2x^2 + 2x + 14 + \dfrac{34}{x - 3}$

When there are missing terms, be sure to write 0's for their coefficients.

**EXAMPLES** Use synthetic division to divide.

**9.** $(2x^3 + 7x^2 - 5) \div (x + 3)$

There is no $x$-term, so we must write a 0 for its coefficient. Note that $x + 3 = x - (-3)$, so we write $-3$ at the left.

$$
\begin{array}{r}
-3\,\underline{|2 \quad 7 \quad 0 \quad -5} \\
\phantom{-3|2} -6 \quad -3 \quad 9 \\
\hline
2 \quad 1 \quad -3\,|\, 4
\end{array}
$$

The answer is $2x^2 + x - 3$, R 4; or $2x^2 + x - 3 + \dfrac{4}{x + 3}$.

**10.** $(x^3 + 4x^2 - x - 4) \div (x + 4)$

Note that $x + 4 = x - (-4)$, so we write $-4$ at the left.

$$
\begin{array}{r}
-4\,\underline{|1 \quad 4 \quad -1 \quad -4} \\
\phantom{-4|1} -4 \quad 0 \quad 4 \\
\hline
1 \quad 0 \quad -1\,|\, 0
\end{array}
$$

The answer is $x^2 - 1$.

**11.** $(x^4 - 1) \div (x - 1)$

The divisor is $x - 1$, so we write 1 at the left.

$$
\begin{array}{r}
1\,\underline{|1 \quad 0 \quad 0 \quad 0 \quad -1} \\
\phantom{1|1} 1 \quad 1 \quad 1 \quad 1 \\
\hline
1 \quad 1 \quad 1 \quad 1\,|\, 0
\end{array}
$$

The answer is $x^3 + x^2 + x + 1$.

**12.** $(8x^5 - 6x^3 + x - 8) \div (x + 2)$

Note that $x + 2 = x - (-2)$, so we write $-2$ at the left.

$$
\begin{array}{r}
-2\,\underline{|8 \quad 0 \quad -6 \quad 0 \quad 1 \quad -8} \\
\phantom{-2|8} -16 \quad 32 \quad -52 \quad 104 \quad -210 \\
\hline
8 \quad -16 \quad 26 \quad -52 \quad 105\,|\, -218
\end{array}
$$

The answer is $8x^4 - 16x^3 + 26x^2 - 52x + 105$, R $-218$; or

$$8x^4 - 16x^3 + 26x^2 - 52x + 105 + \dfrac{-218}{x + 2}.$$

Use synthetic division to divide.

**11.** $(x^3 - 2x^2 + 5x - 4) \div (x + 2)$

**12.** $(y^3 + 1) \div (y + 1)$

Do Exercises 11 and 12.

*Answers*

**11.** $x^2 - 4x + 13$, R $-30$;
or $x^2 - 4x + 13 + \dfrac{-30}{x + 2}$    **12.** $y^2 - y + 1$

**a**  Divide and check.

1. $\dfrac{24x^6 + 18x^5 - 36x^2}{6x^2}$

2. $\dfrac{30y^8 - 15y^6 + 40y^4}{5y^4}$

3. $\dfrac{45y^7 - 20y^4 + 15y^2}{5y^2}$

4. $\dfrac{60x^8 + 44x^5 - 28x^3}{4x^3}$

5. $(32a^4b^3 + 14a^3b^2 - 22a^2b) \div (2a^2b)$

6. $(7x^3y^4 - 21x^2y^3 + 28xy^2) \div (7xy)$

**b**  Divide.

7. $(x^2 + 10x + 21) \div (x + 3)$

8. $(y^2 - 8y + 16) \div (y - 4)$

9. $(a^2 - 8a - 16) \div (a + 4)$

10. $(y^2 - 10y - 25) \div (y - 5)$

11. $(x^2 + 7x + 14) \div (x + 5)$

12. $(t^2 - 7t - 9) \div (t - 3)$

13. $(4y^3 + 6y^2 + 14) \div (2y + 4)$

14. $(6x^3 - x^2 - 10) \div (3x + 4)$

15. $(10y^3 + 6y^2 - 9y + 10) \div (5y - 2)$

16. $(6x^3 - 11x^2 + 11x - 2) \div (2x - 3)$

17. $(2x^4 - x^3 - 5x^2 + x - 6) \div (x^2 + 2)$

18. $(3x^4 + 2x^3 - 11x^2 - 2x + 5) \div (x^2 - 2)$

19. $(2x^5 - x^4 + 2x^3 - x) \div (x^2 - 3x)$

20. $(2x^5 + 3x^3 + x^2 - 4) \div (x^2 + x)$

Use synthetic division to divide.

**21.** $(x^3 - 2x^2 + 2x - 5) \div (x - 1)$

**22.** $(x^3 - 2x^2 + 2x - 5) \div (x + 1)$

**23.** $(a^2 + 11a - 19) \div (a + 4)$

**24.** $(a^2 + 11a - 19) \div (a - 4)$

**25.** $(x^3 - 7x^2 - 13x + 3) \div (x - 2)$

**26.** $(x^3 - 7x^2 - 13x + 3) \div (x + 2)$

**27.** $(3x^3 + 7x^2 - 4x + 3) \div (x + 3)$

**28.** $(3x^3 + 7x^2 - 4x + 3) \div (x - 3)$

**29.** $(y^3 - 3y + 10) \div (y - 2)$

**30.** $(x^3 - 2x^2 + 8) \div (x + 2)$

**31.** $(3x^4 - 25x^2 - 18) \div (x - 3)$

**32.** $(6y^4 + 15y^3 + 28y + 6) \div (y + 3)$

**33.** $(x^3 - 8) \div (x - 2)$

**34.** $(y^3 + 125) \div (y + 5)$

**35.** $(y^4 - 16) \div (y - 2)$

**36.** $(x^5 - 32) \div (x - 2)$

**37.** $(y^8 - 1) \div (y + 1)$

**38.** $(y^6 - 2) \div (y - 1)$

## Skill Maintenance

Graph.  [3.7b]

**39.** $2x - 3y < 6$

**40.** $5x + 3y \leq 15$

**41.** $y > 4$

**42.** $x \leq -2$

Graph.  [2.2c]

**43.** $f(x) = x^2$

**44.** $g(x) = x^2 - 3$

**45.** $f(x) = 3 - x^2$

**46.** $f(x) = x^2 + 6x + 6$

Solve.  [4.8a]

**47.** $x^2 - 5x = 0$

**48.** $25y^2 = 64$

**49.** $12x^2 = 17x + 5$

**50.** $12x^2 + 11x + 2 = 0$

## Synthesis

**51.** Let $f(x) = 4x^3 + 16x^2 - 3x - 45$. Find $f(-3)$ and then solve $f(x) = 0$.

**52.** Let $f(x) = 6x^3 - 13x^2 - 79x + 140$. Find $f(4)$ and then solve $f(x) = 0$.

**53.** When $x^2 - 3x + 2k$ is divided by $x + 2$, the remainder is 7. Find $k$.

**54.** Find $k$ such that when $x^3 - kx^2 + 3x + 7k$ is divided by $x + 2$, the remainder is 0.

Divide.

**55.** $(4a^3b + 5a^2b^2 + a^4 + 2ab^3) \div (a^2 + 2b^2 + 3ab)$

**56.** $(a^7 + b^7) \div (a + b)$

# 5.4 Complex Rational Expressions

**a**

A **complex rational expression** is a rational expression that contains rational expressions within its numerator and/or its denominator. Here are some examples:

$$\frac{\frac{2}{3}}{\frac{4}{5}}, \quad \frac{1 + \frac{5}{x}}{4x}, \quad \frac{\frac{x-y}{x+y}}{\frac{2x-y}{3x+y}}, \quad \frac{\frac{3x}{5} - \frac{2}{x}}{\frac{4x}{3} + \frac{7}{6x}}.$$

The rational expressions within each complex rational expression are red.

There are two methods that can be used to simplify complex rational expressions. We will consider both of them.

## Method 1: Multiplying by the LCM of All the Denominators

*Method 1.* To simplify a complex rational expression:

1. First, find the LCM of all the denominators of all the rational expressions occurring within both the numerator and the denominator of the (original) complex rational expression.
2. Multiply by 1 using LCM/LCM.
3. If possible, simplify.

**EXAMPLE 1** Simplify: $\dfrac{x + \frac{1}{5}}{x - \frac{1}{3}}$.

We first find the LCM of all the denominators of all the rational expressions occurring in both the numerator and the denominator of the complex rational expression. The denominators are 3 and 5. The LCM of these denominators is $3 \cdot 5$, or 15. We multiply by 15/15.

$$\frac{x + \frac{1}{5}}{x - \frac{1}{3}} = \left(\frac{x + \frac{1}{5}}{x - \frac{1}{3}}\right) \cdot \frac{15}{15} \qquad \text{Multiplying by 1}$$

$$= \frac{\left(x + \frac{1}{5}\right) \cdot 15}{\left(x - \frac{1}{3}\right) \cdot 15} \qquad \begin{array}{l}\text{Multiplying the numerators}\\\text{and the denominators}\end{array}$$

$$= \frac{15x + \frac{1}{5} \cdot 15}{15x - \frac{1}{3} \cdot 15} \qquad \begin{array}{l}\text{Carrying out the multiplications}\\\text{using the distributive laws}\end{array}$$

$$= \frac{15x + 3}{15x - 5}, \text{ or } \frac{3(5x + 1)}{5(3x - 1)} \qquad \text{No further simplification is possible.}$$

**SKILL TO REVIEW**
Objective 5.1e: Divide rational expressions and simplify.

Divide and simplify.

1. $\dfrac{5x - 10}{x} \div \dfrac{x - 2}{x^5}$

2. $\dfrac{a^2 - 49}{a + 3} \div \dfrac{a + 7}{a + 3}$

*To the instructor and the student:* Students can be instructed to try both methods and then choose the one that works best for them, or one method can be chosen by the instructor.

**Answers**

*Skill to Review:*
1. $5x^4$    2. $a - 7$

In Example 1, if you feel more comfortable doing so, you can always write denominators of 1 where there are no denominators written. In this case, you could start out by writing

$$\frac{\dfrac{x}{1} + \dfrac{1}{5}}{\dfrac{x}{1} - \dfrac{1}{3}}.$$

Do Exercise 1.

**1.** Simplify. Use method 1.

$$\frac{y + \dfrac{1}{2}}{y - \dfrac{1}{7}}$$

**EXAMPLE 2**  Simplify: $\dfrac{1 + \dfrac{1}{x}}{1 - \dfrac{1}{x^2}}$.

We first find the LCM of all the denominators of all the rational expressions occurring in both the numerator and the denominator of the complex rational expression. The denominators are $x$ and $x^2$. The LCM of these denominators is $x^2$. We multiply by $x^2/x^2$.

$$\frac{1 + \dfrac{1}{x}}{1 - \dfrac{1}{x^2}} = \left(\frac{1 + \dfrac{1}{x}}{1 - \dfrac{1}{x^2}}\right) \cdot \frac{x^2}{x^2} \qquad \text{The LCM of the denominators is } x^2.$$
$$\text{We multiply by 1: } \frac{x^2}{x^2}.$$

$$= \frac{\left(1 + \dfrac{1}{x}\right) \cdot x^2}{\left(1 - \dfrac{1}{x^2}\right) \cdot x^2} \qquad \text{Multiplying the numerators and the denominators}$$

$$= \frac{x^2 + \dfrac{1}{x} \cdot x^2}{x^2 - \dfrac{1}{x^2} \cdot x^2} \qquad \text{Carrying out the multiplications using the distributive laws}$$

$$= \frac{x^2 + x}{x^2 - 1}$$

$$= \frac{x(x + 1)}{(x + 1)(x - 1)} \qquad \text{Factoring}$$

$$= \frac{x\cancel{(x + 1)}}{\cancel{(x + 1)}(x - 1)} \qquad \text{Removing a factor of 1: } \frac{x + 1}{x + 1} = 1$$

$$= \frac{x}{x - 1}$$

Do Exercise 2.

**2.** Simplify. Use method 1.

$$\frac{1 - \dfrac{1}{x}}{1 - \dfrac{1}{x^2}}$$

**Answers**

**1.** $\dfrac{14y + 7}{14y - 2}$, or $\dfrac{7(2y + 1)}{2(7y - 1)}$   **2.** $\dfrac{x}{x + 1}$

**EXAMPLE 3** Simplify: $\dfrac{\dfrac{1}{a} + \dfrac{1}{b}}{\dfrac{1}{a^3} + \dfrac{1}{b^3}}$.

The denominators are $a$, $b$, $a^3$, and $b^3$. The LCM of these denominators is $a^3b^3$. We multiply by $a^3b^3/(a^3b^3)$.

$$\dfrac{\dfrac{1}{a} + \dfrac{1}{b}}{\dfrac{1}{a^3} + \dfrac{1}{b^3}} = \left(\dfrac{\dfrac{1}{a} + \dfrac{1}{b}}{\dfrac{1}{a^3} + \dfrac{1}{b^3}}\right) \cdot \dfrac{a^3b^3}{a^3b^3} \qquad \text{The LCM of the denominators is } a^3b^3. \text{ We multiply by 1: } \dfrac{a^3b^3}{a^3b^3}.$$

$$= \dfrac{\left(\dfrac{1}{a} + \dfrac{1}{b}\right) \cdot a^3b^3}{\left(\dfrac{1}{a^3} + \dfrac{1}{b^3}\right) \cdot a^3b^3} \qquad \text{Multiplying the numerators and the denominators}$$

$$= \dfrac{\dfrac{1}{a} \cdot a^3b^3 + \dfrac{1}{b} \cdot a^3b^3}{\dfrac{1}{a^3} \cdot a^3b^3 + \dfrac{1}{b^3} \cdot a^3b^3} \qquad \text{Carrying out the multiplications using a distributive law}$$

$$= \dfrac{a^2b^3 + a^3b^2}{b^3 + a^3} = \dfrac{a^2b^2(b + a)}{(b + a)(b^2 - ba + a^2)} \qquad \text{Factoring}$$

$$= \dfrac{a^2b^2\cancel{(b + a)}}{\cancel{(b + a)}(b^2 - ba + a^2)} \qquad \text{Removing a factor of 1: } \dfrac{b + a}{b + a} = 1$$

$$= \dfrac{a^2b^2}{b^2 - ba + a^2}.$$

Do Exercises 3 and 4.

Simplify. Use method 1.

3. $\dfrac{\dfrac{1}{a} + \dfrac{1}{b}}{\dfrac{1}{a} - \dfrac{1}{b}}$

4. $\dfrac{\dfrac{1}{a} - \dfrac{1}{b}}{\dfrac{1}{a^3} - \dfrac{1}{b^3}}$

## Method 2: Adding or Subtracting in the Numerator and the Denominator

*Method 2.* To simplify a complex rational expression:

1. Add or subtract, as necessary, to get a single rational expression in the numerator.
2. Add or subtract, as necessary, to get a single rational expression in the denominator.
3. Divide the numerator by the denominator.
4. If possible, simplify.

We will redo Examples 1–3 using this method.

**EXAMPLE 4** Simplify: $\dfrac{x + \dfrac{1}{5}}{x - \dfrac{1}{3}}$.

$$\frac{x + \dfrac{1}{5}}{x - \dfrac{1}{3}} = \frac{x \cdot \dfrac{5}{5} + \dfrac{1}{5}}{x - \dfrac{1}{3}} = \frac{\dfrac{5x + 1}{5}}{x - \dfrac{1}{3}}$$

To get a single rational expression in the numerator, we note that the LCM in the numerator is 5. We multiply by 1 and add.

$$= \frac{\dfrac{5x + 1}{5}}{x \cdot \dfrac{3}{3} - \dfrac{1}{3}} = \frac{\dfrac{5x + 1}{5}}{\dfrac{3x - 1}{3}}$$

To get a single rational expression in the denominator, we note that the LCM in the denominator is 3. We multiply by 1 and subtract.

$$= \frac{5x + 1}{5} \cdot \frac{3}{3x - 1}$$

Multiplying by the reciprocal of the denominator

$$= \frac{15x + 3}{15x - 5}, \text{ or } \frac{3(5x + 1)}{5(3x - 1)}$$

No further simplification is possible.

**EXAMPLE 5** Simplify: $\dfrac{1 + \dfrac{1}{x}}{1 - \dfrac{1}{x^2}}$.

$$\frac{1 + \dfrac{1}{x}}{1 - \dfrac{1}{x^2}} = \frac{1 \cdot \dfrac{x}{x} + \dfrac{1}{x}}{1 \cdot \dfrac{x^2}{x^2} - \dfrac{1}{x^2}}$$

Finding the LCM in the numerator and multiplying by 1

Finding the LCM in the denominator and multiplying by 1

$$= \frac{\dfrac{x}{x} + \dfrac{1}{x}}{\dfrac{x^2}{x^2} - \dfrac{1}{x^2}}$$

$$= \frac{\dfrac{x + 1}{x}}{\dfrac{x^2 - 1}{x^2}}$$

Adding in the numerator and subtracting in the denominator

$$= \frac{x + 1}{x} \cdot \frac{x^2}{x^2 - 1}$$

Multiplying by the reciprocal of the denominator

$$= \frac{(x + 1) \cdot x \cdot x}{x(x - 1)(x + 1)}$$

Factoring and removing a factor of 1: $\dfrac{x(x + 1)}{x(x + 1)} = 1$

$$= \frac{x}{x - 1}$$

Do Exercises 5 and 6.

Simplify. Use method 2.

**5.** $\dfrac{y + \dfrac{1}{2}}{y - \dfrac{1}{7}}$

**6.** $\dfrac{1 - \dfrac{1}{x}}{1 - \dfrac{1}{x^2}}$

*Answers*

**5.** $\dfrac{14y + 7}{14y - 2}$, or $\dfrac{7(2y + 1)}{2(7y - 1)}$ **6.** $\dfrac{x}{x + 1}$

**EXAMPLE 6** Simplify: $\dfrac{\dfrac{1}{a} + \dfrac{1}{b}}{\dfrac{1}{a^3} + \dfrac{1}{b^3}}$.

The LCM in the numerator is $ab$, and the LCM in the denominator is $a^3b^3$.

$$\dfrac{\dfrac{1}{a} + \dfrac{1}{b}}{\dfrac{1}{a^3} + \dfrac{1}{b^3}} = \dfrac{\dfrac{1}{a} \cdot \dfrac{b}{b} + \dfrac{1}{b} \cdot \dfrac{a}{a}}{\dfrac{1}{a^3} \cdot \dfrac{b^3}{b^3} + \dfrac{1}{b^3} \cdot \dfrac{a^3}{a^3}}$$

$$= \dfrac{\dfrac{b}{ab} + \dfrac{a}{ab}}{\dfrac{b^3}{a^3b^3} + \dfrac{a^3}{a^3b^3}}$$

$$= \dfrac{\dfrac{b + a}{ab}}{\dfrac{b^3 + a^3}{a^3b^3}} \qquad \text{Adding in the numerator and the denominator}$$

$$= \dfrac{b + a}{ab} \cdot \dfrac{a^3b^3}{b^3 + a^3} \qquad \text{Multiplying by the reciprocal of the denominator}$$

$$= \dfrac{(b + a)a^3b^3}{ab(b^3 + a^3)}$$

$$= \dfrac{\cancel{(b + a)} \cdot \cancel{ab} \cdot a^2b^2}{\cancel{ab}\cancel{(b + a)}(b^2 - ba + a^2)} \qquad \text{Factoring and removing a factor of 1: } \dfrac{ab(b + a)}{ab(b + a)} = 1$$

$$= \dfrac{a^2b^2}{b^2 - ba + a^2}$$

Do Exercises 7 and 8.

Simplify. Use method 2.

**7.** $\dfrac{\dfrac{1}{a} + \dfrac{1}{b}}{\dfrac{1}{a} - \dfrac{1}{b}}$

**8.** $\dfrac{\dfrac{1}{a} - \dfrac{1}{b}}{\dfrac{1}{a^3} - \dfrac{1}{b^3}}$

## STUDY TIPS

### TIME MANAGEMENT

Here are some additional tips to help you with time management.

- **Keep on schedule.** Your course syllabus provides a plan for the semester's schedule. Use a write-on calendar, daily planner, PDA, or laptop computer to outline your time for the semester. Be sure to note deadlines involving writing assignments and exams so that you can begin a big task early, breaking it down into smaller segments that will not overwhelm you.

- **Are you a morning or an evening person?** If you are an evening person, it might be best to avoid scheduling early-morning classes. If you are a morning person, you will probably want to schedule morning classes if your work schedule and family obligations will allow it. Nothing can drain your study time and effectiveness like fatigue.

*Answers*

**7.** $\dfrac{b + a}{b - a}$  **8.** $\dfrac{a^2b^2}{b^2 + ab + a^2}$

**a** Simplify.

1. $\dfrac{2 + \dfrac{3}{5}}{4 - \dfrac{1}{2}}$

2. $\dfrac{\dfrac{3}{8} - 5}{\dfrac{2}{3} + 6}$

3. $\dfrac{\dfrac{2}{3} + \dfrac{4}{5}}{\dfrac{3}{4} - \dfrac{1}{2}}$

4. $\dfrac{\dfrac{5}{8} - \dfrac{2}{3}}{\dfrac{3}{4} + \dfrac{5}{6}}$

5. $\dfrac{\dfrac{x}{y^2}}{\dfrac{y^3}{x^2}}$

6. $\dfrac{\dfrac{a^3}{b^5}}{\dfrac{a^4}{b^2}}$

7. $\dfrac{\dfrac{9x^2 - y^2}{xy}}{\dfrac{3x - y}{y}}$

8. $\dfrac{\dfrac{a^2 - 16b^2}{ab}}{\dfrac{a + 4b}{b}}$

9. $\dfrac{\dfrac{1}{a} + 2}{\dfrac{1}{a} - 1}$

10. $\dfrac{\dfrac{1}{t} + 6}{\dfrac{1}{t} - 5}$

11. $\dfrac{x - \dfrac{1}{x}}{x + \dfrac{1}{x}}$

12. $\dfrac{y + \dfrac{1}{y}}{y - \dfrac{1}{y}}$

13. $\dfrac{\dfrac{3}{x} + \dfrac{4}{y}}{\dfrac{4}{x} - \dfrac{3}{y}}$

14. $\dfrac{\dfrac{2}{y} + \dfrac{5}{z}}{\dfrac{1}{y} - \dfrac{4}{z}}$

15. $\dfrac{a - \dfrac{3a}{b}}{b - \dfrac{b}{a}}$

16. $\dfrac{1 - \dfrac{2}{3x}}{x - \dfrac{4}{9x}}$

17. $\dfrac{\dfrac{1}{a} + \dfrac{1}{b}}{\dfrac{a^2 - b^2}{ab}}$

18. $\dfrac{\dfrac{1}{x} - \dfrac{1}{y}}{\dfrac{x^2 - y^2}{xy}}$

19. $\dfrac{\dfrac{1}{x + h} - \dfrac{1}{x}}{h}$

20. $\dfrac{\dfrac{1}{a - h} - \dfrac{1}{a}}{h}$

It may help you to write $h$ as $\dfrac{h}{1}$.

21. $\dfrac{\dfrac{x^2 - x - 12}{x^2 - 2x - 15}}{\dfrac{x^2 + 8x + 12}{x^2 - 5x - 14}}$

22. $\dfrac{\dfrac{y^2 - y - 6}{y^2 - 5y - 14}}{\dfrac{y^2 + 6y + 5}{y^2 - 6y - 7}}$

23. $\dfrac{\dfrac{1}{x + 2} + \dfrac{4}{x - 3}}{\dfrac{2}{x - 3} - \dfrac{7}{x + 2}}$

24. $\dfrac{\dfrac{1}{y - 4} + \dfrac{1}{y + 5}}{\dfrac{6}{y + 5} + \dfrac{2}{y - 4}}$

**25.** $\dfrac{\dfrac{6}{x^2 - 4} - \dfrac{5}{x + 2}}{\dfrac{7}{x^2 - 4} - \dfrac{4}{x - 2}}$

**26.** $\dfrac{\dfrac{1}{x^2 - 1} + \dfrac{5}{x^2 - 5x + 4}}{\dfrac{1}{x^2 - 1} + \dfrac{2}{x^2 + 3x + 2}}$

**27.** $\dfrac{\dfrac{1}{z^2} - \dfrac{1}{w^2}}{\dfrac{1}{z^3} + \dfrac{1}{w^3}}$

**28.** $\dfrac{\dfrac{1}{b^2} - \dfrac{1}{c^2}}{\dfrac{1}{b^3} - \dfrac{1}{c^3}}$

**29.** $\dfrac{\dfrac{3}{x^2 + 2x - 3} - \dfrac{1}{x^2 - 3x - 10}}{\dfrac{3}{x^2 - 6x + 5} - \dfrac{1}{x^2 + 5x + 6}}$

**30.** $\dfrac{\dfrac{1}{a^2 + 7a + 12} + \dfrac{1}{a^2 + a - 6}}{\dfrac{1}{a^2 + 2a - 8} + \dfrac{1}{a^2 + 5a + 4}}$

## Skill Maintenance

Solve.  [1.3a]

**31.** *Moving Freight.*  Most freight in the United States is moved by truck. The total percent of freight moved by truck and rail is 84%. If the percent of freight moved by truck is 9% more than four times the percent moved by rail, what percent is moved by truck?

Source: U.S. Freight Transportation Forecast to 2020

**32.** *Tax Code.*  The 1969 publication explaining the tax code contained 16,500 pages. The 2009 publication contained 12,180 fewer pages than five times the number of pages for 1969. How long was the tax code for 2009?

Source: CCH Inc.

Factor.  [4.3a], [4.4a], [4.6d]

**33.** $4x^3 + 20x^2 + 6x$

**34.** $y^3 + 8$

**35.** $y^3 - 8$

**36.** $2x^3 - 32x^2 + 126x$

**37.** $1000x^3 + 1$

**38.** $1 - 1000a^3$

**39.** $y^3 - 64x^3$

**40.** $\frac{1}{8}a^3 - 343$

**41.** Solve for $s$:  $T = \dfrac{r + s}{3}$.  [1.2a]

**42.** Graph: $f(x) = -3x + 2$.  [2.2c]

**43.** Given that $f(x) = x^2 - 3$, find $f(-5)$.  [2.2b]

**44.** Solve: $|2x - 5| = 7$.  [1.6c]

## Synthesis

For each function in Exercises 45–48, find and simplify $\dfrac{f(a + h) - f(a)}{h}$.

**45.** $f(x) = \dfrac{3}{x^2}$

**46.** $f(x) = \dfrac{5}{x}$

**47.** $f(x) = \dfrac{1}{1 - x}$

**48.** $f(x) = \dfrac{x}{1 + x}$

Simplify.

**49.** $\dfrac{5x^{-1} - 5y^{-1} + 10x^{-1}y^{-1}}{6x^{-1} - 6y^{-1} + 12x^{-1}y^{-1}}$

**50.** $\left[ \dfrac{\dfrac{x + 3}{x - 3} + 1}{\dfrac{x + 3}{x - 3} - 1} \right]^8$

Find the reciprocal and simplify.

**51.** $x^2 - \dfrac{1}{x}$

**52.** $\dfrac{1 - \dfrac{1}{a}}{a - 1}$

**53.** $\dfrac{a^3 + b^3}{a + b}$

**54.** $x^2 + x + 1 + \dfrac{1}{x} + \dfrac{1}{x^2}$

## Concept Reinforcement

Determine whether each statement is true or false.

_____ **1.** For synthetic division, the divisor must be in the form $x - a$.  [5.3c]

_____ **2.** The sum of two rational expressions is the sum of the numerators over the sum of the denominators.  [5.2b]

_____ **3.** The domain of $f(x) = \dfrac{(x - 5)(x + 4)}{x - 4}$ is $\{x | x \neq 5 \ and \ x \neq -4 \ and \ x \neq 4\}$.  [5.1a]

## Guided Solutions

Fill in each blank with the number or expression that creates a correct solution.

**4.** Subtract: $\dfrac{7x - 2}{x - 4} - \dfrac{x + 1}{x + 3}$.  [5.2b]

$$\dfrac{7x - 2}{x - 4} - \dfrac{x + 1}{x + 3} = \dfrac{7x - 2}{x - 4} \cdot \dfrac{\square}{\square} - \dfrac{x + 1}{x + 3} \cdot \dfrac{\square}{\square}$$

$$= \dfrac{7x^2 + \square x - \square}{(\square)(x + 3)} - \dfrac{x^2 - \square x - \square}{(\square)(x - 4)}$$

$$= \dfrac{\square x^2 + 19x - 6 - \square + \square + 4}{(\square)(x + 3)}$$

$$= \dfrac{\square x^2 + \square x - \square}{(x - 4)(\square)}$$

**5.** Simplify: $\dfrac{\dfrac{1}{m} + 3}{\dfrac{1}{m} - 5}$.  [5.4a]

$$\dfrac{\dfrac{1}{m} + 3}{\dfrac{1}{m} - 5} = \dfrac{\dfrac{1}{m} + 3}{\dfrac{1}{m} - 5} \cdot \dfrac{\square}{\square} = \dfrac{\square + 3\square}{\square - 5\square}$$

## Mixed Review

Find the domain of each function.  [5.1a]

**6.** $f(x) = \dfrac{x + 5}{x^2 - 100}$

**7.** $g(x) = \dfrac{-3}{x - 7}$

**8.** $h(x) = \dfrac{x^2 - 9}{x^2 + 8x - 9}$

Simplify.  [5.1c]

**9.** $\dfrac{24p^2}{36p^9}$

**10.** $\dfrac{42y - 3}{33}$

**11.** $\dfrac{x^2 - y^2}{x^3 + y^3}$

**12.** $\dfrac{x^2 - x - 30}{x^2 - 4x - 12}$

**13.** $\dfrac{9a - 18}{9a + 18}$

**14.** $\dfrac{3 - t}{t^2 - t - 6}$

Find the LCM.  [5.2a]

**15.** $x^3$, $14x^2y$, $35x^4y^5$

**16.** $x^2 - 25$, $x^2 - 10x + 25$, $x^2 + 3x - 40$

Perform the indicated operations and simplify.

**17.** $\dfrac{45}{x^2 - 1} \div \dfrac{x + 1}{x - 1}$  [5.1e]

**18.** $\dfrac{3x - 1}{x + 6} + \dfrac{x}{x - 2}$  [5.2b]

**19.** $\dfrac{q}{q + 2} - \dfrac{q + 1}{q}$  [5.2b]

**20.** $\dfrac{2y}{y^2 + 2y - 3} - \dfrac{3y + 1}{y^2 + y - 2}$  [5.2b]

**21.** $\dfrac{\dfrac{1}{b} - 1}{\dfrac{1}{b^2} - 1}$  [5.4a]

**22.** $\dfrac{w^2 - z^2}{5w - 5z} \cdot \dfrac{w - z}{w + z}$  [5.1d]

**23.** $\dfrac{t^3 - 8}{2t + 3} \cdot \dfrac{2t^2 + t - 3}{t - 2}$  [5.1d]

**24.** $\dfrac{5c}{3} + \dfrac{2a}{5c}$  [5.2b]

**25.** $\dfrac{x^2 - 4x}{x^2 + 2x} \div \dfrac{x^2 - 8x + 16}{x^2 + 4x + 4}$  [5.1e]

Divide and if there is a remainder, express it in two ways. Use synthetic division in Exercises 28–30.  [5.3b, c]

**26.** $(6x^2 - 5x + 11) \div (2x - 3)$

**27.** $(x^4 - 1) \div (x + 1)$

**28.** $(2x^3 - x^2 + 5x - 4) \div (x + 2)$

**29.** $(x^2 - 4x - 12) \div (x - 6)$

**30.** $(x^4 - 3x^2 + 2) \div (x + 3)$

**31.** $(15x^2 - 2x + 6) \div (5x + 1)$

## Understanding Through Discussion and Writing

**32.** Explain how synthetic division can be useful when factoring a polynomial.  [5.3c]

**33.** Do addition, subtraction, multiplication, and division of polynomials always result in a polynomial? Why or why not?  [5.1d], [5.2b], [5.3b]

**34.** Is it possible to understand how to simplify rational expressions without first understanding how to multiply? Why or why not?  [5.1c]

**35.** Janine found that the sum of two rational expressions was $(3 - x)/(x - 5)$, but the answer at the back of the book was $(x - 3)/(5 - x)$. Was Janine's answer correct? Why or why not?  [5.2b]

**36.** Nancy *incorrectly* simplifies $(x + 2)/x$ as follows:

$$\dfrac{x + 2}{x} = \dfrac{\cancel{x} + 2}{\cancel{x}} = 1 + 2 = 3.$$

She insists that this is correct because when $x$ is replaced with 1, her answer checks. Explain her error.  [5.1c]

**37.** Explain why it is easier to use method 1 than method 2 to simplify the following expression.  [5.4a]

$$\dfrac{\dfrac{a}{b} + \dfrac{c}{d}}{\dfrac{a}{b} - \dfrac{c}{d}}$$

# 5.5

# Solving Rational Equations

## OBJECTIVE

**a** Solve rational equations.

**SKILL TO REVIEW**
Objective 4.8a: Solve quadratic and other polynomial equations by first factoring and then using the principle of zero products.

Solve.

**1.** $x^2 - 3x - 18 = 0$

**2.** $3x^2 - 12x = 0$

## **a** Rational Equations

In Sections 5.1–5.4, we studied operations with *rational expressions*. These expressions do not have equals signs. Although we can perform the operations and simplify, we cannot solve them. Note the following examples:

$$\frac{x^2 - 6x + 9}{x^2 - 4} \cdot \frac{x - 2}{x - 3}, \qquad \frac{x + y}{x - y} \div \frac{x^2 + y}{x^2 - y^2}, \quad \text{and} \quad \frac{a + 7}{a^2 - 16} + \frac{5}{5a - 15}.$$

Operation signs occur. There are no equals signs!

Most often, the result of our calculation is another rational expression that is not cleared of fractions.

Equations *do have* equals signs, and we can clear them of fractions as we did in Section 1.1. A **rational**, or **fraction, equation** is an equation containing one or more rational expressions. Here are some examples:

$$\frac{2}{3} - \frac{5}{6} = \frac{1}{x}, \qquad x + \frac{6}{x} = 5, \quad \text{and} \quad \frac{2x}{x - 3} - \frac{6}{x} = \frac{18}{x^2 - 3x}.$$

There are equals signs as well as operation signs.

> **SOLVING RATIONAL EQUATIONS**
>
> To solve a rational equation, the first step is to clear the equation of fractions. To do this, multiply all terms on both sides of the equation by the LCM of all the denominators. Then carry out the equation-solving process as discussed in Chapters 1 and 4.

**EXAMPLE 1** Solve: $\dfrac{2}{3} - \dfrac{5}{6} = \dfrac{1}{x}$.

The LCM of all the denominators is $6x$, or $2 \cdot 3 \cdot x$. Using the multiplication principle of Chapter 1, we multiply all terms on both sides of the equation by the LCM.

$$(2 \cdot 3 \cdot x) \cdot \left(\frac{2}{3} - \frac{5}{6}\right) = (2 \cdot 3 \cdot x) \cdot \frac{1}{x} \qquad \text{Multiplying both sides by the LCM}$$

$$2 \cdot 3 \cdot x \cdot \frac{2}{3} - 2 \cdot 3 \cdot x \cdot \frac{5}{6} = 2 \cdot 3 \cdot x \cdot \frac{1}{x} \qquad \text{Multiplying to remove parentheses}$$

> When clearing fractions, be sure to multiply *every* term in the equation by the LCM.

$$2 \cdot x \cdot 2 - x \cdot 5 = 2 \cdot 3$$

$$4x - 5x = 6$$

$$-x = 6$$

$$-1 \cdot x = 6$$

$$x = -6$$

*Answers*

*Skill to Review:*

**1.** $-3, 6$   **2.** $0, 4$

Check:  $\dfrac{2}{3} - \dfrac{5}{6} = \dfrac{1}{x}$

$$\dfrac{2}{3} - \dfrac{5}{6} \ ? \ \dfrac{1}{-6}$$

$$\dfrac{4}{6} - \dfrac{5}{6} \ \bigg| \ -\dfrac{1}{6}$$

$$-\dfrac{1}{6} \ \bigg| \qquad \text{TRUE}$$

The solution is $-6$.

Do Exercise 1.

**1.** Solve: $\dfrac{2}{3} + \dfrac{5}{6} = \dfrac{1}{x}$.

**EXAMPLE 2**  Solve: $\dfrac{x + 1}{2} - \dfrac{x - 3}{3} = 3$.

The LCM of all the denominators is $2 \cdot 3$, or 6. We multiply all terms on both sides of the equation by the LCM.

$$2 \cdot 3 \cdot \left( \dfrac{x + 1}{2} - \dfrac{x - 3}{3} \right) = 2 \cdot 3 \cdot 3 \qquad \text{Multiplying both sides by the LCM}$$

$$2 \cdot 3 \cdot \dfrac{x + 1}{2} - 2 \cdot 3 \cdot \dfrac{x - 3}{3} = 2 \cdot 3 \cdot 3 \qquad \text{Multiplying to remove parentheses}$$

$$3(x + 1) - 2(x - 3) = 18 \qquad \text{Simplifying}$$

$$3x + 3 - 2x + 6 = 18 \left.\vphantom{\dfrac{1}{1}}\right\} \qquad \text{Multiplying and collecting like terms}$$

$$x + 9 = 18$$

$$x = 9$$

Check:  $\dfrac{x + 1}{2} - \dfrac{x - 3}{3} = 3$

$$\dfrac{9 + 1}{2} - \dfrac{9 - 3}{3} \ ? \ 3$$

$$5 - 2 \ \bigg|$$

$$3 \ \bigg| \qquad \text{TRUE}$$

---------- *Caution!* ----------

*Clearing fractions* is a valid procedure only when solving equations, *not* when adding, subtracting, multiplying, or dividing rational expressions.

The solution is 9.

Do Exercise 2.

**2.** Solve: $\dfrac{y - 4}{5} - \dfrac{y + 7}{2} = 5$.

**CHECKING POSSIBLE SOLUTIONS**

When we multiply all terms on both sides of an equation by the LCM, the resulting equation might yield numbers that are *not* solutions of the original equation. Thus we must *always* check possible solutions in the original equation.

1.  If you have carried out all algebraic procedures correctly, you need only check to see whether a number makes a denominator 0 in the original equation. If it does, it is not a solution.

2.  To be sure that no computational errors have been made and that you indeed have a solution, a complete check is necessary, as we did in Examples 1 and 2 above.

The next example illustrates the importance of checking all possible solutions.

*Answers*

1. $\dfrac{2}{3}$    2. $-31$

**EXAMPLE 3**  Solve: $\dfrac{2x}{x-3} - \dfrac{6}{x} = \dfrac{18}{x^2 - 3x}$.

The LCM of the denominators is $x(x-3)$. We multiply all terms on both sides by $x(x-3)$.

$$x(x-3)\left(\dfrac{2x}{x-3} - \dfrac{6}{x}\right) = x(x-3)\left(\dfrac{18}{x^2-3x}\right) \qquad \text{Multiplying both sides by the LCM}$$

$$x(x-3)\cdot\dfrac{2x}{x-3} - x(x-3)\cdot\dfrac{6}{x} = x(x-3)\left(\dfrac{18}{x^2-3x}\right) \qquad \text{Multiplying to remove parentheses}$$

$$2x^2 - 6(x-3) = 18 \qquad \text{Simplifying}$$
$$2x^2 - 6x + 18 = 18$$
$$2x^2 - 6x = 0$$
$$2x(x-3) = 0 \qquad \text{Factoring}$$
$$2x = 0 \quad or \quad x - 3 = 0 \qquad \text{Using the principle of zero products}$$
$$x = 0 \quad or \qquad x = 3$$

The numbers 0 and 3 are possible solutions. We look at the original equation and see that each makes a denominator 0, so neither is a solution. We can carry out a check, as follows.

Check:

For 0:

$$\dfrac{2x}{x-3} - \dfrac{6}{x} = \dfrac{18}{x^2-3x}$$

$$\dfrac{2(0)}{0-3} - \dfrac{6}{0} \enspace \overset{?}{\enspace} \enspace \dfrac{18}{0^2 - 3(0)}$$

$$0 - \dfrac{6}{0} \enspace\Big|\enspace \dfrac{18}{0} \qquad \text{NOT DEFINED}$$

For 3:

$$\dfrac{2x}{x-3} - \dfrac{6}{x} = \dfrac{18}{x^2-3x}$$

$$\dfrac{2(3)}{3-3} - \dfrac{6}{3} \enspace \overset{?}{\enspace} \enspace \dfrac{18}{3^2 - 3(3)}$$

$$\dfrac{6}{0} - 2 \enspace\Big|\enspace \dfrac{18}{0} \qquad \text{NOT DEFINED}$$

The equation has *no solution*.

Do Exercise 3.

**3.** Solve:

$$\dfrac{4x}{x+5} + \dfrac{20}{x} = \dfrac{100}{x^2+5x}.$$

**EXAMPLE 4**  Solve: $\dfrac{x^2}{x-2} = \dfrac{4}{x-2}$.

The LCM of the denominators is $x-2$. We multiply all terms on both sides by $x-2$.

$$(x-2)\cdot\dfrac{x^2}{x-2} = (x-2)\cdot\dfrac{4}{x-2}$$
$$x^2 = 4 \qquad \text{Simplifying}$$
$$x^2 - 4 = 0$$
$$(x+2)(x-2) = 0$$
$$x+2 = 0 \quad or \quad x-2 = 0 \qquad \text{Using the principle of zero products}$$
$$x = -2 \quad or \qquad x = 2$$

*Answer*

**3.** No solution

Check:  For 2:

$$\frac{x^2}{x - 2} = \frac{4}{x - 2}$$

$$\frac{2^2}{2 - 2} \overset{?}{\phantom{=}} \frac{4}{2 - 2}$$

$$\frac{4}{0} \;\Big|\; \frac{4}{0} \qquad \text{NOT DEFINED}$$

For $-2$:

$$\frac{x^2}{x - 2} = \frac{4}{x - 2}$$

$$\frac{(-2)^2}{-2 - 2} \overset{?}{\phantom{=}} \frac{4}{-2 - 2}$$

$$\frac{4}{-4} \;\Big|\; \frac{4}{-4}$$

$$-1 \;\Big|\; -1 \qquad \text{TRUE}$$

The number $-2$ is a solution, but 2 is not (it results in division by 0).

Do Exercise 4.

**EXAMPLE 5**  Solve: $\dfrac{2}{x - 1} = \dfrac{3}{x + 1}$.

The LCM of the denominators is $(x - 1)(x + 1)$. We multiply all terms on both sides by $(x - 1)(x + 1)$.

$$(x - 1)(x + 1) \cdot \frac{2}{x - 1} = (x - 1)(x + 1) \cdot \frac{3}{x + 1} \qquad \text{Multiplying}$$

$$2(x + 1) = 3(x - 1) \qquad \text{Simplifying}$$

$$2x + 2 = 3x - 3$$

$$5 = x$$

The check is left to the student. The number 5 checks and is the solution.

**EXAMPLE 6**  Solve: $\dfrac{2}{x + 5} + \dfrac{1}{x - 5} = \dfrac{16}{x^2 - 25}$.

The LCM of the denominators is $(x + 5)(x - 5)$. We multiply all terms on both sides by $(x + 5)(x - 5)$.

$$(x + 5)(x - 5) \cdot \left[ \frac{2}{x + 5} + \frac{1}{x - 5} \right] = (x + 5)(x - 5) \cdot \frac{16}{x^2 - 25}$$

$$(x + 5)(x - 5) \cdot \frac{2}{x + 5} + (x + 5)(x - 5) \cdot \frac{1}{x - 5} = (x + 5)(x - 5) \cdot \frac{16}{x^2 - 25}$$

$$2(x - 5) + (x + 5) = 16$$

$$2x - 10 + x + 5 = 16$$

$$3x - 5 = 16$$

$$3x = 21$$

$$x = 7$$

**4.** Solve: $\dfrac{x^2}{x - 3} = \dfrac{9}{x - 3}$.

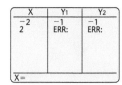

**Calculator Corner**

**Checking Solutions of Rational Equations**  We can use a table to check possible solutions of rational equations. Consider the equation in Example 4,

$$\frac{x^2}{x - 2} = \frac{4}{x - 2},$$

and the possible solutions that were found, $-2$ and 2. To check these solutions, we enter $y_1 = x^2/(x - 2)$ and $y_2 = 4/(x - 2)$ on the equation-editor screen. Then, with a table set in ASK mode, we enter $x = -2$. (See p. 83.) Since $y_1$ and $y_2$ have the same value, we know that the equation is true when $x = -2$, and thus $-2$ is a solution. Now we enter $x = 2$. The ERROR messages indicate that 2 is not a solution because it is not an allowable replacement for $x$ in the equation.

| X | Y₁ | Y₂ |
|---|---|---|
| -2 | -1 | -1 |
| 2 | ERR: | ERR: |
| X= | | |

**Exercises:**

1. Use a graphing calculator to check the possible solutions found in Examples 1, 2, and 3.

2. Use a graphing calculator to check the possible solutions you found in Margin Exercises 1–4.

*Answer*

**4.** $-3$

Solve.

**5.** $\dfrac{2}{x-1} = \dfrac{3}{x+2}$

**6.** $\dfrac{2}{x^2-9} + \dfrac{5}{x-3} = \dfrac{3}{x+3}$

Check:
$$\begin{array}{c|c} \dfrac{2}{x+5} + \dfrac{1}{x-5} & = \dfrac{16}{x^2-25} \\ \hline \dfrac{2}{7+5} + \dfrac{1}{7-5} & ?\ \dfrac{16}{7^2-25} \\ \dfrac{2}{12} + \dfrac{1}{2} & \dfrac{16}{49-25} \\ \dfrac{8}{12} & \dfrac{16}{24} \\ \dfrac{2}{3} & \dfrac{2}{3} \end{array} \quad \text{TRUE}$$

The solution is 7.

Do Exercises 5 and 6.

**EXAMPLE 7** Given that $f(x) = x + 6/x$, find all values of $x$ for which $f(x) = 5$.

Since $f(x) = x + 6/x$, we want to find all values of $x$ for which

$$x + \frac{6}{x} = 5.$$

The LCM of the denominators is $x$. We multiply all terms on both sides by $x$:

$$x\left(x + \frac{6}{x}\right) = x \cdot 5 \qquad \text{Multiplying by } x \text{ on both sides}$$
$$x \cdot x + x \cdot \frac{6}{x} = 5x$$
$$x^2 + 6 = 5x \qquad \text{Simplifying}$$
$$x^2 - 5x + 6 = 0 \qquad \text{Getting 0 on one side}$$
$$(x-3)(x-2) = 0 \qquad \text{Factoring}$$
$$x - 3 = 0 \quad or \quad x - 2 = 0 \qquad \text{Using the principle of zero products}$$
$$x = 3 \quad or \quad x = 2.$$

Check: For $x = 3$, $f(3) = 3 + \dfrac{6}{3} = 3 + 2 = 5$.

For $x = 2$, $f(2) = 2 + \dfrac{6}{2} = 2 + 3 = 5$.

The solutions are 2 and 3.

Do Exercise 7.

## Algebraic–Graphical Connection

Let's make a visual check of Example 7 by looking at a graph. We can think of the equation

$$x + \frac{6}{x} = 5$$

as the intersection of the graphs of

$$f(x) = x + \frac{6}{x} \quad \text{and} \quad g(x) = 5.$$

We see in the graph that there are two points of intersection, at $x = 2$ and at $x = 3$.

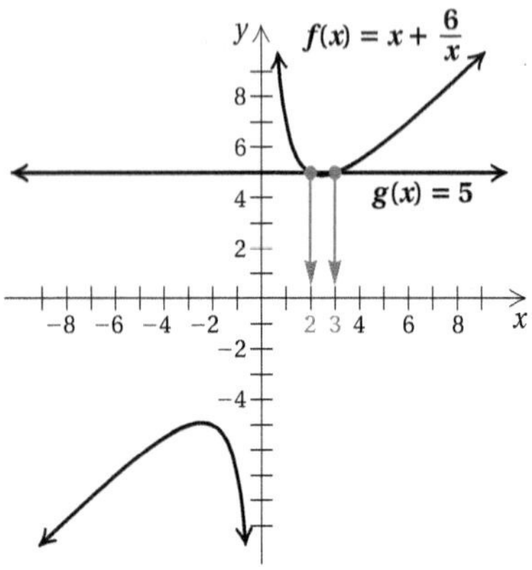


**7.** Given that $f(x) = x - 12/x$, find all values of $x$ for which $f(x) = 1$.

### Caution!

In this section, we have introduced a new use of the LCM. Before, you used the LCM in adding or subtracting rational expressions. Now we are working with equations. There are equals signs. We clear the fractions by multiplying all terms on both sides of the equation by the LCM. This eliminates the denominators. *Do not* make the mistake of trying to "clear the fractions" when you do not have an equation!

*Answers*

5. 7 6. −13 7. 4, −3

### ARE YOU CALCULATING OR SOLVING?

One of the common difficulties with this chapter is knowing for sure the task at hand. Are you combining expressions using operations to get another *rational expression*, or are you solving equations for which the results are numbers that are *solutions* of an equation? To learn to make these decisions, complete the following list by writing in the blank the type of answer you should get: "Rational expression" or "Solutions." You need not complete the mathematical operations. Answers can be found at the back of the book.

| TASK | TYPE OF ANSWER (Just write "Rational expression" or "Solutions.") |
|---|---|
| **1.** Add: $\dfrac{4}{x-2} + \dfrac{1}{x+2}$. | |
| **2.** Solve: $\dfrac{4}{x-2} = \dfrac{1}{x+2}$. | |
| **3.** Subtract: $\dfrac{4}{x-2} - \dfrac{1}{x+2}$. | |
| **4.** Multiply: $\dfrac{4}{x-2} \cdot \dfrac{1}{x+2}$. | |
| **5.** Divide: $\dfrac{4}{x-2} \div \dfrac{1}{x+2}$. | |
| **6.** Solve: $\dfrac{4}{x-2} + \dfrac{1}{x+2} = \dfrac{26}{x^2-4}$. | |
| **7.** Perform the indicated operations and simplify: $\dfrac{4}{x-2} + \dfrac{1}{x+2} - \dfrac{26}{x^2-4}$. | |
| **8.** Solve: $\dfrac{x^2}{x-1} = \dfrac{1}{x-1}$. | |
| **9.** Solve: $\dfrac{2}{y^2-25} = \dfrac{3}{y-5} + \dfrac{1}{y-5}$. | |
| **10.** Solve: $\dfrac{x}{x+4} - \dfrac{4}{x-4} = \dfrac{x^2+16}{x^2-16}$. | |
| **11.** Perform the indicated operations and simplify: $\dfrac{x}{x+4} - \dfrac{4}{x-4} - \dfrac{x^2+16}{x^2-16}$. | |
| **12.** Solve: $\dfrac{5}{y-3} - \dfrac{30}{y^2-9} = 1$. | |
| **13.** Add: $\dfrac{5}{y-3} + \dfrac{30}{y^2-9} + 1$. | |

**a**   Solve. Don't forget to check!

1. $\dfrac{y}{10} = \dfrac{2}{5} + \dfrac{3}{8}$

2. $\dfrac{3}{8} + \dfrac{1}{3} = \dfrac{t}{12}$

3. $\dfrac{1}{4} - \dfrac{5}{6} = \dfrac{1}{a}$

4. $\dfrac{5}{8} - \dfrac{2}{5} = \dfrac{1}{y}$

5. $\dfrac{x}{3} - \dfrac{x}{4} = 12$

6. $\dfrac{y}{5} - \dfrac{y}{3} = 15$

7. $x + \dfrac{8}{x} = -9$

8. $y + \dfrac{22}{y} = -13$

9. $\dfrac{3}{y} + \dfrac{7}{y} = 5$

10. $\dfrac{4}{3y} - \dfrac{3}{y} = \dfrac{10}{3}$

11. $\dfrac{1}{2} = \dfrac{z - 5}{z + 1}$

12. $\dfrac{x - 6}{x + 9} = \dfrac{2}{7}$

13. $\dfrac{3}{y + 1} = \dfrac{2}{y - 3}$

14. $\dfrac{4}{x - 1} = \dfrac{3}{x + 2}$

15. $\dfrac{y - 1}{y - 3} = \dfrac{2}{y - 3}$

16. $\dfrac{x - 2}{x - 4} = \dfrac{2}{x - 4}$

17. $\dfrac{x + 1}{x} = \dfrac{3}{2}$

18. $\dfrac{y + 2}{y} = \dfrac{5}{3}$

19. $\dfrac{1}{2} - \dfrac{4}{9x} = \dfrac{4}{9} - \dfrac{1}{6x}$

20. $-\dfrac{1}{3} - \dfrac{5}{4y} = \dfrac{3}{4} - \dfrac{1}{6y}$

21. $\dfrac{60}{x} - \dfrac{60}{x - 5} = \dfrac{2}{x}$

22. $\dfrac{50}{y} - \dfrac{50}{y - 2} = \dfrac{4}{y}$

23. $\dfrac{7}{5x - 2} = \dfrac{5}{4x}$

24. $\dfrac{5}{y + 4} = \dfrac{3}{y - 2}$

25. $\dfrac{x}{x - 2} + \dfrac{x}{x^2 - 4} = \dfrac{x + 3}{x + 2}$

26. $\dfrac{3}{y - 2} + \dfrac{2y}{4 - y^2} = \dfrac{5}{y + 2}$

27. $\dfrac{6}{x^2 - 4x + 3} - \dfrac{1}{x - 3} = \dfrac{1}{4x - 4}$

28. $\dfrac{1}{2x + 10} = \dfrac{8}{x^2 - 25} - \dfrac{2}{x - 5}$

29. $\dfrac{5}{y + 3} = \dfrac{1}{4y^2 - 36} + \dfrac{2}{y - 3}$

30. $\dfrac{7}{x - 2} - \dfrac{8}{x + 5} = \dfrac{1}{2x^2 + 6x - 20}$

31. $\dfrac{a}{2a - 6} - \dfrac{3}{a^2 - 6a + 9} = \dfrac{a - 2}{3a - 9}$

**32.** $\dfrac{1}{x-2} = \dfrac{2}{x+4} + \dfrac{2x-1}{x^2+2x-8}$

**33.** $\dfrac{2x+3}{x-1} = \dfrac{10}{x^2-1} + \dfrac{2x-3}{x+1}$

**34.** $\dfrac{y}{y+1} + \dfrac{3y+5}{y^2+4y+3} = \dfrac{2}{y+3}$

**35.** $\dfrac{3x}{x+2} + \dfrac{72}{x^3+8} = \dfrac{24}{x^2-2x+4}$

**36.** $\dfrac{4}{x+3} + \dfrac{7}{x^2-3x+9} = \dfrac{108}{x^3+27}$

**37.** $\dfrac{5x}{x-7} - \dfrac{35}{x+7} = \dfrac{490}{x^2-49}$

**38.** $\dfrac{3x}{x+2} + \dfrac{6}{x} + 4 = \dfrac{12}{x^2+2x}$

**39.** $\dfrac{x^2}{x^2-4} = \dfrac{x}{x+2} - \dfrac{2x}{2-x}$

For the given rational function $f$, find all values of $x$ for which $f(x)$ has the indicated value.

**40.** $f(x) = 2x - \dfrac{15}{x}$; $f(x) = 1$

**41.** $f(x) = 2x - \dfrac{6}{x}$; $f(x) = 1$

**42.** $f(x) = \dfrac{x-5}{x+1}$; $f(x) = \dfrac{3}{5}$

**43.** $f(x) = \dfrac{x-3}{x+2}$; $f(x) = \dfrac{1}{5}$

**44.** $f(x) = \dfrac{12}{x} - \dfrac{12}{2x}$; $f(x) = 8$

**45.** $f(x) = \dfrac{6}{x} - \dfrac{6}{2x}$; $f(x) = 5$

## Skill Maintenance

Factor.  [4.6d]

**46.** $4t^3 + 500$

**47.** $1 - t^6$

**48.** $a^3 + 8b^3$

**49.** $a^3 - 8b^3$

Solve.  [4.8a]

**50.** $x^2 - 6x + 9 = 0$

**51.** $(x-3)(x+4) = 0$

**52.** $x^2 - 49 = 0$

**53.** $12x^2 - 11x + 2 = 0$

Solve.  [2.4c]

**54.** *Unemployment Benefits.*  In December 2007, there were 2.6 million people in the United States collecting state unemployment benefits. By March 2009, the number of people collecting benefits had grown to 5.5 million. Find the rate of change of the number of people collecting unemployment benefits with respect to time, in months. Round the answer to the nearest hundredth of a million.
**Source:** National Association of State Workforce Agencies

**55.** *Bird Collisions.*  In 1990, in the United States, there were 179 reports of large-bird collisions with aircraft. The number of reports increased to 550 in 2007. Find the rate of change of the number of large-bird collisions reported with respect to time, in years.
**Source:** Federal Aviation Administration, USA TODAY Research

## Synthesis

**56.** 

**a)** Use the INTERSECT feature of a graphing calculator to find the points of intersection of the graphs of

$$f(x) = \dfrac{1}{1+x} + \dfrac{x}{1-x} \quad \text{and} \quad g(x) = \dfrac{1}{1-x} - \dfrac{x}{1+x}.$$

**b)** Use the algebraic methods of this section to check your answers to part (a).

**c)** Explain which procedure you prefer.

**57.** 

**a)** Use the INTERSECT feature of a graphing calculator to find the points of intersection of the graphs of

$$f(x) = \dfrac{x+3}{x+2} - \dfrac{x+4}{x+3} \quad \text{and} \quad g(x) = \dfrac{x+5}{x+4} - \dfrac{x+6}{x+5}.$$

**b)** Use the algebraic methods of this section to check your answers to part (a).

**c)** Explain which procedure you prefer.

## Key Terms, Properties, and Formulas

rational expression, p. 412
synthetic division, p. 438
complex rational expression, p. 443
rational equation, p. 452
fraction equation, p. 452
proportion, p. 463

proportional, p. 463
direct variation, p. 478
equation of direct variation, p. 478
variation constant, p. 478
constant of proportionality, p. 478
$y$ varies directly as $x$, p. 478

$y$ is directly proportional to $x$, p. 478
inverse variation, p. 480
equation of inverse variation, p. 480
$y$ varies inversely as $x$, p. 480
$y$ is inversely proportional to $x$, p. 483
joint variation, p. 483

*Direct Variation*: $y = kx$     *Inverse Variation*: $y = \dfrac{k}{x}$     *Joint Variation*: $y = kxz$

*Work Principle*:    $\dfrac{t}{a} + \dfrac{t}{b} = 1$, where $a$ is the time needed for A to complete the job alone, $b$ is the time needed for B to complete the job alone, and $t$ is the time needed for A and B to complete the job working together.

## Concept Reinforcement

Determine whether each statement is true or false.

_____ **1.** The expressions $a - b$ and $-(b - a)$ are opposites, or additive inverses, of each other. [5.2a]

_____ **2.** If $y$ is inversely proportional to $x$, then the rational function $f(x) = k/x$ can model the situation. [5.8c]

_____ **3.** Clearing fractions is a valid procedure only when solving equations, not when adding, subtracting, multiplying, or dividing rational expressions. [5.5a]

## Important Concepts

**Objective 5.1a**   Find all numbers for which a rational expression is not defined or that are not in the domain of a rational function, and state the domain of the function.

**Example**   Find the domain of $f(x) = \dfrac{x^2 - 12x + 27}{x^2 + 6x - 16}$.

    The rational expression is not defined for a replacement that makes the denominator 0. We set the denominator equal to 0 and solve for $x$.

$$x^2 + 6x - 16 = 0$$
$$(x + 8)(x - 2) = 0$$
$$x + 8 = 0 \quad or \quad x - 2 = 0$$
$$x = -8 \quad or \quad \qquad x = 2$$

The expression is not defined for replacements $-8$ and $2$. Thus the domain is

    $\{x \mid x$ is a real number *and* $x \neq -8$ *and* $x \neq 2\}$, or
    $(-\infty, -8) \cup (-8, 2) \cup (2, \infty)$.

**Practice Exercise**

**1.** Find the domain of
$$f(x) = \dfrac{x^2 + 3x - 28}{x^2 + 3x - 54}.$$

**Objective 5.1c**  Simplify rational expressions.

**Example**  Simplify: $\dfrac{a^2 - 1}{a^2 + 7a - 8}$.

$\dfrac{a^2 - 1}{a^2 + 7a - 8} = \dfrac{(a + 1)(a - 1)}{(a + 8)(a - 1)} = \dfrac{a + 1}{a + 8} \cdot \dfrac{a - 1}{a - 1} = \dfrac{a + 1}{a + 8}$

**Practice Exercise**

**2.** Simplify:

$\dfrac{b^2 - 9}{b^2 - 5b - 24}$.

---

**Objective 5.1e**  Divide rational expressions and simplify.

**Example**  Divide and simplify: $\dfrac{t^2 + 2t + 4}{3t^2 + 6t} \div \dfrac{t^3 - 8}{t^3 + 2t^2}$.

$\dfrac{t^2 + 2t + 4}{3t^2 + 6t} \div \dfrac{t^3 - 8}{t^3 + 2t^2} = \dfrac{t^2 + 2t + 4}{3t^2 + 6t} \cdot \dfrac{t^3 + 2t^2}{t^3 - 8}$

$= \dfrac{(t^2 + 2t + 4)(t)(t)(t + 2)}{3t(t + 2)(t - 2)(t^2 + 2t + 4)}$

$= \dfrac{t}{3(t - 2)}$

**Practice Exercise**

**3.** Divide and simplify:

$\dfrac{w^3 - 125}{w^3 + 8w^2 + 15w} \div \dfrac{w - 5}{w^3 - 25w}$.

---

**Objective 5.2a**  Find the LCM of several algebraic expressions by factoring.

**Example**  Find the LCM of $x^2$, $16x^2 - 25$, and $4x^3 - 15x^2 - 25x$.

We factor each expression completely:

$x^2 = x \cdot x$;

$16x^2 - 25 = (4x + 5)(4x - 5)$;

$4x^3 - 15x^2 - 25x = x(4x + 5)(x - 5)$.

LCM $= x \cdot x \cdot (4x + 5)(4x - 5)(x - 5)$;

$= x^2(4x + 5)(4x - 5)(x - 5)$

**Practice Exercise**

**4.** Find the LCM of $x^4$, $x^5 - 9x^3$, and $2x^2 + 11x + 15$.

---

**Objective 5.2b**  Add and subtract rational expressions.

**Example**  Subtract:

$\dfrac{x - y}{x^2 + 3xy + 2y^2} - \dfrac{3y}{x^2 + 6xy + 5y^2}$.

First, we factor the denominator of each term.

$\dfrac{x - y}{(x + 2y)(x + y)} - \dfrac{3y}{(x + 5y)(x + y)}$    The LCM is $(x + 2y)(x + y)(x + 5y)$.

$= \dfrac{x - y}{(x + 2y)(x + y)} \cdot \dfrac{x + 5y}{x + 5y} - \dfrac{3y}{(x + 5y)(x + y)} \cdot \dfrac{x + 2y}{x + 2y}$

$= \dfrac{(x - y)(x + 5y)}{(x + 2y)(x + y)(x + 5y)} - \dfrac{3y(x + 2y)}{(x + 5y)(x + y)(x + 2y)}$

$= \dfrac{(x^2 + 4xy - 5y^2) - (3xy + 6y^2)}{(x + 2y)(x + y)(x + 5y)}$

$= \dfrac{x^2 + 4xy - 5y^2 - 3xy - 6y^2}{(x + 2y)(x + y)(x + 5y)} = \dfrac{x^2 + xy - 11y^2}{(x + 2y)(x + y)(x + 5y)}$

**Practice Exercise**

**5.** Subtract:

$\dfrac{r + s}{r^2 + rs - 2s^2} - \dfrac{5s}{r^2 - s^2}$.

**Objective 5.3b**   Divide a polynomial by a divisor that is not a monomial, and if there is a remainder, express the result in two ways.

**Example**   Divide: $(y^2 - 2y + 13) \div (y + 2)$.

$$
\begin{array}{r}
y - 4 \\
y + 2 \overline{)\,y^2 - 2y + 13} \\
\underline{y^2 + 2y\phantom{ + 13}} \\
-4y + 13 \\
\underline{-4y -\phantom{0} 8} \\
21
\end{array}
$$

The answer is $y - 4$, R 21; or $y - 4 + \dfrac{21}{y + 2}$.

**Practice Exercise**

6. Divide:
$$(y^2 - 5y + 9) \div (y - 1).$$

---

**Objective 5.3c**   Use synthetic division to divide a polynomial by a binomial of the type $x - a$.

**Example**   Use synthetic division to divide:
$$(x^3 - 2x^2 - 6) \div (x + 2).$$

There is no $x$-term, so we write 0 for its coefficient. Note that $x + 2 = x - (-2)$, so we write $-2$ on the left.

$$
\begin{array}{r|rrrr}
-2 & 1 & -2 & 0 & -6 \\
   &   & -2 & 8 & -16 \\
\hline
   & 1 & -4 & 8 & -22
\end{array}
$$

The answer is $x^2 - 4x + 8$, R $-22$; or $x^2 - 4x + 8 + \dfrac{-22}{x + 2}$.

**Practice Exercise**

7. Use synthetic division to divide:
$$(x^3 - 5x^2 - 1) \div (x + 3).$$

---

**Objective 5.4a**   Simplify complex rational expressions.

**Example**   Simplify: $\dfrac{\dfrac{2}{x} - \dfrac{5}{y}}{\dfrac{5}{x} + \dfrac{2}{y}}$.

The LCM of all denominators is $xy$.

$$
\frac{\dfrac{2}{x} - \dfrac{5}{y}}{\dfrac{5}{x} + \dfrac{2}{y}} = \frac{\dfrac{2}{x} - \dfrac{5}{y}}{\dfrac{5}{x} + \dfrac{2}{y}} \cdot \frac{xy}{xy} = \frac{\dfrac{2}{x} \cdot xy - \dfrac{5}{y} \cdot xy}{\dfrac{5}{x} \cdot xy + \dfrac{2}{y} \cdot xy} = \frac{2y - 5x}{5y + 2x}
$$

**Practice Exercise**

8. Simplify:
$$\frac{\dfrac{2}{a} + \dfrac{8}{b}}{\dfrac{8}{a} - \dfrac{2}{b}}.$$

---

**Objective 5.5a**   Solve rational equations.

**Example**   Solve:
$$\frac{12}{x^2 - 6x - 7} - \frac{3}{x - 7} = \frac{1}{x + 1}.$$

The LCM of the denominators is $(x - 7)(x + 1)$. We multiply all terms on both sides by $(x - 7)(x + 1)$.

$$(x - 7)(x + 1)\left(\frac{12}{x^2 - 6x - 7} - \frac{3}{x - 7}\right) = (x - 7)(x + 1) \cdot \frac{1}{x + 1}$$

$$
\begin{aligned}
12 - 3(x + 1) &= x - 7 \\
12 - 3x - 3 &= x - 7 \\
9 - 3x &= x - 7 \\
-4x &= -16 \\
x &= 4
\end{aligned}
$$

We must always check possible solutions. The number 4 checks in the original equation. The solution is 4.

**Practice Exercise**

9. Solve:
$$\frac{5}{x - 4} - \frac{3}{x + 5} = \frac{4}{x^2 + x - 20}.$$

**Objective 5.8a** Find an equation of direct variation given a pair of values of the variables.

**Example** Find the variation constant and an equation of variation in which $y$ varies directly as $x$, and $y = 44$ when $x = \frac{11}{5}$.

$$y = kx \qquad \text{Direct variation}$$
$$44 = k \cdot \tfrac{11}{5} \qquad \text{Substituting}$$
$$\tfrac{5}{11} \cdot 44 = k$$
$$20 = k$$

The variation constant is 20. The equation of variation is $y = 20x$.

**Practice Exercise**

10. Find the variation constant and an equation of variation in which $y$ varies directly as $x$, and $y = 62$ when $x = \frac{2}{3}$.

---

**Objective 5.8c** Find an equation of inverse variation given a pair of values of the variables.

**Example** Find the variation constant and an equation of variation in which $y$ varies inversely as $x$, and $y = \frac{5}{18}$ when $x = 2$.

$$y = \frac{k}{x} \qquad \text{Inverse variation}$$

$$\frac{5}{18} = \frac{k}{2} \qquad \text{Substituting}$$

$$2 \cdot \frac{5}{18} = k$$

$$\frac{5}{9} = k$$

The variation constant is $\frac{5}{9}$. The equation of variation is

$$y = \frac{\frac{5}{9}}{x}, \text{ or } y = \frac{5}{9x}.$$

**Practice Exercise**

11. Find the variation constant and an equation of variation in which $y$ varies inversely as $x$, and $y = \frac{3}{10}$ when $x = 15$.

---

## Review Exercises

1. Find all numbers for which the rational expression
$$\frac{x^2 - 3x + 2}{x^2 - 9}$$
is not defined.   [5.1a]

2. Find the domain of $f$ where
$$f(x) = \frac{x^2 - 3x + 2}{x^2 - 9}. \qquad \text{[5.1a]}$$

Simplify.   [5.1c]

3. $\dfrac{4x^2 - 7x - 2}{12x^2 + 11x + 2}$

4. $\dfrac{a^2 + 2a + 4}{a^3 - 8}$

Find the LCM.   [5.2a]

5. $6x^3$, $16x^2$

6. $x^2 - 49$, $3x + 1$

7. $x^2 + x - 20$, $x^2 + 3x - 10$

Perform the indicated operations and simplify.   [5.1d, e], [5.2b, c]

8. $\dfrac{y^2 - 64}{2y + 10} \cdot \dfrac{y + 5}{y + 8}$

9. $\dfrac{x^3 - 8}{x^2 - 25} \cdot \dfrac{x^2 + 10x + 25}{x^2 + 2x + 4}$

10. $\dfrac{9a^2 - 1}{a^2 - 9} \div \dfrac{3a + 1}{a + 3}$

11. $\dfrac{x^3 - 64}{x^2 - 16} \div \dfrac{x^2 + 5x + 6}{x^2 - 3x - 18}$

12. $\dfrac{x}{x^2 + 5x + 6} - \dfrac{2}{x^2 + 3x + 2}$

**13.** $\dfrac{2x^2}{x-y} + \dfrac{2y^2}{x+y}$

**14.** $\dfrac{3}{y+4} - \dfrac{y}{y-1} + \dfrac{y^2+3}{y^2+3y-4}$

Divide.

**15.** $(16ab^3c - 10ab^2c^2 + 12a^2b^2c) \div (4ab)$    [5.3a]

**16.** $(y^2 - 20y + 64) \div (y - 6)$    [5.3b]

**17.** $(6x^4 + 3x^2 + 5x + 4) \div (x^2 + 2)$    [5.3b]

Divide using synthetic division. Show your work.    [5.3c]

**18.** $(x^3 + 5x^2 + 4x - 7) \div (x - 4)$

**19.** $(3x^4 - 5x^3 + 2x - 7) \div (x + 1)$

Simplify.    [5.4a]

**20.** $\dfrac{3 + \dfrac{3}{y}}{4 + \dfrac{4}{y}}$

**21.** $\dfrac{\dfrac{2}{a} + \dfrac{2}{b}}{\dfrac{4}{a^3} + \dfrac{4}{b^3}}$

**22.** $\dfrac{\dfrac{x^2 - 5x - 36}{x^2 - 36}}{\dfrac{x^2 + x - 12}{x^2 - 12x + 36}}$

**23.** $\dfrac{\dfrac{4}{x+3} - \dfrac{2}{x^2 - 3x + 2}}{\dfrac{3}{x-2} + \dfrac{1}{x^2 + 2x - 3}}$

Solve.    [5.5a]

**24.** $\dfrac{x}{4} + \dfrac{x}{7} = 1$

**25.** $\dfrac{5}{3x+2} = \dfrac{3}{2x}$

**26.** $\dfrac{4x}{x+1} + \dfrac{4}{x} + 9 = \dfrac{4}{x^2 + x}$

**27.** $\dfrac{90}{x^2 - 3x + 9} - \dfrac{5x}{x+3} = \dfrac{405}{x^3 + 27}$

**28.** $\dfrac{2}{x-3} + \dfrac{1}{4x+20} = \dfrac{1}{x^2 + 2x - 15}$

**29.** Given that

$$f(x) = \dfrac{6}{x} + \dfrac{4}{x},$$

find all $x$ for which $f(x) = 5$.

**30.** *House Painting.*   David can paint the outside of a house in 12 hr. Bill can paint the same house in 9 hr. How long would it take them working together to paint the house?    [5.6a]

**31.** *Boat Travel.*   The current of the Gold River is 6 mph. A boat travels 50 mi downstream in the same time that it takes to travel 30 mi upstream. Complete the table below and then find the speed of the boat in still water.    [5.6c]

|  | DISTANCE | SPEED | TIME |
|---|---|---|---|
| DOWNSTREAM |  |  |  |
| UPSTREAM |  |  |  |

**32.** *Travel Distance.* Fred operates a potato-chip delivery route. He drives 800 mi in 3 days. How far will he travel in 15 days? [5.6b]

Solve for the indicated letter. [5.7a]

**33.** $W = \dfrac{cd}{c + d}$, for $d$; for $c$

**34.** $S = \dfrac{p}{a} + \dfrac{t}{b}$, for $b$; for $t$

**35.** Find an equation of variation in which $y$ varies directly as $x$, and $y = 100$ when $x = 25$. [5.8a]

**36.** Find an equation of variation in which $y$ varies inversely as $x$, and $y = 100$ when $x = 25$. [5.8c]

**37.** *Pumping Time.* The time $t$ required to empty a tank varies inversely as the rate $r$ of pumping. If a pump can empty a tank in 35 min at the rate of 800 kL per minute, how long will it take the pump to empty the same tank at the rate of 1400 kL per minute? [5.8d]

**38.** *Test Score.* The score $N$ on a test varies directly as the number of correct responses $a$. Ellen answers 28 questions correctly and earns a score of 87. What would Ellen's score have been if she had answered 25 questions correctly? [5.8b]

**39.** *Power of Electric Current.* The power $P$ expended by heat in an electric circuit of fixed resistance varies directly as the square of the current $C$ in the circuit. A circuit expends 180 watts when a current of 6 amperes is flowing. What is the amount of heat expended when the current is 10 amperes? [5.8f]

**40.** Find the domain of $f(x) = \dfrac{x^2 - x}{x^2 - 2x - 35}$. [5.1a]

   **A.** $(0, 1)$
   **B.** $(-\infty, -5) \cup (-5, 7) \cup (7, \infty)$
   **C.** $(-5, 7)$
   **D.** $(-\infty, 0) \cup (0, 1) \cup (1, \infty)$

**41.** Find the LCM of $x^5$, $x - 4$, $x^2 - 4$, and $x^2 - 4x$. [5.2a]

   **A.** $x(x - 4)^2$
   **B.** $(x - 4)(x + 4)$
   **C.** $x^5(x - 4)(x - 2)(x + 2)$
   **D.** $x^5(x - 4)^2$

## Synthesis

**42.** Find the reciprocal and simplify: $\dfrac{a - b}{a^3 - b^3}$. [5.1c, e]

**43.** Solve: $\dfrac{5}{x - 13} - \dfrac{5}{x} = \dfrac{65}{x^2 - 13x}$. [5.5a]

# Understanding Through Discussion and Writing

**1.** Discuss at least three different uses of the LCM studied in this chapter. [5.2b], [5.4a], [5.5a]

**2.** You have learned to solve a new kind of equation in this chapter. Explain how this type differs from those you have studied previously and how the equation-solving process differs. [5.5a]

**3.** Explain why it is sufficient, when checking a possible solution of a rational equation, to verify that the number in question does not make a denominator 0. [5.5a]

**4.** If $y$ varies directly as $x$ and $x$ varies inversely as $z$, how does $y$ vary with regard to $z$? Why? [5.8a, c, e]

**5.** Explain how you might easily create rational equations for which there is no solution. (See Example 4 of Section 5.5 for a hint.) [5.5a]

**6.** Which is easier to solve for $x$? Explain why. [5.7a]

$$\frac{1}{38} + \frac{1}{47} = \frac{1}{x} \quad \text{or} \quad \frac{1}{a} + \frac{1}{b} = \frac{1}{x}$$

CHAPTER
5

Test

For Extra Help

CHAPTER
Test Prep
VIDEOS

Step-by-step test solutions are found on the Chapter Test Prep Videos available via the Video Resources on DVD, in *MyMathLab*, and on You Tube (search "BittingerInterAlgPB" and click on "Channels").

1. Find all numbers for which the rational expression
$$\frac{x^2 - 16}{x^2 - 3x + 2}$$
is not defined.

2. Find the domain of $f$ where
$$f(x) = \frac{x^2 - 16}{x^2 - 3x + 2}.$$

Simplify.

3. $\dfrac{12x^2 + 11x + 2}{4x^2 - 7x - 2}$

4. $\dfrac{p^3 + 1}{p^2 - p - 2}$

5. Find the LCM of $x^2 + x - 6$ and $x^2 + 8x + 15$.

Perform the indicated operations and simplify.

6. $\dfrac{2x^2 + 20x + 50}{x^2 - 4} \cdot \dfrac{x + 2}{x + 5}$

7. $\dfrac{x}{x^2 + 11x + 30} - \dfrac{5}{x^2 + 9x + 20}$

8. $\dfrac{y^2 - 16}{2y + 6} \div \dfrac{y - 4}{y + 3}$

9. $\dfrac{x^2}{x - y} + \dfrac{y^2}{y - x}$

10. $\dfrac{1}{x + 1} - \dfrac{x + 2}{x^2 - 1} + \dfrac{3}{x - 1}$

11. $\dfrac{a}{a - b} + \dfrac{b}{a^2 + ab + b^2} - \dfrac{2}{a^3 - b^3}$

Divide.

12. $(20r^2s^3 + 15r^2s^2 - 10r^3s^3) \div (5r^2s)$

13. $(y^3 + 125) \div (y + 5)$

14. $(4x^4 + 3x^3 - 5x - 2) \div (x^2 + 1)$

Divide using synthetic division. Show your work.

15. $(x^3 + 3x^2 + 2x - 6) \div (x - 3)$

16. $(3x^3 + 22x^2 - 160) \div (x + 4)$

Simplify.

17. $\dfrac{1 - \dfrac{1}{x^2}}{1 - \dfrac{1}{x}}$

18. $\dfrac{\dfrac{1}{a^3} + \dfrac{1}{b^3}}{\dfrac{1}{a} + \dfrac{1}{b}}$

19. Given that
$$f(x) = \frac{2}{x - 1} + \frac{2}{x + 2},$$
find all $x$ for which $f(x) = 1$.

Solve.

**20.** $\dfrac{2}{x-1} = \dfrac{3}{x+3}$

**21.** $\dfrac{7x}{x+3} + \dfrac{21}{x-3} = \dfrac{126}{x^2-9}$

**22.** $\dfrac{2x}{x+7} = \dfrac{5}{x+1}$

**23.** $\dfrac{1}{3x-6} - \dfrac{1}{x^2-4} = \dfrac{3}{x+2}$

**24.** *Completing a Puzzle.* Working together, Rachel and Jessie can complete a jigsaw puzzle in 1.5 hr. Rachel takes 4 hr longer than Jessie does when working alone. How long would it take Jessie to complete the puzzle?

**25.** *Bicycle Travel.* David can bicycle at a rate of 12 mph when there is no wind. Against the wind, David bikes 8 mi in the same time that it takes to bike 14 mi with the wind. What is the speed of the wind?

**26.** *Predicting Paint Needs.* Logan and Noah run a summer painting company to defray their college expenses. They need 4 gal of paint to paint 1700 ft$^2$ of clapboard. How much paint would they need for a building with 6000 ft$^2$ of clapboard?

Solve for the indicated letter.

**27.** $T = \dfrac{ab}{a-b}$, for $a$; for $b$

**28.** $Q = \dfrac{2}{a} - \dfrac{t}{b}$, for $a$

**29.** Find an equation of variation in which $Q$ varies jointly as $x$ and $y$, and $Q = 25$ when $x = 2$ and $y = 5$.

**30.** Find an equation of variation in which $y$ varies inversely as $x$, and $y = 10$ when $x = 25$.

**31.** *Income vs Time.* Kaylee's income $I$ varies directly as the time $t$ worked. She gets a job that pays $550 for 40 hr of work. What is she paid for working 72 hr, assuming that there is no change in pay scale for overtime?

**32.** *Time and Speed.* The time $t$ required to drive a fixed distance varies inversely as the speed $r$. It takes 5 hr at 60 km/h to drive a fixed distance. How long would it take to drive that same distance at 40 km/h?

**33.** *Area of a Balloon.* The surface area of a balloon varies directly as the square of its radius. The area is 314 cm$^2$ when the radius is 5 cm. What is the area when the radius is 7 cm?

**34.** Find the LCM of $6x^2$, $3x^2 - 3y^2$, and $x^2 - 2xy - 3y^2$.
 **A.** $3x^2(2x+y)(x-3y)$
 **B.** $6x(x+y)(x-y)(x-3y)$
 **C.** $3x^2(x+y)^2(x-y)$
 **D.** $6x^2(x+y)(x-y)(x-3y)$

## Synthesis

**35.** Solve: $\dfrac{6}{x-15} - \dfrac{6}{x} = \dfrac{90}{x^2-15x}$.

**36.** Find the $x$- and $y$-intercepts of the function $f$ given by

$$f(x) = \dfrac{\dfrac{5}{x+4} - \dfrac{3}{x-2}}{\dfrac{2}{x-3} + \dfrac{1}{x+4}}.$$

# Cumulative Review

Graph.

**1.** $y = -5x + 4$

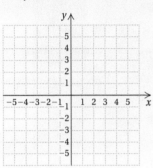

**2.** $3x - 18 = 0$

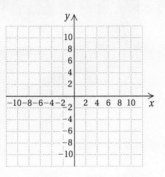

**3.** $x + 3y < 4$

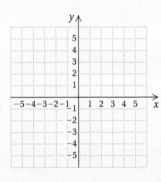

**4.** $x + y \geq 4$,
$x - y > 1$

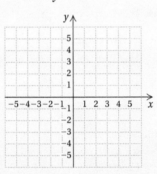

**5.** Given that $g(x) = |x - 4| + 5$, find $g(-2)$.

**6.** Given that

$$f(x) = \frac{x - 2}{x^2 - 25},$$

find the domain.

**7.** Find the domain and the range of the function graphed below.

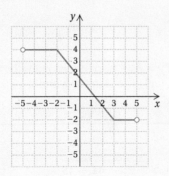

Simplify.

**8.** $(6m - n)^2$

**9.** $(3a - 4b)(5a + 2b)$

**10.** $\dfrac{y^2 - 4}{3y + 33} \cdot \dfrac{y + 11}{y + 2}$

**11.** $\dfrac{9x^2 - 25}{x^2 - 16} \div \dfrac{3x + 5}{x - 4}$

**12.** $\dfrac{2x + 1}{4x - 12} - \dfrac{x - 2}{5x - 15}$

**13.** $\dfrac{1 - \dfrac{2}{y^2}}{1 - \dfrac{1}{y^3}}$

**14.** $(6p^2 - 2p + 5) - (-10p^2 + 6p + 5)$

**15.** $\dfrac{2}{x + 2} + \dfrac{3}{x - 2} - \dfrac{x + 1}{x^2 - 4}$

**16.** $(2x^3 - 7x^2 + x - 3) \div (x + 2)$

Solve.

**17.** $9y - (5y - 3) = 33$

**18.** $-3 < -2x - 6 < 0$

**19.** $\dfrac{3x}{x - 2} - \dfrac{6}{x + 2} = \dfrac{24}{x^2 - 4}$

**20.** $P = \dfrac{3a}{a + b}$, for $a$

**21.** $F = \dfrac{9}{5}C + 32$, for $C$

**22.** $|x| \geq 2.1$

**23.** $\dfrac{6}{x - 5} = \dfrac{2}{2x}$

**24.** $8x = 1 + 16x^2$

**25.** $14 + 3x = 2x^2$

Solve.

**26.** $4x - 2y = 6,$
$6x - 3y = 9$

**27.** $4x + 5y = -3,$
$x = 1 - 3y$

**28.** $x + 2y - 2z = 9,$
$2x - 3y + 4z = -4,$
$5x - 4y + 2z = 5$

**29.** $x + 6y + 4z = -2,$
$4x + 4y + z = 2,$
$3x + 2y - 4z = 5$

Factor.

**30.** $4x^3 + 18x^2$

**31.** $8a^3 - 4a^2 - 6a + 3$

**32.** $x^2 + 8x - 84$

**33.** $6x^2 + 11x - 10$

**34.** $16y^2 - 81$

**35.** $t^2 - 16t + 64$

**36.** $64x^3 + 8$

**37.** $0.027b^3 - 0.008c^3$

**38.** $x^6 - x^2$

**39.** $20x^2 + 7x - 3$

**40.** Find an equation of the line with slope $-\frac{1}{2}$ passing through the point $(2, -2)$.

**41.** Find an equation of the line that is perpendicular to the line $2x + y = 5$ and passes through the point $(3, -1)$.

**42.** *Hockey Results.* A hockey team played 81 games in a season. They won 1 fewer game than three times the number of ties and lost 8 fewer games than they won. How many games did they win? lose? tie?

**43.** *Waste Generation.* The amount of waste generated by a fast-food restaurant varies directly as the number of customers served. A typical restaurant that serves 2000 customers per day generates 238 lb of waste daily. How many pounds of waste would be generated daily by a restaurant that serves 1700 customers a day?

**44.** Solve: $\dfrac{x}{x - 4} - \dfrac{4}{x + 3} = \dfrac{28}{x^2 - x - 12}$.

**A.** No solution
**B.** 0
**C.** $-4, 3$
**D.** $4, -3$

**45.** Solve: $x^2 - x - 6 = 6$.

**A.** $4, 9$
**B.** $3, 8$
**C.** $4, -3$
**D.** $0, 1$

**46.** *Tank Filling.* An oil storage tank can be filled in 10 hr by ship A working alone and in 15 hr by ship B working alone. How many hours would it take to fill the oil storage tank if both ships A and B are working?

**A.** 8 hr
**B.** 6 hr
**C.** $12\frac{1}{2}$ hr
**D.** 25 hr

## Synthesis

**47.** The graph of $y = ax^2 + bx + c$ contains the three points $(4, 2), (2, 0),$ and $(1, 2)$. Find $a$, $b$, and $c$.

Solve.

**48.** $16x^3 = x$

**49.** $\dfrac{18}{x - 9} + \dfrac{10}{x + 5} = \dfrac{28x}{x^2 - 4x - 45}$

# Radical Expressions, Equations, and Functions

## Real-World Application

The geologically formed, open-air Red Rocks Amphitheatre near Denver, Colorado, hosts a series of concerts. A scientific instrument at one of these concerts determined that the sound of the music was traveling at a rate of 1170 ft/sec. What was the air temperature at the concert?

*This problem appears as Example 9 in Section 6.6.*

499

# 6.1

## Radical Expressions and Functions

### OBJECTIVES

**a** Find principal square roots and their opposites, approximate square roots, identify radicands, find outputs of square-root functions, graph square-root functions, and find the domains of square-root functions.

**b** Simplify radical expressions with perfect-square radicands.

**c** Find cube roots, simplifying certain expressions, and find outputs of cube-root functions.

**d** Simplify expressions involving odd roots and even roots.

In this section, we consider roots, such as square roots and cube roots. We define the symbolism and consider methods of manipulating symbols to get equivalent expressions.

### a  Square Roots and Square-Root Functions

When we raise a number to the second power, we say that we have **squared** the number. Sometimes we may need to find the number that was squared. We call this process **finding a square root** of a number.

---
**SQUARE ROOT**

The number $c$ is a **square root** of $a$ if $c^2 = a$.

---

For example:

$5$ is a *square root* of 25 because $5^2 = 5 \cdot 5 = 25$;

$-5$ is a *square root* of 25 because $(-5)^2 = (-5)(-5) = 25$.

The number $-4$ does not have a real-number square root because there is no real number $c$ such that $c^2 = -4$.

---
**PROPERTIES OF SQUARE ROOTS**

Every positive real number has two real-number square roots.

The number 0 has just one square root, 0 itself.

Negative numbers do not have real-number square roots.*

---

**Find the square roots.**

**1.** 9

**2.** 36

**3.** 121

**EXAMPLE 1**  Find the two square roots of 64.

The square roots of 64 are 8 and $-8$ because $8^2 = 64$ and $(-8)^2 = 64$.

Do Exercises 1–3.

---
**PRINCIPAL SQUARE ROOT**

The **principal square root** of a nonnegative number is its nonnegative square root. The symbol $\sqrt{a}$ represents the principal square root of $a$. To name the negative square root of $a$, we can write $-\sqrt{a}$.

---

Simplify.

**4.** $\sqrt{1}$          **5.** $\sqrt{36}$

**6.** $\sqrt{\dfrac{81}{100}}$          **7.** $\sqrt{0.0064}$

*Answers*

**1.** 3, −3   **2.** 6, −6   **3.** 11, −11
**4.** 1   **5.** 6   **6.** $\dfrac{9}{10}$   **7.** 0.08

---

*In Section 6.8, we wil consider a number system in which negative numbers do have square roots.

**EXAMPLES** Simplify.

**2.** $\sqrt{25} = 5$ 

> Remember: $\sqrt{\phantom{x}}$ indicates the principal (nonnegative) square root.

**3.** $-\sqrt{25} = -5$

**4.** $\sqrt{\dfrac{81}{64}} = \dfrac{9}{8}$ because $\left(\dfrac{9}{8}\right)^2 = \dfrac{9}{8} \cdot \dfrac{9}{8} = \dfrac{81}{64}$.

**5.** $\sqrt{0.0049} = 0.07$ because $(0.07)^2 = (0.07)(0.07) = 0.0049$.

**6.** $-\sqrt{0.000001} = -0.001$

**7.** $\sqrt{0} = 0$

**8.** $\sqrt{-25}$   Does not exist as a real number. Negative numbers do not have real-number square roots.

> Do Exercises 4–13. (Exercises 4–7 are on the preceding page.)

We found exact square roots in Examples 1–8. We often need to use rational numbers to *approximate* square roots that are irrational. (See Section R.1.) Such expressions can be found using a calculator with a square-root key.

**EXAMPLES** Use a calculator to approximate each of the following.

| Number | Using a calculator with a 10-digit readout | Rounded to three decimal places |
|---|---|---|
| **9.** $\sqrt{11}$ | 3.316624790 | 3.317 |
| **10.** $\sqrt{487}$ | 22.06807649 | 22.068 |
| **11.** $-\sqrt{7297.8}$ | $-85.42716196$ | $-85.427$ |
| **12.** $\sqrt{\dfrac{463}{557}}$ | .9117229728 | 0.912 |

> Do Exercises 14–19.

> ### RADICAL; RADICAL EXPRESSION; RADICAND
>
> The symbol $\sqrt{\phantom{x}}$ is called a **radical**.
>
> An expression written with a radical is called a **radical expression**.
>
> The expression written under the radical is called the **radicand**.

These are radical expressions:

$$\sqrt{5}, \quad \sqrt{a}, \quad -\sqrt{5x}, \quad \sqrt{y^2 + 7}.$$

The radicands in these expressions are 5, $a$, $5x$, and $y^2 + 7$, respectively.

**EXAMPLE 13** Identify the radicand in $x\sqrt{x^2 - 9}$.

The radicand is the expression under the radical, $x^2 - 9$.

> Do Exercises 20 and 21 on the following page.

---

Find each of the following.

**8. a)** $\sqrt{16}$      **9. a)** $\sqrt{49}$
   **b)** $-\sqrt{16}$      **b)** $-\sqrt{49}$
   **c)** $\sqrt{-16}$      **c)** $\sqrt{-49}$

**10.** $\sqrt{\dfrac{25}{64}}$      **11.** $\sqrt{\dfrac{16}{9}}$

**12.** $-\sqrt{0.81}$      **13.** $\sqrt{1.44}$

It would be helpful to memorize the following table of exact square roots.

| TABLE OF COMMON SQUARE ROOTS | |
|---|---|
| $\sqrt{1} = 1$ | $\sqrt{196} = 14$ |
| $\sqrt{4} = 2$ | $\sqrt{225} = 15$ |
| $\sqrt{9} = 3$ | $\sqrt{256} = 16$ |
| $\sqrt{16} = 4$ | $\sqrt{289} = 17$ |
| $\sqrt{25} = 5$ | $\sqrt{324} = 18$ |
| $\sqrt{36} = 6$ | $\sqrt{361} = 19$ |
| $\sqrt{49} = 7$ | $\sqrt{400} = 20$ |
| $\sqrt{64} = 8$ | $\sqrt{441} = 21$ |
| $\sqrt{81} = 9$ | $\sqrt{484} = 22$ |
| $\sqrt{100} = 10$ | $\sqrt{529} = 23$ |
| $\sqrt{121} = 11$ | $\sqrt{576} = 24$ |
| $\sqrt{144} = 12$ | $\sqrt{625} = 25$ |
| $\sqrt{169} = 13$ | |

Use a calculator to approximate each square root to three decimal places.

**14.** $\sqrt{17}$      **15.** $\sqrt{40}$

**16.** $\sqrt{1138}$      **17.** $-\sqrt{867.6}$

**18.** $\sqrt{\dfrac{22}{35}}$      **19.** $-\sqrt{\dfrac{2103.4}{67.82}}$

*Answers*

**8.** (a) 4; (b) $-4$; (c) does not exist as a real number   **9.** (a) 7; (b) $-7$; (c) does not exist as a real number   **10.** $\dfrac{5}{8}$   **11.** $\dfrac{4}{3}$   **12.** $-0.9$
**13.** 1.2   **14.** 4.123   **15.** 6.325   **16.** 33.734
**17.** $-29.455$   **18.** 0.793   **19.** $-5.569$

Identify the radicand.

**20.** $5\sqrt{28 + x}$

**21.** $\sqrt{\dfrac{y}{y + 3}}$

For the given function, find the indicated function values.

**22.** $g(x) = \sqrt{6x + 4}$;  $g(0), g(3)$, and $g(-5)$

**23.** $f(x) = -\sqrt{x}$;  $f(4), f(7)$, and $f(-3)$

---

Since each nonnegative real number $x$ has exactly one principal square root, the symbol $\sqrt{x}$ represents exactly one real number and thus can be used to define a square-root function:

$$f(x) = \sqrt{x}.$$

The domain of this function is the set of nonnegative real numbers. In interval notation, the domain is $[0, \infty)$. This function will be discussed further in Example 16.

**EXAMPLE 14**  For the given function, find the indicated function values:

$$f(x) = \sqrt{3x - 2}; \quad f(1), f(5), \text{ and } f(0).$$

We have

$$
\begin{aligned}
f(1) &= \sqrt{3 \cdot 1 - 2} && \text{Substituting 1 for } x\\
&= \sqrt{3 - 2} = \sqrt{1} = 1; && \text{Simplifying and taking the square root}\\
f(5) &= \sqrt{3 \cdot 5 - 2} && \text{Substituting 5 for } x\\
&= \sqrt{13} \approx 3.606; && \text{Simplifying and approximating}\\
f(0) &= \sqrt{3 \cdot 0 - 2} && \text{Substituting 0 for } x\\
&= \sqrt{-2}. && \text{Negative radicand. No real-number function}\\
& && \text{value exists; 0 is not in the domain of } f.
\end{aligned}
$$

Do Exercises 22 and 23.

**EXAMPLE 15**  Find the domain of $g(x) = \sqrt{x + 2}$.

The expression $\sqrt{x + 2}$ is a real number only when $x + 2$ is nonnegative. Thus the domain of $g(x) = \sqrt{x + 2}$ is the set of all $x$-values for which $x + 2 \geq 0$. We solve as follows:

$$x + 2 \geq 0$$
$$x \geq -2. \quad \text{Adding } -2$$

The domain of $g = \{x \mid x \geq -2\} = [-2, \infty)$.

**EXAMPLE 16**  Graph: **(a)** $f(x) = \sqrt{x}$;  **(b)** $g(x) = \sqrt{x + 2}$.

We first find outputs as we did in Example 14. We can either select inputs that have exact outputs or use a calculator to make approximations. Once ordered pairs have been calculated, a smooth curve can be drawn.

**a)**

| $x$ | $f(x) = \sqrt{x}$ | $(x, f(x))$ |
|---|---|---|
| 0 | 0 | $(0, 0)$ |
| 1 | 1 | $(1, 1)$ |
| 3 | 1.7 | $(3, 1.7)$ |
| 4 | 2 | $(4, 2)$ |
| 7 | 2.6 | $(7, 2.6)$ |
| 9 | 3 | $(9, 3)$ |

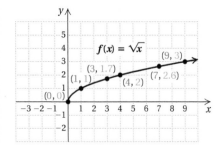

We can see from the table and the graph that the domain of $f$ is $[0, \infty)$. The range is also the set of nonnegative real numbers $[0, \infty)$.

---

*Answers*

**20.** $28 + x$  **21.** $\dfrac{y}{y + 3}$
**22.** 2; $\sqrt{22} \approx 4.690$; does not exist as a real number  **23.** $-2$; $-\sqrt{7} \approx -2.646$; does not exist as a real number

**b)**

| $x$ | $g(x) = \sqrt{x + 2}$ | $(x, g(x))$ |
|-----|------------------------|-------------|
| $-2$ | $0$ | $(-2, 0)$ |
| $-1$ | $1$ | $(-1, 1)$ |
| $0$ | $1.4$ | $(0, 1.4)$ |
| $3$ | $2.2$ | $(3, 2.2)$ |
| $5$ | $2.6$ | $(5, 2.6)$ |
| $10$ | $3.5$ | $(10, 3.5)$ |

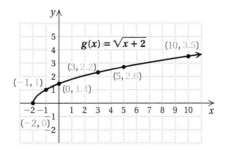

We can see from the table, the graph, and Example 15 that the domain of $g$ is $[-2, \infty)$. The range is the set of nonnegative real numbers $[0, \infty)$.

Do Exercises 24–27.

## b Finding $\sqrt{a^2}$

In the expression $\sqrt{a^2}$, the radicand is a perfect square. It is tempting to think that $\sqrt{a^2} = a$, but we see below that this is not the case.

Suppose $a = 5$. Then we have $\sqrt{5^2}$, which is $\sqrt{25}$, or $5$.
Suppose $a = -5$. Then we have $\sqrt{(-5)^2}$, which is $\sqrt{25}$, or $5$.
Suppose $a = 0$. Then we have $\sqrt{0^2}$, which is $\sqrt{0}$, or $0$.

The symbol $\sqrt{a^2}$ never represents a negative number. It represents the principal square root of $a^2$. Note the following.

> **SIMPLIFYING $\sqrt{a^2}$**
>
> $a \geq 0 \longrightarrow \sqrt{a^2} = a$
>
> If $a$ is positive or 0, the principal square root of $a^2$ is $a$.
>
> $a < 0 \longrightarrow \sqrt{a^2} = -a$
>
> If $a$ is negative, the principal square root of $a^2$ is the opposite of $a$.

In all cases, the radical expression represents the absolute value of $a$.

> **PRINCIPAL SQUARE ROOT OF $a^2$**
>
> For any real number $a$, $\sqrt{a^2} = |a|$. The principal (nonnegative) square root of $a^2$ is the absolute value of $a$.

The absolute value is used to ensure that the principal square root is nonnegative, which is as it is defined.

---

Find the domain of each function.

**24.** $f(x) = \sqrt{x - 5}$

**25.** $g(x) = \sqrt{2x + 3}$

Graph.

**26.** $g(x) = -\sqrt{x}$

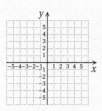

**27.** $f(x) = 2\sqrt{x + 3}$

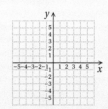

*Answers*

**24.** $\{x \,|\, x \geq 5\}$, or $[5, \infty)$
**25.** $\{x \,|\, x \geq -\frac{3}{2}\}$, or $\left[-\frac{3}{2}, \infty\right)$
**26.**

[graph of $g(x) = -\sqrt{x}$]

**27.**

[graph of $f(x) = 2\sqrt{x + 3}$]

Find each of the following. Assume that letters can represent *any* real number.

**28.** $\sqrt{y^2}$

**29.** $\sqrt{(-24)^2}$

**30.** $\sqrt{(5y)^2}$

**31.** $\sqrt{16y^2}$

**32.** $\sqrt{(x+7)^2}$

**33.** $\sqrt{4(x-2)^2}$

**34.** $\sqrt{49(y+5)^2}$

**35.** $\sqrt{x^2-6x+9}$

**EXAMPLES** Find each of the following. Assume that letters can represent any real number.

**17.** $\sqrt{(-16)^2} = |-16|$, or 16

**18.** $\sqrt{(3b)^2} = |3b| = |3| \cdot |b| = 3|b|$

$|3b|$ can be simplified to $3|b|$ because the absolute value of any product is the product of the absolute values. That is, $|a \cdot b| = |a| \cdot |b|$.

**19.** $\sqrt{(x-1)^2} = |x-1|$

**20.** $\sqrt{x^2 + 8x + 16} = \sqrt{(x+4)^2}$
$= |x+4|$

---- *Caution!* ----

$|x+4|$ is *not* the same as $|x| + 4$.

Do Exercises 28–35.

## (c) Cube Roots

**CUBE ROOT**

The number $c$ is the **cube root** of $a$, written $\sqrt[3]{a}$, if the third power of $c$ is $a$—that is, if $c^3 = a$, then $\sqrt[3]{a} = c$.

For example:

2 is the *cube root* of 8 because $2^3 = 2 \cdot 2 \cdot 2 = 8$;

$-4$ is the *cube root* of $-64$ because $(-4)^3 = (-4)(-4)(-4) = -64$.

We talk about *the* cube root of a number rather than *a* cube root because of the following.

Every real number has exactly one cube root in the system of real numbers. The symbol $\sqrt[3]{a}$ represents *the* cube root of $a$.

**EXAMPLES** Find each of the following.

**21.** $\sqrt[3]{8} = 2$ because $2^3 = 8$.

**22.** $\sqrt[3]{-27} = -3$

**23.** $\sqrt[3]{-\dfrac{216}{125}} = -\dfrac{6}{5}$

**24.** $\sqrt[3]{0.001} = 0.1$

**25.** $\sqrt[3]{x^3} = x$

**26.** $\sqrt[3]{-8} = -2$

**27.** $\sqrt[3]{0} = 0$

**28.** $\sqrt[3]{-8y^3} = \sqrt[3]{(-2y)^3} = -2y$

Find each of the following.

**36.** $\sqrt[3]{-64}$

**37.** $\sqrt[3]{27y^3}$

**38.** $\sqrt[3]{8(x+2)^3}$

**39.** $\sqrt[3]{-\dfrac{343}{64}}$

When we are determining a cube root, no absolute-value signs are needed because a real number has just one cube root. The real-number cube root of a positive number is positive. The real-number cube root of a negative number is negative. The cube root of 0 is 0. That is, $\sqrt[3]{a^3} = a$ whether $a > 0$, $a < 0$, or $a = 0$.

Do Exercises 36–39.

Since the symbol $\sqrt[3]{x}$ represents exactly one real number, it can be used to define a cube-root function: $f(x) = \sqrt[3]{x}$.

**EXAMPLE 29** For the given function, find the indicated function values:

$$f(x) = \sqrt[3]{x}; \quad f(125), f(0), f(-8), \text{ and } f(-10).$$

We have

$$f(125) = \sqrt[3]{125} = 5;$$
$$f(0) = \sqrt[3]{0} = 0;$$
$$f(-8) = \sqrt[3]{-8} = -2;$$
$$f(-10) = \sqrt[3]{-10} \approx -2.154.$$

Do Exercise 40.

Do Exercise 40.

**40.** For the given function, find the indicated function values:
$$g(x) = \sqrt[3]{x - 4}; \quad g(-23),$$
$$g(4), g(-1), \text{ and } g(11).$$

The graph of $f(x) = \sqrt[3]{x}$ is shown below for reference. Note that both the domain and the range consist of the entire set of real numbers, $(-\infty, \infty)$.

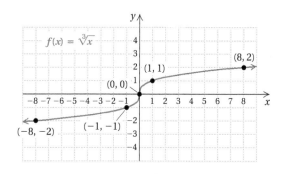

## d Odd and Even *k*th Roots

In the expression $\sqrt[k]{a}$, we call $k$ the **index** and assume $k \geq 2$.

### Odd Roots

The 5th root of a number $a$ is the number $c$ for which $c^5 = a$. There are also 7th roots, 9th roots, and so on. Whenever the number $k$ in $\sqrt[k]{\phantom{a}}$ is an odd number, we say that we are taking an **odd root**.

Every number has just one real-number odd root. For example, $\sqrt[3]{8} = 2$, $\sqrt[3]{-8} = -2$, and $\sqrt[3]{0} = 0$. If the number is positive, then the root is positive. If the number is negative, then the root is negative. If the number is 0, then the root is 0. Absolute-value signs are *not* needed when we are finding odd roots.

If $k$ is an *odd* natural number, then for any real number $a$,
$$\sqrt[k]{a^k} = a.$$

*Answer*

**40.** $-3; 0; \sqrt[3]{-5} \approx -1.710; \sqrt[3]{7} \approx 1.913$

Find each of the following.

**41.** $\sqrt[5]{243}$        **42.** $\sqrt[5]{-243}$

**43.** $\sqrt[5]{x^5}$        **44.** $\sqrt[7]{y^7}$

**45.** $\sqrt[5]{0}$        **46.** $\sqrt[5]{-32x^5}$

**47.** $\sqrt[7]{(3x+2)^7}$

**EXAMPLES** Find each of the following.

**30.** $\sqrt[5]{32} = 2$        **31.** $\sqrt[5]{-32} = -2$

**32.** $-\sqrt[5]{32} = -2$        **33.** $-\sqrt[5]{-32} = -(-2) = 2$

**34.** $\sqrt[7]{x^7} = x$        **35.** $\sqrt[7]{128} = 2$

**36.** $\sqrt[7]{-128} = -2$        **37.** $\sqrt[7]{0} = 0$

**38.** $\sqrt[5]{a^5} = a$        **39.** $\sqrt[9]{(x-1)^9} = x-1$

Do Exercises 41–47.

## Even Roots

When the index $k$ in $\sqrt[k]{\phantom{x}}$ is an even number, we say that we are taking an **even root**. When the index is 2, we do not write it. Every positive real number has two real-number $k$th roots when $k$ is even. One of those roots is positive and one is negative. Negative real numbers do not have real-number $k$th roots when $k$ is even. When we are finding even $k$th roots, absolute-value signs are sometimes necessary, as we have seen with square roots. For example,

$$\sqrt{64} = 8, \qquad \sqrt[6]{64} = 2, \qquad -\sqrt[6]{64} = -2, \qquad \sqrt[6]{64x^6} = \sqrt[6]{(2x)^6} = |2x| = 2|x|.$$

Note that in $\sqrt[6]{64x^6}$, we need absolute-value signs because a variable is involved.

**EXAMPLES** Find each of the following. Assume that variables can represent any real number.

**40.** $\sqrt[4]{16} = 2$

**41.** $-\sqrt[4]{16} = -2$

**42.** $\sqrt[4]{-16}$        Does not exist as a real number.

**43.** $\sqrt[4]{81x^4} = \sqrt[4]{(3x)^4} = |3x| = 3|x|$

**44.** $\sqrt[6]{(y+7)^6} = |y+7|$

**45.** $\sqrt{81y^2} = \sqrt{(9y)^2} = |9y| = 9|y|$

The following is a summary of how absolute value is used when we are taking even roots or odd roots.

Find each of the following. Assume that letters can represent any real number.

**48.** $\sqrt[4]{81}$        **49.** $-\sqrt[4]{81}$

**50.** $\sqrt[4]{-81}$        **51.** $\sqrt[4]{0}$

**52.** $\sqrt[4]{16(x-2)^4}$        **53.** $\sqrt[6]{x^6}$

**54.** $\sqrt[8]{(x+3)^8}$        **55.** $\sqrt[7]{(x+3)^7}$

**56.** $\sqrt[5]{243x^5}$

---

### SIMPLIFYING

For any real number $a$:

a) $\sqrt[k]{a^k} = |a|$ when $k$ is an *even* natural number. We use absolute value when $k$ is even unless $a$ is nonnegative.

b) $\sqrt[k]{a^k} = a$ when $k$ is an *odd* natural number greater than 1. We do not use absolute value when $k$ is odd.

---

Do Exercises 48–56.

**a** Find the square roots.

**1.** 16

**2.** 225

**3.** 144

**4.** 9

**5.** 400

**6.** 81

Simplify.

**7.** $-\sqrt{\dfrac{49}{36}}$

**8.** $-\sqrt{\dfrac{361}{9}}$

**9.** $\sqrt{196}$

**10.** $\sqrt{441}$

**11.** $\sqrt{0.0036}$

**12.** $\sqrt{0.04}$

**13.** $\sqrt{-225}$

**14.** $\sqrt{-64}$

Use a calculator to approximate to three decimal places.

**15.** $\sqrt{347}$

**16.** $-\sqrt{1839.2}$

**17.** $\sqrt{\dfrac{285}{74}}$

**18.** $\sqrt{\dfrac{839.4}{19.7}}$

Identify the radicand.

**19.** $9\sqrt{y^2 + 16}$

**20.** $-3\sqrt{p^2 - 10}$

**21.** $x^4 y^5 \sqrt{\dfrac{x}{y-1}}$

**22.** $a^2 b^2 \sqrt{\dfrac{a^2 - b}{b}}$

For the given function, find the indicated function values.

**23.** $f(x) = \sqrt{5x - 10};\quad f(6), f(2), f(1),$ and $f(-1)$

**24.** $t(x) = -\sqrt{2x + 1};\quad t(4), t(0), t(-1),$ and $t\left(-\tfrac{1}{2}\right)$

**25.** $g(x) = \sqrt{x^2 - 25};\quad g(-6), g(3), g(6),$ and $g(13)$

**26.** $F(x) = \sqrt{x^2 + 1};\quad F(0), F(-1),$ and $F(-10)$

**27.** Find the domain of the function $f$ in Exercise 23.

**28.** Find the domain of the function $t$ in Exercise 24.

**29.** *Parking-Lot Arrival Spaces.* The attendants at a parking lot park cars in temporary spaces before the cars are taken to long-term parking stalls. The number $N$ of such spaces needed is approximated by the function

$$N(a) = 2.5\sqrt{a},$$

where $a$ is the average number of arrivals in peak hours. What is the number of spaces needed when the average number of arrivals is 66? 100?

**30.** *Body Surface Area.* Body surface area $B$ can be estimated using the Mosteller formula

$$B = \sqrt{\dfrac{h \times w}{3600}},$$

where $B$ is in square meters, $h$ is height, in centimeters, and $w$ is weight, in kilograms. Estimate the body surface area of a woman whose height is 165 cm and whose weight is 63 kg; of a man whose height is 183 cm and whose weight is 100 kg. Round to the nearest tenth.

Graph.

**31.** $f(x) = 2\sqrt{x}$

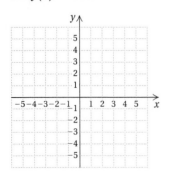

**32.** $g(x) = 3 - \sqrt{x}$

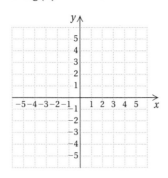

**33.** $F(x) = -3\sqrt{x}$

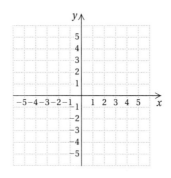

**34.** $f(x) = 2 + \sqrt{x - 1}$

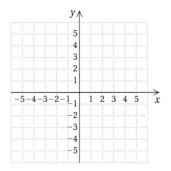

**35.** $f(x) = \sqrt{x}$

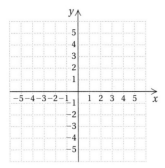

**36.** $g(x) = -\sqrt{x}$

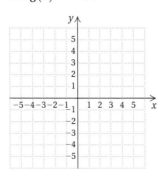

**37.** $f(x) = \sqrt{x - 2}$

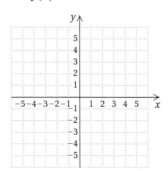

**38.** $g(x) = \sqrt{x + 3}$

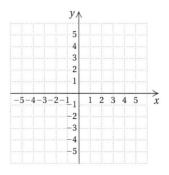

**39.** $f(x) = \sqrt{12 - 3x}$

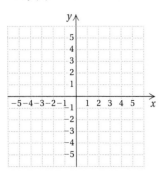

**40.** $g(x) = \sqrt{8 - 4x}$

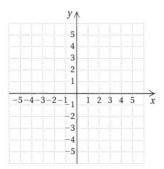

**41.** $g(x) = \sqrt{3x + 9}$

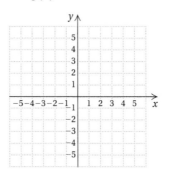

**42.** $f(x) = \sqrt{3x - 6}$

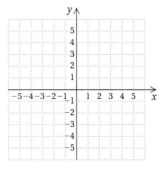

**b** Find each of the following. Assume that letters can represent *any* real number.

**43.** $\sqrt{16x^2}$

**44.** $\sqrt{25t^2}$

**45.** $\sqrt{(-12c)^2}$

**46.** $\sqrt{(-9d)^2}$

**47.** $\sqrt{(p + 3)^2}$

**48.** $\sqrt{(2 - x)^2}$

**49.** $\sqrt{x^2 - 4x + 4}$

**50.** $\sqrt{9t^2 - 30t + 25}$

**51.** $\sqrt[3]{27}$

**52.** $-\sqrt[3]{64}$

**53.** $\sqrt[3]{-64x^3}$

**54.** $\sqrt[3]{-125y^3}$

**55.** $\sqrt[3]{-216}$

**56.** $-\sqrt[3]{-1000}$

**57.** $\sqrt[3]{0.343(x+1)^3}$

**58.** $\sqrt[3]{0.000008(y-2)^3}$

For the given function, find the indicated function values.

**59.** $f(x) = \sqrt[3]{x+1}$;   $f(7), f(26), f(-9),$ and $f(-65)$

**60.** $g(x) = -\sqrt[3]{2x-1}$;   $g(-62), g(0), g(-13),$ and $g(63)$

**61.** $f(x) = -\sqrt[3]{3x+1}$;   $f(0), f(-7), f(21),$ and $f(333)$

**62.** $g(t) = \sqrt[3]{t-3}$;   $g(30), g(-5), g(1),$ and $g(67)$

**d**   Find each of the following. Assume that letters can represent *any* real number.

**63.** $-\sqrt[4]{625}$

**64.** $-\sqrt[4]{256}$

**65.** $\sqrt[5]{-1}$

**66.** $\sqrt[5]{-32}$

**67.** $\sqrt[5]{-\dfrac{32}{243}}$

**68.** $\sqrt[5]{-\dfrac{1}{32}}$

**69.** $\sqrt[6]{x^6}$

**70.** $\sqrt[8]{y^8}$

**71.** $\sqrt[4]{(5a)^4}$

**72.** $\sqrt[4]{(7b)^4}$

**73.** $\sqrt[10]{(-6)^{10}}$

**74.** $\sqrt[12]{(-10)^{12}}$

**75.** $\sqrt[414]{(a + b)^{414}}$

**76.** $\sqrt[1999]{(2a + b)^{1999}}$

**77.** $\sqrt[7]{y^7}$

**78.** $\sqrt[3]{(-6)^3}$

**79.** $\sqrt[5]{(x - 2)^5}$

**80.** $\sqrt[9]{(2xy)^9}$

## Skill Maintenance

Solve. [4.8a]

**81.** $x^2 + x - 2 = 0$

**82.** $x^2 + x = 0$

**83.** $4x^2 - 49 = 0$

**84.** $2x^2 - 26x + 72 = 0$

**85.** $3x^2 + x = 10$

**86.** $4x^2 - 20x + 25 = 0$

**87.** $4x^3 - 20x^2 + 25x = 0$

**88.** $x^3 - x^2 = 0$

Simplify. [R.7a, b]

**89.** $(a^3b^2c^5)^3$

**90.** $(5a^7b^8)(2a^3b)$

## Synthesis

**91.** Find the domain of
$$f(x) = \frac{\sqrt{x + 3}}{\sqrt{2 - x}}.$$

**92.** 📈 Use a graphing calculator to check your answers to Exercises 35, 39, and 41.

**93.** Use only the graph of $f(x) = \sqrt{x}$, shown below, to approximate $\sqrt{3}$, $\sqrt{5}$, and $\sqrt{10}$. Answers may vary.

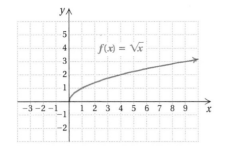

**94.** Use only the graph of $f(x) = \sqrt[3]{x}$, shown below, to approximate $\sqrt[3]{4}$, $\sqrt[3]{6}$, and $\sqrt[3]{-5}$. Answers may vary.

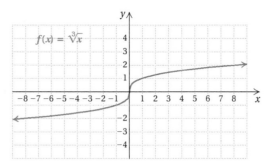

**95.** 📈 Use the TABLE, TRACE, and GRAPH features of a graphing calculator to find the domain and the range of each of the following functions.

**a)** $f(x) = \sqrt[3]{x}$

**b)** $g(x) = \sqrt[3]{4x - 5}$

**c)** $q(x) = 2 - \sqrt{x + 3}$

**d)** $h(x) = \sqrt[4]{x}$

**e)** $t(x) = \sqrt[4]{x - 3}$

# 6.2 Rational Numbers as Exponents

In this section, we give meaning to expressions such as $a^{1/3}, 7^{-1/2}$, and $(3x)^{0.84}$, which have rational numbers as exponents. We will see that using such notation can help simplify certain radical expressions.

## a  Rational Exponents

Expressions like $a^{1/2}, 5^{-1/4}$, and $(2y)^{4/5}$ have not yet been defined. We will define such expressions so that the general properties of exponents hold.

Consider $a^{1/2} \cdot a^{1/2}$. If we want to multiply by adding exponents, it must follow that $a^{1/2} \cdot a^{1/2} = a^{1/2+1/2}$, or $a^1$. Thus we should define $a^{1/2}$ to be a square root of $a$. Similarly, $a^{1/3} \cdot a^{1/3} \cdot a^{1/3} = a^{1/3+1/3+1/3}$, or $a^1$, so $a^{1/3}$ should be defined to mean $\sqrt[3]{a}$.

> **$a^{1/n}$**
>
> For any *nonnegative* real number $a$ and any natural number index $n$ ($n \neq 1$),
>
> $$a^{1/n} \quad \text{means} \quad \sqrt[n]{a} \quad \text{(the nonnegative } n\text{th root of } a\text{)}.$$

Whenever we use rational exponents, we assume that the bases are nonnegative.

**EXAMPLES**  Rewrite without rational exponents, and simplify, if possible.

1. $27^{1/3} = \sqrt[3]{27} = 3$
2. $(abc)^{1/5} = \sqrt[5]{abc}$
3. $x^{1/2} = \sqrt{x}$   An index of 2 is not written.

> Do Exercises 1–5.

**EXAMPLES**  Rewrite with rational exponents.

4. $\sqrt[5]{7xy} = (7xy)^{1/5}$

> We need parentheses around the radicand here.

5. $8\sqrt[3]{xy} = 8(xy)^{1/3}$

6. $\sqrt[7]{\dfrac{x^3 y}{9}} = \left(\dfrac{x^3 y}{9}\right)^{1/7}$

> Do Exercises 6–9.

How should we define $a^{2/3}$? If the general properties of exponents are to hold, we have $a^{2/3} = (a^{1/3})^2$, or $(a^2)^{1/3}$, or $\left(\sqrt[3]{a}\right)^2$, or $\sqrt[3]{a^2}$. We define this accordingly.

> **$a^{m/n}$**
>
> For any natural numbers $m$ and $n$ ($n \neq 1$) and any nonnegative real number $a$,
>
> $$a^{m/n} \quad \text{means} \quad \sqrt[n]{a^m}, \quad \text{or} \quad \left(\sqrt[n]{a}\right)^m.$$

Rewrite without rational exponents, and simplify, if possible.

1. $y^{1/4}$
2. $(3a)^{1/2}$
3. $16^{1/4}$
4. $(125)^{1/3}$
5. $(a^3 b^2 c)^{1/5}$

Rewrite with rational exponents.

6. $\sqrt[3]{19ab}$
7. $19\sqrt[3]{ab}$
8. $\sqrt[5]{\dfrac{x^2 y}{16}}$
9. $7\sqrt[4]{2ab}$

**Answers**

1. $\sqrt[4]{y}$  2. $\sqrt{3a}$  3. 2  4. 5
5. $\sqrt[5]{a^3 b^2 c}$  6. $(19ab)^{1/3}$  7. $19(ab)^{1/3}$
8. $\left(\dfrac{x^2 y}{16}\right)^{1/5}$  9. $7(2ab)^{1/4}$

Rewrite without rational exponents, and simplify, if possible.

**10.** $x^{3/5}$          **11.** $8^{2/3}$

**12.** $4^{5/2}$

Rewrite with rational exponents.

**13.** $\left(\sqrt[3]{7abc}\right)^4$          **14.** $\sqrt[5]{6^7}$

Rewrite with positive exponents, and simplify, if possible.

**15.** $16^{-1/4}$          **16.** $(3xy)^{-7/8}$

**17.** $81^{-3/4}$          **18.** $7p^{3/4}q^{-6/5}$

**19.** $\left(\dfrac{11m}{7n}\right)^{-2/3}$

**EXAMPLES**   Rewrite without rational exponents, and simplify, if possible.

**7.** $(27)^{2/3} = \sqrt[3]{27^2}$
$= \left(\sqrt[3]{27}\right)^2$
$= 3^2$
$= 9$

**8.** $4^{3/2} = \sqrt[2]{4^3}$
$= \left(\sqrt[2]{4}\right)^3$
$= 2^3$
$= 8$

Do Exercises 10–12.

**EXAMPLES**   Rewrite with rational exponents.

The index becomes the denominator of the rational exponent.

**9.** $\sqrt[3]{9^4} = 9^{4/3}$          **10.** $\left(\sqrt[4]{7xy}\right)^5 = (7xy)^{5/4}$

Do Exercises 13 and 14.

## b   Negative Rational Exponents

Negative rational exponents have a meaning similar to that of negative integer exponents.

---

**$a^{-m/n}$**

For any rational number $m/n$ and any positive real number $a$,

$$a^{-m/n} \quad \text{means} \quad \frac{1}{a^{m/n}};$$

that is, $a^{m/n}$ and $a^{-m/n}$ are reciprocals.

---

**EXAMPLES**   Rewrite with positive exponents, and simplify, if possible.

**11.** $9^{-1/2} = \dfrac{1}{9^{1/2}} = \dfrac{1}{\sqrt{9}} = \dfrac{1}{3}$

**12.** $(5xy)^{-4/5} = \dfrac{1}{(5xy)^{4/5}}$

**13.** $64^{-2/3} = \dfrac{1}{64^{2/3}} = \dfrac{1}{\left(\sqrt[3]{64}\right)^2} = \dfrac{1}{4^2} = \dfrac{1}{16}$

**14.** $4x^{-2/3}y^{1/5} = 4 \cdot \dfrac{1}{x^{2/3}} \cdot y^{1/5} = \dfrac{4y^{1/5}}{x^{2/3}}$

**15.** $\left(\dfrac{3r}{7s}\right)^{-5/2} = \left(\dfrac{7s}{3r}\right)^{5/2}$   Since $\left(\dfrac{a}{b}\right)^{-n} = \left(\dfrac{b}{a}\right)^{n}$

Do Exercises 15–19.

*Answers*

**10.** $\sqrt[5]{x^3}$   **11.** 4   **12.** 32   **13.** $(7abc)^{4/3}$

**14.** $6^{7/5}$   **15.** $\dfrac{1}{2}$   **16.** $\dfrac{1}{(3xy)^{7/8}}$   **17.** $\dfrac{1}{27}$

**18.** $\dfrac{7p^{3/4}}{q^{6/5}}$   **19.** $\left(\dfrac{7n}{11m}\right)^{2/3}$

**Rational Exponents**  We can use a graphing calculator to approximate rational roots of real numbers. To approximate $7^{2/3}$, we press ⑦ ▲ ( ② ÷ ③ ) **ENTER**. Note that the parentheses around the exponent are necessary. If they are not used, the calculator will read the expression as $7^2 \div 3$. To approximate $14^{-1.9}$, we press ① ④ ▲ (-) ① · ⑨ **ENTER**. Parentheses are not required when a rational exponent is expressed in a single decimal number. The display indicates that $7^{2/3} \approx 3.659$ and $14^{-1.9} \approx 0.007$.

```
7^(2/3)
            3.65930571
14^-1.9
            .006642885
```

**Exercises:**  Approximate each of the following.

**1.** $5^{3/4}$

**2.** $8^{4/7}$

**3.** $29^{-3/8}$

**4.** $73^{0.56}$

**5.** $34^{-2.78}$

**6.** $32^{0.2}$

## (c) Laws of Exponents

The same laws hold for rational-number exponents as for integer exponents. We list them for review.

For any real number $a$ and any rational exponents $m$ and $n$:

**1.** $a^m \cdot a^n = a^{m+n}$  In multiplying, we can add exponents if the bases are the same.

**2.** $\dfrac{a^m}{a^n} = a^{m-n}$  In dividing, we can subtract exponents if the bases are the same.

**3.** $(a^m)^n = a^{m \cdot n}$  To raise a power to a power, we can multiply the exponents.

**4.** $(ab)^m = a^m b^m$  To raise a product to a power, we can raise each factor to the power.

**5.** $\left(\dfrac{a}{b}\right)^n = \dfrac{a^n}{b^n}$  To raise a quotient to a power, we can raise both the numerator and the denominator to the power.

**EXAMPLES**  Use the laws of exponents to simplify.

**16.** $3^{1/5} \cdot 3^{3/5} = 3^{1/5+3/5} = 3^{4/5}$    Adding exponents

**17.** $\dfrac{7^{1/4}}{7^{1/2}} = 7^{1/4-1/2} = 7^{1/4-2/4} = 7^{-1/4} = \dfrac{1}{7^{1/4}}$    Subtracting exponents

**18.** $(7.2^{2/3})^{3/4} = 7.2^{2/3 \cdot 3/4} = 7.2^{6/12} = 7.2^{1/2}$    Multiplying exponents

**19.** $(a^{-1/3} b^{2/5})^{1/2} = a^{-1/3 \cdot 1/2} \cdot b^{2/5 \cdot 1/2}$    Raising a product to a power and multiplying exponents

$$= a^{-1/6} b^{1/5} = \dfrac{b^{1/5}}{a^{1/6}}$$

Do Exercises 20–23.

Use the laws of exponents to simplify.

**20.** $7^{1/3} \cdot 7^{3/5}$

**21.** $\dfrac{5^{7/6}}{5^{5/6}}$

**22.** $(9^{3/5})^{2/3}$

**23.** $(p^{-2/3} q^{1/4})^{1/2}$

***Answers***

**20.** $7^{14/15}$   **21.** $5^{1/3}$   **22.** $9^{2/5}$   **23.** $\dfrac{q^{1/8}}{p^{1/3}}$

## (d) Simplifying Radical Expressions

Rational exponents can be used to simplify some radical expressions. The procedure is as follows.

> **SIMPLIFYING RADICAL EXPRESSIONS**
>
> 1. Convert radical expressions to exponential expressions.
> 2. Use arithmetic and the laws of exponents to simplify.
> 3. Convert back to radical notation when appropriate.
>
> *Important*: This procedure works only when we assume that a negative number has not been raised to an even power in the radicand. With this assumption, no absolute-value signs will be needed.

**EXAMPLES** Use rational exponents to simplify.

**20.** $\sqrt[6]{x^3} = x^{3/6}$     Converting to an exponential expression

$\phantom{\sqrt[6]{x^3}} = x^{1/2}$     Simplifying the exponent

$\phantom{\sqrt[6]{x^3}} = \sqrt{x}$     Converting back to radical notation

**21.** $\sqrt[6]{4} = 4^{1/6}$     Converting to exponential notation

$\phantom{\sqrt[6]{4}} = (2^2)^{1/6}$     Renaming 4 as $2^2$

$\phantom{\sqrt[6]{4}} = 2^{2/6}$     Using $(a^m)^n = a^{mn}$; multiplying exponents

$\phantom{\sqrt[6]{4}} = 2^{1/3}$     Simplifying the exponent

$\phantom{\sqrt[6]{4}} = \sqrt[3]{2}$     Converting back to radical notation

**22.** $\sqrt[8]{a^2b^4} = (a^2b^4)^{1/8}$     Converting to exponential notation

$\phantom{\sqrt[8]{a^2b^4}} = a^{2/8} \cdot b^{4/8}$     Using $(ab)^n = a^n b^n$

$\phantom{\sqrt[8]{a^2b^4}} = a^{1/4} \cdot b^{1/2}$     Simplifying the exponents

$\phantom{\sqrt[8]{a^2b^4}} = a^{1/4} \cdot b^{2/4}$     Rewriting $\frac{1}{2}$ with a denominator of 4

$\phantom{\sqrt[8]{a^2b^4}} = (ab^2)^{1/4}$     Using $a^n b^n = (ab)^n$

$\phantom{\sqrt[8]{a^2b^4}} = \sqrt[4]{ab^2}$     Converting back to radical notation

Do Exercises 24–29.

---

**Use rational exponents to simplify.**

**24.** $\sqrt[4]{a^2}$     **25.** $\sqrt[4]{x^4}$

**26.** $\sqrt[6]{8}$     **27.** $\sqrt[12]{x^3y^6}$

**28.** $\sqrt[6]{a^{12}b^3}$     **29.** $\sqrt[5]{a^5b^{10}}$

---

We can use properties of rational exponents to write a single radical expression for a product or a quotient.

**EXAMPLE 23** Use rational exponents to write a single radical expression for $\sqrt[3]{5} \cdot \sqrt{2}$.

$\sqrt[3]{5} \cdot \sqrt{2} = 5^{1/3} \cdot 2^{1/2}$     Converting to exponential notation

$\phantom{\sqrt[3]{5} \cdot \sqrt{2}} = 5^{2/6} \cdot 2^{3/6}$     Rewriting so that exponents have a common denominator

$\phantom{\sqrt[3]{5} \cdot \sqrt{2}} = (5^2 \cdot 2^3)^{1/6}$     Using $a^n b^n = (ab)^n$

$\phantom{\sqrt[3]{5} \cdot \sqrt{2}} = \sqrt[6]{5^2 \cdot 2^3}$     Converting back to radical notation

$\phantom{\sqrt[3]{5} \cdot \sqrt{2}} = \sqrt[6]{200}$     Multiplying under the radical

Do Exercise 30.

**30.** Use rational exponents to write a single radical expression for

$\sqrt[4]{7} \cdot \sqrt{3}$.

---

*Answers*

**24.** $\sqrt{a}$    **25.** $x$    **26.** $\sqrt{2}$    **27.** $\sqrt[4]{xy^2}$
**28.** $a^2\sqrt{b}$    **29.** $ab^2$    **30.** $\sqrt[4]{63}$

**EXAMPLE 24** Write a single radical expression for $a^{1/2}b^{-1/2}c^{5/6}$.

$$a^{1/2}b^{-1/2}c^{5/6} = a^{3/6}b^{-3/6}c^{5/6}$$     Rewriting so that exponents have a common denominator

$$= (a^3b^{-3}c^5)^{1/6}$$     Using $a^nb^n = (ab)^n$

$$= \sqrt[6]{a^3b^{-3}c^5}$$     Converting to radical notation

**EXAMPLE 25** Write a single radical expression for $\dfrac{x^{5/6} \cdot y^{3/8}}{x^{4/9} \cdot y^{1/4}}$.

$$\frac{x^{5/6} \cdot y^{3/8}}{x^{4/9} \cdot y^{1/4}} = x^{5/6-4/9} \cdot y^{3/8-1/4}$$     Subtracting exponents

$$= x^{15/18-8/18} \cdot y^{3/8-2/8}$$     Finding common denominators so that exponents can be subtracted

$$= x^{7/18} \cdot y^{1/8}$$     Carrying out the subtraction of exponents

$$= x^{28/72} \cdot y^{9/72}$$     Rewriting so that all exponents have a common denominator

$$= (x^{28}y^9)^{1/72}$$     Using $a^nb^n = (ab)^n$

$$= \sqrt[72]{x^{28}y^9}$$     Converting to radical notation

Do Exercises 31 and 32.

**EXAMPLES** Use rational exponents to simplify.

**26.** $\sqrt[6]{(5x)^3} = (5x)^{3/6}$     Converting to exponential notation

$$= (5x)^{1/2}$$     Simplifying the exponent

$$= \sqrt{5x}$$     Converting back to radical notation

**27.** $\sqrt[5]{t^{20}} = t^{20/5}$     Converting to exponential notation

$$= t^4$$     Simplifying the exponent

**28.** $\left(\sqrt[3]{pq^2c}\right)^{12} = (pq^2c)^{12/3}$     Converting to exponential notation

$$= (pq^2c)^4$$     Simplifying the exponent

$$= p^4q^8c^4$$     Using $(ab)^n = a^nb^n$

**29.** $\sqrt{\sqrt[3]{x}} = \sqrt{x^{1/3}}$     Converting the radicand to exponential notation

$$= (x^{1/3})^{1/2}$$     Try to go directly to this step.

$$= x^{1/6}$$     Multiplying exponents

$$= \sqrt[6]{x}$$     Converting back to radical notation

Do Exercises 33–36.

Write a single radical expression.
**31.** $x^{2/3}y^{1/2}z^{5/6}$

**32.** $\dfrac{a^{1/2}b^{3/8}}{a^{1/4}b^{1/8}}$

Use rational exponents to simplify.
**33.** $\sqrt[14]{(5m)^2}$     **34.** $\sqrt[18]{m^3}$

**35.** $\left(\sqrt[6]{a^5b^3c}\right)^{24}$     **36.** $\sqrt[5]{\sqrt{x}}$

***Answers***
**31.** $\sqrt[6]{x^4y^3z^5}$   **32.** $\sqrt[4]{ab}$   **33.** $\sqrt[7]{5m}$
**34.** $\sqrt[6]{m}$   **35.** $a^{20}b^{12}c^4$   **36.** $\sqrt[10]{x}$

**6.2** **Exercise Set**

For Extra Help

*MyMathLab*

Math XL
PRACTICE

WATCH

DOWNLOAD

READ

REVIEW

**a** Rewrite without rational exponents, and simplify, if possible.

**1.** $y^{1/7}$

**2.** $x^{1/6}$

**3.** $8^{1/3}$

**4.** $16^{1/2}$

**5.** $(a^3b^3)^{1/5}$

**6.** $(x^2y^2)^{1/3}$

**7.** $16^{3/4}$

**8.** $4^{7/2}$

**9.** $49^{3/2}$

**10.** $27^{4/3}$

Rewrite with rational exponents.

**11.** $\sqrt{17}$

**12.** $\sqrt{x^3}$

**13.** $\sqrt[3]{18}$

**14.** $\sqrt[3]{23}$

**15.** $\sqrt[5]{xy^2z}$

**16.** $\sqrt[7]{x^3y^2z^2}$

**17.** $\left(\sqrt{3mn}\right)^3$

**18.** $\left(\sqrt[3]{7xy}\right)^4$

**19.** $\left(\sqrt[7]{8x^2y}\right)^5$

**20.** $\left(\sqrt[6]{2a^5b}\right)^7$

**b** Rewrite with positive exponents, and simplify, if possible.

**21.** $27^{-1/3}$

**22.** $100^{-1/2}$

**23.** $100^{-3/2}$

**24.** $16^{-3/4}$

**25.** $3x^{-1/4}$

**26.** $8y^{-1/7}$

**27.** $(2rs)^{-3/4}$

**28.** $(5xy)^{-5/6}$

**29.** $2a^{3/4}b^{-1/2}c^{2/3}$

**30.** $5x^{-2/3}y^{4/5}z$

**31.** $\left(\dfrac{7x}{8yz}\right)^{-3/5}$

**32.** $\left(\dfrac{2ab}{3c}\right)^{-5/6}$

**33.** $\dfrac{1}{x^{-2/3}}$

**34.** $\dfrac{1}{a^{-7/8}}$

**35.** $2^{-1/3}x^4y^{-2/7}$

**36.** $3^{-5/2}a^3b^{-7/3}$

**37.** $\dfrac{7x}{\sqrt[3]{z}}$

**38.** $\dfrac{6a}{\sqrt[4]{b}}$

**39.** $\dfrac{5a}{3c^{-1/2}}$

**40.** $\dfrac{2z}{5x^{-1/3}}$

**c** Use the laws of exponents to simplify. Write the answers with positive exponents.

**41.** $5^{3/4} \cdot 5^{1/8}$

**42.** $11^{2/3} \cdot 11^{1/2}$

**43.** $\dfrac{7^{5/8}}{7^{3/8}}$

**44.** $\dfrac{3^{5/8}}{3^{-1/8}}$

**45.** $\dfrac{4.9^{-1/6}}{4.9^{-2/3}}$

**46.** $\dfrac{2.3^{-3/10}}{2.3^{-1/5}}$

**47.** $(6^{3/8})^{2/7}$

**48.** $(3^{2/9})^{3/5}$

**49.** $a^{2/3} \cdot a^{5/4}$

**50.** $x^{3/4} \cdot x^{2/3}$

**51.** $(a^{2/3} \cdot b^{5/8})^4$      **52.** $(x^{-1/3} \cdot y^{-2/5})^{-15}$      **53.** $(x^{2/3})^{-3/7}$      **54.** $(a^{-3/2})^{2/9}$

**55.** $\left(\dfrac{x^{3/4}}{y^{1/2}}\right)^{-2/3}$      **56.** $\left(\dfrac{a^{-3/2}}{b^{-5/3}}\right)^{1/3}$      **57.** $(m^{-1/4} \cdot n^{-5/6})^{-12/5}$      **58.** $(x^{3/8} \cdot y^{5/2})^{4/3}$

(**d**)   Use rational exponents to simplify. Write the answer in radical notation if appropriate.

**59.** $\sqrt[6]{a^2}$      **60.** $\sqrt[6]{t^4}$      **61.** $\sqrt[3]{x^{15}}$      **62.** $\sqrt[4]{a^{12}}$      **63.** $\sqrt[6]{x^{-18}}$

**64.** $\sqrt[5]{a^{-10}}$      **65.** $\left(\sqrt[3]{ab}\right)^{15}$      **66.** $\left(\sqrt[7]{cd}\right)^{14}$      **67.** $\sqrt[14]{128}$      **68.** $\sqrt[6]{81}$

**69.** $\sqrt[6]{4x^2}$      **70.** $\sqrt[3]{8y^6}$      **71.** $\sqrt{x^4y^6}$      **72.** $\sqrt[4]{16x^4y^2}$      **73.** $\sqrt[5]{32c^{10}d^{15}}$

Use rational exponents to write a single radical expression.

**74.** $\sqrt[3]{3}\sqrt{3}$      **75.** $\sqrt[3]{7} \cdot \sqrt[4]{5}$      **76.** $\sqrt{11} \cdot \sqrt[6]{13}$      **77.** $\sqrt[4]{5} \cdot \sqrt[5]{7}$      **78.** $\sqrt[3]{y}\sqrt[5]{3y}$

**79.** $\sqrt{x}\sqrt[3]{2x}$      **80.** $\left(\sqrt[3]{x^2y^5}\right)^{12}$      **81.** $\left(\sqrt[5]{a^2b^4}\right)^{15}$      **82.** $\sqrt[4]{\sqrt{x}}$      **83.** $\sqrt[3]{\sqrt[6]{m}}$

**84.** $a^{2/3} \cdot b^{3/4}$      **85.** $x^{1/3} \cdot y^{1/4} \cdot z^{1/6}$      **86.** $\dfrac{x^{8/15} \cdot y^{7/5}}{x^{1/3} \cdot y^{-1/5}}$      **87.** $\left(\dfrac{c^{-4/5}d^{5/9}}{c^{3/10}d^{1/6}}\right)^3$      **88.** $\sqrt[3]{\sqrt[4]{xy}}$

## Skill Maintenance

Solve.   |5.7a|

**89.** $A = \dfrac{ab}{a + b}$, for $a$      **90.** $Q = \dfrac{st}{s - t}$, for $s$      **91.** $Q = \dfrac{st}{s - t}$, for $t$      **92.** $\dfrac{1}{t} = \dfrac{1}{a} - \dfrac{1}{b}$, for $b$

## Synthesis

**93.** Use the SIMULTANEOUS mode to graph
$$y_1 = x^{1/2}, \quad y_2 = 3x^{2/5}, \quad y_3 = x^{4/7}, \quad y_4 = \tfrac{1}{5}x^{3/4}.$$
Then, looking only at coordinates, match each graph with its equation.

**94.** Simplify:
$$\left(\sqrt[10]{\sqrt[5]{x^{15}}}\right)^5 \left(\sqrt[5]{\sqrt[10]{x^{15}}}\right)^5.$$

# 6.3

# Simplifying Radical Expressions

## OBJECTIVES

**a** Multiply and simplify radical expressions.

**b** Divide and simplify radical expressions.

## a  Multiplying and Simplifying Radical Expressions

Note that $\sqrt{4}\sqrt{25} = 2 \cdot 5 = 10$. Also $\sqrt{4 \cdot 25} = \sqrt{100} = 10$. Likewise,

$$\sqrt[3]{27}\sqrt[3]{8} = 3 \cdot 2 = 6 \quad \text{and} \quad \sqrt[3]{27 \cdot 8} = \sqrt[3]{216} = 6.$$

These examples suggest the following.

---

**THE PRODUCT RULE FOR RADICALS**

For any nonnegative real numbers $a$ and $b$ and any index $k$,

$$\sqrt[k]{a} \cdot \sqrt[k]{b} = \sqrt[k]{a \cdot b}, \quad \text{or} \quad a^{1/k} \cdot b^{1/k} = (ab)^{1/k}.$$

The index must be the same throughout.

(To multiply, multiply the radicands.)

---

**EXAMPLES**  Multiply.

**1.** $\sqrt{3} \cdot \sqrt{5} = \sqrt{3 \cdot 5} = \sqrt{15}$

**2.** $\sqrt{5a}\sqrt{2b} = \sqrt{5a \cdot 2b} = \sqrt{10ab}$

**3.** $\sqrt[3]{4}\sqrt[3]{5} = \sqrt[3]{4 \cdot 5} = \sqrt[3]{20}$

**4.** $\sqrt[4]{\dfrac{y}{5}} \sqrt[4]{\dfrac{7}{x}} = \sqrt[4]{\dfrac{y}{5} \cdot \dfrac{7}{x}} = \sqrt[4]{\dfrac{7y}{5x}}$

*Caution!*

A common error is to omit the index in the answer.

Multiply.

**1.** $\sqrt{19}\,\sqrt{7}$

**2.** $\sqrt{3p}\,\sqrt{7q}$

**3.** $\sqrt[4]{403}\,\sqrt[4]{7}$

**4.** $\sqrt[3]{\dfrac{5}{p}} \cdot \sqrt[3]{\dfrac{2}{q}}$

Do Exercises 1–4.

Keep in mind that the product rule can be used only when the indexes are the same. When indexes differ, we can use rational exponents as we did in Examples 23 and 24 of Section 6.2.

**EXAMPLE 5**  Multiply: $\sqrt{5x} \cdot \sqrt[4]{3y}$.

$$\begin{aligned}
\sqrt{5x} \cdot \sqrt[4]{3y} &= (5x)^{1/2}(3y)^{1/4} & \text{Converting to exponential notation} \\
&= (5x)^{2/4}(3y)^{1/4} & \text{Rewriting so that exponents have a common denominator} \\
&= [(5x)^2(3y)]^{1/4} & \text{Using } a^n b^n = (ab)^n \\
&= [(25x^2)(3y)]^{1/4} & \text{Squaring } 5x \\
&= \sqrt[4]{(25x^2)(3y)} & \text{Converting back to radical notation} \\
&= \sqrt[4]{75x^2y} & \text{Multiplying under the radical}
\end{aligned}$$

Multiply.

**5.** $\sqrt{5}\,\sqrt[3]{2}$

**6.** $\sqrt[4]{x}\,\sqrt[3]{2y}$

Do Exercises 5 and 6.

*Answers*

**1.** $\sqrt{133}$   **2.** $\sqrt{21pq}$   **3.** $\sqrt[4]{2821}$

**4.** $\sqrt[3]{\dfrac{10}{pq}}$   **5.** $\sqrt[6]{500}$   **6.** $\sqrt[12]{16x^3y^4}$

We can reverse the product rule to simplify a product. We simplify the root of a product by taking the root of each factor separately.

---

**FACTORING RADICAL EXPRESSIONS**

For any nonnegative real numbers $a$ and $b$ and any index $k$,

$$\sqrt[k]{ab} = \sqrt[k]{a} \cdot \sqrt[k]{b}, \quad \text{or} \quad (ab)^{1/k} = a^{1/k} \cdot b^{1/k}.$$

(Take the $k$th root of each factor separately.)

---

Compare the following:

$$\sqrt{50} = \sqrt{10 \cdot 5} = \sqrt{10}\,\sqrt{5};$$
$$\sqrt{50} = \sqrt{25 \cdot 2} = \sqrt{25}\,\sqrt{2} = 5\sqrt{2}.$$

In the second case, the radicand is written with the perfect-square factor 25. If you do not recognize perfect-square factors, try factoring the radicand into its prime factors. For example,

$$\sqrt{50} = \sqrt{2 \cdot \underline{5 \cdot 5}} = 5\sqrt{2}.$$

$\uparrow$

Perfect square (a pair of the same numbers)

Square-root radical expressions in which the radicand has no perfect-square factors, such as $5\sqrt{2}$, are considered to be in simplest form. A procedure for simplifying $k$th roots follows.

---

**SIMPLIFYING $k$th ROOTS**

To simplify a radical expression by factoring:

1. Look for the largest factors of the radicand that are perfect $k$th powers (where $k$ is the index).
2. Then take the $k$th root of the resulting factors.
3. A radical expression, with index $k$, is *simplified* when its radicand has no factors that are perfect $k$th powers.

---

**EXAMPLES**  Simplify by factoring.

6. $\sqrt{50} = \sqrt{25 \cdot 2} = \sqrt{25} \cdot \sqrt{2} = \sqrt{5 \cdot 5} \cdot \sqrt{2} = 5\sqrt{2}$

> This factor is a perfect square.

7. $\sqrt[3]{32} = \sqrt[3]{8 \cdot 4} = \sqrt[3]{8} \cdot \sqrt[3]{4} = \sqrt[3]{2 \cdot 2 \cdot 2} \cdot \sqrt[3]{2 \cdot 2} = 2\sqrt[3]{4}$

> This factor is a perfect cube (third power).

8. $\sqrt[4]{48} = \sqrt[4]{16 \cdot 3} = \sqrt[4]{16} \cdot \sqrt[4]{3} = \sqrt[4]{2 \cdot 2 \cdot 2 \cdot 2} \cdot \sqrt[4]{3} = 2\sqrt[4]{3}$

> This factor is a perfect fourth power.

Simplify by factoring.

7. $\sqrt{32}$    8. $\sqrt[3]{80}$

Do Exercises 7 and 8.

*Answers*

7. $4\sqrt{2}$    8. $2\sqrt[3]{10}$

**EXAMPLES** Simplify by factoring. Assume that no radicands were formed by raising negative numbers to even powers.

**9.** $\sqrt{5x^2} = \sqrt{5 \cdot x^2}$     Factoring the radicand

$= \sqrt{5} \cdot \sqrt{x^2}$     Factoring into two radicals

$= \sqrt{5} \cdot x$     Taking the square root of $x^2$

> Absolute-value notation is not needed because we assume that $x$ is not negative.

**10.** $\sqrt{18x^2y} = \sqrt{9 \cdot 2 \cdot x^2 \cdot y}$     Factoring the radicand and looking for perfect-square factors

$= \sqrt{9 \cdot x^2 \cdot 2 \cdot y}$

$= \sqrt{9} \cdot \sqrt{x^2} \cdot \sqrt{2} \cdot \sqrt{y}$     Factoring into several radicals

$= 3x\sqrt{2y}$     Taking square roots

**11.** $\sqrt{216x^5y^3} = \sqrt{36 \cdot 6 \cdot x^4 \cdot x \cdot y^2 \cdot y}$     Factoring the radicand and looking for perfect-square factors

$= \sqrt{36 \cdot x^4 \cdot y^2 \cdot 6 \cdot x \cdot y}$

$= \sqrt{36}\,\sqrt{x^4}\,\sqrt{y^2}\,\sqrt{6xy}$     Factoring into several radicals

$= 6x^2y\sqrt{6xy}$     Taking square roots

Let's look at this example another way. We do a complete factorization and look for pairs of factors. Each pair of factors makes a square:

$\sqrt{216x^5y^3} = \sqrt{2 \cdot 2 \cdot 2 \cdot 3 \cdot 3 \cdot 3 \cdot x \cdot x \cdot x \cdot x \cdot x \cdot y \cdot y \cdot y}$     Each pair of factors makes a perfect square.

$= 2 \cdot 3 \cdot x \cdot x \cdot y \cdot \sqrt{2 \cdot 3 \cdot x \cdot y}$

$= 6x^2y\sqrt{6xy}.$

**12.** $\sqrt[3]{16a^7b^{11}} = \sqrt[3]{8 \cdot 2 \cdot a^6 \cdot a \cdot b^9 \cdot b^2}$     Factoring the radicand. The index is 3, so we look for the largest powers that are multiples of 3 because these are perfect cubes.

$= \sqrt[3]{8} \cdot \sqrt[3]{a^6} \cdot \sqrt[3]{b^9} \cdot \sqrt[3]{2ab^2}$     Factoring into radicals

$= 2a^2b^3\sqrt[3]{2ab^2}$     Taking cube roots

Let's look at this example another way. We do a complete factorization and look for triples of factors. Each triple of factors makes a cube:

$\sqrt[3]{16a^7b^{11}}$

$= \sqrt[3]{2 \cdot 2 \cdot 2 \cdot 2 \cdot a \cdot a \cdot a \cdot a \cdot a \cdot a \cdot a \cdot b \cdot b \cdot b \cdot b \cdot b \cdot b \cdot b \cdot b \cdot b \cdot b \cdot b}$

Each triple of factors makes a cube.

$= 2 \cdot a \cdot a \cdot b \cdot b \cdot b \cdot \sqrt[3]{2 \cdot a \cdot b \cdot b}$

$= 2a^2b^3\sqrt[3]{2ab^2}.$

Do Exercises 9–14.

Simplify by factoring. Assume that no radicands were formed by raising negative numbers to even powers.

**9.** $\sqrt{300}$       **10.** $\sqrt{36y^2}$

**11.** $\sqrt{12a^2b}$       **12.** $\sqrt{12ab^3c^2}$

**13.** $\sqrt[3]{16}$       **14.** $\sqrt[3]{81x^4y^8}$

*Answers*

**9.** $10\sqrt{3}$   **10.** $6y$   **11.** $2a\sqrt{3b}$
**12.** $2bc\sqrt{3ab}$   **13.** $2\sqrt[3]{2}$   **14.** $3xy^2\sqrt[3]{3xy^2}$

Sometimes after we have multiplied, we can simplify by factoring.

**EXAMPLES** Multiply and simplify. Assume that no radicands were formed by raising negative numbers to even powers.

**13.** $\sqrt{20}\sqrt{8} = \sqrt{20 \cdot 8} = \sqrt{\underline{4} \cdot 5 \cdot \underline{4} \cdot 2} = 4\sqrt{10}$

**14.** $3\sqrt[3]{25} \cdot 2\sqrt[3]{5} = 3 \cdot 2 \cdot \sqrt[3]{25} \cdot \sqrt[3]{5} = 6 \cdot \sqrt[3]{25 \cdot 5}$
$$= 6 \cdot \sqrt[3]{5 \cdot 5 \cdot 5}$$
$$= 6 \cdot 5 = 30$$

**15.** $\sqrt[3]{18y^3}\,\sqrt[3]{4x^2} = \sqrt[3]{18y^3 \cdot 4x^2}$    Multiplying radicands
$$= \sqrt[3]{2 \cdot 3 \cdot 3 \cdot y \cdot y \cdot y \cdot 2 \cdot 2 \cdot x \cdot x}$$
$$= 2 \cdot y \cdot \sqrt[3]{3 \cdot 3 \cdot x \cdot x}$$
$$= 2y\sqrt[3]{9x^2}$$

Do Exercises 15-18.

Multiply and simplify. Assume that no radicands were formed by raising negative numbers to even powers.

**15.** $\sqrt{3}\,\sqrt{6}$

**16.** $\sqrt{18y}\,\sqrt{14y}$

**17.** $\sqrt[3]{3x^2y}\,\sqrt[3]{36x}$

**18.** $\sqrt{7a}\,\sqrt{21b}$

## **b** Dividing and Simplifying Radical Expressions

Note that $\dfrac{\sqrt[3]{27}}{\sqrt[3]{8}} = \dfrac{3}{2}$ and that $\sqrt[3]{\dfrac{27}{8}} = \dfrac{3}{2}$. This example suggests the following.

---

**THE QUOTIENT RULE FOR RADICALS**

For any nonnegative number $a$, any positive number $b$, and any index $k$,

$$\frac{\sqrt[k]{a}}{\sqrt[k]{b}} = \sqrt[k]{\frac{a}{b}}, \quad \text{or} \quad \frac{a^{1/k}}{b^{1/k}} = \left(\frac{a}{b}\right)^{1/k}.$$

(To divide, divide the radicands. After doing this, you can sometimes simplify by taking roots.)

---

**EXAMPLES** Divide and simplify. Assume that no radicands were formed by raising negative numbers to even powers.

**16.** $\dfrac{\sqrt{80}}{\sqrt{5}} = \sqrt{\dfrac{80}{5}} = \sqrt{16} = 4$    We divide the radicands.

**17.** $\dfrac{5\sqrt[3]{32}}{\sqrt[3]{2}} = 5\sqrt[3]{\dfrac{32}{2}} = 5\sqrt[3]{16} = 5\sqrt[3]{8 \cdot 2} = 5\sqrt[3]{8}\,\sqrt[3]{2} = 5 \cdot 2\sqrt[3]{2} = 10\sqrt[3]{2}$

**18.** $\dfrac{\sqrt{72xy}}{2\sqrt{2}} = \dfrac{1}{2}\dfrac{\sqrt{72xy}}{\sqrt{2}} = \dfrac{1}{2}\sqrt{\dfrac{72xy}{2}} = \dfrac{1}{2}\sqrt{36xy} = \dfrac{1}{2}\sqrt{36}\,\sqrt{xy}$
$$= \dfrac{1}{2} \cdot 6\sqrt{xy} = 3\sqrt{xy}$$

Do Exercises 19-22.

Divide and simplify. Assume that no radicands were formed by raising negative numbers to even powers.

**19.** $\dfrac{\sqrt{75}}{\sqrt{3}}$

**20.** $\dfrac{14\sqrt{128xy}}{2\sqrt{2}}$

**21.** $\dfrac{\sqrt{50a^3}}{\sqrt{2a}}$

**22.** $\dfrac{4\sqrt[3]{250}}{7\sqrt[3]{2}}$

*Answers*

**15.** $3\sqrt{2}$   **16.** $6y\sqrt{7}$   **17.** $3x\sqrt[3]{4y}$
**18.** $7\sqrt{3ab}$   **19.** 5   **20.** $56\sqrt{xy}$   **21.** $5a$
**22.** $\dfrac{20}{7}$

We can reverse the quotient rule to simplify a quotient. We simplify the root of a quotient by taking the roots of the numerator and of the denominator separately.

---

**kth ROOTS OF QUOTIENTS**

For any nonnegative number $a$, any positive number $b$, and any index $k$,

$$\sqrt[k]{\frac{a}{b}} = \frac{\sqrt[k]{a}}{\sqrt[k]{b}}, \quad \text{or} \quad \left(\frac{a}{b}\right)^{1/k} = \frac{a^{1/k}}{b^{1/k}}.$$

(Take the $k$th roots of the numerator and of the denominator separately.)

---

**EXAMPLES** Simplify by taking the roots of the numerator and the denominator. Assume that no radicands were formed by raising negative numbers to even powers.

**19.** $\sqrt[3]{\dfrac{27}{125}} = \dfrac{\sqrt[3]{27}}{\sqrt[3]{125}} = \dfrac{3}{5}$ ← We take the cube root of the numerator and of the denominator.

**20.** $\sqrt{\dfrac{25}{y^2}} = \dfrac{\sqrt{25}}{\sqrt{y^2}} = \dfrac{5}{y}$ ← We take the square root of the numerator and of the denominator.

Simplify by taking the roots of the numerator and the denominator. Assume that no radicands were formed by raising negative numbers to even powers.

**23.** $\sqrt{\dfrac{25}{36}}$     **24.** $\sqrt{\dfrac{x^2}{100}}$

**25.** $\sqrt[3]{\dfrac{54x^5}{125}}$

**21.** $\sqrt{\dfrac{16x^3}{y^4}} = \dfrac{\sqrt{16x^3}}{\sqrt{y^4}} = \dfrac{\sqrt{16x^2 \cdot x}}{\sqrt{y^4}} = \dfrac{\sqrt{16x^2} \cdot \sqrt{x}}{\sqrt{y^4}} = \dfrac{4x\sqrt{x}}{y^2}$

**22.** $\sqrt[3]{\dfrac{27y^5}{343x^3}} = \dfrac{\sqrt[3]{27y^5}}{\sqrt[3]{343x^3}} = \dfrac{\sqrt[3]{27y^3 \cdot y^2}}{\sqrt[3]{343x^3}} = \dfrac{\sqrt[3]{27y^3} \cdot \sqrt[3]{y^2}}{\sqrt[3]{343x^3}} = \dfrac{3y\sqrt[3]{y^2}}{7x}$

We are assuming here that no variable represents 0 or a negative number. Thus we need not be concerned about zero denominators.

Do Exercises 23–25.

When indexes differ, we can use rational exponents.

**EXAMPLE 23** Divide and simplify: $\dfrac{\sqrt[3]{a^2b^4}}{\sqrt{ab}}$.

**26.** Divide and simplify:
$$\dfrac{\sqrt[4]{x^3y^2}}{\sqrt[3]{x^2y}}.$$

$$\dfrac{\sqrt[3]{a^2b^4}}{\sqrt{ab}} = \dfrac{(a^2b^4)^{1/3}}{(ab)^{1/2}} \qquad \text{Converting to exponential notation}$$

$$= \dfrac{a^{2/3}b^{4/3}}{a^{1/2}b^{1/2}} \qquad \text{Using the product and power rules}$$

$$= a^{2/3-1/2}b^{4/3-1/2} \qquad \text{Subtracting exponents}$$

$$= a^{4/6-3/6}b^{8/6-3/6} \qquad \text{Finding common denominators so exponents can be subtracted}$$

$$= a^{1/6}b^{5/6}$$

$$= (ab^5)^{1/6} \qquad \text{Using } a^n b^n = (ab)^n$$

$$= \sqrt[6]{ab^5} \qquad \text{Converting back to radical notation}$$

Do Exercise 26.

*Answers*

**23.** $\dfrac{5}{6}$    **24.** $\dfrac{x}{10}$    **25.** $\dfrac{3x\sqrt[3]{2x^2}}{5}$    **26.** $\sqrt[12]{xy^2}$

**a** Simplify by factoring. Assume that no radicands were formed by raising negative numbers to even powers.

**1.** $\sqrt{24}$      **2.** $\sqrt{20}$      **3.** $\sqrt{90}$      **4.** $\sqrt{18}$

**5.** $\sqrt[3]{250}$      **6.** $\sqrt[3]{108}$      **7.** $\sqrt{180x^4}$      **8.** $\sqrt{175y^6}$

**9.** $\sqrt[3]{54x^8}$      **10.** $\sqrt[3]{40y^3}$      **11.** $\sqrt[3]{80t^8}$      **12.** $\sqrt[3]{108x^5}$

**13.** $\sqrt[4]{80}$      **14.** $\sqrt[4]{32}$      **15.** $\sqrt{32a^2b}$      **16.** $\sqrt{75p^3q^4}$

**17.** $\sqrt[4]{243x^8y^{10}}$      **18.** $\sqrt[4]{162c^4d^6}$      **19.** $\sqrt[5]{96x^7y^{15}}$      **20.** $\sqrt[5]{p^{14}q^9r^{23}}$

Multiply and simplify. Assume that no radicands were formed by raising negative numbers to even powers.

**21.** $\sqrt{10}\,\sqrt{5}$      **22.** $\sqrt{6}\,\sqrt{3}$      **23.** $\sqrt{15}\,\sqrt{6}$      **24.** $\sqrt{2}\,\sqrt{32}$

**25.** $\sqrt[3]{2}\,\sqrt[3]{4}$      **26.** $\sqrt[3]{9}\,\sqrt[3]{3}$      **27.** $\sqrt{45}\,\sqrt{60}$      **28.** $\sqrt{24}\,\sqrt{75}$

**29.** $\sqrt{3x^3}\,\sqrt{6x^5}$      **30.** $\sqrt{5a^7}\,\sqrt{15a^3}$      **31.** $\sqrt{5b^3}\,\sqrt{10c^4}$      **32.** $\sqrt{2x^3y}\,\sqrt{12xy}$

**33.** $\sqrt[3]{5a^2}\ \sqrt[3]{2a}$

**34.** $\sqrt[3]{7x}\ \sqrt[3]{3x^2}$

**35.** $\sqrt[3]{y^4}\ \sqrt[3]{16y^5}$

**36.** $\sqrt[3]{s^2t^4}\ \sqrt[3]{s^4t^6}$

**37.** $\sqrt[4]{16}\ \sqrt[4]{64}$

**38.** $\sqrt[5]{64}\ \sqrt[5]{16}$

**39.** $\sqrt{12a^3b}\ \sqrt{8a^4b^2}$

**40.** $\sqrt{30x^3y^4}\ \sqrt{18x^2y^5}$

**41.** $\sqrt{2}\ \sqrt[3]{5}$

**42.** $\sqrt{6}\ \sqrt[3]{5}$

**43.** $\sqrt[4]{3}\ \sqrt{2}$

**44.** $\sqrt[3]{5}\ \sqrt[4]{2}$

**45.** $\sqrt{a}\ \sqrt[4]{a^3}$

**46.** $\sqrt[3]{x^2}\ \sqrt[6]{x^5}$

**47.** $\sqrt[5]{b^2}\ \sqrt{b^3}$

**48.** $\sqrt[4]{a^3}\ \sqrt[3]{a^2}$

**49.** $\sqrt{xy^3}\ \sqrt[3]{x^2y}$

**50.** $\sqrt{y^5z}\ \sqrt[3]{yz^4}$

**51.** $\sqrt{2a^3b}\ \sqrt[4]{8ab^2}$

**52.** $\sqrt[4]{9ab^3}\ \sqrt{3a^4b}$

**b** Divide and simplify. Assume that all expressions under radicals represent positive numbers.

**53.** $\dfrac{\sqrt{90}}{\sqrt{5}}$

**54.** $\dfrac{\sqrt{98}}{\sqrt{2}}$

**55.** $\dfrac{\sqrt{35q}}{\sqrt{7q}}$

**56.** $\dfrac{\sqrt{30x}}{\sqrt{10x}}$

**57.** $\dfrac{\sqrt[3]{54}}{\sqrt[3]{2}}$

**58.** $\dfrac{\sqrt[3]{40}}{\sqrt[3]{5}}$

**59.** $\dfrac{\sqrt{56xy^3}}{\sqrt{8x}}$

**60.** $\dfrac{\sqrt{52ab^3}}{\sqrt{13a}}$

**61.** $\dfrac{\sqrt[3]{96a^4b^2}}{\sqrt[3]{12a^2b}}$

**62.** $\dfrac{\sqrt[3]{189x^5y^7}}{\sqrt[3]{7x^2y^2}}$

**63.** $\dfrac{\sqrt{128xy}}{2\sqrt{2}}$

**64.** $\dfrac{\sqrt{48ab}}{2\sqrt{3}}$

**65.** $\dfrac{\sqrt[4]{48x^9y^{13}}}{\sqrt[4]{3xy^5}}$

**66.** $\dfrac{\sqrt[5]{64a^{11}b^{28}}}{\sqrt[5]{2ab^2}}$

**67.** $\dfrac{\sqrt[3]{a}}{\sqrt{a}}$

**68.** $\dfrac{\sqrt{x}}{\sqrt[4]{x}}$

**69.** $\dfrac{\sqrt[3]{a^2}}{\sqrt[4]{a}}$

**70.** $\dfrac{\sqrt[3]{x^2}}{\sqrt[5]{x}}$

**71.** $\dfrac{\sqrt[4]{x^2y^3}}{\sqrt[3]{xy}}$

**72.** $\dfrac{\sqrt[5]{a^4b^2}}{\sqrt[3]{ab^2}}$

Simplify.

**73.** $\sqrt{\dfrac{25}{36}}$

**74.** $\sqrt{\dfrac{49}{64}}$

**75.** $\sqrt{\dfrac{16}{49}}$

**76.** $\sqrt{\dfrac{100}{81}}$

**77.** $\sqrt[3]{\dfrac{125}{27}}$

**78.** $\sqrt[3]{\dfrac{343}{1000}}$

**79.** $\sqrt{\dfrac{49}{y^2}}$

**80.** $\sqrt{\dfrac{121}{x^2}}$

**81.** $\sqrt{\dfrac{25y^3}{x^4}}$

**82.** $\sqrt{\dfrac{36a^5}{b^6}}$

**83.** $\sqrt[3]{\dfrac{81y^5}{64}}$

**84.** $\sqrt[3]{\dfrac{8z^7}{125}}$

**85.** $\sqrt[3]{\dfrac{27a^4}{8b^3}}$

**86.** $\sqrt[3]{\dfrac{64x^7}{216y^6}}$

**87.** $\sqrt[4]{\dfrac{81x^4}{16}}$

**88.** $\sqrt[4]{\dfrac{256}{81x^8}}$

**89.** $\sqrt[4]{\dfrac{16a^{12}}{b^4c^{16}}}$

**90.** $\sqrt[4]{\dfrac{81x^4}{y^8z^4}}$

**91.** $\sqrt[5]{\dfrac{32x^8}{y^{10}}}$

**92.** $\sqrt[5]{\dfrac{32b^{10}}{243a^{20}}}$

**93.** $\sqrt[5]{\dfrac{w^7}{z^{10}}}$

**94.** $\sqrt[5]{\dfrac{z^{11}}{w^{20}}}$

**95.** $\sqrt[6]{\dfrac{x^{13}}{y^6z^{12}}}$

**96.** $\sqrt[6]{\dfrac{p^9q^{24}}{r^{18}}}$

## Skill Maintenance

Solve.

**97.** *Boating.* A paddleboat moves at a rate of 14 km/h in still water. If the river's current moves at a rate of 7 km/h, how long will it take the boat to travel 56 km downstream? 56 km upstream?  [1.3b]

**98.** *Triangle Dimensions.* The base of a triangle is 2 in. longer than the height. The area is 12 in². Find the height and the base.  [4.8b]

Solve.  [5.5a]

**99.** $\dfrac{12x}{x-4} - \dfrac{3x^2}{x+4} = \dfrac{384}{x^2-16}$

**100.** $\dfrac{2}{3} + \dfrac{1}{t} = \dfrac{4}{5}$

**101.** $\dfrac{18}{x^2-3x} = \dfrac{2x}{x-3} - \dfrac{6}{x}$

**102.** $\dfrac{4x}{x+5} + \dfrac{20}{x} = \dfrac{100}{x^2+5x}$

## Synthesis

**103.** *Pendulums.* The **period** of a pendulum is the time it takes to complete one cycle, swinging to and fro. For a pendulum that is $L$ centimeters long, the period $T$ is given by the function

$$T(L) = 2\pi\sqrt{\dfrac{L}{980}},$$

where $T$ is in seconds. Find, to the nearest hundredth of a second, the period of a pendulum of length **(a)** 65 cm; **(b)** 98 cm; **(c)** 120 cm. Use a calculator's $\pi$ key if possible.

Simplify.

**104.** $\dfrac{\sqrt[3]{x^3-y^3}}{\sqrt[3]{x-y}}$

**105.** $\dfrac{\sqrt{44x^2y^9z}\,\sqrt{22y^9z^6}}{\left(\sqrt{11xy^8z^2}\right)^2}$

**106.** Use a graphing calculator to check your answers to Exercises 7, 12, 30, and 56.

# 6.4 Addition, Subtraction, and More Multiplication

## a Addition and Subtraction

Any two real numbers can be added. For example, the sum of 7 and $\sqrt{3}$ can be expressed as $7 + \sqrt{3}$. We cannot simplify this sum. However, when we have **like radicals** (radicals having the same index and radicand), we can use the distributive laws to simplify by collecting like radical terms. For example,

$$7\sqrt{3} + \sqrt{3} = 7\sqrt{3} + 1 \cdot \sqrt{3} = (7 + 1)\sqrt{3} = 8\sqrt{3}.$$

**EXAMPLES** Add or subtract. Simplify by collecting like radical terms, if possible.

**1.** $6\sqrt{7} + 4\sqrt{7} = (6 + 4)\sqrt{7}$    Using a distributive law $\left(\text{factoring out } \sqrt{7}\right)$
$= 10\sqrt{7}$

**2.** $8\sqrt[3]{2} - 7x\sqrt[3]{2} + 5\sqrt[3]{2} = (8 - 7x + 5)\sqrt[3]{2}$    Factoring out $\sqrt[3]{2}$
$= (13 - 7x)\sqrt[3]{2}$

> These parentheses *are* necessary!

**3.** $6\sqrt[5]{4x} + 4\sqrt[5]{4x} - \sqrt[3]{4x} = (6 + 4)\sqrt[5]{4x} - \sqrt[3]{4x}$
$= 10\sqrt[5]{4x} - \sqrt[3]{4x}$

> Note that these expressions have the same *radicand*, but they are not like radicals because they do not have the same *index*.

Do Margin Exercises 1 and 2.

Add or subtract. Simplify by collecting like radical terms, if possible.
**1.** $5\sqrt{2} + 8\sqrt{2}$

**2.** $7\sqrt[4]{5x} + 3\sqrt[4]{5x} - \sqrt{7}$

Sometimes we need to simplify radicals by factoring in order to obtain terms with like radicals.

**EXAMPLES** Add or subtract. Simplify by collecting like radical terms, if possible.

**4.** $3\sqrt{8} - 5\sqrt{2} = 3\sqrt{4 \cdot 2} - 5\sqrt{2}$    Factoring 8
$= 3\sqrt{4} \cdot \sqrt{2} - 5\sqrt{2}$    Factoring $\sqrt{4 \cdot 2}$ into two radicals
$= 3 \cdot 2\sqrt{2} - 5\sqrt{2}$    Taking the square root of 4
$= 6\sqrt{2} - 5\sqrt{2}$
$= (6 - 5)\sqrt{2}$    Collecting like radical terms
$= \sqrt{2}$

**5.** $5\sqrt{2} - 4\sqrt{3}$    No simplification possible

**6.** $5\sqrt[3]{16y^4} + 7\sqrt[3]{2y} = 5\sqrt[3]{8y^3 \cdot 2y} + 7\sqrt[3]{2y}$   ⎫
$= 5\sqrt[3]{8y^3} \cdot \sqrt[3]{2y} + 7\sqrt[3]{2y}$   ⎬ Factoring the first radical
$= 5 \cdot 2y \cdot \sqrt[3]{2y} + 7\sqrt[3]{2y}$   ⎭ Taking the cube root of $8y^3$
$= 10y\sqrt[3]{2y} + 7\sqrt[3]{2y}$
$= (10y + 7)\sqrt[3]{2y}$    Collecting like radical terms

Do Exercises 3–5.

Add or subtract. Simplify by collecting like radical terms, if possible.
**3.** $7\sqrt{45} - 2\sqrt{5}$

**4.** $3\sqrt[3]{y^5} + 4\sqrt[3]{y^2} + \sqrt[3]{8y^6}$

**5.** $\sqrt{25x - 25} - \sqrt{9x - 9}$

## b More Multiplication

To multiply expressions in which some factors contain more than one term, we use the procedures for multiplying polynomials.

**EXAMPLES** Multiply.

7. $\sqrt{3}(x - \sqrt{5}) = \sqrt{3} \cdot x - \sqrt{3} \cdot \sqrt{5}$     Using a distributive law

$\qquad\qquad\qquad = x\sqrt{3} - \sqrt{15}$     Multiplying radicals

8. $\sqrt[3]{y}(\sqrt[3]{y^2} + \sqrt[3]{2}) = \sqrt[3]{y} \cdot \sqrt[3]{y^2} + \sqrt[3]{y} \cdot \sqrt[3]{2}$     Using a distributive law

$\qquad\qquad\qquad\quad = \sqrt[3]{y^3} + \sqrt[3]{2y}$     Multiplying radicals

$\qquad\qquad\qquad\quad = y + \sqrt[3]{2y}$     Simplifying $\sqrt[3]{y^3}$

Do Exercises 6 and 7.

**EXAMPLE 9** Multiply: $(4\sqrt{3} + \sqrt{2})(\sqrt{3} - 5\sqrt{2})$.

$\qquad\qquad\qquad\qquad\qquad\qquad\qquad$ F $\qquad$ O $\qquad$ I $\qquad$ L

$(4\sqrt{3} + \sqrt{2})(\sqrt{3} - 5\sqrt{2}) = 4(\sqrt{3})^2 - 20\sqrt{3} \cdot \sqrt{2} + \sqrt{2} \cdot \sqrt{3} - 5(\sqrt{2})^2$

$\qquad\qquad\qquad\qquad\qquad = 4 \cdot 3 - 20\sqrt{6} + \sqrt{6} - 5 \cdot 2$

$\qquad\qquad\qquad\qquad\qquad = 12 - 20\sqrt{6} + \sqrt{6} - 10$

$\qquad\qquad\qquad\qquad\qquad = 2 - 19\sqrt{6}$     Collecting like terms

**EXAMPLE 10** Multiply: $(\sqrt{a} + \sqrt{3})(\sqrt{b} + \sqrt{3})$. Assume that all expressions under radicals represent nonnegative numbers.

$(\sqrt{a} + \sqrt{3})(\sqrt{b} + \sqrt{3}) = \sqrt{a}\sqrt{b} + \sqrt{a}\sqrt{3} + \sqrt{3}\sqrt{b} + \sqrt{3}\sqrt{3}$

$\qquad\qquad\qquad\qquad = \sqrt{ab} + \sqrt{3a} + \sqrt{3b} + 3$

**EXAMPLE 11** Multiply: $(\sqrt{5} + \sqrt{7})(\sqrt{5} - \sqrt{7})$.

$(\sqrt{5} + \sqrt{7})(\sqrt{5} - \sqrt{7}) = (\sqrt{5})^2 - (\sqrt{7})^2$     This is now a difference of two squares: $(A - B)(A + B) = A^2 - B^2$.

$\qquad\qquad\qquad\qquad = 5 - 7 = -2$

**EXAMPLE 12** Multiply: $(\sqrt{a} + \sqrt{b})(\sqrt{a} - \sqrt{b})$. Assume that no radicands were formed by raising negative numbers to even powers.

$(\sqrt{a} + \sqrt{b})(\sqrt{a} - \sqrt{b}) = (\sqrt{a})^2 - (\sqrt{b})^2$

$\qquad\qquad\qquad\qquad = a - b$     No radicals

Expressions of the form $\sqrt{a} + \sqrt{b}$ and $\sqrt{a} - \sqrt{b}$ are called **conjugates**. Their product is always an expression that has no radicals.

Do Exercises 8–11.

**EXAMPLE 13** Multiply: $(\sqrt{3} + x)^2$.

$(\sqrt{3} + x)^2 = (\sqrt{3})^2 + 2x\sqrt{3} + x^2$     Squaring a binomial

$\qquad\qquad = 3 + 2x\sqrt{3} + x^2$

Do Exercises 12 and 13.

---

Multiply. Assume that no radicands were formed by raising negative numbers to even powers.

6. $\sqrt{2}(5\sqrt{3} + 3\sqrt{7})$

7. $\sqrt[3]{a^2}(\sqrt[3]{3a} - \sqrt[3]{2})$

Multiply. Assume that no radicands were formed by raising negative numbers to even powers.

8. $(\sqrt{3} - 5\sqrt{2})(2\sqrt{3} + \sqrt{2})$

9. $(\sqrt{a} + 2\sqrt{3})(3\sqrt{b} - 4\sqrt{3})$

10. $(\sqrt{2} + \sqrt{5})(\sqrt{2} - \sqrt{5})$

11. $(\sqrt{p} - \sqrt{q})(\sqrt{p} + \sqrt{q})$

Multiply.

12. $(2\sqrt{5} - y)^2$     13. $(3\sqrt{6} + 2)^2$

**Answers**

6. $5\sqrt{6} + 3\sqrt{14}$    7. $a\sqrt[3]{3} - \sqrt[3]{2a^2}$
8. $-4 - 9\sqrt{6}$
9. $3\sqrt{ab} - 4\sqrt{3a} + 6\sqrt{3b} - 24$    10. $-3$
11. $p - q$    12. $20 - 4y\sqrt{5} + y^2$
13. $58 + 12\sqrt{6}$

**a** Add or subtract. Then simplify by collecting like radical terms, if possible. Assume that no radicands were formed by raising negative numbers to even powers.

**1.** $7\sqrt{5} + 4\sqrt{5}$

**2.** $2\sqrt{3} + 9\sqrt{3}$

**3.** $6\sqrt[3]{7} - 5\sqrt[3]{7}$

**4.** $13\sqrt[5]{3} - 8\sqrt[5]{3}$

**5.** $4\sqrt[3]{y} + 9\sqrt[3]{y}$

**6.** $6\sqrt[4]{t} - 3\sqrt[4]{t}$

**7.** $5\sqrt{6} - 9\sqrt{6} - 4\sqrt{6}$

**8.** $3\sqrt{10} - 8\sqrt{10} + 7\sqrt{10}$

**9.** $4\sqrt[3]{3} - \sqrt{5} + 2\sqrt[3]{3} + \sqrt{5}$

**10.** $5\sqrt{7} - 8\sqrt[4]{11} + \sqrt{7} + 9\sqrt[4]{11}$

**11.** $8\sqrt{27} - 3\sqrt{3}$

**12.** $9\sqrt{50} - 4\sqrt{2}$

**13.** $8\sqrt{45} + 7\sqrt{20}$

**14.** $9\sqrt{12} + 16\sqrt{27}$

**15.** $18\sqrt{72} + 2\sqrt{98}$

**16.** $12\sqrt{45} - 8\sqrt{80}$

**17.** $3\sqrt[3]{16} + \sqrt[3]{54}$

**18.** $\sqrt[3]{27} - 5\sqrt[3]{8}$

**19.** $2\sqrt{128} - \sqrt{18} + 4\sqrt{32}$

**20.** $5\sqrt{50} - 2\sqrt{18} + 9\sqrt{32}$

**21.** $\sqrt{5a} + 2\sqrt{45a^3}$

**22.** $4\sqrt{3x^3} - \sqrt{12x}$

**23.** $\sqrt[3]{24x} - \sqrt[3]{3x^4}$

**24.** $\sqrt[3]{54x} - \sqrt[3]{2x^4}$

**25.** $7\sqrt{27x^3} + \sqrt{3x}$

**26.** $2\sqrt{45x^3} - \sqrt{5x}$

**27.** $\sqrt{4} + \sqrt{18}$

**28.** $\sqrt[3]{8} - \sqrt[3]{24}$

**29.** $5\sqrt[3]{32} - \sqrt[3]{108} + 2\sqrt[3]{256}$

**30.** $3\sqrt[3]{8x} - 4\sqrt[3]{27x} + 2\sqrt[3]{64x}$

**31.** $\sqrt[3]{6x^4} + \sqrt[3]{48x} - \sqrt[3]{6x}$

**32.** $\sqrt[4]{80x^5} - \sqrt[4]{405x^9} + \sqrt[4]{5x}$

**33.** $\sqrt{4a-4} + \sqrt{a-1}$

**34.** $\sqrt{9y+27} + \sqrt{y+3}$

**35.** $\sqrt{x^3-x^2} + \sqrt{9x-9}$

**36.** $\sqrt{4x-4} + \sqrt{x^3-x^2}$

**b**    Multiply. Assume that no radicands were formed by raising negative numbers to even powers.

**37.** $\sqrt{5}\left(4 - 2\sqrt{5}\right)$

**38.** $\sqrt{6}\left(2 + \sqrt{6}\right)$

**39.** $\sqrt{3}\left(\sqrt{2} - \sqrt{7}\right)$

**40.** $\sqrt{2}\left(\sqrt{5} - \sqrt{2}\right)$

**41.** $\sqrt{3}\left(-4\sqrt{3} + 6\right)$

**42.** $\sqrt{2}\left(-5\sqrt{2} - 7\right)$

**43.** $\sqrt{3}\left(2\sqrt{5} - 3\sqrt{4}\right)$

**44.** $\sqrt{2}\left(3\sqrt{10} - 2\sqrt{2}\right)$

**45.** $\sqrt[3]{2}\left(\sqrt[3]{4} - 2\sqrt[3]{32}\right)$

**46.** $\sqrt[3]{3}\left(\sqrt[3]{9} - 4\sqrt[3]{21}\right)$

**47.** $3\sqrt[3]{y}\left(2\sqrt[3]{y^2} - 4\sqrt[3]{y}\right)$

**48.** $2\sqrt[3]{y^2}\left(5\sqrt[3]{y} + 4\sqrt[3]{y^2}\right)$

**49.** $\sqrt[3]{a}\left(\sqrt[3]{2a^2} + \sqrt[3]{16a^2}\right)$

**50.** $\sqrt[3]{x}\left(\sqrt[3]{3x^2} - \sqrt[3]{81x^2}\right)$

**51.** $\left(\sqrt{3} - \sqrt{2}\right)\left(\sqrt{3} + \sqrt{2}\right)$

**52.** $\left(\sqrt{5} + \sqrt{6}\right)\left(\sqrt{5} - \sqrt{6}\right)$

**53.** $\left(\sqrt{8} + 2\sqrt{5}\right)\left(\sqrt{8} - 2\sqrt{5}\right)$

**54.** $\left(\sqrt{18} + 3\sqrt{7}\right)\left(\sqrt{18} - 3\sqrt{7}\right)$

**55.** $\left(7 + \sqrt{5}\right)\left(7 - \sqrt{5}\right)$

**56.** $\left(4 - \sqrt{3}\right)\left(4 + \sqrt{3}\right)$

**57.** $\left(2 - \sqrt{3}\right)\left(2 + \sqrt{3}\right)$

**58.** $\left(11 - \sqrt{2}\right)\left(11 + \sqrt{2}\right)$

**59.** $\left(\sqrt{8} + \sqrt{5}\right)\left(\sqrt{8} - \sqrt{5}\right)$

**60.** $\left(\sqrt{6} - \sqrt{7}\right)\left(\sqrt{6} + \sqrt{7}\right)$

**61.** $\left(3 + 2\sqrt{7}\right)\left(3 - 2\sqrt{7}\right)$

**62.** $\left(6 - 3\sqrt{2}\right)\left(6 + 3\sqrt{2}\right)$

**63.** $\left(\sqrt{a} + \sqrt{b}\right)\left(\sqrt{a} - \sqrt{b}\right)$

**64.** $\left(\sqrt{x} - \sqrt{y}\right)\left(\sqrt{x} + \sqrt{y}\right)$

**65.** $\left(3 - \sqrt{5}\right)\left(2 + \sqrt{5}\right)$

**66.** $\left(2 + \sqrt{6}\right)\left(4 - \sqrt{6}\right)$

**67.** $\left(\sqrt{3} + 1\right)\left(2\sqrt{3} + 1\right)$

**68.** $\left(4\sqrt{3} + 5\right)\left(\sqrt{3} - 2\right)$

**69.** $\left(2\sqrt{7} - 4\sqrt{2}\right)\left(3\sqrt{7} + 6\sqrt{2}\right)$

**70.** $\left(4\sqrt{5} + 3\sqrt{3}\right)\left(3\sqrt{5} - 4\sqrt{3}\right)$

**71.** $\left(\sqrt{a} + \sqrt{2}\right)\left(\sqrt{a} + \sqrt{3}\right)$

**72.** $\left(2 - \sqrt{x}\right)\left(1 - \sqrt{x}\right)$

**73.** $\left(2\sqrt[3]{3} + \sqrt[3]{2}\right)\left(\sqrt[3]{3} - 2\sqrt[3]{2}\right)$

**74.** $\left(3\sqrt[3]{7} + \sqrt[3]{6}\right)\left(2\sqrt[3]{7} - 3\sqrt[3]{6}\right)$

**75.** $\left(2 + \sqrt{3}\right)^2$

**76.** $\left(\sqrt{5} + 1\right)^2$

**77.** $\left(\sqrt[5]{9} - \sqrt[5]{3}\right)\left(\sqrt[5]{8} + \sqrt[5]{27}\right)$

**78.** $\left(\sqrt[3]{8x} - \sqrt[3]{5y}\right)^2$

## Skill Maintenance

Multiply or divide and simplify.   [5.1d, e]

**79.** $\dfrac{x^3 + 4x}{x^2 - 16} \div \dfrac{x^2 + 8x + 15}{x^2 + x - 20}$

**80.** $\dfrac{a^2 - 4}{a} \div \dfrac{a - 2}{a + 4}$

**81.** $\dfrac{a^3 + 8}{a^2 - 4} \cdot \dfrac{a^2 - 4a + 4}{a^2 - 2a + 4}$

**82.** $\dfrac{y^3 - 27}{y^2 - 9} \cdot \dfrac{y^2 - 6y + 9}{y^2 + 3y + 9}$

Simplify.   [5.4a]

**83.** $\dfrac{x - \dfrac{1}{3}}{x + \dfrac{1}{4}}$

**84.** $\dfrac{1 - \dfrac{1}{x}}{1 - \dfrac{1}{x^2}}$

**85.** $\dfrac{\dfrac{1}{p} - \dfrac{1}{q}}{\dfrac{1}{p^2} - \dfrac{1}{q^2}}$

**86.** $\dfrac{\dfrac{1}{a} + \dfrac{1}{b}}{\dfrac{1}{a^3} + \dfrac{1}{b^3}}$

Solve.   [1.6c, d, e]

**87.** $|3x + 7| = 22$

**88.** $|3x + 7| < 22$

**89.** $|3x + 7| \geq 22$

**90.** $|3x + 7| = |2x - 5|$

## Synthesis

**91.** Graph the function $f(x) = \sqrt{(x - 2)^2}$. What is the domain?

**92.** Use a graphing calculator to check your answers to Exercises 5, 22, and 72.

Multiply and simplify.

**93.** $\sqrt{9 + 3\sqrt{5}}\,\sqrt{9 - 3\sqrt{5}}$

**94.** $\left(\sqrt{x + 2} - \sqrt{x - 2}\right)^2$

**95.** $\left(\sqrt{3} + \sqrt{5} - \sqrt{6}\right)^2$

**96.** $\sqrt[3]{y}\left(1 - \sqrt[3]{y}\right)\left(1 + \sqrt[3]{y}\right)$

**97.** $\left(\sqrt[3]{9} - 2\right)\left(\sqrt[3]{9} + 4\right)$

**98.** $\left[\sqrt{3 + \sqrt{2 + \sqrt{1}}}\right]^4$

# Mid-Chapter Review

## Concept Reinforcement

Determine whether each statement is true or false.

_____ **1.** Every real number has two real-number square roots.   [6.1a]

_____ **2.** If $\sqrt[3]{q}$ is negative, then $q$ is negative.   [6.1c]

_____ **3.** $a^{m/n}$ and $a^{n/m}$ are reciprocals.   [6.2b]

_____ **4.** To multiply radicals with the same index, we multiply the radicands.   [6.3a]

## Guided Solutions

Fill in each blank with the number that creates a correct statement or solution.

Perform the indicated operations and simplify.   [6.3a], [6.4a]

**5.** $\sqrt{6}\sqrt{10} = \sqrt{6 \cdot \square} = \sqrt{2 \cdot \square \cdot 2 \cdot \square} = \square\sqrt{\square}$

**6.** $5\sqrt{32} - 3\sqrt{18} = 5\sqrt{\square \cdot 2} - 3\sqrt{\square \cdot 2}$

$= 5 \cdot \square\sqrt{2} - 3 \cdot \square\sqrt{2}$

$= \square\sqrt{2} - \square\sqrt{2}$

$= \square\sqrt{2}$

## Mixed Review

Simplify.   [6.1a]

**7.** $\sqrt{81}$

**8.** $-\sqrt{144}$

**9.** $\sqrt{\dfrac{16}{25}}$

**10.** $\sqrt{-9}$

**11.** For $f(x) = \sqrt{2x + 3}$, find $f(3)$ and $f(-2)$.   [6.1a]

**12.** Find the domain of $f(x) = \sqrt{4 - x}$.   [6.1a]

Graph.   [6.1a]

**13.** $f(x) = -2\sqrt{x}$

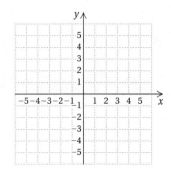

**14.** $g(x) = \sqrt{x + 1}$

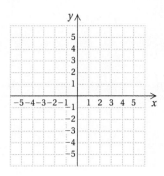

Find each of the following. Assume that letters can represent *any* real number.   [6.1b, c, d]

**15.** $\sqrt{36z^2}$

**16.** $\sqrt{x^2 - 8x + 16}$

**17.** $\sqrt[3]{-64}$

**18.** $-\sqrt[3]{27a^3}$

**19.** $\sqrt[5]{32}$

**20.** $\sqrt[10]{y^{10}}$

Rewrite without rational exponents and simplify, if possible. [6.2a]

**21.** $125^{1/3}$

**22.** $\left(a^3b\right)^{1/4}$

Rewrite with rational exponents. [6.2a]

**23.** $\sqrt[5]{16}$

**24.** $\sqrt[3]{6m^2n}$

Simplify. Write the answer with positive exponents. [6.2c]

**25.** $3^{1/4} \cdot 3^{-5/8}$

**26.** $\dfrac{7^{6/5}}{7^{2/5}}$

**27.** $\left(x^{3/4}y^{-2/3}\right)^2$

**28.** $\left(n^{-3/5}\right)^{5/4}$

Use rational exponents to simplify. Write the answer in radical notation. [6.2d]

**29.** $\sqrt[6]{16}$

**30.** $\left(\sqrt[10]{ab}\right)^5$

Use rational exponents to write a single radical expression. [6.2d]

**31.** $\sqrt{y}\,\sqrt[3]{y}$

**32.** $a^{2/3}b^{3/5}$

Perform the indicated operation and simplify. Assume that no radicands were formed by raising negative numbers to even powers. [6.3a, b], [6.4a, b]

**33.** $\sqrt{5}\sqrt{15}$

**34.** $\sqrt[3]{4x^2y}\,\sqrt[3]{6xy^4}$

**35.** $\dfrac{\sqrt[3]{80}}{\sqrt[3]{2}}$

**36.** $\sqrt{\dfrac{49a^5}{b^8}}$

**37.** $5\sqrt{7} + 6\sqrt{7}$

**38.** $3\sqrt{18x^3} - 6\sqrt{32x}$

**39.** $\sqrt{3}\left(2 - 5\sqrt{3}\right)$

**40.** $\left(1 - \sqrt{x}\right)\left(3 - \sqrt{x}\right)$

**41.** $\left(\sqrt{m} - \sqrt{n}\right)\left(\sqrt{m} + \sqrt{n}\right)$

**42.** $\left(\sqrt{7} + 2\right)^2$

**43.** $\left(2\sqrt{3} + 3\sqrt{5}\right)\left(3\sqrt{3} - 4\sqrt{5}\right)$

# Understanding Through Discussion and Writing

**44.** Does the $n$th root of $x^2$ always exist? Why or why not? [6.1a]

**45.** Explain how to formulate a radical expression that can be used to define a function $f$ with a domain of $\{x|x \le 5\}$. [6.1a]

**46.** Explain why $\sqrt[3]{x^6} = x^2$ for any value of $x$, but $\sqrt{x^6} = x^3$ only when $x \ge 0$. [6.2d]

**47.** Is the quotient of two irrational numbers always an irrational number? Why or why not? [6.3b]

# 6.5 More on Division of Radical Expressions

## a Rationalizing Denominators

**OBJECTIVES**

**a** Rationalize the denominator of a radical expression having one term in the denominator.

**b** Rationalize the denominator of a radical expression having two terms in the denominator.

Sometimes in mathematics it is useful to find an equivalent expression without a radical in the denominator. This provides a standard notation for expressing results. The procedure for finding such an expression is called **rationalizing the denominator**. We carry this out by multiplying by 1.

**EXAMPLE 1** Rationalize the denominator: $\sqrt{\dfrac{7}{3}}$.

We multiply by 1, using $\sqrt{3}/\sqrt{3}$. We do this so that the denominator of the radicand will be a perfect square.

$$\sqrt{\frac{7}{3}} = \frac{\sqrt{7}}{\sqrt{3}} \cdot \frac{\sqrt{3}}{\sqrt{3}}$$

$$= \frac{\sqrt{7} \cdot \sqrt{3}}{\sqrt{3} \cdot \sqrt{3}}$$

$$= \frac{\sqrt{21}}{\sqrt{3^2}} = \frac{\sqrt{21}}{3}$$

The radicand is a perfect square.

Do Margin Exercise 1.

**EXAMPLE 2** Rationalize the denominator: $\sqrt[3]{\dfrac{7}{25}}$.

We first factor the denominator:

$$\sqrt[3]{\frac{7}{25}} = \sqrt[3]{\frac{7}{5 \cdot 5}}.$$

To get a perfect cube in the denominator, we consider the index 3 and the factors. We have 2 factors of 5, and we need 3 factors of 5. We achieve this by multiplying by 1, using $\sqrt[3]{5}/\sqrt[3]{5}$.

$$\sqrt[3]{\frac{7}{25}} = \sqrt[3]{\frac{7}{5 \cdot 5}} \cdot \frac{\sqrt[3]{5}}{\sqrt[3]{5}}$$

Multiplying by $\dfrac{\sqrt[3]{5}}{\sqrt[3]{5}}$ to make the denominator of the radicand a perfect cube

$$= \frac{\sqrt[3]{7} \cdot \sqrt[3]{5}}{\sqrt[3]{5 \cdot 5} \cdot \sqrt[3]{5}}$$

$$= \frac{\sqrt[3]{35}}{\sqrt[3]{5^3}}$$

The radicand is a perfect cube.

$$= \frac{\sqrt[3]{35}}{5}$$

Do Exercise 2.

**SKILL TO REVIEW**

Objective 4.2d: Use a rule to multiply a sum and a difference of the same two terms.

Multiply.

**1.** $(x + 3)(x - 3)$

**2.** $(2y + 5)(2y - 5)$

**1.** Rationalize the denominator:

$$\sqrt{\frac{2}{5}}.$$

**2.** Rationalize the denominator:

$$\sqrt[3]{\frac{5}{4}}.$$

***Answers***

*Skill to Review:*
1. $x^2 - 9$   2. $4y^2 - 25$

*Margin Exercises:*
1. $\dfrac{\sqrt{10}}{5}$   2. $\dfrac{\sqrt[3]{10}}{2}$

**EXAMPLE 3** Rationalize the denominator: $\sqrt{\dfrac{2a}{5b}}$. Assume that no radicands were formed by raising negative numbers to even powers.

$$\sqrt{\frac{2a}{5b}} = \frac{\sqrt{2a}}{\sqrt{5b}} \qquad \text{Converting to a quotient of radicals}$$

$$= \frac{\sqrt{2a}}{\sqrt{5b}} \cdot \frac{\sqrt{5b}}{\sqrt{5b}} \qquad \text{Multiplying by 1}$$

$$= \frac{\sqrt{10ab}}{\sqrt{5^2 b^2}} \qquad \begin{array}{l}\text{The radicand in the denominator}\\ \text{is a perfect square.}\end{array}$$

$$= \frac{\sqrt{10ab}}{5b}$$

**3.** Rationalize the denominator:
$$\sqrt{\frac{4a}{3b}}.$$

Do Exercise 3.

**EXAMPLE 4** Rationalize the denominator: $\dfrac{\sqrt[3]{a}}{\sqrt[3]{9x}}$.

We factor the denominator:

$$\frac{\sqrt[3]{a}}{\sqrt[3]{9x}} = \frac{\sqrt[3]{a}}{\sqrt[3]{3 \cdot 3 \cdot x}}.$$

To choose the symbol for 1, we look at $3 \cdot 3 \cdot x$. To make it a cube, we need another 3 and two more $x$'s. Thus we multiply by 1, using $\sqrt[3]{3x^2}/\sqrt[3]{3x^2}$:

$$\frac{\sqrt[3]{a}}{\sqrt[3]{9x}} = \frac{\sqrt[3]{a}}{\sqrt[3]{3 \cdot 3 \cdot x}} \cdot \frac{\sqrt[3]{3x^2}}{\sqrt[3]{3x^2}} \qquad \text{Multiplying by 1}$$

$$= \frac{\sqrt[3]{3ax^2}}{\sqrt[3]{3^3 x^3}} \qquad \begin{array}{l}\text{The radicand in the denominator}\\ \text{is a perfect cube.}\end{array}$$

$$= \frac{\sqrt[3]{3ax^2}}{3x}.$$

Rationalize the denominator.

**4.** $\dfrac{\sqrt[4]{7}}{\sqrt[4]{2}}$      **5.** $\sqrt[3]{\dfrac{3x^5}{2y}}$

Do Exercises 4 and 5.

**EXAMPLE 5** Rationalize the denominator: $\dfrac{3x}{\sqrt[5]{2x^2 y^3}}$.

$$\frac{3x}{\sqrt[5]{2x^2 y^3}} = \frac{3x}{\sqrt[5]{2 \cdot x \cdot x \cdot y \cdot y \cdot y}}$$

$$= \frac{3x}{\sqrt[5]{2x^2 y^3}} \cdot \frac{\sqrt[5]{2^4 x^3 y^2}}{\sqrt[5]{2^4 x^3 y^2}}$$

$$= \frac{3x \sqrt[5]{16x^3 y^2}}{\sqrt[5]{2^5 x^5 y^5}} \qquad \begin{array}{l}\text{The radicand in the denominator}\\ \text{is a perfect fifth power.}\end{array}$$

$$= \frac{3x \sqrt[5]{16x^3 y^2}}{2xy}$$

$$= \frac{x}{x} \cdot \frac{3 \sqrt[5]{16x^3 y^2}}{2y}$$

$$= \frac{3 \sqrt[5]{16x^3 y^2}}{2y}$$

**6.** Rationalize the denominator:
$$\frac{7x}{\sqrt[3]{4xy^5}}.$$

Do Exercise 6.

*Answers*

**3.** $\dfrac{2\sqrt{3ab}}{3b}$    **4.** $\dfrac{\sqrt[4]{56}}{2}$    **5.** $\dfrac{x\sqrt[3]{12x^2 y^2}}{2y}$

**6.** $\dfrac{7\sqrt[3]{2x^2 y}}{2y^2}$

## b Rationalizing When There Are Two Terms

Do Exercises 7 and 8.

Certain pairs of expressions containing square roots, such as $c - \sqrt{b}$, $c + \sqrt{b}$ and $\sqrt{a} - \sqrt{b}$, $\sqrt{a} + \sqrt{b}$, are called **conjugates**. The product of such a pair of conjugates has no radicals in it. (See Example 12 of Section 6.4.) Thus when we wish to rationalize a denominator that has two terms and one or more of them involves a square-root radical, we multiply by 1 using the conjugate of the denominator to write a symbol for 1.

**EXAMPLES** In each of the following, what symbol for 1 would you use to rationalize the denominator?

*Expression     Symbol for 1*

**6.** $\dfrac{3}{x + \sqrt{7}}$     $\dfrac{x - \sqrt{7}}{x - \sqrt{7}}$

> Change the operation sign in the denominator to obtain the conjugate. Use the conjugate for the numerator and denominator of the symbol for 1.

**7.** $\dfrac{\sqrt{7} + 4}{3 - 2\sqrt{5}}$     $\dfrac{3 + 2\sqrt{5}}{3 + 2\sqrt{5}}$

Do Exercises 9 and 10.

**EXAMPLE 8** Rationalize the denominator: $\dfrac{4}{\sqrt{3} + x}$.

$$\frac{4}{\sqrt{3} + x} = \frac{4}{\sqrt{3} + x} \cdot \frac{\sqrt{3} - x}{\sqrt{3} - x}$$

$$= \frac{4(\sqrt{3} - x)}{(\sqrt{3} + x)(\sqrt{3} - x)}$$

$$= \frac{4\sqrt{3} - 4x}{3 - x^2}$$

**EXAMPLE 9** Rationalize the denominator: $\dfrac{4 + \sqrt{2}}{\sqrt{5} - \sqrt{2}}$.

$$\frac{4 + \sqrt{2}}{\sqrt{5} - \sqrt{2}} = \frac{4 + \sqrt{2}}{\sqrt{5} - \sqrt{2}} \cdot \frac{\sqrt{5} + \sqrt{2}}{\sqrt{5} + \sqrt{2}}$$   Multiplying by 1, using the conjugate of $\sqrt{5} - \sqrt{2}$, which is $\sqrt{5} + \sqrt{2}$

$$= \frac{(4 + \sqrt{2})(\sqrt{5} + \sqrt{2})}{(\sqrt{5} - \sqrt{2})(\sqrt{5} + \sqrt{2})}$$   Multiplying numerators and denominators

$$= \frac{4\sqrt{5} + 4\sqrt{2} + \sqrt{2}\sqrt{5} + (\sqrt{2})^2}{(\sqrt{5})^2 - (\sqrt{2})^2}$$   Using $(A - B)(A + B) = A^2 - B^2$ in the denominator

$$= \frac{4\sqrt{5} + 4\sqrt{2} + \sqrt{10} + 2}{5 - 2}$$

$$= \frac{4\sqrt{5} + 4\sqrt{2} + \sqrt{10} + 2}{3}$$

Do Exercises 11 and 12.

---

Multiply.

**7.** $(c - \sqrt{b})(c + \sqrt{b})$

**8.** $(\sqrt{a} + \sqrt{b})(\sqrt{a} - \sqrt{b})$

What symbol for 1 would you use to rationalize the denominator?

**9.** $\dfrac{\sqrt{5} + 1}{\sqrt{3} - y}$     **10.** $\dfrac{1}{\sqrt{2} + \sqrt{3}}$

Rationalize the denominator.

**11.** $\dfrac{14}{3 + \sqrt{2}}$     **12.** $\dfrac{5 + \sqrt{2}}{1 - \sqrt{2}}$

*Answers*

**7.** $c^2 - b$   **8.** $a - b$   **9.** $\dfrac{\sqrt{3} + y}{\sqrt{3} + y}$

**10.** $\dfrac{\sqrt{2} - \sqrt{3}}{\sqrt{2} - \sqrt{3}}$   **11.** $6 - 2\sqrt{2}$

**12.** $-7 - 6\sqrt{2}$

**a** Rationalize the denominator. Assume that no radicands were formed by raising negative numbers to even powers.

**1.** $\sqrt{\dfrac{5}{3}}$

**2.** $\sqrt{\dfrac{8}{7}}$

**3.** $\sqrt{\dfrac{11}{2}}$

**4.** $\sqrt{\dfrac{17}{6}}$

**5.** $\dfrac{2\sqrt{3}}{7\sqrt{5}}$

**6.** $\dfrac{3\sqrt{5}}{8\sqrt{2}}$

**7.** $\sqrt[3]{\dfrac{16}{9}}$

**8.** $\sqrt[3]{\dfrac{1}{3}}$

**9.** $\dfrac{\sqrt[3]{3a}}{\sqrt[3]{5c}}$

**10.** $\dfrac{\sqrt[3]{7x}}{\sqrt[3]{3y}}$

**11.** $\dfrac{\sqrt[3]{2y^4}}{\sqrt[3]{6x^4}}$

**12.** $\dfrac{\sqrt[3]{3a^4}}{\sqrt[3]{7b^2}}$

**13.** $\dfrac{1}{\sqrt[4]{st}}$

**14.** $\dfrac{1}{\sqrt[3]{yz}}$

**15.** $\sqrt{\dfrac{3x}{20}}$

**16.** $\sqrt{\dfrac{7a}{32}}$

**17.** $\sqrt[3]{\dfrac{4}{5x^5y^2}}$

**18.** $\sqrt[3]{\dfrac{7c}{100ab^5}}$

**19.** $\sqrt[4]{\dfrac{1}{8x^7y^3}}$

**20.** $\dfrac{2x}{\sqrt[5]{18x^8y^6}}$

**21.** $\dfrac{9}{6 - \sqrt{10}}$

**22.** $\dfrac{3}{8 + \sqrt{5}}$

**23.** $\dfrac{-4\sqrt{7}}{\sqrt{5} + \sqrt{3}}$

**24.** $\dfrac{-5\sqrt{2}}{\sqrt{7} - \sqrt{5}}$

**25.** $\dfrac{6\sqrt{3}}{3\sqrt{2} - \sqrt{5}}$

**26.** $\dfrac{34\sqrt{5}}{2\sqrt{5} - \sqrt{3}}$

**27.** $\dfrac{3 + \sqrt{5}}{\sqrt{2} + \sqrt{5}}$

**28.** $\dfrac{2 + \sqrt{3}}{\sqrt{3} + \sqrt{5}}$

**29.** $\dfrac{\sqrt{3} - \sqrt{2}}{\sqrt{3} - \sqrt{7}}$

**30.** $\dfrac{\sqrt{5} - \sqrt{3}}{\sqrt{5} - \sqrt{2}}$

**31.** $\dfrac{\sqrt{5} - 2\sqrt{6}}{\sqrt{3} - 4\sqrt{5}}$

**32.** $\dfrac{\sqrt{6} - 3\sqrt{5}}{\sqrt{3} - 2\sqrt{7}}$

**33.** $\dfrac{2 - \sqrt{a}}{3 + \sqrt{a}}$

**34.** $\dfrac{5 + \sqrt{x}}{8 - \sqrt{x}}$

**35.** $\dfrac{2 + 3\sqrt{x}}{3 + 2\sqrt{x}}$

**36.** $\dfrac{5 + 2\sqrt{y}}{4 + 3\sqrt{y}}$

**37.** $\dfrac{5\sqrt{3} - 3\sqrt{2}}{3\sqrt{2} - 2\sqrt{3}}$

**38.** $\dfrac{7\sqrt{2} + 4\sqrt{3}}{4\sqrt{3} - 3\sqrt{2}}$

**39.** $\dfrac{\sqrt{x} - \sqrt{y}}{\sqrt{x} + \sqrt{y}}$

**40.** $\dfrac{\sqrt{a} + \sqrt{b}}{\sqrt{a} - \sqrt{b}}$

## Skill Maintenance

Solve.   [5.5a]

**41.** $\dfrac{1}{2} - \dfrac{1}{3} = \dfrac{5}{t}$

**42.** $\dfrac{5}{x - 1} + \dfrac{9}{x^2 + x + 1} = \dfrac{15}{x^3 - 1}$

Divide and simplify.   [5.1e]

**43.** $\dfrac{1}{x^3 - y^3} \div \dfrac{1}{(x - y)(x^2 + xy + y^2)}$

**44.** $\dfrac{2x^2 - x - 6}{x^2 + 4x + 3} \div \dfrac{2x^2 + x - 3}{x^2 - 1}$

## Synthesis

**45.**  Use a graphing calculator to check your answers to Exercises 15 and 16.

**46.** Express each of the following as the product of two radical expressions.

    **a)** $x - 5$         **b)** $x - a$

Simplify. (*Hint*: Rationalize the denominator.)

**47.** $\sqrt{a^2 - 3} - \dfrac{a^2}{\sqrt{a^2 - 3}}$

**48.** $\dfrac{1}{4 + \sqrt{3}} + \dfrac{1}{\sqrt{3}} + \dfrac{1}{\sqrt{3} - 4}$

# 6.6

# Solving Radical Equations

## OBJECTIVES

a) Solve radical equations with one radical term.

b) Solve radical equations with two radical terms.

c) Solve applied problems involving radical equations.

**SKILL TO REVIEW**
Objective 4.8a: Solve quadratic and other polynomial equations by first factoring and then using the principle of zero products.

Solve.

1. $x^2 - x = 6$

2. $x^2 - x = 2x + 4$

## a) The Principle of Powers

A **radical equation** has variables in one or more radicands—for example,

$$\sqrt[3]{2x} + 1 = 5, \qquad \sqrt{x} + \sqrt{4x - 2} = 7.$$

To solve such an equation, we need a new equation-solving principle. Suppose that an equation $a = b$ is true. If we square both sides, we get another true equation: $a^2 = b^2$. This can be generalized.

---

**THE PRINCIPLE OF POWERS**

For any natural number $n$, if an equation $a = b$ is true, then $a^n = b^n$ is true.

---

However, if an equation $a^n = b^n$ is true, it *may not* be true that $a = b$, if $n$ is even. For example, $3^2 = (-3)^2$ is true, but $3 = -3$ is not true. Thus we *must check* the possible solutions when we solve an equation using the principle of powers.

To solve an equation with a radical term, we first isolate the radical term on one side of the equation. Then we use the principle of powers.

**EXAMPLE 1** Solve: $\sqrt{x} - 3 = 4$.

We have

$$
\begin{aligned}
\sqrt{x} - 3 &= 4 \\
\sqrt{x} &= 7 && \text{Adding to isolate the radical} \\
(\sqrt{x})^2 &= 7^2 && \text{Using the principle of powers (squaring)} \\
x &= 49. && \sqrt{x} \cdot \sqrt{x} = x
\end{aligned}
$$

The number 49 is a possible solution. But we *must* check in order to be sure!

Check:
$$
\begin{array}{c|c}
\sqrt{x} - 3 = 4 \\
\hline
\sqrt{49} - 3 \;?\; 4 \\
7 - 3 \\
4 & \text{TRUE}
\end{array}
$$

The solution is 49.

---------- *Caution!* ----------

The principle of powers does not always give equivalent equations. For this reason, a check is a must!

---

*Answers*

*Skill to Review:*

1. $-2, 3$    2. $-1, 4$

**EXAMPLE 2**  Solve: $\sqrt{x} = -3$.

We might observe at the outset that this equation has no solution because the principal square root of a number is never negative. Let's continue as above for comparison.

$$\sqrt{x} = -3$$
$$\left(\sqrt{x}\right)^2 = (-3)^2$$
$$x = 9$$

Check:  $$\frac{\sqrt{x} = -3}{\sqrt{9} \; ? \; -3}$$
$$\phantom{\sqrt{9}} 3 \; | \qquad \text{FALSE}$$

The number 9 does *not* check. Thus the equation $\sqrt{x} = -3$ has no real-number solution. Note that the solution of the equation $x = 9$ is 9, but the equation $\sqrt{x} = -3$ has *no* solution. Thus the equations $x = 9$ and $\sqrt{x} = -3$ are *not* equivalent equations.

Do Exercises 1 and 2.

Solve.

**1.** $\sqrt{x} - 7 = 3$

**2.** $\sqrt{x} = -2$

**EXAMPLE 3**  Solve: $x - 7 = 2\sqrt{x + 1}$.

The radical term is already isolated. We proceed with the principle of powers:

$$x - 7 = 2\sqrt{x + 1}$$
$$(x - 7)^2 = \left(2\sqrt{x + 1}\right)^2 \qquad \text{Using the principle of powers (squaring)}$$
$$(x - 7) \cdot (x - 7) = \left(2\sqrt{x + 1}\right)\left(2\sqrt{x + 1}\right)$$
$$x^2 - 14x + 49 = 2^2\left(\sqrt{x + 1}\right)^2$$
$$x^2 - 14x + 49 = 4(x + 1)$$
$$x^2 - 14x + 49 = 4x + 4$$
$$x^2 - 18x + 45 = 0$$
$$(x - 3)(x - 15) = 0 \qquad \text{Factoring}$$
$$x - 3 = 0 \quad or \quad x - 15 = 0 \qquad \text{Using the principle of zero products}$$
$$x = 3 \quad or \qquad x = 15.$$

The possible solutions are 3 and 15. We check.

For 3:
$$\frac{x - 7 = 2\sqrt{x + 1}}{3 - 7 \; ? \; 2\sqrt{3 + 1}}$$
$$\phantom{xx} -4 \; \Big| \; 2\sqrt{4}$$
$$\phantom{xxxx} \Big| \; 2(2)$$
$$\phantom{xxxx} \Big| \; 4 \qquad \text{FALSE}$$

For 15:
$$\frac{x - 7 = 2\sqrt{x + 1}}{15 - 7 \; ? \; 2\sqrt{15 + 1}}$$
$$\phantom{xxx} 8 \; \Big| \; 2\sqrt{16}$$
$$\phantom{xxxx} \Big| \; 2(4)$$
$$\phantom{xxxx} \Big| \; 8 \qquad \text{TRUE}$$

The number 3 does *not* check, but the number 15 does check. The solution is 15.

The number 3 in Example 3 is what is sometimes called an *extraneous solution*, but such terminology is risky to use at best because the number 3 is in *no way* a *solution* of the original equation.

Do Exercises 3 and 4.

Solve.

**3.** $x + 2 = \sqrt{2x + 7}$

**4.** $x + 1 = 3\sqrt{x - 1}$

## ✳ Algebraic-Graphical Connection

We can visualize or check the solutions of a radical equation graphically. Consider the equation of Example 3: $x - 7 = 2\sqrt{x + 1}$. We can examine the solutions by graphing the equations

$$y = x - 7 \quad \text{and} \quad y = 2\sqrt{x + 1}$$

using the same set of axes. A hand-drawn graph of $y = 2\sqrt{x + 1}$ would involve approximating square roots on a calculator.

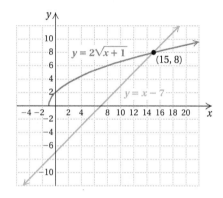

It appears from the graph that when $x = 15$, the values of $y = x - 7$ and $y = 2\sqrt{x + 1}$ are the same, 8. We can check this as we did in Example 3. Note too that the graphs *do not* intersect at $x = 3$, the extraneous solution.

---

### Calculator Corner

**Solving Radical Equations**   We can solve radical equations graphically. Consider the equation in Example 3,

$$x - 7 = 2\sqrt{x + 1}.$$

We first graph each side of the equation. We enter $y_1 = x - 7$ and $y_2 = 2\sqrt{x + 1}$ on the equation-editor screen and graph the equations using the window $[-5, 20, -10, 10]$. Note that there is one point of intersection. We use the INTERSECT feature to find its coordinates. (See the Calculator Corner on p. 246 for the procedure.) The first coordinate, 15, is the value of $x$ for which $y_1 = y_2$, or $x - 7 = 2\sqrt{x + 1}$. It is the solution of the equation. Note that the graph shows a single solution whereas the algebraic solution in Example 3 yields two possible solutions, 3 and 15, that must be checked. The algebraic check shows that 15 is the only solution.

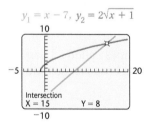

**Exercises:**

**1.** Solve the equations in Examples 1 and 4 graphically.

**2.** Solve the equations in Margin Exercises 1, 3, and 4 graphically.

**EXAMPLE 4**  Solve: $x = \sqrt{x + 7} + 5$.

We have

$$x = \sqrt{x + 7} + 5$$

$$x - 5 = \sqrt{x + 7} \qquad \text{Subtracting 5 to isolate the radical term}$$

$$(x - 5)^2 = \left(\sqrt{x + 7}\right)^2 \qquad \text{Using the principle of powers (squaring both sides)}$$

$$x^2 - 10x + 25 = x + 7$$

$$x^2 - 11x + 18 = 0$$

$$(x - 9)(x - 2) = 0 \qquad \text{Factoring}$$

$$x = 9 \quad or \quad x = 2. \qquad \text{Using the principle of zero products}$$

The possible solutions are 9 and 2. Let's check.

For 9:

$$\begin{array}{c|l} x = \sqrt{x + 7} + 5 \\ \hline 9 \; ? \; \sqrt{9 + 7} + 5 \\ \quad \sqrt{16} + 5 \\ \quad 4 + 5 \\ \quad 9 & \text{TRUE} \end{array}$$

For 2:

$$\begin{array}{c|l} x = \sqrt{x + 7} + 5 \\ \hline 2 \; ? \; \sqrt{2 + 7} + 5 \\ \quad \sqrt{9} + 5 \\ \quad 3 + 5 \\ \quad 8 & \text{FALSE} \end{array}$$

Since 9 checks but 2 does not, the solution is 9.

**EXAMPLE 5**  Solve: $\sqrt[3]{2x + 1} + 5 = 0$.

We have

$$\sqrt[3]{2x + 1} + 5 = 0$$

$$\sqrt[3]{2x + 1} = -5 \qquad \text{Subtracting 5. This isolates the radical term.}$$

$$\left(\sqrt[3]{2x + 1}\right)^3 = (-5)^3 \qquad \text{Using the principle of powers (raising to the third power)}$$

$$2x + 1 = -125$$

$$2x = -126 \qquad \text{Subtracting 1}$$

$$x = -63.$$

Check:

$$\begin{array}{c|l} \sqrt[3]{2x + 1} + 5 = 0 \\ \hline \sqrt[3]{2 \cdot (-63) + 1} + 5 \; ? \; 0 \\ \quad \sqrt[3]{-125} + 5 \\ \quad -5 + 5 \\ \quad 0 & \text{TRUE} \end{array}$$

The solution is $-63$.

Do Exercises 5 and 6.

Solve.

**5.** $x = \sqrt{x + 5} + 1$

**6.** $\sqrt[4]{x - 1} - 2 = 0$

## b Equations with Two Radical Terms

A general strategy for solving radical equations, including those with two radical terms, is as follows.

> **SOLVING RADICAL EQUATIONS**
>
> To solve radical equations:
>
> 1. Isolate one of the radical terms.
> 2. Use the principle of powers.
> 3. If a radical remains, perform steps (1) and (2) again.
> 4. Check possible solutions.

**EXAMPLE 6** Solve: $\sqrt{x-3} + \sqrt{x+5} = 4$.

$$\sqrt{x-3} + \sqrt{x+5} = 4$$

$$\sqrt{x-3} = 4 - \sqrt{x+5}$$     Subtracting $\sqrt{x+5}$. This isolates one of the radical terms.

$$\left(\sqrt{x-3}\right)^2 = \left(4 - \sqrt{x+5}\right)^2$$     Using the principle of powers (squaring both sides)

$$x - 3 = 16 - 8\sqrt{x+5} + (x+5)$$     Using $(A-B)^2 = A^2 - 2AB + B^2$. See this rule in Section 4.2.

$$-3 = 21 - 8\sqrt{x+5}$$     Subtracting $x$ and collecting like terms

$$-24 = -8\sqrt{x+5}$$     Isolating the remaining radical term

$$3 = \sqrt{x+5}$$     Dividing by $-8$

$$3^2 = \left(\sqrt{x+5}\right)^2$$     Squaring

$$9 = x + 5$$

$$4 = x$$

The number 4 checks and is the solution.

**EXAMPLE 7** Solve: $\sqrt{2x-5} = 1 + \sqrt{x-3}$.

$$\sqrt{2x-5} = 1 + \sqrt{x-3}$$

$$\left(\sqrt{2x-5}\right)^2 = \left(1 + \sqrt{x-3}\right)^2$$     One radical is already isolated. We square both sides.

$$2x - 5 = 1 + 2\sqrt{x-3} + \left(\sqrt{x-3}\right)^2$$

$$2x - 5 = 1 + 2\sqrt{x-3} + (x-3)$$

$$x - 3 = 2\sqrt{x-3}$$     Isolating the remaining radical term

$$(x-3)^2 = \left(2\sqrt{x-3}\right)^2$$     Squaring both sides

$$x^2 - 6x + 9 = 4(x-3)$$

$$x^2 - 6x + 9 = 4x - 12$$

$$x^2 - 10x + 21 = 0$$

$$(x-7)(x-3) = 0$$     Factoring

$$x = 7 \quad or \quad x = 3$$     Using the principle of zero products

The possible solutions are 7 and 3. We check.

For 7:

$$\frac{\sqrt{2x-5} = 1 + \sqrt{x-3}}{\begin{array}{c|c} \sqrt{2(7)-5} \; ? \; 1 + \sqrt{7-3} \\ \sqrt{14-5} & 1 + \sqrt{4} \\ \sqrt{9} & 1 + 2 \\ 3 & 3 \end{array}}$$ TRUE

For 3:

$$\frac{\sqrt{2x-5} = 1 + \sqrt{x-3}}{\begin{array}{c|c} \sqrt{2(3)-5} \; ? \; 1 + \sqrt{3-3} \\ \sqrt{6-5} & 1 + \sqrt{0} \\ \sqrt{1} & 1 + 0 \\ 1 & 1 \end{array}}$$ TRUE

The numbers 7 and 3 check and are the solutions.

Do Exercises 7 and 8.

**Solve.**

**7.** $\sqrt{x} - \sqrt{x-5} = 1$

**8.** $\sqrt{2x-5} - 2 = \sqrt{x-2}$

**EXAMPLE 8** Solve: $\sqrt{x+2} - \sqrt{2x+2} + 1 = 0$.

We first isolate one radical.

$$\sqrt{x+2} - \sqrt{2x+2} + 1 = 0$$

$$\sqrt{x+2} + 1 = \sqrt{2x+2} \qquad \text{Adding } \sqrt{2x+2} \text{ to isolate a radical term}$$

$$\left(\sqrt{x+2} + 1\right)^2 = \left(\sqrt{2x+2}\right)^2 \qquad \text{Squaring both sides}$$

$$x + 2 + 2\sqrt{x+2} + 1 = 2x + 2$$

$$2\sqrt{x+2} = x - 1$$

$$\left(2\sqrt{x+2}\right)^2 = (x-1)^2$$

$$4(x+2) = x^2 - 2x + 1$$

$$4x + 8 = x^2 - 2x + 1$$

$$0 = x^2 - 6x - 7$$

$$0 = (x-7)(x+1) \qquad \text{Factoring}$$

$$x - 7 = 0 \quad or \quad x + 1 = 0 \qquad \text{Using the principle of zero products}$$

$$x = 7 \quad or \qquad x = -1$$

The possible solutions are 7 and $-1$. We check.

For 7:

$$\frac{\sqrt{x+2} - \sqrt{2x+2} + 1 = 0}{\begin{array}{c|c} \sqrt{7+2} - \sqrt{2 \cdot 7 + 2} + 1 \; ? \; 0 \\ \sqrt{9} - \sqrt{16} + 1 \\ 3 - 4 + 1 \\ 0 \end{array}}$$ TRUE

For $-1$:

$$\frac{\sqrt{x+2} - \sqrt{2x+2} + 1 = 0}{\begin{array}{c|c} \sqrt{-1+2} - \sqrt{2 \cdot (-1) + 2} + 1 \; ? \; 0 \\ \sqrt{1} - \sqrt{0} + 1 \\ 1 - 0 + 1 \\ 2 \end{array}}$$ FALSE

The number 7 checks, but $-1$ does not. The solution is 7.

Do Exercise 9.

**9.** Solve:
$$\sqrt{3x+1} - 1 - \sqrt{x+4} = 0.$$

## c Applications

*Speed of Sound.* Many applications translate to radical equations. For example, at a temperature of $t$ degrees Fahrenheit, sound travels at a rate of $S$ feet per second, where

$$S = 21.9\sqrt{5t + 2457}.$$

**EXAMPLE 9** *Outdoor Concert.* The geologically formed, open-air Red Rocks Amphitheatre near Denver, Colorado, hosts a series of concerts. A scientific instrument at one of these concerts determined that the sound of the music was traveling at a rate of 1170 ft/sec. What was the air temperature at the concert?

We substitute 1170 for $S$ in the formula $S = 21.9\sqrt{5t + 2457}$:

$$1170 = 21.9\sqrt{5t + 2457}.$$

Then we solve the equation for $t$:

$$1170 = 21.9\sqrt{5t + 2457}$$

$$\frac{1170}{21.9} = \sqrt{5t + 2457} \qquad \text{Dividing by 21.9}$$

$$\left(\frac{1170}{21.9}\right)^2 = \left(\sqrt{5t + 2457}\right)^2 \qquad \text{Squaring both sides}$$

$$2854.2 \approx 5t + 2457 \qquad \text{Simplifying}$$

$$397.2 \approx 5t \qquad \text{Subtracting 2457}$$

$$79 \approx t. \qquad \text{Dividing by 5}$$

The temperature at the concert was about 79°F.

> Do Exercise 10.

**10. Marching Band Performance.** When the Fulton High School marching band performed at half-time of a football game, the speed of sound from the music was measured by a scientific instrument to be 1162 ft/sec. What was the air temperature?

*Answer*

**10.** About 72°F

---

**6.6** **Exercise Set**

For Extra Help

*MyMathLab*

### a Solve.

**1.** $\sqrt{2x - 3} = 4$

**2.** $\sqrt{5x + 2} = 7$

**3.** $\sqrt{6x} + 1 = 8$

**4.** $\sqrt{3x} - 4 = 6$

**5.** $\sqrt{y + 7} - 4 = 4$

**6.** $\sqrt{x - 1} - 3 = 9$

**7.** $\sqrt{5y + 8} = 10$

**8.** $\sqrt{2y + 9} = 5$

**9.** $\sqrt[3]{x} = -1$

**10.** $\sqrt[3]{y} = -2$

**11.** $\sqrt{x + 2} = -4$

**12.** $\sqrt{y - 3} = -2$

**13.** $\sqrt[3]{x + 5} = 2$

**14.** $\sqrt[3]{x - 2} = 3$

**15.** $\sqrt[4]{y - 3} = 2$

**16.** $\sqrt[4]{x + 3} = 3$

**17.** $\sqrt[3]{6x + 9} + 8 = 5$

**18.** $\sqrt[3]{3y + 6} + 2 = 3$

**19.** $8 = \dfrac{1}{\sqrt{x}}$

**20.** $\dfrac{1}{\sqrt{y}} = 3$

**21.** $x - 7 = \sqrt{x - 5}$

**22.** $x - 5 = \sqrt{x + 7}$

**23.** $2\sqrt{x + 1} + 7 = x$

**24.** $\sqrt{2x + 7} - 2 = x$

**25.** $3\sqrt{x - 1} - 1 = x$

**26.** $x - 1 = \sqrt{x + 5}$

**27.** $x - 3 = \sqrt{27 - 3x}$

**28.** $x - 1 = \sqrt{1 - x}$

 Solve.

**29.** $\sqrt{3y + 1} = \sqrt{2y + 6}$

**30.** $\sqrt{5x - 3} = \sqrt{2x + 3}$

**31.** $\sqrt{y - 5} + \sqrt{y} = 5$

**32.** $\sqrt{x - 9} + \sqrt{x} = 1$

**33.** $3 + \sqrt{z - 6} = \sqrt{z + 9}$

**34.** $\sqrt{4x - 3} = 2 + \sqrt{2x - 5}$

**35.** $\sqrt{20 - x} + 8 = \sqrt{9 - x} + 11$

**36.** $4 + \sqrt{10 - x} = 6 + \sqrt{4 - x}$

**37.** $\sqrt{4y + 1} - \sqrt{y - 2} = 3$

**38.** $\sqrt{y + 15} - \sqrt{2y + 7} = 1$

**39.** $\sqrt{x + 2} + \sqrt{3x + 4} = 2$

**40.** $\sqrt{6x + 7} - \sqrt{3x + 3} = 1$

**41.** $\sqrt{3x - 5} + \sqrt{2x + 3} + 1 = 0$

**42.** $\sqrt{2m - 3} + 2 - \sqrt{m + 7} = 0$

**43.** $2\sqrt{t-1} - \sqrt{3t-1} = 0$

**44.** $3\sqrt{2y+3} - \sqrt{y+10} = 0$

**C**   Solve.

*Sighting to the Horizon.*   How far can you see to the horizon from a given height? The function

$$D = 1.2\sqrt{h}$$

can be used to approximate the distance $D$, in miles, that a person can see to the horizon from a height $h$, in feet.

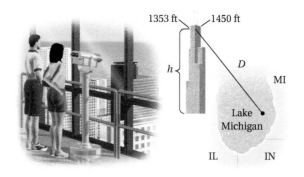

**45.** An observation deck near the top of the Willis Tower (formerly known as the Sears Tower) in Chicago is 1353 ft high. How far can a tourist see to the horizon from this deck?

**46.** The roof of the Willis Tower is 1450 ft high. How far can a worker see to the horizon from the top of the Willis Tower?

**47.** Sarah can see 31.3 mi to the horizon from the top of a cliff. What is the height of Sarah's eyes?

**48.** A technician can see 30.4 mi to the horizon from the top of a radio tower. How high is the tower?

**49.** A steeplejack can see 13 mi to the horizon from the top of a building. What is the height of the steeplejack's eyes?

**50.** A person can see 230 mi to the horizon from an airplane window. How high is the airplane?

*Speed of a Skidding Car.* After an accident, how do police determine the speed at which the car had been traveling? The formula

$$r = 2\sqrt{5L}$$

can be used to approximate the speed $r$, in miles per hour, of a car that has left a skid mark of length $L$, in feet. Use this formula for Exercises 51 and 52.

**51.** How far will a car skid at 55 mph? at 75 mph?

**52.** How far will a car skid at 65 mph? at 100 mph?

*Temperature and the Speed of Sound.* Solve Exercises 53 and 54 using the formula $S = 21.9\sqrt{5t + 2457}$ from Example 9.

**53.** During blasting for avalanche control in Utah's Wasatch Mountains, sound traveled at a rate of 1113 ft/sec. What was the temperature at the time?

**54.** At a recent concert by the Dave Matthews Band, sound traveled at a rate of 1176 ft/sec. What was the temperature at the time?

*Period of a Swinging Pendulum.* The formula $T = 2\pi\sqrt{L/32}$ can be used to find the period $T$, in seconds, of a pendulum of length $L$, in feet.

**55.** What is the length of a pendulum that has a period of 1.0 sec? Use 3.14 for $\pi$.

**56.** What is the length of a pendulum that has a period of 2.0 sec? Use 3.14 for $\pi$.

**57.** The pendulum in Jean's grandfather clock has a period of 2.2 sec. Find the length of the pendulum. Use 3.14 for $\pi$.

**58.** A playground swing has a period of 3.1 sec. Find the length of the swing's chain. Use 3.14 for $\pi$.

## Skill Maintenance

Solve. [5.6a]

**59.** *Painting a Room.* Julia can paint a room in 8 hr. George can paint the same room in 10 hr. How long will it take them, working together, to paint the same room?

**60.** *Delivering Leaflets.* Jeff can drop leaflets in mailboxes three times as fast as Grace can. If they work together, it takes them 1 hr to complete the job. How long would it take each to deliver the leaflets alone?

Solve. [5.6b]

**61.** *Bicycle Travel.* A cyclist traveled 702 mi in 14 days. At this same ratio, how far would the cyclist have traveled in 56 days?

**62.** *Earnings.* Dharma earned $696.64 working for 56 hr at a fruit stand. How many hours must she work in order to earn $1044.96?

Solve. [4.8a]

**63.** $x^2 + 2.8x = 0$

**64.** $3x^2 - 5x = 0$

**65.** $x^2 - 64 = 0$

**66.** $2x^2 = x + 21$

For each of the following functions, find and simplify $f(a + h) - f(a)$. [4.2e]

**67.** $f(x) = x^2$

**68.** $f(x) = x^2 - x$

**69.** $f(x) = 2x^2 - 3x$

**70.** $f(x) = 2x^2 + 3x - 7$

## Synthesis

**71.**  Use a graphing calculator to check your answers to Exercises 4, 9, 33, and 38.

**72.** Consider the equation
$$\sqrt{2x + 1} + \sqrt{5x - 4} = \sqrt{10x + 9}.$$
a) Use a graphing calculator to solve the equation.
b) Solve the equation algebraically.
c) Explain the advantages and disadvantages of using each method. Which do you prefer?

Solve.

**73.** $\sqrt[3]{\dfrac{z}{4}} - 10 = 2$

**74.** $\sqrt[4]{z^2 + 17} = 3$

**75.** $\sqrt{\sqrt{y + 49} - \sqrt{y}} = \sqrt{7}$

**76.** $\sqrt[3]{x^2 + x + 15} - 3 = 0$

**77.** $\sqrt{\sqrt{x^2 + 9x + 34}} = 2$

**78.** $\sqrt{8 - b} = b\sqrt{8 - b}$

**79.** $\sqrt{x - 2} - \sqrt{x + 2} + 2 = 0$

**80.** $6\sqrt{y} + 6y^{-1/2} = 37$

**81.** $\sqrt{a^2 + 30a} = a + \sqrt{5a}$

**82.** $\sqrt{\sqrt{x} + 4} = \sqrt{x} - 2$

**83.** $\dfrac{x - 1}{\sqrt{x^2 + 3x + 6}} = \dfrac{1}{4}$

**84.** $\sqrt{x + 1} - \dfrac{2}{\sqrt{x + 1}} = 1$

**85.** $\sqrt{y^2 + 6} + y - 3 = 0$

**86.** $2\sqrt{x - 1} - \sqrt{3x - 5} = \sqrt{x - 9}$

**87.** $\sqrt{y + 1} - \sqrt{2y - 5} = \sqrt{y - 2}$

**88.** Evaluate: $\sqrt{7 + 4\sqrt{3}} - \sqrt{7 - 4\sqrt{3}}$.

# Summary and Review

## Key Terms and Properties

square of a number, p. 500
square root, p. 500
principal square root, p. 500
radical symbol, p. 501
radical expression, p. 501
radicand, p. 501

cube root, p. 504
index, p. 505
odd root, p. 505
even root, p. 506
rationalizing the denominator, p. 535
conjugates, p. 537

radical equation, p. 540
complex-number system, p. 558
complex number $i$, p. 558
imaginary number, p. 558

$$\sqrt{a^2} = |a|; \quad \sqrt[k]{a^k} = |a|, \text{ when } k \text{ is even;} \quad \sqrt[k]{a^k} = a, \text{ when } k \text{ is odd;}$$

$$\sqrt[k]{ab} = \sqrt[k]{a} \cdot \sqrt[k]{b}; \quad \sqrt[k]{\frac{a}{b}} = \frac{\sqrt[k]{a}}{\sqrt[k]{b}}; \quad a^{1/n} = \sqrt[n]{a};$$

$$a^{m/n} = \sqrt[n]{a^m} = \left(\sqrt[n]{a}\right)^m; \quad a^{-m/n} = \frac{1}{a^{m/n}}$$

*Principle of Powers:*    If $a = b$ is true, then $a^n = b^n$ is true.

*Pythagorean Theorem:*    $a^2 + b^2 = c^2$, in a right triangle.

$i = \sqrt{-1}, \quad i^2 = -1, \quad i^3 = -i, \quad i^4 = 1$

*Imaginary Numbers:*    $bi, i^2 = -1, b \neq 0$

*Complex Numbers:*    $a + bi, i^2 = -1$

*Conjugates:*    $a + bi, a - bi$

## Concept Reinforcement

Determine whether each statement is true or false.

_____ **1.** For any negative number $a$, we have $\sqrt{a^2} = -a$.   [6.1a]

_____ **2.** For any real numbers $\sqrt[m]{a}$ and $\sqrt[n]{b}$, $\sqrt[m]{a} \cdot \sqrt[n]{b} = \sqrt[mn]{ab}$.   [6.3a]

_____ **3.** For any real numbers $\sqrt[n]{a}$ and $\sqrt[n]{b}$, $\sqrt[n]{a} + \sqrt[n]{b} = \sqrt[n]{a + b}$.   [6.4a]

_____ **4.** If $x^2 = 4$, then $x = 2$.   [6.6a]

_____ **5.** All real numbers are complex numbers, but not every complex number is a real number.   [6.8a]

_____ **6.** The product of a complex number and its conjugate is always a real number.   [6.8e]

## Important Concepts

**Objective 6.1b**   Simplify radical expressions with perfect-square radicands.

**Example**   Simplify: $\sqrt{16x^2}$.
$$\sqrt{16x^2} = \sqrt{(4x)^2} = |4x| = |4| \cdot |x| = 4|x|$$

**Example**   Simplify: $\sqrt{x^2 - 6x + 9}$.
$$\sqrt{x^2 - 6x + 9} = \sqrt{(x - 3)^2} = |x - 3|$$

**Practice Exercises**

  **1.** Simplify: $\sqrt{36y^2}$.

  **2.** Simplify: $\sqrt{a^2 + 4a + 4}$.

**Objective 6.2a** Write expressions with or without rational exponents, and simplify, if possible.

**Example** Rewrite $x^{1/4}$ without a rational exponent.
Recall that $a^{1/n}$ means $\sqrt[n]{a}$. Then
$$x^{1/4} = \sqrt[4]{x}.$$

**Example** Rewrite $\left(\sqrt[3]{4xy^2}\right)^4$ with a rational exponent.
Recall that $\left(\sqrt[n]{a}\right)^m$ means $a^{m/n}$. Then
$$\left(\sqrt[3]{4xy^2}\right)^4 = (4xy^2)^{4/3}.$$

**Practice Exercises**

**3.** Rewrite $z^{3/5}$ without a rational exponent.

**4.** Rewrite $\left(\sqrt{6ab}\right)^5$ with a rational exponent.

**Objective 6.2b** Write expressions without negative exponents, and simplify, if possible.

**Example** Rewrite $8^{-2/3}$ with a positive exponent, and simplify, if possible.

Recall that $a^{-m/n}$ means $\dfrac{1}{a^{m/n}}$. Then

$$8^{-2/3} = \frac{1}{8^{2/3}} = \frac{1}{\left(\sqrt[3]{8}\right)^2} = \frac{1}{2^2} = \frac{1}{4}.$$

**Practice Exercise**

**5.** Rewrite $9^{-3/2}$ with a positive exponent, and simplify, if possible.

**Objective 6.2d** Use rational exponents to simplify radical expressions.

**Example** Use rational exponents to simplify: $\sqrt[6]{x^2y^4}$.
$$\begin{aligned}
\sqrt[6]{x^2y^4} &= (x^2y^4)^{1/6} \\
&= x^{2/6}y^{4/6} \\
&= x^{1/3}y^{2/3} \\
&= (xy^2)^{1/3} \\
&= \sqrt[3]{xy^2}
\end{aligned}$$

**Practice Exercise**

**6.** Use rational exponents to simplify: $\sqrt[8]{a^6b^2}$.

**Objective 6.3a** Multiply and simplify radical expressions.

**Example** Multiply and simplify: $\sqrt[3]{6xy^2}\sqrt[3]{9y}$.
$$\begin{aligned}
\sqrt[3]{6xy^2}\,\sqrt[3]{9y} &= \sqrt[3]{6xy^2 \cdot 9y} \\
&= \sqrt[3]{54xy^3} \\
&= \sqrt[3]{27y^3 \cdot 2x} \\
&= \sqrt[3]{27y^3}\sqrt[3]{2x} \\
&= 3y\sqrt[3]{2x}
\end{aligned}$$

**Practice Exercise**

**7.** Multiply and simplify. Assume that all expressions under radicals represent nonnegative numbers.
$$\sqrt{5y}\sqrt{30y}$$

**Objective 6.3b** Divide and simplify radical expressions.

**Example** Divide and simplify: $\dfrac{\sqrt{24x^5}}{\sqrt{6x}}$.

$$\frac{\sqrt{24x^5}}{\sqrt{6x}} = \sqrt{\frac{24x^5}{6x}} = \sqrt{4x^4} = 2x^2$$

**Practice Exercise**

**8.** Divide and simplify: $\dfrac{\sqrt{20a}}{\sqrt{5}}$.

**Objective 6.4a**   Add or subtract with radical notation and simplify.

**Example**   Subtract: $5\sqrt{2} - 4\sqrt{8}$.

$$5\sqrt{2} - 4\sqrt{8} = 5\sqrt{2} - 4\sqrt{4\cdot2}$$
$$= 5\sqrt{2} - 4\sqrt{4}\sqrt{2}$$
$$= 5\sqrt{2} - 4\cdot2\sqrt{2} = 5\sqrt{2} - 8\sqrt{2}$$
$$= (5-8)\sqrt{2} = -3\sqrt{2}$$

**Practice Exercise**

**9.** Subtract: $\sqrt{48} - 2\sqrt{3}$.

---

**Objective 6.4b**   Multiply expressions involving radicals in which some factors contain more than one term.

**Example**   Multiply: $\left(3 - \sqrt{6}\right)\left(2 + 4\sqrt{6}\right)$.

We use FOIL:

$$\left(3 - \sqrt{6}\right)\left(2 + 4\sqrt{6}\right)$$
$$= 3\cdot2 + 3\cdot4\sqrt{6} - \sqrt{6}\cdot2 - \sqrt{6}\cdot4\sqrt{6}$$
$$= 6 + 12\sqrt{6} - 2\sqrt{6} - 4\cdot6$$
$$= 6 + 12\sqrt{6} - 2\sqrt{6} - 24$$
$$= -18 + 10\sqrt{6}.$$

**Practice Exercise**

**10.** Multiply: $\left(5 - \sqrt{x}\right)^2$.

---

**Objective 6.6a**   Solve radical equations with one radical term.

**Example**   Solve: $x = \sqrt{x-2} + 4$.

First, we subtract 4 on both sides to isolate the radical. Then we square both sides of the equation.

$$x = \sqrt{x-2} + 4$$
$$x - 4 = \sqrt{x-2}$$
$$(x-4)^2 = \left(\sqrt{x-2}\right)^2$$
$$x^2 - 8x + 16 = x - 2$$
$$x^2 - 9x + 18 = 0$$
$$(x-3)(x-6) = 0$$
$$x - 3 = 0 \quad or \quad x - 6 = 0$$
$$x = 3 \quad or \qquad x = 6$$

We must check both possible solutions. When we do, we find that 6 checks, but 3 does not. Thus the solution is 6.

**Practice Exercise**

**11.** Solve: $3 + \sqrt{x-1} = x$.

---

**Objective 6.6b**   Solve radical equations with two radical terms.

**Example**   Solve: $1 = \sqrt{x+9} - \sqrt{x}$.

$$1 = \sqrt{x+9} - \sqrt{x}$$
$$\sqrt{x} + 1 = \sqrt{x+9} \qquad \text{Isolating one radical}$$
$$\left(\sqrt{x} + 1\right)^2 = \left(\sqrt{x+9}\right)^2 \qquad \text{Squaring both sides}$$
$$x + 2\sqrt{x} + 1 = x + 9$$
$$2\sqrt{x} = 8 \qquad \text{Isolating the remaining radical}$$
$$\sqrt{x} = 4$$
$$\left(\sqrt{x}\right)^2 = 4^2$$
$$x = 16$$

The number 16 checks. It is the solution.

**Practice Exercise**

**12.** Solve: $\sqrt{x+3} - \sqrt{x-2} = 1$.

**Objective 6.8c**   Multiply complex numbers.

**Example**   Multiply: $(3 - 2i)(4 + i)$.

$$(3 - 2i)(4 + i) = 12 + 3i - 8i - 2i^2 \quad \text{Using FOIL}$$
$$= 12 + 3i - 8i - 2(-1)$$
$$= 12 + 3i - 8i + 2$$
$$= 14 - 5i$$

**Practice Exercise**

**13.** Multiply: $(2 - 5i)^2$.

---

**Objective 6.8e**   Find conjugates of complex numbers and divide complex numbers.

**Example**   Divide and simplify to the form $a + bi$:

$$\frac{5 - i}{4 + 3i}.$$

The conjugate of the denominator is $4 - 3i$, so we multiply by 1 using $\dfrac{4 - 3i}{4 - 3i}$:

$$\frac{5 - i}{4 + 3i} = \frac{5 - i}{4 + 3i} \cdot \frac{4 - 3i}{4 - 3i}$$

$$= \frac{20 - 15i - 4i + 3i^2}{16 - 9i^2}$$

$$= \frac{20 - 19i + 3(-1)}{16 - 9(-1)}$$

$$= \frac{20 - 19i - 3}{16 + 9}$$

$$= \frac{17 - 19i}{25} = \frac{17}{25} - \frac{19}{25}i.$$

**Practice Exercise**

**14.** Divide and simplify to the form $a + bi$: $\dfrac{3 - 2i}{2 + i}$.

---

# Review Exercises

Use a calculator to approximate to three decimal places.
[6.1a]

**1.** $\sqrt{778}$

**2.** $\sqrt{\dfrac{963.2}{23.68}}$

**3.** For the given function, find the indicated function values.   [6.1a]
$$f(x) = \sqrt{3x - 16}; \quad f(0), f(-1), f(1), \text{ and } f\left(\tfrac{41}{3}\right)$$

**4.** Find the domain of the function $f$ in Exercise 3.   [6.1a]

Simplify. Assume that letters represent *any* real number.
[6.1b]

**5.** $\sqrt{81a^2}$

**6.** $\sqrt{(-7z)^2}$

**7.** $\sqrt{(6 - b)^2}$

**8.** $\sqrt{x^2 + 6x + 9}$

Simplify.   [6.1c]

**9.** $\sqrt[3]{-1000}$

**10.** $\sqrt[3]{-\dfrac{1}{27}}$

**11.** For the given function, find the indicated function values.   [6.1c]
$$f(x) = \sqrt[3]{x + 2}; \quad f(6), f(-10), \text{ and } f(25)$$

Simplify. Assume that letters represent *any* real number.
[6.1d]

**12.** $\sqrt[10]{x^{10}}$

**13.** $-\sqrt[13]{(-3)^{13}}$

Rewrite without rational exponents, and simplify, if possible.
[6.2a]

**14.** $a^{1/5}$

**15.** $64^{3/2}$

Rewrite with rational exponents. [6.2a]

**16.** $\sqrt{31}$

**17.** $\sqrt[5]{a^2 b^3}$

Rewrite with positive exponents, and simplify, if possible. [6.2b]

**18.** $49^{-1/2}$

**19.** $(8xy)^{-2/3}$

**20.** $5a^{-3/4} b^{1/2} c^{-2/3}$

**21.** $\dfrac{3a}{\sqrt[4]{t}}$

Use the laws of exponents to simplify. Write answers with positive exponents. [6.2c]

**22.** $(x^{-2/3})^{3/5}$

**23.** $\dfrac{7^{-1/3}}{7^{-1/2}}$

Use rational exponents to simplify. Write the answer in radical notation if appropriate. [6.2d]

**24.** $\sqrt[3]{x^{21}}$

**25.** $\sqrt[3]{27x^6}$

Use rational exponents to write a single radical expression. [6.2d]

**26.** $x^{1/3} y^{1/4}$

**27.** $\sqrt[4]{x}\sqrt[3]{x}$

Simplify by factoring. Assume that all expressions under radicals represent nonnegative numbers. [6.3a]

**28.** $\sqrt{245}$

**29.** $\sqrt[3]{-108}$

**30.** $\sqrt[3]{250a^2 b^6}$

Simplify. Assume that no radicands were formed by raising negative numbers to even powers. [6.3b]

**31.** $\sqrt{\dfrac{49}{36}}$

**32.** $\sqrt[3]{\dfrac{64x^6}{27}}$

**33.** $\sqrt[4]{\dfrac{16x^8}{81y^{12}}}$

Perform the indicated operations and simplify. Assume that no radicands were formed by raising negative numbers to even powers. [6.3a, b], [6.4a]

**34.** $\sqrt{5x}\sqrt{3y}$

**35.** $\sqrt[3]{a^5 b}\sqrt[3]{27b}$

**36.** $\sqrt[3]{a}\sqrt[5]{b^3}$

**37.** $\dfrac{\sqrt[3]{60xy^3}}{\sqrt[3]{10x}}$

**38.** $\dfrac{\sqrt{75x}}{2\sqrt{3}}$

**39.** $\dfrac{\sqrt[3]{x^2}}{\sqrt[4]{x}}$

**40.** $5\sqrt[3]{x} + 2\sqrt[3]{x}$

**41.** $2\sqrt{75} - 7\sqrt{3}$

**42.** $\sqrt{50} + 2\sqrt{18} + \sqrt{32}$

**43.** $\sqrt[3]{8x^4} + \sqrt[3]{xy^6}$

Multiply. [6.4b]

**44.** $\left(\sqrt{5} - 3\sqrt{8}\right)\left(\sqrt{5} + 2\sqrt{8}\right)$

**45.** $\left(1 - \sqrt{7}\right)^2$

**46.** $\left(\sqrt[3]{27} - \sqrt[3]{2}\right)\left(\sqrt[3]{27} + \sqrt[3]{2}\right)$

Rationalize the denominator. [6.5a, b]

**47.** $\sqrt{\dfrac{8}{3}}$

**48.** $\dfrac{2}{\sqrt{a} + \sqrt{b}}$

Solve. [6.6a, b]

**49.** $x - 3 = \sqrt{5 - x}$

**50.** $\sqrt[4]{x + 3} = 2$

**51.** $\sqrt{x + 8} - \sqrt{3x + 1} = 1$

*Automotive Repair.* For an engine with a displacement of 2.8 L, the function given by
$$d(n) = 0.75\sqrt{2.8n}$$
can be used to determine the diameter of the carburetor's opening, $d(n)$, in millimeters, where $n$ is the number of rpm's at which the engine achieves peak performance. [6.6c]

Source: macdizzy.com

**52.** 🖩 If a carburetor's opening is 81 mm, for what number of rpm's will the engine produce peak power?

**53.** 🖩 If a carburetor's opening is 84 mm, for what number of rpm's will the engine produce peak power?

**54.** *Length of a Side of a Square.* The diagonal of a square has length $9\sqrt{2}$ cm. Find the length of a side of the square. [6.7a]

**55.** *Bookcase Width.* A bookcase is 5 ft tall and has a 7-ft diagonal brace, as shown. How wide is the bookcase? [6.7a]

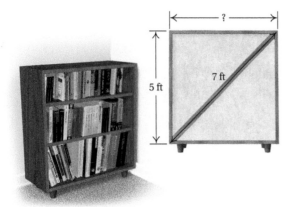

5 ft
7 ft
?

In a right triangle, find the length of the side not given. Give an exact answer and an answer to three decimal places. [6.7a]

**56.** $a = 7$, $b = 24$      **57.** $a = 2$, $c = 5\sqrt{2}$

**58.** Express in terms of $i$: $\sqrt{-25} + \sqrt{-8}$. [6.8a]

Add or subtract. [6.8b]

**59.** $(-4 + 3i) + (2 - 12i)$      **60.** $(4 - 7i) - (3 - 8i)$

Multiply. [6.8c, d]

**61.** $(2 + 5i)(2 - 5i)$      **62.** $i^{13}$

**63.** $(6 - 3i)(2 - i)$

Divide. [6.8e]

**64.** $\dfrac{-3 + 2i}{5i}$      **65.** $\dfrac{1 - 2i}{3 + i}$

**66.** Graph: $f(x) = \sqrt{x}$. [6.1a]

**67.** Which of the following is a solution of $x^2 + 4x + 5 = 0$? [6.8f]

  **A.** $1 - i$      **B.** $1 + i$
  **C.** $2 + i$      **D.** $-2 + i$

## Synthesis

**68.** Simplify: $i \cdot i^2 \cdot i^3 \cdots i^{99} \cdot i^{100}$. [6.8c, d]

**69.** Solve: $\sqrt{11x + \sqrt{6 + x}} = 6$. [6.6a]

# Understanding Through Discussion and Writing

**1.** Find the domain of
$$f(x) = (x + 5)^{1/2}(x + 7)^{-1/2}$$
and explain how you found your answer. [6.1a], [6.2b]

**2.** 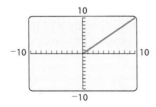 Ron is puzzled. When he uses a graphing calculator to graph $y = \sqrt{x} \cdot \sqrt{x}$, he gets the following screen. Explain why Ron did not get the complete line $y = x$. [6.1a], [6.3a]

10

-10        10

-10

**3.** In what way(s) is collecting like radical terms the same as collecting like monomial terms? [6.4a]

**4.** Is checking solutions of equations necessary when the principle of powers is used with an odd power $n$? Why or why not? [6.1d], [6.6a, b]

**5.** A student *incorrectly* claims that
$$\frac{5 + \sqrt{2}}{\sqrt{18}} = \frac{5 + \sqrt{1}}{\sqrt{9}} = \frac{5 + 1}{3} = 2.$$
How could you convince the student that a mistake has been made? How would you explain the correct way of rationalizing the denominator? [6.5a]

**6.** How are conjugates of complex numbers similar to the conjugates used in Section 6.5? [6.8e]

CHAPTER
6

Test

For Extra Help

Step-by-step test solutions are found on the Chapter Test Prep Videos available via the Video Resources on DVD, in *MyMathLab*, and on You Tube (search "BittingerInterAlgPB" and click on "Channels").

1. Use a calculator to approximate $\sqrt{148}$ to three decimal places.

2. For the given function, find the indicated function values.

   $$f(x) = \sqrt{8 - 4x}; \quad f(1) \text{ and } f(3)$$

3. Find the domain of the function $f$ in Exercise 2.

Simplify. Assume that letters represent *any* real number.

4. $\sqrt{(-3q)^2}$

5. $\sqrt{x^2 + 10x + 25}$

6. $\sqrt[3]{-\dfrac{1}{1000}}$

7. $\sqrt[5]{x^5}$

8. $\sqrt[10]{(-4)^{10}}$

Rewrite without rational exponents, and simplify, if possible.

9. $a^{2/3}$

10. $32^{3/5}$

Rewrite with rational exponents.

11. $\sqrt{37}$

12. $\left(\sqrt{5xy^2}\right)^5$

Rewrite with positive exponents, and simplify, if possible.

13. $1000^{-1/3}$

14. $8a^{3/4}b^{-3/2}c^{-2/5}$

Use the laws of exponents to simplify. Write answers with positive exponents.

15. $(x^{2/3}y^{-3/4})^{12/5}$

16. $\dfrac{2.9^{-5/8}}{2.9^{2/3}}$

Use rational exponents to simplify. Write the answer in radical notation if appropriate. Assume that no radicands were formed by raising negative numbers to even powers.

17. $\sqrt[8]{x^2}$

18. $\sqrt[4]{16x^6}$

Use rational exponents to write a single radical expression.

19. $a^{2/5}b^{1/3}$

20. $\sqrt[4]{2y}\sqrt[3]{y}$

Simplify by factoring. Assume that no radicands were formed by raising negative numbers to even powers.

21. $\sqrt{148}$

22. $\sqrt[4]{80}$

23. $\sqrt[3]{24a^{11}b^{13}}$

Simplify. Assume that no radicands were formed by raising negative numbers to even powers.

24. $\sqrt[3]{\dfrac{16x^5}{y^6}}$

25. $\sqrt{\dfrac{25x^2}{36y^4}}$

Perform the indicated operations and simplify. Assume that no radicands were formed by raising negative numbers to even powers.

**26.** $\sqrt[3]{2x}\sqrt[3]{5y^2}$

**27.** $\sqrt[4]{x^3y^2}\sqrt[4]{xy}$

**28.** $\dfrac{\sqrt[5]{x^3y^4}}{\sqrt[5]{xy^2}}$

**29.** $\dfrac{\sqrt{300a}}{5\sqrt{3}}$

**30.** Add: $3\sqrt{128} + 2\sqrt{18} + 2\sqrt{32}$.

Multiply.

**31.** $\left(\sqrt{20} + 2\sqrt{5}\right)\left(\sqrt{20} - 3\sqrt{5}\right)$

**32.** $\left(3 + \sqrt{x}\right)^2$

**33.** Rationalize the denominator: $\dfrac{1 + \sqrt{2}}{3 - 5\sqrt{2}}$.

Solve.

**34.** $\sqrt[5]{x - 3} = 2$

**35.** $\sqrt{x - 6} = \sqrt{x + 9} - 3$

**36.** $\sqrt{x - 1} + 3 = x$

**37.** *Length of a Side of a Square.* The diagonal of a square has length $7\sqrt{2}$ ft. Find the length of a side of the square.

**38.** *Sighting to the Horizon.* A person can see 72 mi to the horizon from an airplane window. How high is the airplane? Use the formula $D = 1.2\sqrt{h}$, where $D$ is in miles and $h$ is in feet.

In a right triangle, find the length of the side not given. Give an exact answer and an answer to three decimal places.

**39.** $a = 7, \ b = 7$

**40.** $a = 1, \ c = \sqrt{5}$

**41.** Express in terms of $i$: $\sqrt{-9} + \sqrt{-64}$.

**42.** Subtract: $(5 + 8i) - (-2 + 3i)$.

Multiply.

**43.** $(3 - 4i)(3 + 7i)$

**44.** $i^{95}$

**45.** Divide: $\dfrac{-7 + 14i}{6 - 8i}$.

**46.** Determine whether $1 + 2i$ is a solution of
$$x^2 + 2x + 5 = 0.$$

**47.** Which of the following describes the solution(s) of the equation $x - 4 = \sqrt{x - 2}$?

    **A.** There is exactly one solution, and it is positive.

    **B.** There are one positive solution and one negative solution.

    **C.** There are two positive solutions.

    **D.** There is no solution.

## Synthesis

**48.** Simplify: $\dfrac{1 - 4i}{4i(1 + 4i)^{-1}}$.

**49.** Solve: $\sqrt{2x - 2} + \sqrt{7x + 4} = \sqrt{13x + 10}$.

# Cumulative Review

Simplify. Assume that no radicands were formed by raising negative numbers to even powers.

**1.** $(2x^2 - 3x + 1) + (6x - 3x^3 + 7x^2 - 4)$

**2.** $(2x^2 - y)^2$

**3.** $(5x^2 - 2x + 1)(3x^2 + x - 2)$

**4.** $\dfrac{x^3 + 64}{x^2 - 49} \cdot \dfrac{x^2 - 14x + 49}{x^2 - 4x + 16}$

**5.** $\dfrac{\dfrac{y^2 - 5y - 6}{y^2 - 7y - 18}}{\dfrac{y^2 + 3y + 2}{y^2 + 4y + 4}}$

**6.** $\dfrac{x}{x + 2} + \dfrac{1}{x - 3} - \dfrac{x^2 - 2}{x^2 - x - 6}$

**7.** $(y^3 + 3y^2 - 5) \div (y + 2)$

**8.** $\sqrt[3]{-8x^3}$

**9.** $\sqrt{16x^2 - 32x + 16}$

**10.** $9\sqrt{75} + 6\sqrt{12}$

**11.** $\sqrt{2xy^2} \cdot \sqrt{8xy^3}$

**12.** $\dfrac{3\sqrt{5}}{\sqrt{6} - \sqrt{3}}$

**13.** $\sqrt[6]{\dfrac{m^{12}n^{24}}{64}}$

**14.** $6^{2/9} \cdot 6^{2/3}$

**15.** $(6 + i) - (3 - 4i)$

**16.** $\dfrac{2 - i}{6 + 5i}$

Solve.

**17.** $\dfrac{1}{5} + \dfrac{3}{10}x = \dfrac{4}{5}$

**18.** $M = \dfrac{1}{8}(c - 3)$, for $c$

**19.** $3a - 4 < 10 + 5a$

**20.** $-8 < x + 2 < 15$

**21.** $|3x - 6| = 2$

**22.** $625 = 49y^2$

**23.** $3x + 5y = 30,$
$5x + 3y = 34$

**24.** $3x + 2y - z = -7,$
$-x + y + 2z = 9,$
$5x + 5y + z = -1$

**25.** $\dfrac{6x}{x - 5} - \dfrac{300}{x^2 + 5x + 25} = \dfrac{2250}{x^3 - 125}$

**26.** $\dfrac{3x^2}{x + 2} + \dfrac{5x - 22}{x - 2} = \dfrac{-48}{x^2 - 4}$

**27.** $I = \dfrac{nE}{R + nr}$, for $R$

**28.** $\sqrt{4x + 1} - 2 = 3$

**29.** $2\sqrt{1 - x} = \sqrt{5}$

**30.** $13 - x = 5 + \sqrt{x + 4}$

Graph.

**31.** $f(x) = -\dfrac{2}{3}x + 2$

**32.** $4x - 2y = 8$

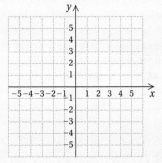
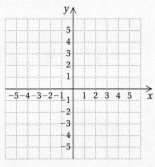

**33.** $4x \geq 5y + 20$

**34.** $y \geq -3,$
$y \leq 2x + 3$

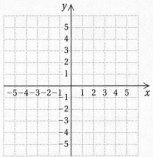
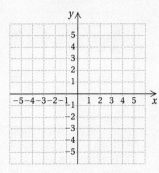

**35.** $g(x) = x^2 - x - 2$

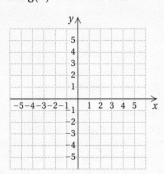

**36.** $f(x) = |x + 4|$

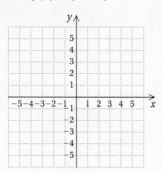

**37.** $g(x) = \dfrac{4}{x - 3}$

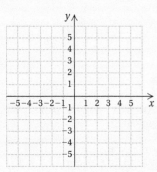

**38.** $f(x) = 2 - \sqrt{x}$

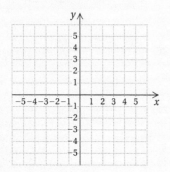

Factor.

**39.** $12x^2y^2 - 30xy^3$

**40.** $3x^2 - 17x - 28$

**41.** $y^2 - y - 132$

**42.** $27y^3 + 8$

**43.** $4x^2 - 625$

Find the domain and the range of each function.

**44.**

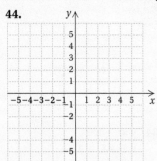

**45.**

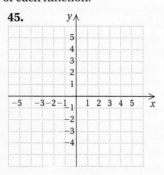

**46.** Find the slope and the $y$-intercept of the line $3x - 2y = 8$.

**47.** Find an equation for the line perpendicular to the line $3x - y = 5$ and passing through $(1, 4)$.

**48.** *Triangle Area.* The height $h$ of triangles of fixed area varies inversely as the base $b$. Suppose the height is 100 ft when the base is 20 ft. Find the height when the base is 16 ft. What is the fixed area?

Solve.

**49.** *Harvesting Time.* One combine can harvest a field in 3 hr. Another combine can harvest the same field in 1.5 hr. How long should it take them to harvest the field together?

**50.** *Warning Dye.* A warning dye is used by people in lifeboats to aid search planes. The volume $V$ of the dye used varies directly as the square of the diameter $d$ of the circular area formed by the dye in the water. If 4 L of dye is required for a 10-m wide circle, how much dye is needed for a 40-m wide circle?

**51.** Rewrite with rational exponents: $\sqrt[5]{xy^4}$.

   **A.** $\dfrac{1}{(xy^4)^5}$        **B.** $(xy^4)^5$

   **C.** $(xy)^{4/5}$         **D.** $(xy^4)^{1/5}$

**52.** A grain bin can be filled in 3 hr if the grain enters through spout A alone or in 15 hr if the grain enters through spout B alone. If grain is entering through both spouts at the same time, how many hours will it take to fill the bin?

   **A.** $\frac{5}{2}$ hr        **B.** 9 hr

   **C.** $22\frac{1}{2}$ hr      **D.** $10\frac{1}{2}$ hr

**53.** Divide: $(x^3 - x^2 + 2x + 4) \div (x - 3)$.

   **A.** $x^2 + 2x + 8,\ \text{R} -28$    **B.** $x^2 + 2x - 4,\ \text{R} -8$

   **C.** $x^2 - 4x - 10,\ \text{R} -26$   **D.** $x^2 - 4x + 14,\ \text{R}\ 46$

**54.** Solve: $2x + 6 = 8 + \sqrt{5x + 1}$.

   **A.** $\frac{1}{4}$         **B.** 3

   **C.** $3, \frac{1}{4}$       **D.** $4, 3$

## Synthesis

**55.** Solve: $\dfrac{x + \sqrt{x + 1}}{x - \sqrt{x + 1}} = \dfrac{5}{11}$.

# Quadratic Equations and Functions

## Real-World Application

Canoes are deepest at the middle of the center line, with the depth decreasing to zero at the edges. Lou and Jen own a company that specializes in producing custom canoes. A customer provided suggested guidelines for measures of the depths $D$, in inches, along the center line of the canoe at distances $x$, in inches, from the edge. The measures are listed in a table on p. 647. Make a scatterplot of the data and decide whether the data seem to fit a quadratic function. Use data points to find a quadratic function that fits the data and use the function to estimate the depth of the canoe 10 in. from the edge along the center line.

*This problem appears as Example 7 in Section 7.7.*

# The Basics of Solving Quadratic Equations

## OBJECTIVES

**a** Solve quadratic equations using the principle of square roots and find the $x$-intercepts of the graph of a related function.

**b** Solve quadratic equations by completing the square.

**c** Solve applied problems using quadratic equations.

**SKILL TO REVIEW**

Objective 4.8a: Solve quadratic and other polynomial equations by first factoring and then using the principle of zero products.

Solve.

**1.** $x^2 + 6x - 16 = 0$

**2.** $6x^2 - 13x - 5 = 0$

**1.** Consider solving the equation
$x^2 - 6x + 8 = 0.$

Below is the graph of
$f(x) = x^2 - 6x + 8.$

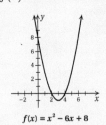

$f(x) = x^2 - 6x + 8$

a) What are the $x$-intercepts of the graph?

b) What are the solutions of $x^2 - 6x + 8 = 0$?

c) What relationship exists between the answers to parts (a) and (b)?

## ※ Algebraic-Graphical Connection

Let's reexamine the graphical connections to the algebraic equation-solving concepts we have studied before.

In Chapter 2, we introduced the graph of a quadratic function:

$$f(x) = ax^2 + bx + c, \quad a \neq 0.$$

For example, the graph of the function $f(x) = x^2 + 6x + 8$ and its $x$-intercepts are shown below.

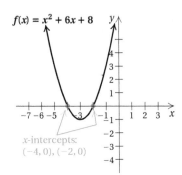

$f(x) = x^2 + 6x + 8$

$x$-intercepts:
$(-4, 0), (-2, 0)$

The $x$-intercepts are $(-4, 0)$ and $(-2, 0)$. These pairs are also the points of intersection of the graphs of $f(x) = x^2 + 6x + 8$ and $g(x) = 0$ (the $x$-axis). We will analyze the graphs of quadratic functions in greater detail in Sections 7.5–7.7.

In Chapter 4, we solved quadratic equations like $x^2 + 6x + 8 = 0$ using factoring, as here:

$$x^2 + 6x + 8 = 0$$
$$(x + 4)(x + 2) = 0 \qquad \text{Factoring}$$
$$x + 4 = 0 \quad or \quad x + 2 = 0 \qquad \text{Using the principle of zero products}$$
$$x = -4 \quad or \qquad x = -2.$$

We see that the solutions of $x^2 + 6x + 8 = 0$, $-4$ and $-2$, are the first coordinates of the $x$-intercepts, $(-4, 0)$ and $(-2, 0)$, of the graph of $f(x) = x^2 + 6x + 8$.

Do Margin Exercise 1.

We now extend our ability to solve quadratic equations.

## a The Principle of Square Roots

The quadratic equation

$$5x^2 + 8x - 2 = 0$$

is said to be in **standard form**. The quadratic equation

$$5x^2 = 2 - 8x$$

is equivalent to the preceding equation, but it is *not* in standard form.

*Answers*

Answers to Skill to Review Exercises 1 and 2 and Margin Exercise 1 are on p. 581.

> ### QUADRATIC EQUATION
>
> An equation of the type $ax^2 + bx + c = 0$, where $a$, $b$, and $c$ are real-number constants and $a > 0$, is called the **standard form of a quadratic equation**.

To find the standard form of the quadratic equation $-5x^2 + 4x - 7 = 0$, we find an equivalent equation by multiplying by $-1$ on both sides:

$$-1(-5x^2 + 4x - 7) = -1(0)$$
$$5x^2 - 4x + 7 = 0. \quad \text{Writing in standard form}$$

In Section 4.8, we studied the use of factoring and the principle of zero products to solve certain quadratic equations. Let's review that procedure and introduce a new one.

### EXAMPLE 1

a)  Solve: $x^2 = 25$.

b)  Find the $x$-intercepts of $f(x) = x^2 - 25$.

a)  We first find standard form and then factor:

$$x^2 - 25 = 0 \qquad \text{Subtracting 25}$$
$$(x - 5)(x + 5) = 0 \qquad \text{Factoring}$$
$$x - 5 = 0 \quad or \quad x + 5 = 0 \qquad \text{Using the principle of zero products}$$
$$x = 5 \quad or \qquad x = -5.$$

The solutions are $5$ and $-5$.

b)  The $x$-intercepts of $f(x) = x^2 - 25$ are $(-5, 0)$ and $(5, 0)$. The solutions of the equation $x^2 = 25$ are the first coordinates of the $x$-intercepts of the graph of $f(x) = x^2 - 25$.

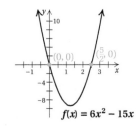

### EXAMPLE 2   Solve: $6x^2 - 15x = 0$.

We factor and use the principle of zero products:

$$6x^2 - 15x = 0$$
$$3x(2x - 5) = 0$$
$$3x = 0 \quad or \quad 2x - 5 = 0$$
$$x = 0 \quad or \qquad 2x = 5$$
$$x = 0 \quad or \qquad x = \tfrac{5}{2}.$$

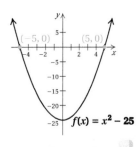

The solutions are $0$ and $\frac{5}{2}$. The check is left to the student.

Do Exercises 2 and 3.

**2. a)** Solve: $x^2 = 16$.

**b)** Find the $x$-intercepts of $f(x) = x^2 - 16$.

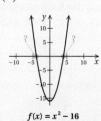

$f(x) = x^2 - 16$

**3. a)** Solve: $4x^2 + 14x = 0$.

**b)** Find the $x$-intercepts of $f(x) = 4x^2 + 14x$.

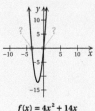

$f(x) = 4x^2 + 14x$

*Answers*

*Skill to Review:*

**1.** $-8, 2$ **2.** $-\dfrac{1}{3}, \dfrac{5}{2}$

*Margin Exercises:*
**1. (a)** $(2, 0)$, $(4, 0)$; **(b)** 2, 4; **(c)** The solutions of $x^2 - 6x + 8 = 0$, 2 and 4, are the first coordinates of the $x$-intercepts, $(2, 0)$ and $(4, 0)$, of the graph of $f(x) = x^2 - 6x + 8$.
**2. (a)** 4 and $-4$; **(b)** $(-4, 0)$, $(4, 0)$
**3. (a)** $0, -\frac{7}{2}$; **(b)** $\left(-\frac{7}{2}, 0\right)$, $(0, 0)$

## EXAMPLE 3

**a)** Solve: $3x^2 = 2 - x$.

**b)** Find the $x$-intercepts of $f(x) = 3x^2 + x - 2$.

**a)** We first find standard form. Then we factor and use the principle of zero products.

$$3x^2 = 2 - x$$

$$3x^2 + x - 2 = 0 \qquad \text{Adding } x \text{ and subtracting 2 to get the standard form}$$

$$(x + 1)(3x - 2) = 0 \qquad \text{Factoring}$$

$$x + 1 = 0 \quad or \quad 3x - 2 = 0 \qquad \text{Using the principle of zero products}$$

$$x = -1 \quad or \qquad 3x = 2$$

$$x = -1 \quad or \qquad x = \tfrac{2}{3}$$

Check:     For $-1$:

$$\begin{array}{c|c}
3x^2 = 2 - x \\
\hline
3(-1)^2 \ ?\ 2 - (-1) \\
3 \cdot 1 \ \big|\ 2 + 1 \\
3 \ \big|\ 3 \qquad \text{TRUE}
\end{array}$$

For $\tfrac{2}{3}$:

$$\begin{array}{c|c}
3x^2 = 2 - x \\
\hline
3\left(\tfrac{2}{3}\right)^2 \ ?\ 2 - \left(\tfrac{2}{3}\right) \\
3 \cdot \tfrac{4}{9} \ \big|\ \tfrac{6}{3} - \tfrac{2}{3} \\
\tfrac{4}{3} \ \big|\ \tfrac{4}{3} \qquad \text{TRUE}
\end{array}$$

The solutions are $-1$ and $\tfrac{2}{3}$.

**b)** The $x$-intercepts of $f(x) = 3x^2 + x - 2$ are $(-1, 0)$ and $\left(\tfrac{2}{3}, 0\right)$. The solutions of the equation $3x^2 = 2 - x$ are the first coordinates of the $x$-intercepts of the graph of $f(x) = 3x^2 + x - 2$.

$f(x) = 3x^2 + x - 2$

**4. a)** Solve: $5x^2 = 8x - 3$.

**b)** Find the $x$-intercepts of $f(x) = 5x^2 - 8x + 3$.

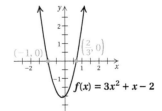

$f(x) = 5x^2 - 8x + 3$

Do Exercise 4.

### Solving Equations of the Type $x^2 = d$

Consider the equation $x^2 = 25$ again. We know from Chapter 6 that the number 25 has two real-number square roots, namely, 5 and $-5$. Note that these are the solutions of the equation in Example 1. This exemplifies the principle of square roots, which provides a quick method for solving equations of the type $x^2 = d$.

---

**THE PRINCIPLE OF SQUARE ROOTS**

The solutions of the equation $x^2 = d$ are $\sqrt{d}$ and $-\sqrt{d}$.

When $d > 0$, the solutions are two real numbers.

When $d = 0$, the only solution is 0.

When $d < 0$, the solutions are two imaginary numbers.

---

*Answer*

**4. (a)** $\tfrac{3}{5}$, 1; **(b)** $\left(\tfrac{3}{5}, 0\right)$, $(1, 0)$

**EXAMPLE 4** Solve: $3x^2 = 6$. Give the exact solutions and approximate the solutions to three decimal places.

We have

$$3x^2 = 6$$
$$x^2 = 2$$
$$x = \sqrt{2} \quad or \quad x = -\sqrt{2}.$$

We often use the symbol $\pm\sqrt{2}$ to represent both of the solutions.

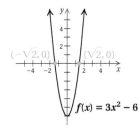

Check: For $\sqrt{2}$: For $-\sqrt{2}$:

$$\frac{3x^2 = 6}{3(\sqrt{2})^2 \; ? \; 6}$$
$$3 \cdot 2 \Big|$$
$$6 \Big| \quad \text{TRUE}$$

$$\frac{3x^2 = 6}{3(-\sqrt{2})^2 \; ? \; 6}$$
$$3 \cdot 2 \Big|$$
$$6 \Big| \quad \text{TRUE}$$

The solutions are $\sqrt{2}$ and $-\sqrt{2}$, or $\pm\sqrt{2}$, which are about $1.414$ and $-1.414$, or $\pm 1.414$, when rounded to three decimal places.

Do Exercise 5.

**5.** Solve: $5x^2 = 15$. Give the exact solution and approximate the solutions to three decimal places.

Sometimes we rationalize denominators to simplify answers.

**EXAMPLE 5** Solve: $-5x^2 + 2 = 0$. Give the exact solutions and approximate the solutions to three decimal places.

$$-5x^2 + 2 = 0$$

$$x^2 = \frac{2}{5} \qquad \text{Subtracting 2 and dividing by } -5$$

$$x = \sqrt{\frac{2}{5}} \quad or \quad x = -\sqrt{\frac{2}{5}} \qquad \text{Using the principle of square roots}$$

$$x = \sqrt{\frac{2}{5} \cdot \frac{5}{5}} \quad or \quad x = -\sqrt{\frac{2}{5} \cdot \frac{5}{5}} \qquad \text{Rationalizing the denominators}$$

$$x = \frac{\sqrt{10}}{5} \quad or \quad x = -\frac{\sqrt{10}}{5}$$

Check: We check both numbers at once, since there is no $x$-term in the equation. We could have checked both numbers at once in Example 4 as well.

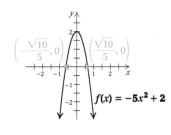

$$\frac{-5x^2 + 2 = 0}{-5\left(\pm\frac{\sqrt{10}}{5}\right)^2 + 2 \; ? \; 0}$$
$$-5\left(\frac{10}{25}\right) + 2 \Big|$$
$$-2 + 2 \Big|$$
$$0 \Big| \quad \text{TRUE}$$

The solutions are $\dfrac{\sqrt{10}}{5}$ and $-\dfrac{\sqrt{10}}{5}$, or $\pm\dfrac{\sqrt{10}}{5}$. We can use a calculator for approximations:

$$\pm\frac{\sqrt{10}}{5} \approx \pm 0.632.$$

*Answer*

**5.** $\sqrt{3}$ and $-\sqrt{3}$, or $\pm\sqrt{3}$; 1.732 and $-1.732$, or $\pm 1.732$

**6.** Solve: $-3x^2 + 8 = 0$. Give the exact solution and approximate the solutions to three decimal places.

Do Exercise 6.

Sometimes we get solutions that are imaginary numbers.

**EXAMPLE 6**   Solve: $4x^2 + 9 = 0$.

$$4x^2 + 9 = 0$$

$$x^2 = -\frac{9}{4} \qquad \text{Subtracting 9 and dividing by 4}$$

$$x = \sqrt{-\frac{9}{4}} \quad \text{or} \quad x = -\sqrt{-\frac{9}{4}} \qquad \text{Using the principle of square roots}$$

$$x = \frac{3}{2}i \quad \text{or} \quad x = -\frac{3}{2}i \qquad \text{Simplifying}$$

Check:
$$\begin{array}{c} 4x^2 + 9 = 0 \\ \hline 4\left(\pm\frac{3}{2}i\right)^2 + 9 \; ? \; 0 \\ 4\left(-\frac{9}{4}\right) + 9 \\ -9 + 9 \\ 0 \quad | \quad \text{TRUE} \end{array}$$

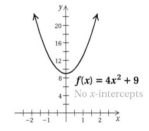

$f(x) = 4x^2 + 9$
No $x$-intercepts

The solutions are $\frac{3}{2}i$ and $-\frac{3}{2}i$, or $\pm\frac{3}{2}i$.

We see that the graph of $f(x) = 4x^2 + 9$ does not cross the $x$-axis. This is true because the equation $4x^2 + 9 = 0$ has *imaginary* complex-number solutions. Only real-number solutions correspond to $x$-intercepts.

**7.** Solve: $2x^2 + 1 = 0$.

Do Exercise 7.

## Solving Equations of the Type $(x + c)^2 = d$

The equation $(x - 2)^2 = 7$ can also be solved using the principle of square roots.

**EXAMPLE 7**

a) Solve: $(x - 2)^2 = 7$.

b) Find the $x$-intercepts of $f(x) = (x - 2)^2 - 7$.

**8. a)** Solve: $(x - 1)^2 = 5$.

**b)** Find the $x$-intercepts of $f(x) = (x - 1)^2 - 5$.

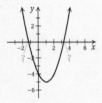

$f(x) = (x-1)^2 - 5$

a) We have

$$(x - 2)^2 = 7$$

$$x - 2 = \sqrt{7} \qquad \text{or} \quad x - 2 = -\sqrt{7} \qquad \text{Using the principle of square roots}$$

$$x = 2 + \sqrt{7} \quad \text{or} \qquad x = 2 - \sqrt{7}.$$

The solutions are $2 + \sqrt{7}$ and $2 - \sqrt{7}$, or $2 \pm \sqrt{7}$.

b) The $x$-intercepts of $f(x) = (x - 2)^2 - 7$ are $\left(2 - \sqrt{7}, 0\right)$ and $\left(2 + \sqrt{7}, 0\right)$.

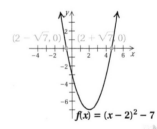

$(2 - \sqrt{7}, 0)$   $(2 + \sqrt{7}, 0)$

$f(x) = (x - 2)^2 - 7$

*Answers*

**6.** $\dfrac{2\sqrt{6}}{3}$ and $-\dfrac{2\sqrt{6}}{3}$, or $\pm\dfrac{2\sqrt{6}}{3}$; 1.633 and $-1.633$, or $\pm1.633$   **7.** $\dfrac{\sqrt{2}}{2}i$ and $-\dfrac{\sqrt{2}}{2}i$, or $\pm\dfrac{\sqrt{2}}{2}i$   **8. (a)** $1 \pm \sqrt{5}$; **(b)** $\left(1 - \sqrt{5}, 0\right)$, $\left(1 + \sqrt{5}, 0\right)$

Do Exercise 8.

If we can express the left side of an equation as the square of a binomial, we can proceed as we did in Example 7.

**EXAMPLE 8** Solve: $x^2 + 6x + 9 = 2$.

We have

$x^2 + 6x + 9 = 2$     The left side is the square of a binomial.

$(x + 3)^2 = 2$

$x + 3 = \sqrt{2}$     or    $x + 3 = -\sqrt{2}$     Using the principle of square roots

$x = -3 + \sqrt{2}$   or      $x = -3 - \sqrt{2}$.

The solutions are $-3 + \sqrt{2}$ and $-3 - \sqrt{2}$, or $-3 \pm \sqrt{2}$.

Do Exercise 9.

**9.** Solve: $x^2 + 16x + 64 = 11$.

## b  Completing the Square

We can solve quadratic equations like $3x^2 = 6$ and $(x - 2)^2 = 7$ by using the principle of square roots. We can also solve an equation such as $x^2 + 6x + 9 = 2$ in like manner because the expression on the left side is the square of a binomial, $(x + 3)^2$. This second procedure is the basis for a method called **completing the square**. *It can be used to solve any quadratic equation.*

Suppose we have the following quadratic equation:

$x^2 + 14x = 4$.

If we could add on both sides of the equation a constant that would make the expression on the left the square of a binomial, we could then solve the equation using the principle of square roots.

How can we determine what to add to $x^2 + 14x$ to construct the square of a binomial? We want to find a number $a$ such that the following equation is satisfied:

$x^2 + 14x + a^2 = (x + a)(x + a) = x^2 + 2ax + a^2$.

Thus, $a$ is such that $2a = 14$. Solving, we get $a = 7$. That is, $a$ is half of the coefficient of $x$ in $x^2 + 14x$. Since $a^2 = \left(\frac{14}{2}\right)^2 = 7^2 = 49$, we add 49 to our original expression:

$x^2 + 14x + 49$ is the square of $x + 7$;

that is,

$x^2 + 14x + 49 = (x + 7)^2$.

> **COMPLETING THE SQUARE**
>
> When solving an equation, to **complete the square** of an expression like $x^2 + bx$, we take half the $x$-coefficient, which is $b/2$, and square it. Then we add that number, $(b/2)^2$, on both sides of the equation.

Returning to solving our original equation, we first add 49 on *both* sides to *complete the square* on the left. Then we solve:

$$x^2 + 14x \qquad = 4 \qquad\qquad \text{Original equation}$$
$$x^2 + 14x + 49 = 4 + 49 \qquad \text{Adding 49: } \left(\tfrac{14}{2}\right)^2 = 7^2 = 49$$
$$(x + 7)^2 = 53$$
$$x + 7 = \sqrt{53} \qquad or \quad x + 7 = -\sqrt{53} \qquad \text{Using the principle}$$
$$\qquad\qquad\qquad\qquad\qquad\qquad\qquad\qquad\qquad \text{of square roots}$$
$$x = -7 + \sqrt{53} \quad or \qquad x = -7 - \sqrt{53}.$$

The solutions are $-7 \pm \sqrt{53}$.

We have seen that a quadratic equation $(x + c)^2 = d$ can be solved using the principle of square roots. Any equation, such as $x^2 - 6x + 8 = 0$, can be put in this form by completing the square. Then we can solve as before.

**EXAMPLE 9**   Solve: $x^2 - 6x + 8 = 0$.

We have

$$x^2 - 6x + 8 = 0$$
$$x^2 - 6x \qquad = -8. \qquad \text{Subtracting 8}$$

We take half of $-6$ and square it, to get 9. Then we add 9 on *both* sides of the equation. This makes the left side the square of a binomial, $x - 3$. We have now *completed the square*.

$$x^2 - 6x + 9 = -8 + 9 \qquad\qquad \text{Adding 9: } \left(\tfrac{-6}{2}\right)^2 = (-3)^2 = 9$$
$$(x - 3)^2 = 1$$
$$x - 3 = 1 \quad or \quad x - 3 = -1 \qquad \text{Using the principle of square roots}$$
$$x = 4 \quad or \qquad x = 2$$

The solutions are 2 and 4.

Do Exercises 10 and 11.

**Solve.**

**10.** $x^2 + 6x + 8 = 0$

**11.** $x^2 - 8x - 20 = 0$

**EXAMPLE 10**   Solve $x^2 + 4x - 7 = 0$ by completing the square.

We have

$$x^2 + 4x - 7 = 0$$
$$x^2 + 4x \qquad = 7 \qquad\qquad \text{Adding 7}$$
$$x^2 + 4x + 4 = 7 + 4 \qquad \text{Adding 4: } \left(\tfrac{4}{2}\right)^2 = (2)^2 = 4$$
$$(x + 2)^2 = 11$$
$$x + 2 = \sqrt{11} \qquad or \quad x + 2 = -\sqrt{11} \qquad \text{Using the principle of}$$
$$\qquad\qquad\qquad\qquad\qquad\qquad\qquad\qquad\qquad \text{square roots}$$
$$x = -2 + \sqrt{11} \quad or \qquad x = -2 - \sqrt{11}.$$

The solutions are $-2 \pm \sqrt{11}$.

Do Exercise 12.

**12.** Solve by completing the square:
$$x^2 + 6x - 1 = 0.$$

When the coefficient of $x^2$ is not 1, we can make it 1, as shown in the following example.

**EXAMPLE 11** Solve $3x^2 + 7x = 2$ by completing the square.

We have

$$3x^2 + 7x = 2$$

$$\frac{1}{3}(3x^2 + 7x) = \frac{1}{3} \cdot 2 \qquad \text{Multiplying by } \tfrac{1}{3} \text{ to make the } x^2\text{-coefficient 1}$$

$$x^2 + \frac{7}{3}x = \frac{2}{3} \qquad \text{Multiplying and simplifying}$$

$$x^2 + \frac{7}{3}x + \frac{49}{36} = \frac{2}{3} + \frac{49}{36} \qquad \text{Adding } \frac{49}{36}\colon \left[\frac{1}{2} \cdot \frac{7}{3}\right]^2 = \frac{49}{36}$$

$$\left(x + \frac{7}{6}\right)^2 = \frac{24}{36} + \frac{49}{36} \qquad \text{Finding a common denominator}$$

$$\left(x + \frac{7}{6}\right)^2 = \frac{73}{36}$$

$$x + \frac{7}{6} = \sqrt{\frac{73}{36}} \qquad or \quad x + \frac{7}{6} = -\sqrt{\frac{73}{36}} \qquad \text{Using the principle of square roots}$$

$$x + \frac{7}{6} = \frac{\sqrt{73}}{6} \qquad or \quad x + \frac{7}{6} = -\frac{\sqrt{73}}{6}$$

$$x = -\frac{7}{6} + \frac{\sqrt{73}}{6} \qquad or \qquad x = -\frac{7}{6} - \frac{\sqrt{73}}{6}.$$

The solutions are $-\dfrac{7}{6} \pm \dfrac{\sqrt{73}}{6}$.

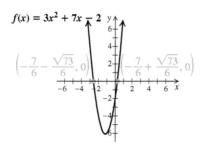

$$f(x) = 3x^2 + 7x - 2$$

Do Exercises 13 and 14.

Solve by completing the square.

**13.** $2x^2 + 6x = 5$

**14.** $3x^2 - 2x = 7$

**EXAMPLE 12** Solve $2x^2 = 3x - 7$ by completing the square.

$$2x^2 = 3x - 7$$

$$2x^2 - 3x = -7 \qquad \text{Subtracting } 3x$$

$$\frac{1}{2}(2x^2 - 3x) = \frac{1}{2} \cdot (-7) \qquad \begin{array}{l}\text{Multiplying by } \frac{1}{2} \text{ to make the}\\ x^2\text{-coefficient 1}\end{array}$$

$$x^2 - \frac{3}{2}x = -\frac{7}{2} \qquad \text{Multiplying and simplifying}$$

$$x^2 - \frac{3}{2}x + \frac{9}{16} = -\frac{7}{2} + \frac{9}{16} \qquad \text{Adding } \frac{9}{16}: \left[\frac{1}{2}\left(-\frac{3}{2}\right)\right]^2 = \left[-\frac{3}{4}\right]^2 = \frac{9}{16}$$

$$\left(x - \frac{3}{4}\right)^2 = -\frac{56}{16} + \frac{9}{16} \qquad \text{Finding a common denominator}$$

$$\left(x - \frac{3}{4}\right)^2 = -\frac{47}{16}$$

$$x - \frac{3}{4} = \sqrt{-\frac{47}{16}} \quad or \quad x - \frac{3}{4} = -\sqrt{-\frac{47}{16}} \qquad \begin{array}{l}\text{Using the principle}\\ \text{of square roots}\end{array}$$

$$x - \frac{3}{4} = \frac{\sqrt{47}}{4}i \quad or \quad x - \frac{3}{4} = -\frac{\sqrt{47}}{4}i \qquad \sqrt{-1} = i$$

$$x = \frac{3}{4} + \frac{\sqrt{47}}{4}i \quad or \quad x = \frac{3}{4} - \frac{\sqrt{47}}{4}i$$

The solutions are $\dfrac{3}{4} \pm \dfrac{\sqrt{47}}{4}i$.

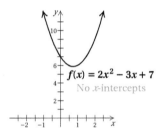

$f(x) = 2x^2 - 3x + 7$

No $x$-intercepts

We see that the graph of $f(x) = 2x^2 - 3x + 7$ does not cross the $x$-axis. This is true because the equation $2x^2 = 3x - 7$ has nonreal complex-number solutions.

Do Exercise 15.

**15.** Solve by completing the square:
$$3x^2 = 2x - 1.$$

---

### SOLVING BY COMPLETING THE SQUARE

To solve an equation $ax^2 + bx + c = 0$ by completing the square:

1. If $a \neq 1$, multiply by $1/a$ so that the $x^2$-coefficient is 1.
2. If the $x^2$-coefficient is 1, add or subtract so that the equation is in the form

$$x^2 + bx = -c, \quad \text{or} \quad x^2 + \frac{b}{a}x = -\frac{c}{a} \text{ if step (1) has been applied.}$$

3. Take half of the $x$-coefficient and square it. Add the result on both sides of the equation.
4. Express the side with the variables as the square of a binomial.
5. Use the principle of square roots and complete the solution.

---

*Answer*

**15.** $\dfrac{1}{3} \pm \dfrac{\sqrt{2}}{3}i$

Completing the square provides a base for proving the quadratic formula in Section 7.2 and for our work with conic sections in Chapter 9.

## c Applications and Problem Solving

**EXAMPLE 13** *Hang Time.* One of the most exciting plays in basketball is the dunk shot. The amount of time $T$ that passes from the moment a player leaves the ground, goes up, makes the shot, and arrives back on the ground is called *hang time*. A function relating an athlete's vertical leap $V$, in inches, to hang time $T$, in seconds, is given by

$$V(T) = 48T^2.$$

a) Hall-of-Famer Michael Jordan had a hang time of about 0.889 sec. What was his vertical leap?

b) Although his height is only 5 ft 7 in., Spud Webb, formerly of the Sacramento Kings, had a vertical leap of about 44 in. What was his hang time?

**Source:** www.vertcoach.com/highest-vertical-leap.html

a) To find Jordan's vertical leap, we substitute 0.889 for $T$ in the function and compute $V$:

$$V(0.889) = 48(0.889)^2 \approx 37.9 \text{ in.}$$

Jordan's vertical leap was about 37.9 in. Surprisingly, Jordan did not have the vertical leap most fans would expect.

b) To find Webb's hang time, we substitute 44 for $V$ and solve for $T$:

$$44 = 48T^2 \qquad \text{Substituting 44 for } V$$
$$\frac{44}{48} = T^2 \qquad \text{Solving for } T^2$$
$$0.91\overline{6} = T^2$$
$$\sqrt{0.91\overline{6}} = T \qquad \text{Hang time is positive.}$$
$$0.957 \approx T. \qquad \text{Using a calculator}$$

Webb's hang time was 0.957 sec. Note that his hang time was greater than Jordan's.

> Do Exercises 16 and 17.

**16. Vertical Leap.** Larry Bird, currently President of Basketball Operations for the Indiana Pacers, played for the Boston Celtics from 1979 though 1992. He had a hang time of about 0.764 sec. What was his vertical leap?

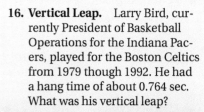

**17. Hang Time.** Vince Carter of the Orlando Magic has a vertical leap of 43 in. What is his hang time?

*Answers*

**16.** About 28 in. **17.** About 0.946 sec

**a**

**1. a)** Solve:
$6x^2 = 30$.
**b)** Find the
$x$-intercepts of
$f(x) = 6x^2 - 30$.

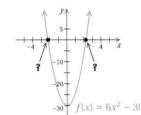

**2. a)** Solve:
$5x^2 = 35$.
**b)** Find the
$x$-intercepts of
$f(x) = 5x^2 - 35$.

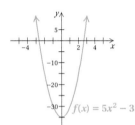

**3. a)** Solve:
$9x^2 + 25 = 0$.
**b)** Find the
$x$-intercepts of
$f(x) = 9x^2 + 25$.

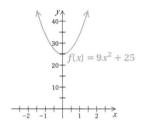

**4. a)** Solve:
$36x^2 + 49 = 0$.
**b)** Find the
$x$-intercepts of
$f(x) = 36x^2 + 49$.

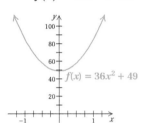

Solve. Give the exact solution and approximate solutions to three decimal places, when appropriate.

**5.** $2x^2 - 3 = 0$

**6.** $3x^2 - 7 = 0$

**7.** $(x + 2)^2 = 49$

**8.** $(x - 1)^2 = 6$

**9.** $(x - 4)^2 = 16$

**10.** $(x + 3)^2 = 9$

**11.** $(x - 11)^2 = 7$

**12.** $(x - 9)^2 = 34$

**13.** $(x - 7)^2 = -4$

**14.** $(x + 1)^2 = -9$

**15.** $(x - 9)^2 = 81$

**16.** $(t - 2)^2 = 25$

**17.** $\left(x - \frac{3}{2}\right)^2 = \frac{7}{2}$

**18.** $\left(y + \frac{3}{4}\right)^2 = \frac{17}{16}$

**19.** $x^2 + 6x + 9 = 64$

**20.** $x^2 + 10x + 25 = 100$

**21.** $y^2 - 14y + 49 = 4$

**22.** $p^2 - 8p + 16 = 1$

**b**  Solve by completing the square. Show your work.

**23.** $x^2 + 4x = 2$

**24.** $x^2 + 2x = 5$

**25.** $x^2 - 22x = 11$

**26.** $x^2 - 18x = 10$

**27.** $x^2 + x = 1$

**28.** $x^2 - x = 3$

**29.** $t^2 - 5t = 7$

**30.** $y^2 + 9y = 8$

**31.** $x^2 + \frac{3}{2}x = 3$

**32.** $x^2 - \frac{4}{3}x = \frac{2}{3}$

**33.** $m^2 - \frac{9}{2}m = \frac{3}{2}$

**34.** $r^2 + \frac{2}{5}r = \frac{4}{5}$

**35.** $x^2 + 6x - 16 = 0$

**36.** $x^2 - 8x + 15 = 0$

**37.** $x^2 + 22x + 102 = 0$     **38.** $x^2 + 18x + 74 = 0$     **39.** $x^2 - 10x - 4 = 0$     **40.** $x^2 + 10x - 4 = 0$

**41. a)** Solve:
$x^2 + 7x - 2 = 0$.
**b)** Find the
$x$-intercepts of
$f(x) = x^2 + 7x - 2$.

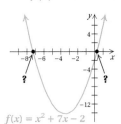

**42. a)** Solve:
$x^2 - 7x - 2 = 0$.
**b)** Find the
$x$-intercepts of
$f(x) = x^2 - 7x - 2$.

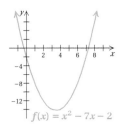

**43. a)** Solve:
$2x^2 - 5x + 8 = 0$.
**b)** Find the
$x$-intercepts of
$f(x) = 2x^2 - 5x + 8$.

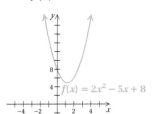

**44. a)** Solve:
$2x^2 - 3x + 9 = 0$.
**b)** Find the
$x$-intercepts of
$f(x) = 2x^2 - 3x + 9$.

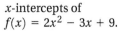
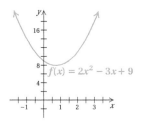

Solve by completing the square. Show your work.

**45.** $x^2 - \frac{3}{2}x - \frac{1}{2} = 0$     **46.** $x^2 + \frac{3}{2}x - 2 = 0$     **47.** $2x^2 - 3x - 17 = 0$     **48.** $2x^2 + 3x - 1 = 0$

**49.** $3x^2 - 4x - 1 = 0$     **50.** $3x^2 + 4x - 3 = 0$     **51.** $x^2 + x + 2 = 0$     **52.** $x^2 - x + 1 = 0$

**53.** $x^2 - 4x + 13 = 0$     **54.** $x^2 - 6x + 13 = 0$

**C**   *Hang Time.*   For Exercises 55 and 56, use the hang-time function $V(T) = 48T^2$, relating vertical leap to hang time.

**55.** The NBA's Shaquille O'Neal, of the Cleveland Cavaliers, has a vertical leap of about 32 in. What is his hang time?

**56.** The NBA's Antonio McDyess, of the San Antonio Spurs, has a vertical leap of 42 in. What is his hang time?

*Free-Falling Objects.* The function $s(t) = 16t^2$ is used to approximate the distance $s$, in feet, that an object falls freely from rest in $t$ seconds. Use the formula for Exercises 57–60.

**57.** Reaching 745 ft above the water, the towers of California's Golden Gate Bridge are the world's tallest bridge towers. How long would it take an object to fall freely from the top?

**58.** Suspended 1053 ft above the water, the bridge over Colorado's Royal Gorge is the world's highest bridge. How long would it take an object to fall freely from the bridge?

**59.** The Washington Monument, near the west end of the National Mall in Washington, D.C., is the world's tallest stone structure and the world's tallest obelisk. It is 555.427 ft tall. How long would it take an object to fall freely from the top of the monument?

**60.** The Gateway Arch in St. Louis is 640 ft high. How long would it take an object to fall freely from the top?

**61.** The Millau viaduct is part of the E11 expressway connecting Paris and Barcelona. The viaduct has the tallest piers ever constructed. The tallest pier is 804 ft high. How long would it take an object to fall freely from the viaduct?

**62.** Completed in 2009, the Burj Dubai, in downtown Dubai, is the tallest free-standing structure in the world. It is 2684 ft tall. How long would it take an object to fall freely from the top?

## Skill Maintenance

**63.** *Record Births.* The following table lists data regarding the number of births in the United States in 1930 and in 2007. [2.6e]

| NUMBER OF YEARS SINCE 1930 | NUMBER OF BIRTHS IN THE UNITED STATES (in millions) |
|---|---|
| 0 | 2.6 |
| 77 | 4.3 |

**Source:** National Center for Health Statistics

**a)** Use the two data points to find a linear function $B(t) = mt + b$ that fits the data.

**b)** Use the function to estimate the number of births in 2012.

**c)** In what year will there be 4.5 million births?

Graph.  [2.2c], [2.5a]

**64.** $f(x) = 5 - 2x^2$

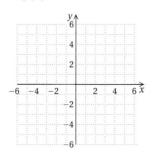

**65.** $f(x) = 5 - 2x$

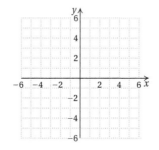

**66.** $2x - 5y = 10$

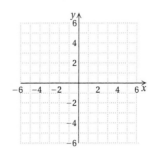

**67.** $f(x) = |5 - 2x|$

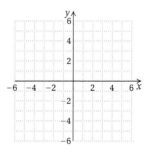

**68.** Simplify: $\sqrt{88}$.  [6.3a]

**69.** Rationalize the denominator: $\sqrt{\dfrac{2}{5}}$.  [6.5a]

Solve.  [6.6a, b]

**70.** $\sqrt{5x - 4} + \sqrt{13 - x} = 7$

**71.** $\sqrt{4x - 4} = \sqrt{x + 4} + 1$

**72.** $\sqrt{7x - 5} = \sqrt{4x + 7}$

**73.** $-35 = \sqrt{2x + 5}$

## Synthesis

**74.** 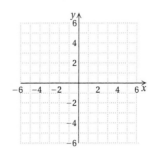 Use a graphing calculator to solve each of the following equations.

  **a)** $25.55x^2 - 1635.2 = 0$
  **b)** $-0.0644x^2 + 0.0936x + 4.56 = 0$
  **c)** $2.101x + 3.121 = 0.97x^2$

**75.** 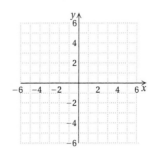 Problems such as those in Exercises 17, 21, and 25 can be solved without first finding standard form by using the INTERSECT feature on a graphing calculator. We let $y_1 = $ the left side of the equation and $y_2 = $ the right side. Use a graphing calculator to solve Exercises 17, 21, and 25 in this manner.

Find $b$ such that the trinomial is a square.

**76.** $x^2 + bx + 75$

**77.** $x^2 + bx + 64$

Solve.

**78.** $\left(x - \frac{1}{3}\right)\left(x - \frac{1}{3}\right) + \left(x - \frac{1}{3}\right)\left(x + \frac{2}{9}\right) = 0$

**79.** $x(2x^2 + 9x - 56)(3x + 10) = 0$

**80.** *Boating.*  A barge and a fishing boat leave a dock at the same time, traveling at right angles to each other. The barge travels 7 km/h slower than the fishing boat. After 4 hr, the boats are 68 km apart. Find the speed of each vessel.

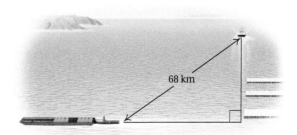

68 km

# 7.2

# The Quadratic Formula

## OBJECTIVE

**a** Solve quadratic equations using the quadratic formula, and approximate solutions using a calculator.

**SKILL TO REVIEW**

Objective 6.8a: Express imaginary numbers as *bi*, where *b* is a nonzero real number, and complex numbers as *a* + *bi*, where *a* and *b* are real numbers.

Express in terms of *i*.

1. $\sqrt{-100}$
2. $10 - \sqrt{-68}$

There are at least two reasons for learning to complete the square. One is to enhance your ability to graph certain equations that are needed to solve problems in Section 7.7. The other is to prove a general formula for solving quadratic equations.

## **a** Solving Using the Quadratic Formula

Each time you solve by completing the square, the procedure is the same. When we do the same kind of procedure many times, we look for a formula to speed up our work. Consider

$$ax^2 + bx + c = 0, \quad a > 0.$$

Note that if $a < 0$, we can get an equivalent form with $a > 0$ by first multiplying by $-1$.

Let's solve by *completing the square*. As we carry out the steps, compare them with Example 12 in the preceding section.

$$x^2 + \frac{b}{a}x + \frac{c}{a} = 0 \qquad \text{Multiplying by } \frac{1}{a}$$

$$x^2 + \frac{b}{a}x \phantom{+ \frac{c}{a}} = -\frac{c}{a} \qquad \text{Subtracting } \frac{c}{a}$$

Half of $\frac{b}{a}$ is $\frac{b}{2a}$. The square is $\frac{b^2}{4a^2}$. We add $\frac{b^2}{4a^2}$ on both sides:

$$x^2 + \frac{b}{a}x + \frac{b^2}{4a^2} = -\frac{c}{a} + \frac{b^2}{4a^2} \qquad \text{Adding } \frac{b^2}{4a^2}$$

$$\left(x + \frac{b}{2a}\right)^2 = -\frac{4ac}{4a^2} + \frac{b^2}{4a^2} \qquad \begin{array}{l}\text{Factoring the left side and finding a} \\ \text{common denominator on the right}\end{array}$$

$$\left(x + \frac{b}{2a}\right)^2 = \frac{b^2 - 4ac}{4a^2}$$

$$x + \frac{b}{2a} = \sqrt{\frac{b^2 - 4ac}{4a^2}} \quad \text{or} \quad x + \frac{b}{2a} = -\sqrt{\frac{b^2 - 4ac}{4a^2}}. \qquad \begin{array}{l}\text{Using the principle} \\ \text{of square roots}\end{array}$$

Since $a > 0$, $\sqrt{4a^2} = 2a$, so we can simplify as follows:

$$x + \frac{b}{2a} = \frac{\sqrt{b^2 - 4ac}}{2a} \quad \text{or} \quad x + \frac{b}{2a} = -\frac{\sqrt{b^2 - 4ac}}{2a}.$$

Thus,

$$x = -\frac{b}{2a} \pm \frac{\sqrt{b^2 - 4ac}}{2a}, \quad \text{or} \quad x = \frac{-b \pm \sqrt{b^2 - 4ac}}{2a}.$$

We now have the following.

---

**THE QUADRATIC FORMULA**

The solutions of $ax^2 + bx + c = 0$ are given by

$$x = \frac{-b \pm \sqrt{b^2 - 4ac}}{2a}.$$

---

*Answers*

*Skill to Review:*
**1.** $10i$  **2.** $10 - 2\sqrt{17}i$

The formula also holds when $a < 0$. A similar proof would show this, but we will not consider it here.

## ✖ Algebraic-Graphical Connection

*The Quadratic Formula (Algebraic).* The solutions of $ax^2 + bx + c = 0$, $a \neq 0$, are given by

$$x = \frac{-b \pm \sqrt{b^2 - 4ac}}{2a}.$$

*The Quadratic Formula (Graphical).*
The $x$-intercepts of the graph of the function $f(x) = ax^2 + bx + c$, $a \neq 0$, if they exist, are given by

$$\left( \frac{-b \pm \sqrt{b^2 - 4ac}}{2a}, 0 \right).$$

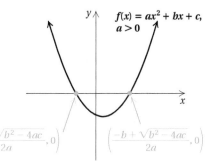

$f(x) = ax^2 + bx + c,$
$a > 0$

$\left( \dfrac{-b - \sqrt{b^2 - 4ac}}{2a}, 0 \right)$  $\left( \dfrac{-b + \sqrt{b^2 - 4ac}}{2a}, 0 \right)$

✖

**EXAMPLE 1**  Solve $5x^2 + 8x = -3$ using the quadratic formula.

We first find standard form and determine $a$, $b$, and $c$:

$$5x^2 + 8x + 3 = 0;$$
$$a = 5, \quad b = 8, \quad c = 3.$$

We then use the quadratic formula:

$$x = \frac{-b \pm \sqrt{b^2 - 4ac}}{2a}$$

$$x = \frac{-8 \pm \sqrt{8^2 - 4 \cdot 5 \cdot 3}}{2 \cdot 5} \quad \text{Substituting}$$

$$x = \frac{-8 \pm \sqrt{64 - 60}}{10}$$

Be sure to write the fraction bar all the way across.

$$x = \frac{-8 \pm \sqrt{4}}{10}$$

$$x = \frac{-8 \pm 2}{10}$$

$$x = \frac{-8 + 2}{10} \quad or \quad x = \frac{-8 - 2}{10}$$

$$x = \frac{-6}{10} \quad or \quad x = \frac{-10}{10}$$

$$x = -\frac{3}{5} \quad or \quad x = -1.$$

The solutions are $-\frac{3}{5}$ and $-1$.

$f(x) = 5x^2 + 8x + 3$

$\left(-\frac{3}{5}, 0\right)$

$(-1, 0)$

**1.** Consider the equation
$$2x^2 = 4 + 7x.$$

 a) Solve using the quadratic formula.

 b) Solve by factoring.

It turns out that we could have solved the equation in Example 1 more easily by factoring, as follows:

$$5x^2 + 8x + 3 = 0$$
$$(5x + 3)(x + 1) = 0$$
$$5x + 3 = 0 \quad or \quad x + 1 = 0$$
$$5x = -3 \quad or \qquad x = -1$$
$$x = -\tfrac{3}{5} \quad or \qquad x = -1.$$

> To solve a quadratic equation:
>
> **1.** Check for the form $x^2 = d$ or $(x + c)^2 = d$. If it is in this form, use the principle of square roots as in Section 7.1.
>
> **2.** If it is not in the form of step (1), write it in standard form $ax^2 + bx + c = 0$ with $a$ and $b$ nonzero.
>
> **3.** Then try factoring.
>
> **4.** If it is not possible to factor or if factoring seems difficult, use the quadratic formula.
>
> The solutions of a quadratic equation cannot always be found by factoring. They can *always* be found using the quadratic formula.

The solutions to all the exercises in this section could also be found by completing the square. However, the quadratic formula is the preferred method because it is faster.

Do Exercise 1.

We will see in Example 2 that we cannot always rely on factoring.

**EXAMPLE 2**  Solve: $5x^2 - 8x = 3$. Give the exact solutions and approximate the solutions to three decimal places.

We first find standard form and determine $a$, $b$, and $c$:

$$5x^2 - 8x - 3 = 0;$$
$$a = 5, \quad b = -8, \quad c = -3.$$

We then use the quadratic formula, $x = \dfrac{-b \pm \sqrt{b^2 - 4ac}}{2a}$:

$$x = \frac{-(-8) \pm \sqrt{(-8)^2 - 4 \cdot 5 \cdot (-3)}}{2 \cdot 5} \qquad \text{Substituting}$$

$$x = \frac{8 \pm \sqrt{64 + 60}}{10} = \frac{8 \pm \sqrt{124}}{10} = \frac{8 \pm \sqrt{4 \cdot 31}}{10}$$

$$x = \frac{8 \pm 2\sqrt{31}}{10} = \frac{2(4 \pm \sqrt{31})}{2 \cdot 5} = \frac{2}{2} \cdot \frac{4 \pm \sqrt{31}}{5} = \frac{4 \pm \sqrt{31}}{5}.$$

↑ *Caution!*

To avoid a common error in simplifying, remember to *factor the numerator and the denominator* and then remove a factor of 1.

---

**Calculator Corner**

**Approximating Solutions of Quadratic Equations**  In Example 2, we find that the solutions of the equation $5x^2 - 8x = 3$ are $\dfrac{4 + \sqrt{31}}{5}$ and $\dfrac{4 - \sqrt{31}}{5}$. We can use a calculator to approximate these solutions. To approximate $\dfrac{4 + \sqrt{31}}{5}$, we press

$\boxed{)}$ $\boxed{\div}$ $\boxed{5}$ $\boxed{\text{ENTER}}$. To approximate $\dfrac{4 - \sqrt{31}}{5}$, we press $\boxed{(}$ $\boxed{4}$ $\boxed{-}$ $\boxed{\text{2ND}}$

$\boxed{\sqrt{\,}}$ $\boxed{3}$ $\boxed{1}$ $\boxed{)}$ $\boxed{)}$ $\boxed{\div}$ $\boxed{5}$ $\boxed{\text{ENTER}}$.
We see that the solutions are approximately 1.914 and −0.314.

| (4+√(31))/5 | |
|---|---|
| | 1.913552873 |
| (4−√(31))/5 | |
| | −.3135528726 |

**Exercises:**  Use a calculator to approximate the solutions in each of the following. Round to three decimal places.

**1.** Example 4

**2.** Margin Exercise 2

**3.** Margin Exercise 4

---

*Answer*

**1.** (a) $-\tfrac{1}{2}$, 4; (b) $-\tfrac{1}{2}$, 4

We can use a calculator to approximate the solutions:

$$\frac{4 + \sqrt{31}}{5} \approx 1.914; \qquad \frac{4 - \sqrt{31}}{5} \approx -0.314.$$

Check:   Checking the exact solutions $\left(4 \pm \sqrt{31}\right)/5$ can be quite cumbersome. It could be done on a calculator or by using the approximations. Here we check 1.914; the check for $-0.314$ is left to the student.

For 1.914:

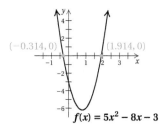

$$\frac{5x^2 - 8x = 3}{5(1.914)^2 - 8(1.914) \; ? \; 3}$$
$$5(3.663396) - 15.312 \quad | $$
$$3.00498 \quad | $$

We do not have a perfect check due to the rounding error. But our check seems to confirm the solutions.

Do Exercise 2.

**2.** Solve using the quadratic formula:
$$3x^2 + 2x = 7.$$
Give the exact solutions and approximate solutions to three decimal places.

Some quadratic equations have solutions that are nonreal complex numbers.

**EXAMPLE 3**   Solve: $x^2 + x + 1 = 0$.

We have $a = 1$, $b = 1$, $c = 1$. We use the quadratic formula:

$$x = \frac{-1 \pm \sqrt{1^2 - 4 \cdot 1 \cdot 1}}{2 \cdot 1}$$

$$x = \frac{-1 \pm \sqrt{1 - 4}}{2}$$

$$x = \frac{-1 \pm \sqrt{-3}}{2}$$

$$x = \frac{-1 \pm \sqrt{3}i}{2}.$$

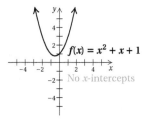

The solutions are

$$\frac{-1 + i\sqrt{3}}{2} \quad \text{and} \quad \frac{-1 - \sqrt{3}i}{2}.$$

The solutions can also be expressed in the form

$$-\frac{1}{2} + \frac{\sqrt{3}}{2}i \quad \text{and} \quad -\frac{1}{2} - \frac{\sqrt{3}}{2}i.$$

Do Exercise 3.

**3.** Solve: $x^2 - x + 2 = 0$.

**EXAMPLE 4**   Solve: $2 + \dfrac{7}{x} = \dfrac{5}{x^2}$. Give the exact solutions and approximate solutions to three decimal places.

We first find an equivalent quadratic equation in standard form:

$$x^2\left(2 + \frac{7}{x}\right) = x^2 \cdot \frac{5}{x^2} \qquad \text{Multiplying by } x^2 \text{ to clear fractions,}$$
$$\text{noting that } x \neq 0$$

$$2x^2 + 7x = 5$$

$$2x^2 + 7x - 5 = 0. \qquad \text{Subtracting 5}$$

***Answers***

**2.** $\dfrac{-1 \pm \sqrt{22}}{3}$; 1.230, $-1.897$

**3.** $\dfrac{1 \pm \sqrt{7}i}{2}$, or $\dfrac{1}{2} \pm \dfrac{\sqrt{7}}{2}i$

Then

$$a = 2, \quad b = 7, \quad c = -5$$

$$x = \frac{-7 \pm \sqrt{7^2 - 4 \cdot 2 \cdot (-5)}}{2 \cdot 2} \quad \text{Substituting}$$

$$x = \frac{-7 \pm \sqrt{49 + 40}}{4} = \frac{-7 \pm \sqrt{89}}{4}$$

$$x = \frac{-7 + \sqrt{89}}{4} \quad \text{or} \quad x = \frac{-7 - \sqrt{89}}{4}.$$

Since we began with a rational equation, we need to check. We cleared the fractions before obtaining a quadratic equation in standard form, and this step could introduce numbers that do not check in the original rational equation. We need to show that neither of the numbers makes a denominator 0. Since neither of them does, the solutions are

$$\frac{-7 + \sqrt{89}}{4} \quad \text{and} \quad \frac{-7 - \sqrt{89}}{4}.$$

We can use a calculator to approximate the solutions:

$$\frac{-7 + \sqrt{89}}{4} \approx 0.608;$$

$$\frac{-7 - \sqrt{89}}{4} \approx -4.108.$$

Do Exercise 4.

**4.** Solve:

$$3 = \frac{5}{x} + \frac{4}{x^2}.$$

Give the exact solutions and approximate solutions to three decimal places.

$f(x) = 2 + \dfrac{7}{x} - \dfrac{5}{x^2}$

$(-4.108, 0)$

$(0.608, 0)$

**Solving Quadratic Equations** A quadratic equation written with 0 on one side of the equals sign can be solved using the ZERO feature of a graphing calculator. See the Calculator Corner on p. 391 for the procedure.

We can also use the INTERSECT feature to solve a quadratic equation. Consider the equation in Exercise 19 in Exercise Set 7.2: $4x(x - 2) - 5x(x - 1) = 2$. First, we enter $y_1 = 4x(x - 2) - 5x(x - 1)$ and $y_2 = 2$ on the equation-editor screen and graph the equations in a window that shows the point(s) of intersection of the graphs.

We use the INTERSECT feature to find the coordinates of the left-hand point of intersection. (See the Calculator Corner on p. 246 for the procedure.) The first coordinate of this point, $-2$, is one solution of the equation. We use the INTERSECT feature again to find the other solution, $-1$.

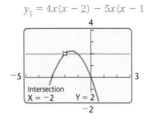

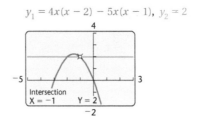

**Exercises:** Solve.

**1.** $5x^2 = -11x + 12$

**2.** $2x^2 - 15 = 7x$

**3.** $6(x - 3) = (x - 3)(x - 2)$

**4.** $(x + 1)(x - 4) = 3(x - 4)$

*Answer*

**4.** $\dfrac{5 \pm \sqrt{73}}{6}$; 2.257, $-0.591$

**a** Solve.

**1.** $x^2 + 8x + 2 = 0$

**2.** $x^2 - 6x - 4 = 0$

**3.** $3p^2 = -8p - 1$

**4.** $3u^2 = 18u - 6$

**5.** $x^2 - x + 1 = 0$

**6.** $x^2 + x + 2 = 0$

**7.** $x^2 + 13 = 4x$

**8.** $x^2 + 13 = 6x$

**9.** $r^2 + 3r = 8$

**10.** $h^2 + 4 = 6h$

**11.** $1 + \dfrac{2}{x} + \dfrac{5}{x^2} = 0$

**12.** $1 + \dfrac{5}{x^2} = \dfrac{2}{x}$

**13. a)** Solve: $3x + x(x - 2) = 0$.
**b)** Find the $x$-intercepts of
$f(x) = 3x + x(x - 2)$.

**14. a)** Solve: $4x + x(x - 3) = 0$.
**b)** Find the $x$-intercepts of
$f(x) = 4x + x(x - 3)$.

**15. a)** Solve: $11x^2 - 3x - 5 = 0$.
**b)** Find the $x$-intercepts of
$f(x) = 11x^2 - 3x - 5$.

**16. a)** Solve: $7x^2 + 8x = -2$.
**b)** Find the $x$-intercepts of
$f(x) = 7x^2 + 8x + 2$.

**17. a)** Solve: $25x^2 = 20x - 4$.
**b)** Find the $x$-intercepts of
$f(x) = 25x^2 - 20x + 4$.

**18. a)** Solve: $49x^2 - 14x + 1 = 0$.
**b)** Find the $x$-intercepts of
$f(x) = 49x^2 - 14x + 1$.

Solve.

**19.** $4x(x - 2) - 5x(x - 1) = 2$

**20.** $3x(x + 1) - 7x(x + 2) = 6$

**21.** $14(x - 4) - (x + 2) = (x + 2)(x - 4)$

**22.** $11(x - 2) + (x - 5) = (x + 2)(x - 6)$

**23.** $5x^2 = 17x - 2$

**24.** $15x = 2x^2 + 16$

**25.** $x^2 + 5 = 4x$

**26.** $x^2 + 5 = 2x$

**27.** $x + \dfrac{1}{x} = \dfrac{13}{6}$

**28.** $\dfrac{3}{x} + \dfrac{x}{3} = \dfrac{5}{2}$

**29.** $\dfrac{1}{y} + \dfrac{1}{y + 2} = \dfrac{1}{3}$

**30.** $\dfrac{1}{x} + \dfrac{1}{x + 4} = \dfrac{1}{7}$

**31.** $(2t - 3)^2 + 17t = 15$

**32.** $2y^2 - (y + 2)(y - 3) = 12$

**33.** $(x - 2)^2 + (x + 1)^2 = 0$

**34.** $(x + 3)^2 + (x - 1)^2 = 0$

**35.** $x^3 - 1 = 0$
(*Hint*: Factor the difference of cubes. Then use the quadratic formula.)

**36.** $x^3 + 27 = 0$

Solve. Give the exact solutions and approximate solutions to three decimal places.

**37.** $x^2 + 6x + 4 = 0$

**38.** $x^2 + 4x - 7 = 0$

**39.** $x^2 - 6x + 4 = 0$

**40.** $x^2 - 4x + 1 = 0$

**41.** $2x^2 - 3x - 7 = 0$

**42.** $3x^2 - 3x - 2 = 0$

**43.** $5x^2 = 3 + 8x$

**44.** $2y^2 + 2y - 3 = 0$

## Skill Maintenance

Solve.   [6.6a, b]

**45.** $x = \sqrt{x + 2}$

**46.** $x = \sqrt{15 - 2x}$

**47.** $\sqrt{x + 2} = \sqrt{2x - 8}$

**48.** $\sqrt{x + 1} + 2 = \sqrt{3x + 1}$

**49.** $\sqrt{x + 5} = -7$

**50.** $\sqrt{2x - 6} + 11 = 2$

**51.** $\sqrt[3]{4x - 7} = 2$

**52.** $\sqrt[4]{3x - 1} = 2$

## Synthesis

**53.** Use a graphing calculator to solve the equations in Exercises 3, 16, 17, and 43 using the INTERSECT feature, letting $y_1 = $ the left side and $y_2 = $ the right side. Then solve $2.2x^2 + 0.5x - 1 = 0$.

**54.** Use a graphing calculator to solve the equations in Exercises 9, 27, and 30. Then solve $5.33x^2 = 8.23x + 3.24$.

Solve.

**55.** $2x^2 - x - \sqrt{5} = 0$

**56.** $\dfrac{5}{x} + \dfrac{x}{4} = \dfrac{11}{7}$

**57.** $ix^2 - x - 1 = 0$

**58.** $\sqrt{3}x^2 + 6x + \sqrt{3} = 0$

**59.** $\dfrac{x}{x + 1} = 4 + \dfrac{1}{3x^2 - 3}$

**60.** $\left(1 + \sqrt{3}\right)x^2 - \left(3 + 2\sqrt{3}\right)x + 3 = 0$

**61.** Let $f(x) = (x - 3)^2$. Find all inputs $x$ such that $f(x) = 13$.

**62.** Let $f(x) = x^2 + 14x + 49$. Find all inputs $x$ such that $f(x) = 36$.

# Mid-Chapter Review

## Concept Reinforcement

Determine whether each statement is true or false.

_____ **1.** Every quadratic equation has exactly two real-number solutions. [7.4a]

_____ **2.** The quadratic formula can be used to find all the solutions of any quadratic equation. [7.2a]

_____ **3.** If the graph of a quadratic equation crosses the $x$-axis, then it has exactly two real-number solutions. [7.4a]

_____ **4.** The $x$-intercepts of $f(x) = x^2 - t$ are $\left(0, \sqrt{t}\right)$ and $\left(0, -\sqrt{t}\right)$. [7.1a]

## Guided Solutions

Fill in each blank with the number that creates a correct solution.

**5.** Solve $5x^2 + 3x = 4$ by completing the square. [7.1b]

$$5x^2 + 3x = 4$$

$$\square(5x^2 + 3x) = \square \cdot 4$$

$$x^2 + \frac{3}{\square}x = \frac{4}{\square}$$

$$x^2 + \frac{3}{5}x + \square = \frac{4}{5} + \square$$

$$\left(x + \square\right)^2 = \frac{\square}{100}$$

$$x + \frac{3}{10} = \sqrt{\square} \qquad \text{or} \qquad x + \frac{3}{10} = -\sqrt{\square}$$

$$x + \frac{3}{10} = \frac{\sqrt{\square}}{\square} \qquad \text{or} \qquad x + \frac{3}{10} = -\frac{\sqrt{\square}}{\square}$$

$$x = -\frac{\square}{10} + \frac{\sqrt{\square}}{10} \qquad \text{or} \qquad x = -\frac{\square}{10} - \frac{\sqrt{\square}}{10}.$$

The solutions are $-\dfrac{\square}{10} \pm \dfrac{\sqrt{\square}}{10}$.

**6.** Use the quadratic formula to solve $5x^2 + 3x = 4$. [7.2a]

$$5x^2 + 3x = 4$$

$$5x^2 + 3x - \square = 0$$

$$5x^2 + 3x + \square = 0$$

$$a = \square, \quad b = \square, \quad c = \square$$

$$x = \frac{-b \pm \sqrt{b^2 - 4ac}}{2a}$$

$$x = \frac{-\square \pm \sqrt{\square^2 - 4 \cdot \square \cdot \square}}{2 \cdot \square}$$

$$x = \frac{-3 \pm \sqrt{\square + \square}}{\square}$$

$$x = \frac{-3 \pm \sqrt{\square}}{\square}$$

$$x = -\frac{3}{10} \pm \frac{\sqrt{\square}}{\square}$$

## Mixed Review

Solve by completing the square. [7.1b]

**7.** $x^2 + 1 = -4x$

**8.** $2x^2 + 5x - 3 = 0$

**9.** $x^2 + 10x - 6 = 0$

**10.** $x^2 - x = 5$

Determine the nature of the solutions of each equation $ax^2 + bx + c = 0$ and the number of $x$-intercepts of the graph of the function $f(x) = ax^2 + bx + c$. [7.4a]

**11.** $x^2 - 10x + 25 = 0$

**12.** $x^2 - 11 = 0$

**13.** $y^2 = \frac{1}{3}y - \frac{4}{7}$

**14.** $x^2 + 5x + 9 = 0$

**15.** $x^2 - 4 = 2x$

**16.** $x^2 - 8x = 0$

Write a quadratic equation having the given numbers as solutions.  [7.4b]

**17.** $-1$ and $10$

**18.** $-13$ and $13$

**19.** $-\sqrt{5}$ and $3\sqrt{5}$

**20.** $-4i$ and $4i$

**21.** $-6$, only solution

**22.** $-\dfrac{4}{3}$ and $\dfrac{2}{7}$

Solve.

**23.** Jacob traveled 780 mi by car. Had he gone 5 mph faster, he could have made the trip in 1 hr less time. Find his speed.  [7.3a]

**24.** $R = as^2$, for $s$  [7.3b]

Solve.  [7.1a], [7.2a], [7.4c]

**25.** $3x^2 + x = 4$

**26.** $x^4 - 8x^2 + 15 = 0$

**27.** $4x^2 = 15x - 5$

**28.** $7x^2 + 2 = -9x$

**29.** $2x + x(x - 1) = 0$

**30.** $(x + 3)^2 = 64$

**31.** $49x^2 + 16 = 0$

**32.** $(x^2 - 2)^2 + 2(x^2 - 2) - 24 = 0$

**33.** $r^2 + 5r = 12$

**34.** $s^2 + 12s + 37 = 0$

**35.** $\left(x - \dfrac{5}{2}\right)^2 = \dfrac{11}{4}$

**36.** $x + \dfrac{1}{x} = \dfrac{7}{3}$

**37.** $4x + 1 = 4x^2$

**38.** $(x - 3)^2 + (x + 5)^2 = 0$

**39.** $b^2 - 16b + 64 = 3$

**40.** $(x - 3)^2 = -10$

**41.** $\dfrac{1}{x} + \dfrac{1}{x + 2} = \dfrac{1}{5}$

**42.** $x - \sqrt{x} - 6 = 0$

## Understanding Through Discussion and Writing

**43.** Given the solutions of a quadratic equation, is it possible to reconstruct the original equation? Why or why not?  [7.4b]

**44.** Explain how the quadratic formula can be used to factor a quadratic polynomial into two binomials. Use it to factor $5x^2 + 8x - 3$.  [7.2a]

**45.** Describe a procedure that could be used to write an equation having the first seven natural numbers as solutions.  [7.4b]

**46.** Describe a procedure that could be used to write an equation that is quadratic in $3x^2 + 1$ and has real-number solutions.  [7.4c]

## Key Terms, Properties, and Formulas

standard form, p. 580
completing the square, p. 585
quadratic formula, p. 594
discriminant, p. 613

parabola, p. 624
line of symmetry, p. 624
axis of symmetry, p. 624
vertex, p. 624

minimum, p. 627
maximum, p. 627
quadratic inequality, p. 653
rational inequality, p. 657

*Principle of Square Roots:* $x^2 = d$ has solutions $\sqrt{d}$ and $-\sqrt{d}$.

*Quadratic Formula:* $\qquad x = \dfrac{-b \pm \sqrt{b^2 - 4ac}}{2a}$ $\qquad$ *Discriminant:* $b^2 - 4ac$

The *vertex* of the graph of $f(x) = ax^2 + bx + c$ is $\left(-\dfrac{b}{2a}, \dfrac{4ac - b^2}{4a}\right)$, or $\left(-\dfrac{b}{2a}, f\left(-\dfrac{b}{2a}\right)\right)$.

The *line of symmetry* of the graph of $f(x) = ax^2 + bx + c$ is $x - -\dfrac{b}{2a}$.

## Concept Reinforcement

Determine whether each statement is true or false.

_____ **1.** The graph of $f(x) = -(-x^2 - 8x - 3)$ opens downward.  [7.5a]

_____ **2.** If $(-5, 7)$ is the vertex of a parabola, then $x = -5$ is the line of symmetry.  [7.6a]

_____ **3.** The graph of $f(x) = -3(x + 2)^2 - 5$ is a translation to the right of the graph of $f(x) = -3x^2 - 5$.  [7.5b]

## Important Concepts

**Objective 7.1a** Solve quadratic equations using the principle of square roots.

**Example** Solve: $(x - 3)^2 = -36$.
$$x - 3 = \sqrt{-36} \quad or \quad x - 3 = -\sqrt{-36}$$
$$x = 3 + 6i \quad or \qquad x = 3 - 6i$$
The solutions are $3 \pm 6i$.

**Practice Exercise**

**1.** Solve: $(x - 2)^2 = -9$.

**Objective 7.1b** Solve quadratic equations by completing the square.

**Example** Solve by completing the square:
$$x^2 - 8x + 13 = 0.$$

$$x^2 - 8x \qquad = -13$$
$$x^2 - 8x + 16 = -13 + 16$$
$$(x - 4)^2 = 3$$
$$x - 4 = \sqrt{3} \qquad or \quad x - 4 = -\sqrt{3}$$
$$x = 4 + \sqrt{3} \quad or \qquad x = 4 - \sqrt{3}$$
The solutions are $4 \pm \sqrt{3}$.

**Practice Exercise**

**2.** Solve by completing the square:
$$x^2 - 12x + 31 = 0.$$

**Objective 7.2a** Solve quadratic equations using the quadratic formula, and approximate solutions using a calculator.

**Example** Solve: $x^2 - 2x = 2$. Give the exact solutions and approximate solutions to three decimal places.

$x^2 - 2x - 2 = 0$     Standard form

     $a = 1, \quad b = -2, \quad c = -2$

$x = \dfrac{-(-2) \pm \sqrt{(-2)^2 - 4 \cdot 1 \cdot (-2)}}{2 \cdot 1}$     Using the quadratic formula

$x = \dfrac{2 \pm \sqrt{4 + 8}}{2} = \dfrac{2 \pm \sqrt{12}}{2} = \dfrac{2 \pm 2\sqrt{3}}{2}$

     $= 1 \pm \sqrt{3}$, or 2.732 and −0.732

**Practice Exercise**

3. Solve: $x^2 - 10x = -23$. Give the exact solutions and approximate solutions to three decimal places.

---

**Objective 7.4a** Determine the nature of the solutions of a quadratic equation.

**Example** Determine the nature of the solutions of the quadratic equation $x^2 - 7x = 1$.

     In standard form, we have $x^2 - 7x - 1 = 0$. Thus, $a = 1$, $b = -7$, and $c = -1$. The discriminant, $b^2 - 4ac$, is $(-7)^2 - 4 \cdot 1 \cdot (-1)$, or 53. Since the discriminant is positive, there are two real solutions.

**Practice Exercise**

4. Determine the nature of the solutions of each quadratic equation.
   a) $x^2 - 3x = 7$
   b) $2x^2 - 5x + 5 = 0$

---

**Objective 7.4b** Write a quadratic equation having two given numbers as solutions.

**Example** Write a quadratic equation whose solutions are 7 and $-\frac{1}{4}$.

     $x = 7$    *or*       $x = -\frac{1}{4}$

   $x - 7 = 0$    *or*    $x + \frac{1}{4} = 0$

   $x - 7 = 0$    *or*    $4x + 1 = 0$     Clearing the fraction

$(x - 7)(4x + 1) = 0$      Using the principle of zero products in reverse

   $4x^2 - 27x - 7 = 0$      Using FOIL

**Practice Exercise**

5. Write a quadratic equation whose solutions are $-\frac{2}{5}$ and 3.

---

**Objective 7.4c** Solve equations that are quadratic in form.

**Example** Solve: $x - 8\sqrt{x} - 9 = 0$.

     Let $u = \sqrt{x}$. Then we substitute $u$ for $\sqrt{x}$ and $u^2$ for $x$ and solve for $u$:

       $u^2 - 8u - 9 = 0$

    $(u - 9)(u + 1) = 0$

         $u = 9$   *or*   $u = -1$.

Next, we substitute $\sqrt{x}$ for $u$ and solve for $x$:

     $\sqrt{x} = 9$   *or*   $\sqrt{x} = -1$.

Squaring each equation, we get

     $x = 81$   *or*   $x = 1$.

Checking both 81 and 1 in $x - 8\sqrt{x} - 9 = 0$, we find that 81 checks but 1 does not. The solution is 81.

**Practice Exercise**

6. Solve:
   $$(x^2 - 3)^2 - 5(x^2 - 3) - 6 = 0.$$

**Objective 7.6a**  For a quadratic function, find the vertex, the line of symmetry, and the maximum or minimum value, and then graph the function.

**Example**  For $f(x) = -2x^2 + 4x + 1$, find the vertex, the line of symmetry, and the maximum or minimum value. Then graph.

We factor out $-2$ from only the first two terms:

$$f(x) = -2(x^2 - 2x) + 1.$$

Next, we complete the square, factor, and simplify:

$$\begin{aligned} f(x) &= -2(x^2 - 2x \quad\quad) + 1 \\ &= -2(x^2 - 2x + 1 - 1) + 1 \\ &= -2(x^2 - 2x + 1) + (-2)(-1) + 1 \\ &= -2(x - 1)^2 + 3. \end{aligned}$$

The vertex is $(1, 3)$. The line of symmetry is $x = 1$. The coefficient of $x^2$ is negative, so the graph opens down. Thus, 3 is the maximum value of the function.

We plot points and graph the parabola.

| $x$ | $y$ |
|-----|-----|
| 1 | 3 |
| 2 | 1 |
| 0 | 1 |
| 3 | $-5$ |
| $-1$ | $-5$ |

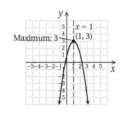

**Practice Exercise**

7. For $f(x) = -x^2 - 2x - 3$, find the vertex, the line of symmetry, and the maximum or minimum value. Then graph.

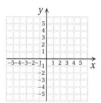

---

**Objective 7.6b**  Find the intercepts of a quadratic function.

**Example**  Find the intercepts of $f(x) = x^2 - 8x + 14$.

Since $f(0) = 0^2 - 8 \cdot 0 + 14$, the $y$-intercept is $(0, 14)$. To find the $x$-intercepts, we solve $0 = x^2 - 8x + 14$. Using the quadratic formula, we have $x = 4 \pm \sqrt{2}$. Thus the $x$-intercepts are $\left(4 - \sqrt{2}, 0\right)$ and $\left(4 + \sqrt{2}, 0\right)$.

**Practice Exercise**

8. Find the intercepts of $f(x) = x^2 - 6x + 4$.

---

**Objective 7.8a**  Solve quadratic inequalities and other polynomial inequalities.

**Example**  Solve: $x^2 - 15 > 2x$.

$$x^2 - 2x - 15 > 0 \quad\text{Adding 15}$$

We set the polynomial equal to 0 and solve. The solutions of $x^2 - 2x - 15 = 0$, or $(x + 3)(x - 5) = 0$, are $-3$ and 5. They divide the number line into three intervals.

$$\xleftarrow{\;\;\;\;\;\;\;\;\;\;\;\;\;\;\;\;\;\;\;\;\;}\xrightarrow{\;\;}$$
$$-6\;-5\;-4\;-3\;-2\;-1\;\;0\;\;1\;\;2\;\;3\;\;4\;\;5\;\;6$$

We try a test point in each interval:

Test $-5$:  $(-5)^2 - 2(-5) - 15 = 20 > 0$;

Test 0:  $0^2 - 2 \cdot 0 - 15 = -15 < 0$;

Test 6:  $6^2 - 2 \cdot 6 - 15 = 9 > 0$.

The expression $x^2 - 2x - 15$ is positive for values of $x$ in the intervals $(-\infty, -3)$ and $(5, \infty)$. The inequality symbol is $>$, so $-3$ and 5 are not solutions. The solution set is $\{x | x < -3 \text{ or } x > 5\}$, or $(-\infty, -3) \cup (5, \infty)$.

**Practice Exercise**

9. Solve: $x^2 + 40 > 14x$.

**Objective 7.8b**  Solve rational inequalities.

**Example**  Solve: $\dfrac{x + 3}{x - 6} \geq 2$.

We first solve the related equation $\dfrac{x + 3}{x - 6} = 2$. The solution is 15. We also need to determine those numbers for which the rational expression is not defined. We set the denominator equal to 0 and solve: $x - 6 = 0$, or $x = 6$. The numbers 6 and 15 divide the number line into three intervals. We test a point in each interval.

4 5 6 7 8 9 10 11 12 13 14 15 16

Test 5:  $\dfrac{5 + 3}{5 - 6} \geq 2$, or $-8 \geq 2$, which is false.

Test 9:  $\dfrac{9 + 3}{9 - 6} \geq 2$, or $4 \geq 2$, which is true.

Test 17:  $\dfrac{17 + 3}{17 - 6} \geq 2$, or $\dfrac{20}{11} \geq 2$, which is false.

The solution set includes the interval $(6, 15)$ and the number 15, the solution of the related equation. The number 6 is not included. It is not an allowable replacement because it results in division by 0. The solution set is $\{x \mid 6 < x \leq 15\}$, or $(6, 15]$.

**Practice Exercise**

**10.**  Solve: $\dfrac{x + 7}{x - 5} \geq 3$.

## Review Exercises

**1. a)** Solve: $2x^2 - 7 = 0$.  [7.1a]
   **b)** Find the $x$-intercepts of $f(x) = 2x^2 - 7$.

Solve.  [7.2a]

**2.** $14x^2 + 5x = 0$

**3.** $x^2 - 12x + 27 = 0$

**4.** $4x^2 + 3x + 1 = 0$

**5.** $x^2 - 7x + 13 = 0$

**6.** $4x(x - 1) + 15 = x(3x + 4)$

**7.** $x^2 + 4x + 1 = 0$. Give exact solutions and approximate solutions to three decimal places.

**8.** $\dfrac{x}{x - 2} + \dfrac{4}{x - 6} = 0$

**9.** $\dfrac{x}{4} - \dfrac{4}{x} = 2$

**10.** $15 = \dfrac{8}{x + 2} - \dfrac{6}{x - 2}$

**11.** Solve $x^2 + 6x + 2 = 0$ by completing the square. Show your work.  [7.1b]

**12.** *Hang Time.*  Use the function $V(T) = 48T^2$. A basketball player has a vertical leap of 39 in. What is his hang time?  [7.1c]

**13.** *DVD Player Screen.*  The width of a rectangular screen on a portable DVD player is 5 cm less than the length. The area is 126 cm$^2$. Find the length and the width.  [7.3a]

**14.** *Picture Matting.*  A picture mat measures 12 in. by 16 in., and 140 in$^2$ of picture shows. Find the width of the mat.  [7.3a]

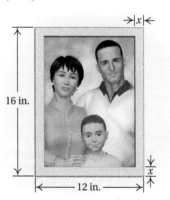

16 in.

12 in.

$\rightarrow |x| \leftarrow$

$x$

**15.** *Motorcycle Travel.* During the first part of a trip, a motorcyclist travels 50 mi. The rider travels 80 mi on the second part of the trip at a speed that is 10 mph slower. The total time for the trip is 3 hr. What is the speed on each part of the trip?  [7.3a]

Determine the nature of the solutions of each equation. [7.4a]

**16.** $x^2 + 3x - 6 = 0$    **17.** $x^2 + 2x + 5 = 0$

Write a quadratic equation having the given solutions. [7.4b]

**18.** $\frac{1}{5}, -\frac{3}{5}$    **19.** $-4$, only solution

Solve for the indicated letter.  [7.3b]

**20.** $N = 3\pi\sqrt{\dfrac{1}{p}}$, for $p$    **21.** $2A = \dfrac{3B}{T^2}$, for $T$

Solve.  [7.4c]

**22.** $x^4 - 13x^2 + 36 = 0$    **23.** $15x^{-2} - 2x^{-1} - 1 = 0$

**24.** $(x^2 - 4)^2 - (x^2 - 4) - 6 = 0$

**25.** $x - 13\sqrt{x} + 36 = 0$

For each quadratic function in Exercises 26–28, find and label **(a)** the vertex, **(b)** the line of symmetry, and **(c)** the maximum or minimum value. Then **(d)** graph the function. [7.5c], [7.6a]

**26.** $f(x) = -\frac{1}{2}(x - 1)^2 + 3$

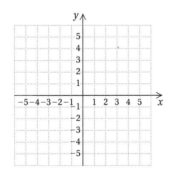

Vertex: (____, ____)
Line of symmetry: $x =$ ____
_____ value: ____

**27.** $f(x) = x^2 - x + 6$

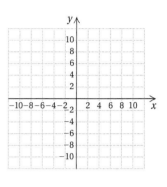

Vertex: (____, ____)
Line of symmetry: $x =$ ____
_____ value: ____

**28.** $f(x) = -3x^2 - 12x - 8$

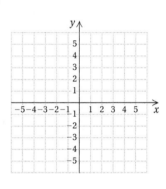

Vertex: (____, ____)
Line of symmetry: $x =$ ____
_____ value: ____

Find the $x$- and $y$-intercepts.  [7.6b]

**29.** $f(x) = x^2 - 9x + 14$

**30.** $g(x) = x^2 - 4x - 3$

**31.** What is the minimum product of two numbers whose difference is 22? What numbers yield this product? [7.7a]

**32.** Find a quadratic function that fits the data points $(0, -2), (1, 3)$, and $(3, 7)$. [7.7b]

**33.** *Live Births by Age.* The average number of live births per 1000 women rises and falls according to age, as seen in the following bar graph. [7.7b]

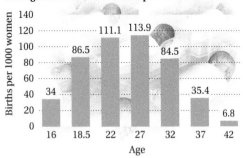

**Average Number of Live Births per 1000 Women**

SOURCE: Centers for Disease Control and Prevention

a) Use the data points $(16, 34)$, $(27, 113.9)$, and $(37, 35.4)$ to fit a quadratic function to the data.

b) Use the quadratic function to estimate the number of live births per 1000 women of age 30.

Solve. [7.8a, b]

**34.** $(x + 2)(x - 1)(x - 2) > 0$

**35.** $\dfrac{(x + 4)(x - 1)}{(x + 2)} < 0$

**36.** Determine the nature of the solutions
$$x^2 - 10x + 25 = 0. \quad [7.4a]$$

**A.** Infinite number of solutions
**B.** One real solution
**C.** Two real solutions
**D.** No real solutions

**37.** Solve: $2x^2 - 6x + 5 = 0$. [7.2a]

**A.** $\dfrac{3}{2} \pm \dfrac{\sqrt{19}}{2}$      **B.** $3 \pm i$

**C.** $3 \pm \sqrt{19}$      **D.** $\dfrac{3}{2} \pm \dfrac{i}{2}$

## Synthesis

**38.** A quadratic function has $x$-intercepts $(-3, 0)$ and $(5, 0)$ and $y$-intercept $(0, -7)$. Find an equation for the function. What is its maximum or minimum value? [7.7a, b]

**39.** Find $h$ and $k$ such that $3x^2 - hx + 4k = 0$, the sum of the solutions is 20, and the product of the solutions is 80. [7.2a], [7.7b]

**40.** The average of two numbers is 171. One of the numbers is the square root of the other. Find the numbers. [7.3a]

# Understanding Through Discussion and Writing

**1.** Does the graph of every quadratic function have a $y$-intercept? Why or why not? [7.6b]

**2.** Explain how the leading coefficient of a quadratic function can be used to determine whether a maximum or minimum function value exists. [7.7a]

**3.** Explain, without plotting points, why the graph of $f(x) = (x + 3)^2 - 4$ looks like the graph of $f(x) = x^2$ translated 3 units to the left and 4 units down. [7.5c]

**4.** Describe a method that could be used to create quadratic inequalities that have no solution. [7.8a]

**5.** Is it possible for the graph of a quadratic function to have only one $x$-intercept if the vertex is off the $x$-axis? Why or why not? [7.6b]

**6.** Explain how the $x$-intercepts of a quadratic function can be used to help find the vertex of the function. What piece of information would still be missing? [7.6a, b]

Test

For Extra Help
CHAPTER
Test Prep
VIDEOS

Step-by-step test solutions are found on the Chapter Test Prep Videos available via the Video Resources on DVD, in *MyMathLab* , and on You Tube (search "BittingerInterAlgPB" and click on "Channels").

**1. a)** Solve: $3x^2 - 4 = 0$.
   **b)** Find the $x$-intercepts of $f(x) = 3x^2 - 4$.

Solve.

**2.** $x^2 + x + 1 = 0$

**3.** $x - 8\sqrt{x} + 7 = 0$

**4.** $4x(x - 2) - 3x(x + 1) = -18$

**5.** $4x^4 - 17x^2 + 15 = 0$

**6.** $x^2 + 4x = 2$. Give exact solutions and approximate solutions to three decimal places.

**7.** $\dfrac{1}{4 - x} + \dfrac{1}{2 + x} = \dfrac{3}{4}$

**8.** Solve $x^2 - 4x + 1 = 0$ by completing the square. Show your work.

**9.** *Free-Falling Objects.* The Peachtree Plaza in Atlanta, Georgia, is 723 ft tall. Use the function $s(t) = 16t^2$ to approximate how long it would take an object to fall from the top.

**10.** *Marine Travel.* The Columbia River flows at a rate of 2 mph for the length of a popular boating route. In order for a motorized dinghy to travel 3 mi upriver and then return in a total of 4 hr, how fast must the boat be able to travel in still water?

**11.** *Memory Board.* A computer-parts company wants to make a rectangular memory board that has a perimeter of 28 cm. What dimensions will allow the board to have the maximum area?

**12.** *Hang Time.* Use the function $V(T) = 48T^2$. Nate Robinson of the New York Knicks has a vertical leap of 43 in. What is his hang time?

**13.** Determine the nature of the solutions of the equation $x^2 + 5x + 17 = 0$.

**14.** Write a quadratic equation having the solutions $\sqrt{3}$ and $3\sqrt{3}$.

**15.** Solve $V = 48T^2$ for $T$.

For the quadratic functions in Exercises 16 and 17, find and label **(a)** the vertex, **(b)** the line of symmetry, and **(c)** the maximum or minimum value. Then **(d)** graph the function.

**16.** $f(x) = -x^2 - 2x$

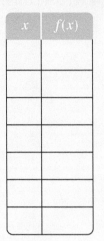

| $x$ | $f(x)$ |
|---|---|
|  |  |
|  |  |
|  |  |
|  |  |
|  |  |
|  |  |

Vertex: ( ____ , ____ )
Line of symmetry: $x =$ ____
_____ value: ____

**17.** $f(x) = 4x^2 - 24x + 41$

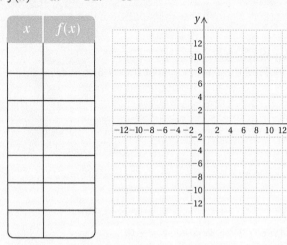

| $x$ | $f(x)$ |
|---|---|
|  |  |
|  |  |
|  |  |
|  |  |
|  |  |
|  |  |

Vertex: ( ____ , ____ )
Line of symmetry: $x =$ ____
_____ value: ____

**18.** Find the $x$- and $y$-intercepts:

$$f(x) = -x^2 + 4x - 1.$$

**19.** What is the minimum product of two numbers whose difference is 8? What numbers yield this product?

**20.** Find the quadratic function that fits the data points $(0, 0)$, $(3, 0)$, and $(5, 2)$.

**21.** *Foreign Adoptions.* The graph at right shows the number of foreign adoptions to the United States for various years. It appears that the graph might be fit by a quadratic function.

**a)** Use the data points $(0, 18.5)$, $(4, 22.9)$, and $(8, 17.4)$ to fit a quadratic function $A(x) = ax^2 + bx + c$ to the data, where $A$ is the number of foreign adoptions to the United States $x$ years since 2000 and $x = 0$ corresponds to 2000.

**b)** Use the quadratic function to estimate the number of adoptions in 2009.

**Foreign Adoptions to the United States**

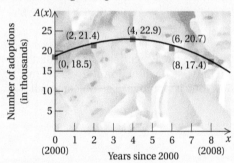

SOURCE: Intercountry Adoption, Office of Children's Issues, U.S. Department of State

Solve.

**22.** $x^2 < 6x + 7$

**23.** $\dfrac{x - 5}{x + 3} < 0$

**24.** $\dfrac{(x - 2)}{(x + 3)(x - 1)} \geq 0$

**25.** Write a quadratic equation whose solutions are $\dfrac{i}{2}$ and $-\dfrac{i}{2}$.

**A.** $4x^2 - 4ix - 1 = 0$

**B.** $x^2 - \dfrac{1}{4} = 0$

**C.** $4x^2 + 1 = 0$

**D.** $x^2 - ix + 1 = 0$

## Synthesis

**26.** A quadratic function has $x$-intercepts $(-2, 0)$ and $(7, 0)$ and $y$-intercept $(0, 8)$. Find an equation for the function. What is its maximum or minimum value?

**27.** One solution of $kx^2 + 3x - k = 0$ is $-2$. Find the other solution.

**1.** *Golf Courses.* Most golf courses have a hole such as the one shown here, where the safe way to the hole is to hit straight out on a first shot (the distance $a$) and then make subsequent shots at a right angle to cover the distance $b$. Golfers are often lured, however, into taking a shortcut over trees, houses, or lakes. If a golfer makes a hole in one on this hole, how long is the shot?

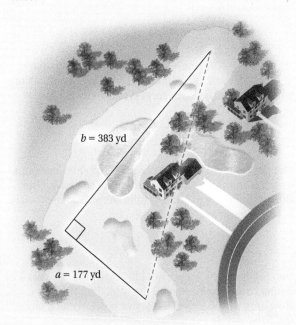

$b = 383$ yd

$a = 177$ yd

Simplify.

**2.** $(4 + 8x^2 - 5x) - (-2x^2 + 3x - 2)$

**3.** $(2x^2 - x + 3)(x - 4)$

**4.** $\dfrac{a^2 - 16}{5a - 15} \cdot \dfrac{2a - 6}{a + 4}$

**5.** $\dfrac{y}{y^2 - y - 42} \div \dfrac{y^2}{y - 7}$

**6.** $\dfrac{2}{m + 1} + \dfrac{3}{m - 5} - \dfrac{m^2 - 1}{m^2 - 4m - 5}$

**7.** $(9x^3 + 5x^2 + 2) \div (x + 2)$

**8.** $\dfrac{\dfrac{1}{x} - \dfrac{1}{y}}{x + y}$

**9.** $\sqrt{0.36}$

**10.** $\sqrt{9x^2 - 36x + 36}$

**11.** $6\sqrt{45} - 3\sqrt{20}$

**12.** $\dfrac{2\sqrt{3} - 4\sqrt{2}}{\sqrt{2} - 3\sqrt{6}}$

**13.** $(8^{2/3})^4$

**14.** $(3 + 2i)(5 - i)$

**15.** $\dfrac{6 - 2i}{3i}$

Factor.

**16.** $2t^2 - 7t - 30$

**17.** $a^2 + 3a - 54$

**18.** $-3a^3 + 12a^2$

**19.** $64a^2 - 9b^2$

**20.** $3a^2 - 36a + 108$

**21.** $\dfrac{1}{27}a^3 - 1$

**22.** $24a^3 + 18a^2 - 20a - 15$

**23.** $(x + 1)(x - 1) + (x + 1)(x + 2)$

Solve.

**24.** $3(4x - 5) + 6 = 3 - (x + 1)$

**25.** $F = \dfrac{mv^2}{r}$, for $r$

**26.** $5 - 3(2x + 1) \le 8x - 3$

**27.** $3x - 2 < -6 \text{ or } x + 3 > 9$

**28.** $|4x - 1| \leq 14$

**29.** $5x + 10y = -10,$
$-2x - 3y = 5$

**30.** $2x + y - z = 9,$
$4x - 2y + z = -9,$
$2x - y + 2z = -12$

**31.** $10x^2 + 28x - 6 = 0$

**32.** $\dfrac{2}{n} - \dfrac{7}{n} = 3$

**33.** $\dfrac{1}{2x - 1} = \dfrac{3}{5x}$

**34.** $A = \dfrac{mh}{m + a}$, for $m$

**35.** $\sqrt{2x - 1} = 6$

**36.** $\sqrt{x - 2} + 1 = \sqrt{2x - 6}$

**37.** $16(t - 1) = t(t + 8)$

**38.** $x^2 - 3x + 16 = 0$

**39.** $\dfrac{18}{x + 1} - \dfrac{12}{x} = \dfrac{1}{3}$

**40.** $P = \sqrt{a^2 - b^2}$, for $a$

**41.** $\dfrac{(x + 3)(x + 2)}{(x - 1)(x + 1)} < 0$

**42.** Solve: $4x^2 - 25 > 0$.

Graph.

**43.** $x + y = 2$

**44.** $y \geq 6x - 5$

**45.** $x < -3$

**46.** $3x - y > 6,$
$4x + y \leq 3$

**47.** $f(x) = x^2 - 1$

**48.** $f(x) = -2x^2 + 3$

**49.** Find an equation of the line with slope $\frac{1}{2}$ and through the point $(-4, 2)$.

**50.** Find an equation of the line parallel to the line $3x + y = 4$ and through the point $(0, 1)$.

**51.** *Marine Travel.* The Connecticut River flows at a rate of 4 km/h for the length of a popular scenic route. In order for a cruiser to travel 60 km upriver and then return in a total of 8 hr, how fast must the boat be able to travel in still water?

**52.** *Architecture.* An architect is designing a rectangular family room with a perimeter of 56 ft. What dimensions will yield the maximum area? What is the maximum area?

**53.** The perimeter of a hexagon with all six sides the same length is the same as the perimeter of a square. One side of the hexagon is 3 less than the side of the square. Find the perimeter of each polygon.

**54.** Two pipes can fill a tank in $1\frac{1}{2}$ hr. One pipe requires 4 hr longer running alone to fill the tank than the other. How long would it take the faster pipe, working alone, to fill the tank?

**55.** Complete the square: $f(x) = 5x^2 - 20x + 15$.
**A.** $f(x) = 5(x - 2)^2 - 5$ **B.** $f(x) = 5(x + 2)^2 + 15$
**C.** $f(x) = 5(x + 2)^2 + 6$ **D.** $f(x) = 5(x + 2)^2 + 11$

**56.** How many times does the graph of $f(x) = x^4 - 6x^2 - 16$ cross the $x$-axis?
**A.** 1          **B.** 2
**C.** 3          **D.** 4

## Synthesis

**57.** Solve: $\dfrac{2x + 1}{x} = 3 + 7\sqrt{\dfrac{2x + 1}{x}}$.

**58.** Factor: $\dfrac{a^3}{8} + \dfrac{8b^3}{729}$.

# Answers

## Exercise Set R.1, p. 9

**1.** $1, 12, \sqrt{25}$ **3.** $-6, 0, 1, -\frac{1}{2}, -4, \frac{7}{9}, 12, -\frac{6}{5}, 3.45, 5\frac{1}{2}, \sqrt{25}, -\frac{12}{3}$
**5.** $-6, 0, 1, -\frac{1}{2}, -4, \frac{7}{9}, 12, -\frac{6}{5}, 3.45, 5\frac{1}{2}, \sqrt{3}, \sqrt{25}, -\frac{12}{3},$
$0.131331333133331\ldots$ **7.** $12, 0$ **9.** $-11, 12, 0$
**11.** $-\sqrt{5}, \pi, -3.565665666566665\ldots$ **13.** $\{m, a, t, h\}$
**15.** $\{1, 2, 3, 4, 5, 6, 7, 8, 9, 10, 11, 12\}$ **17.** $\{2, 4, 6, 8, \ldots\}$
**19.** $\{x \mid x$ is a whole number less than or equal to 5$\}$, or $\{x \mid x$ is a whole number less than 6$\}$ **21.** $\left\{\frac{a}{b} \mid a \text{ and } b \text{ are integers and } b \neq 0\right\}$ **23.** $\{x \mid x > -3\}$ **25.** $>$ **27.** $<$ **29.** $<$
**31.** $<$ **33.** $>$ **35.** $<$ **37.** $>$ **39.** $<$ **41.** $x < -8$
**43.** $y \geq -12.7$ **45.** False **47.** True
**49.**
**51.**
**53.**
**55.** **57.** 6 **59.** 28
**61.** 35 **63.** $\frac{2}{3}$ **65.** 42.8 **67.** 986 **69.** 0 **71.** $\leq$
**73.** $\leq$ **75.** $\frac{1}{8}\%, 0.3\%, 0.009, 1\%, 1.1\%, \frac{9}{100}, \frac{1}{11}, \frac{99}{1000}, 0.11, \frac{1}{8}, \frac{2}{7}, 0.286$

## Exercise Set R.2, p. 19

**1.** $-28$ **3.** 5 **5.** $-16$ **7.** $-4$ **9.** $-10$ **11.** $-26$
**13.** 1.2 **15.** $-8.86$ **17.** $-\frac{1}{3}$ **19.** $-\frac{4}{3}$ **21.** $\frac{1}{10}$ **23.** $\frac{7}{20}$
**25.** 4 **27.** $-3.7$ **29.** $-10$ **31.** 0 **33.** $-4$ **35.** $-14$
**37.** 0 **39.** $-46$ **41.** 5 **43.** 15 **45.** $-11.6$ **47.** $-29.25$
**49.** $-\frac{7}{4}$ **51.** $-\frac{1}{4}$ **53.** $-\frac{19}{12}$ **55.** $-\frac{7}{15}$ **57.** $-21$ **59.** $-8$
**61.** 24 **63.** $-112$ **65.** 34.2 **67.** $-\frac{12}{35}$ **69.** 2 **71.** 60
**73.** 26.46 **75.** 1 **77.** $-\frac{8}{27}$ **79.** $-2$ **81.** $-7$ **83.** 7
**85.** 0.3 **87.** Not defined **89.** 0 **91.** Not defined **93.** $\frac{4}{3}$
**95.** $-\frac{8}{7}$ **97.** $\frac{1}{25}$ **99.** 5 **101.** $-\frac{b}{a}$ **103.** $-\frac{6}{77}$ **105.** 25
**107.** $-6$ **109.** 5 **111.** $-120$ **113.** $-\frac{9}{8}$ **115.** $\frac{5}{3}$ **117.** $\frac{3}{2}$
**119.** $\frac{9}{64}$ **121.** $-2$ **123.** $\frac{12}{13}$, or $0.\overline{923076}$ **125.** $-\frac{81}{50}$, or $-1.62$
**127.** Not defined **129.** $-\frac{2}{3}, \frac{3}{2}, \frac{5}{4}, -\frac{4}{5}; 0$, does not exist; $-1, 1;$
$4.5, -\frac{1}{4.5}; -x, \frac{1}{x}$ **131.** $26, 0$ **132.** 26 **133.** $-13, 26, 0$
**134.** $\sqrt{3}, \pi, 4.57557555755557\ldots$ **135.** $-12.47, -13, 26, 0,$
$-\frac{23}{32}, \frac{7}{11}$ **136.** $\sqrt{3}, -12.47, -13, 26, \pi, 0, -\frac{23}{32}, \frac{7}{11},$
$4.57557555755557\ldots$ **137.** $<$ **138.** $>$ **139.** $<$ **140.** $>$
**141.** $\frac{1}{4}$ **143.** 31,250

## Calculator Corner, p. 27

**1.** 56 **2.** 96 **3.** 262.5 **4.** $-2.\overline{4}$, or $-\frac{22}{9}$

## Exercise Set R.3, p. 28

**1.** $4^5$ **3.** $5^6$ **5.** $m^3$ **7.** $\left(\frac{7}{12}\right)^4$ **9.** $(123.7)^2$ **11.** 128
**13.** $-32$ **15.** $\frac{1}{81}$ **17.** $-64$ **19.** 31.36 **21.** 5 **23.** 1
**25.** 1 **27.** $\frac{7}{8}$ **29.** 16 **31.** $\frac{27}{8}$ **33.** $\frac{1}{y^5}$ **35.** $a^2$ **37.** $-\frac{1}{11}$
**39.** $3^{-4}$ **41.** $b^{-3}$ **43.** $(-16)^{-2}$ **45.** $-4$ **47.** $-117$
**49.** 2 **51.** 8 **53.** $-358$ **55.** 144; 74 **57.** $-576$
**59.** 2599 **61.** 36 **63.** 5619.712 **65.** $-200,167,769$
**67.** 3 **69.** 3 **71.** 16 **73.** $-310$ **75.** 2 **77.** 1875
**79.** 7804.48 **81.** 12 **83.** 8 **85.** 16 **87.** $-86$ **89.** 37
**91.** $-1$ **93.** 22 **95.** $-39$ **97.** 12 **99.** $-549$ **101.** $-144$
**103.** 2 **105.** $-\frac{31}{76}$ **107.** $\frac{61}{13}$ **109.** $\frac{9}{7}$ **110.** 2.3 **111.** 0
**112.** 900 **113.** $-33$ **114.** $-79$ **115.** 33 **116.** $-79$
**117.** $-23$ **118.** 23 **119.** $-23$ **120.** $\frac{5}{8}$ **121.** $25\frac{1}{4}$
**123.** $9 \cdot 5 + 2 - (8 \cdot 3 + 1) = 22$ **125.** 3125
**127.** $(2 + 3)^{-1} = (5)^{-1} = \frac{1}{5}; 2^{-1} + 3^{-1} = \frac{1}{2} + \frac{1}{3} = \frac{3}{6} + \frac{2}{6} = \frac{5}{6};$
so $(2 + 3)^{-1} \neq 2^{-1} + 3^{-1}$.

## Exercise Set R.4, p. 36

**1.** $b + 8$, or $8 + b$ **3.** $c - 13.4$ **5.** $5 + q$, or $q + 5$
**7.** $a + b$, or $b + a$ **9.** $x \div y$, or $\frac{x}{y}$ **11.** $x + w$, or $w + x$
**13.** $n - m$ **15.** $p + q$, or $q + p$ **17.** $3q$ **19.** $-18m$
**21.** $17\% s$, or $0.17s$ **23.** $75t$ **25.** $\$40 - x$ **27.** $-92$
**29.** 3 **31.** 4 **33.** $\frac{45}{2}$, or 22.5 **35.** 16 **37.** 19 **39.** 57
**41.** $\$440.70$ **43.** $A = 2289.06 \text{ in}^2; C = 169.56 \text{ in.}$ **45.** 243
**46.** $-243$ **47.** 100 **48.** 10,000 **49.** 28.09 **50.** $\frac{9}{25}$
**51.** 1 **52.** 4.5 **53.** $3x$ **54.** 1 **55.** $d = r \cdot t$ **57.** 9

## Exercise Set R.5, p. 44

**1.** $-10, -10, 2; 25, 25, -5; 0, 0, 0; 2x + 3x$ and $5x$ are equivalent.
**3.** $-12, -16, -12; 38.4, 51.2, 38.4; 0, 0, 0; 4x + 8x$ and $4(x + 2x)$ are equivalent. **5.** $\frac{7x}{8x}$ **7.** $\frac{6a}{8a}$ **9.** $\frac{5}{3}$ **11.** $-4$ **13.** $3 + w$
**15.** $tr$ **17.** $cd + 4, dc + 4$, or $4 + dc$ **19.** $x + yz,$
$x + zy$, or $zy + x$ **21.** $(m + n) + 2$ **23.** $7 \cdot (x \cdot y)$
**25.** $a + (8 + b), (a + 8) + b, b + (a + 8)$; others are
possible **27.** $(7 \cdot b) \cdot a, b \cdot (a \cdot 7), (b \cdot a) \cdot 7$; others are
possible **29.** $4a + 4$ **31.** $8x - 8y$ **33.** $-10a - 15b$
**35.** $2ab - 2ac + 2ad$ **37.** $2\pi rh + 2\pi r$ **39.** $\frac{1}{2}ha + \frac{1}{2}hb$
**41.** $4a, -5b, 6$ **43.** $2x, -3y, -2z$ **45.** $24(x + y)$
**47.** $7(p - 1)$ **49.** $7(x - 3)$ **51.** $x(y + 1)$
**53.** $2(x - y + z)$ **55.** $3(x + 2y - 1)$ **57.** $4(w - 3z + 2)$
**59.** $4(5x - 9y - 3)$ **61.** $a(b + c - d)$ **63.** $\frac{1}{4}\pi r(r + s)$
**65.** $(x + y)^2$ **66.** $x^2 + y^2$ **67.** $-102$ **68.** $-\frac{1}{2}$ **69.** $\frac{1}{8}$
**70.** $-46$ **71.** No **73.** Yes

## Exercise Set R.6, p. 50

**1.** $12x$   **3.** $-3b$   **5.** $15y$   **7.** $11a$   **9.** $-8t$   **11.** $10x$
**13.** $11x - 5y$   **15.** $-4c + 12d$   **17.** $22x + 18$
**19.** $1.19x + 0.93y$   **21.** $-\frac{2}{15}a - \frac{1}{3}b - 27$   **23.** $P = 2(l + w)$
**25.** $2c$   **27.** $-b - 4$   **29.** $-b + 3$, or $3 - b$   **31.** $-t + y$,
or $y - t$   **33.** $-x - y - z$   **35.** $-8x + 6y - 13$
**37.** $2c - 5d + 3e - 4f$   **39.** $1.2x - 56.7y + 34z + \frac{1}{4}$
**41.** $3a + 5$   **43.** $m + 1$   **45.** $9d - 16$   **47.** $-7x + 14$
**49.** $-9x + 17$   **51.** $17x + 3y - 18$   **53.** $10x - 19$
**55.** $22a - 15$   **57.** $-190$   **59.** $12x + 30$   **61.** $3x + 30$
**63.** $9x - 18$   **65.** $-4x + 808$   **67.** $-14y - 186$   **69.** $-37$
**70.** $-71$   **71.** $-23.1$   **72.** $\frac{5}{24}$   **73.** $-16$   **74.** $16$
**75.** $-16$   **76.** $-\frac{1}{6}$   **77.** $8a - 8b$   **78.** $-16a + 24b - 32$
**79.** $6ax - 6bx + 12cx$   **80.** $16x - 8y + 10$   **81.** $24(a - 1)$
**82.** $8(3a - 2b)$   **83.** $a(b - c + 1)$   **84.** $5(3p + 9q - 2)$
**85.** $(3 - 8)^2 + 9 = 34$   **87.** $5 \cdot 2^3 \div (3 - 4)^4 = 40$
**89.** $23a - 18b + 184$   **91.** $-9z + 5x$   **93.** $-x + 19$

## Calculator Corner, p. 61

**1.** $1.2312 \times 10^{-4}$   **2.** $2.4495 \times 10^3$   **3.** $2.8 \times 10^5$
**4.** $5.4 \times 10^{14}$   **5.** $3 \times 10^{-6}$   **6.** $6 \times 10^5$   **7.** $1.2 \times 10^{-14}$
**8.** $3 \times 10^{12}$

## Exercise Set R.7, p. 61

**1.** $3^9$   **3.** $\frac{1}{6^4}$   **5.** $\frac{1}{8^6}$   **7.** $\frac{1}{b^3}$   **9.** $a^3$   **11.** $72x^5$   **13.** $-28m^5n^5$
**15.** $-\frac{14}{x^{11}}$   **17.** $\frac{105}{x^{2t}}$   **19.** $-\frac{8}{y^{6m}}$   **21.** $8^7$   **23.** $6^5$   **25.** $\frac{1}{10^9}$
**27.** $9^2$   **29.** $\frac{1}{x^{10n}}$   **31.** $\frac{1}{w^{5q}}$   **33.** $a^5$   **35.** $-3x^5z^4$   **37.** $-\frac{4x^9}{3y^2}$
**39.** $\frac{3x^3}{2y^2}$   **41.** $4^6$   **43.** $\frac{1}{8^{12}}$   **45.** $6^{12}$   **47.** $125a^6b^6$   **49.** $\frac{y^{12}}{9x^6}$
**51.** $\frac{a^4}{36b^6c^2}$   **53.** $\frac{1}{4^9 \cdot 3^{12}}$   **55.** $\frac{8x^9y^3}{27}$   **57.** $\frac{a^{10}b^5}{5^{10}}$
**59.** $\frac{6^{30}2^{12}y^{36}}{z^{48}}$   **61.** $\frac{64}{x^{24}y^{12}}$   **63.** $\frac{5^7b^{28}}{3^7a^{35}}$   **65.** $10^a$
**67.** $3a^{-x-4}$   **69.** $\frac{-5x^{a+1}}{y}$   **71.** $8^{4xy}$   **73.** $12^{6b-2ab}$
**75.** $5^{2c}x^{2ac-2c}y^{2bc+2c}$, or $25^cx^{2ac-2c}y^{2bc+2c}$   **77.** $2x^{a+2}y^{b-2}$
**79.** $4.7 \times 10^{10}$   **81.** $1.6 \times 10^{-8}$   **83.** $2.6 \times 10^9$   **85.** $2 \times 10^{-7}$
**87.** $673,000,000$   **89.** $0.000066$ cm   **91.** $\$2,000,000,000,000$
**93.** $9.66 \times 10^{-5}$   **95.** $1.3338 \times 10^{-11}$   **97.** $2.5 \times 10^3$
**99.** $5.0 \times 10^{-4}$   **101.** About $\$1.584 \times 10^8$
**103.** $6.3072 \times 10^{10}$ sec   **105.** About 4.08 light-years
**107.** $3.33 \times 10^{-2}$   **109.** About $2.2 \times 10^{-3}$ lb
**111.** $19x + 4y - 20$   **112.** $-23t + 21$   **113.** $-11$   **114.** $-231$
**115.** $-8$   **116.** $8$   **117.** $2^{21}$   **119.** $\frac{1}{a^{14}b^{27}}$   **121.** $4x^{2a}y^{2b}$

## Summary and Review: Chapter R, p. 66

### Concept Reinforcement

**1.** False   **2.** True   **3.** True   **4.** False   **5.** False   **6.** True
**7.** True   **8.** True

### Review Exercises

**1.** $2, -\frac{2}{3}, 0.45\overline{45}, -23.788$   **2.** $\{x \mid x$ is a real number less than or
equal to $46\}$   **3.** $<$   **4.** $x < 19$   **5.** False   **6.** True
**7.**
**8.**   **9.** $7.23$   **10.** $0$
**11.** $-2$   **12.** $-7.9$   **13.** $-\frac{31}{28}$   **14.** $-5$   **15.** $-26.7$   **16.** $\frac{19}{4}$
**17.** $10.26$   **18.** $-\frac{3}{7}$   **19.** $168$   **20.** $-4$   **21.** $21$   **22.** $-7$
**23.** $-\frac{7}{12}$   **24.** $\frac{8}{3}$   **25.** Not defined   **26.** $-24$   **27.** $7$

**28.** $-2.3$   **29.** $0$   **30.** $a^5$   **31.** $\left(-\frac{7}{8}\right)^3$   **32.** $\frac{1}{a^4}$   **33.** $x^{-8}$
**34.** $59$   **35.** $-116$   **36.** $5x$   **37.** $28\%y$, or $0.28y$   **38.** $t - 9$
**39.** $\frac{a}{b} - 8$   **40.** $-17$   **41.** $-8$   **42.** $84$ ft$^2$   **43.** $-4, 16, 36, 6$;
$95, 225, 25, 105$; $-5, 25, 25, 5$; none are equivalent   **44.** $-16, -9$,
$-16, 12$; $6, 13, 6, 34$; $-14, -7, -14, 14$; $2x - 14$ and $2(x - 7)$ are
equivalent   **45.** $\frac{21x}{9x}$   **46.** $-12$   **47.** $a + 11$   **48.** $y \cdot 8$
**49.** $9 + (a + b)$   **50.** $(8x)y$   **51.** $-6x + 3y$   **52.** $8abc + 4ab$
**53.** $5(x + 2y - z)$   **54.** $pt(r + s)$   **55.** $-3x + 5y$
**56.** $12c - 4$   **57.** $9c - 4d + 3$   **58.** $x + 3$   **59.** $6x + 15$
**60.** $22x - 14$   **61.** $-17m - 12$   **62.** $-\frac{10x^7}{y^5}$   **63.** $-\frac{3y^3}{2x^4}$
**64.** $\frac{a^8}{9b^2c^6}$   **65.** $\frac{81y^{40}}{16x^{24}}$   **66.** $6.875 \times 10^9$   **67.** $1.312 \times 10^{-1}$
**68.** $\$6.7 \times 10^4$   **69.** $1.422 \times 10^{-2}$ m$^3$   **70.** D   **71.** A
**72.** $x^{12y}$   **73.** $32$   **74.** (a), (i); (d), (f); (h), (j)

### Understanding Through Discussion and Writing

**1.** Answers may vary. Five rational numbers that are not
integers are $\frac{1}{3}, -\frac{3}{4}, 6\frac{5}{8}, -0.001$, and $1.7$. They are not integers
because they are not whole numbers or opposites of whole
number.   **2.** The quotient $7/0$ is defined to be the number
that gives a result of 7 when multiplied by 0. There is no such
number, so we say that the quotient is not defined.
**3.** No; the area is quadrupled. For a triangle with base $b$ and
height $h$, $A = \frac{1}{2}bh$. For a triangle with base $2b$ and height $2h$,
$A = \frac{1}{2} \cdot 2b \cdot 2h = 2bh = 4\left(\frac{1}{2}bh\right)$.   **4.** No; the area is
quadrupled. For a parallelogram with base $b$ and height $h$,
$A = bh$. For a parallelogram with base $2b$ and height $2h$,
$A = 2b \cdot 2h = 4(bh)$.   **5.** $\$5$ million in $\$20$ bills contains
$\frac{5 \times 10^6}{20} = 0.25 \times 10^6 = 2.5 \times 10^5$ bills, and $2.5 \times 10^5$ bills
would weigh $2.5 \times 10^5 \times 2.2 \times 10^{-3} = 5.5 \times 10^2$, or 550 lb.
Thus it is not possible that a criminal is carrying $\$5$ million in
$\$20$ bills in a briefcase.   **6.** For $5^n$, where $n$ is a natural
number, the ones digit will be 5. Since this is not the case with
the given calculator readout, we know that the readout is an
approximation.

## Test: Chapter R, p. 71

**1.** [R.1a] $\sqrt{7}, \pi$   **2.** [R.1a] $\{x \mid x$ is a real number greater than $20\}$
**3.** [R.1b] $>$   **4.** [R.1b] $5 \geq a$   **5.** [R.1b] True   **6.** [R.1b] True
**7.** [R.1c]
**8.** [R.1d] $0$   **9.** [R.1d] $\frac{7}{8}$   **10.** [R.2a] $-2$   **11.** [R.2a] $-13.1$
**12.** [R.2a] $-6$   **13.** [R.2c] $-1$   **14.** [R.2c] $-29.7$   **15.** [R.2c] $\frac{25}{4}$
**16.** [R.2d] $-33.62$   **17.** [R.2d] $\frac{3}{4}$   **18.** [R.2d] $-528$
**19.** [R.2e] $15$   **20.** [R.2e] $-5$   **21.** [R.2e] $\frac{8}{3}$   **22.** [R.2e] $-82$
**23.** [R.2e] Not defined   **24.** [R.2b] $13$   **25.** [R.2b] $0$
**26.** [R.3a] $q^4$   **27.** [R.3b] $a^{-9}$   **28.** [R.3c] $0$   **29.** [R.3c] $-\frac{16}{7}$
**30.** [R.4a] $t + 9$, or $9 + t$   **31.** [R.4a] $\frac{x}{y} - 12$   **32.** [R.4b] $18$
**33.** [R.4b] $3.75$ cm$^2$   **34.** [R.5a] Yes   **35.** [R.5a] No
**36.** [R.5b] $\frac{27x}{36x}$   **37.** [R.5b] $\frac{3}{2}$   **38.** [R.5c] $qp$   **39.** [R.5c] $4 + t$
**40.** [R.5c] $(3 + t) + w$   **41.** [R.5c] $4(ab)$
**42.** [R.5d] $-6a + 8b$   **43.** [R.5d] $3\pi rs + 3\pi r$
**44.** [R.5d] $a(b - c + 2d)$   **45.** [R.5d] $h(2a + 1)$
**46.** [R.6a] $10y - 5x$   **47.** [R.6a] $21a + 14$
**48.** [R.6b] $9x - 7y + 22$   **49.** [R.6b] $-7x + 14$
**50.** [R.6b] $10x - 21$   **51.** [R.7a] $-\frac{3y^2}{2x^4}$

**52.** [R.7a] $-\dfrac{6a^9}{b^5}$  **53.** [R.7a] $-50a^{9n}$  **54.** [R.7a] $-\dfrac{5}{x^{4t}}$

**55.** [R.7b] $\dfrac{a^{12}}{81b^8c^4}$  **56.** [R.7b] $\dfrac{16a^{48}}{b^{48}}$  **57.** [R.7c] $4.37 \times 10^{-5}$

**58.** [R.7c] $3.741 \times 10^7$  **59.** [R.7c] $1.875 \times 10^{-6}$  **60.** [R.7c] C
**61.** [R.5c, d], [R.7b] (b), (e); (d), (f), (h); (i), (j)

# CHAPTER 1

## Calculator Corner, p. 83

**1.** Left to the student  **2.** Left to the student

## Exercise Set 1.1, p. 84

**1.** Yes  **3.** No  **5.** No  **7.** No  **9.** Yes  **11.** No  **13.** 7
**15.** $-8$  **17.** 27  **19.** $-39$  **21.** 86.86  **23.** $\frac{1}{6}$  **25.** 6
**27.** $-4$  **29.** $-147$  **31.** 32  **33.** $-6$  **35.** $-\frac{1}{6}$  **37.** 10
**39.** 11  **41.** $-12$  **43.** 8  **45.** 2  **47.** 21  **49.** $-12$
**51.** No solution  **53.** $-1$  **55.** $\frac{18}{5}$  **57.** 0  **59.** 1
**61.** All real numbers  **63.** No solution  **65.** 7  **67.** 2
**69.** 7  **71.** 5  **73.** $-\frac{3}{2}$  **75.** All real numbers  **77.** 5
**79.** $\frac{23}{66}$  **81.** $\frac{5}{32}$  **83.** $\frac{79}{32}$  **85.** $a^{14}$  **86.** $\dfrac{1}{a^{32}}$  **87.** $-\dfrac{18x^2}{y^{11}}$
**88.** $-2x^8y^3$  **89.** $12 - 20x$  **90.** $-5 + 6x$
**91.** $-12x + 8y - 4z$  **92.** $-10x + 35y - 20$  **93.** $2(x - 3y)$
**94.** $-4(x + 6y)$  **95.** $2(2x - 5y + 1)$  **96.** $-5(x - 7y + 4)$
**97.** $\{1, 2, 3, 4, 5, 6, 7, 8, 9\}$; $\{x \mid x \text{ is a positive integer less than } 10\}$
**98.** $\{-8, -7, -6, -5, -4, -3, -2, -1\}$; $\{x \mid x \text{ is a negative integer greater than } -9\}$  **99.** Approximately $-4.176$  **101.** $\frac{3}{2}$
**103.** 8

## Exercise Set 1.2, p. 93

**1.** $r = \dfrac{d}{t}$  **3.** $h = \dfrac{A}{b}$  **5.** $w = \dfrac{P - 2l}{2}$, or $\dfrac{P}{2} - l$  **7.** $b = \dfrac{2A}{h}$

**9.** $a = 2A - b$  **11.** $m = \dfrac{F}{a}$  **13.** $t = \dfrac{I}{Pr}$  **15.** $c^2 = \dfrac{E}{m}$

**17.** $p = 2Q + q$  **19.** $y = \dfrac{c - Ax}{B}$  **21.** $N = \dfrac{1.08T}{I}$

**23.** $m = \dfrac{4}{3}C - 5$, or $\dfrac{4C - 15}{3}$  **25.** $b = 3n - a + c$

**27.** $R = \dfrac{d}{1 - st}$  **29.** $B = \dfrac{T}{1 + qt}$

**31. (a)** About 1930 calories; **(b)** $w = \dfrac{R - 66 - 12.7h + 6.8a}{6.23}$

**33. (a)** About 2340 calories;

**(b)** $a = \dfrac{1015.25 + 6.74w + 7.29h - K}{7.29}$  **35. (a)** 1614 g;

**(b)** $a = \dfrac{P + 299}{9.337d}$  **37. (a)** 50 mg; **(b)** $d = \dfrac{c(a + 12)}{a}$, or

$c + \dfrac{12c}{a}$  **39.** $-5$  **40.** 250  **41.** $-2$  **42.** $-25$  **43.** $\frac{4}{5}$

**44.** 6  **45.** $-6$  **46.** $-5$  **47.** $s = \dfrac{A - \pi r^2}{\pi r}$, or $\dfrac{A}{\pi r} - r$

**49.** $V_1 = \dfrac{P_2 V_2 T_1}{P_1 T_2}$; $P_2 = \dfrac{P_1 V_1 T_2}{T_1 V_2}$  **51.** 0.8 yr
**53. (a)** Approximately 120.5 horsepower;
**(b)** approximately 94.1 horsepower

## Exercise Set 1.3, p. 105

**1.** 6.55 mi  **3.** \$38.1 billion  **5.** $45°, 52°, 83°$  **7.** \$1120
**9.** Length: 94 ft; width: 50 ft  **11.** $66\frac{2}{3}$ cm and $33\frac{1}{3}$ cm
**13.** \$265,000  **15.** 9, 11, 13  **17.** 348 and 349  **19.** 843 sq ft
**21.** \$38,950  **23.** About 2169 incidents  **25. (a)** 68.4 million
laptops; 136.8 million laptops; **(b)** 2010  **27.** 6 min
**29.** Downstream: 1.25 hr; upstream: 1.875 hr  **31.** $\frac{1}{2}$ hr

**33.** $-2442$  **34.** 208  **35.** 49  **36.** $-119$  **37.** 49
**38.** $-119$  **39.** $\frac{78}{1649}$  **40.** $\frac{17}{10}$  **41.** $-1$  **42.** $-256$
**43.** $2^5$, or 32  **44.** $2^{21}$, or 2,097,152  **45.** \$115,243
**47.** 130 novels  **49.** 25% increase  **51.** 62,208,000 sec
**53.** Answers may vary. A piece of material 75 cm long is to be cut into 2 pieces, one of them $\frac{2}{3}$ as long as the other. How should the material be cut?  **55.** $m\angle 2 = 120°$; $m\angle 1 = 60°$

## Mid-Chapter Review: Chapter 1, p. 111

**1.** True  **2.** True  **3.** False  **4.** False
**5.**
$$2x - 5 = 1 - 4x$$
$$2x - 5 + 4x = 1 - 4x + 4x$$
$$6x - 5 = 1$$
$$6x - 5 + 5 = 1 + 5$$
$$6x = 6$$
$$\frac{6x}{6} = \frac{6}{6}$$
$$x = 1$$
**6.**
$$Mx + Ny = T$$
$$Mx + Ny - Mx = T - Mx$$
$$Ny = T - Mx$$
$$y = \frac{T - Mx}{N}$$

**7.** Yes  **8.** No  **9.** No  **10.** Yes  **11.** $-3$  **12.** $-8$
**13.** 4  **14.** 2  **15.** All real numbers  **16.** 2  **17.** $-\frac{5}{2}$
**18.** No solution  **19.** $-\frac{4}{3}$  **20.** 5  **21.** $\frac{3}{2}$  **22.** $-\frac{3}{16}$
**23.** $n = \dfrac{P}{m}$  **24.** $t = \dfrac{z - 3w}{3}$, or $\dfrac{z}{3} - w$  **25.** $s = 4N - r$
**26.** $B = 1.5\dfrac{A}{T}$  **27.** $t = \dfrac{3H + 10}{2}$, or $\dfrac{3H}{2} + 5$  **28.** $g = \dfrac{f}{1 + hm}$
**29.** About \$15.9 billion  **30.** \$5.4 billion  **31.** Length: 7 ft; width: 5 ft  **32.** 1.5 hr; 3 hr  **33.** Equivalent expressions have the same value for all possible replacements. Any replacement that does not make any of the expressions undefined can be substituted for the variable. Equivalent equations have the same solutions(s).  **34.** Answers may vary. A walker who knows how far and how long she walks each day wants to know her average speed each day.  **35.** Answers may vary. A decorator wants to have a carpet cut for a bedroom. The perimeter of the room is 54 ft and its length is 15 ft. How wide should the carpet be?  **36.** We can subtract by adding an opposite, so we can use the addition principle to subtract the same number on both sides of an equation. Similarly, we can divide by multiplying by a reciprocal, so we can use the multiplication principle to divide both sides of an equation by the same number.  **37.** The manner in which a guess or an estimate is manipulated can give insight into the form of the equation to which the problem will be translated.  **38.** Labeling the variable clearly makes the *Translate* step more accurate. It also allows us to determine whether the solution of the equation we translated to provides the information asked for in the original problem.

## Translating for Success, p. 122

**1.** F  **2.** I  **3.** C  **4.** E  **5.** D  **6.** J  **7.** O  **8.** M
**9.** B  **10.** L

## Exercise Set 1.4, p. 123

**1.** No, no, no, yes  **3.** No, yes, yes, no, no  **5.** $(-\infty, 5)$
**7.** $[-3, 3]$  **9.** $(-8, -4)$  **11.** $(-2, 5)$  **13.** $(-\sqrt{2}, \infty)$
**15.** $\{x \mid x > -1\}$, or $(-1, \infty)$  **17.** $\{y \mid y < 6\}$, or $(-\infty, 6)$
**19.** $\{a \mid a \le -22\}$, or $(-\infty, -22]$

**21.** $\{t \mid t \ge -4\}$, or $[-4, \infty)$

**23.** $\{y|y > -6\}$, or $(-6, \infty)$   **25.** $\{x|x \le 9\}$, or $(-\infty, 9]$

**27.** $\{x|x \ge 3\}$, or $[3, \infty)$

**29.** $\{x|x < -60\}$, or $(-\infty, -60)$   **31.** $\{x|x > 3\}$, or $(3, \infty)$

**33.** $\{x|x \le 0.9\}$, or $(-\infty, 0.9]$   **35.** $\left\{x \mid x \le \frac{5}{6}\right\}$, or $\left(-\infty, \frac{5}{6}\right]$

**37.** $\{x|x < 6\}$, or $(-\infty, 6)$   **39.** $\{y|y \le -3\}$, or $(-\infty, -3]$

**41.** $\left\{y \mid y > \frac{2}{3}\right\}$, or $\left(\frac{2}{3}, \infty\right)$   **43.** $\{x|x \ge 11.25\}$, or $[11.25, \infty)$

**45.** $\left\{x \mid x \le \frac{1}{2}\right\}$, or $\left(-\infty, \frac{1}{2}\right]$   **47.** $\left\{y \mid y \le -\frac{75}{2}\right\}$, or $\left(-\infty, -\frac{75}{2}\right]$

**49.** $\left\{x \mid x > -\frac{2}{17}\right\}$, or $\left(-\frac{2}{17}, \infty\right)$   **51.** $\left\{m \mid m > \frac{7}{3}\right\}$, or $\left(\frac{7}{3}, \infty\right)$

**53.** $\{r|r < -3\}$, or $(-\infty, -3)$   **55.** $\{x|x \ge 2\}$, or $[2, \infty)$

**57.** $\{y|y < 5\}$, or $(-\infty, 5)$   **59.** $\left\{x \mid x \le \frac{4}{7}\right\}$, or $\left(-\infty, \frac{4}{7}\right]$

**61.** $\{x|x < 8\}$, or $(-\infty, 8)$   **63.** $\left\{x \mid x \ge \frac{13}{2}\right\}$, or $\left[\frac{13}{2}, \infty\right)$

**65.** $\left\{x \mid x < \frac{11}{18}\right\}$, or $\left(-\infty, \frac{11}{18}\right)$   **67.** $\left\{x \mid x \ge -\frac{51}{31}\right\}$, or $\left[-\frac{51}{31}, \infty\right)$

**69.** $\{a|a \ge 2\}$, or $(-\infty, 2]$   **71.** $\{W|W <$ (approximately)

189.5 lb$\}$   **73.** $\{S|S \ge 84\}$   **75.** $\{B|B \ge \$11,500\}$

**77.** $\{S|S > \$7000\}$   **79.** $\{n|n > 25\}$   **81.** $\{p|p > 80\}$

**83.** $\{s|s > 8\}$   **85. (a)** 8.2 million gal; 9.4 million gal;

10.6 million gal; **(b)** years after 2012   **87.** $-9a + 30b$

**88.** $32x - 72y$   **89.** $-8a + 22b$   **90.** $-6a + 17b$

**91.** $10(3x - 7y - 4)$   **92.** $-6a(2 - 5b)$

**93.** $-4(2x - 6y + 1)$   **94.** $5(2n - 9mn + 20m)$   **95.** $-11.2$

**96.** 6.6   **97.** $-11.2$   **98.** 6.6   **99. (a)** $\{p|p > 10\}$;

**(b)** $\{p|p < 10\}$   **101.** True   **103.** All real numbers

**105.** All real numbers

## Exercise Set 1.5, p. 137

**1.** $\{9, 11\}$   **3.** $\{b\}$   **5.** $\{9, 10, 11, 13\}$   **7.** $\{a, b, c, d, f, g\}$

**9.** $\varnothing$   **11.** $\{3, 5, 7\}$

**13.** ; $(-4, 1]$

**15.** ; $(1, 6)$

**17.** $\{x|-4 \le x < 5\}$, or $[-4, 5)$;

**19.** $\{x|x \ge 2\}$, or $[2, \infty)$;   **21.** $\varnothing$

**23.** $\{x|-8 < x < 6\}$, or $(-8, 6)$

**25.** $\{x|-6 < x \le 2\}$, or $(-6, 2]$

**27.** $\{x|-1 < x \le 6\}$, or $(-1, 6]$

**29.** $\{y|-1 < y \le 5\}$, or $(-1, 5]$

**31.** $\left\{x \mid -\frac{5}{3} \le x \le \frac{4}{3}\right\}$, or $\left[-\frac{5}{3}, \frac{4}{3}\right]$

**33.** $\left\{x \mid -\frac{7}{2} < x \le \frac{11}{2}\right\}$, or $\left(-\frac{7}{2}, \frac{11}{2}\right]$

**35.** $\{x|10 < x \le 14\}$, or $(10, 14]$

**37.** $\left\{x \mid -\frac{13}{3} \le x \le 9\right\}$, or $\left[-\frac{13}{3}, 9\right]$

**39.** ; $(-\infty, -2) \cup (1, \infty)$

**41.** ; $(-\infty, -3] \cup (1, \infty)$

**43.** $\{x|x < -5 \text{ or } x > -1\}$, or $(-\infty, -5) \cup (-1, \infty)$;

**45.** $\left\{x \mid x \le \frac{5}{2} \text{ or } x \ge 4\right\}$, or $\left(-\infty, \frac{5}{2}\right] \cup [4, \infty)$;

**47.** $\{x|x \ge -3\}$, or $[-3, \infty)$;

**49.** $\left\{x \mid x \le -\frac{5}{4} \text{ or } x > -\frac{1}{2}\right\}$, or $\left(-\infty, -\frac{5}{4}\right] \cup \left(-\frac{1}{2}, \infty\right)$

---

**51.** All real numbers, or $(-\infty, \infty)$

**53.** $\{x|x < -4 \text{ or } x > 2\}$, or $(-\infty, -4) \cup (2, \infty)$

**55.** $\left\{x \mid x < \frac{79}{4} \text{ or } x > \frac{89}{4}\right\}$, or $\left(-\infty, \frac{79}{4}\right) \cup \left(\frac{89}{4}, \infty\right)$

**57.** $\left\{x \mid x \le -\frac{13}{2} \text{ or } x \ge \frac{29}{2}\right\}$, or $\left(-\infty, -\frac{13}{2}\right] \cup \left[\frac{29}{2}, \infty\right)$

**59.** $\{d|0 \text{ ft} \le d \le 198 \text{ ft}\}$   **61.** Between 23 beats and 27 beats

**63.** $\{W|140.2 \text{ lb} \le W \le 188.8 \text{ lb}\}$

**65.** $\{d|250 \text{ mg} < d < 500 \text{ mg}\}$   **67.** 3.2   **68.** 12   **69.** 2

**70.** 0   **71.** $-\dfrac{32y^{30}}{x^{20}}$   **72.** $-\dfrac{20b}{a^7}$   **73.** $-\dfrac{4a^{17}}{5b^{15}}$   **74.** $25p^{12}q^{22}$

**75.** $\dfrac{a^6}{8b^6}$   **76.** $25p^{10}q^8$   **77.** $\{x|-4 < x \le 1\}$, or $(-4, 1]$

**79.** $\left\{x \mid \frac{2}{5} \le x \le \frac{4}{5}\right\}$, or $\left[\frac{2}{5}, \frac{4}{5}\right]$   **81.** $\left\{x \mid -\frac{1}{8} < x < \frac{1}{2}\right\}$, or $\left(-\frac{1}{8}, \frac{1}{2}\right)$

**83.** $\{x|10 < x \le 18\}$, or $(10, 18]$   **85.** True   **87.** False

**89.** All real numbers; $\varnothing$

## Exercise Set 1.6, p. 148

**1.** $9|x|$   **3.** $2x^2$   **5.** $2x^2$   **7.** $6|y|$   **9.** $\dfrac{2}{|x|}$   **11.** $\dfrac{x^2}{|y|}$

**13.** $4|x|$   **15.** $\dfrac{y^2}{3}$   **17.** 38   **19.** 19   **21.** 6.3   **23.** 5

**25.** $\{-3, 3\}$   **27.** $\varnothing$   **29.** $\{0\}$   **31.** $\{-9, 15\}$   **33.** $\left\{-\frac{1}{2}, \frac{7}{2}\right\}$

**35.** $\left\{-\frac{5}{4}, \frac{23}{4}\right\}$   **37.** $\{-11, 11\}$   **39.** $\{-291, 291\}$

**41.** $\{-8, 8\}$   **43.** $\{-7, 7\}$   **45.** $\{-2, 2\}$   **47.** $\{-7, 8\}$

**49.** $\{-12, 2\}$   **51.** $\left\{-\frac{5}{2}, \frac{7}{2}\right\}$   **53.** $\varnothing$   **55.** $\left\{-\frac{13}{54}, -\frac{7}{54}\right\}$

**57.** $\left\{-\frac{11}{2}, \frac{3}{4}\right\}$   **59.** $\left\{\frac{3}{2}\right\}$   **61.** $\left\{5, -\frac{3}{5}\right\}$   **63.** All real numbers

**65.** $\left\{-\frac{3}{2}\right\}$   **67.** $\left\{\frac{24}{23}, 0\right\}$   **69.** $\left\{32, \frac{8}{3}\right\}$   **71.** $\{x|-3 < x < 3\}$,

or $(-3, 3)$   **73.** $\{x|x \le -2 \text{ or } x \ge 2\}$, or $(-\infty, -2] \cup [2, \infty)$

**75.** $\{x|0 < x < 2\}$, or $(0, 2)$   **77.** $\{x|-6 \le x \le -2\}$, or

$[-6, -2]$   **79.** $\left\{x \mid -\frac{1}{2} \le x \le \frac{7}{2}\right\}$, or $\left[-\frac{1}{2}, \frac{7}{2}\right]$   **81.** $\left\{y \mid y < -\frac{3}{2} \text{ or } \right.$

$\left. y > \frac{17}{2}\right\}$, or $\left(-\infty, -\frac{3}{2}\right) \cup \left(\frac{17}{2}, \infty\right)$   **83.** $\left\{x \mid x \le -\frac{5}{4} \text{ or } x \ge \frac{23}{4}\right\}$, or

$\left(-\infty, -\frac{5}{4}\right] \cup \left[\frac{23}{4}, \infty\right)$   **85.** $\{y|-9 < y < 15\}$, or $(-9, 15)$

**87.** $\left\{x \mid -\frac{7}{2} \le x \le \frac{1}{2}\right\}$, or $\left[-\frac{7}{2}, \frac{1}{2}\right]$   **89.** $\left\{y \mid y < -\frac{4}{3} \text{ or } y > 4\right\}$, or

$\left(-\infty, -\frac{4}{3}\right) \cup (4, \infty)$ **91.** $\left\{x \mid x \le -\frac{5}{4} \text{ or } x \ge \frac{23}{4}\right\}$, or

$\left(-\infty, -\frac{5}{4}\right] \cup \left[\frac{23}{4}, \infty\right)$ **93.** $\left\{x \mid -\frac{9}{2} < x < 6\right\}$, or $\left(-\frac{9}{2}, 6\right)$

**95.** $\left\{x \mid x \le -\frac{25}{6} \text{ or } x \ge \frac{23}{6}\right\}$, or $\left(-\infty, -\frac{25}{6}\right] \cup \left[\frac{23}{6}, \infty\right)$

**97.** $\{x|-5 < x < 19\}$, or $(-5, 19)$

**99.** $\left\{x \mid x \le -\frac{2}{15} \text{ or } x \ge \frac{14}{15}\right\}$, or $\left(-\infty, -\frac{2}{15}\right] \cup \left[\frac{14}{15}, \infty\right)$

**101.** $\{m|-12 \le m \le 2\}$, or $[-12, 2]$   **103.** $\left\{x \mid \frac{1}{2} \le x \le \frac{5}{2}\right\}$, or

$\left[\frac{1}{2}, \frac{5}{2}\right]$   **105.** $\{x|-1 \le x \le 2\}$, or $[-1, 2]$   **107.** Union

**108.** Disjoint   **109.** At least   **110.** $[a, b]$   **111.** Absolute

value   **112.** Equation   **113.** Equivalent   **114.** Inequality

**115.** $\left\{d \mid 5\frac{1}{2} \text{ ft} \le d \le 6\frac{1}{2} \text{ ft}\right\}$   **117.** $\{x|x \ge -5\}$, or $[-5, \infty)$

**119.** $\left\{1, -\frac{1}{4}\right\}$   **121.** $\varnothing$   **123.** All real numbers

**125.** $|x| < 3$   **127.** $|x| \ge 6$   **129.** $|x + 3| > 5$

## Summary and Review: Chapter 1, p. 152

### Concept Reinforcement

**1.** True   **2.** False   **3.** False   **4.** False   **5.** True   **6.** False

**7.** True

### Important Concepts

**1.** 8   **2.** $h = \dfrac{4F}{g}$

**3.** $\{y|y < -2\}$, or $(-\infty, -2)$;

**4.** $\{z|-2 \le z < 1\}$, or $[-2, 1)$;

**5.** $\{z \mid z < -1 \text{ or } z \geq 1\}$, or $(-\infty, -1) \cup [1, \infty)$;
[number line]

**6.** $\left\{-\frac{8}{5}, 2\right\}$  **7.** $\left\{3, -\frac{1}{2}\right\}$  **8. (a)** $\{x \mid -4 < x < 1\}$, or $(-4, 1)$;
**(b)** $\left\{x \mid x \leq -\frac{10}{3} \text{ or } x \geq 2\right\}$, or $\left(-\infty, -\frac{10}{3}\right] \cup [2, \infty)$

### Review Exercises

**1.** 8  **2.** $\frac{3}{7}$  **3.** $\frac{22}{5}$  **4.** $-\frac{1}{13}$  **5.** $-0.2$  **6.** 5
**7.** $d = \frac{11}{4}(C - 3)$  **8.** $b = \frac{A - 2a}{-3}$, or $\frac{2a - A}{3}$  **9.** 185 and 186
**10.** 15 m, 12 m  **11.** 160,000  **12.** 40 sec  **13.** $[-8, 9)$
**14.** $(-\infty, 40]$  **15.** [number line]; $(-\infty, -2]$
**16.** [number line]; $(1, \infty)$
**17.** $\{a \mid a \leq -21\}$, or $(-\infty, -21]$  **18.** $\{y \mid y \geq -7\}$, or $[-7, \infty)$
**19.** $\{y \mid y > -4\}$, or $(-4, \infty)$  **20.** $\{y \mid y > -30\}$, or $(-30, \infty)$
**21.** $\{x \mid x > -3\}$, or $(-3, \infty)$  **22.** $\left\{y \mid y \leq -\frac{6}{5}\right\}$, or $\left(-\infty, -\frac{6}{5}\right]$
**23.** $\{x \mid x < -3\}$, or $(-\infty, -3)$  **24.** $\{y \mid y > -10\}$, or $(-10, \infty)$
**25.** $\left\{x \mid x \leq -\frac{5}{2}\right\}$, or $\left(-\infty, -\frac{5}{2}\right]$  **26.** $\left\{t \mid t > 4\frac{1}{4} \text{ hr}\right\}$
**27.** \$10,000  **28.** [number line]; $[-2, 5)$
**29.** [number line]; $(-\infty, -2] \cup (5, \infty)$
**30.** $\{1, 5, 9\}$  **31.** $\{1, 2, 3, 5, 6, 9\}$  **32.** $\varnothing$
**33.** $\{x \mid -7 < x \leq 2\}$, or $(-7, 2]$  **34.** $\left\{x \mid -\frac{5}{4} < x < \frac{5}{2}\right\}$, or $\left(-\frac{5}{4}, \frac{5}{2}\right)$
**35.** $\{x \mid x < -3 \text{ or } x > 1\}$, or $(-\infty, -3) \cup (1, \infty)$
**36.** $\{x \mid x < -11 \text{ or } x \geq -6\}$, or $(-\infty, -11) \cup [-6, \infty)$
**37.** $\{x \mid x \leq -6 \text{ or } x \geq 8\}$, or $(-\infty, -6] \cup [8, \infty)$
**38.** $\frac{3}{|x|}$  **39.** $\frac{2|x|}{y^2}$  **40.** $\frac{4}{|y|}$
**41.** 62  **42.** $\{-6, 6\}$  **43.** $\{-5, 9\}$  **44.** $\left\{-14, \frac{4}{3}\right\}$
**45.** $\varnothing$  **46.** $\left\{x \mid -\frac{17}{2} < x < \frac{7}{2}\right\}$, or $\left(-\frac{17}{2}, \frac{7}{2}\right)$
**47.** $\{x \mid x \leq -3.5 \text{ or } x \geq 3.5\}$, or $(-\infty, -3.5] \cup [3.5, \infty)$
**48.** $\left\{x \mid x \leq -\frac{11}{3} \text{ or } x \geq \frac{19}{3}\right\}$, or $\left(-\infty, -\frac{11}{3}\right] \cup \left[\frac{19}{3}, \infty\right)$  **49.** $\varnothing$
**50.** B  **51.** A  **52.** $\left\{x \mid -\frac{8}{3} \leq x \leq -2\right\}$, or $\left[-\frac{8}{3}, -2\right]$

### Understanding Through Discussion and Writing

**1.** When the signs of the quantities on either side of the inequality symbol are changed, their relative positions on the number line are reversed.  **2.** The distance between $x$ and $-5$ is $|x - (-5)|$, or $|x + 5|$. Then the solutions of the inequality $|x + 5| \leq 2$ can be interpreted as "all those numbers $x$ whose distance from $-5$ is at most 2 units."  **3.** When $b \geq c$, then the intervals overlap and $[a, b] \cup [c, d] = [a, d]$.  **4.** The solutions of $|x| \geq 6$ are those numbers whose distance from 0 is greater than or equal to 6. In addition to the numbers in $[6, \infty)$, the distance of the numbers in $(-\infty, -6]$ from 0 is also greater than or equal to 6. Thus, $[6, \infty)$ is only part of the solution of the inequality.  **5. (1)** $-9(x + 2) = -9x - 18$, not $-9x + 2$. **(2)** This would be correct if (1) were correct except that the inequality symbol should not have been reversed. **(3)** If (2) were correct, the right-hand side would be $-5$, not 8. **(4)** The inequality symbol should be reversed. The correct solution is

$$7 - 9x + 6x < -9(x + 2) + 10x$$
$$7 - 9x + 6x < -9x - 18 + 10x$$
$$7 - 3x < x - 18$$
$$-4x < -25$$
$$x > \tfrac{25}{4}.$$

**6.** By definition, the notation $3 < x < 5$ indicates that $3 < x$ *and* $x < 5$. A solution of the disjunction $3 < x \text{ or } x < 5$ must be in at least one of these sets but not necessarily in both, so the disjunction cannot be written as $3 < x < 5$.

### Test: Chapter 1, p. 157

**1.** [1.1b] $-2$  **2.** [1.1c] $\frac{2}{3}$  **3.** [1.1b] $\frac{19}{15}$  **4.** [1.1d] 4
**5.** [1.1d] 1.1  **6.** [1.1d] $-2$  **7.** [1.2a] $B = \dfrac{A + C}{3}$
**8.** [1.2a] $n = \dfrac{m}{1 - t}$  **9.** [1.3a] Length: $14\frac{2}{5}$ ft; width: $9\frac{3}{5}$ ft
**10.** [1.3a] 52,000 copies  **11.** [1.3a] 180,000
**12.** [1.3a] 59°, 60°, 61°  **13.** [1.3b] $2\frac{2}{5}$ hr; 4 hr
**14.** [1.4b] $(-3, 2]$  **15.** [1.4b] $(-4, \infty)$
**16.** [1.4c] [number line]; $(-\infty, 6]$
**17.** [1.4c] [number line]; $(-\infty, -2]$
**18.** [1.4c] $\{x \mid x \geq 10\}$, or $[10, \infty)$  **19.** [1.4c] $\{y \mid y > -50\}$, or $(-50, \infty)$  **20.** [1.4c] $\left\{a \mid a \leq \frac{11}{5}\right\}$, or $\left(-\infty, \frac{11}{5}\right]$
**21.** [1.4c] $\{y \mid y > 1\}$, or $(1, \infty)$  **22.** [1.4c] $\left\{x \mid x > \frac{5}{2}\right\}$, or $\left(\frac{5}{2}, \infty\right)$
**23.** [1.4c] $\left\{x \mid x \leq \frac{7}{4}\right\}$, or $\left(-\infty, \frac{7}{4}\right]$  **24.** [1.4d] $\left\{h \mid h > 2\frac{1}{10} \text{ hr}\right\}$
**25.** [1.5c] $\{d \mid 33 \text{ ft} \leq d \leq 231 \text{ ft}\}$
**26.** [1.5a] [number line]; $[-3, 4]$
**27.** [1.5b] [number line]; $(-\infty, -3) \cup (4, \infty)$
**28.** [1.5a] $\{x \mid x \geq 4\}$, or $[4, \infty)$  **29.** [1.5a] $\{x \mid -1 < x < 6\}$, or $(-1, 6)$  **30.** [1.5a] $\left\{x \mid -\frac{2}{5} < x \leq \frac{9}{5}\right\}$, or $\left(-\frac{2}{5}, \frac{9}{5}\right]$
**31.** [1.5b] $\left\{x \mid x < -4 \text{ or } x > -\frac{5}{2}\right\}$, or $(-\infty, -4) \cup \left(-\frac{5}{2}, \infty\right)$
**32.** [1.5b] All real numbers, or $(-\infty, \infty)$
**33.** [1.5b] $\{x \mid x < 3 \text{ or } x > 6\}$, or $(-\infty, 3) \cup (6, \infty)$
**34.** [1.6a] $\dfrac{7}{|x|}$  **35.** [1.6a] $2|x|$  **36.** [1.6b] 8.4
**37.** [1.5a] $\{3, 5\}$  **38.** [1.5b] $\{1, 3, 5, 7, 9, 11, 13\}$
**39.** [1.6c] $\{-9, 9\}$  **40.** [1.6c] $\{-6, 12\}$  **41.** [1.6d] $\{1\}$
**42.** [1.6c] $\varnothing$  **43.** [1.6e] $\{x \mid -0.875 < x < 1.375\}$, or $(-0.875, 1.375)$  **44.** [1.6e] $\{x \mid x < -3 \text{ or } x > 3\}$, or $(-\infty, -3) \cup (3, \infty)$  **45.** [1.6e] $\{x \mid -99 \leq x \leq 111\}$, or $[-99, 111]$  **46.** [1.6e] $\left\{x \mid x \leq -\frac{13}{5} \text{ or } x \geq \frac{7}{5}\right\}$, or $\left(-\infty, -\frac{13}{5}\right] \cup \left[\frac{7}{5}, \infty\right)$  **47.** [1.1d] C  **48.** [1.6e] $\varnothing$
**49.** [1.5a] $\left\{x \mid \frac{1}{5} < x < \frac{4}{5}\right\}$, or $\left(\frac{1}{5}, \frac{4}{5}\right)$

## CHAPTER 2

### Calculator Corner, p. 164

**1.**  **2.**
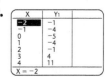

### Calculator Corner, p. 168

**1.** $y = 2x - 1$  **2.** $y = -3x + 2$
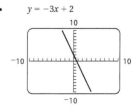

**3.** $y = 5x - 3$  **4.** $y = -4x + 5$
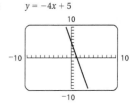

**5.** $y = \frac{2}{3}x - 3$

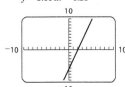

**6.** $y = -\frac{3}{4}x + 4$

**7.** $y = 3.104x - 6.21$

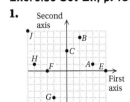

**8.** $y = -2.98x - 1.75$

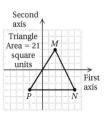

## Exercise Set 2.1, p. 168

**1.**

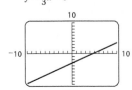

**3.**

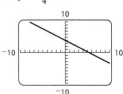

Triangle Area = 21 square units

**5.** Yes    **7.** Yes    **9.** No

**11.** $y = 4 - x$

$$5 \;?\; 4 - (-1)$$
$$\left| \; 4 + 1 \right.$$
$$\left| \; 5 \right. \qquad \text{TRUE}$$

$y = 4 - x;$

$$1 \;?\; 4 - 3$$
$$\left| \; 1 \right. \qquad \text{TRUE}$$

$(-1, 5)$   $(1, 3)$   $(3, 1)$

**13.** $3x + y = 7$

$$3 \cdot 2 + 1 \;?\; 7$$
$$6 + 1 \;\Big|$$
$$7 \;\Big| \qquad \text{TRUE}$$

$3x + y = 7$

$$3 \cdot 4 + (-5) \;?\; 7$$
$$12 - 5 \;\Big|$$
$$7 \;\Big| \qquad \text{TRUE}$$

$(2, 1)$   $(3, -2)$   $(4, -5)$

**15.** $6x - 3y = 3$

$$6 \cdot 1 - 3 \cdot 1 \;?\; 3$$
$$6 - 3 \;\Big|$$
$$3 \;\Big| \qquad \text{TRUE}$$

$6x - 3y = 3$

$$6(-1) - 3(-3) \;?\; 3$$
$$-6 + 9 \;\Big|$$
$$3 \;\Big| \qquad \text{TRUE}$$

$(3, 5)$   $(1, 1)$   $(-1, -3)$

**17.**

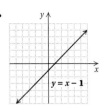

$y = x - 1$

**19.**

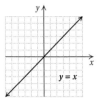

$y = x$

**21.**

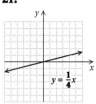

$y = \frac{1}{4}x$

**23.**

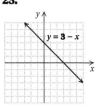

$y = 3 - x$

**25.**

$y = 5x - 2$

**27.**

$y = \frac{1}{2}x + 1$

**29.**

$x + y = 5$

**31.**

$y = -\frac{5}{3}x - 2$

**33.**

$x + 2y = 8$

**35.**

$y = \frac{3}{2}x + 1$

**37.**

$8y + 2x = 4$

**39.**

$8y + 2x = -4$

**41.**

$y = x^2$

**43.**

$y = x^2 + 2$

**45.**

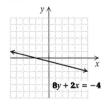

$y = x^2 - 3$

**47.**

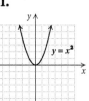

$y = -\frac{1}{x}$

**49.**

$y = |x - 2|$

**51.**

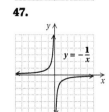

$y = x^3$

**53.** $\left\{ x \mid 1 < x \leq \frac{15}{2} \right\}$, or $\left( 1, \frac{15}{2} \right]$

**54.** $\{ x \mid x > -3 \}$, or $(-3, \infty)$    **55.** $\left\{ x \mid x \leq -\frac{7}{3} \; or \; x \geq \frac{17}{3} \right\}$, or $\left( -\infty, -\frac{7}{3} \right] \cup \left[ \frac{17}{3}, \infty \right)$    **56.** $\{ x \mid -6 < x < 6 \}$, or $(-6, 6)$

**57.** Kidney: 78,170 people; liver: 15,848 people
**58.** 25 ft    **59.** $4\frac{3}{4}$ mi    **60.** $330,000

**61.** $y = x^3 - 3x + 2$

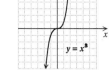

**63.** $y = 1/(x - 2)$

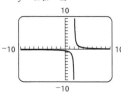

**65.** $y = -x + 4$    **67.** $y = |x| - 3$

## Calculator Corner, p. 177

**1.** $-13.3$    **2.** $-14.4$    **3.** $14$    **4.** $34$

## Calculator Corner, p. 179

**1.** $y = x - 4$
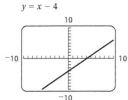

**2.** $y = -2x - 3$
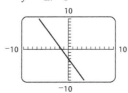

**3.** $y = 1 - x^2$
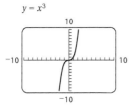

**4.** $y = 3x^2 - 4x + 1$
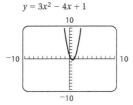

**5.** $y = x^3$
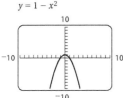

**6.** $y = |x + 3|$
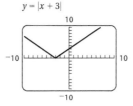

## Exercise Set 2.2, p. 182

**1.** Yes   **3.** Yes   **5.** No   **7.** No   **9.** Yes   **11.** No
**13.** Yes   **15. (a)** 9; **(b)** 12; **(c)** 2; **(d)** 5; **(e)** 7.4; **(f)** $5\frac{2}{3}$
**17. (a)** $-21$; **(b)** 15; **(c)** 2; **(d)** 0; **(e)** $18a$; **(f)** $3a + 3$   **19. (a)** 7;
**(b)** $-17$; **(c)** 6; **(d)** 4; **(e)** $3a - 2$; **(f)** $3a + 3h + 4$   **21. (a)** 0;
**(b)** 5; **(c)** 2; **(d)** 170; **(e)** 65; **(f)** $32a^2 - 12a$   **23. (a)** 1; **(b)** 3;
**(c)** 3; **(d)** 11; **(e)** $|a - 1| + 1$; **(f)** $|a + h| + 1$   **25. (a)** 0; **(b)** $-1$;
**(c)** 8; **(d)** 1000; **(e)** $-125$; **(f)** $-27a^3$   **27.** 2003: about 61 yr; 2009:
about 63 yr   **29.** $1\frac{20}{33}$ atm; $1\frac{10}{11}$ atm; $4\frac{1}{33}$ atm   **31.** 1.792 cm;
2.8 cm; 11.2 cm

**33.**
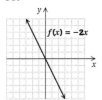

**35.**
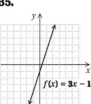

**37.**
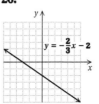

**39.**

**41.**

**43.**
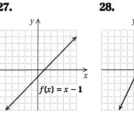

**45.**

**47.**
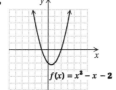

**49.**

**51.**
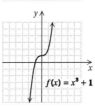

**53.** Yes   **55.** Yes   **57.** No   **59.** No   **61.** About 1150
stations   **63.** About 1.9 billion images   **65.** Quadrants
**66.** Relation   **67.** Function; domain; range; domain; range
**68.** Graph   **69.** Inputs   **70.** Solutions   **71.** Addition
principle   **72.** Vertical-line test   **73.** $g(-2) = 39$
**75.** 26; 99   **77.** $g(x) = \frac{15}{4}x - \frac{13}{4}$

## Exercise Set 2.3, p. 191

**1. (a)** 3; **(b)** $\{-4, -3, -2, -1, 0, 1, 2\}$; **(c)** $-2, 0$; **(d)** $\{1, 2, 3, 4\}$
**3. (a)** $2\frac{1}{2}$; **(b)** $[-3, 5]$; **(c)** $2\frac{1}{4}$; **(d)** $[1, 4]$   **5. (a)** $2\frac{1}{4}$; **(b)** $[-4, 3]$;
**(c)** 0; **(d)** $[-5, 4]$   **7. (a)** 1; **(b)** all real numbers; **(c)** 3; **(d)** all real
numbers   **9. (a)** 1; **(b)** all real numbers; **(c)** $-2, 2$; **(d)** $[0, \infty)$
**11. (a)** $-1$; **(b)** $[-6, 5]$; **(c)** $-4, 0, 3$; **(d)** $[-2, 2]$   **13.** $\{x | x$ is a
real number $and\ x \neq -3\}$, or $(-\infty, -3) \cup (-3, \infty)$
**15.** All real numbers   **17.** All real numbers   **19.** $\{x | x$ is a
real number $and\ x \neq \frac{14}{5}\}$, or $\left(-\infty, \frac{14}{5}\right) \cup \left(\frac{14}{5}, \infty\right)$   **21.** All real
numbers   **23.** $\{x | x$ is a real number $and\ x \neq \frac{7}{4}\}$, or
$\left(-\infty, \frac{7}{4}\right) \cup \left(\frac{7}{4}, \infty\right)$   **25.** $\{x | x$ is a real number $and\ x \neq 1\}$, or
$(-\infty, 1) \cup (1, \infty)$   **27.** All real numbers   **29.** All real
numbers   **31.** $\{x | x$ is a real number $and\ x \neq \frac{5}{2}\}$, or
$\left(-\infty, \frac{5}{2}\right) \cup \left(\frac{5}{2}, \infty\right)$   **33.** All real numbers   **35.** $\{x | x$ is a real
number $and\ x \neq -\frac{5}{4}\}$, or $\left(-\infty, -\frac{5}{4}\right) \cup \left(-\frac{5}{4}, \infty\right)$   **37.** $-8; 0; -2$
**39.** $\{S | S > \$42,500\}$   **40.** $\{x | x \geq 90\}$   **41.** $\{-8, 8\}$
**42.** $\{\ \}$, or $\varnothing$   **43.** $\{-4, 18\}$   **44.** $\{-8, 5\}$   **45.** $\{\frac{1}{2}, 3\}$
**46.** $\{-1, \frac{9}{13}\}$   **47.** $\{\ \}$, or $\varnothing$   **48.** $\{\frac{8}{3}\}$   **49.** $(-\infty, 0) \cup (0, \infty)$;
$[2, \infty); [-4, \infty); [0, \infty)$   **51.** All real numbers

## Mid-Chapter Review: Chapter 2, p. 193

**1.** True   **2.** False   **3.** True   **4.** True   **5.** False

**6.**

| $x$ | $y$ |
|-----|-----|
| 0 | 1 |
| 2 | $-2$ |
| $-2$ | 4 |
| 4 | $-5$ |

**7.**

| $x$ | $f(x)$ |
|-----|--------|
| $-2$ | 0 |
| $-2$ or 3 | 0 |
| 0 | $-6$ |
| 2 | $-4$ |
| $-1$ | $-4$ |
| 1 | $-6$ |

**8.** No   **9.** Yes   **10.** Yes   **11.** No
**12.** Domain: $\{x | -3 \leq x \leq 3\}$, or $[-3, 3]$;
range: $\{y | -2 \leq y \leq 1\}$, or $[-2, 1]$   **13.** $-3$   **14.** $-7$
**15.** 8   **16.** 9   **17.** 9000   **18.** 0   **19.** Yes   **20.** No
**21.** Yes   **22.** $\{x | x$ is a real number $and\ x \neq 4\}$, or
$(-\infty, 4) \cup (4, \infty)$   **23.** All real numbers   **24.** $\{x | x$ is a real
number $and\ x \neq -2\}$, or $(-\infty, -2) \cup (-2, \infty)$   **25.** All real
numbers

**26.**
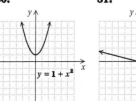

**27.**
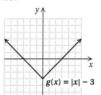

**28.**
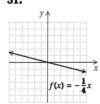

**29.**

**30.**

**31.**

**32.** No; since each input has exactly one output, the number of outputs cannot exceed the number of inputs.  **33.** When $x < 0$, then $y < 0$ and the graph contains points in quadrant III. When $0 < x < 30$, then $y < 0$ and the graph contains points in quadrant IV. When $x > 30$, then $y > 0$ and the graph contains points in quadrant I. Thus the graph passes through three quadrants.  **34.** The output $-3$ corresponds to the input 2. The number $-3$ in the range is paired with the number 2 in the domain. The point $(2, -3)$ is on the graph of the function.  **35.** The domain of a function is the set of all inputs, and the range is the set of all outputs.

### Calculator Corner, p. 195

**1.** The graph of $y_2 = x + 4$ is the same as the graph of $y_1 = x$, but it is moved up 4 units.  **2.** The graph of $y_3 = x - 3$ is the same as the graph of $y_1 = x$, but it is moved down 3 units.  **3.** The graph of $y = x + 8$ will be the same as the graph of $y_1 = x$, but it will be moved up 8 units. The graph of $y = x - 5$ will be the same as the graph of $y_1 = x$, but it will be moved down 5 units.

### Calculator Corner, p. 199

**1.** The graph of $y = 10x$ will slant up from left to right. It will be steeper than the other graphs.  **2.** The graph of $y = 0.005x$ will slant up from left to right. It will be less steep than the other graphs.  **3.** The graph of $y = -10x$ will slant down from left to right. It will be steeper than the other graphs.  **4.** The graph of $y = -0.005x$ will slant down from left to right. It will be less steep than the other graphs.

### Exercise Set 2.4, p. 204

**1.** $m = 4$; $y$-intercept: $(0, 5)$  **3.** $m = -2$; $y$-intercept: $(0, -6)$  **5.** $m = -\frac{3}{8}$; $y$-intercept: $\left(0, -\frac{1}{5}\right)$  **7.** $m = 0.5$; $y$-intercept: $(0, -9)$  **9.** $m = \frac{2}{3}$; $y$-intercept: $\left(0, -\frac{8}{3}\right)$  **11.** $m = 3$; $y$-intercept: $(0, -2)$  **13.** $m = -8$; $y$-intercept: $(0, 12)$  **15.** $m = 0$; $y$-intercept: $\left(0, \frac{4}{17}\right)$  **17.** $m = -\frac{1}{2}$  **19.** $m = \frac{1}{3}$  **21.** $m = 2$  **23.** $m = \frac{2}{3}$  **25.** $m = -\frac{1}{3}$  **27.** $\frac{2}{25}$, or $8\%$  **29.** $\frac{13}{41}$, or about $31.7\%$  **31.** The rate of change is $-2.55$ deaths per year.  **33.** The rate of change is $-\$900$ per year.  **35.** The rate of change is $4313.4$ servicemen per year.  **37.** $-1323$  **38.** $45x + 54$  **39.** $350x - 60y + 120$  **40.** 25  **41.** Square: 15 yd; triangle: 20 yd  **42.** $\left\{x \mid x \le -\frac{24}{5} \, or \, x \ge 8\right\}$, or $\left(-\infty, -\frac{24}{5}\right] \cup [8, \infty)$  **43.** $\left\{x \mid -\frac{24}{5} < x < 8\right\}$, or $\left(-\frac{24}{5}, 8\right)$  **44.** $\left\{-\frac{24}{5}, 8\right\}$  **45.** $\{\ \}$, or $\varnothing$

### Calculator Corner, p. 207

**1.**
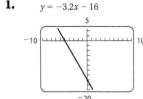
$y = -3.2x - 16$
Xscl = 1, Yscl = 2

**2.**
$y = 4.25x + 85$
Xscl = 5, Yscl = 5

**3.**
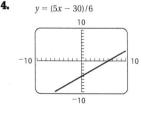
$y = (-6x + 90)/5$
Xscl = 5, Yscl = 5

**4.**
$y = (5x - 30)/6$

**5.**
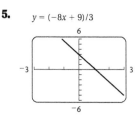
$y = (-8x + 9)/3$

**6.**
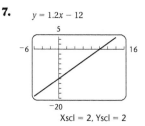
$y = 0.4x - 5$
Xscl = 2, Yscl = 1

**7.**
$y = 1.2x - 12$

**8.**
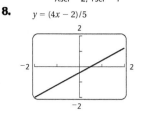
$y = (4x - 2)/5$
Xscl = 2, Yscl = 2

### Visualizing for Success, p. 213

**1.** D  **2.** I  **3.** H  **4.** C  **5.** F  **6.** A  **7.** G  **8.** B  **9.** E  **10.** J

### Exercise Set 2.5, p. 214

**1.**
$x - 2 = y$
$(2, 0)$
$(0, -2)$

**3.**
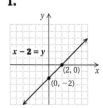
$(0, 2)$
$(6, 0)$
$x + 3y = 6$

**5.**
$(0, 2)$
$(3, 0)$
$2x + 3y = 6$

**7.**
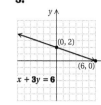
$f(x) = -2 - 2x$
$(-1, 0)$
$(0, -2)$

**9.**
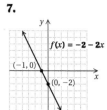
$5y = -15 + 3x$
$(5, 0)$
$(0, -3)$

**11.**
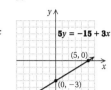
$2x - 3y = 6$
$(3, 0)$
$(0, -2)$

**13.**
$2.8y - 3.5x = -9.8$
$(2.8, 0)$
$(0, -3.5)$

**15.**
$(0, \frac{7}{2})$
$(\frac{7}{5}, 0)$
$5x + 2y = 7$

**17.**
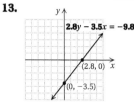
$y = \frac{5}{2}x + 1$

**19.**
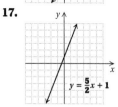
$f(x) = -\frac{5}{2}x - 4$

**21.**
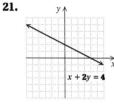
$x + 2y = 4$

**23.**
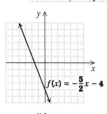
$4x - 3y = 12$

**25.**  $f(x) = \frac{1}{3}x - 4$

**27.** 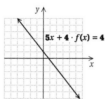 $5x + 4 \cdot f(x) = 4$

**29.** Not defined **31.** $m = 0$

 $x = 1$

 $y = -1$

**33.** $m = 0$ **35.** $m = 0$

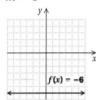 $f(x) = -6$

 $y = 0$

**37.** $m = 0$ **39.** Not defined

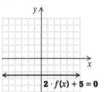 $2 \cdot f(x) + 5 = 0$

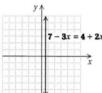 $7 - 3x = 4 + 2x$

**41.** Yes **43.** No **45.** Yes **47.** Yes **49.** Yes **51.** No
**53.** No **55.** Yes **57.** $5.3 \times 10^{10}$ **58.** $4.7 \times 10^{-5}$
**59.** $1.8 \times 10^{-2}$ **60.** $9.9902 \times 10^7$ **61.** $0.0000213$
**62.** $901,000,000$ **63.** $20,000$ **64.** $0.085677$ **65.** $3(3x - 5y)$
**66.** $3a(4 + 7b)$ **67.** $7p(3 - q + 2)$ **68.** $64(x - 2y + 4)$
**69.** $y = 3$ **71.** $a = 2$ **73.** $y = \frac{2}{15}x + \frac{2}{5}$ **75.** $y = 0$; yes
**77.** $m = -\frac{3}{4}$ **79.** **(a)** II; **(b)** IV; **(c)** I; **(d)** III

## Exercise Set 2.6, p. 226

**1.** $y = -8x + 4$ **3.** $y = 2.3x - 1$ **5.** $f(x) = -\frac{7}{3}x - 5$
**7.** $f(x) = \frac{2}{3}x + \frac{5}{8}$ **9.** $y = 5x - 17$ **11.** $y = -3x + 33$
**13.** $y = x - 6$ **15.** $y = -2x + 16$ **17.** $y = -7$
**19.** $y = \frac{2}{3}x - \frac{8}{3}$ **21.** $y = \frac{1}{2}x + \frac{7}{2}$ **23.** $y = x$
**25.** $y = \frac{7}{4}x + 7$ **27.** $y = \frac{3}{2}x$ **29.** $y = \frac{1}{6}x$
**31.** $y = 13x - \frac{15}{4}$ **33.** $y = -\frac{1}{2}x + \frac{17}{2}$ **35.** $y = \frac{5}{7}x - \frac{17}{7}$
**37.** $y = \frac{1}{3}x + 4$ **39.** $y = \frac{1}{2}x + 4$ **41.** $y = \frac{4}{3}x - 6$
**43.** $y = \frac{5}{2}x + 9$ **45.** **(a)** $C(t) = 40t + 85$;
**(b)** 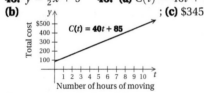 ; **(c)** $345$

**47.** **(a)** $V(t) = 750 - 25t$;
**(b)** 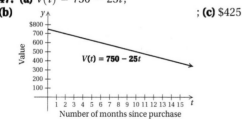 ; **(c)** $425$

---

**49.** **(a)** $W(x) = 379.6x + 2862$; **(b)** 4001 cases; 12,352 cases
**51.** **(a)** $D(x) = -231.88x + 24,026$; **(b)** 21,939 dealerships;
**(c)** about 26 yr after 1991, or in 2017
**53.** **(a)** $M(t) = 0.236t + 71.8$; **(b)** about 75.8 yr
**55.** $\{x | x > 24\}$, or $(24, \infty)$ **56.** $\{-27, 24\}$
**57.** $\{x | x \leq 24\}$, or $(-\infty, 24]$ **58.** $\{x | x \geq \frac{7}{3}\}$, or $[\frac{7}{3}, \infty)$
**59.** $\{x | -8 \leq x \leq 5\}$, or $[-8, 5]$ **60.** $\{-7, \frac{1}{3}\}$
**61.** $\{ \ \}$, or $\varnothing$ **62.** $\{x | -\frac{15}{2} \leq x < 24\}$, or $[-\frac{15}{2}, 24)$

## Summary and Review: Chapter 2, p. 229

### Concept Reinforcement
**1.** False **2.** True **3.** False

### Important Concepts
**1.** 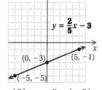 $y = \frac{2}{5}x - 3$ **2.** No

**3.** $g(0) = -2$; $g(-2) = -3$; $g(6) = 1$ **4.** Yes
**5.** Domain: $[-4, 5]$; range: $[-2, 4]$ **6.** $\{x | x$ is a real number
*and* $x \neq -3\}$, or $(-\infty, -3) \cup (-3, \infty)$ **7.** $-2$
**8.** Slope: $-\frac{1}{2}$; $y$-intercept: $(0, 2)$
**9.** 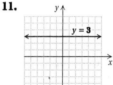 **10.** 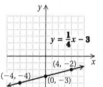 $y = \frac{1}{4}x - 3$

**11.** 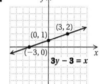 $y = 3$ **12.** $x = -\frac{5}{2}$

**13.** Parallel **14.** Perpendicular **15.** $y = -8x + 0.3$
**16.** $y = -4x - 1$ **17.** $y = -\frac{5}{3}x + \frac{11}{3}$ **18.** $y = \frac{4}{3}x - \frac{23}{3}$
**19.** $y = -\frac{3}{4}x - \frac{7}{2}$

### Review Exercises

**1.**
$$\begin{array}{c} 3x - y = 2 \\ \hline 3 \cdot 0 - (-2) \ ? \ 2 \\ 0 + 2 \ | \\ 2 \ | \quad \text{TRUE} \end{array}$$

$$\begin{array}{c} 3x - y = 2 \\ \hline 3(-1) - (-5) \ ? \ 2 \\ -3 + 5 \ | \\ 2 \ | \quad \text{TRUE} \end{array}$$

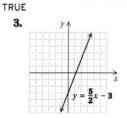

**2.**  $y = -3x + 2$ **3.** $y = \frac{5}{2}x - 3$

**4.**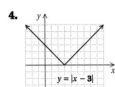

**5.**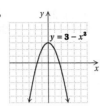

**6.** No    **7.** Yes    **8.** $g(0) = 5; g(-1) = 7$
**9.** $f(0) = 7; f(-1) = 12$    **10.** About $6810    **11.** Yes
**12.** No    **13.** **(a)** $f(2) = 3$; **(b)** $[-2, 4]$; **(c)** $-1$; **(d)** $[1, 5]$
**14.** $\{x | x$ is a real number $and\ x \neq 4\}$, or $(-\infty, 4) \cup (4, \infty)$
**15.** All real numbers    **16.** Slope: $-3$; $y$-intercept: $(0, 2)$
**17.** Slope: $-\frac{1}{2}$; $y$-intercept: $(0, 2)$    **18.** $m = \frac{11}{3}$

**19.**     **20.**     **21.**

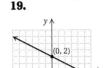
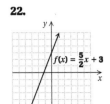

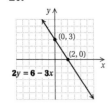

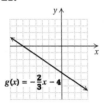

**22.**     **23.**     **24.**

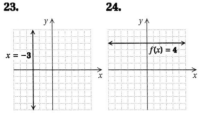

**25.** Perpendicular    **26.** Parallel    **27.** Parallel
**28.** Perpendicular    **29.** $f(x) = 4.7x - 23$    **30.** $y = -3x + 4$
**31.** $y = -\frac{3}{2}x$    **32.** $y = -\frac{5}{7}x + 9$    **33.** $y = \frac{1}{3}x + \frac{1}{3}$
**34.** **(a)** $R(x) = -0.064x + 46.8$; **(b)** about 44.37 sec; 44.24 sec
**35.** C    **36.** A    **37.** $f(x) = 3.09x + 3.75$

## Understanding Through Discussion and Writing

**1.** A line's $x$- and $y$-intercepts are the same only when the line
passes through the origin. The equation for such a line is of the
form $y = mx$.    **2.** The concept of slope is useful in describing
how a line slants. A line with positive slope slants up from left to
right. A line with negative slope slants down from left to right.
The larger the absolute value of the slope, the steeper the slant.
**3.** Find the slope–intercept form of the equation:

$$4x + 5y = 12$$
$$5y = -4x + 12$$
$$y = -\frac{4}{5}x + \frac{12}{5}.$$

This form of the equation indicates that the line has a negative
slope and thus should slant down from left to right. The student
may have graphed $y = \frac{4}{5}x + \frac{12}{5}$.    **4.** For $R(t) = 50t + 35$,
$m = 50$ and $b = 35$; 50 signifies that the cost per hour of a repair
is $50; 35 signifies that the minimum cost of a repair job is $35.

**5.** $m = \dfrac{\text{change in } y}{\text{change in } x}$

As we move from one point to another on a vertical line, the
$y$-coordinate changes but the $x$-coordinate does not. Thus the
change in $y$ is a nonzero number whereas the change in $x$ is 0.
Since division by 0 is undefined, the slope of a vertical line is
undefined.

    As we move from one point to another on a horizontal line,
the $y$-coordinate does not change but the $x$-coordinate does.
Thus the change in $y$ is 0 whereas the change in $x$ is a nonzero
number, so the slope is 0.    **6.** Using algebra, we find that

the slope–intercept form of the equation is $y = \frac{5}{2}x - \frac{3}{2}$. This
indicates that the $y$-intercept is $\left(0, -\frac{3}{2}\right)$, so a mistake has been
made. It appears that the student graphed $y = \frac{5}{2}x + \frac{3}{2}$.

### Test: Chapter 2, p. 238
**1.** [2.1b] Yes    **2.** [2.1b] No
**3.** [2.1c]     **4.** [2.2c]     **5.** [2.2c]

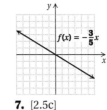

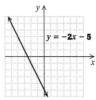

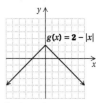

**6.** [2.1d]     **7.** [2.5c]     **8.** [2.5c]

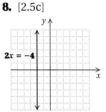

**9.** [2.2e] **(a)** 8.666 yr; **(b)** 1998    **10.** [2.2a] Yes
**11.** [2.2a] No    **12.** [2.2b] $-4; 2$    **13.** [2.2b] 7; 8
**14.** [2.2d] Yes    **15.** [2.2d] No    **16.** [2.3a] $\{x | x$ is a real
number $and\ x \neq -\frac{3}{2}\}$, or $\left(-\infty, -\frac{3}{2}\right) \cup \left(-\frac{3}{2}, \infty\right)$    **17.** [2.3a] All
real numbers    **18.** [2.3a] **(a)** 1; **(b)** $[-3, 4]$; **(c)** $-3$; **(d)** $[-1, 2]$
**19.** [2.4b] Slope: $-\frac{3}{5}$; $y$-intercept: $(0, 12)$
**20.** [2.4b] Slope: $-\frac{2}{5}$; $y$-intercept: $\left(0, -\frac{7}{5}\right)$    **21.** [2.4b] $m = \frac{5}{8}$
**22.** [2.4b] $m = 0$    **23.** [2.4c] $m$ (or rate of change) $= \frac{4}{5}$ km/min
**24.** [2.5a]     **25.** [2.5b]

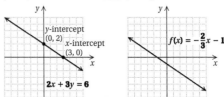

**26.** [2.5d] Parallel    **27.** [2.5d] Perpendicular
**28.** [2.6a] $y = -3x + 4.8$    **29.** [2.6a] $f(x) = 5.2x - \frac{5}{8}$
**30.** [2.6b] $y = -4x + 2$    **31.** [2.6c] $y = -\frac{3}{2}x$
**32.** [2.6d] $y = \frac{1}{2}x - 3$    **33.** [2.6d] $y = 3x - 1$
**34.** [2.6e] **(a)** $A(x) = 0.122x + 23.2$; **(b)** 27.84 yr; 28.69 yr
**35.** [2.6b] B    **36.** [2.6d] $\frac{24}{5}$    **37.** [2.2b] $f(x) = 3$; answers
may vary

### Cumulative Review: Chapters 1–2, p. 241
**1.** [2.6e] **(a)** $R(x) = -0.006x + 3.85$; **(b)** 3.50 min; 3.49 min
**2.** [2.3a] **(a)** 6; **(b)** $[0, 30]$; **(c)** 25; **(d)** $[0, 15]$    **3.** [1.1b] $-22$
**4.** [1.1d] $\frac{15}{88}$    **5.** [1.1c] 20    **6.** [1.1d] $-\frac{21}{4}$    **7.** [1.1d] $-5$
**8.** [1.1d] No solution    **9.** [1.2a] $x = \dfrac{W - By}{A}$

**10.** [1.2a] $A = \dfrac{M}{1 + 4B}$    **11.** [1.4c] $\{y | y \leq 7\}$, or $(-\infty, 7]$
**12.** [1.4c] $\{x | x < -\frac{3}{2}\}$, or $\left(-\infty, -\frac{3}{2}\right)$    **13.** [1.4c] $\{x | x > -\frac{1}{11}\}$,
or $\left(-\frac{1}{11}, \infty\right)$    **14.** [1.5b] All real numbers
**15.** [1.5a] $\{x | -7 < x \leq 4\}$, or $(-7, 4]$
**16.** [1.5a] $\{x | -2 \leq x \leq \frac{3}{2}\}$, or $\left[-2, \frac{3}{2}\right]$    **17.** [1.6c] $\{-8, 8\}$
**18.** [1.6e] $\{y | y < -4\ or\ y > 4\}$, or $(-\infty, -4) \cup (4, \infty)$
**19.** [1.6e] $\{x | -\frac{3}{2} \leq x \leq 2\}$, or $\left[-\frac{3}{2}, 2\right]$
**20.** [2.6d] $y = -4x - 22$    **21.** [2.6d] $y = \frac{1}{4}x - 5$

**22.** [2.1c]

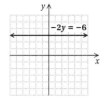

**23.** [2.5a]

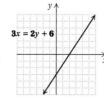

**24.** [2.5c]

**25.** [2.5c]

**26.** [2.2c]

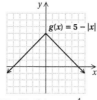

**27.** [2.2c]

**28.** [2.4b] Slope: $\frac{9}{4}$; $y$-intercept: $(0, -3)$   **29.** [2.4b] $m = \frac{4}{3}$
**30.** [2.6b] $y = -3x - 5$   **31.** [2.6c] $y = -\frac{1}{10}x + \frac{12}{5}$
**32.** [1.3a] $w = 17$ m, $l = 23$ m   **33.** [1.3a] $22,500
**34.** [2.5d] (1), (4)   **35.** [2.6e] $151,000
**36.** [1.5a] $\{x|6 < x \leq 10\}$, or $(6, 10]$

## CHAPTER 3

### Calculator Corner, p. 246
**1.** $(2, 3)$   **2.** $(-4, -1)$   **3.** $(-1, 5)$   **4.** $(3, -1)$

### Exercise Set 3.1, p. 250
**1.** $(3, 1)$; consistent; independent   **3.** $(1, -2)$; consistent; independent   **5.** $(4, -2)$; consistent; independent   **7.** $(2, 1)$; consistent; independent   **9.** $\left(\frac{5}{2}, -2\right)$; consistent; independent   **11.** $(3, -2)$; consistent; independent   **13.** No solution; inconsistent; independent   **15.** Infinitely many solutions; consistent; dependent   **17.** $(4, -5)$; consistent; independent   **19.** $(2, -3)$; consistent; independent   **21.** Consistent; independent; F   **23.** Consistent; dependent; B   **25.** Inconsistent; independent; D   **27.** $-3$   **28.** $-20$   **29.** $\frac{9}{20}$   **30.** $-38$   **31.** $(2.23, 1.14)$   **33.** $(3, 3), (-5, 5)$

### Calculator Corner, p. 254
Left to the student

### Exercise Set 3.2, p. 257
**1.** $(2, -3)$   **3.** $\left(\frac{21}{5}, \frac{12}{5}\right)$   **5.** $(2, -2)$   **7.** $(-2, -6)$   **9.** $(-2, 1)$   **11.** $\left(\frac{1}{2}, \frac{1}{2}\right)$   **13.** $\left(\frac{19}{8}, \frac{1}{8}\right)$   **15.** No solution   **17.** Length: 40 ft; width: 20 ft   **19.** $48°$ and $132°$   **21.** Wins: 23; ties: 14

**23.** 1.3   **24.** $-15y - 39$   **25.** $p = \dfrac{7A}{q}$   **26.** $\frac{7}{3}$   **27.** $-23$

**28.** $\frac{29}{22}$   **29.** $m = -\frac{1}{2}; b = \frac{5}{2}$   **31.** Length: 57.6 in.; width: 20.4 in.

### Exercise Set 3.3, p. 265
**1.** $(1, 2)$   **3.** $(-1, 3)$   **5.** $(-1, -2)$   **7.** $(5, 2)$   **9.** Infinitely many solutions   **11.** $\left(\frac{1}{2}, -\frac{1}{2}\right)$   **13.** $(4, 6)$   **15.** No solution   **17.** $(10, -8)$   **19.** $(12, 15)$   **21.** $(10, 8)$   **23.** $(-4, 6)$   **25.** $(10, -5)$   **27.** $(140, 60)$   **29.** 36 and 27   **31.** 18 and $-15$   **33.** $48°$ and $42°$   **35.** Two-point shots: 21; free-throws: 6   **37.** Lanterns: 4; grills: 8   **39.** 1   **40.** 5   **41.** 3   **42.** 291   **43.** 15   **44.** $12a^2 - 2a + 1$   **45.** 53   **46.** 8.92   **47.** $\{x|x$ is a real number $and\ x \neq -7\}$, or $(-\infty, -7) \cup (-7, \infty)$   **48.** Domain: all real numbers; range: $\{y|y \leq 5\}$, or $(-\infty, 5]$

**49.** $y = -\frac{3}{5}x - 7$   **50.** $\dfrac{a^3}{b}$   **51.** $(23.12, -12.04)$

**53.** $A = 2, B = 4$   **55.** $p = 2, q = -\frac{1}{3}$

### Translating for Success, p. 277
**1.** G   **2.** E   **3.** D   **4.** A   **5.** J   **6.** B   **7.** C   **8.** I   **9.** F   **10.** H

### Exercise Set 3.4, p. 278
**1.** 32 brushes at $8.50; 13 brushes at $9.75   **3.** Humulin: 21 vials; Novolin: 29 vials   **5.** 30-sec: 4; 60-sec: 8   **7.** 5 lb of each   **9.** 25% acid: 4 L; 50% acid: 6 L   **11.** 10 silk neckties   **13.** $7500 at 6%; $4500 at 9%   **15.** Whole milk: $169\frac{3}{13}$ lb; cream: $30\frac{10}{13}$ lb   **17.** $5 bills: 7; $1 bills: 15   **19.** $7400 at 5.5%; $10,600 at 4%   **21.** 375 mi   **23.** 14 km/h   **25.** 144 mi   **27.** 2 hr   **29.** $1\frac{1}{3}$ hr   **31.** About 1489 mi   **33.** $-7$   **34.** $-11$   **35.** $-3$   **36.** 33   **37.** $-15$   **38.** $8a - 7$   **39.** $-23$   **40.** 0.2   **41.** $-4$   **42.** $-17$   **43.** $-12h - 7$   **44.** 3993   **45.** $4\frac{4}{7}$ L   **47.** City: 261 mi; highway: 204 mi   **49.** Brown: 0.8 gal; neutral: 0.2 gal

### Mid-Chapter Review: Chapter 3, p. 282
**1.** False   **2.** False   **3.** True   **4.** True
**5.** $x + 2(x - 6) = 3$
$x + 2x - 12 = 3$
$3x - 12 = 3$
$3x = 15$
$x = 5$

$y = 5 - 6$
$y = -1$

The solution is $(5, -1)$.

**6.** $6x - 4y = 10$
$\underline{2x + 4y = 14}$
$8x\phantom{ - 4y} = 24$
$x = 3$

$2 \cdot 3 + 4y = 14$
$6 + 4y = 14$
$4y = 8$
$y = 2$

The solution is $(3, 2)$.

**7.** $(5, -1)$, consistent; independent   **8.** $(0, 3)$; consistent; independent   **9.** Infinitely many solutions; consistent; dependent   **10.** No solution; inconsistent; independent   **11.** $(8, 6)$   **12.** $(2, -3)$   **13.** $(-3, 5)$   **14.** $(-1, -2)$   **15.** $(2, -2)$   **16.** $(5, -4)$   **17.** $(-1, -2)$   **18.** $(3, 1)$   **19.** No solution   **20.** Infinitely many solutions   **21.** $(10, -12)$   **22.** $(-9, 8)$   **23.** Length: 12 ft; width: 10 ft   **24.** $2100 at 2%; $2900 at 3%   **25.** 20% acid: 56 L; 50% acid: 28 L   **26.** 26 mph   **27.** *Graphically*: **1.** Graph $y = \frac{3}{4}x + 2$ and $y = \frac{2}{5}x - 5$ and find the point of intersection. The first coordinate of this point is the solution of the original equation. **2.** Rewrite the equation as $\frac{7}{20}x + 7 = 0$. Then graph $y = \frac{7}{20}x + 7$ and find the $x$-intercept. The first coordinate of this point is the solution of the original equation.
*Algebraically*: **1.** Use the addition and multiplication principles for equations. **2.** Multiply by 20 to clear the fractions and then use the addition and multiplication principles for equations.
**28.** **(a)** Answers may vary.

$x + y = 1,$
$x - y = 7$

**(b)** Answers may vary.

$x + 2y = 5,$
$3x + 6y = 10$

**(c)** Answers may vary.

$x - 2y = 3,$
$3x - 6y = 9$

**29.** Answers may vary. Form a linear expression in two variables and set it equal to two different constants. See Exercises 10 and 19 in this review for examples.   **30.** Answers may vary. Let any linear equation be one equation in the system. Multiply by a

constant on both sides of that equation to get the second equation in the system. See Exercises 9 and 20 in this review for examples.

## Exercise Set 3.5, p. 289

**1.** $(1, 2, -1)$ **3.** $(2, 0, 1)$ **5.** $(3, 1, 2)$ **7.** $(-3, -4, 2)$
**9.** $(2, 4, 1)$ **11.** $(-3, 0, 4)$ **13.** $(2, 2, 4)$ **15.** $\left(\frac{1}{2}, 4, -6\right)$
**17.** $(-2, 3, -1)$ **19.** $\left(\frac{1}{2}, \frac{1}{3}, \frac{1}{6}\right)$ **21.** $(3, -5, 8)$ **23.** $(15, 33, 9)$
**25.** $(4, 1, -2)$ **27.** $(17, 9, 79)$ **28.** $a = \dfrac{F}{3b}$
**29.** $a = \dfrac{Q - 4b}{4}$, or $\dfrac{Q}{4} - b$ **30.** $d = \dfrac{tc - 2F}{t}$, or $c - \dfrac{2F}{t}$
**31.** $c = \dfrac{2F + td}{t}$, or $\dfrac{2F}{t} + d$ **32.** $y = \dfrac{c - Ax}{B}$
**33.** $y = \dfrac{Ax - c}{B}$ **34.** Slope: $-\frac{2}{3}$; $y$-intercept: $\left(0, -\frac{5}{4}\right)$
**35.** Slope: $-4$; $y$-intercept: $(0, 5)$ **36.** Slope: $\frac{2}{5}$; $y$-intercept: $(0, -2)$ **37.** Slope: 1.09375; $y$-intercept: $(0, -3.125)$
**39.** $(1, -2, 4, -1)$

## Exercise Set 3.6, p. 294

**1.** Reading: 502; math: 515; writing: 494 **3.** 32°, 96°, 52°
**5.** $-7, 20, 42$ **7.** Automatic transmission: $865; power door locks: $520; air conditioning: $375 **9.** Small: 10; medium: 16; large: 8 **11.** First fund: $45,000; second fund: $10,000; third fund: $25,000 **13.** Dog: $200; cat: $81; bird: $9 **15.** Roast beef: 2; baked potato: 1; broccoli: 2 **17.** A: 1500 lenses; B: 1900 lenses; C: 2300 lenses **19.** Par-3: 6 holes; par-4: 8 holes; par-5: 4 holes **21.** Two-pointers: 32; three-pointers: 5; foul shots: 13 **23.** At most **24.** Empty set **25.** Linear **26.** Negative **27.** Consistent **28.** Perpendicular **29.** $y$-intercept **30.** Horizontal **31.** 180° **33.** 464

## Visualizing for Success, p. 308

**1.** D **2.** B **3.** E **4.** C **5.** I **6.** G **7.** F **8.** H
**9.** A **10.** J

## Exercise Set 3.7, p. 309

**1.** Yes **3.** Yes
**5.**
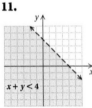
**7.**
**9.**
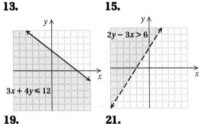

**11.**
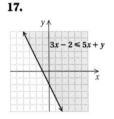
**13.**
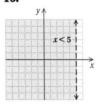
**15.**

**17.**
**19.**
**21.**
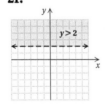

**23.**
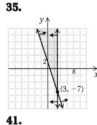
**25.** F **27.** B **29.** C

**31.**
**33.**
**35.**
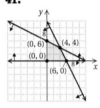

**37.**
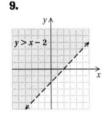
**39.**
**41.**

**43.** $\frac{10}{17}$ **44.** $-\frac{14}{13}$ **45.** $-2$ **46.** $\frac{29}{11}$ **47.** $-12$ **48.** $\frac{333}{245}$
**49.** 2 **50.** 3 **51.** 1 **52.** 8 **53.** 4 **54.** $|2 - 2a|$, or $2|1 - a|$ **55.** 6 **56.** 0.2
**57.** $w > 0$,
$h > 0$,
$w + h + 30 \leq 62$, or
$w + h \geq 32$,
$2w + 2h + 30 \leq 130$, or
$w + h \leq 50$
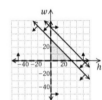

## Summary and Review: Chapter 3, p. 313

### Concept Reinforcement

**1.** False **2.** True **3.** True **4.** False

### Important Concepts

**1.** $(4, -1)$; consistent; independent **2.** $(-1, 4)$ **3.** $(-2, 3)$
**4.** $(3, -5, 1)$
**5.**
**6.**
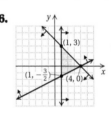

### Review Exercises

**1.** $(-2, 1)$; consistent; independent **2.** Infinitely many solutions; consistent; dependent **3.** No solution; inconsistent; independent **4.** $(1, -1)$ **5.** No solution
**6.** $\left(\frac{2}{5}, -\frac{4}{5}\right)$ **7.** $(6, -3)$ **8.** $(2, 2)$ **9.** $(5, -3)$
**10.** Infinitely many solutions **11.** CD: $18; DVD: $34
**12.** 5 L of each **13.** $5\frac{1}{2}$ hr **14.** $(10, 4, -8)$ **15.** $(-1, 3, -2)$
**16.** $(2, 0, 4)$ **17.** $\left(2, \frac{1}{3}, -\frac{2}{3}\right)$ **18.** 90°, $67\frac{1}{2}$°, $22\frac{1}{2}$°
**19.** $20 bills: 5; $5 bills: 15; $1 bills: 19
**20.**
**21.**
**22.**
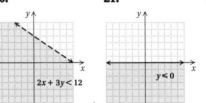

**23.** 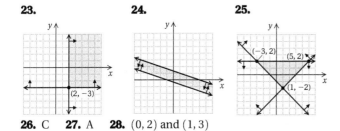 **24.** **25.**

**26.** C  **27.** A  **28.** $(0, 2)$ and $(1, 3)$

## Understanding Through Discussion and Writing

**1.** Answers may vary. One day, a florist sold a total of 23 hanging baskets and flats of petunias. Hanging baskets cost $10.95 each and flats of petunias cost $12.95 each. The sales totaled $269.85. How many of each were sold?  **2.** We know that Eldon, Dana, and Casey can weld 74 linear feet per hour when working together. We also know that Eldon and Dana together can weld 44 linear feet per hour, which leads to the conclusion that Casey can weld $74 - 44$ or 30 linear feet per hour alone. We also know that Eldon and Casey together can weld 50 linear feet per hour. This, along with the earlier conclusion that Casey can weld 30 linear feet per hour alone, leads to two conclusions: Eldon can weld $50 - 30$, or 20 linear feet per hour alone, and Dana can weld $74 - 50$, or 24 linear feet per hour alone.  **3.** Let $x = $ the number of adults in the audience, $y = $ the number of senior citizens, and $z = $ the number of children. The total attendance is 100, so we have equation (1), $x + y + z = 100$. The amount taken in was $100, so equation (2) is $10x + 3y + 0.5z = 100$. There is no other information that can be translated to an equation. Clearing decimals in equation (2) and then eliminating $z$ gives us equation (3), $95x + 25y = 500$. Dividing by 5 on both sides, we have equation (4), $19x + 5y = 100$. Since we have only two equations, it is not possible to eliminate $z$ from another pair of equations. However, in $19x + 5y = 100$, note that 5 is a factor of both $5y$ and 100. Therefore, 5 must also be a factor of $19x$, and hence of $x$, since 5 is not a factor of 19. Then for some positive integer $n$, $x = 5n$. (We require $n$ to be positive, since the number of adults clearly cannot be negative and must also be nonzero since the exercise states that the audience consists of adults, senior citizens, and children.) We have

$$19 \cdot 5n + 5y = 100$$
$$19n + \ y = 20. \qquad \text{Dividing by 5}$$

Since $n$ and $y$ must both be positive, $n = 1$. (If $n > 1$, then $19n + y > 20$.) Then $x = 5 \cdot 1$, or 5.

$$19 \cdot 5 + 5y = 100 \qquad \text{Substituting in (4)}$$
$$y = 1$$

$$5 + 1 + z = 100 \qquad \text{Substituting in (1)}$$
$$z = 94$$

There were 5 adults, 1 senior citizen, and 94 children in the audience.  **4.** No; the symbol $\geq$ does not always yield a graph in which the half-plane above the line is shaded. For the inequality $-y \geq 3$, for example, the half-plane below the line $y = -3$ is shaded.

## Test: Chapter 3, p. 319

**1.** [3.1a] $(-2, 1)$; consistent; independent  **2.** [3.1a] No solution; inconsistent; independent  **3.** [3.1a] Infinitely many solutions; consistent; dependent  **4.** [3.2a] $(2, -3)$
**5.** [3.2a] Infinitely many solutions  **6.** [3.2a] $(-4, 5)$
**7.** [3.3a] $(-1, 1)$  **8.** [3.3a] $\left(-\frac{3}{2}, -\frac{1}{2}\right)$
**9.** [3.3a] No solution  **10.** [3.2b] Length: 93 ft; width: 51 ft
**11.** [3.4b] 120 km/h  **12.** [3.3b], [3.4a] Buckets: 17; dinners: 11
**13.** [3.4a] 20% solution: 12 L; 45% solution: 8 L
**14.** [3.5a] $\left(2, -\frac{1}{2}, -1\right)$  **15.** [3.6a] 3.5 hr

**16.** [3.7b]   **17.** [3.7b]

**18.** [3.7c] 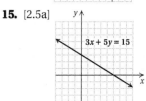  **19.** [3.7c]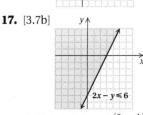

**20.** [3.6a] B  **21.** [3.3a] $m = 7$; $b = 10$

## Cumulative Review: Chapters 1–3; p. 321

**1.** [1.1d] $\frac{10}{9}$  **2.** [1.1d] 6  **3.** [1.2a] $h = \dfrac{A}{\pi r^2}$
**4.** [1.2a] $p = \dfrac{3L}{m} - k$, or $\dfrac{3L - km}{m}$  **5.** [1.4c] $\{x | x > -1\}$, or $(-1, \infty)$  **6.** [1.5a] $\left\{x | \frac{1}{3} < x \leq \frac{13}{3}\right\}$, or $\left(\frac{1}{3}, \frac{13}{3}\right]$
**7.** [1.5b] $\{x | x \leq 3 \text{ or } x \geq 7\}$, or $(-\infty, 3] \cup [7, \infty)$
**8.** [1.6c] $\{-5, 3\}$  **9.** [1.6e] $\left\{y | y \leq -\frac{3}{2} \text{ or } y \geq \frac{9}{4}\right\}$, or $\left(-\infty, -\frac{3}{2}\right] \cup \left[\frac{9}{4}, \infty\right)$  **10.** [1.6d] $\{-5, 1\}$  **11.** [1.6b] 11
**12.** [2.5c] **13.** [2.2c]

**14.** [2.5b] **15.** [2.5a]

**16.** [3.7b] **17.** [3.7b]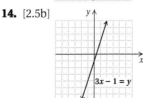

**18.** [3.1a] $(3, -1)$; consistent; independent  **19.** [3.2a] $\left(\frac{8}{5}, -\frac{1}{5}\right)$
**20.** [3.3a] $(1, -1)$  **21.** [3.3a] $(-1, 3)$  **22.** [3.5a] $(2, 0, -1)$
**23.** [3.7b] **24.** [3.7c]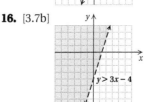

**25.** [2.3a] **(a)** $\{-5, -3, -1, 1, 3\}$; **(b)** $\{-3, -2, 1, 4, 5\}$; **(c)** $-2$;
**(d)** 3  **26.** [2.3a] $\{x | x \text{ is a real number } and \ x \neq \frac{1}{2}\}$, or $\left(-\infty, \frac{1}{2}\right) \cup \left(\frac{1}{2}, \infty\right)$  **27.** [2.2b] $-1$; 1; $-17$
**28.** [2.4b] Slope: $\frac{4}{5}$; $y$-intercept: $(0, 4)$  **29.** [2.6b] $y = -3x + 17$
**30.** [2.6c] $y = -4x - 7$  **31.** [2.5d] Perpendicular
**32.** [2.6d] $y = \frac{1}{3}x + 4$  **33.** [1.3a] 4 m; 6 m
**34.** [1.4d] $\{S | S \geq 88\}$  **35.** [3.3b] Scientific: 18; graphing: 27
**36.** [3.4a] 15%: 21 L; 25%: 9 L  **37.** [3.4b] 720 km
**38.** [3.6a] $120  **39.** [2.6e] $151,000
**40.** [3.3a] $m = -\frac{5}{9}$; $b = -\frac{2}{9}$

# CHAPTER 4

## Calculator Corner, p. 330
**1.** Correct **2.** Incorrect **3.** Correct **4.** Correct
**5.** Incorrect **6.** Incorrect

## Exercise Set 4.1, p. 331
**1.** $-9x^4, -x^3, 7x^2, 6x, -8; 4, 3, 2, 1, 0; 4; -9x^4; -9; -8$
**3.** $t^3, 4t^7, s^2t^4, -2; 3, 7, 6, 0; 7; 4t^7; 4; -2$
**5.** $u^7, 8u^2v^6, 3uv, 4u, -1; 7, 8, 2, 1, 0; 8; 8u^2v^6; 8; -1$
**7.** $-4y^3 - 6y^2 + 7y + 23$ **9.** $-xy^3 + x^2y^2 + x^3y + 1$
**11.** $-9b^5y^5 - 8b^2y^3 + 2by$ **13.** $5 + 12x - 4x^3 + 8x^5$
**15.** $3xy^3 + x^2y^2 - 9x^3y + 2x^4$
**17.** $-7ab + 4ax - 7ax^2 + 4x^6$ **19.** $45; 21; 5$
**21.** $-168; -9; 4; -7\frac{7}{8}$ **23. (a)** 144 ft; **(b)** 1024 ft
**25. (a)** About 340 mg; **(b)** about 190 mg; **(c)** $M(5) \approx 65$;
**(d)** $M(3) \approx 300$ **27. (a)** \$10,750; **(b)** \$18,287.50
**29.** $P(x) = -x^2 + 280x - 7000$ **31.** 17 **33.** 8 **35.** $2x^2$
**37.** $3x + 4y$ **39.** $7a + 14$ **41.** $-6a^2b - 2b^2$
**43.** $9x^2 + 2xy + 15y^2$ **45.** $-x^2y + 4y + 9xy^2$
**47.** $5x^2 + 2y^2 + 5$ **49.** $6a + b + c$ **51.** $-4a^2 - b^2 + 3c^2$
**53.** $-3x^2 + 2x + xy - 1$ **55.** $5x^2y - 4xy^2 + 5xy$
**57.** $9r^2 + 9r - 9$ **59.** $-\frac{2}{15}xy + \frac{19}{12}xy^2 + 1.7x^2y$
**61.** $-(5x^3 - 7x^2 + 3x - 6); -5x^3 + 7x^2 - 3x + 6$
**63.** $-(-13y^2 + 6ay^4 - 5by^2); 13y^2 - 6ay^4 + 5by^2$
**65.** $11x - 7$ **67.** $-4x^2 - 3x + 13$ **69.** $2a + 3c - 4b$
**71.** $-2x^2 + 6x$ **73.** $-4a^2 + 8ab - 5b^2$
**75.** $16ab + 8a^2b + 3ab^2$
**77.** $0.06y^4 + 0.032y^3 - 0.94y^2 + 0.93$
**79.** $x^4 - x^2 - 1$

**81.**
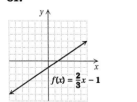
$f(x) = \frac{2}{3}x - 1$

**82.**

$g(x) = |x| - 1$

**83.**
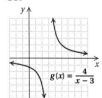
$g(x) = \frac{4}{x-3}$

**84.**
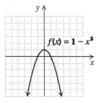
$f(x) = 1 - x^2$

**85.** $3y - 6$ **86.** $-10x - 20y + 70$
**87.** $-42p + 28q + 140$ **88.** $8w - 6t + 20$
**89.**
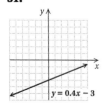
$y = \frac{4}{3}x + 2$

**90.**

$y = -0.4x + 1$

**91.**
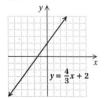
$y = 0.4x - 3$

**92.**
$y = -\frac{2}{3}x - 4$

**93.** 494.55 cm³ **95.** $47x^{4a} + 40x^{3a} + 30x^{2a} + x^a + 4$
**97.** Left to the student

## Calculator Corner, p. 339
**1.** Correct **2.** Incorrect **3.** Correct **4.** Incorrect
**5.** Incorrect **6.** Correct

## Exercise Set 4.2, p. 343
**1.** $24y^3$ **3.** $-20x^3y$ **5.** $-10x^6y^7$ **7.** $14z - 2zx$
**9.** $6a^2b + 6ab^2$ **11.** $15c^3d^2 - 25c^2d^3$ **13.** $15x^2 + x - 2$
**15.** $s^2 - 9t^2$ **17.** $x^2 - 2xy + y^2$ **19.** $x^6 + 3x^3 - 40$
**21.** $a^4 - 5a^2b^2 + 6b^4$ **23.** $x^3 - 64$ **25.** $x^3 + y^3$
**27.** $a^4 + 5a^3 - 2a^2 - 9a + 5$
**29.** $4a^3b^2 + 4a^3b - 10a^2b^2 - 2a^2b + 3ab^3 + 7ab^2 - 6b^3$
**31.** $x^2 + \frac{1}{2}x + \frac{1}{16}$ **33.** $\frac{1}{8}x^2 - \frac{2}{9}$ **35.** $3.25x^2 - 0.9xy - 28y^2$
**37.** $a^2 + 13a + 40$ **39.** $y^2 + 3y - 28$ **41.** $9a^2 + 3a + \frac{1}{4}$
**43.** $x^2 - 4xy + 4y^2$ **45.** $b^2 - \frac{5}{6}b + \frac{1}{6}$ **47.** $2x^2 + 13x + 18$
**49.** $400a^2 - 6.4ab + 0.0256b^2$ **51.** $4x^2 - 4xy - 3y^2$
**53.** $x^6 + 4x^3 + 4$ **55.** $4x^4 - 12x^2y^2 + 9y^4$
**57.** $a^6b^4 + 2a^3b^2 + 1$ **59.** $0.01a^4 - a^2b + 25b^2$
**61.** $A = P + 2Pi + Pi^2$ **63.** $a^2 - 64$ **65.** $4c^2 - 9$
**67.** $36m^2 - 25n^2$ **69.** $x^4 - y^2z^2$ **71.** $m^4 - m^2n^2$
**73.** $16p^4 - 9p^2q^2$ **75.** $\frac{1}{4}p^2 - \frac{4}{9}q^2$ **77.** $x^4 - 1$
**79.** $a^4 - 2a^2b^2 + b^4$ **81.** $a^2 + 2ab + b^2 - 1$
**83.** $4x^2 + 12xy + 9y^2 - 16$
**85.** $t^2 + 3t - 4, p^2 + 7p + 6, h^2 + 2ah + 5h,$
$t^2 + t - 6 + c, a^2 + 5a + 5$ **87.** $3t^2 - 13t + 18,$
$3p^2 - p + 4, 3h^2 + 6ah - 7h, 3t^2 - 19t + 34 + c,$
$3a^2 - 7a + 13$ **89.** $-t^2 + 7t - 6, -p^2 + 3p + 4,$
$-h^2 - 2ah + 5h, -t^2 + 9t - 14 + c, -a^2 + 5a + 5$
**91.** $-t^2 + 5t, -p^2 + p + 6, -h^2 - 2ah + 3h,$
$-t^2 + 7t - 6 + c, -a^2 + 3a + 9$
**93.** 5.5 hr **94.** 180 mph **95.** $\left(\frac{4}{3}, -\frac{14}{27}\right)$ **96.** $(1, 3)$
**97.** Infinitely many solutions **98.** $\left(\frac{10}{21}, \frac{11}{14}\right)$
**99.** Left to the student **101.** $z^{5n^5}$
**103.** $r^8 - 2r^4s^4 + s^8$ **105.** $9x^{10} - \frac{30}{11}x^5 + \frac{25}{121}$
**107.** $x^{4a} - y^{4b}$ **109.** $x^6 - 1$

## Calculator Corner, p. 350
**1.** Correct **2.** Correct **3.** Incorrect **4.** Incorrect
**5.** Incorrect **6.** Correct **7.** Incorrect **8.** Correct

## Exercise Set 4.3, p. 351
**1.** $3a(2a + 1)$ **3.** $x^2(x + 9)$ **5.** $4x^2(2 - x^2)$
**7.** $4xy(x - 3y)$ **9.** $3(y^2 - y - 3)$ **11.** $2a(2b - 3c + 6d)$
**13.** $5(2a^4 + 3a^2 - 5a - 6)$ **15.** $3x^2y^4z^3(5y - 4x^2z^4)$
**17.** $7a^3b^3c^3(2ac^2 + 3b^2c - 5ab)$ **19.** $-5(x + 9)$
**21.** $-6(a + 14)$ **23.** $-2(x^2 - x + 12)$ **25.** $-3y(y - 8)$
**27.** $-(a^4 - 2a^3 + 13a^2 + 1)$ **29.** $-3(y^3 - 4y^2 + 5y - 8)$
**31.** $\pi r^2\left(h + \frac{4}{3}r\right),$ or $\frac{1}{3}\pi r^2(3h + 4r)$
**33. (a)** $h(t) = -8t(2t - 9)$; **(b)** $h(2) = 80$ in each
**35.** $R(x) = 0.4x(700 + x)$ **37.** $(b - 2)(a + c)$
**39.** $(x - 2)(2x + 13)$ **41.** $(y - 7)(y^7 + 1)$
**43.** $(c + d)(a + b)$ **45.** $(b - 1)(b^2 + 2)$
**47.** $(y + 8)(y^2 - 5)$ **49.** $12(x^2 + 3)(2x - 3)$
**51.** $a(a^3 - a^2 + a + 1)$ **53.** $(y^2 + 3)(2y^2 - 5)$
**55.** Slope–intercept **56.** Equivalent **57.** Down
**58.** Inconsistent **59.** Point–slope **60.** Supplementary
**61.** Ascending **62.** Constant
**63.** $x^5y^4 + x^4y^6 = x^3y(x^2y^3 + xy^5)$
**65.** $(x^2 - x + 5)(r + s)$ **67.** $(x^4 + x^2 + 5)(a^4 + a^2 + 5)$
**69.** $x^{1/3}(1 - 7x)$ **71.** $x^{1/3}(1 - 5x^{1/6} + 3x^{5/12})$
**73.** $3a^n(a + 2 - 5a^2)$ **75.** $y^{a+b}(7y^a - 5 + 3y^b)$

**Exercise Set 4.4, p. 358**

**1.** $(x + 4)(x + 9)$ **3.** $(t - 5)(t - 3)$ **5.** $(x - 11)(x + 3)$
**7.** $2(y - 4)(y - 4)$ **9.** $(p + 9)(p - 6)$
**11.** $(x + 3)(x + 9)$ **13.** $\left(y - \frac{1}{3}\right)\left(y - \frac{1}{3}\right)$
**15.** $(t - 3)(t - 1)$ **17.** $(x + 7)(x - 2)$
**19.** $(x + 2)(x + 3)$ **21.** $-1(x - 8)(x + 7)$, or
$(-x + 8)(x + 7)$, or $(x - 8)(-x - 7)$
**23.** $-y(y - 8)(y + 4)$, or $y(-y + 8)(y + 4)$, or
$y(y - 8)(-y - 4)$ **25.** $(x^2 + 16)(x^2 - 5)$
**27.** Not factorable **29.** $(x + 9y)(x + 3y)$
**31.** $2(x - 9)(x + 5)$ **33.** $-1(z + 12)(z - 3)$, or
$(-z - 12)(z - 3)$, or $(z + 12)(-z + 3)$
**35.** $(x^2 + 49)(x^2 + 1)$ **37.** $(x^3 + 9)(x^3 + 2)$
**39.** $(x^4 - 3)(x^4 - 8)$ **41.** $(y - 0.4)(y - 0.4)$
**43.** $(4 + b^{10})(3 - b^{10})$, or $-1(b^{10} + 4)(b^{10} - 3)$
**45.** Countryside: $9\frac{3}{8}$ lb; Mystic: $15\frac{5}{8}$ lb **46.** 8 weekdays
**47.** Yes **48.** No **49.** No **50.** Yes
**51.** All real numbers **52.** All real numbers
**53.** $\{x \mid x$ is a real number $and$ $x \neq \frac{7}{4}\}$, or $\left(-\infty, \frac{7}{4}\right) \cup \left(\frac{7}{4}, \infty\right)$
**54.** All real numbers **55.** $76, -76, 28, -28, 20, -20$
**57.** $x - 365$

**Mid-Chapter Review: Chapter 4, p. 360**

**1.** True **2.** False **3.** True **4.** False **5.** True
**6.**
$$\qquad F \qquad O \qquad I \qquad L$$
$(8w - 3)(w - 5) = (8w)(w) + (8w)(-5) + (-3)(w) + (-3)(-5)$
$$= 8w^2 - 40w - 3w + 15$$
$$= 8w^2 - 43w + 15$$
**7.** $c^3 - 8c^2 - 48c = c \cdot c^2 - c \cdot 8c - c \cdot 48$
$$= c(c^2 - 8c - 48) = c(c + 4)(c - 12)$$
**8.** $x^{20} + 8x^{10} - 9 = (x^{10})^2 + 8(x^{10}) - 9$
$$= (x^{10} + 9)(x^{10} - 1)$$
**9.** $5y^3 + 20y^2 - y - 4 = 5y^2(y + 4) + (-1)(y + 4)$
$$= (y + 4)(5y^2 - 1)$$
**10.** Terms: $-a^7, a^4, -a, 8$; degree of each term: 7, 4, 1, 0; degree of polynomial: 7; leading term: $-a^7$; leading coefficient: $-1$; constant term: 8 **11.** Terms: $3x^4, 2x^3w^5, -12x^2w, 4x^2, -1$; degree of each term: 4, 8, 3, 2, 0; degree of polynomial: 8; leading term: $2x^3w^5$; leading coefficient: 2; constant term: $-1$
**12.** $5 - 2y - y^3 - 2y^4 + y^9$
**13.** $2x^5 - 4qx^2 + 2qx - 9qr$
**14.** $h(0) = 5; h(-2) = 21; h\left(\frac{1}{2}\right) = 2\frac{7}{8}$, or $\frac{23}{8}$
**15.** $f(-1) = 1\frac{1}{2}$, or $\frac{3}{2}; f(1) = -\frac{1}{2}; f(0) = 0$
**16.** $f(a - 2) = a^2 - 2a - 9; f(a + h) - f(a) = 2ah + h^2 + 2h$ **17.** $-2a^2 - 3b - 4ab - 1$ **18.** $11x^2 + 7x - 8$
**19.** $b^2 - 11b - 12$ **20.** $3c^4 - c^5$ **21.** $y^8 - 3y^4 - 18$
**22.** $4y^3 + 6y^2 - 2y$ **23.** $9x - 12$ **24.** $16x^2 - 40x + 25$
**25.** $4x^2 + 20x + 25$ **26.** $0.11x - 3y$ **27.** $-130x^3y$
**28.** $x^3 - x^2y + xy^2 + 3y^3$ **29.** $10x^2 + 31x - 63$
**30.** $81x^2 - 16$ **31.** $h(5h + 7)$ **32.** $(x + 10)(x - 2)$
**33.** $(7 + b)(3 - b)$ **34.** $\left(m + \frac{1}{7}\right)^2$ **35.** $(2 - x)(xy + 5)$
**36.** $3(w - 1)^2$ **37.** $(t + 3)(t^2 + 1)$
**38.** $8xy^3z(3y^3z^3 - 2x^3)$ **39.** Not factorable
**40.** One explanation is as follows. The expression $-(a - b)$ is the opposite of $a - b$. Since $(a - b) + (b - a) = 0$, then $-(a - b) = b - a$. **41.** No; if the coefficients of at least one pair of like terms are opposites, then the sum is a monomial. For example, $(2x + 3) + (-2x + 1) = 4$, a monomial. **42.** No; consider the polynomial $3x^{11} + 5x^7$. All the coefficients and exponents are prime numbers, yet the polynomial can be factored so it is not prime. **43.** When coefficients and/or exponents are large, a polynomial is more easily evaluated after it has been factored. **44.** **(a)** The middle term, $2 \cdot a \cdot 3$, is missing from the righthand side.
$$(a + 3)^2 = a^2 + 6a + 9$$

**(b)** The middle term, $-2ab$, is missing from the righthand side and the sign preceding $b^2$ is incorrect.
$$(a - b)(a - b) = a^2 - 2ab + b^2$$
**(c)** The product of the outside terms and the product of the inside terms are missing from the righthand side.
$$(x + 3)(x - 4) = x^2 - x - 12$$
**(d)** There should be a minus sign between the terms of the product.
$$(p + 7)(p - 7) = p^2 - 49$$
**(e)** The middle term, $-2 \cdot t \cdot 3$, is missing from the righthand side and the sign preceding 9 is incorrect.
$$(t - 3)^2 = t^2 - 6t + 9$$
**45.** Answers may vary. For the polynomial $4a^3 - 12a$, an incorrect factorization is $4a(a - 3)$. Evaluating both the polynomial and the factorization for $a = 0$, we get 0 in each case. Thus the evaluation does not catch the mistake.

**Exercise Set 4.5, p. 368**

**1.** $(3x + 1)(x - 5)$ **3.** $y(5y - 7)(2y + 3)$
**5.** $(3c - 8)(c - 4)$ **7.** $(5y + 2)(7y + 4)$
**9.** $2(5t - 3)(t + 1)$ **11.** $4(2x + 1)(x - 4)$
**13.** $3(3a - 1)(2a - 5)$ **15.** $5(3t + 1)(2t + 5)$
**17.** $x(3x - 4)(4x - 5)$ **19.** $x^2(7x + 1)(2x - 3)$
**21.** $(3a - 4)(a + 1)$ **23.** $(3x + 1)(3x + 4)$
**25.** $-1(z - 3)(12z + 1)$, or $(-z + 3)(12z + 1)$, or
$(z - 3)(-12z - 1)$ **27.** $-1(2t - 3)(2t + 5)$, or
$(-2t + 3)(2t + 5)$, or $(2t - 3)(-2t - 5)$
**29.** $x(3x + 1)(x - 2)$ **31.** $(24x + 1)(x - 2)$
**33.** $-2t(2t + 5)(2t - 3)$ **35.** $-x(24x + 1)(x - 2)$
**37.** $(7x + 3)(3x + 4)$ **39.** $4(10x^4 + 4x^2 - 3)$
**41.** $(4a - 3b)(3a - 2b)$ **43.** $(2x - 3y)(x + 2y)$
**45.** $2(3x - 4y)(2x - 7y)$ **47.** $(3x - 5y)(3x - 5y)$
**49.** $(3x^3 - 2)(x^3 + 2)$ **51.** **(a)** 224 ft; 288 ft; 320 ft; 288 ft; 128 ft; **(b)** $h(t) = -16(t - 7)(t + 2)$ **53.** $(2, -1, 0)$
**54.** $\left(\frac{3}{2}, -4, 3\right)$ **55.** $(1, -1, 2)$ **56.** $(2, 4, 1)$ **57.** Parallel
**58.** Parallel **59.** Neither **60.** Perpendicular
**61.** $y = -\frac{1}{7}x - \frac{23}{7}$ **62.** $y = -\frac{1}{3}x - \frac{7}{3}$ **63.** $y = -\frac{7}{17}x - \frac{19}{17}$
**64.** $y = -\frac{5}{2}x - \frac{2}{3}$ **65.** Left to the student
**67.** $(7a + 6)(ab + 1)$ **69.** $(9xy - 4)(xy + 1)$
**71.** $(x^a + 8)(x^a - 3)$

**Visualizing for Success, p. 377**

**1.** A, E **2.** F, J **3.** G, K **4.** L, S **5.** P, Q **6.** C, I
**7.** D, H **8.** M, O **9.** N, T **10.** B, R

**Exercise Set 4.6, p. 378**

**1.** $(x - 2)^2$ **3.** $(y + 9)^2$ **5.** $(x + 1)^2$ **7.** $(3y + 2)^2$
**9.** $y(y - 9)^2$ **11.** $3(2a + 3)^2$ **13.** $2(x - 10)^2$
**15.** $(1 - 4d)^2$, or $(4d - 1)^2$ **17.** $3a(a - 1)^2$
**19.** $(0.5x + 0.3)^2$ **21.** $(p - q)^2$ **23.** $(a + 2b)^2$
**25.** $(5a - 3b)^2$ **27.** $(y^3 + 13)^2$ **29.** $(4x^5 - 1)^2$
**31.** $(x^2 + y^2)^2$ **33.** $(p + 7)(p - 7)$
**35.** $(y + 2)^2(y - 2)^2$ **37.** $(pq + 5)(pq - 5)$
**39.** $6(x + y)(x - y)$ **41.** $4x(y^2 + z^2)(y + z)(y - z)$
**43.** $a(2a + 7)(2a - 7)$
**45.** $3(x^4 + y^4)(x^2 + y^2)(x + y)(x - y)$
**47.** $a^2(3a + 5b^2)(3a - 5b^2)$ **49.** $\left(\frac{1}{6} + z\right)\left(\frac{1}{6} - z\right)$
**51.** $(0.2x + 0.3y)(0.2x - 0.3y)$
**53.** $(m - 7)(m + 2)(m - 2)$ **55.** $(a - 2)(a + b)(a - b)$
**57.** $(a + b + 10)(a + b - 10)$
**59.** $(12 - p + 8)(12 + p - 8)$, or $(20 - p)(4 + p)$
**61.** $(a + b + 3)(a + b - 3)$ **63.** $(r - 1 + 2s)(r - 1 - 2s)$
**65.** $2(m + n + 5b)(m + n - 5b)$

**67.** $[3 + (a + b)][3 - (a + b)]$, or $(3 + a + b)(3 - a - b)$
**69.** $(z + 3)(z^2 - 3z + 9)$    **71.** $(x - 1)(x^2 + x + 1)$
**73.** $(y + 5)(y^2 - 5y + 25)$    **75.** $(2a + 1)(4a^2 - 2a + 1)$
**77.** $(y - 2)(y^2 + 2y + 4)$    **79.** $(2 - 3b)(4 + 6b + 9b^2)$
**81.** $(4y + 1)(16y^2 - 4y + 1)$    **83.** $(2x + 3)(4x^2 - 6x + 9)$
**85.** $(a - b)(a^2 + ab + b^2)$    **87.** $\left(a + \frac{1}{2}\right)\left(a^2 - \frac{1}{2}a + \frac{1}{4}\right)$
**89.** $2(y - 4)(y^2 + 4y + 16)$    **91.** $3(2a + 1)(4a^2 - 2a + 1)$
**93.** $r(s + 4)(s^2 - 4s + 16)$    **95.** $5(x - 2z)(x^2 + 2xz + 4z^2)$
**97.** $(x + 0.1)(x^2 - 0.1x + 0.01)$
**99.** $8(2x^2 - t^2)(4x^4 + 2x^2t^2 + t^4)$
**101.** $2y(y - 4)(y^2 + 4y + 16)$
**103.** $(z - 1)(z^2 + z + 1)(z + 1)(z^2 - z + 1)$
**105.** $(t^2 + 4y^2)(t^4 - 4t^2y^2 + 16y^4)$
**107.** $(2w^3 - z^3)(4w^6 + 2w^3z^3 + z^6)$
**109.** $\left(\frac{1}{2}c + d\right)\left(\frac{1}{4}c^2 - \frac{1}{2}cd + d^2\right)$
**111.** $(0.1x - 0.2y)(0.01x^2 + 0.02xy + 0.04y^2)$
**113.** $\left(-\frac{41}{53}, \frac{148}{53}\right)$    **114.** $\left(-\frac{26}{7}, -\frac{134}{7}\right)$    **115.** $(1, 13)$
**116.** No solution
**117.**                      **118.**

**119.**                      **120.**

**121.** $y = x - 2; y = -x - 6$    **122.** $y = \frac{2}{3}x - \frac{23}{3}; y = -\frac{3}{2}x - \frac{11}{2}$
**123.** $y = -\frac{1}{2}x + 7; y = 2x - 3$    **124.** $y = \frac{1}{4}x - \frac{3}{2};$
$y = -4x + 24$    **125.** $h(3a^2 + 3ah + h^2)$
**127.** (a) $\pi h(R + r)(R - r)$; (b) $3,014,400$ cm$^3$
**129.** $5(c^{50} + 4d^{50})(c^{25} + 2d^{25})(c^{25} - 2d^{25})$
**131.** $(x^{2a} + y^b)(x^{4a} - x^{2a}y^b + y^{2b})$
**133.** $3(x^a + 2y^b)(x^{2a} - 2x^ay^b + 4y^{2b})$
**135.** $\frac{1}{3}\left(\frac{1}{2}xy + z\right)\left(\frac{1}{4}x^2y^2 - \frac{1}{2}xyz + z^2\right)$    **137.** $y(3x^2 + 3xy + y^2)$
**139.** $4(3a^2 + 4)$

### Exercise Set 4.7, p. 385

**1.** $(y + 15)(y - 15)$    **3.** $(2x + 3)(x + 4)$
**5.** $5(x^2 + 2)(x^2 - 2)$    **7.** $(p + 6)^2$    **9.** $2(x - 11)(x + 6)$
**11.** $(3x + 5y)(3x - 5y)$    **13.** $4(m^2 + 5)(m^2 - 5)$
**15.** $6(w - 1)(w + 3)$    **17.** $2x(y + 5)(y - 5)$
**19.** $(18 - a)(12 + a)$
**21.** $(m + 1)(m^2 - m + 1)(m - 1)(m^2 + m + 1)$
**23.** $(x + 3 + y)(x + 3 - y)$
**25.** $2(5x - 4y)(25x^2 + 20xy + 16y^2)$
**27.** $(m^3 + 10)(m^3 - 2)$    **29.** $(a + d)(c - b)$
**31.** $(5b - a)(10b + a)$    **33.** $(2x - 7)(x^2 + 2)$
**35.** $2(x + 3)(x + 2)(x - 2)$
**37.** $2(2x + 3)(4x^2 - 6xy + 9y^2)$    **39.** $-3y(5x + 2)(4x - 1)$,
or $3y(-5x - 2)(4x - 1)$, or $3y(5x + 2)(-4x + 1)$
**41.** $(a^4 + b^4)(a^2 + b^2)(a + b)(a - b)$
**43.** $ab(a + 4b)(a - 4b)$    **45.** $\left(\frac{1}{4}x - \frac{1}{3}y^2\right)^2$
**47.** $5(x - y)^2(x + y)$    **49.** $(9ab + 2)(3ab + 4)$
**51.** $y(2y - 5)(4y^2 + 10y + 25)$
**53.** $(a - b - 3)(a + b + 3)$    **55.** $(q - 5 + r)(q - 5 - r)$

**57.** Correct answers: 55; incorrect answers: 20    **58.** $\frac{80}{7}$
**59.** $(6y^2 - 5x)(5y^2 - 12x)$    **61.** $5\left(x - \frac{1}{3}\right)\left(x^2 + \frac{1}{3}x + \frac{1}{9}\right)$
**63.** $x(x - 2p)$    **65.** $y(y - 1)^2(y - 2)$
**67.** $(2x + y - r + 3s)(2x + y + r - 3s)$    **69.** $c(c^w + 1)^2$
**71.** $3x(x + 5)$    **73.** $(x - 1)^3(x^2 + 1)(x + 1)$
**75.** $y(y^4 + 1)(y^2 + 1)(y + 1)(y - 1)$

### Calculator Corner, p. 391
**1.** Left to the student

### Translating for Success, p. 395
**1.** Q    **2.** F    **3.** B    **4.** A    **5.** P    **6.** D    **7.** O    **8.** H
**9.** I    **10.** J

### Exercise Set 4.8, p. 396
**1.** $-7, 4$    **3.** $3$    **5.** $-10$    **7.** $-5, -4$    **9.** $0, -8$    **11.** $-5, 5$
**13.** $-12, 12$    **15.** $7, -9$    **17.** $-4, 8$    **19.** $-2, -\frac{2}{3}$    **21.** $\frac{1}{2}, \frac{3}{4}$
**23.** $0, 6$    **25.** $\frac{2}{3}, -\frac{3}{4}$    **27.** $-1, 1$    **29.** $\frac{2}{3}, -\frac{5}{7}$    **31.** $0, \frac{1}{5}$
**33.** $7, -2$    **35.** $0, -2, 3$    **37.** $0, -8, 8$    **39.** $5, -5, 1, -1$
**41.** $-6, 6$    **43.** $-\frac{7}{4}, \frac{4}{3}$    **45.** $-8, -4$    **47.** $-4, \frac{3}{2}$
**49.** $-9, -3$
**51.** $\{x | x$ is a real number $and\ x \neq -1\ and\ x \neq 5\}$
**53.** $\{x | x$ is a real number $and\ x \neq -3\ and\ x \neq 3\}$
**55.** $\{x | x$ is a real number $and\ x \neq \frac{1}{5}\}$
**57.** $\{x | x$ is a real number $and\ x \neq 0\ and\ x \neq 2\ and\ x \neq 5\}$
**59.** $x$-intercepts: $(-5, 0)$ and $(9, 0)$; solutions: $-5, 9$
**61.** $x$-intercepts: $(-4, 0)$ and $(8, 0)$; solutions: $-4, 8$
**63.** Length: 12 cm; width: 7 cm    **65.** Height: 6 ft; base: 4 ft
**67.** 6 cm    **69.** $d = 12$ ft; $h = 16$ ft    **71.** 16, 18, 20
**73.** Length: 12 ft; width: 8 ft    **75.** 3 cm    **77.** 150 ft by 200 ft
**79.** 24 m, 25 m    **81.** 24 ft, 25 ft    **83.** 11 sec    **85.** 7
**86.** 1    **87.** 7    **88.** 2.5    **89.** 1.3    **90.** $\frac{19}{15}$    **91.** 691
**92.** 1023    **93.** $y = \frac{11}{6}x + \frac{32}{3}$    **94.** $y = -\frac{11}{10}x + \frac{24}{5}$
**95.** $y = -\frac{3}{10}x + \frac{32}{5}$    **96.** $y = \frac{26}{31}x + \frac{934}{31}$
**97.** $\{-3, 1\}$; $\{x | -4 \leq x \leq 2\}$, or $[-4, 2]$    **99.** Left to the
student    **101.** (a) 1.2522305, 3.1578935;
(b) $-0.3027756, 0, 3.3027756$; (c) 2.1387475, 2.7238657;
(d) $-0.7462555, 3.3276509$

### Summary and Review: Chapter 4, p. 401
#### Concept Reinforcement
**1.** False    **2.** True    **3.** False

#### Important Concepts
**1.** Terms: $-6x^4, 5x^3, -x^2, 10x, -1$; degree of each term: 4, 3, 2,
1, 0; degree of polynomial: 4; leading term: $-6x^4$; leading
coefficient: $-6$; constant term: $-1$
**2.** Descending: $-x^4 + 2x^3 + 8x^2 - 3x - 7$;
ascending: $-7 - 3x + 8x^2 + 2x^3 - x^4$
**3.** $2y^3 + 2y^2 + 17y - 8$    **4.** $3x^2 + xy - 10y^2$
**5.** $4y^2 + 28y + 49$    **6.** $25d^2 - 100$
**7.** $f(x + 1) = 3x^2 + 5x + 4; f(a + h) - f(a) =$
$3h^2 + 6ah - h$    **8.** $6x(3y + 7z - 4w)$    **9.** $(y + 3)(y^2 - 8)$
**10.** $(3x - 8)(x + 9)$    **11.** $(2x - 7)(5x + 1)$    **12.** $(9x - 4)^2$
**13.** $(10t + 1)(10t - 1)$    **14.** $(6x + 1)(36x^2 - 6x + 1)$
**15.** $(10y - 3)(100y^2 + 30y + 9)$    **16.** $-2, \frac{7}{3}$

#### Review Exercises
**1.** (a) 7, 11, 3, 2; 11; (b) $-7x^8y^3$; $-7$;
(c) $-3x^2 + 2x^3 + 3x^6y - 7x^8y^3$;
(d) $-7x^8y^3 + 3x^6y + 2x^3 - 3x^2$, or
$-7x^8y^3 + 3x^6y - 3x^2 + 2x^3$    **2.** 0; $-6$    **3.** 4; $-31$
**4.** $-7x + 23y$    **5.** $ab + 12ab^2 + 4$    **6.** (a) About 230,000;
(b) about 389,000    **7.** $-x^3 + 2x^2 + 5x + 2$
**8.** $x^3 + 6x^2 - x - 4$    **9.** $13x^2y - 8xy^2 + 4xy$    **10.** $9x - 7$
**11.** $-2a + 6b + 7c$    **12.** $16p^2 - 8p$    **13.** $4x^2 - 7xy + 3y^2$

**14.** $-18x^3y^4$    **15.** $x^8 - x^6 + 5x^2 - 3$
**16.** $8a^2b^2 + 2abc - 3c^2$    **17.** $4x^2 - 25y^2$
**18.** $4x^2 - 20xy + 25y^2$    **19.** $20x^4 - 18x^3 - 47x^2 + 69x - 27$
**20.** $x^4 + 8x^2y^3 + 16y^6$    **21.** $x^3 - 125$    **22.** $x^2 - \frac{1}{2}x + \frac{1}{18}$
**23.** $a^2 - 4a - 4; 2ah + h^2 - 2h$    **24.** $3y^2(3y^2 - 1)$
**25.** $3x(5x^3 - 6x^2 + 7x - 3)$    **26.** $(a - 9)(a - 3)$
**27.** $(3m + 2)(m + 4)$    **28.** $(5x + 2)^2$
**29.** $4(y + 2)(y - 2)$    **30.** $(a + 2b)(x - y)$
**31.** $4(x^4 + x^2 + 5)$    **32.** $(3x - 2)(9x^2 + 6x + 4)$
**33.** $(0.4b - 0.5c)(0.16b^2 + 0.2bc + 0.25c^2)$
**34.** $y(y^2 + 1)(y + 1)(y - 1)$    **35.** $2z^6(z^2 - 8)$
**36.** $2y(3x^2 - 1)(9x^4 + 3x^2 + 1)$    **37.** $(1 + a)(1 - a + a^2)$
**38.** $4(3x - 5)^2$    **39.** $(3t + p)(2t + 5p)$
**40.** $(x + 2)(x + 3)(x - 3)$    **41.** $(a - b + 2t)(a - b - 2t)$
**42.** $10$    **43.** $\frac{2}{3}, \frac{3}{2}$    **44.** $0, \frac{7}{4}$    **45.** $-4, 4$    **46.** $-4, 11$
**47.** $\{x | x \text{ is a real number } and \ x \neq \frac{2}{3} \ and \ x \neq -7\}$
**48.** Length: 8 in.; width: 5 in.    **49.** $-7, -5, -3; 3, 5, 7$
**50.** $7$    **51.** A    **52.** C
**53.** $2(2x + y)(4x^2 - 2xy + y^2)(2x - y)(4x^2 + 2xy + y^2)$
**54.** $2(3x^2 + 1)$    **55.** $a^3 - (b - 1)^3$    **56.** $0, \frac{1}{8}, -\frac{1}{8}$

## Understanding Through Discussion and Writing

**1.** A sum of two squares can be factored when there is a common factor that is a perfect square. For example, consider $4 + 4x^2$:

$$4 + 4x^2 = 4(1 + x^2).$$

**2.** See the procedure on p. 366 of the text.    **3.** Add the opposite of the polynomial being subtracted.    **4.** To solve $P(x) = 0$, find the first coordinate(s) of the $x$-intercept(s) of $y = P(x)$. To solve $P(x) = 4$, find the first coordinate(s) of the points of intersection of the graphs of $y_1 = P(x)$ and $y_2 = 4$.
**5.** To use factoring, write $x^3 - 8 = (x - 2)(x^2 + 2x + 4)$ and $(x - 2)^3 = (x - 2)(x - 2)(x - 2)$. Since $(x - 2)(x^2 + 2x + 4) \neq (x - 2)(x - 2)(x - 2)$, then $x^3 - 8 \neq (x - 2)^3$. To use graphing, enter $y_1 = x^3 - 8$ and $y_2 = (x - 2)^3$ and show that the graphs are different.
**6.** Both are correct. The factorizations are equivalent:
$$\begin{aligned}(a - b)(x - y) &= -1(b - a)(-1)(y - x) \\ &= (-1)(-1)(b - a)(y - x) \\ &= (b - a)(y - x)\end{aligned}$$

**7.**
$$x = 5 \quad or \quad x = -3$$
$$x - 5 = 0 \quad or \quad x + 3 = 0$$
$$(x - 5)(x + 3) = 0$$
$$x^2 - 2x - 15 = 0;$$

No; there cannot be more than two solutions of a quadratic equation. This is because a quadratic equation is factorable into at most two different linear factors. Each of these has one solution when set equal to zero as required by the principle of zero products.
**8.** The discussion could include the following points:
**(a)** We can now solve certain polynomial equations. **(b)** Whereas most linear equations have exactly one solution, nonlinear polynomial equations can have more than one solution. **(c)** We used factoring and the principle of zero products to solve polynomial equations.

## Test: Chapter 4, p. 407

**1.** [4.1a] **(a)** 4, 3, 9, 5; 9; **(b)** $5x^5y^4$; 5;
**(c)** $3xy^3 - 4x^2y - 2x^4y + 5x^5y^4$;
**(d)** $5x^5y^4 + 3xy^3 - 4x^2y - 2x^4y$, or $5x^5y^4 + 3xy^3 - 2x^4y - 4x^2y$    **2.** [4.1b] 4; 2    **3.** [4.1b] **(a)** About $1.66 billion;
**(b)** about $2.8 billion    **4.** [4.1c] $3xy + 3xy^2$    **5.** [4.1c] $-3x^3 + 3x^2 - 6y - 7y^2$    **6.** [4.1c] $7a^3 - 6a^2 + 3a - 3$
**7.** [4.1c] $7m^3 + 2m^2n + 3mn^2 - 7n^3$    **8.** [4.1d] $6a - 8b$
**9.** [4.1d] $7x^2 - 7x + 13$    **10.** [4.1d] $2y^2 + 5y + y^3$
**11.** [4.2a] $64x^3y^3$    **12.** [4.2b] $12a^2 - 4ab - 5b^2$

**13.** [4.2a] $x^3 - 2x^2y + y^3$    **14.** [4.2a] $-3m^4 - 13m^3 + 5m^2 + 26m - 10$    **15.** [4.2c] $16y^2 - 72y + 81$    **16.** [4.2d] $x^2 - 4y^2$    **17.** [4.2e] $a^2 + 15a + 50; 2ah + h^2 - 5h$
**18.** [4.3a] $x(9x + 7)$    **19.** [4.3a] $8y^2(3y + 2)$
**20.** [4.6c] $(y + 5)(y + 2)(y - 2)$    **21.** [4.4a] $(p - 14)(p + 2)$
**22.** [4.5a, b] $(6m + 1)(2m + 3)$    **23.** [4.6b] $(3y + 5)(3y - 5)$
**24.** [4.6d] $3(r - 1)(r^2 + r + 1)$    **25.** [4.6a] $(3x - 5)^2$
**26.** [4.6b] $(z + 1 + b)(z + 1 - b)$
**27.** [4.6b] $(x^4 + y^4)(x^2 + y^2)(x + y)(x - y)$
**28.** [4.6c] $(y + 4 + 10t)(y + 4 - 10t)$
**29.** [4.6b] $5(2a + b)(2a - b)$
**30.** [4.5a, b] $2(4x - 1)(3x - 5)$
**31.** [4.6d] $2ab(2a^2 + 3b^2)(4a^4 - 6a^2b^2 + 9b^4)$
**32.** [4.8a] $-3, 6$    **33.** [4.8a] $-5, 5$    **34.** [4.8a] $-\frac{3}{2}, -7$
**35.** [4.8a] $0, 5$    **36.** [4.8a] $\{x | x \text{ is a real number } and \ x \neq -1\}$, or $(-\infty, -1) \cup (-1, \infty)$    **37.** [4.8b] Length: 8 cm; width: 5 cm
**38.** [4.8b] 24 ft    **39.** [4.8b] 5    **40.** [4.3a] $f(n) = \frac{1}{2}n(n - 1)$
**41.** [4.6d] C    **42.** [4.7a] $(3x^n + 4)(2x^n - 5)$    **43.** [4.2c] 19

## Cumulative Review: Chapters 1-4, p. 409

**1.** [4.1c] $-2x^2 + x - xy - 1$    **2.** [4.1d] $-2x^2 + 6x$
**3.** [4.2a] $a^4 + a^3 - 8a^2 - 3a + 9$
**4.** [4.2b] $x^2 + 13x + 36$    **5.** [1.1d] 2    **6.** [1.1d] 13
**7.** [1.2a] $b = \dfrac{2A - ha}{h}$, or $\dfrac{2A}{h} - a$
**8.** [1.4c] $\{x | x \geq -\frac{7}{9}\}$, or $[-\frac{7}{9}, \infty)$    **9.** [1.5b] $\{x | x < \frac{5}{4} \ or \ x > 4\}$, or $(-\infty, \frac{5}{4}) \cup (4, \infty)$    **10.** [1.6e] $\{x | -2 < x < 5\}$, or $(-2, 5)$
**11.** [3.5a] $(1, 3, -9)$    **12.** [3.3a] $(4, -2)$    **13.** [3.3a] $(\frac{19}{8}, \frac{1}{8})$
**14.** [3.5a] $(-1, 0, -1)$    **15.** [4.8a] $-3, -8$    **16.** [4.8a] $\frac{1}{2}, 7$
**17.** [4.8a] $\frac{2}{3}, -2$
**18.** [4.8a] $\{x | x \text{ is a real number } and \ x \neq 5 \ and \ x \neq -3\}$
**19.** [4.3a] $3x^2(x - 4)$
**20.** [4.3b], [4.6d] $(2x + 1)(x + 1)(x^2 - x + 1)$
**21.** [4.4a] $(x - 2)(x + 7)$    **22.** [4.5a, b] $(4a - 3)(5a - 2)$
**23.** [4.6b] $(2x + 5)(2x - 5)$    **24.** [4.6a] $2(x - 7)^2$
**25.** [4.6d] $(a + 4)(a^2 - 4a + 16)$
**26.** [4.6d] $(4x - 1)(16x^2 + 4x + 1)$
**27.** [4.4a] $(a^3 + 6)(a^3 - 2)$
**28.** [4.6b] $x^2y^2(2x + y)(2x - y)$
**29.** [3.6a] A: 1500 bearings; B: 1900 bearings; C: 2300 bearings
**30.** [1.5b]

**31.** [2.1c]    **32.** [2.5c]    **33.** [3.7b]

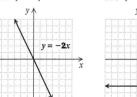

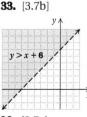

**34.** [2.2c]    **35.** [2.2c]    **36.** [3.7c]

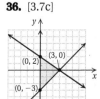

**37.** [2.6d] $y = -\frac{1}{2}x + \frac{17}{2}$    **38.** [2.6d] $y = \frac{4}{3}x - 6$
**39.** [2.6c] $y = 4x + 8$    **40.** [2.6b] $y = -3x + 7$
**41.** [2.4c] About 2897 horses per year    **42. (a)** [4.1b] 30 games;
**(b)** [4.8b] 9 teams    **43.** [4.8b] 11 cm by 10 cm
**44.** [1.6e] $\{x | x \leq 1\}$, or $(-\infty, 1]$

# CHAPTER 5

**Calculator Corner, p. 416**
**1.** Correct   **2.** Correct   **3.** Incorrect   **4.** Incorrect
**5.** Correct

**Calculator Corner, p. 419**
Left to the student

**Exercise Set 5.1, p. 420**
**1.** $-\frac{17}{3}$   **3.** $-7, -5$   **5.** $\{x|x \text{ is a real number } and \ x \neq -7\}$,
or $(-\infty, -7) \cup (-7, \infty)$   **7.** $\{x|x \text{ is a real number } and$
$x \neq 0 \ and \ x \neq 3\}$, or $(-\infty, 0) \cup (0, 3) \cup (3, \infty)$
**9.** $\{x|x \text{ is a real number } and \ x \neq -\frac{17}{3}\}$, or $\left(-\infty, -\frac{17}{3}\right) \cup$
$\left(-\frac{17}{3}, \infty\right)$   **11.** $\{x|x \text{ is a real number } and \ x \neq -7 \ and$
$x \neq -5\}$, or $(-\infty, -7) \cup (-7, -5) \cup (-5, \infty)$
**13.** $\dfrac{7x(x + 2)}{7x(x + 8)}$   **15.** $\dfrac{(q - 5)(q + 5)}{(q + 3)(q + 5)}$   **17.** $3y$   **19.** $\dfrac{2}{3p^4}$
**21.** $a - 3$   **23.** $\dfrac{4x - 5}{7}$   **25.** $\dfrac{y - 3}{y + 3}$   **27.** $\dfrac{t + 4}{t - 4}$
**29.** $\dfrac{x - 8}{x + 4}$   **31.** $\dfrac{w^2 + wz + z^2}{w + z}$   **33.** $\dfrac{1}{3x^3}$
**35.** $\dfrac{(x - 4)(x + 4)}{x(x + 3)}$   **37.** $\dfrac{y + 4}{2}$   **39.** $\dfrac{(2x + 3)(x + 5)}{7x}$
**41.** $c - 2$   **43.** $\dfrac{1}{x + y}$   **45.** $\dfrac{3x^5}{2y^3}$   **47.** 3
**49.** $\dfrac{(y - 3)(y + 2)}{y}$   **51.** $\dfrac{2a + 1}{a + 2}$   **53.** $\dfrac{(x + 4)(x + 2)}{3(x - 5)}$
**55.** $\dfrac{y(y^2 + 3)}{(y + 3)(y - 2)}$   **57.** $\dfrac{x^2 + 4x + 16}{(x + 4)(x + 4)}$
**59.** $\dfrac{4y^2 - 6y + 9}{(4y - 1)(2y - 3)}$   **61.** $\dfrac{2s}{r + 2s}$   **63.** $\dfrac{y^5}{(y + 2)^3(y + 4)}$
**65.** Domain $= \{-4, -2, 0, 2, 4, 6\}$; range $= \{-3, -2, 0, 1, 3, 4\}$
**66.** Domain $= [-4, 5]$; range $= [-3, 2]$
**67.** Domain $= [-5, 5]$; range $= [-4, 4]$
**68.** Domain $= [-4, 5]$; range $= [0, 2]$
**69.** $(3a - 5b)(2a + 5b)$   **70.** $(3a - 5b)^2$
**71.** $10(x - 7)(x - 1)$   **72.** $(5x - 4)(2x - 1)$
**73.** $(7p + 5)(3p - 2)$   **74.** $2(3m + 1)(2m - 5)$
**75.** $2x(x - 11)(x + 3)$   **76.** $10(y + 13)(y - 5)$
**77.** $y = -\frac{2}{3}x - 5$   **78.** $y = -\frac{2}{7}x + \frac{48}{7}$
**79.** $\dfrac{x - 3}{(x + 1)(x + 3)}$   **81.** $\dfrac{m - t}{m + t + 1}$
**83.** $\frac{13}{19}$; $-3$; not defined; $\dfrac{2a + 2h + 3}{4a + 4h - 1}$

**Calculator Corner, p. 430**
Left to the student

**Exercise Set 5.2, p. 431**
**1.** 120   **3.** 144   **5.** 210   **7.** 45   **9.** $\frac{11}{10}$   **11.** $\frac{17}{72}$   **13.** $\frac{251}{240}$
**15.** $21x^2y$   **17.** $10(y - 10)(y + 10)$   **19.** $30a^3b^2$
**21.** $5(y - 3)^2$   **23.** $(y + 5)(y - 5)$, or $(y + 5)(5 - y)$
**25.** $(2r + 3)(r - 4)(3r - 1)(r + 4)$
**27.** $x^3(x - 2)^2(x^2 + 4)$   **29.** $10x^3(x - 1)^2(x + 1)(x^2 + 1)$
**31.** $\dfrac{2x + 7y}{x + y}$   **33.** $\dfrac{3y + 5}{y - 2}$   **35.** $a + b$   **37.** $\dfrac{13}{y}$   **39.** $\dfrac{1}{a + 7}$
**41.** $a^2 + ab + b^2$   **43.** $\dfrac{2(y^2 + 11)}{(y + 4)(y - 5)}$   **45.** $\dfrac{x + y}{x - y}$
**47.** $\dfrac{3x - 4}{(x - 2)(x - 1)}$   **49.** $\dfrac{8x + 1}{(x + 1)(x - 1)}$   **51.** $\dfrac{2(x - 7)}{15(x + 5)}$

**53.** $\dfrac{-a^2 + 7ab - b^2}{(a + b)(a - b)}$   **55.** $\dfrac{y}{(y - 2)(y - 3)}$
**57.** $\dfrac{3y - 10}{(y - 5)(y + 4)}$   **59.** $\dfrac{3y^2 - 3y - 29}{(y + 8)(y - 3)(y - 4)}$
**61.** $\dfrac{2x^2 - 13x + 7}{(x + 3)(x - 1)(x - 3)}$   **63.** 0   **65.** $\dfrac{4y - 11}{(y + 4)(y - 4)}$
**67.** $\dfrac{-2y - 3}{(y + 4)(y - 4)}$   **69.** $\dfrac{-3x^2 - 3x - 4}{(x + 1)(x - 1)}$   **71.** $\dfrac{-2}{x - y}$, or
$\dfrac{2}{y - x}$   **73.** $\dfrac{1}{x - 3}$
**75.** 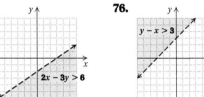   **76.**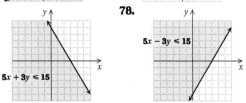
**77.**   **78.**
**79.** $(t - 2)(t^2 + 2t + 4)$   **80.** $(q + 5)(q^2 - 5q + 25)$
**81.** $23x(x + 1)(x^2 - x + 1)$
**82.** $(4a - 3b)(16a^2 + 12ab + 9b^2)$   **83.** $y = -\frac{8}{3}x + \frac{14}{3}$
**84.** $y = \frac{5}{4}x + \frac{11}{2}$   **85.** Domain $= (-\infty, 2) \cup (2, \infty)$;
range $= (-\infty, 0) \cup (0, \infty)$
**87.** $x^4(x + 1)(x - 1)(x^2 + 1)(x^2 + x + 1)(x^2 - x + 1)$
**89.** $-1$   **91.** $\dfrac{-x^3 + x^2y + x^2 - xy^2 + xy + y^3}{(x + y)(x + y)(x - y)(x^2 + y^2)}$

**Exercise Set 5.3, p. 441**
**1.** $4x^4 + 3x^3 - 6$   **3.** $9y^5 - 4y^2 + 3$
**5.** $16a^2b^2 + 7ab - 11$   **7.** $x + 7$   **9.** $a - 12$, R 32; or
$a - 12 + \dfrac{32}{a + 4}$   **11.** $x + 2$, R 4; or $x + 2 + \dfrac{4}{x + 5}$
**13.** $2y^2 - y + 2$, R 6; or $2y^2 - y + 2 + \dfrac{6}{2y + 4}$
**15.** $2y^2 + 2y - 1$, R 8; or $2y^2 + 2y - 1 + \dfrac{8}{5y - 2}$
**17.** $2x^2 - x - 9$, R $(3x + 12)$; or $2x^2 - x - 9 + \dfrac{3x + 12}{x^2 + 2}$
**19.** $2x^3 + 5x^2 + 17x + 51$, R $152x$; or $2x^3 + 5x^2 + 17x +$
$51 + \dfrac{152x}{x^2 - 3x}$   **21.** $x^2 - x + 1$, R $-4$; or $x^2 - x + 1 + \dfrac{-4}{x - 1}$
**23.** $a + 7$, R $-47$; or $a + 7 + \dfrac{-47}{a + 4}$
**25.** $x^2 - 5x - 23$, R $-43$; or $x^2 - 5x - 23 + \dfrac{-43}{x - 2}$
**27.** $3x^2 - 2x + 2$, R $-3$; or $3x^2 - 2x + 2 + \dfrac{-3}{x + 3}$
**29.** $y^2 + 2y + 1$, R 12; or $y^2 + 2y + 1 + \dfrac{12}{y - 2}$
**31.** $3x^3 + 9x^2 + 2x + 6$   **33.** $x^2 + 2x + 4$
**35.** $y^3 + 2y^2 + 4y + 8$
**37.** $y^7 - y^6 + y^5 - y^4 + y^3 - y^2 + y - 1$

**39.**
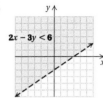

**40.**
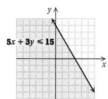

**41.**
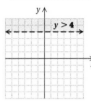

**42.**

**43.**

**44.**
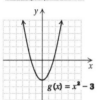

**45.**
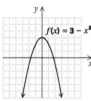

**46.**
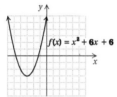

**47.** $0, 5$    **48.** $-\frac{8}{5}, \frac{8}{5}$    **49.** $-\frac{1}{4}, \frac{5}{3}$    **50.** $-\frac{1}{4}, -\frac{2}{3}$
**51.** $0; -3, -\frac{5}{2}, \frac{3}{2}$    **53.** $-\frac{3}{2}$    **55.** $a^2 + ab$

## Calculator Corner, p. 444
Left to the student

## Exercise Set 5.4, p. 448
**1.** $\frac{26}{35}$   **3.** $\frac{88}{15}$   **5.** $\frac{x^3}{y^5}$   **7.** $\frac{3x + y}{x}$   **9.** $\frac{1 + 2a}{1 - a}$   **11.** $\frac{x^2 - 1}{x^2 + 1}$

**13.** $\frac{3y + 4x}{4y - 3x}$   **15.** $\frac{a^2(b - 3)}{b^2(a - 1)}$   **17.** $\frac{1}{a - b}$   **19.** $\frac{-1}{x(x + h)}$

**21.** $\frac{(x - 4)(x - 7)}{(x - 5)(x + 6)}$   **23.** $\frac{x + 1}{5 - x}$   **25.** $\frac{5x - 16}{4x + 1}$

**27.** $\frac{zw(w - z)}{w^2 - wz + z^2}$   **29.** $\frac{2x^2 - 11x - 27}{2x^2 + 21x + 13}$   **31.** 69%
**32.** 70,320 pages   **33.** $2x(2x^2 + 10x + 3)$
**34.** $(y + 2)(y^2 - 2y + 4)$   **35.** $(y - 2)(y^2 + 2y + 4)$
**36.** $2x(x - 9)(x - 7)$   **37.** $(10x + 1)(100x^2 - 10x + 1)$
**38.** $(1 - 10a)(1 + 10a + 100a^2)$
**39.** $(y - 4x)(y^2 + 4xy + 16x^2)$
**40.** $\left(\frac{1}{2}a - 7\right)\left(\frac{1}{4}a^2 + \frac{7}{2}a + 49\right)$   **41.** $s = 3T - r$
**42.**
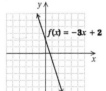

**43.** 22   **44.** $-1, 6$

**45.** $\frac{-3(2a + h)}{a^2(a + h)^2}$   **47.** $\frac{1}{(1 - a - h)(1 - a)}$   **49.** $\frac{5}{6}$

**51.** $\frac{x}{x^3 - 1}$   **53.** $\frac{1}{a^2 - ab + b^2}$

## Mid-Chapter Review: Chapter 5, p. 450
**1.** True    **2.** False    **3.** False

**4.** $\dfrac{7x - 2}{x - 4} - \dfrac{x + 1}{x + 3} = \dfrac{7x - 2}{x - 4} \cdot \dfrac{x + 3}{x + 3} - \dfrac{x + 1}{x + 3} \cdot \dfrac{x - 4}{x - 4}$

$$= \frac{7x^2 + 19x - 6}{(x - 4)(x + 3)} - \frac{x^2 - 3x - 4}{(x + 3)(x - 4)}$$

$$= \frac{7x^2 + 19x - 6 - x^2 + 3x + 4}{(x - 4)(x + 3)}$$

$$= \frac{6x^2 + 22x - 2}{(x - 4)(x + 3)}$$

**5.** $\dfrac{\dfrac{1}{m} + 3}{\dfrac{1}{m} - 5} = \dfrac{\dfrac{1}{m} + 3}{\dfrac{1}{m} - 5} \cdot \dfrac{m}{m} = \dfrac{1 + 3m}{1 - 5m}$

**6.** $\{x | x$ is a real number *and* $x \ne -10$ *and* $x \ne 10\}$, or $(-\infty, -10) \cup (-10, 10) \cup (10, \infty)$   **7.** $\{x | x$ is a real number *and* $x \ne 7\}$, or $(-\infty, 7) \cup (7, \infty)$   **8.** $\{x | x$ is a real number *and* $x \ne -9$ *and* $x \ne 1\}$, or $(-\infty, -9) \cup (-9, 1) \cup (1, \infty)$
**9.** $\dfrac{2}{3p^7}$   **10.** $\dfrac{14y - 1}{11}$   **11.** $\dfrac{x - y}{x^2 - xy + y^2}$   **12.** $\dfrac{x + 5}{x + 2}$
**13.** $\dfrac{a - 2}{a + 2}$   **14.** $\dfrac{-1}{t + 2}$   **15.** $70x^4y^5$

**16.** $(x - 5)^2(x + 5)(x + 8)$   **17.** $\dfrac{45}{(x + 1)^2}$

**18.** $\dfrac{4x^2 - x + 2}{(x + 6)(x - 2)}$   **19.** $\dfrac{-3q - 2}{q(q + 2)}$

**20.** $\dfrac{-y^2 - 6y - 3}{(y - 1)(y + 3)(y + 2)}$   **21.** $\dfrac{b}{1 + b}$   **22.** $\dfrac{w - z}{5}$

**23.** $(t - 1)(t^2 + 2t + 4)$   **24.** $\dfrac{25c^2 + 6a}{15c}$   **25.** $\dfrac{x + 2}{x - 4}$

**26.** $3x + 2$, R 17; or $3x + 2 + \dfrac{17}{2x - 3}$   **27.** $x^3 - x^2 + x - 1$

**28.** $2x^2 - 5x + 15$, R $-34$; or $2x^2 - 5x + 15 + \dfrac{-34}{x + 2}$
**29.** $x + 2$   **30.** $x^3 - 3x^2 + 6x - 18$, R 56; or $x^3 - 3x^2 + 6x - 18 + \dfrac{56}{x + 3}$   **31.** $3x - 1$, R 7; or $3x - 1 + \dfrac{7}{5x + 1}$
**32.** For $a$, a remainder of 0 indicates that $x - a$ is a factor. The quotient is a polynomial of one less degree and can be factored further, if possible, using synthetic division again or another factoring method.   **33.** Addition, subtraction, and multiplication of polynomials always result in a polynomial, because each is defined in terms of addition, subtraction, or multiplication of monomials, and the sum, difference, and product of monomials is a monomial. Division of polynomials does not always result in a polynomial, because the quotient is not always a monomial or a sum of monomials. Example 1 in Section 5.3 in the text illustrates this.   **34.** No; when we simplify a rational expression by removing a factor of 1, we are actually reversing the multiplication process.   **35.** Janine's answer was correct. It is equivalent to the answer at the back of the book:

$$\frac{3 - x}{x - 5} = \frac{-x + 3}{x - 5} = \frac{-1(-x + 3)}{-1(x - 5)} = \frac{x - 3}{-x + 5} = \frac{x - 3}{5 - x}.$$

**36.** Nancy's misconception is that $x$ is a factor of the numerator. $\left(\dfrac{x + 2}{x} = 3 \text{ only for } x = 1.\right)$   **37.** Most would agree that it is easier to find the LCM of all the denominators, $bd$, and then to multiply by $bd/(bd)$ than it is to add in the numerator, subtract in the denominator, and then divide the numerator by the denominator.

## Calculator Corner, p. 455

**1.** Left to the student   **2.** Left to the student

## Study Tips, p. 457

**1.** Rational expression   **2.** Solutions   **3.** Rational expression   **4.** Rational expression   **5.** Rational expression   **6.** Solutions   **7.** Rational expression   **8.** Solutions   **9.** Solutions   **10.** Solutions   **11.** Rational expression   **12.** Solutions   **13.** Rational expression

## Exercise Set 5.5, p. 458

**1.** $\frac{31}{4}$   **3.** $-\frac{12}{7}$   **5.** 144   **7.** $-1, -8$   **9.** 2   **11.** 11   **13.** 11   **15.** No solution   **17.** 2   **19.** 5   **21.** $-145$   **23.** $-\frac{10}{3}$   **25.** $-3$   **27.** $\frac{31}{5}$   **29.** $\frac{85}{12}$   **31.** $-6, 5$   **33.** No solution   **35.** 2   **37.** No solution   **39.** $-1, 0$   **41.** $-\frac{3}{2}, 2$   **43.** $\frac{17}{4}$   **45.** $\frac{3}{5}$   **46.** $4(t + 5)(t^2 - 5t + 25)$   **47.** $(1 - t)(1 + t + t^2)(1 + t)(1 - t + t^2)$   **48.** $(a + 2b)(a^2 - 2ab + 4b^2)$   **49.** $(a - 2b)(a^2 + 2ab + 4b^2)$   **50.** 3   **51.** $-4, 3$   **52.** $-7, 7$   **53.** $\frac{1}{4}, \frac{2}{3}$   **54.** About 0.19 million people per month   **55.** About 22 reports per year   **57. (a)** $(-3.5, 1.\overline{3})$; **(b), (c)** left to the student

## Translating for Success, p. 468

**1.** N   **2.** B   **3.** A   **4.** C   **5.** E   **6.** G   **7.** I   **8.** K   **9.** M   **10.** O

## Exercise Set 5.6, p. 469

**1.** $15\frac{3}{4}$ hr   **3.** $1\frac{5}{7}$ hr   **5.** 4.375 hr, or $4\frac{3}{8}$ hr   **7.** Machine A: 2 hr; machine B: 6 hr   **9.** Samantha: $1\frac{1}{3}$ hr; Elizabeth: 4 hr   **11.** 287 trout   **13.** 3.84 g   **15.** About 27.16 in.   **17.** 28.8 lb   **19.** About 20,658 kg   **21.** $10\frac{1}{2}$ ft; $17\frac{1}{2}$ ft   **23.** 36 touchdown passes   **25.** 35 mph   **27.** 7 mph   **29.** 5.2 ft/sec   **31.** Bus: 60 mph; trolley: 45 mph   **33.** Domain: $[-5, 5]$; range: $[-4, 3]$   **34.** Domain: $\{-4, -2, 0, 1, 2, 4\}$; range: $\{-2, 0, 2, 4, 5\}$   **35.** Domain: $[-5, 5]$; range: $[-5, 3]$   **36.** Domain: $[-5, 5]$; range: $[-5, 0]$

**37.**

**38.**

**39.**

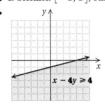

**40.**

**41.** $t = \frac{2}{3}$ hr   **43.** City: 261 mi; highway: 204 mi   **45.** 30 mi

## Exercise Set 5.7, p. 476

**1.** $W_2 = \dfrac{d_2 W_1}{d_1}$   **3.** $r_2 = \dfrac{R r_1}{r_1 - R}$   **5.** $t = \dfrac{2s}{v_1 + v_2}$   **7.** $s = \dfrac{Rg}{g - R}$   **9.** $p = \dfrac{qf}{q - f}$   **11.** $a = \dfrac{bt}{b - t}$   **13.** $E = \dfrac{Inr}{n - I}$   **15.** $H^2 = \dfrac{704.5W}{I}$   **17.** $r = \dfrac{eR}{E - e}$   **19.** $R = \dfrac{3V + \pi h^3}{3\pi h^2}$   **21.** $h = \dfrac{S - 2\pi r^2}{2\pi r}$   **23.** $t_2 = \dfrac{d_2 - d_1 + t_1 v}{v}$   **25.** $Q = \dfrac{2Tt - 2AT}{A - q}$

**27.** Dimes: 2 rolls; nickels: 5 rolls; quarters: 5 rolls   **28.** $-6$   **29.** 6   **30.** 0   **31.** $8a^3 - 2a$   **32.** $-\frac{4}{5}$   **33.** $y = -\frac{4}{5}x + \frac{17}{5}$

## Exercise Set 5.8, p. 485

**1.** 5; $y = 5x$   **3.** $\frac{2}{15}$; $y = \frac{2}{15}x$   **5.** $\frac{9}{4}$; $y = \frac{9}{4}x$   **7.** 175 semi trucks   **9.** 135,209,760 cans   **11.** 90 g   **13.** 40 kg   **15.** 98; $y = \dfrac{98}{x}$   **17.** 36; $y = \dfrac{36}{x}$   **19.** 0.05; $y = \dfrac{0.05}{x}$   **21.** 3.5 hr   **23.** $\frac{2}{9}$ ampere   **25.** 960 lb   **27.** $5\frac{5}{7}$ hr   **29.** $y = 15x^2$   **31.** $y = \dfrac{0.0015}{x^2}$   **33.** $y = xz$   **35.** $y = \frac{3}{10}xz^2$   **37.** $y = \dfrac{xz}{5wp}$   **39.** 2.5 m   **41.** 199.4 lb   **43.** 95 earned runs   **45.** 729 gal   **47.** Like   **48.** Complementary   **49.** Opposites; additive   **50.** Vertical   **51.** Intersection   **52.** Linear   **53.** Multiplication principle   **54.** $(0, a)$   **55. (a)** Inversely; **(b)** neither; **(c)** directly; **(d)** directly   **57.** $7.20

## Summary and Review: Chapter 5, p. 489

### Concept Reinforcement

**1.** False   **2.** True   **3.** True

### Important Concepts

**1.** $\{x \mid x \text{ is a real number } and\ x \neq -9\ and\ x \neq 6\}$, or $(-\infty, -9) \cup (-9, 6) \cup (6, \infty)$   **2.** $\dfrac{b - 3}{b - 8}$   **3.** $\dfrac{(w - 5)(w^2 + 5w + 25)}{w + 3}$   **4.** $x^4(x - 3)(x + 3)(2x + 5)$   **5.** $\dfrac{r^2 - 3rs - 9s^2}{(r + 2s)(r - s)(r + s)}$   **6.** $y - 4$, R 5; or $y - 4 + \dfrac{5}{y - 1}$   **7.** $x^2 - 8x + 24$, R $-73$; or $x^2 - 8x + 24 + \dfrac{-73}{x + 3}$   **8.** $\dfrac{b + 4a}{4b - a}$   **9.** $-\frac{33}{2}$   **10.** $k = 93$; $y = 93x$   **11.** $k = \frac{9}{2}$; $y = \dfrac{9}{2x}$

### Review Exercises

**1.** $-3, 3$   **2.** $\{x \mid x \text{ is a real number } and\ x \neq -3\ and\ x \neq 3\}$, or $(-\infty, -3) \cup (-3, 3) \cup (3, \infty)$   **3.** $\dfrac{x - 2}{3x + 2}$   **4.** $\dfrac{1}{a - 2}$   **5.** $48x^3$   **6.** $(x - 7)(x + 7)(3x + 1)$   **7.** $(x + 5)(x - 4)(x - 2)$   **8.** $\dfrac{y - 8}{2}$   **9.** $\dfrac{(x - 2)(x + 5)}{x - 5}$   **10.** $\dfrac{3a - 1}{a - 3}$   **11.** $\dfrac{(x^2 + 4x + 16)(x - 6)}{(x + 4)(x + 2)}$   **12.** $\dfrac{x - 3}{(x + 1)(x + 3)}$   **13.** $\dfrac{2x^3 + 2x^2 y + 2xy^2 - 2y^3}{(x - y)(x + y)}$   **14.** $\dfrac{-y}{(y + 4)(y - 1)}$   **15.** $4b^2 c - \frac{5}{2}bc^2 + 3abc$   **16.** $y - 14$, R $-20$; or $y - 14 + \dfrac{-20}{y - 6}$   **17.** $6x^2 - 9$, R $(5x + 22)$; or $6x^2 - 9 + \dfrac{5x + 22}{x^2 + 2}$   **18.** $x^2 + 9x + 40$, R 153; or $x^2 + 9x + 40 + \dfrac{153}{x - 4}$   **19.** $3x^3 - 8x^2 + 8x - 6$, R $-1$; or $3x^3 - 8x^2 + 8x - 6 + \dfrac{-1}{x + 1}$   **20.** $\frac{3}{4}$   **21.** $\dfrac{a^2 b^2}{2(a^2 - ab + b^2)}$   **22.** $\dfrac{(x - 9)(x - 6)}{(x - 3)(x + 6)}$

**23.** $\dfrac{2(x^2 - 7x + 1)}{3x^2 + 7x - 11}$   **24.** $\frac{28}{11}$   **25.** 6   **26.** No solution
**27.** 3   **28.** $-\frac{11}{3}$   **29.** 2   **30.** $5\frac{1}{7}$ hr
**31.**

|  | Distance | Speed | Time |
|---|---|---|---|
| **Downstream** | 50 mi | $x + 6$ | $t$ |
| **Upstream** | 30 mi | $x - 6$ | $t$ |

24 mph

**32.** 4000 mi   **33.** $d = \dfrac{Wc}{c - W}; c = \dfrac{Wd}{d - W}$   **34.** $b = \dfrac{ta}{Sa - p}$;
$t = \dfrac{Sab - pb}{a}$   **35.** $y = 4x$   **36.** $y = \dfrac{2500}{x}$   **37.** 20 min
**38.** About 77.7   **39.** 500 watts   **40.** B   **41.** C
**42.** $a^2 + ab + b^2$   **43.** All real numbers except 0 and 13

## Understanding Through Discussion and Writing

**1.** When adding or subtracting rational expressions, we use the LCM of the denominators (the LCD). When solving a rational equation or when solving a formula for a given letter, we multiply by the LCM of all the denominators to clear fractions. When simplifying a complex rational expression, we can use the LCM in either of two ways. We can multiply by $a/a$, where $a$ is the LCM of all the denominators occurring in the expression. Or we can use the LCM to add or subtract as necessary in the numerator and in the denominator.   **2.** Rational equations differ from those previously studied because they contain variables in denominators. Because of this, possible solutions must be checked in the original equation to avoid division by 0.   **3.** Assuming all algebraic procedures have been performed correctly, a possible solution of a rational equation would fail to be an actual solution only if it were not in the domain of one of the rational expressions in the equation. This occurs when the number in question makes a denominator 0.
**4.** Let $y = k_1 x$ and $x = \dfrac{k_2}{z}$. Then $y = k_1 \cdot \dfrac{k_2}{z}$, or $y = \dfrac{k_1 k_2}{z}$, so $y$ varies inversely as $z$.   **5.** Answers may vary. From Example 4 of Section 5.5, we see that one form of such an equation is $\dfrac{x^2}{x - a} = \dfrac{a^2}{x - a}$.   **6.** Answers may vary. Many would probably argue that it is easier to solve $\dfrac{1}{a} + \dfrac{1}{b} = \dfrac{1}{x}$ since it is easier to multiply $a$ and $b$ than 38 and 47. Others might argue that it is easier to solve $\dfrac{1}{38} + \dfrac{1}{47} = \dfrac{1}{x}$ since it is easier to work with constants than variables.

## Test: Chapter 5, p. 495

**1.** [5.1a] 1, 2   **2.** [5.1a] $\{x | x$ is a real number $and\ x \neq 1\ and\ x \neq 2\}$, or $(-\infty, 1) \cup (1, 2) \cup (2, \infty)$   **3.** [5.1c] $\dfrac{3x + 2}{x - 2}$
**4.** [5.1c] $\dfrac{p^2 - p + 1}{p - 2}$   **5.** [5.2a] $(x + 3)(x - 2)(x + 5)$
**6.** [5.1d] $\dfrac{2(x + 5)}{x - 2}$   **7.** [5.2b] $\dfrac{x - 6}{(x + 4)(x + 6)}$
**8.** [5.1e] $\dfrac{y + 4}{2}$   **9.** [5.2b] $x + y$   **10.** [5.2c] $\dfrac{3x}{(x - 1)(x + 1)}$
**11.** [5.2c] $\dfrac{a^3 + a^2 b + ab^2 + ab - b^2 - 2}{(a - b)(a^2 + ab + b^2)}$
**12.** [5.3a] $4s^2 + 3s - 2rs^2$   **13.** [5.3b] $y^2 - 5y + 25$
**14.** [5.3b] $4x^2 + 3x - 4$, R $(-8x + 2)$; or
$4x^2 + 3x - 4 + \dfrac{-8x + 2}{x^2 + 1}$   **15.** [5.3c] $x^2 + 6x + 20$, R 54; or

$x^2 + 6x + 20 + \dfrac{54}{x - 3}$   **16.** [5.3c] $3x^2 + 10x - 40$
**17.** [5.4a] $\dfrac{x + 1}{x}$   **18.** [5.4a] $\dfrac{b^2 - ab + a^2}{a^2 b^2}$   **19.** [5.5a] $-1, 4$
**20.** [5.5a] 9   **21.** [5.5a] No solution   **22.** [5.5a] $-\frac{7}{2}$, 5
**23.** [5.5a] $\frac{17}{8}$   **24.** [5.6a] 2 hr   **25.** [5.6c] $3\frac{3}{11}$ mph
**26.** [5.6b] $14\frac{2}{17}$ gal   **27.** [5.7a] $a = \dfrac{Tb}{T - b}; b = \dfrac{Ta}{a + T}$
**28.** [5.7a] $a = \dfrac{2b}{Qb + t}$   **29.** [5.8e] $Q = \frac{5}{2}xy$
**30.** [5.8c] $y = \dfrac{250}{x}$   **31.** [5.8b] \$990   **32.** [5.8d] $7\frac{1}{2}$ hr
**33.** [5.8f] 615.44 cm$^2$   **34.** [5.2a] D   **35.** [5.5a] All real numbers except 0 and 15   **36.** [5.4a], [5.5a] $x$-intercept: $(11, 0)$; $y$-intercept: $\left(0, -\frac{33}{5}\right)$

## Cumulative Review: Chapters 1-5, p. 497

**1.** [2.1c]   **2.** [2.5c]

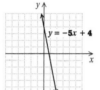   

**3.** [3.7b]   **4.** [3.7c]

**5.** [2.2b] 11   **6.** [5.1a] $\{x | x$ is a real number $and\ x \neq -5\ and\ x \neq 5\}$, or $(-\infty, -5) \cup (-5, 5) \cup (5, \infty)$   **7.** [2.3a] Domain: $[-5, 5]$; range: $[-2, 4]$   **8.** [4.2c] $36m^2 - 12mn + n^2$
**9.** [4.2b] $15a^2 - 14ab - 8b^2$   **10.** [5.1d] $\dfrac{y - 2}{3}$
**11.** [5.1e] $\dfrac{3x - 5}{x + 4}$   **12.** [5.2b] $\dfrac{6x + 13}{20(x - 3)}$   **13.** [5.4a] $\dfrac{y^3 - 2y}{y^3 - 1}$
**14.** [4.1d] $16p^2 - 8p$   **15.** [5.2c] $\dfrac{4x + 1}{(x + 2)(x - 2)}$
**16.** [5.3b] $2x^2 - 11x + 23 + \dfrac{-49}{x + 2}$   **17.** [1.1d] $\frac{15}{2}$
**18.** [1.5a] $\{x | -3 < x < -\frac{3}{2}\}$, or $\left(-3, -\frac{3}{2}\right)$
**19.** [5.5a] No solution   **20.** [5.7a] $a = \dfrac{bP}{3 - P}$
**21.** [1.2a] $C = \frac{5}{9}(F - 32)$   **22.** [1.6e] $\{x | x \leq -2.1\ or\ x \geq 2.1\}$, or $(-\infty, -2.1] \cup [2.1, \infty)$   **23.** [5.5a] $-1$   **24.** [4.8a] $\frac{1}{4}$
**25.** [4.8a] $-2, \frac{7}{2}$   **26.** [3.2a], [3.3a] Infinite number of solutions   **27.** [3.2a], [3.3a] $(-2, 1)$   **28.** [3.5a] $(3, 2, -1)$
**29.** [3.5a] $\left(\frac{5}{8}, \frac{1}{16}, -\frac{3}{4}\right)$   **30.** [4.3a] $2x^2(2x + 9)$
**31.** [4.3b] $(2a - 1)(4a^2 - 3)$   **32.** [4.4a] $(x - 6)(x + 14)$
**33.** [4.5a, b] $(2x + 5)(3x - 2)$   **34.** [4.6b] $(4y + 9)(4y - 9)$
**35.** [4.6a] $(t - 8)^2$   **36.** [4.6d] $8(2x + 1)(4x^2 - 2x + 1)$
**37.** [4.6b] $(0.3b - 0.2c)(0.09b^2 + 0.06bc + 0.04c^2)$
**38.** [4.7a] $x^2(x^2 + 1)(x + 1)(x - 1)$
**39.** [4.5a, b] $(4x - 1)(5x + 3)$   **40.** [2.6b] $y = -\frac{1}{2}x - 1$
**41.** [2.6d] $y = \frac{1}{2}x - \frac{5}{2}$   **42.** [3.6a] Win: 38 games; lose: 30 games; tie: 13 games   **43.** [5.8b] About 202.3 lb
**44.** [5.5a] A   **45.** [4.8a] C   **46.** [5.6a] B
**47.** [3.6a] $a = 1, b = -5, c = 6$   **48.** [4.8a] $0, \frac{1}{4}, -\frac{1}{4}$
**49.** [5.5a] All real numbers except 9 and $-5$

# CHAPTER 6

## Exercise Set 6.1, p. 507

**1.** $4, -4$ **3.** $12, -12$ **5.** $20, -20$ **7.** $-\frac{7}{6}$ **9.** $14$
**11.** $0.06$ **13.** Does not exist as a real number **15.** $18.628$
**17.** $1.962$ **19.** $y^2 + 16$ **21.** $\frac{x}{y-1}$ **23.** $\sqrt{20} \approx 4.472; 0;$
does not exist as a real number; does not exist as a real number
**25.** $\sqrt{11} \approx 3.317$; does not exist as a real number;
$\sqrt{11} \approx 3.317; 12$ **27.** Domain $= \{x | x \geq 2\} = [2, \infty)$
**29.** 21 spaces; 25 spaces

**31.**
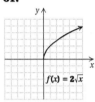

**33.**
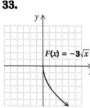

**35.**
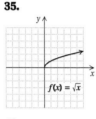

**37.**
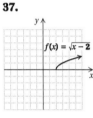

**39.**
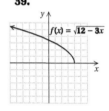

**41.**
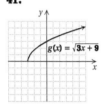

**43.** $4|x|$ **45.** $12|c|$ **47.** $|p + 3|$ **49.** $|x - 2|$ **51.** 3
**53.** $-4x$ **55.** $-6$ **57.** $0.7(x + 1)$ **59.** $2; 3; -2; -4$
**61.** $-1; \sqrt[3]{-20}$, or $\sqrt[3]{20} \approx 2.714; -4; -10$ **63.** $-5$
**65.** $-1$ **67.** $-\frac{2}{3}$ **69.** $|x|$ **71.** $5|a|$ **73.** 6 **75.** $|a + b|$
**77.** $y$ **79.** $x - 2$ **81.** $-2, 1$ **82.** $-1, 0$ **83.** $-\frac{7}{2}, \frac{7}{2}$
**84.** $4, 9$ **85.** $-2, \frac{5}{3}$ **86.** $\frac{5}{2}$ **87.** $0, \frac{5}{2}$ **88.** $0, 1$
**89.** $a^9 b^6 c^{15}$ **90.** $10 a^{10} b^9$
**91.** Domain $= \{x | -3 \leq x < 2\} = [-3, 2)$ **93.** $1.7; 2.2; 3.2$
**95.** **(a)** Domain: $(-\infty, \infty)$; range: $(-\infty, \infty)$;
**(b)** domain: $(-\infty, \infty)$; range: $(-\infty, \infty)$;
**(c)** domain: $[-3, \infty)$; range: $(-\infty, 2]$; **(d)** domain: $[0, \infty)$;
range: $[0, \infty)$; **(e)** domain: $[3, \infty)$; range: $[0, \infty)$

## Calculator Corner, p. 513

**1.** $3.344$ **2.** $3.281$ **3.** $0.283$ **4.** $11.053$ **5.** $5.527 \times 10^{-5}$
**6.** 2

## Exercise Set 6.2, p. 516

**1.** $\sqrt[7]{y}$ **3.** 2 **5.** $\sqrt[5]{a^3 b^3}$ **7.** 8 **9.** 343 **11.** $17^{1/2}$
**13.** $18^{1/3}$ **15.** $(xy^2 z)^{1/5}$ **17.** $(3mn)^{3/2}$ **19.** $(8x^2 y)^{5/7}$
**21.** $\frac{1}{3}$ **23.** $\frac{1}{1000}$ **25.** $\frac{3}{x^{1/4}}$ **27.** $\frac{1}{(2rs)^{3/4}}$ **29.** $\frac{2a^{3/4} c^{2/3}}{b^{1/2}}$
**31.** $\left(\frac{8yz}{7x}\right)^{3/5}$ **33.** $x^{2/3}$ **35.** $\frac{x^4}{2^{1/3} y^{2/7}}$ **37.** $\frac{7x}{z^{1/3}}$
**39.** $\frac{5ac^{1/2}}{3}$ **41.** $5^{7/8}$ **43.** $7^{1/4}$ **45.** $4.9^{1/2}$ **47.** $6^{3/28}$
**49.** $a^{23/12}$ **51.** $a^{8/3} b^{5/2}$ **53.** $\frac{1}{x^{2/7}}$ **55.** $\frac{y^{1/3}}{x^{1/2}}$ **57.** $m^{3/5} n^2$
**59.** $\sqrt[3]{a}$ **61.** $x^5$ **63.** $\frac{1}{x^3}$ **65.** $a^5 b^5$ **67.** $\sqrt{2}$ **69.** $\sqrt[3]{2x}$
**71.** $x^2 y^3$ **73.** $2c^2 d^3$ **75.** $\sqrt[12]{7^4 \cdot 5^3}$ **77.** $\sqrt[20]{5^5 \cdot 7^4}$
**79.** $\sqrt[6]{4x^5}$ **81.** $a^6 b^{12}$ **83.** $\sqrt[18]{m}$ **85.** $\sqrt[12]{x^4 y^3 z^2}$
**87.** $\sqrt[30]{\frac{d^{35}}{c^{99}}}$ **89.** $a = \frac{Ab}{b - A}$ **90.** $s = \frac{Qt}{Q - t}$
**91.** $t = \frac{Qs}{s + Q}$ **92.** $b = \frac{ta}{t - a}$ **93.** Left to the student

## Exercise Set 6.3, p. 523

**1.** $2\sqrt{6}$ **3.** $3\sqrt{10}$ **5.** $5\sqrt[3]{2}$ **7.** $6x^2\sqrt{5}$ **9.** $3x^2\sqrt[3]{2x^2}$
**11.** $2t^2\sqrt[3]{10t^2}$ **13.** $2\sqrt[4]{5}$ **15.** $4a\sqrt{2b}$ **17.** $3x^2 y^2\sqrt[4]{3y^2}$
**19.** $2xy^3\sqrt[5]{3x^2}$ **21.** $5\sqrt{2}$ **23.** $3\sqrt{10}$ **25.** 2 **27.** $30\sqrt{3}$
**29.** $3x^4\sqrt{2}$ **31.** $5bc^2\sqrt{2b}$ **33.** $a\sqrt[3]{10}$ **35.** $2y^3\sqrt[3]{2}$
**37.** $4\sqrt[4]{4}$ **39.** $4a^3 b\sqrt{6ab}$ **41.** $\sqrt[6]{200}$ **43.** $\sqrt[4]{12}$
**45.** $a\sqrt[4]{a}$ **47.** $b\sqrt[10]{b^9}$ **49.** $xy\sqrt[6]{xy^5}$ **51.** $2ab\sqrt[4]{2a^3}$
**53.** $3\sqrt{2}$ **55.** $\sqrt[4]{5}$ **57.** 3 **59.** $y\sqrt{7y}$ **61.** $2\sqrt[3]{a^2 b}$
**63.** $4\sqrt{xy}$ **65.** $2x^2 y^2$ **67.** $\frac{1}{\sqrt[6]{a}}$ **69.** $\sqrt[12]{a^5}$
**71.** $\sqrt[12]{x^2 y^5}$ **73.** $\frac{5}{6}$ **75.** $\frac{4}{7}$ **77.** $\frac{5}{3}$ **79.** $\frac{7}{y}$ **81.** $\frac{5y\sqrt{y}}{x^2}$
**83.** $\frac{3y\sqrt[3]{3y^2}}{4}$ **85.** $\frac{3a\sqrt[4]{a}}{2b}$ **87.** $\frac{3x}{2}$ **89.** $\frac{2a^3}{bc^4}$ **91.** $\frac{2x\sqrt[5]{x^3}}{y^2}$
**93.** $\frac{w\sqrt[5]{w^2}}{z^2}$ **95.** $\frac{x^2\sqrt[6]{x}}{yz^2}$ **97.** $2\frac{2}{3}$ hr; 8 hr **98.** Height: 4 in.;
base: 6 in. **99.** 8 **100.** $\frac{15}{2}$ **101.** No solution
**102.** No solution **103.** **(a)** 1.62 sec; **(b)** 1.99 sec; **(c)** 2.20 sec
**105.** $2yz\sqrt{2z}$

## Exercise Set 6.4, p. 529

**1.** $11\sqrt{5}$ **3.** $\sqrt[3]{7}$ **5.** $13\sqrt[3]{y}$ **7.** $-8\sqrt{6}$ **9.** $6\sqrt[3]{3}$
**11.** $21\sqrt{3}$ **13.** $38\sqrt{5}$ **15.** $122\sqrt{2}$ **17.** $9\sqrt[3]{2}$
**19.** $29\sqrt{2}$ **21.** $(1 + 6a)\sqrt{5a}$ **23.** $(2 - x)\sqrt[3]{3x}$
**25.** $(21x + 1)\sqrt{3x}$ **27.** $2 + 3\sqrt{2}$ **29.** $15\sqrt[3]{4}$
**31.** $(x + 1)\sqrt[3]{6x}$ **33.** $3\sqrt{a - 1}$ **35.** $(x + 3)\sqrt{x - 1}$
**37.** $4\sqrt{5} - 10$ **39.** $\sqrt{6} - \sqrt{21}$ **41.** $-12 + 6\sqrt{3}$
**43.** $2\sqrt{15} - 6\sqrt{3}$ **45.** $-6$ **47.** $6y - 12\sqrt[3]{y^2}$ **49.** $3a\sqrt[3]{2}$
**51.** 1 **53.** $-12$ **55.** 44 **57.** 1 **59.** 3 **61.** $-19$
**63.** $a - b$ **65.** $1 + \sqrt{5}$ **67.** $7 + 3\sqrt{3}$ **69.** $-6$
**71.** $a + \sqrt{3a} + \sqrt{2a} + \sqrt{6}$ **73.** $2\sqrt[3]{9} - 3\sqrt[3]{6} - 2\sqrt[3]{4}$
**75.** $7 + 4\sqrt{3}$ **77.** $\sqrt[5]{72} + 3 - \sqrt[5]{24} - \sqrt[5]{81}$
**79.** $\frac{x(x^2 + 4)}{(x + 4)(x + 3)}$ **80.** $\frac{(a + 2)(a + 4)}{a}$ **81.** $a - 2$
**82.** $\frac{(y - 3)(y - 3)}{y + 3}$ **83.** $\frac{4(3x - 1)}{3(4x + 1)}$ **84.** $\frac{x}{x + 1}$ **85.** $\frac{pq}{q + p}$
**86.** $\frac{a^2 b^2}{b^2 - ab + a^2}$ **87.** $-\frac{29}{3}, 5$ **88.** $\{x | -\frac{29}{3} < x < 5\}$,
or $\left(-\frac{29}{3}, 5\right)$ **89.** $\{x | x \leq -\frac{29}{3} \text{ or } x \geq 5\}$, or $\left(-\infty, -\frac{29}{3}\right] \cup [5, \infty)$
**90.** $-12, -\frac{2}{5}$ **91.** Domain $= (-\infty, \infty)$ **93.** 6
**95.** $14 + 2\sqrt{15} - 6\sqrt{2} - 2\sqrt{30}$ **97.** $3\sqrt[3]{3} + 2\sqrt[3]{9} - 8$

## Mid-Chapter Review: Chapter 6, p. 533

**1.** False **2.** True **3.** False **4.** True
**5.** $\sqrt{6}\sqrt{10} = \sqrt{6 \cdot 10} = \sqrt{2 \cdot 3 \cdot 2 \cdot 5} = 2\sqrt{15}$
**6.** $5\sqrt{32} - 3\sqrt{18} = 5\sqrt{16 \cdot 2} - 3\sqrt{9 \cdot 2} = 5 \cdot 4\sqrt{2} - 3 \cdot 3\sqrt{2} = 20\sqrt{2} - 9\sqrt{2} = 11\sqrt{2}$ **7.** 9 **8.** $-12$ **9.** $\frac{4}{5}$
**10.** Does not exist as a real number **11.** 3; does not exist as a
real number **12.** Domain $= \{x | x \leq 4\} = (-\infty, 4]$

**13.**

**14.**

**15.** $6|z|$ **16.** $|x - 4|$ **17.** $-4$ **18.** $-3a$ **19.** 2 **20.** $|y|$
**21.** 5 **22.** $\sqrt[4]{a^3 b}$ **23.** $16^{1/5}$ **24.** $(6m^2 n)^{1/3}$ **25.** $\frac{1}{3^{3/8}}$
**26.** $7^{4/5}$ **27.** $\frac{x^{3/2}}{y^{4/3}}$ **28.** $\frac{1}{n^{3/4}}$ **29.** $\sqrt[3]{4}$ **30.** $\sqrt{ab}$

**31.** $\sqrt[6]{y^5}$  **32.** $\sqrt[15]{a^{10}b^9}$  **33.** $5\sqrt{3}$  **34.** $2xy\sqrt[3]{3y^2}$
**35.** $2\sqrt[3]{5}$  **36.** $\dfrac{7a^2\sqrt{a}}{b^4}$  **37.** $11\sqrt{7}$  **38.** $(9x-24)\sqrt{2x}$
**39.** $2\sqrt{3}-15$  **40.** $3-4\sqrt{x}+x$  **41.** $m-n$
**42.** $11+4\sqrt{7}$  **43.** $-42+\sqrt{15}$  **44.** Yes; since $x^2$ is nonnegative for any value of $x$, the $n$th root of $x^2$ exists regardless of whether $n$ is even or odd. Thus the $n$th root of $x^2$ always exists.  **45.** Formulate an expression containing a radical term with an even index and a radicand $R$ such that the solution of the inequality $R \geq 0$ is $\{x \mid x \leq 5\}$. One expression is $\sqrt{5-x}$. Other expressions could be formulated as $a\sqrt[k]{b(5-x)}+c$, where $a \neq 0$, $b > 0$, and $k$ is an even integer.
**46.** Since $x^6 \geq 0$ and $x^2 \geq 0$ for any value of $x$, then $\sqrt[3]{x^6}=x^2$. However, $x^3 \geq 0$ only for $x \geq 0$, so $\sqrt{x^6}=x^3$ only when $x \geq 0$.
**47.** No; for example, $\dfrac{\sqrt{8}}{\sqrt{2}}=\sqrt{\dfrac{8}{2}}=\sqrt{4}=2$.

### Exercise Set 6.5, p. 538

**1.** $\dfrac{\sqrt{15}}{3}$  **3.** $\dfrac{\sqrt{22}}{2}$  **5.** $\dfrac{2\sqrt{15}}{35}$  **7.** $\dfrac{2\sqrt[3]{6}}{3}$  **9.** $\dfrac{\sqrt[3]{75ac^2}}{5c}$
**11.** $\dfrac{y\sqrt[3]{9yx^2}}{3x^2}$  **13.** $\dfrac{\sqrt[4]{s^3t^3}}{st}$  **15.** $\dfrac{\sqrt{15x}}{10}$  **17.** $\dfrac{\sqrt[3]{100xy}}{5x^2y}$
**19.** $\dfrac{\sqrt[4]{2xy}}{2x^2y}$  **21.** $\dfrac{54+9\sqrt{10}}{26}$  **23.** $-2\sqrt{35}+2\sqrt{21}$
**25.** $\dfrac{18\sqrt{6}+6\sqrt{15}}{13}$  **27.** $\dfrac{3\sqrt{2}-3\sqrt{5}+\sqrt{10}-5}{-3}$
**29.** $\dfrac{3+\sqrt{21}-\sqrt{6}-\sqrt{14}}{-4}$  **31.** $\dfrac{\sqrt{15}+20-6\sqrt{2}-8\sqrt{30}}{-77}$
**33.** $\dfrac{6-5\sqrt{a}+a}{9-a}$  **35.** $\dfrac{6+5\sqrt{x}-6x}{9-4x}$  **37.** $\dfrac{3\sqrt{6}+4}{2}$
**39.** $\dfrac{x-2\sqrt{xy}+y}{x-y}$  **41.** 30  **42.** $-\dfrac{19}{5}$  **43.** 1  **44.** $\dfrac{x-2}{x+3}$

**45.** Left to the student  **47.** $-\dfrac{3\sqrt{a^2-3}}{a^2-3}$

### Calculator Corner, p. 542

**1.** Left to the student  **2.** Left to the student

### Exercise Set 6.6, p. 546

**1.** $\dfrac{19}{2}$  **3.** $\dfrac{49}{6}$  **5.** 57  **7.** $\dfrac{92}{5}$  **9.** $-1$  **11.** No solution
**13.** 3  **15.** 19  **17.** $-6$  **19.** $\dfrac{1}{64}$  **21.** 9  **23.** 15
**25.** 2, 5  **27.** 6  **29.** 5  **31.** 9  **33.** 7  **35.** $\dfrac{80}{9}$
**37.** 2, 6  **39.** $-1$  **41.** No solution  **43.** 3  **45.** About 44.1 mi
**47.** About 680 ft  **49.** About 117 ft  **51.** 151.25 ft; 281.25 ft
**53.** About 25°F  **55.** About 0.81 ft  **57.** About 3.9 ft
**59.** $4\frac{4}{9}$ hr  **60.** Jeff: $1\frac{1}{3}$ hr; Grace: 4 hr  **61.** 2808 mi
**62.** 84 hr  **63.** $0, -2.8$  **64.** $0, \dfrac{5}{3}$  **65.** $-8, 8$  **66.** $-3, \dfrac{7}{2}$
**67.** $2ah+h^2$  **68.** $2ah+h^2-h$  **69.** $4ah+2h^2-3h$
**70.** $4ah+2h^2+3h$  **71.** Left to the student  **73.** 6912
**75.** 0  **77.** $-6, -3$  **79.** 2  **81.** $0, \dfrac{125}{4}$  **83.** 2  **85.** $\dfrac{1}{2}$
**87.** 3

### Translating for Success, p. 553

**1.** J  **2.** B  **3.** O  **4.** M  **5.** K  **6.** I  **7.** G  **8.** E
**9.** F  **10.** A

### Exercise Set 6.7, p. 554

**1.** $\sqrt{34}$; 5.831  **3.** $\sqrt{450}$; 21.213  **5.** 5  **7.** $\sqrt{43}$; 6.557
**9.** $\sqrt{12}$; 3.464  **11.** $\sqrt{n-1}$  **13.** $\sqrt{116}$ ft; 10.770 ft
**15.** 7.1 ft  **17.** 50 ft  **19.** $\sqrt{10{,}561}$ ft; 102.767 ft
**21.** $s+s\sqrt{2}$  **23.** $\sqrt{181}$ cm; 13.454 cm  **25.** $(3,0), (-3,0)$
**27.** $\sqrt{340}+8$ ft; 26.439 ft  **29.** $\sqrt{420.125}$ in.; 20.497 in.
**31.** Flash: $67\frac{2}{3}$ mph; Crawler: $53\frac{2}{3}$ mph  **32.** $3\frac{3}{4}$ mph

**33.** $-7, \dfrac{3}{2}$  **34.** 3, 8  **35.** 1  **36.** $-2, 2$  **37.** 13  **38.** 7
**39.** 26 packets  **41.** $\sqrt{75}$ cm

### Calculator Corner, p. 563

**1.** $-2-9i$  **2.** $20+17i$  **3.** $-47-161i$  **4.** $-\dfrac{151}{290}+\dfrac{73}{290}i$
**5.** $-20$  **6.** $-28.373$  **7.** $-\dfrac{16}{25}-\dfrac{1}{50}i$  **8.** 81  **9.** $117+118i$
**10.** $-\dfrac{14}{169}+\dfrac{34}{169}i$

### Exercise Set 6.8, p. 565

**1.** $i\sqrt{35}$, or $\sqrt{35}i$  **3.** $4i$  **5.** $-2i\sqrt{3}$, or $-2\sqrt{3}i$
**7.** $i\sqrt{3}$, or $\sqrt{3}i$  **9.** $9i$  **11.** $7i\sqrt{2}$, or $7\sqrt{2}i$
**13.** $-7i$  **15.** $4-2\sqrt{15}i$, or $4-2i\sqrt{15}$  **17.** $\left(2+2\sqrt{3}\right)i$
**19.** $12-4i$  **21.** $9-5i$  **23.** $7+4i$  **25.** $-4-4i$
**27.** $-1+i$  **29.** $11+6i$  **31.** $-18$  **33.** $-\sqrt{14}$  **35.** 21
**37.** $-6+24i$  **39.** $1+5i$  **41.** $18+14i$  **43.** $38+9i$
**45.** $2-46i$  **47.** $5-12i$  **49.** $-24+10i$  **51.** $-5-12i$
**53.** $-i$  **55.** 1  **57.** $-1$  **59.** $i$  **61.** $-1$  **63.** $-125i$
**65.** 8  **67.** $1-23i$  **69.** 0  **71.** 0  **73.** 1  **75.** $5-8i$
**77.** $2-\dfrac{\sqrt{6}}{2}i$  **79.** $\dfrac{9}{10}+\dfrac{13}{10}i$  **81.** $-i$  **83.** $-\dfrac{3}{7}-\dfrac{8}{7}i$
**85.** $\dfrac{6}{5}-\dfrac{2}{5}i$  **87.** $-\dfrac{8}{41}+\dfrac{10}{41}i$  **89.** $-\dfrac{4}{3}i$  **91.** $-\dfrac{1}{2}-\dfrac{1}{4}i$
**93.** $-\dfrac{3}{5}+\dfrac{4}{5}i$
**95.**
$$x^2-2x+5=0$$
$$\overline{(1-2i)^2-2(1-2i)+5}\;\overset{?}{\;}\;0$$
$$1-4i+4i^2-2+4i+5$$
$$1-4i-4-2+4i+5$$
$$\qquad\qquad 0 \;\Big|\; \text{TRUE}$$
Yes
**97.**
$$x^2-4x-5=0$$
$$\overline{(2+i)^2-4(2+i)-5}\;\overset{?}{\;}\;0$$
$$4+4i+i^2-8-4i-5$$
$$4+4i-1-8-4i-5$$
$$\qquad\qquad -10 \;\Big|\; \text{FALSE}$$
No
**99.** Rational  **100.** Difference of squares  **101.** Coordinates
**102.** Positive  **103.** Proportion  **104.** Trinomial square
**105.** Negative  **106.** Zero products  **107.** $-4-8i; -2+4i$;
$8-6i$  **109.** $-3-4i$  **111.** $-88i$  **113.** 8  **115.** $\dfrac{3}{5}+\dfrac{9}{5}i$
**117.** 1

### Summary and Review: Chapter 6, p. 569

#### Concept Reinforcement

**1.** True  **2.** False  **3.** False  **4.** False  **5.** True  **6.** True

#### Important Concepts

**1.** $6|y|$  **2.** $|a+2|$  **3.** $\sqrt[5]{z^3}$  **4.** $(6ab)^{5/2}$  **5.** $\dfrac{1}{9^{3/2}}=\dfrac{1}{27}$
**6.** $\sqrt[4]{a^3b}$  **7.** $5y\sqrt{6}$  **8.** $2\sqrt{a}$  **9.** $2\sqrt{3}$  **10.** $25-10\sqrt{x}+x$
**11.** 5  **12.** 6  **13.** $-21-20i$  **14.** $\dfrac{4}{5}-\dfrac{7}{5}i$

#### Review Exercises

**1.** 27.893  **2.** 6.378  **3.** $f(0), f(-1)$, and $f(1)$ do not exist as real numbers; $f\left(\dfrac{41}{3}\right)=5$  **4.** Domain $=\left\{x \mid x \geq \dfrac{16}{3}\right\}$, or $\left[\dfrac{16}{3}, \infty\right)$
**5.** $9|a|$  **6.** $7|z|$  **7.** $|6-b|$  **8.** $|x+3|$  **9.** $-10$  **10.** $-\dfrac{1}{3}$
**11.** $2; -2; 3$  **12.** $|x|$  **13.** 3  **14.** $\sqrt[5]{a}$  **15.** 512  **16.** $31^{1/2}$
**17.** $(a^2b^3)^{1/5}$  **18.** $\dfrac{1}{7}$  **19.** $\dfrac{1}{4x^{2/3}y^{2/3}}$  **20.** $\dfrac{5b^{1/2}}{a^{3/4}c^{2/3}}$
**21.** $\dfrac{3a}{t^{1/4}}$  **22.** $\dfrac{1}{x^{2/5}}$  **23.** $7^{1/6}$  **24.** $x^7$  **25.** $3x^2$
**26.** $\sqrt[12]{x^4y^3}$  **27.** $\sqrt[12]{x^7}$  **28.** $7\sqrt{5}$  **29.** $-3\sqrt[3]{4}$
**30.** $5b^2\sqrt[3]{2a^2}$  **31.** $\dfrac{7}{6}$  **32.** $\dfrac{4x^2}{3}$  **33.** $\dfrac{2x^2}{3y^3}$  **34.** $\sqrt{15xy}$
**35.** $3a\sqrt[3]{a^2b^2}$  **36.** $\sqrt[15]{a^5b^9}$  **37.** $y\sqrt[3]{6}$  **38.** $\dfrac{5}{2}\sqrt{x}$

39. $\sqrt[12]{x^5}$  40. $7\sqrt[3]{x}$  41. $3\sqrt{3}$  42. $15\sqrt{2}$
43. $(2x+y^2)\sqrt[3]{x}$  44. $-43-2\sqrt{10}$  45. $8-2\sqrt{7}$
46. $9-\sqrt[3]{4}$  47. $\frac{2\sqrt{6}}{3}$  48. $\frac{2\sqrt{a}-2\sqrt{b}}{a-b}$  49. 4  50. 13
51. 1  52. About 4166 rpm  53. 4480 rpm  54. 9 cm
55. $\sqrt{24}$ ft; 4.899 ft  56. 25  57. $\sqrt{46}$; 6.782
58. $(5+2\sqrt{2})i$  59. $-2-9i$  60. $1+i$  61. 29  62. $i$
63. $9-12i$  64. $\frac{2}{5}+\frac{3}{5}i$  65. $\frac{1}{10}-\frac{7}{10}i$
66.

$f(x)=\sqrt{x}$

67. D  68. $-1$  69. 3

## Understanding Through Discussion and Writing

1. $f(x)=(x+5)^{1/2}(x+7)^{-1/2}$. Consider $(x+5)^{1/2}$. Since the exponent is $\frac{1}{2}$, $x+5$ must be nonnegative. Then $x+5\ge 0$, or $x\ge -5$. Consider $(x+7)^{-1/2}$. Since the exponent is $-\frac{1}{2}$, $x+7$ must be positive. Then $x+7>0$, or $x>-7$. Then the domain of $f=\{x|x\ge -5\ and\ x>-7\}$, or $\{x|x\ge -5\}$. 2. Since $\sqrt{x}$ exists only for $\{x|x\ge 0\}$, this is the domain of $y=\sqrt{x}\cdot\sqrt{x}$. 3. The distributive law is used to collect radical expressions with the same indices and radicands just as it is used to collect monomials with the same variables and exponents. 4. No; when $n$ is odd, it is true that if $a^n=b^n$, then $a=b$. 5. Use a calculator to show that $\frac{5+\sqrt{2}}{\sqrt{18}}\ne 2$. Explain that we multiply by 1 to rationalize a denominator. In this case, we would write 1 as $\sqrt{2}/\sqrt{2}$. 6. When two radical expressions are conjugates, their product contains no radicals. Similarly, the product of a complex number and its conjugate does not contain $i$.

## Test: Chapter 6, p. 575

1. [6.1a] 12.166  2. [6.1a] 2; does not exist as a real number
3. [6.1a] Domain $=\{x|x\le 2\}$, or $(-\infty,2]$  4. [6.1b] $3|q|$
5. [6.1b] $|x+5|$  6. [6.1c] $-\frac{1}{10}$  7. [6.1d] $x$  8. [6.1d] 4
9. [6.2a] $\sqrt[3]{a^2}$  10. [6.2a] 8  11. [6.2a] $37^{1/2}$
12. [6.2a] $(5xy^2)^{5/2}$  13. [6.2b] $\frac{1}{10}$  14. [6.2b] $\frac{8a^{3/4}}{b^{3/2}c^{2/5}}$
15. [6.2c] $\frac{x^{8/5}}{y^{9/5}}$  16. [6.2c] $\frac{1}{2.9^{31/24}}$  17. [6.2d] $\sqrt[4]{x}$
18. [6.2d] $2x\sqrt{x}$  19. [6.2d] $\sqrt[15]{a^6b^5}$  20. [6.2d] $\sqrt[12]{8y^7}$
21. [6.3a] $2\sqrt{37}$  22. [6.3a] $2\sqrt[4]{5}$  23. [6.3a] $2a^3b^4\sqrt[3]{3a^2b}$
24. [6.3b] $\frac{2x\sqrt[3]{2x^2}}{y^2}$  25. [6.3b] $\frac{5x}{6y^2}$  26. [6.3a] $\sqrt[3]{10xy^2}$
27. [6.3a] $xy\sqrt[4]{x}$  28. [6.3b] $\sqrt[5]{x^2y^2}$  29. [6.3b] $2\sqrt{a}$
30. [6.4a] $38\sqrt{2}$  31. [6.4b] $-20$  32. [6.4b] $9+6\sqrt{x}+x$
33. [6.5b] $\frac{13+8\sqrt{2}}{-41}$  34. [6.6a] 35  35. [6.6b] 7
36. [6.6a] 5  37. [6.7a] 7 ft  38. [6.6c] 3600 ft
39. [6.7a] $\sqrt{98}$; 9.899  40. [6.7a] 2  41. [6.8a] $11i$
42. [6.8b] $7+5i$  43. [6.8c] $37+9i$  44. [6.8d] $-i$
45. [6.8e] $-\frac{77}{50}+\frac{7}{25}i$  46. [6.8f] No  47. [6.6a] A
48. [6.8c, e] $-\frac{17}{4}i$  49. [6.6b] 3

## Cumulative Review: Chapters 1–6, p. 577

1. [4.1c] $-3x^3+9x^2+3x-3$  2. [4.2c] $4x^4-4x^2y+y^2$
3. [4.2a] $15x^4-x^3-9x^2+5x-2$  4. [5.1d] $\frac{(x+4)(x-7)}{x+7}$

5. [5.4a] $\frac{y-6}{y-9}$  6. [5.2c] $\frac{-2x+4}{(x+2)(x-3)}$, or $\frac{-2(x-2)}{(x+2)(x-3)}$
7. [5.3b, c] $y^2+y-2+\frac{-1}{y+2}$  8. [6.1c] $-2x$
9. [6.3a] $4(x-1)$  10. [6.4a] $57\sqrt{3}$  11. [6.3a] $4xy^2\sqrt{y}$
12. [6.5b] $\sqrt{30}+\sqrt{15}$  13. [6.1d] $\frac{m^2n^4}{2}$  14. [6.2c] $6^{8/9}$
15. [6.8b] $3+5i$  16. [6.8e] $\frac{7}{61}-\frac{16}{61}i$  17. [1.1d] 2
18. [1.2a] $c=8M+3$  19. [1.4c] $\{a|a>-7\}$, or $(-7,\infty)$
20. [1.5a] $\{x|-10<x<13\}$, or $(-10,13)$  21. [1.6c] $\frac{4}{3},\frac{8}{3}$
22. [4.8a] $\frac{25}{7},-\frac{25}{7}$  23. [3.3a] (5,3)  24. [3.5a] (-1,0,4)
25. [5.5a] $-5$  26. [5.5a] $\frac{1}{3}$  27. [5.7a] $R=\frac{nE-nrI}{I}$
28. [6.6a] 6  29. [6.6b] $-\frac{1}{4}$  30. [6.6a] 5
31. [2.2c]  32. [2.5a]  33. [3.7b]

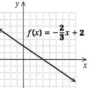
$f(x)=-\frac{2}{3}x+2$

$4x-2y=8$

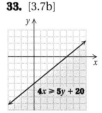
$4x\ge 5y+20$

34. [3.7c]  35. [2.2c]  36. [2.2c]

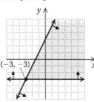
(-3, -3)

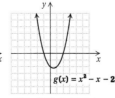
$g(x)=x^2-x-2$

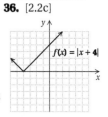
$f(x)=|x+4|$

37. [2.2c]  38. [2.2c], [6.1a]

$g(x)=\frac{4}{x-3}$

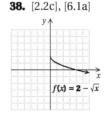
$f(x)=2-\sqrt{x}$

39. [4.3a] $6xy^2(2x-5y)$  40. [4.5a, b] $(3x+4)(x-7)$
41. [4.4a] $(y+11)(y-12)$  42. [4.6d] $(3y+2)(9y^2-6y+4)$
43. [4.6b] $(2x+25)(2x-25)$  44. [2.3a] Domain: $[-5,5]$; range: $[-3,4]$  45. [2.3a] Domain: $(-\infty,\infty)$; range: $[-5,\infty)$
46. [2.4b] Slope: $\frac{3}{2}$; y-intercept: $(0,-4)$  47. [2.6d] $y=-\frac{1}{3}x+\frac{13}{3}$
48. [5.8d] 125 ft; 1000 ft²  49. [5.6a] 1 hr  50. [5.8f] 64 L
51. [6.2a] D  52. [5.6a] A  53. [5.3b, c] A  54. [6.6a] B
55. [6.6b] $-\frac{8}{9}$

## CHAPTER 7

### Calculator Corner, p. 584

The calculator returns an ERROR message because the graph of $y=4x^2+9$ has no x-intercepts. This indicates that the equation $4x^2+9=0$ has no real-number solutions.

### Exercise Set 7.1, p. 590

1. (a) $\sqrt{5},-\sqrt{5}$, or $\pm\sqrt{5}$; (b) $(-\sqrt{5},0),(\sqrt{5},0)$  3. (a) $\frac{5}{3}i$, $-\frac{5}{3}i$, or $\pm\frac{5}{3}i$; (b) no x-intercepts  5. $\pm\frac{\sqrt{6}}{2}$; $\pm1.225$  7. $5,-9$
9. $8,0$  11. $11\pm\sqrt{7}$; 13.646, 8.354  13. $7\pm2i$  15. $18,0$
17. $\frac{3}{2}\pm\frac{\sqrt{14}}{2}$; 3.371, -0.371  19. $5,-11$  21. $9,5$
23. $-2\pm\sqrt{6}$  25. $11\pm2\sqrt{33}$  27. $-\frac{1}{2}\pm\frac{\sqrt{5}}{2}$

**29.** $\frac{5}{2} \pm \frac{\sqrt{53}}{2}$  **31.** $-\frac{3}{4} \pm \frac{\sqrt{57}}{4}$  **33.** $\frac{9}{4} \pm \frac{\sqrt{105}}{4}$  **35.** $2, -8$

**37.** $-11 \pm \sqrt{19}$  **39.** $5 \pm \sqrt{29}$  **41.** (a) $-\frac{7}{2} \pm \frac{\sqrt{57}}{2}$;

**(b)** $\left(-\frac{7}{2} - \frac{\sqrt{57}}{2}, 0\right), \left(-\frac{7}{2} + \frac{\sqrt{57}}{2}, 0\right)$  **43.** (a) $\frac{5}{4} \pm \frac{\sqrt{39}}{4}i$;

**(b)** no $x$-intercepts  **45.** $\frac{3}{4} \pm \frac{\sqrt{17}}{4}$  **47.** $\frac{3}{4} \pm \frac{\sqrt{145}}{4}$

**49.** $\frac{2}{3} \pm \frac{\sqrt{7}}{3}$  **51.** $-\frac{1}{2} \pm \frac{\sqrt{7}}{2}i$  **53.** $2 + 3i$  **55.** About

0.866 sec  **57.** About 6.8 sec  **59.** About 5.9 sec  **61.** About
7.1 sec  **63.** (a) $B(t) = 0.022t + 2.6$, where $t$ is the number of
years since 1930; **(b)** about 4.4 million; **(c)** 2016
**64.**    **65.**

**66.**    **67.**

**68.** $2\sqrt{22}$  **69.** $\frac{\sqrt{10}}{5}$  **70.** 4  **71.** 5  **72.** 4

**73.** No solution  **75.** Left to the student  **77.** $16, -16$
**79.** $0, \frac{7}{2}, -8, -\frac{10}{3}$

**Calculator Corner, p. 596**
**1.–3.** Left to the student

**Calculator Corner, p. 598**
**1.** $-3, 0.8$  **2.** $-1.5, 5$  **3.** $3, 8$  **4.** $2, 4$

**Exercise Set 7.2, p. 599**
**1.** $-4 \pm \sqrt{14}$  **3.** $\frac{-4 \pm \sqrt{13}}{3}$  **5.** $\frac{1}{2} \pm \frac{\sqrt{3}}{2}i$  **7.** $2 \pm 3i$

**9.** $\frac{-3 \pm \sqrt{41}}{2}$  **11.** $-1 \pm 2i$  **13.** (a) $0, -1$; **(b)** $(0, 0), (-1, 0)$

**15.** (a) $\frac{3 \pm \sqrt{229}}{22}$; **(b)** $\left(\frac{3 + \sqrt{229}}{22}, 0\right), \left(\frac{3 - \sqrt{229}}{22}, 0\right)$

**17.** (a) $\frac{2}{5}$; **(b)** $\left(\frac{2}{5}, 0\right)$  **19.** $-1, -2$  **21.** $5, 10$  **23.** $\frac{17 \pm \sqrt{249}}{10}$

**25.** $2 \pm i$  **27.** $\frac{2}{3}, \frac{3}{2}$  **29.** $2 \pm \sqrt{10}$  **31.** $\frac{3}{4}, -2$  **33.** $\frac{1}{2} \pm \frac{3}{2}i$

**35.** $1, -\frac{1}{2} \pm \frac{\sqrt{3}}{2}i$  **37.** $-3 \pm \sqrt{5}; -0.764, -5.236$

**39.** $3 \pm \sqrt{5}; 5.236, 0.764$  **41.** $\frac{3 \pm \sqrt{65}}{4}; 2.766, -1.266$

**43.** $\frac{4 \pm \sqrt{31}}{5}; 1.914, -0.314$  **45.** 2  **46.** 3  **47.** 10  **48.** 8

**49.** No solution  **50.** No solution  **51.** $\frac{15}{4}$  **52.** $\frac{17}{3}$

**53.** Left to the student; $-0.797, 0.570$  **55.** $\frac{1 \pm \sqrt{1 + 8\sqrt{5}}}{4}$

**57.** $\frac{-i \pm i\sqrt{1 + 4i}}{2}$  **59.** $\frac{-1 \pm 3\sqrt{5}}{6}$  **61.** $3 \pm \sqrt{13}$

**Translating for Success, p. 607**
**1.** B  **2.** G  **3.** F  **4.** L  **5.** N  **6.** C  **7.** J  **8.** E
**9.** K  **10.** A

**Exercise Set 7.3, p. 608**
**1.** Length: 9 ft; width: 2 ft  **3.** Length: 18 yd; width: 9 yd
**5.** Height: 16 m; base: 7 m  **7.** Length: $\frac{51 + \sqrt{122,399}}{2}$ ft;

width: $\frac{\sqrt{122,399} - 51}{2}$ ft  **9.** 2 in.  **11.** 6 ft, 8 ft

**13.** 28 and 29  **15.** Length: $2 + \sqrt{14}$ ft $\approx 5.742$ ft; width:

$\sqrt{14} - 2$ ft $\approx 1.742$ ft  **17.** $\frac{17 - \sqrt{109}}{2}$ in. $\approx 3.280$ in.

**19.** $7 + \sqrt{239}$ ft $\approx 22.460$ ft; $\sqrt{239} - 7$ ft $\approx 8.460$ ft
**21.** First part: 60 mph; second part: 50 mph  **23.** 40 mph
**25.** Cessna: 150 mph; Beechcraft: 200 mph; or Cessna:
200 mph; Beechcraft: 250 mph  **27.** To Hillsboro: 10 mph;
return trip: 4 mph  **29.** About 11 mph

**31.** $s = \sqrt{\frac{A}{6}}$  **33.** $r = \sqrt{\frac{Gm_1m_2}{F}}$  **35.** $c = \sqrt{\frac{E}{m}}$

**37.** $b = \sqrt{c^2 - a^2}$  **39.** $k = \frac{3 + \sqrt{9 + 8N}}{2}$

**41.** $r = \frac{-\pi h + \sqrt{\pi^2 h^2 + 2\pi A}}{2\pi}$  **43.** $g = \frac{4\pi^2 L}{T^2}$

**45.** $H = \sqrt{\frac{703W}{I}}$  **47.** $v = \frac{c\sqrt{m^2 - (m_0)^2}}{m}$  **49.** $\frac{1}{x - 2}$

**50.** $\frac{(x + 1)(x^2 + 2)}{(x - 1)(x^2 + x + 1)}$  **51.** $\frac{-x}{(x + 3)(x - 1)}$  **52.** $3x^2\sqrt{x}$

**53.** $2i\sqrt{5}$  **54.** $\frac{3(x + 1)}{3x + 1}$  **55.** $\frac{4b}{a(3b^2 - 4a)}$  **57.** $\pm\sqrt{2}$

**59.** $A(S) = \frac{\pi S}{6}$  **61.** $l = \frac{w + w\sqrt{5}}{2}$

**Exercise Set 7.4, p. 618**
**1.** One real  **3.** Two nonreal  **5.** Two real  **7.** One real
**9.** Two nonreal  **11.** Two real  **13.** Two real
**15.** One real  **17.** $x^2 - 16 = 0$  **19.** $x^2 + 16 = 0$
**21.** $x^2 - 16x + 64 = 0$  **23.** $25x^2 - 20x - 12 = 0$
**25.** $12x^2 - (4k + 3m)x + km = 0$  **27.** $x^2 - \sqrt{3}x - 6 = 0$
**29.** $x^2 + 36 = 0$  **31.** $\pm\sqrt{3}$  **33.** $1, 81$  **35.** $-1, 1, 5, 7$
**37.** $-\frac{1}{4}, \frac{1}{9}$  **39.** 1  **41.** $-1, 1, 4, 6$  **43.** $\pm 2, \pm 5$  **45.** $-1, 2$

**47.** $\pm\frac{\sqrt{15}}{3}, \pm\frac{\sqrt{6}}{2}$  **49.** $-1, 125$  **51.** $-\frac{11}{6}, -\frac{1}{6}$  **53.** $-\frac{3}{2}$

**55.** $\frac{9 \pm \sqrt{89}}{2}, -1 \pm \sqrt{3}$  **57.** $\left(\frac{4}{25}, 0\right)$  **59.** $(4, 0), (-1, 0)$,

$\left(\frac{3 + \sqrt{33}}{2}, 0\right), \left(\frac{3 - \sqrt{33}}{2}, 0\right)$  **61.** $(-8, 0), (1, 0)$

**63.** Kenyan: 30 lb; Peruvian: 20 lb  **64.** Solution A: 4 L;
solution B: 8 L  **65.** $4x$  **66.** $3x^2$  **67.** $3a\sqrt[4]{2a}$  **68.** 4
**69.**    **70.**

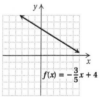    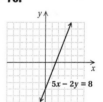

**71.**    **72.**

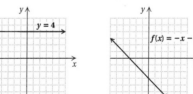

**73.** Left to the student   **75.** (a) $-\frac{3}{5}$; (b) $-\frac{1}{3}$
**77.** $x^2 - \sqrt{3}x + 8 = 0$   **79.** $a = 1, b = 2, c = -3$   **81.** $\frac{100}{99}$
**83.** 259   **85.** 1, 3

## Mid-Chapter Review: Chapter 7, p. 622

**1.** False   **2.** True   **3.** True   **4.** False
**5.**
$$5x^2 + 3x = 4$$
$$\frac{1}{5}(5x^2 + 3x) = \frac{1}{5} \cdot 4$$
$$x^2 + \frac{3}{5}x = \frac{4}{5}$$
$$x^2 + \frac{3}{5}x + \frac{9}{100} = \frac{4}{5} + \frac{9}{100}$$
$$\left(x + \frac{3}{10}\right)^2 = \frac{89}{100}$$
$$x + \frac{3}{10} = \sqrt{\frac{89}{100}} \quad or \quad x + \frac{3}{10} = -\sqrt{\frac{89}{100}}$$
$$x + \frac{3}{10} = \frac{\sqrt{89}}{10} \quad or \quad x + \frac{3}{10} = -\frac{\sqrt{89}}{10}$$
$$x = -\frac{3}{10} + \frac{\sqrt{89}}{10} \quad or \quad x = -\frac{3}{10} - \frac{\sqrt{89}}{10}$$

The solutions are $-\frac{3}{10} \pm \frac{\sqrt{89}}{10}$.

**6.**
$$5x^2 + 3x = 4$$
$$5x^2 + 3x - 4 = 0$$
$$5x^2 + 3x + (-4) = 0$$
$$a = 5, \quad b = 3, \quad c = -4$$
$$x = \frac{-b \pm \sqrt{b^2 - 4ac}}{2a}$$
$$x = \frac{-3 \pm \sqrt{3^2 - 4 \cdot 5 \cdot (-4)}}{2 \cdot 5}$$
$$x = \frac{-3 \pm \sqrt{9 + 80}}{10}$$
$$x = \frac{-3 \pm \sqrt{89}}{10}$$
$$x = -\frac{3}{10} \pm \frac{\sqrt{89}}{10}$$

**7.** $-2 \pm \sqrt{3}$   **8.** $-3, \frac{1}{2}$   **9.** $-5 \pm \sqrt{31}$   **10.** $\frac{1}{2} \pm \frac{\sqrt{21}}{2}$

**11.** One real solution; one $x$-intercept   **12.** Two real solutions; two $x$-intercepts   **13.** Two nonreal solutions; no $x$-intercepts
**14.** Two nonreal solutions; no $x$-intercepts   **15.** Two real solutions; two $x$-intercepts   **16.** Two real solutions; two $x$-intercepts   **17.** $x^2 - 9x - 10 = 0$   **18.** $x^2 - 169 = 0$
**19.** $x^2 - 2\sqrt{5}x - 15 = 0$   **20.** $x^2 + 16 = 0$
**21.** $x^2 + 12x + 36 = 0$   **22.** $21x^2 + 22x - 8 = 0$
**23.** 60 mph   **24.** $s = \sqrt{\frac{R}{a}}$   **25.** $-\frac{4}{3}, 1$   **26.** $\pm\sqrt{3}, \pm\sqrt{5}$
**27.** $\frac{15 \pm \sqrt{145}}{8}$   **28.** $-1, -\frac{2}{7}$   **29.** $-1, 0$   **30.** $-11, 5$
**31.** $\pm\frac{4}{7}i$   **32.** $\pm\sqrt{6}, \pm 2i$   **33.** $\frac{-5 \pm \sqrt{73}}{2}$   **34.** $-6 \pm i$
**35.** $\frac{5 \pm \sqrt{11}}{2}$   **36.** $\frac{7 \pm \sqrt{13}}{6}$   **37.** $\frac{1 \pm \sqrt{2}}{2}$   **38.** $-1 \pm 4i$
**39.** $8 \pm \sqrt{3}$   **40.** $3 \pm \sqrt{10}i$   **41.** $4 \pm \sqrt{26}$   **42.** 9
**43.** Given the solutions of a quadratic equation, it is possible to find an equation equivalent to the original equation but not necessarily expressed in the same form as the original equation. For example, we can find a quadratic equation with solutions $-2$ and 4:
$$[x - (-2)](x - 4) = 0$$
$$(x + 2)(x - 4) = 0$$
$$x^2 - 2x - 8 = 0.$$

Now $x^2 - 2x - 8 = 0$ has solutions $-2$ and 4. However, the original equation might have been in another form, such as $2x(x - 3) - x(x - 4) = 8$.   **44.** Given the quadratic equation $ax^2 + bx + c = 0$, we find $x = \dfrac{-b + \sqrt{b^2 - 4ac}}{2a}$ or

$x = \dfrac{-b - \sqrt{b^2 - 4ac}}{2a}$ using the quadratic formula.

Then we have $ax^2 + bx + c =$
$\left(x - \dfrac{-b + \sqrt{b^2 - 4ac}}{2a}\right)\left(x - \dfrac{-b - \sqrt{b^2 - 4ac}}{2a}\right)$.

Consider $5x^2 + 8x - 3$. First, we use the quadratic formula to solve $5x^2 + 8x - 3 = 0$:
$$x = \frac{-8 \pm \sqrt{8^2 - 4 \cdot 5 \cdot (-3)}}{2 \cdot 5}$$
$$x = \frac{-8 \pm \sqrt{124}}{10} = \frac{-8 \pm 2\sqrt{31}}{10}$$
$$x = \frac{-4 \pm \sqrt{31}}{5}.$$

Then $5x^2 + 8x - 3 = \left(x - \dfrac{-4 - \sqrt{31}}{5}\right)\left(x - \dfrac{-4 + \sqrt{31}}{5}\right)$.

**45.** Set the product
$$(x - 1)(x - 2)(x - 3)(x - 4)(x - 5)(x - 6)(x - 7)$$

equal to 0.   **46.** Write an equation of the form $a(3x^2 + 1)^2 + b(3x^2 + 1) + c = 0$, where $a \neq 0$. To ensure that this equation has real-number solutions, select $a, b,$ and $c$ so that $b^2 - 4ac \geq 0$ and $3x^2 + 1 \geq 0$.

## Exercise Set 7.5, p. 630

**1.**

| $x$ | $f(x)$ |
|---|---|
| 0 | 0 |
| 1 | 4 |
| 2 | 16 |
| $-1$ | 4 |
| $-2$ | 16 |

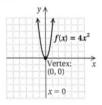

**3.**

| $x$ | $f(x)$ |
|---|---|
| 0 | 0 |
| 1 | $\frac{1}{3}$ |
| 2 | $\frac{4}{3}$ |
| $-1$ | $\frac{1}{3}$ |
| $-2$ | $\frac{4}{3}$ |

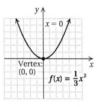

**5.**

| $x$ | $f(x)$ |
|---|---|
| $-3$ | 0 |
| $-2$ | 1 |
| $-1$ | 4 |
| $-4$ | 1 |
| $-5$ | 4 |

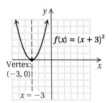

**7.**

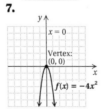

**9.**

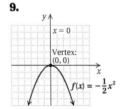

**11.**

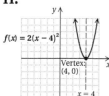

$f(x) = 2(x - 4)^2$
Vertex: (4, 0)
$x = 4$

**13.**

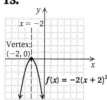

$x = -2$
Vertex: (-2, 0)
$f(x) = -2(x + 2)^2$

**15.**

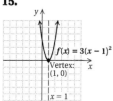

$f(x) = 3(x - 1)^2$
Vertex: (1, 0)
$x = 1$

**17.**

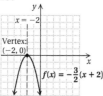

$x = -2$
Vertex: (-2, 0)
$f(x) = -\frac{3}{2}(x + 2)^2$

**19.**

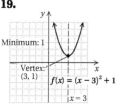

Minimum: 1
Vertex: (3, 1)
$f(x) = (x - 3)^2 + 1$
$x = 3$

**21.**

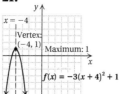

$x = -4$
Vertex: (-4, 1)
Maximum: 1
$f(x) = -3(x + 4)^2 + 1$

**23.**

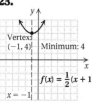

Vertex: (-1, 4)   Minimum: 4
$f(x) = \frac{1}{2}(x + 1)^2 + 4$
$x = -1$

**25.**

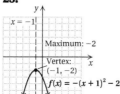

$x = -1$
Maximum: -2
Vertex: (-1, -2)
$f(x) = -(x + 1)^2 - 2$

**27.** $5xy^2\sqrt[4]{x}$   **28.** $12a^2b^2$

## Visualizing for Success, p. 638

**1.** F   **2.** H   **3.** A   **4.** I   **5.** C   **6.** J   **7.** G   **8.** B
**9.** E   **10.** D

## Exercise Set 7.6, p. 639

**1.**

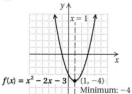

$x = 1$
$f(x) = x^2 - 2x - 3$   (1, -4)
Minimum: -4

**3.**

$x = -2$
(-2, 2)   Maximum: 2
$f(x) = -x^2 - 4x - 2$

**5.**

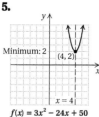

Minimum: 2   (4, 2)
$x = 4$
$f(x) = 3x^2 - 24x + 50$

**7.**

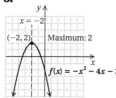

$\left(-\frac{1}{2}, \frac{7}{2}\right)$   Maximum: $\frac{7}{2}$
$x = -\frac{1}{2}$   $f(x) = -2x^2 - 2x + 3$

**9.**

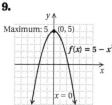

Maximum: 5   (0, 5)
$f(x) = 5 - x^2$
$x = 0$

**11.**

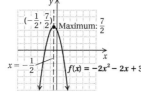

$x = -\frac{5}{4}$
$f(x) = 2x^2 + 5x - 2$
$\left(-\frac{5}{4}, -\frac{41}{8}\right)$   Minimum: $-\frac{41}{8}$

**13.** $y$-intercept: $(0, 1)$; $x$-intercepts: $\left(3 + 2\sqrt{2}, 0\right), \left(3 - 2\sqrt{2}, 0\right)$
**15.** $y$-intercept: $(0, 20)$; $x$-intercepts: $(5, 0), (-4, 0)$
**17.** $y$-intercept: $(0, 9)$; $x$-intercept: $\left(-\frac{3}{2}, 0\right)$   **19.** $y$-intercept:
$(0, 8)$; $x$-intercepts: none   **21.** $D = 15w$   **22.** $C = \frac{89}{6}t$
**23.** $250$; $y = \dfrac{250}{x}$   **24.** $250$; $y = \dfrac{250}{x}$   **25.** $\frac{125}{2}$; $y = \frac{125}{2}x$
**26.** $\frac{2}{125}$; $y = \frac{2}{125}x$   **27.** **(a)** Minimum: $-6.954$;
**(b)** maximum: $7.014$

**29.**

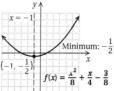

$f(x) = |x^2 - 1|$

**31.**

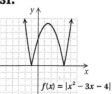

$f(x) = |x^2 - 3x - 4|$

**33.** $f(x) = \frac{5}{16}x^2 - \frac{15}{8}x - \frac{35}{16}$, or $f(x) = \frac{5}{16}(x - 3)^2 - 5$
**35.**

$x = -1$
$\left(-1, -\frac{1}{2}\right)$   Minimum: $-\frac{1}{2}$
$f(x) = \frac{x^2}{8} + \frac{x}{4} - \frac{3}{8}$

## Calculator Corner, p. 644

**1.** Minimum: 1   **2.** Minimum: 4.875   **3.** Maximum: 6
**4.** Maximum: 0.5625

## Exercise Set 7.7, p. 649

**1.** 180 ft by 180 ft   **3.** 3.5 in.   **5.** 3.5 hundred, or 350
**7.** 200 ft²; 10 ft by 20 ft   **9.** 11 days after the concert was
announced; about 62 tickets   **11.** $P(x) = -x^2 + 980x - 3000$;
$237,100$ at $x = 490$   **13.** 121; 11 and 11   **15.** $-4$; 2 and $-2$
**17.** 36; $-6$ and $-6$   **19.** $f(x) = mx + b$
**21.** $f(x) = ax^2 + bx + c, a > 0$   **23.** Polynomial, neither
quadratic nor linear   **25.** $f(x) = ax^2 + bx + c, a < 0$
**27.** $f(x) = 2x^2 + 3x - 1$   **29.** $f(x) = -\frac{1}{4}x^2 + 3x - 5$
**31.** **(a)** $A(s) = \frac{3}{16}s^2 - \frac{135}{4}s + 1750$; **(b)** about 531 per 200,000,000
kilometers driven   **33.** $D(x) = -0.008x^2 + 0.8x$; 15 ft
**35.** Radical; radicand   **36.** Dependent   **37.** Sum
**38.** At least one   **39.** Inverse   **40.** Independent
**41.** Descending   **42.** $x$-intercept   **43.** $b = 19$ cm,
$h = 19$ cm; $A = 180.5$ cm²

## Calculator Corner, p. 654

**1.** $\{x | x < -4 \text{ or } x > 1\}$, or $(-\infty, -4) \cup (1, \infty)$
**2.** $\{x | -2 < x < 3\}$, or $(-2, 3)$
**3.** $\{x | x \leq -2 \text{ or } 0 \leq x \leq 0.5\}$, or $(-\infty, -2] \cup [0, 0.5]$
**4.** $\{x | -4 \leq x \leq 0 \text{ or } x \geq 4\}$, or $[-4, 0] \cup [4, \infty)$

## Exercise Set 7.8, p. 659

**1.** $\{x | x < -2 \text{ or } x > 6\}$, or $(-\infty, -2) \cup (6, \infty)$
**3.** $\{x | -2 \leq x \leq 2\}$, or $[-2, 2]$   **5.** $\{x | -1 \leq x \leq 4\}$, or $[-1, 4]$
**7.** $\{x | -1 < x < 2\}$, or $(-1, 2)$   **9.** All real numbers, or
$(-\infty, \infty)$   **11.** $\{x | 2 < x < 4\}$, or $(2, 4)$
**13.** $\{x | x < -2 \text{ or } 0 < x < 2\}$, or $(-\infty, -2) \cup (0, 2)$
**15.** $\{x | -9 < x < -1 \text{ or } x > 4\}$, or $(-9, -1) \cup (4, \infty)$
**17.** $\{x | x < -3 \text{ or } -2 < x < 1\}$, or $(-\infty, -3) \cup (-2, 1)$
**19.** $\{x | x < 6\}$, or $(-\infty, 6)$   **21.** $\{x | x < -1 \text{ or } x > 3\}$, or
$(-\infty, -1) \cup (3, \infty)$   **23.** $\{x | -\frac{2}{3} \leq x < 3\}$, or $\left[-\frac{2}{3}, 3\right)$
**25.** $\{x | 2 < x < \frac{5}{2}\}$, or $\left(2, \frac{5}{2}\right)$   **27.** $\{x | x < -1 \text{ or } 2 < x < 5\}$, or
$(-\infty, -1) \cup (2, 5)$   **29.** $\{x | -3 \leq x < 0\}$, or $[-3, 0)$
**31.** $\{x | 1 < x < 2\}$, or $(1, 2)$   **33.** $\{x | x < -4 \text{ or } 1 < x < 3\}$,
or $(-\infty, -4) \cup (1, 3)$   **35.** $\{x | 0 < x < \frac{1}{3}\}$, or $\left(0, \frac{1}{3}\right)$

**37.** $\{x | x < -3 \ or -2 < x < 1 \ or \ x > 4\}$, or

$(-\infty, -3) \cup (-2, 1) \cup (4, \infty)$    **39.** $\frac{5}{3}$    **40.** $\frac{5}{2a}$    **41.** $\frac{4a}{b^2}\sqrt{a}$

**42.** $\frac{3c}{7d}\sqrt[3]{c^2}$    **43.** $\sqrt{2}$    **44.** $17\sqrt{5}$    **45.** $(10a + 7)\sqrt[3]{2a}$

**46.** $3\sqrt{10} - 4\sqrt{5}$    **47.** Left to the student
**49.** $\{x | 1 - \sqrt{3} \le x \le 1 + \sqrt{3}\}$, or $[1 - \sqrt{3}, 1 + \sqrt{3}]$
**51.** All real numbers except 0, or $(-\infty, 0) \cup (0, \infty)$
**53.** $\{x | x < \frac{1}{4} \ or \ x > \frac{5}{2}\}$, or $\left(-\infty, \frac{1}{4}\right) \cup \left(\frac{5}{2}, \infty\right)$
**55. (a)** $\{t | 0 < t < 2\}$, or $(0, 2)$; **(b)** $\{t | t > 10\}$, or $(10, \infty)$

## Summary and Review: Chapter 7, p. 661

### Concept Reinforcement
**1.** False    **2.** True    **3.** False

### Important Concepts
**1.** $2 \pm 3i$    **2.** $6 \pm \sqrt{5}$    **3.** $5 \pm \sqrt{2}$, or $6.414$ and $3.586$
**4. (a)** Two real solutions; **(b)** two nonreal solutions
**5.** $5x^2 - 13x - 6 = 0$    **6.** $\pm\sqrt{2}, \pm3$
**7.** Vertex: $(-1, -2)$; line of symmetry: $x = -1$;
maximum: $-2$;

**8.** $y$-intercept: $(0, 4)$; $x$-intercepts: $\left(3 - \sqrt{5}, 0\right)$ and $\left(3 + \sqrt{5}, 0\right)$
**9.** $\{x | x < 4 \ or \ x > 10\}$, or $(-\infty, 4) \cup (10, \infty)$
**10.** $\{x | 5 < x \le 11\}$, or $(5, 11]$

### Review Exercises

**1. (a)** $\pm\frac{\sqrt{14}}{2}$; **(b)** $\left(-\frac{\sqrt{14}}{2}, 0\right), \left(\frac{\sqrt{14}}{2}, 0\right)$    **2.** $0, -\frac{5}{14}$    **3.** $3, 9$

**4.** $-\frac{3}{8} \pm \frac{\sqrt{7}}{8}i$    **5.** $\frac{7}{2} \pm \frac{\sqrt{3}}{2}i$    **6.** $3, 5$    **7.** $-2 \pm \sqrt{3}$;

$-0.268, -3.732$    **8.** $4, -2$    **9.** $4 \pm 4\sqrt{2}$    **10.** $\frac{1 \pm \sqrt{481}}{15}$

**11.** $-3 \pm \sqrt{7}$    **12.** $0.901$ sec    **13.** Length: 14 cm; width: 9 cm
**14.** 1 in.    **15.** First part: 50 mph; second part: 40 mph
**16.** Two real    **17.** Two nonreal    **18.** $25x^2 + 10x - 3 = 0$
**19.** $x^2 + 8x + 16 = 0$    **20.** $p = \frac{9\pi^2}{N^2}$    **21.** $T = \sqrt{\frac{3B}{2A}}$

**22.** $2, -2, 3, -3$    **23.** $3, -5$    **24.** $\pm\sqrt{7}, \pm\sqrt{2}$    **25.** $81, 16$
**26. (a)** $(1, 3)$; **(b)** $x = 1$; **(c)** maximum: 3;
**(d)**

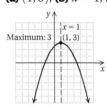

$f(x) = -\frac{1}{2}(x - 1)^2 + 3$

**27. (a)** $\left(\frac{1}{2}, \frac{23}{4}\right)$; **(b)** $x = \frac{1}{2}$; **(c)** minimum: $\frac{23}{4}$;
**(d)**

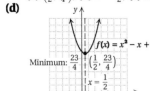

**28. (a)** $(-2, 4)$; **(b)** $x = -2$; **(c)** maximum: 4;

**(d)**

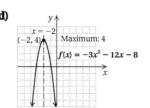

**29.** $y$-intercept: $(0, 14)$; $x$-intercepts: $(2, 0), (7, 0)$
**30.** $y$-intercept: $(0, -3)$; $x$-intercepts: $\left(2 - \sqrt{7}, 0\right)$ and
$\left(2 + \sqrt{7}, 0\right)$    **31.** $-121$; 11 and $-11$
**32.** $f(x) = -x^2 + 6x - 2$    **33. (a)** $N(x) = -0.720x^2 +$
$38.211x - 393.127$; **(b)** about 105 live births
**34.** $\{x | -2 < x < 1 \ or \ x > 2\}$, or $(-2, 1) \cup (2, \infty)$
**35.** $\{x | x < -4 \ or -2 < x < 1\}$, or $(-\infty, -4) \cup (-2, 1)$
**36.** B    **37.** D    **38.** $f(x) = \frac{7}{15}x^2 - \frac{14}{15}x - 7$; minimum: $-\frac{112}{15}$
**39.** $h = 60, k = 60$    **40.** 18 and 324

### Understanding Through Discussion and Writing
**1.** Yes; for any quadratic function $f(x) = ax^2 + bx + c, f(0) = c$,
so the graph of every quadratic function has a $y$-intercept, $(0, c)$.
**2.** If the leading coefficient is positive, the graph of the function
opens up and hence has a minimum value. If the leading
coefficient is negative, the graph of the function opens down
and hence has a maximum value.    **3.** When an input of
$y = (x + 3)^2$ is 3 less than (or 3 units to the left of) an input of
$y = x^2$, the outputs are the same. In addition, for any input, the
output of $f(x) = (x + 3)^2 - 4$ is 4 less than (or 4 units down
from) the output of $f(x) = (x + 3)^2$. Thus the graph of
$f(x) = (x + 3)^2 - 4$ looks like the graph of $f(x) = x^2$ translated
3 units to the left and 4 units down.    **4.** Find a quadratic
function $f(x)$ whose graph lies entirely above the $x$-axis or a
quadratic function $g(x)$ whose graph lies entirely below the
$x$-axis. Then write $f(x) < 0, f(x) \le 0, g(x) > 0$, or $g(x) \ge 0$.
For example, the quadratic inequalities $x^2 + 1 < 0$ and
$-x^2 - 5 \ge 0$ have no solution.    **5.** No; if the vertex is off
the $x$-axis, then due to symmetry, the graph has either no
$x$-intercept or two $x$-intercepts.    **6.** The $x$-coordinate of
the vertex lies halfway between the $x$-coordinates of the
$x$-intercepts. The function must be evaluated for this value of $x$
in order to determine the maximum or minimum value.

### Test: Chapter 7, p. 667

**1.** [7.1a] **(a)** $\pm\frac{2\sqrt{3}}{3}$; **(b)** $\left(\frac{2\sqrt{3}}{3}, 0\right), \left(-\frac{2\sqrt{3}}{3}, 0\right)$

**2.** [7.2a] $-\frac{1}{2} \pm \frac{\sqrt{3}}{2}i$    **3.** [7.4c] 49, 1    **4.** [7.2a] 9, 2

**5.** [7.4c] $\pm\frac{\sqrt{5}}{2}, \pm\sqrt{3}$    **6.** [7.2a] $-2 \pm \sqrt{6}$; 0.449, $-4.449$

**7.** [7.2a] 0, 2    **8.** [7.1b] $2 \pm \sqrt{3}$    **9.** [7.1c] About 6.7 sec
**10.** [7.3a] About 2.89 mph    **11.** [7.3a] 7 cm by 7 cm
**12.** [7.1c] About 0.946 sec    **13.** [7.4a] Two nonreal

**14.** [7.4b] $x^2 - 4\sqrt{3}x + 9 = 0$    **15.** [7.3b] $T = \sqrt{\frac{V}{48}}$, or $\frac{\sqrt{3V}}{12}$

**16.** [7.6a] **(a)** $(-1, 1)$; **(b)** $x = -1$; **(c)** maximum: 1;
**(d)**

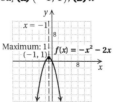

**17.** [7.6a] **(a)** $(3, 5)$; **(b)** $x = 3$; **(c)** minimum: 5;

**(d)**

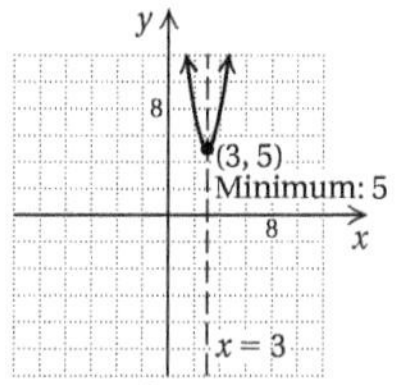


**18.** [7.6b] $y$-intercept: $(0, -1)$; $x$-intercepts: $\left(2 - \sqrt{3}, 0\right)$, $\left(2 + \sqrt{3}, 0\right)$ **19.** [7.7a] $-16$; 4 and $-4$
**20.** [7.7b] $f(x) = \frac{1}{5}x^2 - \frac{3}{5}x$
**21.** [7.7b] **(a)** $A(x) = -0.3x^2 + 2.3x + 18.5$; **(b)** about 14.9 thousand adoptions **22.** [7.8a] $\{x \mid -1 < x < 7\}$, or $(-1, 7)$
**23.** [7.8b] $\{x \mid -3 < x < 5\}$, or $(-3, 5)$
**24.** [7.8b] $\{x \mid -3 < x < 1 \text{ or } x \geq 2\}$, or $(-3, 1) \cup [2, \infty)$
**25.** [7.4b] A **26.** [7.6a, b] $f(x) = -\frac{4}{7}x^2 + \frac{20}{7}x + 8$; maximum: $\frac{81}{7}$ **27.** [7.2a] $\frac{1}{2}$

### Cumulative Review: Chapters 1–7, p. 669

**1.** [6.7a] About 422 yd **2.** [4.1d] $10x^2 - 8x + 6$
**3.** [4.2a] $2x^3 - 9x^2 + 7x - 12$ **4.** [5.1d] $\dfrac{2(a-4)}{5}$
**5.** [5.1e] $\dfrac{1}{y^2 + 6y}$ **6.** [5.2c] $\dfrac{(m-3)(m-2)}{(m+1)(m-5)}$
**7.** [5.3b, c] $9x^2 - 13x + 26 + \dfrac{-50}{x+2}$ **8.** [5.4a] $\dfrac{y-x}{xy(x+y)}$
**9.** [6.1b] 0.6 **10.** [6.1b] $3(x-2)$ **11.** [6.4a] $12\sqrt{5}$
**12.** [6.5b] $\dfrac{\sqrt{6} + 9\sqrt{2} - 12\sqrt{3} - 4}{-26}$ **13.** [6.4a] 256
**14.** [6.8c] $17 + 7i$ **15.** [6.8e] $-\frac{2}{3} - 2i$
**16.** [4.5a, b] $(2t+5)(t-6)$ **17.** [4.4a] $(a+9)(a-6)$
**18.** [4.3a] $-3a^2(a-4)$ **19.** [4.6b] $(8a+3b)(8a-3b)$
**20.** [4.6a] $3(a-6)^2$ **21.** [4.6d] $\left(\frac{1}{3}a - 1\right)\left(\frac{1}{9}a^2 + \frac{1}{3}a + 1\right)$
**22.** [4.3b] $(4a+3)(6a^2-5)$ **23.** [4.3a] $(x+1)(2x+1)$
**24.** [1.1d] $\frac{11}{13}$ **25.** [1.2a] $r = \dfrac{mv^2}{F}$ **26.** [1.4c] $\left\{x \mid x \geq \frac{5}{14}\right\}$, or $\left[\frac{5}{14}, \infty\right)$ **27.** [1.5b] $\left\{x \mid x < -\dfrac{4}{3} \text{ or } x > 6\right\}$, or $\left(-\infty, -\dfrac{4}{3}\right) \cup (6, \infty)$ **28.** [1.6e] $\left\{x \mid -\frac{13}{4} \leq x \leq \frac{15}{4}\right\}$, or $\left[-\frac{13}{4}, \frac{15}{4}\right]$ **29.** [3.3a] $(-4, 1)$ **30.** [3.5a] $\left(\frac{1}{2}, 3, -5\right)$
**31.** [4.8a] $\frac{1}{5}, -3$ **32.** [5.5a] $-\frac{5}{3}$ **33.** [5.5a] 3
**34.** [5.7a] $m = \dfrac{aA}{h - A}$ **35.** [6.6a] $\frac{37}{2}$ **36.** [6.6b] 11
**37.** [4.8a] 4 **38.** [7.2a] $\dfrac{3}{2} \pm \dfrac{\sqrt{55}}{2}i$ **39.** [7.2a] $\dfrac{17 \pm \sqrt{145}}{2}$
**40.** [7.3b] $a = \sqrt{P^2 + b^2}$ **41.** [7.8b] $\{x \mid -3 < x < -2 \text{ or } -1 < x < 1\}$, or $(-3, -2) \cup (-1, 1)$
**42.** [7.8a] $\left\{x \mid x < -\frac{5}{2} \text{ or } x > \frac{5}{2}\right\}$, or $\left(-\infty, -\frac{5}{2}\right) \cup \left(\frac{5}{2}, \infty\right)$
**43.** [2.5a] **44.** [3.7b] **45.** [3.7b]

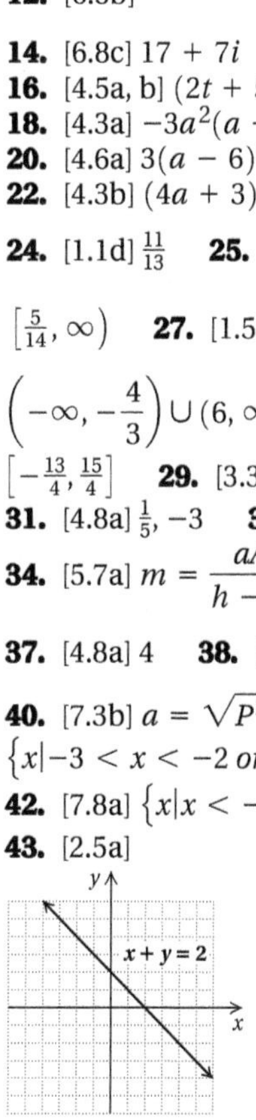


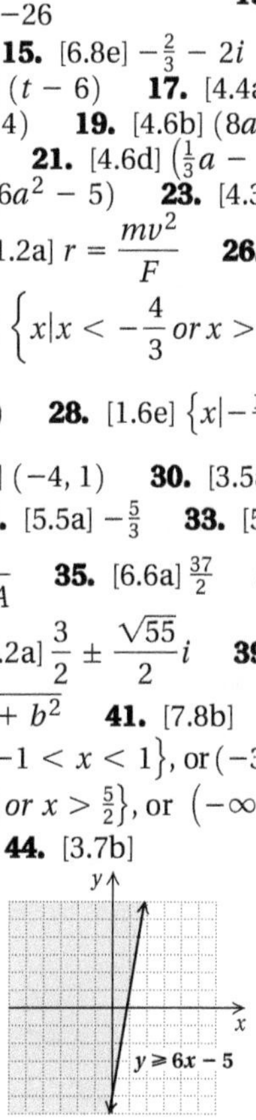


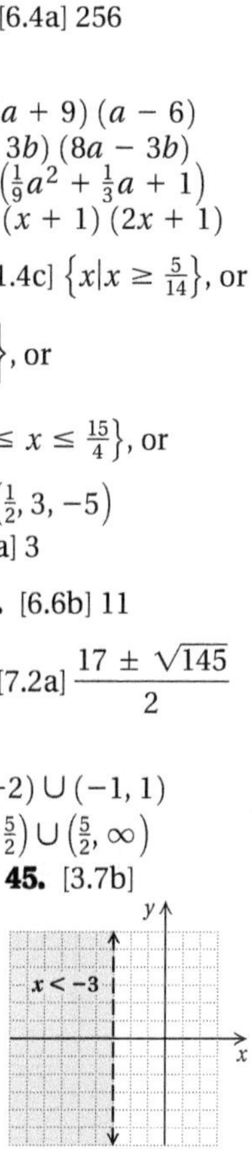


**46.** [3.7c] **47.** [7.6a] **48.** [7.6a]

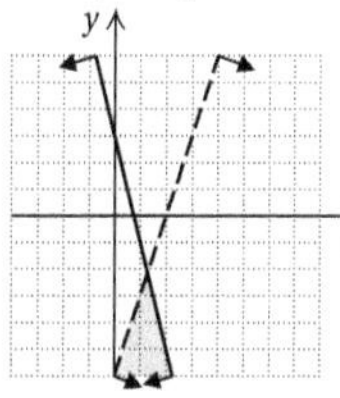

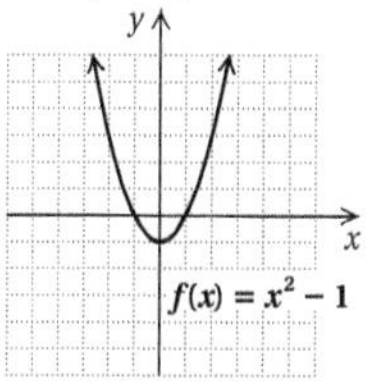


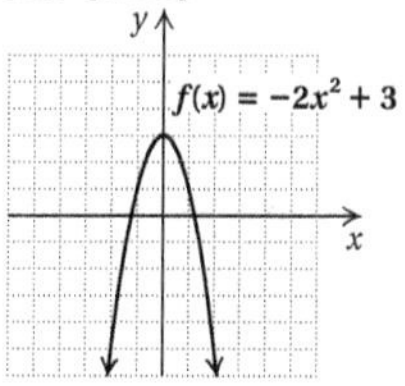


**49.** [2.6b] $y = \frac{1}{2}x + 4$ **50.** [2.6d] $y = -3x + 1$
**51.** [7.3a] 16 km/h **52.** [7.7a] 14 ft by 14 ft; 196 ft$^2$
**53.** [3.2b], [3.3b] 36 **54.** [5.6a] 2 hr **55.** [7.1b] A
**56.** [7.4c] B **57.** [7.4c] $\dfrac{2}{51 + 7\sqrt{61}}$, or $\dfrac{-51 + 7\sqrt{61}}{194}$
**58.** [4.6d] $\left(\dfrac{a}{2} + \dfrac{2b}{9}\right)\left(\dfrac{a^2}{4} - \dfrac{ab}{9} + \dfrac{4b^2}{81}\right)$

## CHAPTER 8

### Calculator Corner, p. 676

**1.** Left to the student **2.** Left to the student

### Calculator Corner, p. 680

**1.** \$1040.60 **2.** \$1049.12 **3.** \$30,372.65 **4.** **(a)** \$10,540; **(b)** \$10,547.29; **(c)** \$10,551.03; **(d)** \$10,554.80; **(e)** \$10,554.84

### Exercise Set 8.1, p. 681

**1.**

| $x$ | $f(x)$ |
|---|---|
| 0 | 1 |
| 1 | 2 |
| 2 | 4 |
| 3 | 8 |
| −1 | $\frac{1}{2}$ |
| −2 | $\frac{1}{4}$ |
| −3 | $\frac{1}{8}$ |

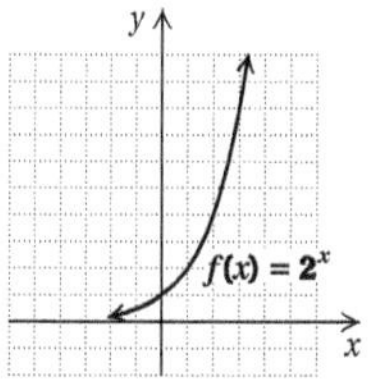


**3.**

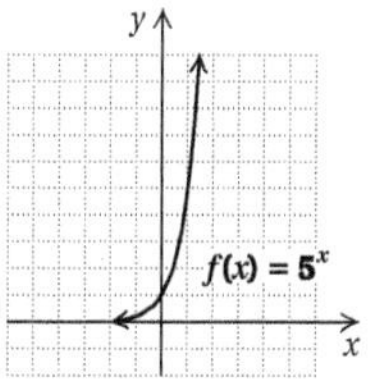


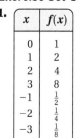

**5.**

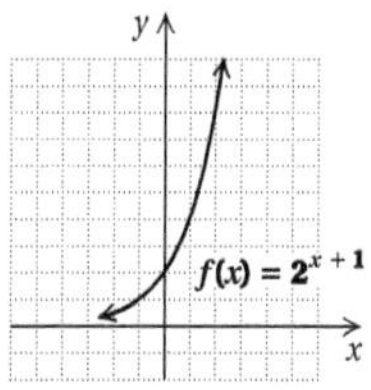


**7.**

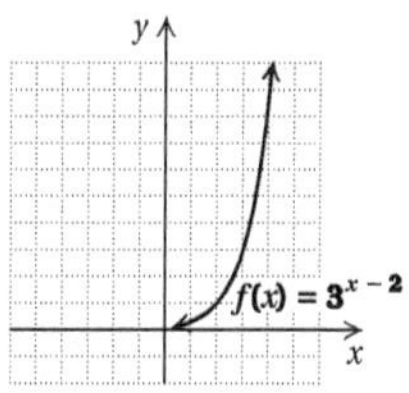


**9.**

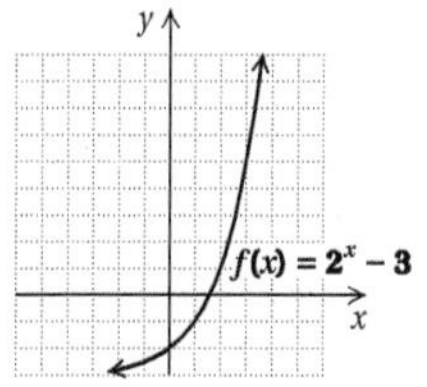


**11.**

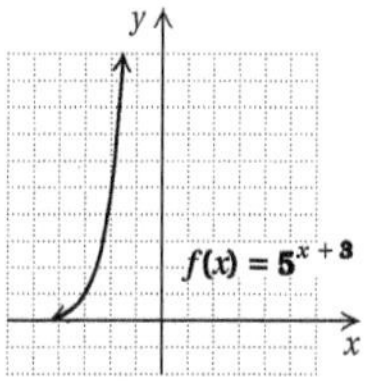


**13.**

| $x$ | $f(x)$ |
|---|---|
| 0 | 1 |
| 1 | $\frac{1}{2}$ |
| 2 | $\frac{1}{4}$ |
| 3 | $\frac{1}{8}$ |
| −1 | 2 |
| −2 | 4 |
| −3 | 8 |

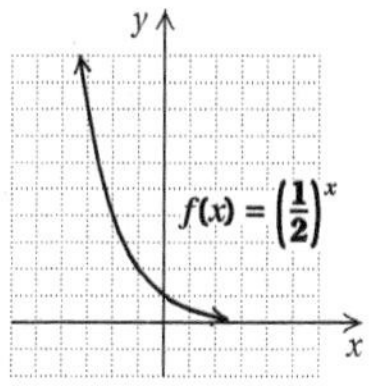

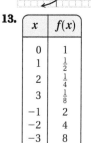

**15.**

**17.**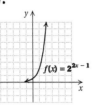

**19.**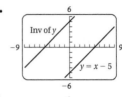

**21.**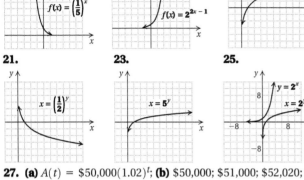

**23.**

**25.**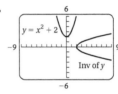

**55.**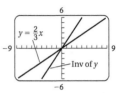

**57.** Left to the student

**27. (a)** $A(t) = \$50,000(1.02)^t$; **(b)** $50,000; $51,000; $52,020; $54,121.61; $58,582.97; $60,949.72; $74,297.37;

**(c)**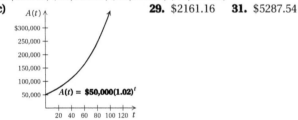

**29.** $2161.16    **31.** $5287.54

**33. (a)** 12,279 MW; 24,274 MW; 47,986 MW;

**(b)**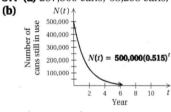

**35. (a)** $5105; $2487; $1212; **(b)**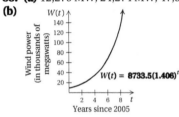

**37. (a)** 257,500 cans; 68,295 cans; 4804 cans;

**(b)**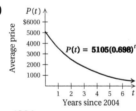

**39.** $\dfrac{1}{x^2}$    **40.** $\dfrac{1}{x^{12}}$    **41.** 1    **42.** 1    **43.** $\frac{2}{3}$    **44.** 2.7

**45.** $\dfrac{1}{x^7}$    **46.** $\dfrac{1}{x^{10}}$    **47.** $x$    **48.** $x$    **49.** $5^4$, or 625

**51.** 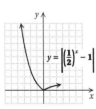    **53.**

### Calculator Corner, p. 694

**1.** 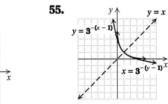    **2.**

**3.** 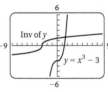    **4.**

### Exercise Set 8.2, p. 698

**1.** Inverse: $\{(2, 1)\}, (-3, 6), (-5, -3)\}$

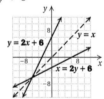

**3.** Inverse: $x = 2y + 6$

| x | y |
|---|---|
| 4 | −1 |
| 6 | 0 |
| 8 | 1 |
| 10 | 2 |
| 12 | 3 |

**5.** Yes    **7.** No    **9.** No    **11.** Yes    **13.** $f^{-1}(x) = \dfrac{x + 2}{5}$

**15.** $f^{-1}(x) = \dfrac{-2}{x}$    **17.** $f^{-1}(x) = \frac{3}{4}(x - 7)$

**19.** $f^{-1}(x) = \dfrac{2}{x} - 5$    **21.** Not one-to-one

**23.** $f^{-1}(x) = \dfrac{1 - 3x}{5x - 2}$    **25.** $f^{-1}(x) = \sqrt[3]{x + 1}$

**27.** $f^{-1}(x) = x^3$

**29.** $f^{-1}(x) = 2x + 6$

| x | f(x) |
|---|------|
| −4 | −5 |
| 0 | −3 |
| 2 | −2 |
| 4 | −1 |

| x | $f^{-1}(x)$ |
|---|-------------|
| −5 | −4 |
| −3 | 0 |
| −2 | 2 |
| −1 | 4 |

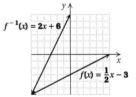

**31.** $f^{-1}(x) = \sqrt[3]{x}$

| $x$ | $f(x)$ |
|---|---|
| 0 | 0 |
| 1 | 1 |
| 2 | 8 |
| 3 | 27 |
| $-1$ | $-1$ |
| $-2$ | $-8$ |
| $-3$ | $-27$ |

| $x$ | $f^{-1}(x)$ |
|---|---|
| 0 | 0 |
| 1 | 1 |
| 8 | 2 |
| 27 | 3 |
| $-1$ | $-1$ |
| $-8$ | $-2$ |
| $-27$ | $-3$ |

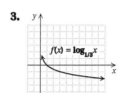

**33.** $-8x + 9$; $-8x + 18$  **35.** $12x^2 - 12x + 5$; $6x^2 + 3$

**37.** $\dfrac{16}{x^2} - 1$; $\dfrac{2}{4x^2 - 1}$  **39.** $x^4 - 10x^2 + 30$; $x^4 + 10x^2 + 20$

**41.** $f(x) = x^2$, $g(x) = 5 - 3x$  **43.** $f(x) = \sqrt{x}$, $g(x) = 5x + 2$

**45.** $f(x) = \dfrac{1}{x}$, $g(x) = x - 1$  **47.** $f(x) = \dfrac{1}{\sqrt{x}}$, $g(x) = 7x + 2$

**49.** $f(x) = x^4$, $g(x) = \sqrt{x} + 5$

**51.** $(f^{-1} \circ f)(x) = f^{-1}(f(x)) = f^{-1}\left(\frac{4}{5}x\right) = \frac{5}{4}\left(\frac{4}{5}x\right) = x$;
$(f \circ f^{-1})(x) = f(f^{-1}(x)) = f\left(\frac{5}{4}x\right) = \frac{4}{5}\left(\frac{5}{4}x\right) = x$

**53.** $(f^{-1} \circ f)(x) = f^{-1}(f(x)) = f^{-1}\left(\dfrac{x+7}{2}\right)$
$= 2\left(\dfrac{x+7}{2}\right) - 7 = x + 7 - 7 = x$;
$(f \circ f^{-1})(x) = f(f^{-1}(x)) = f(2x - 7)$
$= \dfrac{2x - 7 + 7}{2} = \dfrac{2x}{2} = x$

**55.** $(f^{-1} \circ f)(x) = f^{-1}(f(x)) = f^{-1}\left(\dfrac{1-x}{x}\right)$
$= \dfrac{1}{\dfrac{1-x}{x} + 1} = \dfrac{1}{\dfrac{1}{x}} = x$;
$(f \circ f^{-1})(x) = f(f^{-1}(x)) = f\left(\dfrac{1}{x+1}\right)$
$= \dfrac{1 - \dfrac{1}{x+1}}{\dfrac{1}{x+1}} = \dfrac{\dfrac{x}{x+1}}{\dfrac{1}{x+1}} = x$

**57.** $f^{-1}(x) = \frac{1}{3}x$  **59.** $f^{-1}(x) = -x$  **61.** $f^{-1}(x) = x^3 + 5$

**63.** **(a)** 40, 42, 46, 50; **(b)** $f^{-1}(x) = x - 32$; **(c)** 8, 10, 14, 18

**65.** $\sqrt[3]{a}$  **66.** $\sqrt[3]{x^2}$  **67.** $a^2b^3$  **68.** $2t^2$  **69.** $\sqrt{3}$  **70.** $2\sqrt[4]{2}$

**71.** $\sqrt{2xy}$  **72.** $\sqrt[4]{p^2t}$  **73.** $2a^3b^8$  **74.** $10x^3y^6$  **75.** $3a^2b^2$

**76.** $3pq^3$  **77.** No  **79.** Yes  **81.** (1) C; (2) A; (3) B; (4) D

**83.**
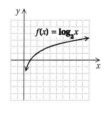

**85.** $f(x) = \frac{1}{2}x + 3$;
$g(x) = 2x - 6$; yes

**Exercise Set 8.3, p. 710**

**1.** $x = 2^y$

| $x$, or $2^y$ | $y$ |
|---|---|
| 1 | 0 |
| 2 | 1 |
| 4 | 2 |
| 8 | 3 |
| $\frac{1}{2}$ | $-1$ |
| $\frac{1}{4}$ | $-2$ |
| $\frac{1}{8}$ | $-3$ |

**3.**
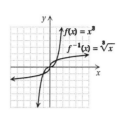

**5.**
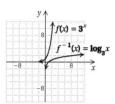

**7.** $3 = \log_{10} 1000$  **9.** $-3 = \log_5 \dfrac{1}{125}$  **11.** $\frac{1}{3} = \log_8 2$

**13.** $0.3010 = \log_{10} 2$  **15.** $2 = \log_e t$  **17.** $t = \log_Q x$

**19.** $2 = \log_e 7.3891$  **21.** $-2 = \log_e 0.1353$  **23.** $4^w = 10$

**25.** $6^2 = 36$  **27.** $10^{-2} = 0.01$  **29.** $10^{0.9031} = 8$

**31.** $e^{4.6052} = 100$  **33.** $t^k = Q$  **35.** 9  **37.** 4  **39.** 4

**41.** 3  **43.** 25  **45.** 1  **47.** $\frac{1}{2}$  **49.** 2  **51.** 2  **53.** $-1$

**55.** 0  **57.** 4  **59.** 2  **61.** 3  **63.** $-2$  **65.** 0  **67.** 1

**69.** $\frac{2}{3}$  **71.** 4.8970  **73.** $-0.1739$  **75.** Does not exist as a real

number  **77.** 0.9464  **79.** $6 = 10^{0.7782}$; $84 = 10^{1.9243}$;

$987{,}606 = 10^{5.9946}$; $0.00987606 = 10^{-2.0054}$; $98{,}760.6 = 10^{4.9946}$;

$70{,}000{,}000 = 10^{7.8451}$; $7000 = 10^{3.8451}$  **81.** Conjugate

**82.** Direct  **83.** Leading term  **84.** Quadratic; discriminant

**85.** Inconsistent  **86.** Parabolas  **87.** Line of symmetry

**88.** $a + bi$  **89.**  **91.** 25  **93.** 32

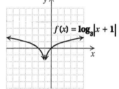

**95.** $-\frac{7}{16}$  **97.** 3  **99.** 0  **101.** $-2$

**Calculator Corner, p. 715**

**1.** Not correct  **2.** Correct  **3.** Not correct  **4.** Correct
**5.** Not correct  **6.** Correct  **7.** Not correct  **8.** Not correct

**Exercise Set 8.4, p. 718**

**1.** $\log_2 32 + \log_2 8$  **3.** $\log_4 64 + \log_4 16$  **5.** $\log_a Q + \log_a x$

**7.** $\log_b 252$  **9.** $\log_c Ky$  **11.** $4 \log_c y$  **13.** $6 \log_b t$

**15.** $-3 \log_b C$  **17.** $\log_a 67 - \log_a 5$  **19.** $\log_b 2 - \log_b 5$

**21.** $\log_c \frac{22}{3}$  **23.** $2 \log_a x + 3 \log_a y + \log_a z$

**25.** $\log_b x + 2 \log_b y - 3 \log_b z$  **27.** $\frac{4}{3}\log_c x - \log_c y - \frac{2}{3}\log_c z$

**29.** $2 \log_a m + 3 \log_a n - \frac{3}{4} - \frac{5}{4}\log_a b$  **31.** $\log_a \dfrac{x^{2/3}}{y^{1/2}}$,

or $\log_a \dfrac{\sqrt[3]{x^2}}{\sqrt{y}}$  **33.** $\log_a \dfrac{2x^4}{y^3}$  **35.** $\log_a \dfrac{\sqrt{a}}{x}$  **37.** 2.708

**39.** 0.51  **41.** $-1.609$  **43.** $\frac{1}{2}$  **45.** 2.609  **47.** Cannot be

found using the properties of logarithms  **49.** $t$  **51.** 5

**53.** 7  **55.** $-7$  **57.** $i$  **58.** $-1$  **59.** 5  **60.** $\frac{3}{5} + \frac{4}{5}i$

**61.** $23 - 18i$  **62.** $10i$  **63.** $-34 - 31i$  **64.** $3 - 4i$

**65.** Left to the student  **67.** $\log_a(x^6 - x^4y^2 + x^2y^4 - y^6)$

**69.** $\frac{1}{2}\log_a(1 - s) + \frac{1}{2}\log_a(1 + s)$  **71.** False  **73.** True

**75.** False

**Mid-Chapter Review: Chapter 8, p. 720**

**1.** False  **2.** True  **3.** False  **4.** True

**5.** $\log_5 x = 3$
$5^3 = x$
$125 = x$

**6.** **(a)** $\log_a 18 = \log_a(2 \cdot 9) = \log_a 2 + \log_a 9 = 0.648 + 2.046 = $
$2.694$; **(b)** $\log_a \frac{1}{2} = \log_a 1 - \log_a 2 = 0 - 0.648 = -0.648$

**7.**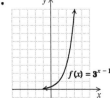

**8.**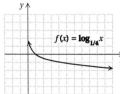

**9.**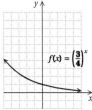

**10.**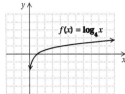

**11. (a)** $A(t) = \$500(1.04)^t$; **(b)** $500$; $584.93$; $740.12$

**12.** $1580.49$    **13.** $f^{-1}(x) = \dfrac{x-1}{3}$    **14.** $f^{-1}(x) = \sqrt[3]{x-2}$

**15.** $1 - 2x; 8 - 2x$    **16.** $9x^2 - 6x + 2; 3x^2 + 2$

**17.** $f(x) = \dfrac{3}{x}; g(x) = x + 4$    **18.** $f(x) = \sqrt{x}; g(x) = 6x - 7$

**19.** $(f^{-1} \circ f)(x) = f^{-1}(f(x)) = f^{-1}\left(\dfrac{x}{3}\right) = 3\left(\dfrac{x}{3}\right) = x$;

$(f \circ f^{-1})(x) = f(f^{-1}(x)) = f(3x) = \dfrac{3x}{3} = x$

**20.** $(f^{-1} \circ f)(x) = f^{-1}(f(x)) = f^{-1}\left(\sqrt[3]{x+4}\right)$

$= \left(\sqrt[3]{x+4}\right)^3 - 4 = x + 4 - 4 = x$;

$(f \circ f^{-1})(x) = f(f^{-1}(x)) = f(x^3 - 4)$

$= \sqrt[3]{x^3 - 4 + 4} = \sqrt[3]{x^3} = x$

**21.** $3 = \log_7 343$    **22.** $-4 = \log_3 \dfrac{1}{81}$    **23.** $6^t = 12$

**24.** $n^m = T$    **25.** $3$    **26.** $2$    **27.** $2$    **28.** $5$    **29.** $2.3869$

**30.** $-0.6383$    **31.** $\log_b 2 + \log_b x + 2 \log_b y - 3 \log_b z$

**32.** $\frac{2}{3} \log_a x + \frac{5}{3} \log_a y - \frac{4}{3} \log_a z$    **33.** $\log_a \dfrac{x\sqrt{z}}{y^2}$

**34.** $\log_m (b - 4)$    **35.** $0$    **36.** $1$    **37.** $-3$    **38.** $5$

**39.** $V^{-1}(t)$ could be used to predict when the value of the stamp will be $t$, where $V^{-1}(t)$ is the number of years after 1999.
**40.** $\log_a b$ is the number to which $a$ is raised to get $c$. Since

$\log_a b = c$, then $a^c = b$.    **41.** Express $\dfrac{x}{5}$ as $x \cdot 5^{-1}$ and then use

the product rule and the power rule to get $\log_a\left(\dfrac{x}{5}\right) =$

$\log_a (x \cdot 5^{-1}) = \log_a x + \log_a 5^{-1} = \log_a x + (-1)\log_a 5 =$
$\log_a x - \log_a 5$.    **42.** The student didn't subtract the logarithm of the entire denominator after using the quotient rule. The correct procedure is as follows:

$\log_b \dfrac{1}{x} = \log_b \dfrac{x}{xx}$

$= \log_b x - \log_b xx$

$= \log_b x - (\log_b x + \log_b x)$

$= \log_b x - \log_b x - \log_b x$

$= -\log_b x.$

(Note that $-\log_b x$ is equivalent to $\log_b 1 - \log_b x$.)

### Calculator Corner, p. 726

**1.** $y = \log_2 x$

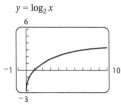

**2.** $y = \log_3 x$

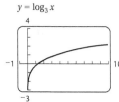

**3.** $y = \log_{1/2} x$

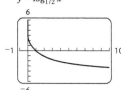

**5.** $y = \log_{2/3} x$

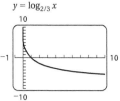

### Visualizing for Success, p. 727

**1.** J    **2.** B    **3.** O    **4.** G    **5.** N    **6.** F    **7.** A    **8.** H
**9.** I    **10.** K

### Exercise Set 8.5, p. 728

**1.** $0.6931$    **3.** $4.1271$    **5.** $8.3814$    **7.** $-5.0832$    **9.** $-1.6094$
**11.** Does not exist    **13.** $-1.7455$    **15.** $1$    **17.** $15.0293$
**19.** $0.0305$    **21.** $109.9472$    **23.** $5$    **25.** $2.5702$    **27.** $6.6439$
**29.** $2.1452$    **31.** $-2.3219$    **33.** $-2.3219$    **35.** $4.6284$

**37.**

| $x$ | $f(x)$ |
|---|---|
| 0 | 1 |
| 1 | 2.7 |
| 2 | 7.4 |
| 3 | 20.1 |
| $-1$ | 0.4 |
| $-2$ | 0.1 |
| $-3$ | 0.05 |

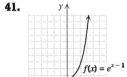

**39.**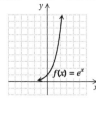

**41.**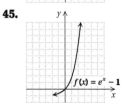

**43.**

**45.**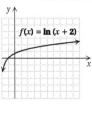

**47.**

| $x$ | $f(x)$ |
|---|---|
| 0 | 0.7 |
| 1 | 1.1 |
| 2 | 1.4 |
| 3 | 1.6 |
| $-0.5$ | 0.4 |
| $-1$ | 0 |
| $-1.5$ | $-0.7$ |

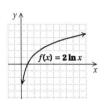

**49.**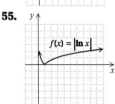

**51.**

**53.**

**55.**

**57.** $16, 256$　　**58.** $\frac{1}{4}, 9$　　**59.** $49, 121$　　**60.** $\pm 3, \pm 4$
**61.** Domain: $(-\infty, \infty)$; range: $[0, \infty)$
**63.** Domain: $(-\infty, \infty)$; range: $(-\infty, 100)$　　**65.** $\left(\frac{5}{2}, \infty\right)$

## Calculator Corner, p. 733

Left to the student

## Exercise Set 8.6, p. 736

**1.** $3$　　**3.** $4$　　**5.** $\frac{5}{2}$　　**7.** $\frac{3}{5}$　　**9.** $3.4594$　　**11.** $5.4263$　　**13.** $\frac{5}{2}$
**15.** $-3, -1$　　**17.** $\frac{3}{2}$　　**19.** $4.6052$　　**21.** $2.3026$　　**23.** $140.6705$
**25.** $2.7095$　　**27.** $3.2220$　　**29.** $256$　　**31.** $\frac{1}{32}$　　**33.** $10$　　**35.** $\frac{1}{100}$
**37.** $e^2 \approx 7.3891$　　**39.** $\frac{1}{e} \approx 0.3679$　　**41.** $121$　　**43.** $10$　　**45.** $\frac{1}{3}$
**47.** $3$　　**49.** $\frac{2}{5}$　　**51.** $5$　　**53.** No solution　　**55.** $\pm 10, \pm 2$
**56.** $-64, 8$　　**57.** $-2, -3, \dfrac{-5 \pm \sqrt{41}}{2}$　　**58.** $-\frac{1}{10}, 1$　　**59.** $\dfrac{y^{4/3}}{25x^2 z^4}$
**60.** $-i$　　**61.** $1$　　**63. (a)** $0.3770$; **(b)** $-1.9617$; **(c)** $0.9036$;
**(d)** $-1.5318$　　**65.** $3, 4$　　**67.** $-4$　　**69.** $2$　　**71.** $\pm\sqrt{34}$
**73.** $10^{100,000}$　　**75.** $1, 100$　　**77.** $3, -7$　　**79.** $1, \dfrac{\log 5}{\log 3} \approx 1.465$

## Translating for Success, p. 746

**1.** D　　**2.** M　　**3.** I　　**4.** A　　**5.** E　　**6.** H　　**7.** C　　**8.** G
**9.** N　　**10.** B

## Exercise Set 8.7, p. 747

**1.** $90$ dB　　**3.** $10^{-7.5}\,\text{W/m}^2$, or about $3.2 \times 10^{-8}\,\text{W/m}^2$;
$-10^{-6}\,\text{W/m}^2$　　**5.** About $6.8$　　**7.** $1.58 \times 10^{-8}$ moles per liter
**9.** $2.36$ ft/sec　　**11.** $2.99$ ft/sec　　**13. (a)** $\$27.87$ billion;
**(b)** $2013$; **(c)** about $4$ yr　　**15.** About $560,664$ PB per month;
**(b)** $2010$; **(c)** about $0.77$ yr　　**17. (a)** $P(t) = P_0 e^{0.03t}$;
**(b)** $\$5152.27$; $\$5309.18$; $\$6749.29$; **(c)** in $23.1$ yr
**19.** $P(t) = 6.8e^{0.01188t}$; **(b)** $7.2$ billion; **(c)** $2076$; **(d)** $58.3$ yr
**21. (a)** $k \approx 0.076$; $C(t) = 80e^{0.076t}$; **(b)** about $\$426$ billion;
**(c)** $2014$　　**23.** About $2103$ yr　　**25.** About $7.2$ days
**27.** $69.3\%$ per year　　**29. (a)** $k \approx 0.103$; $D(t) = 29.7e^{-0.103t}$;
**(b)** about $1.84\%$; **(c)** $1996$　　**31. (a)** $k \approx 0.004$;
$P(t) = 2.431e^{-0.004t}$; **(b)** $2.244$ million; **(c)** $2027$
**33. (a)** $k \approx 0.134$; $V(t) = 640,500e^{0.134t}$; **(b)** $\$1,094,715$;
**(c)** $5.2$ yr; **(d)** $2008$　　**35.** $-1$　　**36.** $1$　　**37.** $i$　　**38.** $i$
**39.** $-1 - i$　　**40.** $-2$　　**41.** $\frac{63}{65} - \frac{16}{65}i$　　**42.** $-\frac{2}{41} + \frac{23}{41}i$
**43.** $41$　　**44.** $91 + 60i$　　**45.** $-0.937, 1.078, 58.770$
**47.** $-0.767, 2, 4$　　**49.** $\$13.4$ million

## Summary and Review: Chapter 8, p. 752

### Concept Reinforcement

**1.** True　　**2.** False　　**3.** False　　**4.** True　　**5.** True　　**6.** True
**7.** False　　**8.** True

### Important Concepts

**1.**
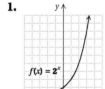

**2.** Yes　　**3.** $g^{-1}(x) = 4 - x$

**4.**

**5.** $8x + 2; 8x + 1$

**6.** $f(x) = \dfrac{1}{x}$, $g(x) = 3x + 2$; answers may vary

**7.**
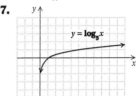

**8.** $\frac{3}{5}\log_a x - \frac{2}{5}\log_a y$　　**9.** $\log_a \dfrac{\sqrt{x}}{y^3}$, or $\log_a \dfrac{x^{1/2}}{y^3}$

**10.**
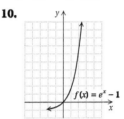

**11.**
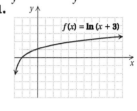

**12.** $\frac{4}{3}$　　**13.** $3$

### Review Exercises

**1.** $\{(2, -4), (-7, 5), (-2, -1), (11, 10)\}$　　**2.** Not one-to-one
**3.** $g^{-1}(x) = \dfrac{7x + 3}{2}$　　**4.** $f^{-1}(x) = \frac{1}{2}\sqrt[3]{x}$　　**5.** $f^{-1}(x) = \dfrac{3x - 4}{2x}$

**6.**
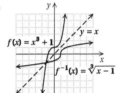

**7.**

| $x$ | $f(x)$ |
|-----|--------|
| $0$ | $\frac{1}{3}$ |
| $1$ | $1$ |
| $2$ | $3$ |
| $3$ | $9$ |
| $-1$ | $\frac{1}{9}$ |
| $-2$ | $\frac{1}{27}$ |
| $-3$ | $\frac{1}{81}$ |

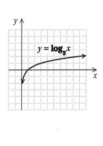

**8.** $3^y$

| $x$, or $3^y$ | $y$ |
|---------------|-----|
| $1$ | $0$ |
| $3$ | $1$ |
| $9$ | $2$ |
| $27$ | $3$ |
| $\frac{1}{3}$ | $-1$ |
| $\frac{1}{9}$ | $-2$ |
| $\frac{1}{27}$ | $-3$ |

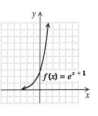

**9.**

| $x$ | $f(x)$ |
|-----|--------|
| $0$ | $2.7$ |
| $1$ | $7.4$ |
| $2$ | $20.1$ |
| $3$ | $54.6$ |
| $-1$ | $1$ |
| $-2$ | $0.4$ |
| $-3$ | $0.1$ |

**10.**

$f(x) = \ln(x - 1)$

**11.** $(f \circ g)(x) = 9x^2 - 30x + 25; (g \circ f)(x) = 3x^2 - 5$
**12.** $f(x) = \sqrt{x}, g(x) = 4 - 7x$; answers may vary
**13.** $4 = \log 10{,}000$ **14.** $\frac{1}{2} = \log_{25} 5$ **15.** $4^x = 16$
**16.** $\left(\frac{1}{2}\right)^{-3} = 8$ **17.** 2 **18.** $-1$ **19.** 1 **20.** 0
**21.** $-2.7425$ **22.** Does not exist as a real number
**23.** $4 \log_a x + 2 \log_a y + 3 \log_a z$ **24.** $\frac{1}{2} \log z - \frac{3}{4} \log x - \frac{1}{4} \log y$
**25.** $\log_a 120$ **26.** $\log \dfrac{a^{1/2}}{bc^2}$ **27.** 17 **28.** $-7$ **29.** 8.7601
**30.** 3.2698 **31.** 2.54995 **32.** $-3.6602$ **33.** $-2.6921$
**34.** 0.3753 **35.** 18.3568 **36.** 0 **37.** Does not exist
**38.** 1 **39.** 0.4307 **40.** 1.7097 **41.** $\frac{1}{9}$ **42.** 2 **43.** $\dfrac{1}{10{,}000}$
**44.** $e^{-2} \approx 0.1353$ **45.** $\frac{7}{2}$ **46.** $1, -5$ **47.** $\dfrac{\log 8.3}{\log 4} \approx 1.5266$
**48.** $\dfrac{\ln 0.03}{-0.1} \approx 35.0656$ **49.** 2 **50.** 8 **51.** $\frac{17}{5}$ **52.** $\sqrt{43}$
**53.** 137 dB **54.** (a) 85.0 million returns; 98.4 million returns; 113.9 million returns; **(b)** 2014; **(c)** about 9.5 yr
**(d)**

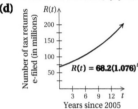

$R(t) = 68.2(1.076)^t$

Number of tax returns e-filed (in millions)

Years since 2005

**55.** (a) $k \approx 0.094$; $V(t) = 40{,}000e^{0.094t}$; **(b)** \$102,399; **(c)** 2017
**56.** $k \approx 0.231$ **57.** About 20.4 yr **58.** About 3463 yr
**59.** C **60.** D **61.** $e^{e^3}$ **62.** $\left(\frac{8}{3}, -\frac{2}{3}\right)$

### Understanding Through Discussion and Writing

**1.** Reflect the graph of $f(x) = e^x$ across the line $y = x$ and then translate it up one unit. **2.** Christina mistakenly thinks that, because negative numbers do not have logarithms, negative numbers cannot be solutions of logarithmic equations.

**3.** $C(x) = \dfrac{100 + 5x}{x}$

$y = \dfrac{100 + 5x}{x}$    Replace $C(x)$ with $y$.

$x = \dfrac{100 + 5y}{y}$    Interchange variables.

$y = \dfrac{100}{x - 5}$;    Solve for $y$.

$C^{-1}(x) = \dfrac{100}{x - 5}$    Replace $y$ with $C^{-1}(x)$.

$C^{-1}(x)$ gives the number of people in the group, where $x$ is the cost per person, in dollars.
**4.** To solve $\ln x = 3$, graph $f(x) = \ln x$ and $g(x) = 3$ on the same set of axes. The solution is the first coordinate of the point of intersection of the two graphs. **5.** You cannot take the logarithm of a negative number because logarithm bases are positive and there is no real-number power to which a positive number can be raised to yield a negative number. **6.** Answers will vary.

### Test: Chapter 8, p. 760

**1.** [8.1a]

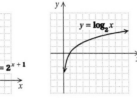

$f(x) = 2^{x+1}$

**2.** [8.3a]

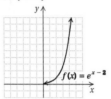

$y = \log_2 x$

**3.** [8.5c]

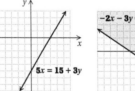

$f(x) = e^{x-2}$

**4.** [8.5c]

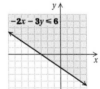

$f(x) = \ln(x - 4)$

**5.** [8.2a] $\{(3, -4), (-8, 5), (-3, -1), (12, 10)\}$
**6.** [8.2b, c] $f^{-1}(x) = \dfrac{x + 3}{4}$ **7.** [8.2b, c] $f^{-1}(x) = \sqrt[3]{x} - 1$
**8.** [8.2b] Not one-to-one **9.** [8.2d] $(f \circ g)(x) = 25x^2 - 15x + 2$, $(g \circ f)(x) = 5x^2 + 5x - 2$ **10.** [8.3b] $\log_{256} 16 = \frac{1}{2}$
**11.** [8.3b] $7^m = 49$ **12.** [8.3c] 3 **13.** [8.4e] 23 **14.** [8.3c] 0
**15.** [8.3d] $-1.9101$ **16.** [8.3d] Does not exist as a real number **17.** [8.4d] $3 \log a + \frac{1}{2} \log b - 2 \log c$
**18.** [8.4d] $\log_a \dfrac{x^{1/3} z^2}{y^3}$ **19.** [8.4d] $-0.544$ **20.** [8.4d] 1.079
**21.** [8.5a] 6.6938 **22.** [8.5a] 107.7701 **23.** [8.5a] 0
**24.** [8.5b] 1.1881 **25.** [8.6b] 5 **26.** [8.6b] 2
**27.** [8.6b] 10,000 **28.** [8.6b] $e^{1/4} \approx 1.2840$
**29.** [8.6a] $\dfrac{\log 1.2}{\log 7} \approx 0.0937$ **30.** [8.6b] 9 **31.** [8.6b] 1
**32.** [8.7a] 4.2 **33.** [8.7b] (a) \$3.18 trillion; **(b)** 2018; **(c)** about 9.5 yr
**34.** [8.7b] (a) $k \approx 0.028$, or 2.8%; $P(t) = 1000e^{0.028t}$; **(b)** \$1251.07; **(c)** after 13 yr; **(d)** about 24.8 yr
**35.** [8.7b] About 3% **36.** [8.7b] About 4684 yr **37.** [8.6b] B
**38.** [8.6b] $44, -37$ **39.** [8.4d] 2

### Cumulative Review: Chapters 1–8, p. 763

**1.** [1.1d] $\frac{11}{2}$ **2.** [4.8a] $-2, 5$ **3.** [3.3a] $(3, -1)$
**4.** [3.5a] $(1, -2, 0)$ **5.** [5.5a] $\frac{9}{2}$ **6.** [6.6b] 5 **7.** [7.4c] 9, 25
**8.** [7.4c] $\pm 2, \pm 3$ **9.** [8.6b] 8 **10.** [8.6a] $\dfrac{\log 7}{5 \log 3} \approx 0.3542$
**11.** [8.6b] $\frac{80}{9}$ **12.** [7.8a] $\{x \mid x < -5 \text{ or } x > 1\}$, or $(-\infty, -5) \cup (1, \infty)$ **13.** [1.6e] $\{x \mid x \le -3 \text{ or } x \ge 6\}$, or $(-\infty, -3] \cup [6, \infty)$ **14.** [7.2a] $-3 \pm 2\sqrt{5}$
**15.** [5.7a] $a = \dfrac{Db}{b - D}$ **16.** [5.7a] $q = \dfrac{pf}{p - f}$
**17.** [5.1a] $\left(-\infty, -\frac{1}{3}\right) \cup \left(-\frac{1}{3}, 2\right) \cup (2, \infty)$ **18.** [5.6a] $\frac{60}{11}$ min, or $5\frac{5}{11}$ min **19.** [8.7a] (a) 78; **(b)** 67.5
**20.** [3.4a] Swim Clean: 60 L; Pure Swim: 40 L **21.** [5.6c] $2\frac{7}{9}$ km/h
**22.** [8.7b] (a) $P(t) = 196e^{0.012t}$, where $P(t)$ is in millions and $t$ is the number of years after 2008; **(b)** about 205.6 million, about 213.2 million; **(c)** about 57.8 yr **23.** [4.8b] 10 ft **24.** [5.8e] 18
**25.** [2.5a] **26.** [3.7b] **27.** [7.6a]

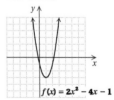

$5x = 15 + 3y$

$-2x - 3y \le 6$

$f(x) = 2x^2 - 4x - 1$

**28.** [8.1a]

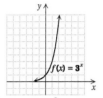

**29.** [8.3a]

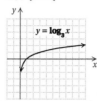

**30.** [4.1d] $8x^2 - 11x - 1$    **31.** [4.2c] $9x^4 - 12x^2y + 4y^2$

**32.** [4.2b] $10a^2 - 9ab - 9b^2$    **33.** [5.1e] $\dfrac{(x+4)(x-3)}{2(x-1)}$

**34.** [5.4a] $\dfrac{1}{x-4}$    **35.** [5.2c] $\dfrac{7x+4}{(x+6)(x-6)}$

**36.** [4.6d] $(1-5x)(1+5x+25x^2)$
**37.** [4.3a], [4.5a, b] $2(3x-2y)(x+2y)$
**38.** [4.3b] $(x^3+7)(x-4)$    **39.** [4.3a], [4.6a] $2(m+3n)^2$
**40.** [4.6b] $(x-2y)(x+2y)(x^2+4y^2)$
**41.** [2.2b] $-12$    **42.** [5.3b, c] $x^3 - 2x^2 - 4x - 12 + \dfrac{-42}{x-3}$

**43.** [6.3a] $14xy^2\sqrt{x}$    **44.** [6.3b] $2y^2\sqrt[3]{y}$

**45.** [6.5b] $\dfrac{6 + \sqrt{y} - y}{4 - y}$    **46.** [6.8c] $12 + 4\sqrt{3}i$

**47.** [8.2c] $f^{-1}(x) = \dfrac{x-7}{-2}$, or $\dfrac{7-x}{2}$    **48.** [2.6d] $y = \frac{1}{2}x + \frac{13}{2}$

**49.** [8.4d] $\log\left(\dfrac{x^3}{y^{1/2}z^2}\right)$    **50.** [8.3b] $a^x = 5$    **51.** [8.3d] $-1.2545$

**52.** [8.3d] $776.2471$    **53.** [8.5a] $2.5479$    **54.** [8.5a] $0.2466$
**55.** [7.6a] D    **56.** [7.3b] D    **57.** [5.5a] All real numbers

except 1 and $-2$    **58.** [8.6b] $\dfrac{1}{3}$, $\dfrac{10{,}000}{3}$    **59.** [5.6c] 35 mph

# CHAPTER 9

## Calculator Corner, p. 769

**1.** $x = y^2 + 4y + 7$

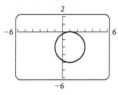

**2.** $x = -2y^2 + 10y - 7$

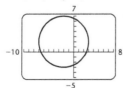

**3.** $x = 4y^2 - 12y + 5$

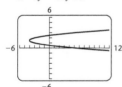

## Calculator Corner, p. 774

**1.** $(x-1)^2 + (y+2)^2 = 4$

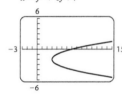

**2.** $(x+2)^2 + (y-2)^2 = 25$

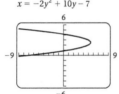

**3.** $x^2 + y^2 - 16 = 0$

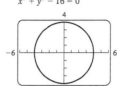

**4.** $4x^2 + 4y^2 = 100$

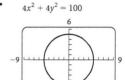

**5.** $x^2 + y^2 - 10x - 11 = 0$

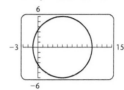

## Exercise Set 9.1, p. 775

**1.** $y = x^2$

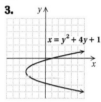

**3.** $x = y^2 + 4y + 1$

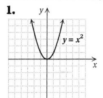

**5.** $y = -x^2 + 4x - 5$

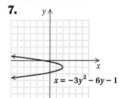

**7.** $x = -3y^2 - 6y - 1$

**9.** 5    **11.** $\sqrt{29} \approx 5.385$    **13.** $\sqrt{648} \approx 25.456$    **15.** 7.1
**17.** $\dfrac{\sqrt{41}}{7} \approx 0.915$    **19.** $\sqrt{6970} \approx 83.487$    **21.** $\sqrt{a^2 + b^2}$
**23.** $\sqrt{17 + 2\sqrt{14} + 2\sqrt{15}} \approx 5.677$
**25.** $\sqrt{9{,}672{,}400} \approx 3110.048$    **27.** $\left(\frac{3}{2}, \frac{7}{2}\right)$    **29.** $\left(0, \frac{11}{2}\right)$
**31.** $\left(-1, -\frac{17}{2}\right)$    **33.** $(-0.25, -0.3)$    **35.** $\left(-\frac{1}{12}, \frac{1}{24}\right)$
**37.** $\left(\dfrac{\sqrt{2} + \sqrt{3}}{2}, \dfrac{3}{2}\right)$    **39.**

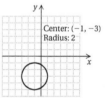

Center: $(-1, -3)$
Radius: 2

$(x+1)^2 + (y+3)^2 = 4$

**41.**

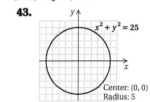

Center: $(3, 0)$
Radius: $\sqrt{2}$

$(x-3)^2 + y^2 = 2$

**43.** $x^2 + y^2 = 25$

Center: $(0, 0)$
Radius: 5

**45.** $x^2 + y^2 = 49$    **47.** $(x+5)^2 + (y-3)^2 = 7$
**49.** $(-4, 3), r = 2\sqrt{10}$    **51.** $(4, -1), r = 2$    **53.** $(2, 0), r = 2$
**55.** $(9, 2)$    **56.** $(-8, 16)$    **57.** $\left(-\frac{21}{5}, -\frac{73}{5}\right)$    **58.** $(1, 2)$
**59.** No solution    **60.** $(2a + b)(2a - b)$    **61.** $(x - 4)(x + 4)$
**62.** $(a - 3b)(a + 3b)$    **63.** $(8p - 9q)(8p + 9q)$
**64.** $25(4cd - 3)(4cd + 3)$    **65.** $x^2 + y^2 = 2$
**67.** $(x + 3)^2 + (y + 2)^2 = 9$    **69.** $\sqrt{49 + k^2}$
**71.** $8\sqrt{m^2 + n^2}$    **73.** Yes    **75.** $(2, 4\sqrt{2})$
**77.** **(a)** $(0, -8467.8)$; **(b)** 8487.3 mm

## Calculator Corner, p. 782

**1.**
$$y_1 = \sqrt{\frac{36 - 4x^2}{9}},$$
$$y_2 = -\sqrt{\frac{36 - 4x^2}{9}}$$

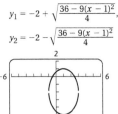

**2.**
$$y_1 = \sqrt{\frac{144 - 16x^2}{9}},$$
$$y_2 = -\sqrt{\frac{144 - 16x^2}{9}}$$

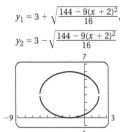

**3.**
$$y_1 = -2 + \sqrt{\frac{36 - 9(x - 1)^2}{4}},$$
$$y_2 = -2 - \sqrt{\frac{36 - 9(x - 1)^2}{4}}$$

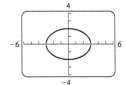

**4.**
$$y_1 = 3 + \sqrt{\frac{144 - 9(x + 2)^2}{16}},$$
$$y_2 = 3 - \sqrt{\frac{144 - 9(x + 2)^2}{16}}$$

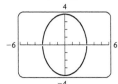

## Exercise Set 9.2, p. 784

**1.**
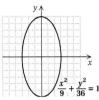
$$\frac{x^2}{9} + \frac{y^2}{36} = 1$$

**3.**

$$\frac{x^2}{1} + \frac{y^2}{4} = 1$$

**5.**
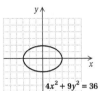
$$4x^2 + 9y^2 = 36$$

**7.**

$$x^2 + 4y^2 = 4$$

**9.**
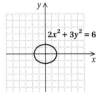
$$2x^2 + 3y^2 = 6$$

**11.**
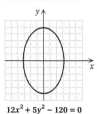
$$12x^2 + 5y^2 - 120 = 0$$

**13.**
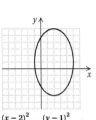
$$\frac{(x - 2)^2}{9} + \frac{(y - 1)^2}{25} = 1$$

**15.**
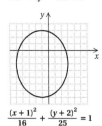
$$\frac{(x + 1)^2}{16} + \frac{(y + 2)^2}{25} = 1$$

**17.**

$$12(x - 1)^2 + 3(y + 2)^2 = 48$$

**19.**

$$(x + 3)^2 + 4(y + 1)^2 - 10 = 6$$

**21.** $\dfrac{1 \pm 2i\sqrt{5}}{3}$  **22.** $\dfrac{6 \pm \sqrt{15}}{3}$  **23.** $\dfrac{-1 \pm i\sqrt{7}}{2}$

**24.** $-1 \pm \sqrt{11}$  **25.** $-1 \pm 3\sqrt{2}$; 3.2, −5.2

**26.** $1 \pm \sqrt{11}$; 4.3, −2.3  **27.** $\dfrac{17 \pm \sqrt{337}}{8}$; 4.4, −0.2

**28.** $\dfrac{-3 \pm \sqrt{41}}{4}$; 0.9, −2.4  **29.** $\log_a b = -t$

**30.** $\log_8 17 = a$  **31.** $e^{3.1781} = 24$  **32.** $e^p = W$

**33.** $\dfrac{x^2}{49} + \dfrac{y^2}{25} = 1$  **35.** $\dfrac{x^2}{9} + \dfrac{y^2}{25} = 1$

## Mid-Chapter Review: Chapter 9, p. 787

**1.** True  **2.** True  **3.** True  **4.** False

**5. (a)** $d = \sqrt{(x_2 - x_1)^2 + (y_2 - y_1)^2} =$
$$\sqrt{(4 - (-6))^2 + (-1 - 2)^2} = \sqrt{(10)^2 + (-3)^2} =$$
$$\sqrt{100 + 9} = \sqrt{109} \approx 10.440;$$ **(b)** $\left(\dfrac{x_1 + x_2}{2}, \dfrac{y_1 + y_2}{2}\right) =$
$$\left(\dfrac{-6 + 4}{2}, \dfrac{2 + (-1)}{2}\right) = \left(\dfrac{-2}{2}, \dfrac{1}{2}\right) = \left(-1, \dfrac{1}{2}\right)$$

**6.**
$$x^2 - 20x + y^2 + 4y = -79$$
$$x^2 - 20x + 100 + y^2 + 4y + 4 = -79 + 100 + 4$$
$$(x - 10)^2 + (y + 2)^2 = 25$$
$$(x - 10)^2 + (y - (-2))^2 = 5^2$$
Center: $(10, -2)$; radius: 5

**7.** $3\sqrt{2} \approx 4.243$  **8.** $\sqrt{120.53} \approx 10.979$  **9.** $\sqrt{11} \approx 3.317$
**10.** $\left(-\frac{19}{2}, \frac{15}{2}\right)$  **11.** $\left(-\frac{1}{6}, \frac{3}{8}\right)$  **12.** $(-1.5, -3.9)$  **13.** Center: $(0, 0)$; radius: 11  **14.** Center: $(13, -9)$; radius: $\sqrt{109}$
**15.** Center: $(0, 5)$; radius: $\sqrt{14}$  **16.** Center: $(-3, 7)$; radius: 4
**17.** $x^2 + y^2 = 1$  **18.** $\left(x + \frac{1}{2}\right)^2 + \left(y - \frac{3}{4}\right)^2 = \frac{81}{4}$
**19.** $(x + 8)^2 + (y - 6)^2 = 17$  **20.** $(x - 3)^2 + (y + 5)^2 = 20$

**21.**
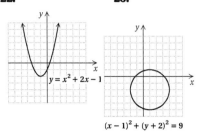
$$\frac{x^2}{4} + \frac{y^2}{36} = 1$$

**22.**
$$y = x^2 + 2x - 1$$

**23.**
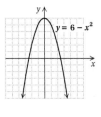
$$(x - 1)^2 + (y + 2)^2 = 9$$

**24.**
$$x = y^2 - 2$$

**25.**
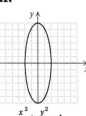
$$x^2 + y^2 = \frac{9}{4}$$

**26.**
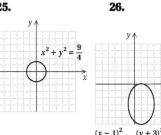
$$\frac{(x - 1)^2}{4} + \frac{(y + 3)^2}{9} = 1$$

**27.**
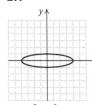
$$\frac{x^2}{16} + \frac{y^2}{1} = 1$$

**28.**
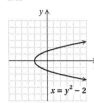
$$y = 6 - x^2$$

**29.** One method is to graph $y = ax^2 + bx + c$ and then use the DrawInv feature to graph the inverse relation, $x = ay^2 + by + c$. Another method is to use the quadratic formula to solve $x = ay^2 + by + c$, or $ay^2 + bx + c - x = 0$. The solutions are

$\dfrac{-b \pm \sqrt{b^2 - 4a(c - x)}}{2a}$. Then graph

$y_1 = \dfrac{-b + \sqrt{b^2 - 4a(c - x)}}{2a}$ and

$y_2 = \dfrac{-b - \sqrt{b^2 - 4a(c - x)}}{2a}$ on the same screen.

**30.** No; a circle is defined to be the set of points in a plane that are a fixed distance from the center. Thus, unless $r = 0$ and the "circle" is one point, the center is not part of the circle.
**31.** Bank shots originating at one focus (the tiny dot) are deflected to the other focus (the hole).
**32. (a)**

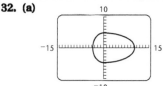

**(b)** Some other factors are the wind speed, the amount of rainfall in the preceding months, and the composition of the forest.

### Calculator Corner, p. 792

**1.**
$y_1 = \sqrt{\dfrac{15x^2 - 240}{4}}$,

$y_2 = -\sqrt{\dfrac{15x^2 - 240}{4}}$

**2.**
$y_1 = \sqrt{\dfrac{16x^2 - 320}{5}}$,

$y_2 = -\sqrt{\dfrac{16x^2 - 320}{5}}$

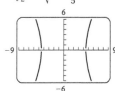

**3.**
$y_1 = \sqrt{\dfrac{16x^2 - 48}{3}}$,

$y_2 = -\sqrt{\dfrac{16x^2 - 48}{3}}$

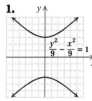

**4.**
$y_1 = \sqrt{\dfrac{45x^2 - 405}{9}}$,

$y_2 = -\sqrt{\dfrac{45x^2 - 405}{9}}$

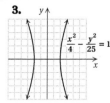

### Visualizing for Success, p. 793

**1.** C   **2.** E   **3.** G   **4.** J   **5.** B   **6.** F   **7.** A   **8.** H
**9.** I   **10.** D

### Exercise Set 9.3, p. 794

**1.**

$\dfrac{y^2}{9} - \dfrac{x^2}{9} = 1$

**3.**

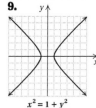

$\dfrac{x^2}{4} - \dfrac{y^2}{25} = 1$

**5.**

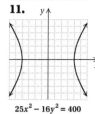

$\dfrac{y^2}{36} - \dfrac{x^2}{9} = 1$

**7.**

$y^2 - x^2 = 25$

**9.**

$x^2 = 1 + y^2$

**11.**

$25x^2 - 16y^2 = 400$

**13.**

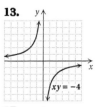
$xy = -4$

**15.**

$xy = 3$

**17.**

$xy = -2$

**19.**

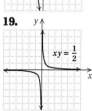
$xy = \frac{1}{2}$

**21.** Discriminant   **22.** Vertex   **23.** Vertical line
**24.** Common   **25.** Exponent   **26.** Horizontal line
**27.** Function   **28.** Half-life   **29.** Left to the student
**31.** Circle   **33.** Parabola   **35.** Ellipse   **37.** Circle
**39.** Hyperbola   **41.** Circle

### Calculator Corner, p. 799

**1.** Left to the student   **2.** Left to the student

### Exercise Set 9.4, p. 803

**1.** $(-8, -6), (6, 8)$   **3.** $(2, 0), (0, 3)$   **5.** $(-2, 1)$
**7.** $\left(\dfrac{5 + \sqrt{70}}{3}, \dfrac{-1 + \sqrt{70}}{3}\right), \left(\dfrac{5 - \sqrt{70}}{3}, \dfrac{-1 - \sqrt{70}}{3}\right)$
**9.** $\left(\dfrac{7}{3}, \dfrac{1}{3}\right), (1, -1)$   **11.** $(-7, 1), (1, -7)$   **13.** $(3, -5), (-1, 3)$
**15.** $\left(\dfrac{8 + 3i\sqrt{6}}{2}, \dfrac{-8 + 3i\sqrt{6}}{2}\right), \left(\dfrac{8 - 3i\sqrt{6}}{2}, \dfrac{-8 - 3i\sqrt{6}}{2}\right)$
**17.** $(-5, 0), (4, 3), (4, -3)$   **19.** $(3, 0), (-3, 0)$   **21.** $(2, 4)$,
$(-2, -4), (4, 2), (-4, -2)$   **23.** $(2, 3), (-2, -3), (3, 2)$,
$(-3, -2)$   **25.** $(2, 1), (-2, -1)$   **27.** $(5, 2), (-5, 2), \left(2, -\dfrac{4}{5}\right)$,
$\left(-2, -\dfrac{4}{5}\right)$   **29.** $(\sqrt{2}, -\sqrt{2}), (-\sqrt{2}, \sqrt{2})$
**31.** $\left(\dfrac{8i\sqrt{5}}{5}, \dfrac{3\sqrt{105}}{5}\right), \left(-\dfrac{8i\sqrt{5}}{5}, \dfrac{3\sqrt{105}}{5}\right)$,
$\left(\dfrac{8i\sqrt{5}}{5}, -\dfrac{3\sqrt{105}}{5}\right), \left(-\dfrac{8i\sqrt{5}}{5}, -\dfrac{3\sqrt{105}}{5}\right)$
**33.** Length: 4 ft; width: 2 ft   **35.** Length: 7 in.; width: 2 in.
**37.** Length: 12 ft; width: 5 ft   **39.** 24 ft; 16 ft
**41.** Length: $\sqrt{2}$ m; width: 1 m   **43.** Length: 24.8 cm; height:
18.6 cm   **45.** $f^{-1}(x) = \dfrac{x + 5}{2}$   **46.** $f^{-1}(x) = \dfrac{7x + 3}{2x}$
**47.** $f^{-1}(x) = \dfrac{3x + 2}{1 - x}$   **48.** $f^{-1}(x) = \dfrac{4x + 8}{5x - 3}$   **49.** Does not
exist   **50.** Does not exist   **51.** $f^{-1}(x) = \log x$
**52.** $f^{-1}(x) = \ln x$   **53.** $f^{-1}(x) = \sqrt[3]{x + 4}$
**54.** $f^{-1}(x) = x^3 - 2$   **55.** $f^{-1}(x) = e^x$   **56.** $f^{-1}(x) = 10^x$
**57.** Left to the student   **59.** One piece: $38\frac{12}{25}$ cm; other piece:
$61\frac{13}{25}$ cm   **61.** 30 units   **63.** $\left(\frac{1}{2}, \frac{1}{3}\right), \left(\frac{1}{3}, \frac{1}{2}\right)$

### Summary and Review: Chapter 9, p. 807

**Concept Reinforcement**
**1.** False   **2.** True   **3.** False

**Important Concepts**
**1.**

$(-2, 3)$

$y = -x^2 - 4x - 1$

**2.** $\sqrt{10} \approx 3.162$   **3.** $(4, -8)$

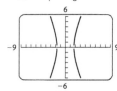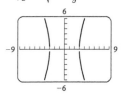

**4.** Center: $(2, -1)$; radius: 4;

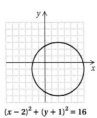

$(x - 2)^2 + (y + 1)^2 = 16$

**5.** $x^2 + (y - 3)^2 = 36$

**6.**

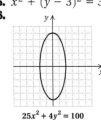

$25x^2 + 4y^2 = 100$

**7.**

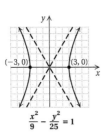

$(-3, 0)$ $(3, 0)$

$\dfrac{x^2}{9} - \dfrac{y^2}{25} = 1$

**8.** $(-6, 0)$ and $(0, 2)$

## Review Exercises

**1.** 4   **2.** 5   **3.** $\sqrt{90.1} \approx 9.492$   **4.** $\sqrt{9 + 4a^2}$   **5.** $(4, 6)$

**6.** $\left(-3, \frac{5}{2}\right)$   **7.** $\left(\frac{3}{4}, \frac{\sqrt{3} - \sqrt{2}}{2}\right)$   **8.** $\left(\frac{1}{2}, 2a\right)$   **9.** $(-2, 3)$, $\sqrt{2}$

**10.** $(5, 0)$, 7   **11.** $(3, 1)$, 3   **12.** $(-4, 3)$, $\sqrt{35}$

**13.** $(x + 4)^2 + (y - 3)^2 = 48$   **14.** $(x - 7)^2 + (y + 2)^2 = 20$

**15.**

$\dfrac{x^2}{16} + \dfrac{y^2}{4} = 1$

**16.**

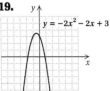

$\dfrac{y^2}{9} - \dfrac{x^2}{4} = 1$

**17.**

$x^2 + y^2 = 16$

**18.**

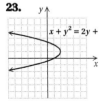

$x = y^2 + 2y - 2$

**19.**

$y = -2x^2 - 2x + 3$

**20.**

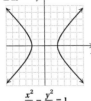

$x^2 + y^2 + 2x - 4y - 4 = 0$

**21.**

$\dfrac{(x - 3)^2}{9} + \dfrac{(y + 4)^2}{4} = 1$

**22.**

$xy = 9$

**23.**

$x + y^2 = 2y + 1$

**24.**

$\dfrac{x^2}{4} - \dfrac{y^2}{4} = 1$

**25.** $(7, 4)$   **26.** $(2, 2), \left(\frac{32}{9}, -\frac{10}{9}\right)$   **27.** $(0, -3), (2, 1)$

**28.** $(4, 3), (4, -3), (-4, 3), (-4, -3)$

**29.** $(2, 1), \left(\sqrt{3}, 0\right), (-2, 1), \left(-\sqrt{3}, 0\right)$   **30.** $(3, -3), \left(-\frac{3}{5}, \frac{21}{5}\right)$

**31.** $(6, 8), (6, -8), (-6, 8), (-6, -8)$

**32.** $(2, 2), (-2, -2), \left(2\sqrt{2}, \sqrt{2}\right), \left(-2\sqrt{2}, -\sqrt{2}\right)$

**33.** Length: 4 in.; width: 3 in.   **34.** 11 ft, 3 ft   **35.** 4 and 8

**36.** Length: 12 m; width: 7 m   **37.** B   **38.** D

**39.** $\left(-5, -4\sqrt{2}\right), \left(-5, 4\sqrt{2}\right), \left(3, -2\sqrt{2}\right), \left(3, 2\sqrt{2}\right)$

**40.** $(x - 2)^2 + (y + 1)^2 = 25$   **41.** $\dfrac{x^2}{49} + \dfrac{y^2}{9} = 1$   **42.** $\left(\frac{9}{4}, 0\right)$

**43.** Parabola   **44.** Hyperbola   **45.** Circle   **46.** Ellipse
**47.** Circle   **48.** Hyperbola

### Understanding Through Discussion and Writing

**1.** Earlier, we studied systems of linear equations. In this chapter, we studied systems of two equations in which at least one equation is of second degree.   **2.** Parabolas of the form $y = ax^2 + bx + c$ and hyperbolas of the form $xy = c$ pass the vertical-line test, so they are functions. Circles, ellipses, parabolas of the form $x = ay^2 + by + c$, and hyperbolas of the form $\dfrac{x^2}{a^2} - \dfrac{y^2}{b^2} = 1$ or $\dfrac{y^2}{b^2} - \dfrac{x^2}{a^2} = 1$ fail the vertical-line test, and hence are not functions.   **3.** The graph of a parabola has one branch whereas the graph of a hyperbola has two branches. A hyperbola has asymptotes, but a parabola does not.   **4.** The asymptotes are $y = x$ and $y = -x$, because for $a = b$, $\pm\dfrac{b}{a} = \pm 1$.

### Test: Chapter 9, p. 813

**1.** [9.1b] $\sqrt{180} \approx 13.416$   **2.** [9.1b] $\sqrt{36 + 4a^2}$, or $2\sqrt{9 + a^2}$
**3.** [9.1c] $(0, 5)$   **4.** [9.1c] $(0, 0)$   **5.** [9.1d] Center: $(-2, 3)$; radius: 8   **6.** [9.1d] Center: $(-2, 3)$; radius: 3
**7.** [9.1d] $(x + 2)^2 + (y + 5)^2 = 18$
**8.** [9.1a]

$y = x^2 - 4x - 1$

**9.** [9.1d]

$x^2 + y^2 = 36$

**10.** [9.3a]

$\dfrac{x^2}{9} - \dfrac{y^2}{4} = 1$

**11.** [9.2a]

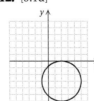

$\dfrac{(x + 2)^2}{16} + \dfrac{(y - 3)^2}{9} = 1$

**12.** [9.1d]

$x^2 + y^2 - 4x + 6y + 4 = 0$

**13.** [9.2a]

$9x^2 + y^2 = 36$

**14.** [9.3b]

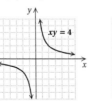

$xy = 4$

**15.** [9.1a]

$x = -y^2 + 4y$

**16.** [9.4a] $(0, 3), (4, 0)$   **17.** [9.4a] $(4, 0), (-4, 0)$
**18.** [9.4b] 16 ft by 12 ft   **19.** [9.4b] $1200, 6\%
**20.** [9.4b] 11 yd by 2 yd   **21.** [9.4b] $\sqrt{5}$ m, $\sqrt{3}$ m   **22.** [9.4a] B

**23.** [9.2a] $\dfrac{(x-6)^2}{25} + \dfrac{(y-3)^2}{9} = 1$

**24.** [9.1d] $\{(x,y)|(x-8)^2 + y^2 = 100\}$  **25.** [9.4b] 9

**26.** [9.1b] $\left(0, -\dfrac{31}{4}\right)$

## Cumulative Review: Chapters 1–9, p. 815

**1.** [1.4c] $\{x|x \geq -1\}$, or $[-1, \infty)$

**2.** [1.6e] $\{x|x < -6.4 \, or \, x > 6.4\}$, or $(-\infty, -6.4) \cup (6.4, \infty)$

**3.** [1.5a] $\{x|-1 \leq x < 6\}$, or $[-1, 6)$  **4.** [3.2a], [3.3a] $\left(-\dfrac{1}{3}, 5\right)$

**5.** [7.4c] $-3, -2, 2, 3$  **6.** [4.8a] $-1, \dfrac{3}{2}$  **7.** [5.5a] $-\dfrac{2}{3}, 3$

**8.** [6.6a] 4  **9.** [4.8a] $-7, -3$  **10.** [7.2a] $-\dfrac{1}{4} \pm i\dfrac{\sqrt{7}}{4}$

**11.** [8.6a] 1.748  **12.** [7.8b] $\{x|x < -1 \, or \, x > 2\}$, or $(-\infty, -1) \cup (2, \infty)$  **13.** [8.6b] 9

**14.** [7.8a] $\{x|x \leq -1 \, or \, x \geq 1\}$, or $(-\infty, -1] \cup [1, \infty)$

**15.** [8.6b] 1  **16.** [5.7a] $p = \dfrac{qf}{q-f}$  **17.** [3.5a] $(-1, 2, 3)$

**18.** [9.4a] $(1, 2), (-1, 2), (1, -2,), (-1, -2)$  **19.** [5.5a] $-16$

**20.** [1.2a] $N = \dfrac{4P - 3M}{6}$  **21.** [8.1c], [8.7b] **(a)** About 80.52 billion ft$^3$, about 84.94 billion ft$^3$; **(b)** about 39 yr;

**(c)**

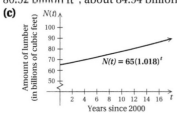

**22.** [8.7b] **(a)** $A(t) = \$50,000(1.04)^t$; **(b)** $50,000; $58,492.93; $68,428.45; $74,012.21;

**(c)**

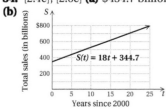

**23.** [4.2a] $2x^3 - x^2 - 8x - 3$  **24.** [4.1d] $-x^3 + 3x^2 - x - 6$

**25.** [5.1d] $\dfrac{2m-1}{m+1}$  **26.** [5.2c] $\dfrac{x+2}{x+1}$  **27.** [5.4a] $\dfrac{1}{x+1}$

**28.** [5.3b, c] $x^3 + 2x^2 - 2x + 1 + \dfrac{3}{x+1}$

**29.** [6.3b] $5x^2\sqrt{y}$  **30.** [6.4a] $11\sqrt{2}$  **31.** [6.2d] 8

**32.** [6.8c] $16 + i\sqrt{2}$  **33.** [6.8e] $\dfrac{3}{10} + \dfrac{11}{10}i$

**34.** [2.4c], [2.6e] **(a)** $434.7 billion, $488.7 billion, $524.7 billion;

**(b)**

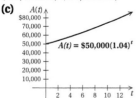

**(c)** $(0, 344.7)$; **(d)** 18; **(e)** an increase of $18 billion per year

**35.** [2.6c] $y = 2x + 2$  **36.** [2.6d] $y = -\dfrac{1}{2}x + \dfrac{5}{2}$

**37.** [2.5a]

**38.** [3.7b]

**39.** [9.2a]

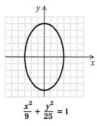

**40.** [9.1d]

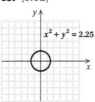

**41.** [3.7c]

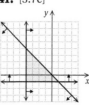

**42.** [9.3a]

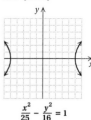

$\dfrac{x^2}{25} - \dfrac{y^2}{16} = 1$

**43.** [9.1d]

$(x-1)^2 + (y+1)^2 = 9$

**44.** [7.6a]

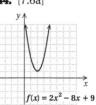

**45.** [2.5c]

**46.** [9.1a]

**47.** [8.5c]

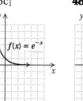

**48.** [8.3a]

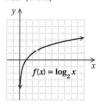

**49.** [4.3b] $(x-6)(2x^3 + 1)$  **50.** [4.4a] $3(a-9b)(a+5b)$

**51.** [4.4a] $(x-8)(x-9)$

**52.** [4.6b] $(9m^2 + n^2)(3m+n)(3m-n)$

**53.** [4.6a] $4(2x-1)^2$  **54.** [4.6d] $3(3a-2)(9a^2 + 6a + 4)$

**55.** [4.5a, b] $2(5x-2)(x+7)$  **56.** [4.5a, b] $3x(2x-1)(x+5)$

**57.** [9.1d] Center: $(8, -3)$; radius: $\sqrt{5}$

**58.** [8.2c] $f^{-1}(x) = \dfrac{1}{2}(x+3)$  **59.** [5.8e] $\dfrac{4}{5}$  **60.** [2.2b] $-10$

**61.** [9.1b] 10  **62.** [9.1c] $\left(1, -\dfrac{3}{2}\right)$  **63.** [6.5b] $\dfrac{15 + 8\sqrt{a} + a}{9 - a}$

**64.** [5.1a] $\left(-\infty, -\dfrac{1}{3}\right) \cup \left(-\dfrac{1}{3}, 0\right) \cup (0, \infty)$  **65.** [4.8a] $-1, \dfrac{2}{3}$

**66.** [1.4d] More than 4  **67.** [3.4b] 612 mi  **68.** [1.3a] $11\dfrac{3}{7}$

**69.** [3.4a] 24 L of A; 56 L of B  **70.** [5.6c] 350 mph

**71.** [5.6a] $8\dfrac{2}{5}$ min  **72.** [5.8f] 20  **73.** [9.4b] 5 ft by 12 ft

**74.** [9.4b] Length: 20 ft; width: 15 ft  **75.** [7.7a] 1250 ft$^2$

**76.** [8.7b] 2397 yr  **77.** [5.8d] 3360 kg

**78.** [2.6c] $f(x) = -\dfrac{1}{3}x - \dfrac{7}{3}$

**79.** [7.7b] $f(x) = -\dfrac{17}{18}x^2 - \dfrac{59}{18}x + \dfrac{11}{9}$  **80.** [8.3b] $\log r = 6$

**81.** [8.3b] $3^x = Q$  **82.** [8.4d] $\log_b\left(\dfrac{x^7}{yz^8}\right)^{1/5}$, or $\log_b \dfrac{x^{7/5}}{y^{1/5}z^{8/5}}$

**83.** [8.4d] $-6\log_b x - 30\log_b y + 6\log_b z$  **84.** [7.7a] 169

**85.** [8.2b] No  **86.** [2.3a] **(a)** $-5$; **(b)** $(-\infty, \infty)$; **(c)** $-2, -1, 1, 2$; **(d)** $[-7, \infty)$  **87.** **(a)** [8.7b] $P(t) = 1{,}998{,}257e^{0.03t}$; **(b)** [8.7b] 3,133,891; **(c)** [8.7b] about 2019  **88.** [5.5a] All real numbers except 0 and $-12$  **89.** [8.6b] 81  **90.** [9.1d] Circle centered at the origin with radius $|a|$  **91.** [1.3a] 84 yr

## APPENDIXES

### Exercise Set A, p. 824

**1.** 68 ft  **3.** 45 g  **5.** $15\dfrac{\text{mi}}{\text{hr}}$  **7.** $3.3\dfrac{\text{m}}{\text{sec}}$  **9.** $4\dfrac{\text{in.-lb}}{\text{sec}}$

**11.** 12 yd  **13.** 16 ft$^3$  **15.** $\dfrac{\$970}{\text{day}}$  **17.** 51.2 oz

**19.** 3080 ft/min  **21.** 96 in.  **23.** Approximately 0.03 yr

**25.** Approximately 31,710 yr  **27.** $80\dfrac{\text{oz}}{\text{in.}}$  **29.** 172,800 sec

**31.** $\dfrac{3}{2}$ ft$^2$  **33.** $1.08\dfrac{\text{ton}}{\text{yd}^3}$

## Exercise Set B, p. 829

**1.** 10 **3.** 0 **5.** −48 **7.** 0 **9.** −10 **11.** −3 **13.** 5
**15.** 0 **17.** $(2, 0)$ **19.** $\left(-\frac{25}{2}, -\frac{11}{2}\right)$ **21.** $\left(\frac{3}{2}, \frac{5}{2}\right)$ **23.** $(-4, 3)$
**25.** $(2, -1, 4)$ **27.** $(1, 2, 3)$ **29.** $\left(\frac{3}{2}, -4, 3\right)$ **31.** $(2, -2, 1)$

## Exercise Set C, p. 834

**1.** $\left(\frac{3}{2}, \frac{5}{2}\right)$ **3.** $(-4, 3)$ **5.** $\left(\frac{1}{2}, \frac{3}{2}\right)$ **7.** $(10, -10)$
**9.** $\left(\frac{3}{2}, -4, 3\right)$ **11.** $(2, -2, 1)$ **13.** $(0, 2, 1)$ **15.** $\left(4, \frac{1}{2}, -\frac{1}{2}\right)$
**17.** $(w, x, y, z) = (1, -3, -2, -1)$

## Exercise Set D, p. 837

**1.** 1 **3.** −41 **5.** 12 **7.** $\frac{13}{18}$ **9.** 5 **11.** 2
**13.** $x^2 - x + 1$ **15.** 21 **17.** 5 **19.** $-x^3 + 4x^2 + 3x - 12$
**21.** 42 **23.** $-\frac{3}{4}$ **25.** $\frac{1}{6}$

**27.** $x^2 + 3x - 4$; $x^2 - 3x + 4$; $3x^3 - 4x^2$; $\dfrac{x^2}{3x - 4}$

**29.** $\dfrac{1}{x - 2} + 4x^3$; $\dfrac{1}{x - 2} - 4x^3$; $\dfrac{4x^3}{x - 2}$; $\dfrac{1}{4x^3(x - 2)}$

**31.** $\dfrac{3}{x - 2} + \dfrac{5}{4 - x}$; $\dfrac{3}{x - 2} - \dfrac{5}{4 - x}$; $\dfrac{15}{(x - 2)(4 - x)}$; $\dfrac{3(4 - x)}{5(x - 2)}$

# Glossary

## A

**Abscissa**   The first coordinate in an ordered pair of numbers

**Absolute value**   The distance that a number is from 0 on the number line

***ac*-method**   A method for factoring trinomials of the type $ax^2 + bx + c, a \neq 1$, involving the product, $ac$, of the leading coefficient $a$ and the last term $c$

**Additive identity**   The number 0

**Additive inverse**   A number's opposite; two numbers are additive inverses of each other if their sum is 0

**Algebraic expression**   An expression consisting of variables, numbers, and operation signs

**Ascending order**   When a polynomial in one variable is arranged so that the exponents increase from left to right, it is said to be in ascending order.

**Associative law of addition**   The statement that when three numbers are added, regrouping the addends gives the same sum

**Associative law of multiplication**   The statement that when three numbers are multiplied, regrouping the factors gives the same product

**Asymptote**   A line that a graph approaches more and more closely as $x$ increases or as $x$ decreases

**Axes**   Two perpendicular number lines used to locate points in a plane

**Axis of symmetry**   A line that can be drawn through a graph such that the part of the graph on one side of the line is an exact reflection of the part on the opposite side; also called *line of symmetry*.

## B

**Base**   In exponential notation, the number being raised to a power

**Binomial**   A polynomial composed of two terms

**Break-even point**   In business, the point of intersection of the revenue function and the cost function

## C

**Circle**   The set of all points in a plane that are a fixed distance $r$, called the radius, from a fixed point $(h, k)$, called the center

**Circumference**   The distance around a circle

**Coefficient**   The numerical multiplier of a variable

**Common logarithm**   A logarithm with base 10

**Commutative law of addition**   The statement that when two numbers are added, changing the order in which the numbers are added does not affect the sum

**Commutative law of multiplication**   The statement that when two numbers are multiplied, changing the order in which the numbers are multiplied does not affect the product

**Complementary angles**   Angles whose sum is 90°

**Completing the square**   Adding a particular constant to an expression so that the resulting sum is a perfect square

**Complex number**   Any number that can be named $a + bi$, where $a$ and $b$ are any real numbers

**Complex number $i$**   The square root of $-1$; that is, $i = \sqrt{-1}$ and $i^2 = -1$

**Complex rational expression**   A rational expression that contains rational expressions within its numerator and/or denominator

**Complex-number system**   A number system that contains the real-number system and is designed so that negative numbers have defined square roots

**Composite function**   A function in which a quantity depends on a variable that, in turn, depends on another variable

**Compound inequality**   A statement in which two or more inequalities are joined by the word *and* or the word *or*

**Compound interest**   Interest computed on the sum of an original principal and the interest previously accrued by that principal

**Conic section**   A curve formed by the intersection of a plane and a cone

**Conjugate of a complex number**   The conjugate of a complex number $a + bi$ is $a - bi$ and the conjugate of $a - bi$ is $a + bi$.

**Conjugates of radical terms**   Pairs of radical terms, like $\sqrt{a} + \sqrt{b}$ and $\sqrt{a} - \sqrt{b}$ or $c + \sqrt{d}$ and $c - \sqrt{d}$, for which the product does not have a radical term

**Conjunction** A statement in which two or more sentences are joined by the word *and*

**Consecutive even integers** Even integers that are two units apart

**Consecutive integers** Integers that are one unit apart

**Consecutive odd integers** Odd integers that are two units apart

**Consistent system of equations** A system of equations that has at least one solution

**Constant** A known number

**Constant function** A function given by an equation of the form $y = b$, or $f(x) = b$, where $b$ is a real number

**Constant of proportionality** The constant in an equation of direct or inverse variation

**Coordinates** The numbers in an ordered pair

**Cube root** The number $c$ is the cube root of $a$, written $\sqrt[3]{a}$, if the third power of $c$ is $a$.

**D**

**Decay rate** The variable $k$ in the exponential decay model $P(t) = P_0 e^{-kt}$

**Degree of a polynomial** The degree of the term of highest degree in a polynomial

**Degree of a term** The sum of the exponents of the variables

**Dependent equations** The equations in a system are dependent if one equation can be removed without changing the solution set. There are infinitely many solutions to the equations.

**Descending order** When a polynomial is arranged so that the exponents decrease from left to right, it is said to be in descending order.

**Determinant** The determinant of a two-by-two matrix $\begin{bmatrix} a_1 & b_1 \\ a_2 & b_2 \end{bmatrix}$ is denoted $\begin{vmatrix} a_1 & b_1 \\ a_2 & b_2 \end{vmatrix}$ and represents $a_1 b_1 - a_2 b_2$.

**Diameter** A segment that passes through the center of a circle and has its endpoints on the circle

**Difference of cubes** Any expression that can be written in the form $A^3 - B^3$

**Difference of squares** Any expression that can be written in the form $A^2 - B^2$

**Direct variation** A situation that gives rise to a linear function $f(x) = kx$, or $y = kx$, where $k$ is a positive constant

**Discriminant** The expression, $b^2 - 4ac$, from the quadratic formula

**Disjoint sets** Two sets with an empty intersection

**Disjunction** A statement in which two or more sentences are joined by the word *or*

**Distributive law of multiplication over addition** The statement that multiplying a factor by the sum of two numbers gives the same result as multiplying the factor by each of the two numbers and then adding

**Distributive law of multiplication over subtraction** The statement that multiplying a factor by the difference of two numbers gives the same result as multiplying the factor by each of the two numbers and then subtracting

**Domain** The set of all first coordinates of the ordered pairs in a function

**Doubling time** The time necessary for a population to double in size

**E**

**Elimination method** An algebraic method that uses the addition principle to solve a system of equations

**Ellipse** The set of all points in a plane for which the sum of the distances from two fixed points $F_1$ and $F_2$ is constant

**Empty set** The set without members

**Equation** A number sentence that says that the expressions on either side of the equals sign, $=$, represent the same number

**Equation of direct variation** An equation described by $y = kx$, with $k$ a positive constant, used to represent direct variation

**Equation of inverse variation** An equation described by $y = k/x$, with $k$ a positive constant, used to represent inverse variation

**Equivalent equations** Equations with the same solutions

**Equivalent expressions** Expressions that have the same value for all allowable replacements

**Equivalent inequalities** Inequalities that have the same solution set

**Evaluate** To substitute a value for each occurrence of a variable in an expression

**Even root** When the number $k$ in $\sqrt[k]{\phantom{x}}$ is an even number, we say that we are taking an even root.

**Exponent** In expressions of the form $a^n$, the number $n$ is an exponent. For $n$ a natural number, $a^n$ represents $n$ factors of $a$.

**Exponential decay model** A decrease in quantity over time that can be modeled by an exponential function of the form $P(t) = P_0 e^{-kt}, k > 0$

**Exponential equation** An equation in which a variable appears as an exponent

**Exponential function** The function $f(x) = a^x$, where $a$ is a positive constant different from 1

**Exponential growth model** An increase in quantity over time that can be modeled by an exponential function of the form $P(t) = P_0 e^{kt}, k > 0$

**Exponential growth rate** The variable $k$ in the exponential growth model $P(t) = P_0 e^{kt}$

**Exponential notation** A representation of a number using a base raised to a power

**F**

**Factor** *Verb*: To write an equivalent expression that is a product. *Noun*: A multiplier

**Factorization of a polynomial** An expression that names the polynomial as a product of factors

**Focus**   One of two fixed points that determine the points of an ellipse

**FOIL**   To multiply two binomials by multiplying the First terms, the Outside terms, the Inside terms, and then the Last terms

**Formula**   An equation that uses numbers or letters to represent a relationship between two or more quantities

**Fraction equation**   An equation containing one or more rational expressions; also called a *rational equation*

**Function**   A correspondence that assigns to each member of a set called the domain *exactly one* member of a set called the range

## G

**Grade**   The measure of a road's steepness

**Graph**   A picture or diagram of the data in a table; a line, curve, or collection of points that represents all the solutions of an equation

**Greatest common factor (GCF)**   The common factor of a polynomial with the largest possible coefficient and the largest possible exponent(s)

## H

**Half-life**   The amount of time necessary for half of a quantity to decay

**Hyperbola**   The set of all points in a plane for which the difference of the distances from two fixed points $F_1$ and $F_2$ is constant

**Hypotenuse**   In a right triangle, the side opposite the right angle

## I

**Identity property of 1**   The statement that the product of a number and 1 is always the original number

**Identity property of 0**   The statement that the sum of a number and 0 is always the original number

**Imaginary number**   A number that can be named $bi$, where $b$ is some real number and $b \neq 0$

**Inconsistent system of equations**   A system of equations for which there is no solution

**Independent equations**   Equations that are not dependent and there exists either one or no solution

**Independent variable**   The variable that represents the input of a function

**Index**   In the expression $\sqrt[k]{a}$, the number $k$ is called the index.

**Inequality**   A mathematical sentence using $<, >, \leq, \geq,$ or $\neq$

**Input**   A member of the domain of a function

**Integers**   The whole numbers and their opposites

**Intercept**   The point at which a graph intersects the $x$- or $y$-axis

**Intersection of sets $A$ and $B$**   The set of all members that are common to $A$ and $B$

**Interval notation**   The use of a pair of numbers inside parentheses and brackets to represent the set of all numbers between those two numbers

**Inverse relation**   The relation formed by interchanging the coordinates of the ordered pairs in a relation

**Inverse variation**   A situation that gives rise to a function $f(x) = k/x$, or $y = k/x$, where $k$ is a positive constant

**Irrational number**   A real number whose decimal representation neither terminates nor has a repeating block of digits and it can be represented as a quotient of two integers

## J

**Joint variation**   A situation that gives rise to an equation of the form $y = kxz$, where $k$ is a constant

## L

**Leading coefficient**   The coefficient of the term of highest degree in a polynomial

**Leading term**   The term of highest degree in a polynomial

**Least common denominator (LCD)**   The least common multiple of the denominators

**Least common multiple (LCM)**   The smallest number that is a multiple of two or more numbers

**Legs**   In a right triangle, the two sides that form the right angle

**Like radicals**   Radicals having the same index and radicand

**Like terms**   Terms that have exactly the same variable factors; also called *similar terms*

**Line of symmetry**   A line that can be drawn through a graph such that the part of the graph on one side of the line is an exact reflection of the part on the opposite side

**Linear equation**   Any equation that can be written in the form $y = mx + b$ or $Ax + By = C$, where $x$ and $y$ are variables; also called *axis of symmetry*

**Linear function**   A function that can be described by an equation of the form $y = mx + b$, where $x$ and $y$ are variables

**Linear inequality**   An inequality whose related equation is a linear equation

**Logarithmic equation**   An equation containing a logarithmic expression

**Logarithmic function, base $a$**   The inverse of an exponential function $f(x) = a^x$

## M

**Mathematical model**   A model in which the essential parts of a problem are described in mathematical language

**Matrix**   A rectangular array of numbers

**Maximum**   The largest function value (output) achieved by a function

**Minimum**   The smallest function value (output) achieved by a function

**Monomial**   A constant, or a constant times a variable or variables raised to powers that are nonnegative integers

**Motion formula**   The formula
Distance = Rate (or Speed) · Time
**Multiplication property of 0**   The statement that the product of 0 and any real number is 0
**Multiplicative identity**   The number 1
**Multiplicative inverses**   Reciprocals; two numbers whose product is 1

## N

**Natural logarithm**   A logarithm with base $e$
**Natural numbers**   The counting numbers: 1, 2, 3, 4, 5, …
**Negative integers**   The integers to the left of zero on the number line
**Nonlinear equation**   An equation whose graph is not a straight line
**Nonlinear function**   A function whose graph is not a straight line

## O

**Odd root**   When the number $k$ in $\sqrt[k]{\phantom{x}}$ is an odd number, we say that we are taking an odd root.
**One-to-one function**   A function for which different inputs have different outputs
**Opposite**   The opposite, or additive inverse, of a number $a$ is denoted $-a$. Opposites are the same distance from 0 on the number line but on different sides of 0.
**Opposite of a polynomial**   To find the opposite of a polynomial, replace each term with its opposite—that is, change the sign of every term.
**Ordered pair**   A pair of numbers of the form $(h, k)$ for which the order in which the numbers are listed is important
**Ordinate**   The second coordinate in an ordered pair of numbers
**Origin**   The point on a graph where the two axes intersect
**Output**   A member of the range of a function

## P

**Parabola**   A graph of a quadratic function
**Parallel lines**   Lines in the same plane that never intersect. Two lines are parallel if they have the same slope and different $y$-intercepts.
**Perfect square**   A rational number $p$ for which there exists a number $a$ for which $a^2 = p$
**Perfect-square trinomial**   A trinomial that is the square of a binomial
**Perimeter**   The sum of the lengths of the sides of a polygon
**Perpendicular lines**   Lines that form a right angle
**Pi ($\pi$)**   The number that results when the circumference of a circle is divided by its diameter; $\pi \approx 3.14$, or 22/7
**Point–slope equation**   An equation of the form $y - y_1 = m(x - x_1)$, where $m$ is the slope and $(x_1, y_1)$ is a point on the line
**Polynomial**   A monomial or a combination of sums and/or differences of monomials

**Polynomial equation**   An equation in which two polynomials are set equal to each other
**Positive integers**   The natural numbers or the integers to the right of zero on the number line
**Prime polynomial**   A polynomial that cannot be factored using only integer coefficients
**Principal square root**   The nonnegative square root of a number
**Principle of zero products**   The statement that an equation $ab = 0$ is true if and only if $a = 0$ is true or $b = 0$ is true, or both are true
**Proportion**   An equation stating that two ratios are equal
**Proportional numbers**   Two pairs of numbers having the same ratio
**Pythagorean theorem**   In any right triangle, if $a$ and $b$ are the lengths of the legs and $c$ is the length of the hypotenuse, then $a^2 + b^2 = c^2$.

## Q

**Quadrants**   The four regions into which the axes divide a plane
**Quadratic equation**   An equation of the type $ax^2 + bx + c = 0$, where $a$, $b$, and $c$ are real-number constants and $a > 0$
**Quadratic formula**   The solutions of $ax^2 + bx + c = 0$ are given by the equation $x = \dfrac{-b \pm \sqrt{b^2 - 4ac}}{2a}$.
**Quadratic inequality**   A second-degree polynomial inequality in one variable

## R

**Radical equation**   An equation in which a variable appears in one or more radicands
**Radical expression**   An algebraic expression written with a radical
**Radical**   The symbol $\sqrt{\phantom{x}}$
**Radicand**   The expression written under the radical
**Radius**   A segment with one endpoint on the center of a circle and the other endpoint on the circle
**Range**   The set of all second coordinates of the ordered pairs in a function
**Rate**   The ratio of two different kinds of measure
**Ratio**   Any rational expression $a/b$
**Rational equation**   An equation containing one or more rational expressions; also called a *fraction equation*
**Rational expression**   A quotient of two polynomials
**Rational inequality**   An inequality containing a rational expression
**Rational number**   A number that can be written in the form $p/q$, where $p$ and $q$ are integers and $q \neq 0$
**Rationalizing the denominator**   A procedure for finding an equivalent expression without a radical in the denominator
**Real numbers**   All rational and irrational numbers; the set of all numbers corresponding to points on the number line

**Reciprocal**   A multiplicative inverse. Two numbers are reciprocals if their product is 1.

**Rectangle**   A four-sided polygon with four right angles

**Relation**   A correspondence between a first set, called the domain, and a second set, called the range, such that each member of the domain corresponds to *at least one* member of the range

**Repeating decimal**   A decimal in which a number pattern repeats indefinitely

**Right triangle**   A triangle that includes a 90° angle

**Rise**   The change in the second coordinate between two points on a line

**Roster method**   A way of naming sets by listing all the elements in the set

**Run**   The change in the first coordinate between two points on a line

## S

**Scientific notation**   A representation of a number of the form $M \times 10^n$, where $n$ is an integer, $1 \le M < 10$, and $M$ is expressed in decimal notation

**Set**   A collection of objects

**Set-builder notation**   The naming of a set by describing basic characteristics of the elements in the set

**Similar terms**   Terms that have exactly the same variable factors; also called *like terms*

**Simplify**   To rewrite an expression in an equivalent, abbreviated, form

**Slope**   The ratio of the rise to the run for any two points on a line

**Slope–intercept equation**   An equation of the form $y = mx + b$, where $x$ and $y$ are variables, the slope is $m$, and the $y$-intercept is $(0, b)$

**Solution**   A replacement for the variable that makes an equation or inequality true

**Solution of a system of equations**   An ordered pair $(x, y)$ that makes *both* equations true

**Solution of a system of linear inequalities**   An ordered pair $(x, y)$ that is a solution of *both* inequalities

**Solution of a system of three equations**   An ordered triple $(x, y, z)$ that makes *all three* equations true

**Solution set**   The set of all solutions of an equation, an inequality, or a system of equations or inequalities

**Solve**   To find all solutions of an equation, an inequality, or a system of equations or inequalities; to find the solution(s) of a problem

**Square**   A four-sided polygon with four right angles and all sides of equal length

**Square of a number**   A number multiplied by itself

**Square root**   The number $c$ is a square root of $a$ if $c^2 = a$.

**Standard form of a quadratic equation**   A quadratic equation in the form $ax^2 + bx + c = 0$, where $a \ne 0$

**Subsets**   Sets that are contained within other sets

**Substitute**   To replace a variable with a number

**Substitution method**   A nongraphical method for solving systems of equations

**Sum of cubes**   An expression that can be written in the form $A^3 + B^3$

**Sum of squares**   An expression that can be written in the form $A^2 + B^2$

**Supplementary angles**   Angles whose sum is 180°

**Synthetic division**   A simplified process for dividing a polynomial by a binomial of the type $x - a$

**System of equations**   A set of two or more equations that are to be solved simultaneously

**System of linear inequalities**   A set of two or more inequalities that are to be solved simultaneously

## T

**Term**   A number, a variable, or a product or a quotient of numbers and/or variables

**Terminating decimal**   A decimal that can be written using a finite number of decimal places

**Trinomial**   A polynomial that is composed of three terms

**Trinomial square**   The square of a binomial expressed as three terms

## U

**Union of sets $A$ and $B$**   The set of all elements belonging to $A$ and/or $B$

## V

**Value**   The numerical result after a number has been substituted into an expression

**Variable**   A letter that represents an unknown number

**Variation constant**   The constant in an equation of direct or inverse variation

**Vertex**   The point at which the graph of a quadratic equation crosses its axis of symmetry

**Vertical-line test**   The statement that a graph represents a function if it is impossible to draw a vertical line that intersects the graph more than once

## W

**Whole numbers**   The natural numbers and 0: 0, 1, 2, 3, …

## X

**$x$-intercept**   The point at which a graph crosses the $x$-axis

## Y

**$y$-intercept**   The point at which a graph crosses the $y$-axis

# Index